MODERN CONTROL PRINCIPLES AND APPLICATIONS

MODERN CONTROL PRINCIPLES AND APPLICATIONS

Jay C. Hsu, Ph. D.
Bell Telephone Laboratories, Incorporated

Andrew U. Meyer, Ph. D.
Department of Electrical Engineering
Newark College of Engineering

McGRAW-HILL BOOK COMPANY

New York San Francisco Toronto London Sydney

MODERN CONTROL PRINCIPLES AND APPLICATIONS

 Library of Congress Catalog Card Number 68-13627

30635

1234567890 MAMM 7543210698

To IRENE and ELISABETH

Preface

This book is intended for those who wish to obtain a reasonably detailed working knowledge of the pertinent modern theories of control without wading through the myriad of publications in the field. It also is intended for those who wish to apply these theories to concrete problems.

There is currently an impression that in order to appreciate some of the newer control theories, one must be steeped in certain modern branches of mathematics. This is true only to a degree. There is, generally speaking, no substitute for a thorough and deep mathematical grounding. Nevertheless, we feel that the essence of these theories can be imparted without wallowing in the jargon of the mathematics. We try to avoid lengthy chapters on set theory, linear vector spaces, and the like. Instead, we introduce most of the needed mathematics in the text proper, in order to indicate the exact part that the mathematics plays relative to the given problems. Thus our presentation is made in such a way that plausibility arguments generally accompany the mathematical detail. Where called for, we present the mathematics without undue compromise. The mathematical levels of the chapters are however graduated, such that the more difficult concepts are introduced in the later parts of the book.

This book is aimed at first-year graduate students and qualified undergraduates. It is also intended for the large class of working engineers who wish to keep abreast of the development in modern control theory. The subject matter evolved from a course given at the Bell Telephone Laboratories and later tried out at the Newark College of Engineering, as well as at Utah State University in a summer course sponsored by the National Science Foundation.

The book covers what to us are the two most important areas of automatic control: stability and performance. It is a universal fact that, if the loop gain is sufficiently high, a closed-loop system can become unstable even without input. When all the system components are essentially operating in their linear ranges, there is a relatively clear understanding of the conditions for instability. This is, however, not the case for nonlinear systems. The extent that modern theories can allow us to determine stability in certain classes of nonlinear systems is a chief topic of the text.

Even in the case of linear systems, how to specify good performance has always been a question that has nagged system designers. This frequently reduces to a question of specifying a suitable criterion of performance (in practice, a single criterion is frequently not enough). Modern optimal control theory skirts this issue and takes the opposite stand: given a suitable performance criterion, find a control system that is best for the purpose. While this is not completely satisfactory from the engineering viewpoint, it does represent an important step forward. Moreover, the problem has certain aesthetic appeal. We treat this fascinating topic in some depth in order to accentuate the power and pitfalls of the theories in this area, particularly in relation to applications.

One interesting aspect of our presentation is that it clearly shows the return to prominence of the frequency-domain techniques in nonlinear system analysis. Theoretical interest in the frequency domain was apparently eclipsed when engineers rediscovered the so-called state-space approach to differential systems. However, it was soon appreciated that most nonlinear systems about which we can develop some understanding boast a linear time-invariant part. By representing the linear part in the frequency domain, new results often can be derived and new insights can be gained. Thus, Popov and others obtained new stability results in the frequency domain. Even in the area of optimal control theory, some new and useful frequency-domain criteria have been derived.

One important benefit derived from the use of the frequency domain for linear time-invariant systems is the intuition it provides in determining the soundness of a system. We try to show how this intuition could be used to assess the workability of the system to be analyzed.

The prime prerequisites for digesting the contents of the text include a course in linear control systems theory, some understanding of differential equations, and the theory of functions of a complex variable. In addition, we assume a level of maturity equivalent to that of a first-year graduate student. An understanding of the theory of matrices, calculus of variations, and sampled-data systems will be helpful but not essential.

Whenever possible, we attempt to share with the reader our practical experience. To this end, in addition to many remarks in the text proper, we have incorporated a number of examples. They are backed up by exercises of varying degrees of difficulty.

For lack of space, two topics are regretfully omitted. One is discrete systems and the other is systems with uncertainties. The first omission is not judged to be too serious, for it is possible, with some effort, to extrapolate to the discrete case most of the results pertaining to the continuous systems. The second omission is more difficult to rationalize, as there is, in practice, no system without uncertainty. However, the problems related to systems with noise are extremely difficult to solve and generally speaking, a clear understanding of the noise-free case is prerequisite for appreciating problems with uncertainty. We feel that the present choice of topics will provide the necessary grounding for handling uncertainty later.

Even with the above omissions, it is not possible to give an adequate coverage of all the important topics in deterministic nonlinear automatic control theory. We try to indicate other relevant results by means of comments, footnotes, and exercises. Because of the nature of the topics covered and because of the manner in which the exposition is given, solving at least part of the exercises should be considered an integral part of the reading effort. Further, in order for the reader to participate actively in "thinking along" with the authors, the text is liberally sprinkled with small challenges ("why," "show this," etc.). These challenges are designed to test the reader's mastery of the text material and in most cases can be readily answered.

A bibliography is appended at the end of the book. All references in the text are made by alphamerics (enclosed in brackets), referring to specific entries in the bibliography. Our references fall into two categories. Those which are judged to be basic for the subject matter of a given chapter are given at the end of each chapter with appropriate annotations. More specialized references are cited in the footnotes. The above policy is in line with our intention to guide the reader through the field of modern control theory with a reasonable expenditure of time and effort. No effort is made to make the bibliography complete.

We are indebted to a number of individuals in the course of preparing the text. Special thanks to our colleagues G. A. Ford, W. C. Grimmell, H. Heffes, J. M. Holtzman, S. Horing, S. H. Kyong, Y. S. Lim, J. C. Lozier, V. O. Mowery, M. A. Murray-Lasso, W. L. Nelson, J. A. Norton, S. Pyati, F. A. Russell, I. W. Sandberg, J. A. Stiles, H. C. Torng, P. P. Wang, and H. S. Witsenhausen for their thorough comments in the course of preparation of the manuscript. We are grateful to G. S. Axelby and J. G. Truxal for their painstaking review of the book and for their valuable suggestions. Particular credit should go to our students at Bell Telephone Laboratories, Newark College of Engineering, and Utah State University; their incisive questions and suggestions did much to improve the constitution of the book. Our gratitude also is due Mrs. Gertrude Martin, who proofread our entire manuscript and lent invaluable editorial aid; Mrs. Nancy Campbell and her group of mathematical typists, particularly Miss Norma Lockwood, who typed and retyped our work with distinction; and C. W. Christ and his draftsmen, who rendered yeoman service with the illustrations.

JAY C. HSU
ANDREW U. MEYER

Symbols*

$\equiv$ identically equal to (p. 41)
$\simeq$ approximately equal to (p. 184)
$\triangleq$ defined as (p. 21)
$|a|$ the absolute value of a, where a is a scalar (p. 51)
$||\mathbf{x}||$ the norm of the vector $\mathbf{x}$ (p. 49)
$||\mathbf{A}||$ the norm of the matrix $\mathbf{A}$ (p. 177)
$\hat{x}$ the peak value of the sinusoidal function $x(t)$ (p. 184)
$\in$ belongs to (p. 364)
sgn $[x(t)]$ (p. 93)
sat $[x(t)]$ (p. 625)
dez $[x(t)]$ (p. 577)
$\angle z$ the angle $\tan^{-1}(b/a)$ of a complex variable $a + jb$ (p. 207)
$\overline{x(t)}$ the average value of $x(t)$ (p. 210)
$\nabla V(\mathbf{x})$ the gradient of the function $V(\mathbf{x})$, also given as grad $V(\mathbf{x})$ (p. 322)
Σ summation (p. 21)
Π product (p. 31)
$\mathcal{R}e[z]$ the real part of the complex variable z (p. 189)
$\mathcal{I}m[z]$ the imaginary part of the complex variable z (p. 189)
$[x : x \in A]$ the set of all values of x that belong to A (p. 547)
$\dfrac{\partial \mathbf{f}}{\partial \mathbf{x}}$ the matrix whose ij entry is $\dfrac{\partial f_i}{\partial x_j}$ (p. 150)
$\dfrac{\partial H}{\partial x}$ the vector whose ith component is $\dfrac{\partial H}{\partial x_i}$ (p. 600)
$\min[a, b]$ the smaller of the two quantities a and b (p. 52)
$\max\limits_{t_1 \le t \le t_2} [x(t)]$ the largest value of $x(t)$ in the range $t_1 \le t \le t_2$ (p. 450)
$\mu_{-1}(t)$ the unit step input function applied at $t = 0$ (p. 282)
$\mu_0(t)$ the unit impulse function applied at $t = 0$ (p. 58)
◆◆ designation of the start and finish of theorems, lemmas, examples and definitions (p. 19)

*The page at which the symbol first appears is given in parentheses.

Contents

PART III OPTIMUM SYSTEM PERFORMANCE ANALYSIS

PART I

INTRODUCTION AND BASIC TECHNIQUES

1

Modern Automatic Control Systems

The space age challenges the control engineer to master the necessary techniques and obtain the needed insights to permit him to attack and solve nonlinear control systems problems. This means that he must gain sophistication in several almost unrelated fields. First, he must acquire deeper knowledge of modern mathematics. Second, he must develop ever keener physical insight into systems and components in their nonlinear range of operation. Third, he must become well acquainted with the capabilities and limitations of modern digital and analog (and hybrid) computers.

Let us briefly examine how these areas are related to the field of automatic control, and take a quick look into the problems in the field of nonlinear control systems.

1.1 The Role of Mathematics in Modern Control Engineering

Two important trends in automatic controls today are the increasing use of abstract mathematics by the control engineers and the increasing awareness of the problems of automatic control by some mathematicians. By degree, we see publications in the control field becoming mathematically sophisticated. Many old mathematical tools are rediscovered and put to use. At the same time, new mathematical techniques suited to the peculiar demands of the control field are being developed.

But elegance does not imply usefulness. It is important to inquire what benefits, if any, the practitioners of the control science (and art) can directly derive from the results of these forays into the mathematical domain.

It is appropriate to comment on the place of mathematics in engineering. As is well known to the practitioners of control, when a problem has been sufficiently well-characterized so that mathematics can be applied, the completion of the task of designing or synthesizing a control system is usually close at hand. That is to say, at this stage, a competent engineer can quite readily determine if the particular job can or cannot be done and, if it can be done, he can usually evolve at least a workable solution. The major part of the design work still lies in the characterization of a system.

System characterization is more in the area of experimental science in which inductive reasoning rather than deductive reasoning plays the major role. Experience and physical insight have a great deal to do with this part of control engineering. Using them, the engineer can exercise the necessary judgment to arrive finally at a mathematical model for the system. From this point on, mathematical competence plays a bigger role.

Even when the characterization of a system has been completed so that mathematics can be applied, experience and insight can go a long way toward making the mathematics fit the problem. There is a tendency for new graduates in control engineering to adapt a problem to a method rather than vice versa; thus mathematical sophistication is taken as the end rather than the means. Such an approach is generally time-consuming and unpromising, because that elusive quantity sometimes called "engineering feel" is lacking.

What then is the role of mathematics in control engineering? Mathematics from the engineer's point of view is but a set of useful tools. If the user is completely familiar with their power, potentialities, and dangers, he can use them with great benefit in well-defined situations. When a system is fully characterized, mathematics can sometimes give "yes" or "no" answers concerning certain types of system stability phenomena; it can sometimes yield information on the performance of the system in a given condition, and it can sometimes give an upperbound when a single performance criterion is given.

There is no question that in order to master the available tools, the analyst must absorb and digest a wide range of modern mathematical topics. In this book, the mathematical techniques that we develop and make use of include the vector-matrix approach to the analysis of dynamic systems described by differential equations; some topological ideas which permit us to develop the idea of stability and optimality intelligently; some approximation methods related to the classical approach of Ritz and Galerkin; the use of the advanced z-transformation; some glimpse of elements of functional analysis; elementary use of calculus of variations and its two modern extensions—the maximum principle and dynamic programming; and, finally, some computational ideas derived from the time-honored techniques of Newton and Raphson and from the technique of steepest descent.

The quantity of mathematical techniques treated is, of course, hardly a measuring index for a book. The value of a mathematical technique is the particular viewpoint that it adopts and the particular light it sheds on a problem. Often, by using a new technique, another facade of a problem is clearly shown and a more suitable path is thus revealed to attack the problem. In this volume, where possible, we try to bring several techniques to bear on a given class of problems. In so doing, we hope to bring about new understanding.

An area of equal importance in describing a mathematical technique is the indication of its pitfalls and drawbacks. We make a serious effort in this regard, as we feel that only by this means can the state of the art be truly appreciated.

1.2 Linear and Nonlinear Control Systems

We shall be dealing mainly with control systems whose dynamics are well characterized by finite-order ordinary differential equations. Such systems will be called *differential systems*.

When a linear block is involved, we will occasionally go beyond the requirement of differential systems. Here sometimes all that is needed is to stipulate that the input-output relationship of the linear block be given in terms of an impulse response, and hence an integral equation. This permits us, for example, to treat as linear, systems such as transmission lines, which are describable by linear partial differential equations.

The linear systems have a number of features which make their behavior easy to characterize. These features are founded on the fact that superposition is directly applicable. Superposition implies the dual properties of additivity and homogeneity* with respect both to the input and to initial conditions.

As a direct result of the property of superposition, the linear system in the absence of input but with arbitrary initial conditions can behave in only the following three ways:

1) The system output decreases eventually to zero.
2) The system output increases without bound.
3) The system output oscillates in such a way that the size of the oscillation is directly proportional to the size of the initial condition.

*For a system that is additive with respect to the input, suppose in the absence of initial conditions, input $r_1(t)$ gives rise to output $y_1(t)$ and input $r_2(t)$ gives rise to output $y_2(t)$, then input $r_1(t) + r_2(t)$ will give rise to an output $y_1(t) + y_2(t)$. For a system that is homogeneous with respect to the input, if, in the absence of initial conditions, an input $r_1(t)$ gives rise to an output $y_1(t)$, then an input $kr_1(t)$ will give rise to an output $ky_1(t)$ for any real constant k. (These two properties are not equivalent, see Ref. [Z1]). The definition of a system that is additive and homogeneous with respect to initial conditions follows readily from the above.

A further subclass of the linear systems is the class of linear time-invariant systems. For these systems, the input-output relation will be unchanged under a translation in time; i.e., in the absence of initial conditions, if $y(t)$ results when $r(t)$ is applied, then $y(t - T)$ results when $r(t - T)$ is applied for any constant value of T. This property makes the linear time-invariant systems amenable to analysis by the transform methods. The well-known frequency-domain techniques thus become the basic tool of analysis, though these can also be complemented significantly by time-domain techniques. An important subclass of the linear time-invariant systems is the class of systems whose dynamics are well characterized by finite-order linear ordinary differential equations with constant coefficients. To date, the linear time-invariant system remains the only one for which a general mathematical method has been developed for its analysis.

When we come to the study of more general differential systems and, in particular, those systems that are not linear, the situation is far from satisfactory. From the 1950s onward, control systems analysts have developed some tools useful in attacking nonlinear problems. The results obtained, however, are quite limited in applicability.

To date, the most significant results have been achieved for a system reducible to the form of a single-loop system at least part of which is linear. Such a system is shown in Fig. 1-1a.

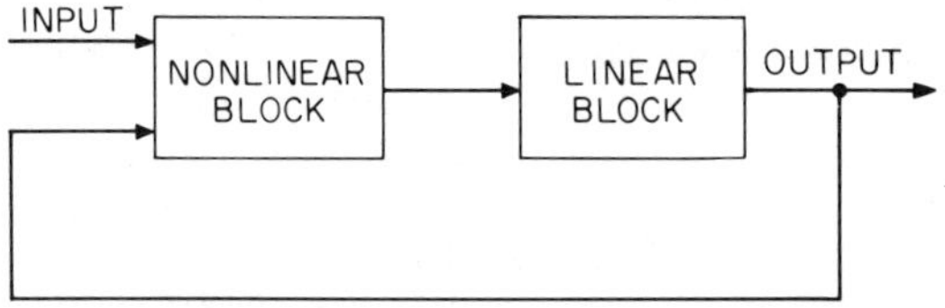

Fig. 1-1a. A single-loop system with a linear part.

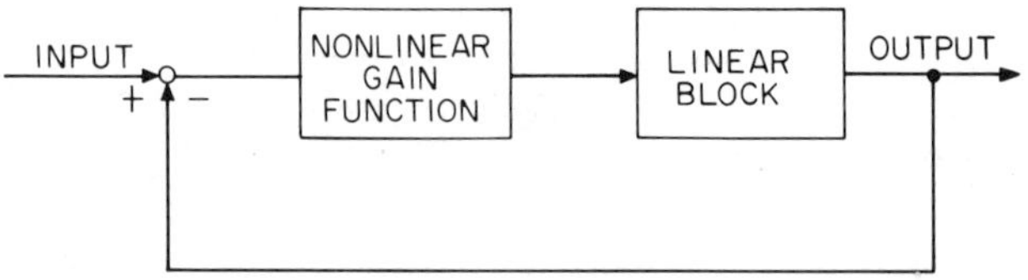

Fig. 1-1b. A special case of the system of Fig. 1-1a.

The restrictions to be imposed on the nonlinear portion of the system depend on whether an approximate or an exact answer is wanted, or whether a qualitative or a quantitative answer is desired. In many cases, the nonlinear portion can only be a nonlinear gain function or a relay-type function, operating on the difference between the input and output (see Fig. 1-1b), although when an approximate answer is sought, the nonlinear block can be a much more general one.

In theory, there needs to be no restriction on the linear block, although in practice due to computational difficulties in certain approaches, the linear system is often restricted to a low order. Generally speaking, if the approach involves the use of time-domain techniques, then the computational steps required increase rapidly with the order of the system and there exists a stage beyond which it is inadvisable to apply the method. If, however, the approach involves the use of frequency-domain techniques, then the computational steps required increase much more slowly with the order of the system and it is possible to study high-order systems with these techniques.

As a tool for obtaining approximate answers, the frequency-domain describing function technique has always been an important part of a design engineer's repertoire. Recently however, a number of *exact* frequency-domain methods have also been developed. Such methods are exemplified by the method of Popov and its extension, mentioned in Chaps. 10 and 11. Wherever a frequency-domain technique exists, it enjoys the traditional advantages over the time-domain methods; namely, ease in computation and manipulations, particularly with high-order systems, and in the imparting of insights.

Why has the progress into the field of nonlinear control systems been so painful and slow? The answer must lie in the fact that there are so many ways that a nonlinear system can "go wrong." It is useful to enumerate some of these at the outset, so as to set the tune for our subsequent discussions.

1) *Finite escape time*—The output of an unstable linear system goes to infinity as time approaches infinity; a nonlinear system's output, however, can go to infinity in a finite time. It is easy to demonstrate that a system modeled by the first-order differential equation $\dot{x} = x^2$ with the starting condition $x = x_0$ at $t = 0$ will have this behavior at $t = 1/x_0$.
2) *Multiple equilibrium states or an equilibrium zone*—For linear systems that are stable, the output ultimately converges to zero in the absence of input. This need not be the case for nonlinear systems. The output may converge to one of a number of values in the absence of input (a "flip-flop" is of this type), or it may converge to any one of a continuum of values, depending on the initial conditions on the system.
3) *Limit cycles*—For a linear time-invariant differential system to oscillate, there must be a pair of poles on the

imaginary axis (which would be a rare occurrence even if we deliberately try to design it this way). The magnitude of the resultant oscillation is directly proportional to the magnitude of the initial conditions of the system. For a nonlinear system, this need not be the case. Quite frequently there are systems which can go into an oscillation of a *fixed* amplitude and period, irrespective of initial conditions. This type of oscillation is known as a limit cycle. Indeed in real life, any stable oscillator must of necessity be of this type.

4) *Subharmonic, harmonic, or almost-periodic oscillations under a periodic input*—A stable linear system under a periodic input produces an output of the same period. For a nonlinear system, the system behavior under a periodic excitation can be quite different. Since a nonlinear element can generate harmonics under a sinusoidal input, it is perhaps not surprising that sometimes under a periodic input, the output periodicity is a submultiple of that of the input. More surprising is the fact that some nonlinear systems generate subharmonics, so that the output periodicity is a multiple of that of the input. Even more intriguing is the generation of an almost-periodic output under a periodic input, which is also possible for certain nonlinear systems.

5) *Multiple modes of behavior*—It is not unusual for two or more modes of behavior to be exhibited for the same nonlinear system. Thus, for a system without input, depending on the initial conditions, the system output may either converge to one (or more) steady value(s) or go into a limit-cycle type oscillation. Indeed, a system may exhibit more than one limit cycle. Similarly for a system under periodic excitation, the output may exhibit harmonic, subharmonic, or almost-periodic oscillations depending on the amplitude and the period of the input. Two further manifestations of these multiple modes of behavior are listed separately below.

6) *The jump phenomenon*—In some nonlinear systems under a periodic excitation, when the amplitude or period of the excitation is smoothly changed, the output sometimes undergoes a discontinuous change in amplitude. This is known as the jump phenomenon.

7) *Frequency entrainment or synchronization*—When some nonlinear systems are driven by a sinusoidal input of small amplitude, the output oscillates at a period that is a submultiple of that of the input. As input amplitude is increased, there is a point at which the output period suddenly is changed to that of the input. This phenomenon is made use of, for example, in television synchronization circuits.

8) *More complex jump phenomenon*—Simultaneous discontinuous jumps in both the period and amplitude can also occur.

1.3 Stability Performance and Optimization

Rather than enumerate the anomalous modes of behavior for nonlinear systems, it is more useful to define the modes of behavior that are considered acceptable.

The most basic acceptable mode of behavior is encompassed in the word *stability*. Stability in a system implies that small changes in the system input, in initial conditions, or in the system parameter do not result in large changes in the system output. Generally speaking, it is the minimum criterion of goodness that must be met in a system. For linear time-invariant systems, stability is relatively easy to define and analyze. Powerful tests such as those of Routh and Hurwitz exist, which provide not only the necessary but also the sufficient conditions for stability. When a linear time-invariant system passes the test for stability, it means that (1) in the absence of input, the output tends toward zero irrespective of the initial conditions, and (2) when the system is excited by a bounded input, the output is bounded.

For nonlinear systems, because of the possible existence of multiple equilibrium states and other anomalies, the concept of stability is difficult even to define. Furthermore, stability with or without input can be two entirely different matters for nonlinear systems.

Since stability almost always is a prerequisite for acceptable performance, we shall devote the first portion of the book to its study.

Within the boundaries of parameter variations permitted by stability considerations, we can then seek to improve the system performance. Here there is a burgeoning area of research which has taken over much of the limelight. This is the study of systems that yield the optimal performance in accordance to a given measure of the goodness of performance. This is the topic that will be taken up in much of the second half of the book. The bulk of the useful results in this area of optimal control systems concerns the control of linear time-invariant systems under the relatively simple constraint that the control signal is amplitude-limited. A number of computational algorithms have been devised to find *specific* solutions for more general systems, but their efficacy has not been completely determined.

Optimal control systems are useful in that they can serve as standards of comparison for practical designs; these systems also give the engineers a feeling for what steps to take to design a system more efficiently. In the second half of this book we try to make a fair assessment of the significance and the state of development of optimal control systems.

1.4 Large-Scaled Systems and Approximation Techniques

Sophisticated technology also gives rise to complex systems. Today it is not rare to encounter systems that can only be adequately described by variables that number in the hundreds or thousands. Some writers tend to suggest that the complex systems can always be analyzed by a straightforward extension of methods which have been developed for simpler systems. This is generally speaking not true, for higher order systems usually bring about added problems undreamed of when only simple systems are considered. The "curse of dimensionality" thus runs deeper than it first seems.

Indeed, the high-order complex systems are responsible for the dichotomy of the industrial and academic viewpoints. An academically oriented individual new to industry tends to view the real world in terms of the low-order world of the textbooks. He is usually frustrated on finding that the tools at his command appear to be rather inadequate to analyze the large-scaled systems in industry.

Large-scaled systems can be attacked successfully, however, even with our limited store of tools. Indeed, if the *essence* of the textbook methods is grasped, analysis of the large-scaled systems often becomes possible.

Let us be more specific and consider this question in terms of the topics covered in this book. First of all, we know that stability is always an issue, and for large-scaled systems, stability is even more difficult to determine *exactly*. However, the many exact techniques available (such as those based on the Lyapunov second method and the method of Popov) do tend to give us an appreciation of the *degree of stability* in various simple situations. It is the task, or indeed the duty, of the engineer to extrapolate the exact results toward what can be established using approximate results (such as those obtainable using the describing function method or the dual-input describing function method). And in fact, he can try to tailor the approximate methods to the large-scaled system, as we shall be doing in Chap. 6.

Again, when the order of a system becomes sufficiently large, it becomes unprofitable or even impossible to optimize the system. But improvement in the performance of the system can still be attempted. Sometimes, by approximating a higher order system by a lower order one, the best ways can be determined to bring about improvements in performance. The extent of improvements that are possible can sometimes also be assessed.

Because of the difficulty of arriving at a performance criterion that adequately describes the need of a system, frequently suboptimal systems, favoring certain less tangible aspects of system design, are preferred.

To sum up, for the large-scaled industrial systems that are in existence, it is the spirit, rather than the letter of the modern theories, that must be invoked. With such a point of view, a proper blend of the exact and approximate methods can yield a highly useful procedure.

1.5 The Role of Computers in Modern Control Engineering

The space age ushers in an era of free use of large-scaled computers, both analog and digital. There is no doubt that the control engineer is greatly benefited by the general availability of computers. Indeed, in some cases, a computer is an integral part of the modern control systems. While it is beyond the planned scope of this volume to discuss the capability of the computers in control, it is clear that they are now a most important design tool.

The free reliance on computers is, of course, not without its pitfalls. Improperly programmed, they will yield wrong answers. This is a most obvious trouble area—albeit a very real one. It is relatively easy to use a wrong integration routine in the case of a digital computer and to take too much liberty with function generation in the case of an analog computer. Since the system simulated cannot usually be solved analytically, the form the solutions should take is not known *a priori*. Here a keen appreciation of what the simulated system is expected to do will be most helpful.

Even when the computer is properly programmed, it must be realized that only *specific solutions* can be given by the simulation. Since the behavior of a nonlinear system is highly dependent on the magnitude of initial conditions and the form of the input, enough specific solutions must be run to ensure that no anomalous behavior remains uncovered in the normal system regime of operation.

Finally, the issue of the efficient use of the computers is becoming ever pressing; particularly in a situation where a computer is used on-line or in a time-shared arrangement. There is currently some indication that the development of computer "software" has not kept pace with the "hardware." This situation of course need not be a permanent one. It does, however, suggest that programming has not yet reached the automatic stage. It is usually not sufficient at present to say that a task can be done; the engineer must aid in working out the details to accomplish the task. By avoiding the pitfalls, the analyst can then begin to use the computer in an intelligent manner.

A particularly useful area is that of simulation. It is almost certain that any large-scaled system encountered in the industry will defy exact analysis, but it often can be simulated and analyzed by trial and error. Indeed, a competent engineer well gounded in the principles of nonlinear system analysis can make excellent use of a man-machine symbiosis involving the engineer and a large-scaled simulation. Here again the scientific process involved will be that of induction rather than deduction and the spirit of inquiry is experimental rather than axiomatic.

Not completely divorced from simulation is the use of the computer as an aid to computation and other routine work. Today most companies can develop root-locus plots and Nyquist and/or Bode diagrams for very high-order linear time-invariant systems as a matter of routine through the use of the computer. Computers are also called upon to draw diagrams and correct manuscripts. Further, comprehensive time-sharing schemes are being developed to permit engineers to do calculations "on-line" such that iterative type computations can be efficiently carried out. These on-line type arrangements are particularly useful for numerically solving optimal control problems, where iterative calculations usually appear.

It is safe to say that the intelligent use of the computer is only in its infancy. An area of great potential is the development of systems where a computer is an integral part of the control loop. Such systems can greatly increase the scope of automatic controls. This is an area where ultimately many of the theoretical results for optimal control can be used in regulating real-life systems. It is clear that the computer can be used to (1) predict the input and (2) simulate the system to be controlled (both faster than real time) and then (3) effect the necessary decisions to cause the system to (4) adapt to the changing input. This type of system already exists, and some mention of such a system will be made in Chap. 17.

1.6 Some Historical Perspectives

It is instructive to trace the chronolgoical and historical development of automatic control theory. While the relevant theories had been developed well before the Second World War, widespread applications of linear automatic control techniques came only after the war. In 1950, with the discovery of the root-locus method by Evans, the development of linear control theory for single-input, single-output time-invariant systems was essentially complete.*

Analytical techniques for nonlinear control systems, however, were in their infancy before 1950. Only the phase-plane method,

*There is, however, much room for further study for multi-input, multi-output linear systems.

suitable for analyzing second-order systems, was available. Other than that there were only isolated attempts to adapt approximation methods such as those of Krylov and Bogoliubov to nonlinear system analysis. Around 1950, at least five investigators in various parts of the world succeeded in developing the latter approach into one easily applicable to closed-loop systems. The describing function method was the result. It remains to this day one of the most versatile approximation methods in control engineering.

Also around 1950, Tsypkin in the Soviet Union and Hamel in France managed to develop the theory of relay control systems to a significant degree of completeness. In the late 1950s, the work of Lyapunov (done in the 1890s) was rediscovered in the United States and, in particular, his so-called second method attracted widespread attention. There followed a concerted effort to translate and digest the Russian control and mathematical literature. It was found that, among other achievements, the Soviet researchers had extended the work of Lyapunov to a fairly sophisticated degree.

In the meantime, two important approaches were revolutionizing the field of optimal control. These were the method of dynamic programming of Bellman (in the U.S.) and the maximum principle of Pontryagin (in the U.S.S.R.). Both were advanced around 1956.*

In 1959, the Rumanian V. M. Popov discovered an exact frequency domain condition for the stability of a class of nonlinear systems. This achievement, along with later extensions by other investigators, brought the spotlight back to the frequency-domain approaches.

In the meantime, the Polish scientist Kulikowski and others were seeking to extend the mathematical discipline of functional analysis to the study of control systems. They contributed significantly to the area of optimal controls. Attempts were also made to use functional analysis for stability studies. Sandberg (U.S.) and Zames (U.S.) made important contributions in this direction.

1.7 An Outline of the Book

The book is divided into three parts. The first part (Chaps. 2 through 4) gives a summary of the state-space approach to system analysis. It is for the benefit of those who have not had training in this area. The major equations and results are collected. Many universities today have undergraduate courses in the use of

*It was only later that the contributions of the University of Chicago group headed by Bliss became fully known. Their extensions to calculus of variations done in the 1930s clearly foreshadowed the maximum principle. See chap. 13.

the state-space approach. Students with sufficient background in state-space techniques can proceed directly to Chap. 5.

The second part (Chaps. 5 through 11) presents the major results in stability analysis for differential systems. It begins with a general treatment of linearization about system equilibrium points and particular trajectories. The results of stability analysis using the linearized equations (Lyapunov's first method) are stated. The important case of uniform asymptotic stability useful for time-varying systems is discussed. Finally, the concept of orbital stability and extension is treated.

Chapters 6 and 7 deal with the powerful approximate methods of describing function and dual-input describing function. When used with care, they can extend considerably the results obtainable by exact methods. We show how their scope of applicability can be enlarged beyond that at present.

Chapter 8 covers the relay control systems in some detail. Several new approaches are brought to bear on this practically important class of systems.

Chapter 9 treats the second method of Lyapunov, detailing its usefulness and drawbacks.

Chapter 10 is concerned with the method of Popov and its extensions. The approach uses an integral representation of the system and adopts an essentially functional analysis point of view. We show that the fundamental theories of Popov and the well-known circle-criterion are related merely by a bilinear transformation via a "pole-shifting" technique. In Chap 11, some new results in the area of system input-output stability are given. The useful contraction-mapping fixed-point theorem is introduced, as are some results in the use of inequalities.

In Chaps. 12 through 17, we discuss the modern results in optimization. Some fundamental concepts and intuitive insights are given in Chap. 12 toward the special way of formulation and solution of the problems. The basic tools of calculus of variations in a form suitable to treat optimal control problems are introduced in Chap. 13. It is shown that, by adding a sufficient number of variables, almost all solvable problems in optimal control can be attacked and solved by calculus of variations. However, the maximum principle of Pontryagin is more adapted to the special formulation of the optimal control problems because the same results can be obtained more readily. Chapter 14 discusses the maximum principle from a geometrical point of view. It is felt that better appreciation of the meaning of the principle can be gained with this viewpoint.

Dynamic programming of Bellman is a third useful method for optimization problems. With this approach, the optimal control problem is looked at from the standpoint of the optimum criterion function defined over the state space. From this, further useful insights can be obtained. In particular, it is convenient to view the class of systems known as the linear optimal control systems in the light of dynamic programming.

Some of the difficulties involved with optimal control problems are discussed in Chaps. 16 and 17. Chapter 16 deals with the so-called singular control problems in which the usual necessary conditions for determining the optimal control functions are satisfied in a trivial way and hence the problems must be solved by other means. Because of this class of problems, the unwary can obtain wrong results in an optimal control problem.

Chapter 17 treats some computational approaches that are commonly used for optimal control functions. The chapter ends with a discussion of practical utilization of optimal control results.

Three appendices are given at the end of the book. In Appendix A, we give the basic ideas and results in matrix analysis. Appendix B gives a capsule review of the principles of z-transforms and advanced z-transforms, which we find occasion to use in Chap. 8. In Appendix C, we present the rather lengthy proof of the fundamental theory in the method of Popov as well as some other mathematical results.

2

The State-Space Approach to System Analysis

For a differential system, when for any reason analysis in the time domain is to be preferred, the use of the so-called state-space approach will offer a great deal of convenience conceptually, notationally, and, sometimes, analytically. The conceptual convenience is derived from the elegant representation of the instantaneous condition of the system by the notion of the system *state*, which can be visualized as a point in a suitable Euclidean space. The behavior of the system as time progresses is then given by a trajectory which is traced out by the point.

The notational and analytical conveniences come through the use of vector-matrix representation which allows the system equations and the *form* of the solutions to be written compactly.

When the system to be investigated contains time-varying or nonlinear elements, the utility of the well-known frequency-domain approaches—such as the transform methods—becomes restricted. However, these systems can still be cast in a time-domain form and the resulting equations can at least be solved numerically by computers. Here the state-space representation is especially useful.

The state-space approach as such is not new, being directly related to methods of dynamic system analysis using the Lagrange-Hamilton formalism. In its modern guise, however, the state-space approach, particularly when applied to linear (but not necessarily time-invariant) systems, permits ready application of many mathematical methods which have been developed for the solution or qualitative discussion of these systems.

In this chapter and the following one, we shall develop some of the results of the state-space approach. These will then serve as the basis for subsequent discussion of time-domain techniques.

2.1 A Control System

A typical control system may be represented by a block diagram such as that shown in Fig. 2-1. The plant is that part of the system which is to be controlled: for example, a rotating antenna mount in a satellite tracking loop or a missile in a radar guidance system. Generally, the plant represents the high-power output end of the system designed to achieve such a purpose as positioning a reflector dish in the case of a rotating antenna mount or orienting a missile flying toward a target. The dynamic characteristics of the plant (in terms of available torque or maximum steering moments, structural resonance characteristics, etc.) are generally determined by the available equipment. In this book, we shall assume that the plant parameters cannot be changed by the designer.

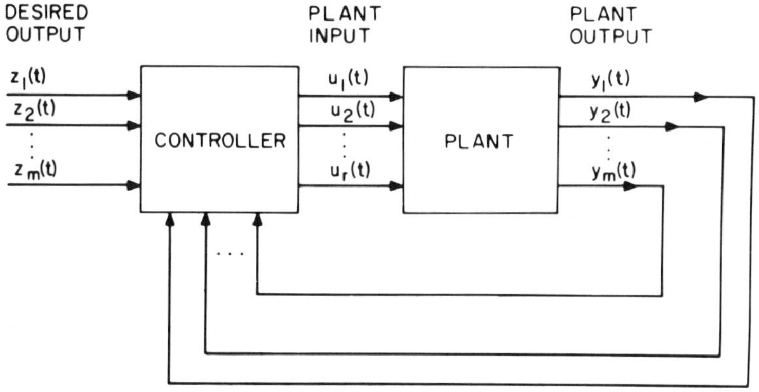

Fig. 2-1. A typical control system.

A plant can have several inputs and outputs. The outputs are those quantities which can be measured, and whose values give an indication of the plant performance; the inputs are those quantities which can be changed or controlled by external means at the disposal of the control engineer. In a well-designed system, each input should influence one or more outputs. In the case of an antenna mount the inputs are the signals which actuate the motors or the hydraulic drives and the outputs are the angular positions of the antenna in elevation and azimuth and their respective rates of change. In the case of a missile the inputs are signals to move the control vanes or to swivel the thrust direction; the outputs may be the missile position and velocity.

We shall designate the plant inputs by the set of r time functions $u_1(t), \ldots, u_r(t)$, and the outputs by the set of m time functions $y_1(t), \ldots, y_m(t)$.

The controller is the device designed to ensure that the system performs in an acceptable manner. Its outputs, the control signals, are the plant inputs $u_1(t), \ldots, u_r(t)$. Thus the task of the controller is to so manipulate the values of the $u(t)$'s so that the plant performs in an acceptable manner.

To render the concept of acceptable performance more precise, we can think in the following terms: In a given situation there usually is, at least implicity, a set of desired output values $z_1(t), \ldots, z_m(t)$ which we should like the actual outputs to approach. Therefore, the controller at least needs to generate the control $u(t)$'s as a function of the desired output $z(t)$'s. If, however, the controller outputs do not depend on the actual values of the plant output $y(t)$'s, then the controller-plant complex forms an *open-loop control system*. When the controller also uses the $y(t)$'s to form the control signals, then there is said to be *feedback* and the controller-plant complex forms a *closed-loop control system*.

Practically all control systems can be cast into the form of Fig. 2-1. As an example, consider a linear follow-up control system with a lead-lag compensator in the forward path; the lead-lag network is then the controller, whose input is the desired output. The controller generates a control signal by performing a linear operation on the difference of the desired and actual output.

The major task of the control engineer is to design an acceptable controller for a plant. Before discussing how to accomplish this end, however, it is first necessary to consider how to characterize the plant and the rest of the system. The reader is assumed to have a familiarity with the frequency-domain method of characterizing a linear constant parameter plant. For the remainder of this chapter, we shall concern ourselves with a method of system characterization in the time domain.

2.2 The Vector-Matrix Representation of the Plant Dynamics

We shall be dealing mainly with plants representable by n ordinary differential equations of the following form:

$$\frac{dx_i(t)}{dt} = f_i\Big(x_1(t), \ldots, x_n(t);\ u_1(t), \ldots, u_r(t);\ t\Big) \qquad i = 1, \ldots, n \tag{2-1a}$$

where the variables $x_i(t)$, $i = 1, \ldots, n$ are related to the m outputs $y_j(t)$, $j = 1, \ldots, m$, by equations of the form

$$y_j(t) = g_j\Big(x_1(t), \ldots, x_n(t);\ u_1(t), \ldots, u_r(t);\ t\Big) \qquad j = 1, \ldots, m \tag{2-1b}$$

Equations (2–1) give a convenient and fairly general representation of a dynamic system. For example, the nth-order differential equation

$$\frac{d^n y}{dt^n} = f\left(\frac{d^{n-1}y}{dt^{n-1}}, \frac{d^{n-2}y}{dt^{n-2}}, \ldots, y; u_1, \ldots, u_r; t\right) \tag{2–2a}$$

can be brought into form (2–1) by setting $x_1 = y$, $x_2 = dy/dt, \ldots,$ $x_n = d^{n-1}y/dt^{n-1}$, giving

$$\dot{x}_1 = x_2, \dot{x}_2 = x_3, \ldots, \dot{x}_{n-1} = x_n, \dot{x}_n = f(x_1, \ldots, x_{n-1}; u_1, \ldots, u_r; t) \tag{2–2b}$$

and

$$y = x_1$$

♦♦Example 2-1. Consider a vertically ascending rocket under thrust. The forces acting on the vehicle include aerodynamic drag, which is assumed to be proportional to the square of the velocity, and the gravitational acceleration, g. The instantaneous thrust is proportional to $dm(t)/dt$, where $m(t)$ is the instantaneous mass of the rocket. Letting h be the height of the vehicle from its launch point, then the equation of motion of the rocket is

$$m(t)\frac{d^2h}{dt^2} + k\left(\frac{dh}{dt}\right)^2 + m(t)g = c\frac{dm(t)}{dt}$$

where k and c are positive constants.

If $dm(t)/dt$ can be controlled, it is the input. Letting $x_1(t) = h$, $x_2(t) = dh/dt$, $x_3(t) = m(t)$ and $u(t) = c[dm(t)/dt]$, the rocket equation of motion becomes

$$\dot{x}_1 = x_2(t)$$

$$\dot{x}_2 = -\frac{k}{x_3(t)}x_2^2(t) - g + \frac{u(t)}{x_3(t)}$$

$$\dot{x}_3 = \frac{1}{c}u(t)$$

If the height $h(t)$ is considered to be the output, then the output Eq. (2–1b) is given by $y(t) = x_1(t)$. If the velocity dh/dt is considered to be the output, then $y(t) = x_2(t)$.♦♦

Returning now to the general form (2–1), we can portray the system signal flow in more detail by means of a block diagram as shown in Fig. 2–2. In this, the system is represented by function generators and integrators. This is the same form that is used for simulation of the system on an analog computer. Compared to Fig. 2-1, we see that between the input functions $u_i(t)$ and the output function $y_j(t)$ there appears an auxiliary set of variables $x_1(t)$, $x_2(t), \ldots, x_n(t)$. The actual outputs are in turn some linear combination of these auxiliary variables.

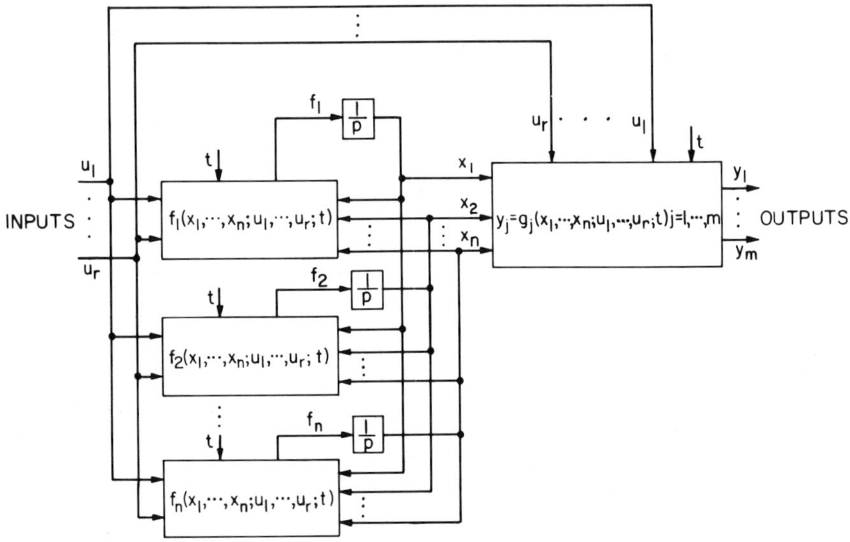

Fig. 2-2. The block diagram of a system represented by Eqs. (2-1*a*) and (2-1*b*).

For the time being we shall view Eqs. (2-1) as the defining equations for these new variables. In this light we see that *the* $x(t)$'s *are a minimal collection of quantities that, through Eqs. (2-1), provide a complete description of the plant output in terms of the plant input and time*. The $x(t)$'s are more than just the output in the conventional sense. We shall call the $x(t)$'s the state variables of the system. The number n will be referred to as the *order* of the system (2-1).

Collectively the set of Eqs. (2-1) will be referred to as the state equations of the system. Scrutinizing this set, we discern the following property of the state of a system:

If the state of a system $x_1(t), \ldots, x_n(t)$ *is known at one instant of time* t_0*, and if the system inputs* $u_1(t), \ldots, u_r(t)$ *are specified for* $t_0 \leq t \leq t_1$*, then the state of a system can be determined at time* t_1.

This property is true for all t_0 and t_1.

Thus far, we seem to have gained little by converting the plant from the form (2-2a) to the form (2-2b); but the gain becomes apparent if we introduce vector-matrix notation. To do this, we note that the system state may be represented by a vector in n-dimensional Euclidean space $\mathcal{E}_n$. We shall call this vector the *state vector* $\mathbf{x}(t)$ of the system, where*

$$\mathbf{x}(t) \triangleq \begin{bmatrix} x_1(t) \\ x_2(t) \\ \vdots \\ x_n(t) \end{bmatrix} \tag{2-3}$$

Similarly, we can consider the sets of variables $f_i (i = 1, \ldots, n)$, $u_i (i = 1, \ldots, r)$, $y_i (i = 1, \ldots, m)$ and $g_i (i = 1, \ldots, m)$ as column vectors in $\mathcal{E}_n$, $\mathcal{E}_r$, and $\mathcal{E}_m$:

$$\mathbf{f} = \begin{bmatrix} f_1 \\ \vdots \\ f_n \end{bmatrix}; \quad \mathbf{u} = \begin{bmatrix} u_1 \\ \vdots \\ u_r \end{bmatrix}; \quad \mathbf{y} = \begin{bmatrix} y_1 \\ \vdots \\ y_m \end{bmatrix}; \quad \mathbf{g} = \begin{bmatrix} g_1 \\ \vdots \\ g_m \end{bmatrix} \tag{2-4}$$

Using Eqs. (2-3) and (2-4) we can write Eq. (2-1) in the compact form**

$$\dot{\mathbf{x}} = \mathbf{f}(\mathbf{x},\mathbf{u},t); \qquad \mathbf{y} = \mathbf{g}(\mathbf{x},\mathbf{u},t) \tag{2-5}$$

Equation (2-5) can be represented in the block diagram shown in Fig. 2-3. In this the flow of a vector quantity is represented by double-line arrow. The block between $\dot{x}$ and x represents the operation $\mathbf{x} = (1/p)\mathbf{I}\dot{\mathbf{x}}$ (or $\dot{\mathbf{x}} = p\,\mathbf{x}$) where $\mathbf{I}$ is the identity matrix and $1/p$ represents the integration operator. The block between $\mathbf{u}$, $\mathbf{x}$, and $\mathbf{y}$ represents $\mathbf{y} = \mathbf{g}(\mathbf{x},\mathbf{u},t)$.

For a linear plant, the functions $f_i(x_1, \ldots, x_n;\ u_1, \ldots, u_r;\ t)$ and $g_j(x_1, \ldots, x_n;\ u_1, \ldots, u_r;\ t)$ are linear combinations of the state variables; that is, there are functions of time $a_{ij}(t)$ and $b_{ik}(t)$ $(i,j = 1, \ldots, n;\ k = 1, \ldots, r)$ such that

$$f_i(x_1, \ldots, x_n;\ u_1, \ldots, u_r;\ t) = \sum_{j=1}^{n} a_{ij}(t)x_j(t) + \sum_{k=1}^{r} b_{ik}(t)u_k(t) \tag{2-6}$$

*We use boldface lowercase letters $\mathbf{x}$, $\mathbf{y}$, $\mathbf{z}$ to denote vector quantities, and boldface uppercase letters $\mathbf{A}$, $\mathbf{B}$, $\mathbf{C}$ to denote matrices. The symbol $\triangleq$ indicates "defined as".

** We use $\dot{\mathbf{x}}$ to denote $d\mathbf{x}/dt$ which in turn represents the set of equations $\dot{x}_1 = dx_i/dt$ $(i = 1, \ldots, n)$.

and further, there are functions $c_{ij}(t)$ and $d_{ik}(t)$ $(i = 1, \ldots, m;$ $j = 1, \ldots, n;\ k = 1, \ldots, r)$ such that

$$g_i(x_1, \ldots, x_n;\ u_1, \ldots, u_r;\ t) = \sum_{j=1}^{n} c_{ij}(t) x_j(t) + \sum_{k=1}^{r} d_{ik}(t) u_k(t) \qquad (2\text{-}7)$$

and Eqs. (2-5) become

$$\dot{\mathbf{x}} = \mathbf{A}(t)\mathbf{x} + \mathbf{B}(t)\mathbf{u}; \qquad \mathbf{y} = \mathbf{C}(t)\mathbf{x} + \mathbf{D}(t)\mathbf{u} \qquad (2\text{-}8)$$

where

$$\mathbf{A}(t) \triangleq \begin{bmatrix} a_{11}(t) & \cdots & a_{1n}(t) \\ \vdots & & \\ a_{n1}(t) & \cdots & a_{nn}(t) \end{bmatrix}, \quad \mathbf{B}(t) \triangleq \begin{bmatrix} b_{11}(t) & \cdots & b_{1r}(t) \\ \vdots & & \\ b_{n1}(t) & \cdots & b_{nr}(t) \end{bmatrix}$$

$$(2\text{-}9)$$

$$\mathbf{C}(t) \triangleq \begin{bmatrix} c_{11}(t) & \cdots & c_{1n}(t) \\ \vdots & & \\ c_{m1}(t) & \cdots & c_{mn}(t) \end{bmatrix}, \quad \mathbf{D}(t) \triangleq \begin{bmatrix} d_{11}(t) & \cdots & d_{1r}(t) \\ \vdots & & \\ d_{m1}(t) & \cdots & d_{mr}(t) \end{bmatrix}$$

$\mathbf{A}(t)$, $\mathbf{B}(t)$, $\mathbf{C}(t)$, and $\mathbf{D}(t)$ are time-varying $n \times n$, $n \times r$, $m \times n$, and $m \times r$ matrices respectively.

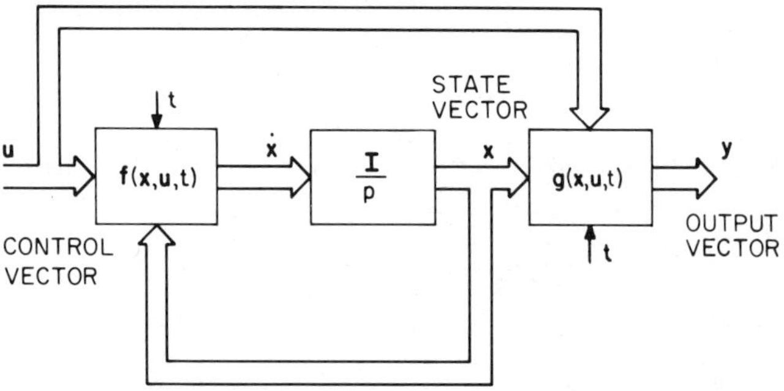

Fig. 2-3. The block diagram of a system represented by Eqs. (2-1*a*) and (2-1*b*) in vector representation.

A special case of particular interest is that of a plant with a single input u and a single output y. u and y are then one-dimensional vectors or scalars. Equations (2-8) can now be put in the form

$$\dot{\mathbf{x}} = \mathbf{A}(t)\mathbf{x} + \mathbf{b}(t)u, \qquad y = \mathbf{c}^T(t)\mathbf{x} + d(t)u \tag{2-10}$$

where

$$\mathbf{b}(t) = \begin{bmatrix} b_1(t) \\ \vdots \\ b_n(t) \end{bmatrix}, \quad \mathbf{c}(t) = \begin{bmatrix} c_1(t) \\ \vdots \\ c_n(t) \end{bmatrix} \tag{2-11}$$

and $\mathbf{c}^T(t)$ is the transpose* of the (column) vector $\mathbf{c}(t)$.

Relations of the form (2-5), (2-8), or (2-10) will be referred to as the *state equations* of a system. It will develop that the *state equations of a system are not unique*, i.e., there exist more than one set of state variables in terms of which the system behavior can be completely described.** However, any two sets of state variables are uniquely related. In a particular case, the state equation resulting from a given choice of state variables may prove to be simpler in form than other choices of state equations. Here, judgment is frequently necessary.

To gain some practical appreciation of how a typical system can be reduced to a set of equations of the form (2-1), consider:

◆◆Example 2-2. The angular equation of motion of an artificial satellite with jet-type actuators can be given by the Euler dynamical equations:

$$\dot{\omega}_1 = -\frac{(I_3 - I_2)}{I_1}\omega_2\omega_3 + \frac{u_1(t)}{I_1}$$

$$\dot{\omega}_2 = -\frac{(I_1 - I_3)}{I_2}\omega_3\omega_1 + \frac{u_2(t)}{I_2}$$

$$\dot{\omega}_3 = -\frac{(I_2 - I_1)}{I_3}\omega_1\omega_2 + \frac{u_3(t)}{I_3}$$

*See Appendix A.

** We do not, of course, count the obvious cases of different ordering of the same set of equations.

where I_i, ω_i, u_i $(i = 1,2,3)$ are respectively the moment of inertia, the angular rate component, and applied torque, each with respect to the ith principal axis of the satellite.

If the angular rate components along the principal axes ω_1, ω_2, ω_3 are chosen as the states, then the Euler dynamical equations are already in the form of Eq. (2-1a) with $x_i = \omega_i$, $i = 1,2,3$ and with f_1, for example, given by $f_1 = -(I_3 - I_2/I_1)\, x_2 x_3 + [u_1(t)]/I_1$ etc.

The components of angular rates can be measured by means of rate gyros appropriately mounted. These can be taken as the system outputs. If the gyros are ideal and properly aligned, then the outputs are the same as the system states or $y_i = x_i = \omega_i$. If the gyros are ideal but are, however, mounted with some misalignment, then each gyro will be sensitive to the angular rates about the other two axes and the outputs will be a linear combination of the states. This means that y_i's will be of the form $y_i = a_i x_1 + b_i x_2 + c_i x_3$ with a_i, b_i, c_i constants $(i = 1,2,3)$. This then means that the functions g_i's will be of the form (2-7).

If on the other hand, the gyros are properly aligned but each has a hard saturation characteristic, as is typical of a practical unit, then the functions g_i's will be nonlinear, and given by a characteristic such as shown in Fig. 2-4.◆◆

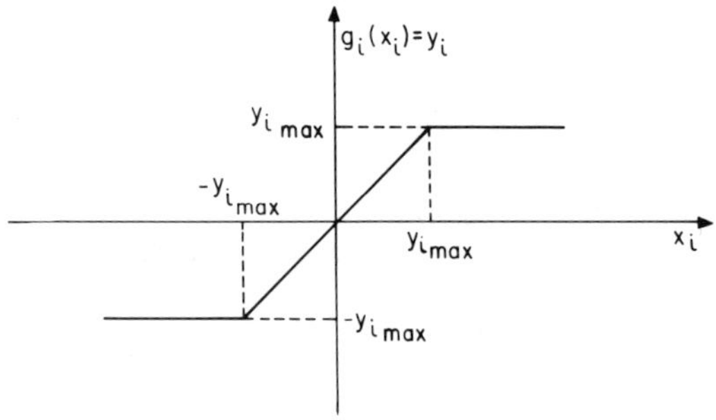

Fig. 2-4. A nonlinear characteristic.

2.3 Linear Systems in Operational Form

An nth order linear differential system with a single input and a single output is representable by an nth order ordinary differential equation of the following form:

$$L(p,t)\,y = M(p,t)\,u \tag{2-12}$$

Here y is the output of the system, u is the input, and p is the operator

$$p \overset{\Delta}{=} \frac{d}{dt}$$

The operators $L(p,t)$ and $M(p,t)$ are polynomials in p with time-varying coefficients:

$$L(p,t) = \sum_{i=0}^{n} a_{n-i}(t)\,p^i$$
$$M(p,t) = \sum_{j=0}^{l} c_{l-j}(t)\,p^j \qquad (2\text{-}13)$$

In the special case of a time-invariant system, Eq. (2-12) becomes

$$L(p)y = M(p)u \qquad (2\text{-}14)$$

where $L(p)$ and $M(p)$ are then polynomials in p with constant coefficients:

$$L(p) = \sum_{i=0}^{n} a_{n-i}p^i, \quad M(p) = \sum_{j=0}^{l} c_{l-j}p^j \qquad (2\text{-}15)$$

System (2-14) can be put in the more familiar form of Fig. 2-5a, where a transfer function $G(s) = M(s)/L(s)$ may be used to characterize the system in the transform domain. In many cases there is no need to invoke the transform domain, and we shall represent the system of (2-12) by a block $G(p) \triangleq M(p)/L(p)$ as in Fig. 2-5b with the understanding that the figure is to mean no more than Eq. (2-14). Thus $G(p)$ is a time-domain operating block.

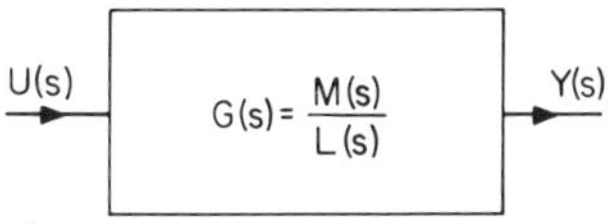

Fig. 2-5a. Block diagram representation of the system of Eq. (2-14) in the transform domain.

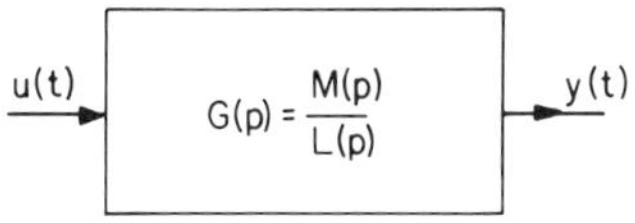

Fig. 2-5b. Block diagram representation of the system of Eq. (2-14) in the time domain.

We can now examine the main ways of finding system state equations of the form (2-8) for systems which can be characterized by differential equations of the form (2-12) or (2-14).

2.4 State Equations for Linear Time-Invariant Systems with No Numerator Dynamics

A system of the form (2-14) has the roots of $L(p)$ as its poles and the roots of $M(p)$ as its zeros. When $M(p)$ is a constant, we say that the system has no numerator dynamics. In this case, the input $u(t)$ does not directly appear in the expression for the output $y(t)$ (i.e., d in (2-10) is 0) and there are several simple methods for the finding of the system state equations, some of which follow.

1. The Method of Partial Fraction Expansion — Canonical Forms

Without loss of generality we can consider the system $G(p) = 1/L(p)$, whereby

$$L(p)y = u \tag{2-16}$$

Assuming for the time being that $L(p)$ has simple zeros, it may be written:

$$L(p) = \prod_{i=1}^{n} (p - \lambda_i) \tag{2-17}$$

where λ_i are the poles of the system $G(p)$ or the roots of the polynomial $L(\lambda)$. By a partial fraction expansion of $1/L(p)$, we obtain

$$\frac{1}{L(p)} = \sum_{i=1}^{n} \frac{c_i}{p - \lambda_i} \tag{2-18}$$

or

$$\left(\sum_{i=1}^{n} \frac{c_i}{p - \lambda_1}\right) u(t) = y(t)$$

If we let

$$x_i(t) = \frac{1}{p - \lambda_i} u(t) \tag{2-19}$$

then

$$y(t) = \sum_{i=1}^{n} c_i x_i(t) \tag{2-20}$$

Now x_i, by Eq. (2-19), satisfies the first-order differential equation

$$\dot{x}_i - \lambda_i x_i = u , \qquad i = 1, \ldots, n \tag{2-21}$$

Equation (2-21) is equivalent to the set

$$\dot{\mathbf{x}} = \mathbf{A}\,\mathbf{x} + \mathbf{b}\,u \tag{2-22}$$

where

$$\mathbf{A} = \begin{bmatrix} \lambda_1 & & 0 \\ & \ddots & \\ 0 & & \lambda_n \end{bmatrix} \triangleq \Lambda, \qquad \mathbf{b} = \begin{bmatrix} 1 \\ \vdots \\ 1 \end{bmatrix} \tag{2-23}$$

In addition we have

$$y = \mathbf{c}^T \mathbf{x} \tag{2-24}$$

where $\mathbf{c}$ is the column vector of the residues

$$\begin{bmatrix} c_1 \\ \vdots \\ c_n \end{bmatrix}$$

Equations (2-22) and (2-24) completely characterize the system and constitute the state equations of the system.

This particular method of forming state equations has the advantage of giving an $\mathbf{A}$ matrix which is diagonal and hence is much simpler to manipulate. Moreover, the eigenvalues or poles of the system are clearly displayed.

A block diagram of the system corresponding to Eqs. (2-22) and (2-24) is as shown in Fig. 2-6. It is seen that each dominant mode of the block $G(p)$ is separated.

It should also be recognized that the roots λ_1 need not be real in order for this particular method to apply. If λ_1 and λ_2 are complex conjugates, their output states x_1 and x_2 will also be complex conjugates.

◆◆Example 2-3. Consider the system given by $(p^2 + 1)y = u$. By partial fraction expansion

$$\frac{1}{p^2 + 1} = \frac{-j/2}{p - j} + \frac{j/2}{p + j}$$

where $j = \sqrt{-1}$, thus

$$\mathbf{A} = \begin{bmatrix} j & 0 \\ 0 & -j \end{bmatrix}, \quad \mathbf{b} = \begin{bmatrix} 1 \\ 1 \end{bmatrix} \quad \text{and} \quad \mathbf{c} = \begin{bmatrix} -\frac{j}{2} \\ \frac{j}{2} \end{bmatrix}$$ ♦♦

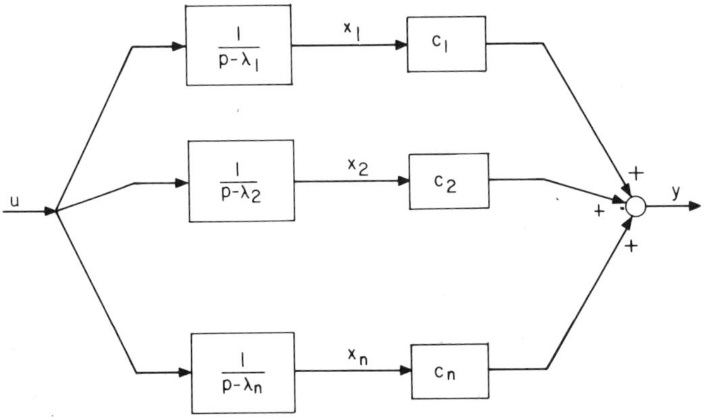

Fig. 2-6. Block diagram of a linear time-invariant system in the canonical form.

We should recognize, however, that it is quite inconvenient in many cases to carry complex values for the state components. For one thing it will deprive us of our ability to portray an n-dimensional state in an n-dimensional space. Practically, it is generally advisable, therefore, to avoid the use of any imaginary number in writing state equations. Thus the canonical form representation is usually avoided if there are complex poles.

In the case of multiple roots, the partial fraction expansion method can still be used, as is shown below:

♦♦Example 2-4. Consider the system with $M(p) = 1$ and $L(p) = (p - \lambda_1)^2(p - \lambda_2)$.

Here,

$$G(p) = \frac{c_1}{(p - \lambda_1)^2} + \frac{c_2}{(p - \lambda_1)} + \frac{c_3}{(p - \lambda_2)}$$

where $c_1 = 1/(\lambda_1 - \lambda_2)$, $c_2 = -1/(\lambda_1 - \lambda_2)^2 = -c_3$. The circuit diagram corresponding to the above is as shown in Fig. 2-7, and the corresponding state equation is

$$\dot{x}_1 = \lambda_1 x_1 + x_2, \quad \dot{x}_2 = \lambda_1 x_2 + u, \quad \dot{x}_3 = \lambda_2 x_3 + u$$

or:

$$\begin{bmatrix} \dot{x}_1 \\ \dot{x}_2 \\ \dot{x}_3 \end{bmatrix} = \begin{bmatrix} \lambda_1 & 1 & 0 \\ 0 & \lambda_1 & 0 \\ 0 & 0 & \lambda_2 \end{bmatrix} \begin{bmatrix} x_1 \\ x_2 \\ x_3 \end{bmatrix} + \begin{bmatrix} 0 \\ 1 \\ 1 \end{bmatrix} u$$

the output is still $y = \mathbf{c}^T\mathbf{x}$, where

$$\mathbf{c} = \begin{bmatrix} c_1 \\ c_2 \\ c_3 \end{bmatrix} \blacklozenge\blacklozenge$$

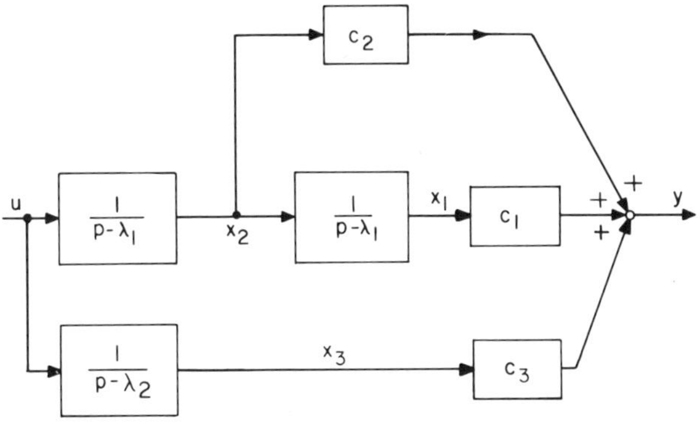

Fig. 2-7. Block diagram of the system of Ex. 2-4.

In the general case $L(p) = (p - \lambda_1)^{k_1}(p - \lambda_2)^{k_2} \ldots (p - \lambda_r)^{k_r}$ (where $k_1 + k_2 + \cdots + k_r = n$), it is not difficult to see that through partial fraction expansion, the system matrix $\mathbf{A}$ takes the Jordan canonical form:

$$\mathbf{A} = \begin{bmatrix} \mathbf{J}_{k_1}(\lambda_1) & 0 & \cdots & 0 \\ 0 & \mathbf{J}_{k_2}(\lambda_2) & & 0 \\ \vdots & & \ddots & \vdots \\ 0 & & & \mathbf{J}_{k_r}(\lambda_r) \end{bmatrix} \triangleq \mathbf{\Lambda}_J \tag{2-25}$$

where each diagonal block $J_{k_i}(\lambda_i)$ is a $k_i \times k_i$ matrix with λ_i at each position of the main diagonal of the matrix and one's or zeros immediately above each of the λ_i's except the first. The rest of the positions are occupied by zeros, that is,

$$J_{k_i}(\lambda_i) = \begin{bmatrix} \lambda_i & h_{i1} & 0 & . & . & 0 \\ 0 & \lambda_i & h_{i2} & & & . \\ \vdots & & & . & & \vdots \\ & & & & . & \\ . & & & & . & h_{ik_i} \\ 0 & & & & & \lambda_i \end{bmatrix} \qquad (2\text{-}26)$$

where each of $h_{i1} \ldots h_{ik_i}$ is either unity or zero.

The vector **b** has unity in the

$$k_1^{\text{th}},\ (k_1 + k_2)^{\text{th}},\ \ldots\ \left(\sum_{i=1}^{r} k_i\right)^{\text{th}}$$

places and zeros in all other places.

The circuit diagram for each of the sub-blocks $J_{k_i}(\lambda_i)$ will be of the form of Fig. 2-8, where the c_{j,k_i}'s are the appropriate residues.

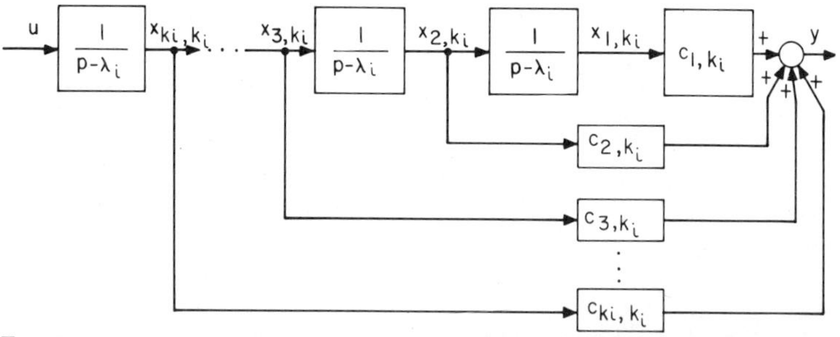

Fig. 2-8. Block diagram of a linear time-invariant system that will have an A matrix that is the Jordan matrix Λ_J.

State equations where the A matrix is either the diagonal matrix of eigenvalues Λ or the Jordan matrix Λ_J will be referred to as *canonical state equations*. In these cases the system is represented in a simple and convenient form for subsequent manipulation.

2. The Method of Simple Factors

Whenever $G(p)$ can be factored, it can be put into the form

$$G(p) = \prod_{i=1}^{n} \frac{1}{(p - \lambda_i)} \tag{2-27}$$

Then a suitable circuit or block diagram may be that shown in Fig. 2-9.

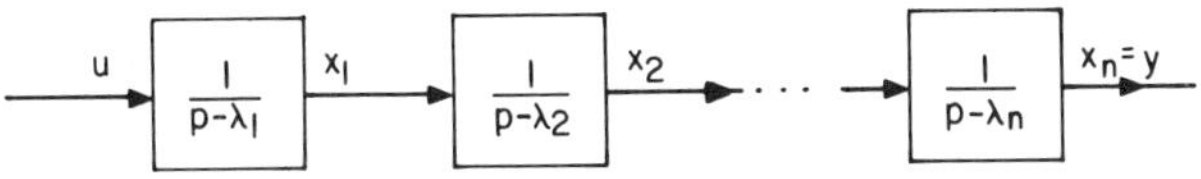

Fig. 2-9. Block diagram of a linear time-invariant system decomposed into simple factors.

Assigning state variables as shown, we see by inspection that

$$\begin{aligned} \dot{x}_1 &= \lambda_1 x_1 + u \\ \dot{x}_2 &= \lambda_2 x_2 + x_1 \\ &\vdots \\ \dot{x}_n &= \lambda_n x_n + x_{n-1} \end{aligned} \tag{2-28}$$

and the output y is simply equal to x_n. Thus, the state equation in vector-matrix form will have

$$\mathbf{A} = \begin{bmatrix} \lambda_1 & & \cdots & 0 & 0 \\ 1 & \lambda_2 & & & \\ & 1 & & & \\ \vdots & & \ddots & & \vdots \\ 0 & & & 1 & \lambda_n \end{bmatrix} \tag{2-29}$$

and

$$\mathbf{b} = \begin{bmatrix} 1 \\ \vdots \\ 0 \\ 0 \end{bmatrix}, \qquad \mathbf{c} = \begin{bmatrix} 0 \\ 0 \\ \vdots \\ 1 \end{bmatrix} \tag{2-30}$$

This method is clearly not restricted to simple roots.

3. Method Derived from Analog Simulation with Feedback

In analog simulation, systems of the form $G(p) = 1/L(p)$ can be simulated by various feedback configurations, using adders, sign changers, and integrators. From these, the system state equation can be written by inspection. It is not necessary to factor $L(p)$.

♦♦Example 2-5. A possible realization for

$$\frac{y}{u} = \frac{1}{p^3 + ap^2 + bp + c} \tag{2-31}$$

is that shown in Fig. 2-10, as can be easily verified.

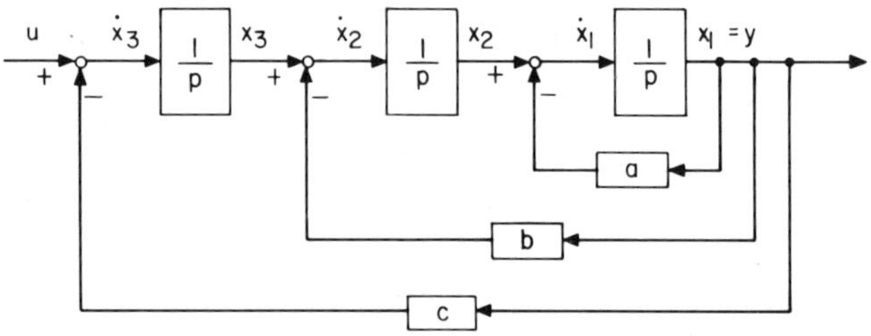

Fig. 2-10. An analog computer realization for the plant of Eq. (2-31).

If the state variables are assigned as shown in Fig. 2-10, then by inspection, the system state equation may be written as:

$$\dot{x}_1 = x_2 - ax_1, \quad \dot{x}_2 = x_3 - bx_1, \quad \dot{x}_3 = -cx_1 + u, \quad y = x_1$$

Thus:

$$\mathbf{A} = \begin{bmatrix} -a & 1 & 0 \\ -b & 0 & 1 \\ -c & 0 & 0 \end{bmatrix}, \quad \mathbf{b} = \begin{bmatrix} 0 \\ 0 \\ 1 \end{bmatrix}, \quad \mathbf{c} = \begin{bmatrix} 1 \\ 0 \\ 0 \end{bmatrix}$$ ♦♦

4. The Normal Form

A classically popular approach is to use as state variables the output and its $n-1$ derivatives. The advantage of this approach lies in the ease of interpreting the significance of the result when the state vector assumes a certain set of values. Moreover, as we have already seen from Eqs. (2-2), a general nonlinear differential system also allows such a representation. If $n = 2$, the system output can be portrayed by trajectories on the classical phase plane; we shall discuss this in Chap. 4. When $n > 2$, the system output can be visualized as trajectories in an n-dimensional "phase space."* It is easy to show that, for

$$L(p) = \sum_{i=0}^{n} a_{n-i}p^i$$

and with the present choice of state variables,

$$x_1 = y, \; x_2 = \dot{x}_1, \; x_3 = \dot{x}_2, \ldots, x_n = \dot{x}_{n-1}$$

the system state equation will have an A matrix of the following form

$$\mathbf{A} = \begin{bmatrix} 0 & 1 & 0 & \cdots & 0 \\ 0 & 0 & 1 & & \cdot \\ \vdots & & & & \vdots \\ \cdot & & & & 1 \\ -\dfrac{a_n}{a_0} & -\dfrac{a_{n-1}}{a_0} & \cdots & \cdots & -\dfrac{a_1}{a_0} \end{bmatrix} \tag{2-32}$$

Also, we will have

$$\mathbf{b} = \begin{bmatrix} 0 \\ \vdots \\ 0 \\ \dfrac{1}{a_0} \end{bmatrix}, \qquad \mathbf{c} = \begin{bmatrix} 1 \\ 0 \\ \vdots \\ 0 \end{bmatrix}$$

Following Zadeh and Desoer [Z1], we shall refer to this set of state variables as the *normal* state variables.

In analog realization, Fig. 2-11 is a representation of the system.

*For this reason, some writers refer to this choice of state variables as *phase variables*. However, we shall not use this notion here.

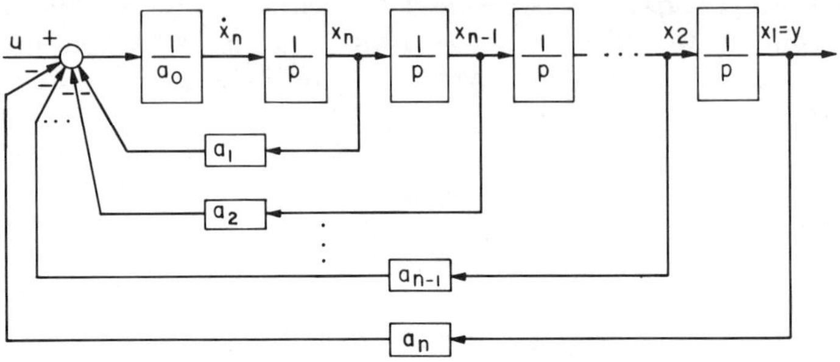

Fig. 2-11. An analog computer realization of a linear time-invariant plant in the normal form.

2.5 State Equations for Linear Time-Invariant Systems with Numerator Dynamics of Order l, $1 \le l \le n$

When the "numerator dynamics" $M(p)$ is of an order less than or equal to $L(p)$, the system can still be represented in the form of Eqs. (2-18) or (2-20). We shall discuss this relative to the various methods as before.

1. The Method of Partial Fraction Expansion

Here no essential difference has been introduced except possibly for the presence of a constant term in the expansion which occurs when $M(p)$ is of the same order as $L(p)$, or $l = n$. Thus y can be of the form

$$y = \mathbf{c}^T\mathbf{x} + du$$

where d is a constant.

All other quantities retain the same form as in the previous case.

2. The Method of Simple Factors

Here if we expand $G(p)$ in terms of its poles and zeros, we have:

$$G(p) = k\prod_{i=1}^{l} \frac{(p - \gamma_i)}{(p - \lambda_i)} \prod_{i=l+1}^{n} \frac{1}{(p - \lambda_i)}$$

where the γ_i's are the zeros of $G(p)$. Since:

$$\frac{p - \gamma_i}{p - \lambda_i} = 1 + \frac{\lambda_i - \gamma_i}{p - \lambda_i}$$

the $G(p)$ above can then be diagrammed as shown in Fig. 2-12. Choosing the state variables as shown, we write by inspection:

$$\dot{x}_1 = \lambda_1 x_1 + (\lambda_1 - \gamma_1) u$$

$$\dot{x}_2 = \lambda_2 x_2 + (\lambda_2 - \gamma_2) x_1 + (\lambda_2 - \gamma_2) u$$

$$\vdots$$

$$\dot{x}_n = \lambda_n x_n + x_{n-1}$$

$$y = k x_n$$

and the system matrices follow directly.

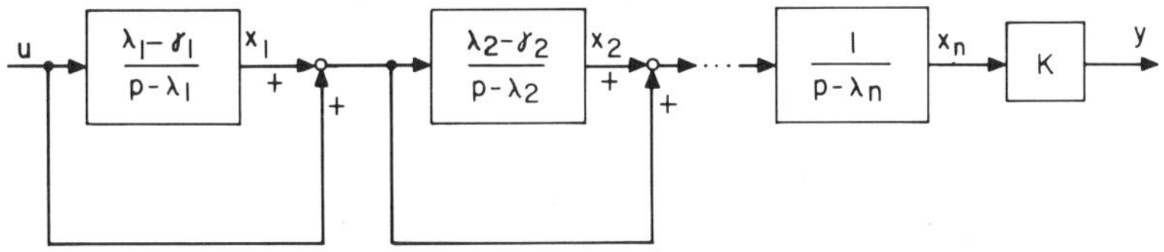

Fig. 2-12. A block diagram realization in terms of simple factors for a linear time-invariant plant with numerator dynamics of order $l < n$.

3. Method Derived from Analog Simulation with Feedback

It is not difficult to show that to add numerator dynamics to a realization such as given in Fig. 2-11, only appropriate feed-forward branches are needed. Thus for the system given by:

$$\frac{y}{u} = \frac{dp^3 + ep^2 + fp + g}{p^3 + ap^2 + bp + c}$$

a realization is given by Fig. 2-13.

The state equation can again be written from inspection:

$$\begin{bmatrix} \dot{x}_1 \\ \dot{x}_2 \\ \dot{x}_3 \end{bmatrix} = \begin{bmatrix} -a & 1 & 0 \\ -b & 0 & 1 \\ -c & 0 & 0 \end{bmatrix} \begin{bmatrix} x_1 \\ x_2 \\ x_3 \end{bmatrix} + \begin{bmatrix} e - ad \\ f - bd \\ g - cd \end{bmatrix} u, \qquad y = \mathbf{c}^T \mathbf{x} + du$$

where $\mathbf{c}^T = (1 \quad 0 \quad 0)$.

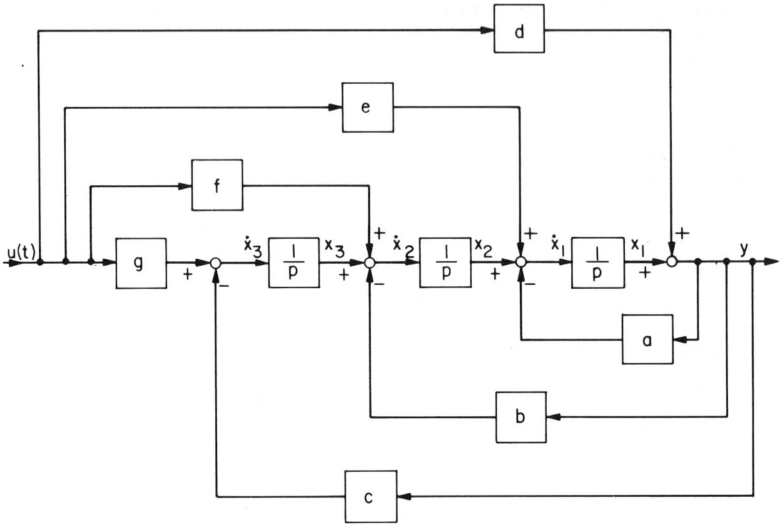

Fig. 2-13. A block diagram realization of a linear time-invariant plant with feed-forward and feedback paths.

Note that A and c are unchanged from those of Example 2-5, though b has been changed and y is now explicitly dependent on u.

4. The Normal Form

The derivatives of $u(t)$ can be avoided and, moreover, a state equation in the normal form can result if suitable changes of variables are made.

♦♦Example 2-6. Consider the system

$$\frac{p + a}{(p + b)(p + c)} = \frac{y}{u}$$

or:

$$\frac{d^2y}{dt^2} + (b + c)\frac{dy}{dt} + (bc)y = \frac{du}{dt} + au \tag{2-33}$$

Instead of the usual substitution $x_1 = y, dx_1/dt = x_2$, etc., let

$$y = x_1 + k_0 u \tag{2-34}$$

$$\frac{dx_1}{dt} = x_2 + k_1 u \tag{2-35}$$

$$\frac{dx_2}{dt} = -(b + c)x_2 - (bc)x_1 + k_2 u \tag{2-36}$$

From (2-34) we have

$$\frac{dy}{dt} = \frac{dx_1}{dt} + k_0 \frac{du}{dt} \tag{2-37}$$

Using (2-35), we obtain

$$x_2 = \frac{dy}{dt} - k_0 \frac{du}{dt} - k_1 u \tag{2-38}$$

From (2-37):

$$\frac{d^2y}{dt^2} = \frac{dx_2}{dt} + k_0 \frac{d^2u}{dt^2} + k_1 \frac{du}{dt} \tag{2-39}$$

and from (2-36), (2-38), and (2-39)

$$\frac{d^2y}{dt^2} - k_0 \frac{d^2u}{dt^2} - k_1 \frac{du}{dt} =$$

$$-(b + c)\left[\frac{du}{dt} - k_0 \frac{du}{dt} - k_1 u\right] - (bc)\,[y - k_0 u] + k_2 u \tag{2-40}$$

Collecting terms and comparing to (2-33) we have

$$k_0 = 0, \qquad k_1 = 1, \qquad k_2 = a - (b + c)$$

Thus with this substitution, the state equation for the system of Eq. (2-33) is

$$\begin{bmatrix} \dot{x}_1 \\ \dot{x}_2 \end{bmatrix} = \begin{bmatrix} 0 & 1 \\ -bc & -(b + c) \end{bmatrix} \begin{bmatrix} x_1 \\ x_2 \end{bmatrix} + \begin{bmatrix} k_1 \\ k_2 \end{bmatrix} u$$ ◆◆

In the general case where

$$L(p) = \sum_{i=0}^{n} a_{n-i} p^i$$

and

$$M(p) = \sum_{j=0}^{n} b_{n-j} p^j$$

with $L(p)$ normalized so that $a_0 = 1$, it is left for the reader to show that the system normal state equation will have an $\mathbf{A}$ matrix that retains the form (2-32), a vector $\mathbf{b}$ of the form

$$\begin{bmatrix} k_1 \\ k_2 \\ \vdots \\ k_n \end{bmatrix}$$

and an output of the form $y = x_1 + k_0 u$ where

$$k_0 = b_0, \quad k_i = b_i - \sum_{m=0}^{i-1} a_{i-m} k_m \tag{2-41}$$

2.6 State Equations for Linear Time-Invariant Systems with Numerator Dynamics of Order $l > n$

When the numerator dynamics exceed the order of the denominator, then derivatives of the input will appear and the state equation will be of the form

$$\begin{aligned} \dot{\mathbf{x}} &= \mathbf{A}\,\mathbf{x} + \mathbf{b}_1 u + \mathbf{b}_2 \dot{u} + \cdots + \mathbf{b}_k \frac{d^k u}{dt^k} \\ \mathbf{y} &= \mathbf{c}^T \mathbf{x} + du \end{aligned} \tag{2-42}$$

Here $G(p)$ must be written in the form

$$G(p) = d_0 p^r + \cdots + d_r p + \frac{b_0 p^n + \cdots + b_n}{a_0 p^n + \cdots + a_n} \tag{2-43}$$

The rational portion can be treated by the various methods previously described; the remaining portion is responsible for the appearance of derivatives of u in Eq. (2-42).

2.7 State Equations for Linear Time-Varying Systems

Here the system is described by Eq. (2-12). Methods derived from partial fraction expansion are awkward to apply to this; the feedback approach and the normal form approach are, however, still valid. In particular, when the numerator is of the same order as the denominator, the method under Part 4 of Sec. 2.5 still applies if the parameters $k_0, k_1, \ldots, k_n$ are treated as functions of time. It may be shown* that for

$$L(p,t) = \sum_{i=0}^{n} a_{n-i}(t)\, p^i$$

where a_n is normalized to unity and

$$M(p,t) = \sum_{j=0}^{n} b_{n-j}(t)\, p^j$$

we will have

$$k_0(t) = b_0(t), \qquad k_i(t) = b_i(t) - \sum_{m=0}^{i-1} \sum_{k=0}^{i-m} \binom{n+k-i}{n-i} a_{i-m-k}(t)\, p^k\, k_m(t) \tag{2-44}$$

Where the symbol $\binom{n}{r}$ is the number of combinations of n items taken r at a time; its value is:

$$\binom{n}{r} = \frac{n!}{r!\,(n-r)!} \tag{2-45}$$

2.8 The Case of Multiple Inputs and Outputs

It is now a relatively straightforward matter to obtain state equations for a system with multiple inputs and outputs. In this case we need matrices $\mathbf{B}$ and $\mathbf{C}$ rather than vectors $\mathbf{b}$ and $\mathbf{c}$ to characterize the system.

♦♦Example 2-7. Consider the system shown in Fig. 2-14, which is a system with two inputs and three outputs. By inspection, the system is sixth order.

*See [Z1] p. 357 and [L1] p. 190.

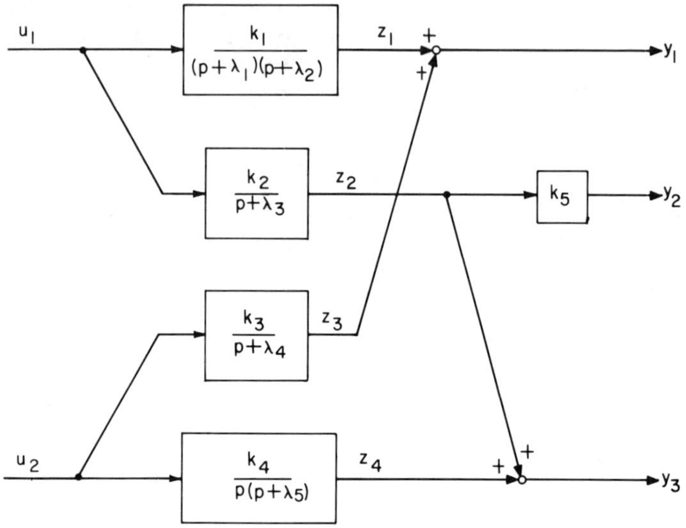

Fig. 2-14. The system of Ex. 2-7.

Choosing the normal coordinates method, we assign the following state variables

$$x_1 = z_1,\ x_2 = \dot{x}_1 = \dot{z}_1,\ x_3 = z_2,\ x_4 = z_3,\ x_5 = z_4,\ x_6 = \dot{x}_5 = \dot{z}_4$$

Then by inspection we obtain $\dot{\mathbf{x}} = \mathbf{A}\,\mathbf{x} + \mathbf{B}\,\mathbf{u}$, $\mathbf{y} = \mathbf{C}\mathbf{x}$, with

$$\mathbf{A} = \begin{bmatrix} 0 & 1 & 0 & 0 & 0 & 0 \\ -\lambda_1\lambda_2 & -(\lambda_1+\lambda_2) & 0 & 0 & 0 & 0 \\ 0 & 0 & -\lambda_3 & 0 & 0 & 0 \\ 0 & 0 & 0 & -\lambda_4 & 0 & 0 \\ 0 & 0 & 0 & 0 & 0 & 1 \\ 0 & 0 & 0 & 0 & 0 & -\lambda_5 \end{bmatrix}, \quad \mathbf{B} = \begin{bmatrix} 0 & 0 \\ k_1 & 0 \\ k_2 & 0 \\ 0 & k_3 \\ 0 & 0 \\ 0 & k_4 \end{bmatrix}$$

$$\mathbf{C} = \begin{bmatrix} 1 & 0 & 0 & 1 & 0 & 0 \\ 0 & 0 & k_5 & 0 & 0 & 0 \\ 0 & 0 & 1 & 0 & 1 & 0 \end{bmatrix} \quad ◆◆$$

2.9 The Characteristic Equations for Time-Invariant Systems

For time-invariant systems of the form of (2-14), it is well known that the polynomial

$$L(\lambda) = 0 \tag{2-46}$$

where λ is a complex variable, is the characteristic equation of the system. The roots of Eq. (2-46) are known as the poles of the system.

When the system (2-14) is described by the state equation

$$\dot{\mathbf{x}} = \mathbf{A}\,\mathbf{x} + \mathbf{B}\,\mathbf{u} \tag{2-47}$$

it can quite readily be shown (exercise for the student) that the characteristic equation can be obtained through the determinant*

$$|\mathbf{A} - \lambda\mathbf{I}| = 0 \tag{2-48}$$

Thus we have

$$L(\lambda) \equiv |\mathbf{A} - \lambda\mathbf{I}|$$

In matrix analysis, the solution of Eq. (2-48) [and hence the poles of the system (2-34)] are known as the eigenvalues or characteristic values of the matrix $\mathbf{A}$.

Equation (2-48) results from finding those vectors $\mathbf{v}$ in the state space which transform under $\mathbf{A}$ into linear multiples of themselves; that is

$$\mathbf{A}\,\mathbf{v} = \lambda\mathbf{v} \tag{2-49}$$

where λ, as in the case of Eq. (2-48), is a complex-valued scalar. Vectors satisfying Eq. (2-49) are known as eigenvectors for the matrix $\mathbf{A}$. A fuller discussion of matrix fundamentals is given in Appendix A.

2.10 Summary

Almost all differential systems can be cast into the vector equations:

$$\dot{\mathbf{x}} = \mathbf{f}(\mathbf{x},\mathbf{u},t), \qquad \mathbf{y} = \mathbf{g}(\mathbf{x},\mathbf{u},t) \tag{2-5}$$

*This will be true if there is no pole-zero cancellation in $G(p)$. One can view pole-zero cancellation as a fortuitous circumstance when a normally n^{th} order system would appear to an external observer as if it were a $(n - 1)^{\text{th}}$ order system provided that all the initial conditions of the system were 0. When this occurs the residue of the cancelled pole will be 0, and so the canonical form flow diagram will have one forward path which is open. If this branch is ignored, there results an A matrix which is $(n - 1) \times (n - 1)$. Pole-zero cancellation is related to the concepts of controllability of a system. We shall discuss it further in the next chapter..

and, in particular, a linear differential system may be put into the vector-matrix form

$$\dot{\mathbf{x}} = \mathbf{A}(t)\mathbf{x} + \mathbf{B}(t)\mathbf{u}, \quad \mathbf{y} = \mathbf{C}(t)\mathbf{x} + \mathbf{D}(t)\mathbf{u} \tag{2-8}$$

The representations (2-5) and (2-8) are known as the *system state equations*. These representations are generally not unique and the selection of a particular representation sometimes depends on the problem at hand.

Several ways to choose the state variables are given in Secs. 2.5 and 2.6. In the case of the linear time-invariant system, two representations are of particular importance:

1) The normal form, where the state vector is composed of the output and its first $n-1$ derivatives; and
2) The canonical form, where the x's are the output variables corresponding to each of the normal modes.

In the case of a linear time-varying system, the normal form representation is still possible but the canonical form is not.

When there is "numerator dynamics" (i.e., the polynomial $M(p,t)$ in (2-12) or $M(p)$ in (2-14) is not a constant), the writing of the normal form representation becomes more complicated. A variable x_1 that is a suitable linear combination of the output and the input needs to be created. x_1 and its $n-1$ derivatives are then used as the state variables. (See Example 2-6 and Sec. 2.7.)

Differential systems with multiple inputs and outputs can also be readily put in the state equation form.

In the next chapter we shall investigate the solutions of the system equations

2.11 Exercises

2-1 Obtain the state equation for the "all-pass" network

$$\frac{Y(p)}{U(p)} = \frac{1 - \tau_1 p}{1 + \tau_1 p}$$

such that the derivative of u does not appear. Exhibit the result in the form of a circuit diagram or signal-flow graph from u to y.

2-2 For the system of Example 2-3, obtain the state equations in normal form and obtain the transformation matrix between the canonical state vector (x_1,x_2) and the normal state vector (y_1,y_2).

2-3 Show that the normal state equations for the linear element of transfer function

$$G(p) = \frac{\sum_{i=0}^{n} b_{n-i} p^i}{\sum_{i=0}^{n-1} a_{n-i} p^i + p^n}$$

can be written as

$$\begin{bmatrix} \dot{x}_1 \\ \dot{x}_2 \\ \cdot \\ \cdot \\ \cdot \\ \dot{x}_{n-1} \\ \dot{x}_n \end{bmatrix} = \begin{bmatrix} 0 & 1 & 0 & \cdots & 0 & 0 \\ 0 & 0 & 1 & & 0 & 0 \\ \cdot & & & & & \\ \cdot & & & & & \\ \cdot & & & & & \\ 0 & 0 & 0 & & 0 & 1 \\ -a_n & -a_{n-1} & -a_{n-2} & \cdots & -a_2 & -a_1 \end{bmatrix} \begin{bmatrix} x_1 \\ x_2 \\ \cdot \\ \cdot \\ \cdot \\ x_{n-1} \\ x_n \end{bmatrix}$$

$$+ \begin{bmatrix} k_1 \\ k_2 \\ \cdot \\ \cdot \\ \cdot \\ k_{n-1} \\ k_n \end{bmatrix} u$$

where the output is given by

$$y = x_1 + k_0 u$$

and the constants k_i are given by

$$k_0 = b_0$$

$$k_i = b_i - \sum_{j=0}^{i-1} k_j a_{i-j} \qquad (i = 1, \ldots, n)$$

2-4 Consider a linear time-invariant system with one input, $u(t)$, and one output, $y(t)$, whose input-output relationship is given by

$$y(t) = G(p)u(t), \quad G(p) = \frac{(p+1)(p+4)}{(p+3)^3(p+2)^2}$$

Obtain state equations for this system and draw appropriate block or signal-flow diagrams

a) for the canonical state equations,
b) for a set of state equations obtained by the method of simple factors,
c) for the normal state equations.

2-5 A fin-controlled missile moving in a vertical plane is as shown in Fig. 2-15. For the missile, when the angle of attack α and the fin-angle are small, we have the following set of linearized state equations*

$$\dot{\theta} = \omega$$

$$\dot{\omega} = \frac{Q}{I} C_{m\alpha}\alpha + \frac{Q}{I} C_{m\delta}\delta$$

$$\dot{\alpha} = \omega - \left[\frac{QC_{L\alpha}}{mV} + \frac{T}{mV}\right]\alpha - \frac{Q}{mV} C_{L\delta}\delta$$

$$a_N = \frac{QC_{N\alpha}}{mg}\alpha + \frac{QC_{N\delta}}{mg}\delta$$

where the first equation represents the definition of the angular rate ω, the second equation represents the sum of all angular acceleration terms, and the third equation represents the sum of all

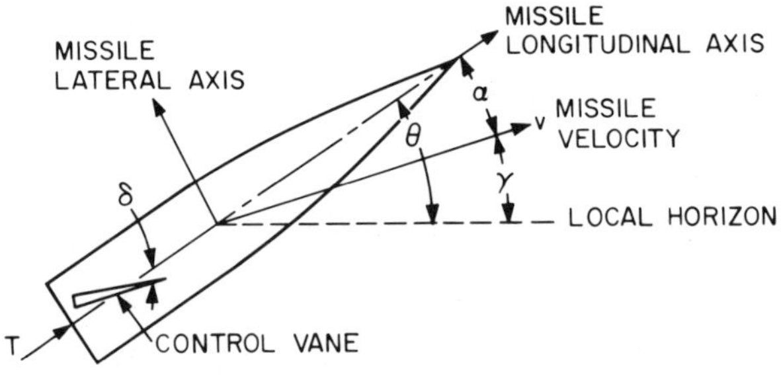

Fig. 2-15. The missile of Exercise 2-5.

*The derivation of this set of equations will be given in Chap. 5.

force terms in the direction perpendicular to the velocity vector. The quantities I, m, and V are respectively the pitch moment of inertia, the mass, and the velocity of the missile. They are all constants for the present problem, as are the quantities T and Q which are respectively the thrust and the dynamic pressure acting on the missile. In addition, the aerodynamic coefficients $C_{m\alpha}$, $C_{m\delta}$, $C_{N\alpha}$, $C_{N\delta}$, $C_{L\alpha}$, and $C_{L\delta}$ are to be taken as constants. The quantity a_N is the lateral acceleration of the missile in g's.

a) Obtain the transfer function $G(p)$ between the input $\delta(t)$ and the output $a_N(t)$.
b) From the result of (a), write the state equations in normal form.
c) From the result of (a), write the state equations in canonical form.

To streamline the calculations in this problem, use the following notation:

$$A_\delta = \frac{C_{m\delta}}{I}, \quad B_\delta = \frac{C_{L\delta}}{mV}, \quad C_\delta = -\frac{C_{N\delta}}{mg}$$

$$a_0 = -\frac{Q}{I} C_{m\alpha}, \quad a_1 = \frac{Q}{mV} C_{L\alpha} + \frac{T}{mV}$$

$$c_0 = -\frac{Q}{I}\left(\frac{C_{m\delta}C_{N\alpha}}{C_{N\delta}} - C_{m\alpha}\right), \quad c_1 = \frac{Q}{mV}(C_{N\alpha} - C_{L\alpha}) - \frac{T}{mV}$$

Moreover, we may assume that

$$C_{N\delta} = C_{L\delta}$$

2-6 Prove that for the $\mathbf{A}$ matrix in normal form, given by Eq. (2-32), the characteristic equation (2-48) yields

$$\lambda^n + \frac{a_1}{a_0}\lambda^{n-1} + \frac{a_2}{a_0}\lambda^{n-2} + \cdots + \frac{a_{n-2}}{a_0}\lambda^2 + \frac{a_{n-1}}{a_0}\lambda + \frac{a_n}{a_0} = 0$$

2-7 From first principles, derive the state equation for a simple pendulum consisting of a mass m suspended at the end of a massless string of length l.

2-8 Find a set of state equations for a network consisting of a voltage source $e(t)$ connected across a network with a resistor, a capacitor and an inductor all in parallel. Do the problem assuming that

a) the resistor, capacitor, and inductor are all constant with values r ohms, c farads, and l henries respectively.
b) the capacitor and resistor are time-varying, with values $c(t)$ farads and $r(t)$ ohms respectively. The inductor of l henries remains time invariant.

2-9 Consider the system

$$\frac{d^3y}{dt^3} + 9\frac{d^2y}{dt^2} + 23\frac{dy}{dt} + 15y = \frac{d^2u}{dt^2} + 2\frac{du}{dt} + 2u$$

By each of the methods given in Sec. 2.5, arrive at the corresponding state equation that does not involve the derivatives of $u(t)$.

2-10 Consider a system with a $G(p)$ of the form

$$G(p) = \frac{M(p)}{(p - \lambda_1)^3}$$

where $M(p)$ is a third-order polynomial in p with constant coefficients.

a) Choose a set of state variables such that the Λ matrix takes the Jordan canonical form.
b) Discuss the conditions on $M(p)$ such that each one of the entries h_{jk} in the Jordan matrix Λ_J [see Eq. (2-26)] vanishes. Under what conditions do more than one of the entries h_{ij} vanish?

2-11 Obtain a set of state equations for a nonlinear system of the form of Fig. 2-16. In the figure, $n(t)$ is a noise input, and $f(e)$ is a nonlinear function relating $u(t)$ with $e(t)$.

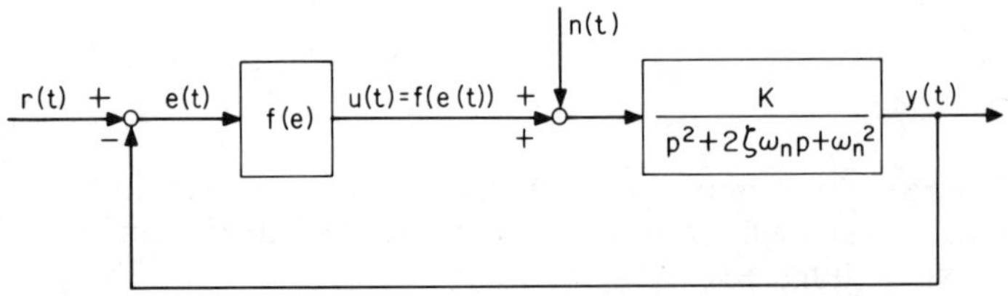

Fig. 2-16. The nonlinear system of Exercise 2-11.

2-12 The linearized equation of motion about the origin for the roll and yaw axes of the gravitational satellite can be shown to be intercoupled and of the form

$$I_1\ddot{\theta}_1 + 4\Omega^2(I_3 - I_2)\theta_1 + \Omega(I_1 - I_3 + I_2)\dot{\theta}_2 = u_1(t)$$

$$I_2\ddot{\theta}_2 + \Omega^2(I_3 - I_1)\theta_2 + \Omega(I_3 - I_1 - I_2)\dot{\theta}_1 = u_2(t)$$

where I_1, I_2, and I_3 are the moments of inertia of the satellite about the roll, yaw, and pitch axes respectively; Ω is the satellite orbiting angular rate; θ_1 and θ_2 are small angle deviations in roll and yaw, respectively; and u_1 and u_2 are control torques exerted about the roll and yaw axes respectively.

a) Show that if $I_3 > I_1 > I_2$, the uncontrolled system will have no eigenvalue in the right half plane.
b) Devise a simple way to decouple the roll and yaw motion by linear feedback of the appropriate state variables.

2.12 References

The topics of this chapter are covered in much more detail in [D2], [O1], [S10], [T3], and [Z1]. The first four references are highly readable introductions to state variables and state equations. They have a wealth of examples and exercises. The last reference is marked by an approach to linear systems that is rigorous and complete. Many stimulating points are raised to challenge those who think that they possess an adequate knowledge of linear system theory.

3

The Solution of the State Equations

One of the advantages of using vector-matrix representation in the form of Eq. (2-5) or Eq. (2-8) is that the system state may be represented in an n-dimensional Euclidean space where n is the order of the system (or the number of the system state variables). This space we have called the state space for the system. As time goes on, we should reasonably expect that the system state would trace out a trajectory in this state space, a trajectory which corresponds to a portrait of the solution of the system differential equation. From our acquaintance with linear systems, we may further expect that the trajectory will be dependent on the input history and on the system initial conditions. In the case of most physical systems, we also would expect the trajectory to be a unique one; that is, the same inputs acting on the same system with the same initial conditions should yield the same solution, but different inputs should not.

In this chapter we will examine the mathematical basis of these expectations. We shall begin by introducing some terminology and definitions relevant to dynamic equations written in the state equation form. Next we shall inquire into the questions of existence and uniqueness of solutions to these equations. Then we shall again concentrate on linear systems; first, by exhibiting the form of their solutions and, second, by considering the important properties of controllability and observability. Finally, we shall consider the use of the so-called adjoint set of equations in the solution of a certain class of linear systems.

3.1 Some Definitions

As previously defined, the vectors $\mathbf{x}$ and $\mathbf{y}$ are the *state* and the *output* of a plant respectively. The vector $\mathbf{u}$ is the control function or forcing function. The *order* or degree of freedom of the system is n; it is the lowest order of differential equation that can represent the dynamic behavior.

Each state $\mathbf{x}$ of a system may be conveniently viewed as a point in an n-dimensional Euclidean space. The coordinates of this space are the quantities $x_1, x_2, \ldots, x_n$.* This space we shall call the *state space* of the system. The null state $x_i = 0$ for $i = 1, \ldots, n$ will be referred to as the origin of the state space or simply as the *origin*; it will be represented by the zero vector $\mathbf{0}$.

We define the Euclidean norm or simply the *norm* of a state $\|\mathbf{x}\|$ as the function

$$\|\mathbf{x}\| = \left(\sum_{i=1}^{n} x_i^2\right)^{1/2} = (\mathbf{x}^T\mathbf{x})^{1/2} \tag{3-1}$$

In the state space given above, the norm of a state is simply the distance (in n-dimensional space) of the state from the origin.

If $\mathbf{u}(t) \equiv 0$ for all t, the plant is said to be *free* or unforced. A closed-loop system whose input is identically zero is also said to be free.

A state $\mathbf{x}_e$ of a dynamical system that is free is called an *equilibrium state*** if, starting at that state, the system will not move from it in the absence of forcing functions. Mathematically, the equilibrium states of a system $\dot{\mathbf{x}} = \mathbf{f}(\mathbf{x}, \mathbf{u}, t)$ comprise all those points $\mathbf{x}_e$ such that

$$\mathbf{f}(\mathbf{x}_e, 0, t) \equiv 0 \quad \text{for all } t \tag{3-2}$$

When every state of a connected region in the state space satisfies this condition we call this set of states an *equilibrium zone*.

♦♦Example 3-1. The system

$$\dot{x}_1 = x_2, \qquad \dot{x}_2 = -x_1$$

is equivalent to the harmonic oscillator

$$(p^2 + 1)x_1 = 0$$

It has the origin $\mathbf{x} = 0$ as the equilibrium state. Indeed, most linear free systems can only have the origin as the equilibrium state. (See Exercise 3-4.)♦♦

*To be mathematically rigorous, a distinction should be made between the system state and the coordinate of the state space in which the state trajectory is to be represented. Some writers thus use different notations for these two different quantities. It is the feeling of the authors, however, that as long as this matter is brought to the attention of the readers, little confusion will result even if no distinction is made notationally.

**In the literature the term "singular point" is sometimes used instead of equilibrium state.

◆◆Example 3-2. For the system

$$\dot{x}_1 = g_1(\mathbf{x}), \quad \dot{x}_2 = g_2(\mathbf{x})$$

where $g_1(\mathbf{x})$ and $g_2(\mathbf{x})$ have the property that

$$g_i(\mathbf{x}) = 0, \quad x_1^2 + x_2^2 \leq 1$$

$$g_i(\mathbf{x}) \neq 0, \quad x_1^2 + x_2^2 > 1 \quad (i = 1,2)$$

The entire circle $x_1^2 + x_2^2 \leq 1$ is an equilibrium zone.◆◆

A system $\dot{\mathbf{x}} = \mathbf{f}$ is time-invariant if $\mathbf{f}$ does not depend explicitly on time. This generally implies that the system does not have parameters that vary with time. Otherwise the system will be known as a *time-varying* system.

An *autonomous* system is one that is both free and time-invariant.

From the foregoing, whenever the system state is not at an equilibrium state or whenever the system input is nonzero, the system state will change with time. This change of system state with time will sometimes be referred to as *motion* of system state, or simply as motion of the system. Given an initial state $\mathbf{x} = \mathbf{x}_0$ at a time $t = t_0$, the set of values that the state takes at times $t \geq t_0$ will be denoted by $\mathbf{x}(t)$ or more precisely, $\mathbf{x}(\mathbf{u},t; \mathbf{x}_0,t_0)$. The set of points traced out by $\mathbf{x}(\mathbf{u},t; \mathbf{x}_0,t_0)$ as t evolves will be called the *state trajectory* of the system.

To distinguish the state trajectory of a free system $[\mathbf{u}(t) \equiv 0]$ from that of a driven system $[\mathbf{u}(t) \not\equiv 0]$, we shall call the trajectory of the free systems the *free trajectory*. Where possible confusion can arise, we shall denote a free trajectory of a system by $\mathbf{x}(t; \mathbf{x}_0,t_0)$.

We see that a state trajectory of a system is a particular solution of the system Eqs. (2-5) or (2-8) when the system initial condition $\mathbf{x} = \mathbf{x}_0$ at $t = t_0$ and the system input $\mathbf{u}(t)$ are specified.

3.2 Sufficient Conditions for the Existence and Uniqueness of Solutions to the System State Equations

Before mathematical techniques can be applied to analyze a system it is usually necessary first to inquire whether the mathematical model of the systems will be well-behaved; otherwise, the method of attack may be limited.

One of the first questions to ask when a system is modeled by a set of differential equations is whether there is any solution at all, and if so, whether the solution is unique, that is, whether there is one and only one solution under the conditions specified.

The existence of a solution to a man-made system is guaranteed, as all systems will do something. Nevertheless, we may have modeled the system so that the equations which represent the system do not have a solution.

More important is the question of uniqueness of solution. Physical systems can have nonunique modes of behavior, in which case their mathematical models will have nonunique solutions. If this happens, many mathematical techniques cannot be applied.

We shall state a general sufficient* condition for the existence and uniqueness of solutions to the system state equations. This will be useful in later chapters when we deal with many mathematical methods which require uniqueness of solutions as a precondition.

Let us note that a $\mathbf{u}(t)$ that is completely specified can be regarded as a time-varying parameter. Thus a system with a fixed $\mathbf{u}(t)$ can be considered to be entirely equivalent to another set of systems with $\mathbf{u}(t) \equiv 0$ and may be studied together as far as the existence and uniqueness of solutions are concerned.

Consider now systems of the type**

$$\dot{\mathbf{x}} = \mathbf{f}(\mathbf{x}, t), \qquad \mathbf{x} = \mathbf{x}_0 \qquad \text{at} \qquad t = t_0 \tag{3-3}$$

or equivalently

$$\dot{\mathbf{x}} = \mathbf{f}\big(\mathbf{x}, \mathbf{u}(t), t\big), \qquad \mathbf{x} = \mathbf{x}_0 \qquad \text{at} \qquad t = t_0 \tag{3-4}$$

where $\mathbf{u}(t)$ is completely specified for all $t \geq t_0$. The following theorem gives a sufficient condition for the existence of a unique solution for the system of (3-3).

♦♦Theorem 3-1. For the system (3-3), let $\mathbf{f}(\mathbf{x}, t)$ be defined and continuous*** with respect to $\mathbf{x}$ and t in the region $\mathcal{R}$ of state space defined by $\|\mathbf{x} - \mathbf{x}_0\| \leq b$ and in the time interval $|t - t_0| \leq c$;

*Since we shall continually be making use of necessary and/or sufficient conditions, we should review the specific meaning of these conditions. When A is a necessary condition for an event B to occur, then whenever B occurs A must also occur. The occurrence of A however does not guarantee that B occurs. This is sometimes written, B occurs *only if* A occurs. When A is a sufficient condition for B to occur, then whenever A occurs B must occur, but the occurrence of B alone does not guarantee the occurrence of A. This is sometimes written, B occurs *if* A occurs. When A is a necessary and sufficient condition for B, then if A occurs, B also occurs *and vice versa*. Then we say B occurs if and only if A occurs.

**Since the system output is not involved in the discussion, we shall omit it in the system equations.

***The definition of continuity in state space is similar to that in functions of n variables and may be stated as follows: A function $\mathbf{f}(\mathbf{x},t_1)$ is continuous at $t = t_1$ if for every $\epsilon > 0$ there exists a $\delta > 0$ such that $\|\mathbf{x}_1 - \mathbf{x}_2\| < \delta$ implies $\|\mathbf{f}(\mathbf{x}_1,t_1) - \mathbf{f}(\mathbf{x}_2,t_1)\| < \epsilon$.

$b, c > 0$. If, for any two state vectors $\mathbf{x}_\alpha, \mathbf{x}_\beta$, the condition

$$\| \mathbf{f}(\mathbf{x}_\alpha, t) - \mathbf{f}(\mathbf{x}_\beta, t) \| \leq k \| \mathbf{x}_\alpha - \mathbf{x}_\beta \| \tag{3-5}$$

is satisfied with $\infty > k > 0$, then there exists a unique solution to systems (3-3) in $\mathcal{R}$ for $|t - t_0| \leq a$ with a obeying

$$a \leq \min \left\{ c, \frac{b}{M} \right\} \tag{3-6}*$$

where M is the maximum value of $\| \mathbf{f}(\mathbf{x}, t) \|$ in the region $\mathcal{R}$ during the time interval $|t - t_0| \leq c$.◆◆

The condition (3-5) is called the ***Lipschitz condition***, and the constant k is called a ***Lipschitz constant***.

When the region $\mathcal{R}$ can only be some small region about $(\mathbf{x}_0, t_0)$, the system is said to satisfy a *local* Lipschitz condition. When the constants b and c of the theorem can both be infinite, then the system is said to satisfy a *global* Lipschitz condition.

The proof of the theorem above can be achieved by using the contraction-mapping fixed-point theorem. It will be given in Chap. 11.

For a first order time-invariant system $\dot{x} = f(x)$, for any values x_α and x_β in the range of interest of x the Lipschitz condition can be written in the form

$$\frac{|f(x_\alpha) - f(x_\beta)|}{|x_\alpha - x_\beta|} \leq k$$

which implies that on a plot of $f(x)$ vs. x, a straight line joining any two points of $f(x)$ cannot have a slope whose *absolute value* is greater than k. Specifically, if $f(x)$ is differentiable and if the largest value of $|df(x)/dx|$ in the range of interest of x is k, then k is the Lipschitz constant for the problem. Note however, the Lipschitz condition can still be applied even when $f(x)$ is not continuously differentiable.

For $n = 2$, if we construct the surface $f(x_1, x_2)$ over the x_1, x_2 plane, then by

$$\frac{\| \mathbf{f}(\mathbf{x}_\alpha) - \mathbf{f}(\mathbf{x}_\beta) \|}{\| \mathbf{x}_\alpha - \mathbf{x}_\beta \|} \leq k$$

the above interpretation in terms of the slope can still be applied.

*The notation $\min\{a,b\}$ means the smaller of the two quantities a and b.

The same concept can be extended to the n-dimensional case by properly exercising our imagination.

♦♦Example 3-3. The function $f(x) = \sqrt{x}$ does not satisfy a Lipschitz condition for $x_0 = 0$ since at 0 the Lipschitz constant k must be ∞.♦♦

♦♦Example 3-4. The function $f(x) = x^2$ does not satisfy a global Lipschitz condition for any x_0, although a local Lipschitz condition can easily be found for any interval of finite length about a given point. (Show this.) ♦♦

♦♦Example 3-5. Any discontinuous function in x does not satisfy a Lipschitz condition at the point of discontinuity.♦♦

In some cases of practical importance $\mathbf{f}(\mathbf{x}, t)$ is discontinuous with respect to t at a finite (or countably infinite) number of points. Here, over those time intervals where the discontinuities do not occur, Theorem 3-1 applies, and there exist unique solutions in those intervals.

In the case of linear unforced systems, corresponding to the Eqs. (3-3) we have

$$\dot{\mathbf{x}} = \mathbf{A}(t)\mathbf{x}, \quad \mathbf{x} = \mathbf{x}_0 \quad \text{at} \quad t = t_0 \tag{3-7}$$

The corresponding theorem for existence and uniqueness is:

♦♦Theorem 3-2. If $\mathbf{A}(t)$ is Riemann-integrable* for some interval of time, there exists a unique solution of (3-7) in that interval.♦♦

In particular, if $\mathbf{A}(t)$ is discontinuous in t at only a finite number of points, then existence and uniqueness of solution are guaranteed.** Finally, we see that the existence and uniqueness of solutions are *always* guaranteed for the case of time-invariant linear systems for all time. This explains, in part, why the linear constant parameter differential systems can be so readily attacked without too much regard for mathematical niceties.

Indeed for linear systems, when the existence of a unique solution for the free system is guaranteed, then under a given input $u(t)$, the existence of a unique output is again guaranteed, as we shall see in the following section.

When a system satisfies the requirements for existence and uniqueness of solutions in a region $\mathcal{R}(x_0, t_0)$, it has the following properties:

1) For all initial conditions $\mathbf{x}_0$ in the region $\mathcal{R}$ and for all time in the interval $|t - t_0| \le c$, there is a trajectory of the system with these initial conditions.
2) If in $\mathcal{R}$ and in the specified time interval there are two solutions with the same initial conditions, then those solutions are identical in $\mathcal{R}$ during the time interval.
3) The trajectories of the system will be continuous with respect to the initial condition $\mathbf{x}_0$ and the initial time t_0. (Why?)

*$\mathbf{A}(t)$ is Riemann integrable if every element of $\mathbf{A}(t)$ is Riemann-integrable.
**At the points of discontinuity of $\mathbf{A}(t)$ however, $\dot{\mathbf{x}}(t)$, and hence Eq. (3-7) is not defined.

Since for an autonomous system the system trajectories are independent of the starting time t_0, then condition (2) above implies that a trajectory of an autonomous system satisfying the existence and uniqueness requirements will not cross itself.

In the sequel we shall assume that all differential systems considered are such that unique solutions are guaranteed.

3.3 The Solution of the Linear State Equations

For the rather general set of Eqs. (2-5), no general form of solution can be displayed unless further restrictions are imposed. Indeed, such systems, except in isolated cases where closed form solutions can be found, require computational solution.

In the linear case (2-8) the situation is different. Although the nonstationary case is not readily solved, it is possible to display the form of the solution in terms of the so-called transition matrix of the system. In the linear constant parameter (stationary) case, the solution can be found explicitly.

Given the linear state equation (2-8) and an initial condition $\mathbf{x}_0$, we wish to find $\mathbf{x}(t)$, or more explicitly, $\mathbf{x}(\mathbf{u},t;\ \mathbf{x}_0, t_0)$ for $\mathbf{u}$ given in the interval between t_0 and t.

To do this we can use the technique of variation of parameters, which is frequently used to solve first-order linear time-varying differential equations.

◆◆Example 3-6. Let us use the method of variation of parameters to solve the first-order linear time-varying differential equation:

$$\dot{x} = a(t)x + u(t), \qquad x(t_0) = x_0$$

The customary approach is to find the homogeneous solution (or the free solution, i.e., for $u(t) \equiv 0$), for which one obtains, on separating the variables and integrating

$$x(t) = k \exp\left[\int_{t_0}^{t} a(\tau)\,d\tau\right] = k\phi(t, t_0)$$

where k is a constant.

The quantity

$$\phi(t,t_0) \triangleq \exp\left[\int_{t_0}^{t} a(\tau)\,d\tau\right]$$

has the properties: (1) it satisfies the equation $\dot{\phi} = a(t)\phi$ and (ii) it has the boundary condition $\phi(t_0,t_0) = 1$.

To find the particular solution through the use of the method of variation of parameters, we allow the quantity k to be a function of time, hence $x(t) = k(t)\phi(t,t_0)$. Taking the time derivative, we have

$$\dot{x}(t) = \frac{dk(t)}{dt}\phi(t,t_0) + k(t)\frac{d}{dt}\phi(t,t_0)$$

but with $x(t) = k(t)\phi(t,t_0)$

$$\dot{x}(t) = a(t)k(t)\phi(t,t_0) + u(t)$$

Then comparing terms, we obtain

$$\frac{dk(t)}{dt}\phi(t,t_0) = u(t)$$

and

$$k(t) = k(t_0) + \int_{t_0}^{t} \phi^{-1}(\tau,t_0)u(\tau)\,d\tau$$

$$= k(t_0) + \int_{t_0}^{t} \exp\left(-\int_{t_0}^{t} a(\nu)\,d\nu\right) u(\tau)\,d\tau$$

Since $k(t_0) = \phi^{-1}(t_0,t_0)x(t_0) = x(t_0)$, we have finally:

$$x(t) = k(t)\phi(t,t_0) = x_0 \exp\left(\int_{t_0}^{t} a(\tau)\,d\tau\right)$$

$$+ \left\{\exp\left(\int_{t_0}^{t} a(\tau)\,d\tau\right)\right\}\int_{t_0}^{t}\left\{\exp\left(-\int_{t_0}^{\tau} a(\nu)\,d\nu\right)\right\}u(\tau)\,d\tau \qquad (3\text{-}8)\blacklozenge\blacklozenge$$

Consider now the linear nth-order system, written in the form

$$\dot{\mathbf{x}} = \mathbf{A}(t)\mathbf{x} + \mathbf{B}(t)\mathbf{u} \qquad (3\text{-}9)$$

We can use the same approach as in the first-order case. Define an $n \times n$ matrix $\Phi(t,t_0)$, called the *transition matrix*, such that

$$\frac{d\mathbf{\Phi}(t,t_0)}{dt} = \mathbf{A}(t)\mathbf{\Phi}(t,t_0), \qquad \mathbf{\Phi}(t_0,t_0) = \mathbf{I} \qquad (3\text{-}10)$$

Now we try a solution of the form $\mathbf{x}(t) = \Phi(t,t_0)\mathbf{k}(t)$, where the parameter k is assumed to be a function of time, yielding:

$$\dot{\mathbf{x}} = \Phi(t,t_0)\frac{d\mathbf{k}}{dt} + \frac{d\Phi(t,t_0)}{dt}\mathbf{k}(t) \tag{3-11}$$

Substitute into Eq. (3-9):

$$\dot{\mathbf{x}} = \Phi(t,t_0)\frac{d\mathbf{k}}{dt} + \mathbf{A}(t)\Phi(t,t_0)\mathbf{k} = \mathbf{A}(t)\Phi(t,t_0)\mathbf{k} + \mathbf{B}(t)\mathbf{u}(t) \tag{3-12}$$

Thus,

$$\Phi(t,t_0)\frac{d\mathbf{k}}{dt} = \mathbf{B}(t)\mathbf{u}(t) \tag{3-13}$$

and therefore:

$$\mathbf{k}(t) = \mathbf{c} + \int_{t_0}^{t} \Phi^{-1}(t_1, t_0)\mathbf{B}(t_1)\mathbf{u}(t_1)\,dt_1 \tag{3-14}$$

where

$$\mathbf{c} = \mathbf{k}(t_0) = \Phi^{-1}(t_0, t_0)\mathbf{x}(t_0) = \mathbf{x}(t_0) \tag{3-15}$$

Hence

$$\mathbf{x}(t) = \Phi(t,t_0)\mathbf{k}(t)$$

$$= \Phi(t,t_0)\mathbf{x}(t_0) + \Phi(t,t_0)\int_{t_0}^{t} \Phi^{-1}(t_1, t_0)\mathbf{B}(t_1)\mathbf{u}(t_1)\,dt_1 \tag{3-16}$$

which is the solution sought.

Let us examine the transition matrix further. First, we may wonder under what conditions $\Phi^{-1}(t,t_0)$ is guaranteed to exist. By inspection of Eq. (3-10), we see that the ith column of the transition matrix may be viewed as the vector $\mathbf{y}_i(t,t_0)$ that satisfies $\dot{\mathbf{y}}_i = \mathbf{A}(t)\mathbf{y}_i$, where $\mathbf{y}_i(t_0, t_0)$ has unity in the ith coordinate and zero elsewhere. Thus the columns of $\Phi(t,t_0)$, whenever $\Phi(t,t_0)$ exists and is unique,* are guaranteed to be a set of n independent solutions $\mathbf{y}_i(t,t_0)$, $i = 1, \ldots, n$ of the system $\dot{\mathbf{y}} = \mathbf{A}\mathbf{y}$. We can use this fact to show that $\Phi(t,t_0)$ is nonsingular for all t; that is, the determinant of the matrix $\Phi(t,t_0)$ will never vanish. Suppose that there is a time t_1 at which $|\Phi(t_1, t_0)| = 0$, then (see Appendix A) at $t = t_1$, the n columns $\mathbf{y}_i(t_1, t_0)$ are linearly dependent, so that we can find a set of n

*The existence and uniqueness properties of Φ are of course the same as those of the vectors y that satisfy $\dot{\mathbf{y}} = \mathbf{A}\mathbf{y}$.

nonzero constants $c_1, \ldots, c_n$ satisfying the relation

$$\sum_{i=1}^{n} c_i \mathrm{y}_i(t_1, t_0) = 0$$

Now since we are dealing with a linear system $\dot{\mathrm{y}} = \mathrm{A}\,\mathrm{y}$, by superposition, the two vectors $c_1 \mathrm{y}_1(t,t_0)$ and

$$-\sum_{i=2}^{n} c_i \mathrm{y}_i(t,t_0)$$

are two solutions which take on the same value at $t = t_1$. By the uniqueness theorem this is only possible if the two vectors are identical for all t. This also implies that

$$\sum_{i=1}^{n} c_1 \mathrm{y}_i(t_0, t_0) = 0$$

which is impossible for nonzero c_i's in view of the original assumption that $\mathrm{y}_i(t_0, t_0)$ has unity in the ith position and zero elsewhere. Thus we have

♦♦Theorem 3-3. In any time interval in which $\mathrm{A}(t)$ is Riemann-integrable, the transition matrix satisfying Eq. (3-10) is nonsingular.♦♦

When the conditions of Theorem 3-3 are satisfied, we are assured that $\Phi^{-1}(t, t_0)$ exists.

Also from Eq. (3-16) we note that the free behavior of $\mathrm{x}(t)$, given an initial condition $\mathrm{x}(t_0)$, can be given by

$$\mathrm{x}(t) = \Phi(t, t_0)\,\mathrm{x}(t_0) \tag{3-17}$$

Thus the transition matrix $\Phi(t, t_0)$ has the property that it transforms the free system from an initial point $\mathrm{x}(t_0)$ to the point $\mathrm{x}(t)$ on its free trajectory at the time t.

Moreover, from Eq. (3-17) some further properties of the transition matrix can be deduced. First, as the solution $\mathrm{x}(t)$ is unique, if

$$\mathrm{x}(t_1) = \Phi(t_1, t_0)\,\mathrm{x}(t_0) \quad \text{and} \quad \mathrm{x}(t_2) = \Phi(t_2, t_1)\,\mathrm{x}(t_1) \tag{3-18}$$

we see that

$$\Phi(t_2, t_0) = \Phi(t_2, t_1)\,\Phi(t_1, t_0) \qquad \text{for all} \quad t_0, t_1, t_2 \tag{3-19}$$

Also, from Eq. (3-19), and the fact that $\Phi(t_0, t_0) = \mathrm{I}$,

$$\Phi(t_0, t_0) = \Phi(t_0, t)\,\Phi(t, t_0) = \mathrm{I} \tag{3-20}$$

Thus

$$\Phi^{-1}(t_0,t) = \Phi(t,t_0) \tag{3-21}$$

Using Eq. (3-19), Eq. (3-16) can be written in an alternate form:

$$\mathbf{x}(t) = \Phi(t,t_0)\mathbf{x}(t_0) + \int_{t_0}^{t} \Phi(t,t_1)\mathbf{B}(t_1)\mathbf{u}(t_1)\,dt_1 \tag{3-22}$$

When there is only a single input $u(t)$, we may write Eq. (3-22) in the expanded form;

$$x_i(t) = \sum_{j=1}^{n} \phi_{ij}(t,t_0)x_j(t_0) + \int_{t_0}^{t} \sum_{j=1}^{n} \phi_{ij}(t,t_1)\,b_j(t_1)\,u(t_1)\,dt_1 \tag{3-23}$$

where ϕ_{ij} is the i, jth entry of the Φ matrix and b_j is the jth component of the $\mathbf{b}$ vector.

Let the initial conditions be all zero so that $x_j(t_0) = 0$ for all j. Let a unit impulse be applied at the time τ. If $\mu_0(t)$ is the unit impulse,* then

$$\begin{aligned} x_i(t) &= \int_{t_0}^{t} \sum_{j=1}^{n} \phi_{ij}(t,t_1)\,b_j(t_1)\,\mu_0(t_1 - \tau)\,dt_1 \\ &= \sum_{j=1}^{n} \phi_{ij}(t,\tau)\,b_j(\tau) \qquad (t \geq t_0) \end{aligned} \tag{3-24}$$

is the response of the ith state coordinate to an impulse at the time τ. We thus see the close relationship between the transition matrix and the system impulse response.

3.4 The Finding of the Transition Matrix for Linear Time-Invariant Systems

In the case of linear time-invariant systems, the transition matrix can be readily found in most cases.

Here we have, from Eq. (3-10)

$$\frac{d\,\Phi(t,t_0)}{dt} = \mathbf{A}\,\Phi(t,t_0), \qquad \Phi(t_0,t_0) = \mathbf{I} \tag{3-25}$$

where $\mathbf{A}$ is a constant matrix.

*$\mu_0(t)$ has the properties: $\mu_0(t) \equiv 0,\ t \neq 0$, and $\int_{-\infty}^{\infty} f(t_1)\mu_0(t_1 - t)\,dt_1 = f(t)$ for all t and for any function $f(t)$.

In the case of a first-order linear time-invariant system, we have

$$\phi(t,t_0) = \exp\left[\int_{t_0}^{t} a\,d\tau\right] = e^{a(t-t_0)}$$

This leads us to try a solution of a form similar to an exponential function of the matrix A.

Suppose we define a matrix exponential function of the matrix A and the elapsed time $(t - t_0)$ as:

$$e^{\mathbf{A}(t-t_0)} \triangleq \sum_{n=0}^{\infty} \frac{\mathbf{A}^n (t-t_0)^n}{n!} \tag{3-26}$$

where

$$\mathbf{A}^0 \triangleq \mathbf{I}$$

If we further define the derivative of a matrix as the matrix of the derivatives of its elements it is clear that if

$$\mathbf{\Phi}(t,t_0) = e^{\mathbf{A}(t-t_0)} \tag{3-27}$$

then Eq. (3-25) is satisfied identically.

Thus the general solution (3-22) reduces, in the special case of a time-invariant system, to

$$\mathbf{x}(t) = e^{\mathbf{A}(t-t_0)}\mathbf{x}(t_0) + \int_{t_0}^{t} e^{\mathbf{A}(t-t_1)}\mathbf{B}(t_1)\mathbf{u}(t_1)\,dt_1 \tag{3-28}$$

and, in the absence of the driving term $\mathbf{u}(t)$, the autonomous behavior of $\mathbf{x}(t)$ is

$$\mathbf{x}(t) = e^{\mathbf{A}(t-t_0)}\mathbf{x}(t_0) \tag{3-29}$$

We have not yet expressed $e^{\mathbf{A}(t-t_0)}$ in closed form. For in order to do this we must be able to find the matrix elements $\phi_{11}(t-t_0)$, $\phi_{12}(t-t_0)$, . . . of

$$\mathbf{\Phi}(t-t_0) = \begin{bmatrix} \phi_{11}(t-t_0) & \cdots & \phi_{1n}(t-t_0) \\ \vdots & & \\ \phi_{n1}(t-t_0) & \cdots & \phi_{nn}(t-t_0) \end{bmatrix} = [\phi_{ij}(t-t_0]$$

Equation (3-26) indicates that $\Phi(t-t_0)$ can theoretically be obtained by means of the infinite matrix series

$$\sum_{n=0}^{\infty} \left(\mathrm{A}^n (t - t_0)^n\right)/n!$$

but this is not practical in general. In particular cases, there are more convenient methods, some of which we now consider.

1. The Constant Matrix A is Diagonal

This occurs for example when an nth-order system is actually made up of n unrelated first-order systems or when the poles of $G(p)$ are distinct and when partial fraction expansion is used, as has been discussed in Chap. 2. Here $\mathrm{A} \equiv \Lambda$ where Λ is the diagonal matrix of the eigenvalues [or poles of $G(p)$], so

$$\mathrm{A}^n = \begin{bmatrix} \lambda_1^{\,n} & & & 0 \\ & \lambda_2^{\,n} & & \\ & & \ddots & \\ 0 & & & \lambda_n^{\,n} \end{bmatrix}$$

and Eq. (3-26) can be used directly to give:

$$e^{\mathrm{A}(t - t_0)} = \begin{bmatrix} e^{\lambda_1 (t - t_0)} & & & 0 \\ & e^{\lambda_2 (t - t_0)} & & \\ & & \ddots & \\ 0 & & & e^{\lambda_n (t - t_0)} \end{bmatrix}$$

This result is clear if we can consider the set of equations as a set of n *decoupled* first-order differential equations.

2. The Eigenvalues of A are Distinct, but A is Not Diagonal

Case 1 suggests that when A is not diagonal we try to find that constant transformation matrix P which can diagonalize A into Λ (see Appendix A); i.e., $\Lambda = \mathrm{P}^{-1} \mathrm{A} \mathrm{P}$. Then $\mathrm{P} \Lambda \mathrm{P}^{-1} = \mathrm{A}$ and since $\mathrm{A}^n = \mathrm{P} \Lambda^n \mathrm{P}^{-1}$, we have

$$e^{\mathrm{A}(t - t_0)} = \mathrm{P}\, e^{\Lambda (t - t_0)}\, \mathrm{P}^{-1}$$

The above is equivalent to the transformation:

$$\Phi(t,t_0) = \mathrm{P}\, \Theta(t,t_0) \tag{3-30}$$

by means of which, we transform from

$$\frac{d\Phi}{dt} = \mathrm{A}\,\Phi, \qquad \Phi(t_0, t_0) = \mathrm{I}$$

to $\mathrm{P}\,\dfrac{d\Theta}{dt} = \mathrm{A\,P}\,\Theta$ or

$$\frac{d\Theta}{dt} = \mathrm{P}^{-1}\mathrm{A\,P}\,\Theta = \Lambda\,\Theta, \qquad \Theta(t_0, t_0) = \mathrm{P}^{-1} \tag{3-31}$$

Since $\mathrm{P}^{-1}\mathrm{A\,P}$ is now diagonal, the elements θ_{ij} of the matrix Θ can readily be found as in Case 1. From the relation between Φ and Θ, namely $\Phi = \mathrm{P}\,\Theta$, we can deduce that each ϕ_{ij} will in this case be a linear combination of terms of form $e^{\lambda_i(t - t_0)}$.

A simple way to find the matrix P in this case is first to find the n eigenvectors v_i (see Sec. 2.9) that satisfy

$$\mathrm{A}\,\mathrm{v}_i = \lambda_i \mathrm{v}_i \qquad i = 1, \ldots, n \tag{3-32}$$

and form the matrix P by having as columns the n vectors v_i.

We can see why this is so if we write $\mathrm{P}^{-1}\mathrm{A\,P} = \Lambda$ as

$$\mathrm{A\,P} = \mathrm{P}\,\Lambda \tag{3-33}$$

If P is formed as described above, it is seen that Eq. (3-33) reduces to Eq. (3-32).

When the system equation is in the normal form, A will have the form of Eq. (2-32) of the previous chapter. For this case a matrix that diagonalizes A into Λ will be the *Vandermonde Matrix.*

$$\mathrm{V} = \begin{bmatrix} 1 & 1 & 1 & \cdots & 1 \\ \lambda_1 & \lambda_2 & \cdot & \cdots & \lambda_n \\ \lambda_1^{\,2} & \lambda_2^{\,2} & \cdot & \cdots & \lambda_n^{\,2} \\ \vdots & & & & \vdots \\ \lambda_1^{\,n-1} & \lambda_2^{\,n-1} & \cdot & \cdots & \lambda_n^{\,n-1} \end{bmatrix} \tag{3-34}$$

Moreover, the matrix that converts a system state from the canonical form into the normal form will be the matrix V C, where C is the matrix $\mathrm{diag}[c_1, \ldots, c_n]$. (See Appendix A.)

To show this, let us list the output y and its $n - 1$ derivatives:

$$y = \sum_{i=1}^{n} c_i x_i, \quad \frac{dy}{dt} = \sum_{i=1}^{n} c_i \frac{dx_i}{dt} = \sum_{i=1}^{n} c_i \lambda_i x_i, \ldots$$

$$\frac{d^{n-1}y}{dt^{n-1}} = \sum_{i=1}^{n} c_i \frac{d^{n-1}x_i}{dt^{n-1}} = \sum_{i=1}^{n} c_i \lambda_i^{n-1} x_i \qquad \text{(3-35) (cont'd)}$$

Thus expressing the normal state vector

$$\mathbf{x}_N = \begin{bmatrix} y \\ \dfrac{dy}{dt} \\ \vdots \\ \dfrac{d^{n-1}y}{dt} \end{bmatrix}$$

in terms of the canonical state vector

$$\mathbf{x}_C = \begin{bmatrix} x_1 \\ \vdots \\ x_n \end{bmatrix}$$

we have

$$\mathbf{x}_N = \begin{bmatrix} c_1 & c_2 & c_3 & \cdot\ \cdot & c_n \\ c_1\lambda_1 & c_2\lambda_2 & \cdot & \cdot\ \cdot & c_n\lambda_n \\ \vdots & & & & \\ & & \cdot & \cdot\ \cdot & \\ c_1\lambda_1^{n-1} & c_2\lambda_2^{n-1} & \cdot & \cdot\ \cdot & c_n\lambda_n^{n-1} \end{bmatrix} \mathbf{x}_C = \mathbf{V}\,\mathbf{C}\,\mathbf{x}_C$$

Since $\mathbf{x}_N$ and $\mathbf{x}_C$ are the state vectors for systems in the normal form and the canonical form respectively, we have proved the second part of our assertion. Now we can write:

$$\mathbf{V}\,\mathbf{C}\,\Lambda(\mathbf{V}\,\mathbf{C})^{-1} = \mathbf{V}\,\mathbf{C}\,\Lambda\,\mathbf{C}^{-1}\mathbf{V}^{-1} = \mathbf{A}_N$$

where $\mathbf{A}_N$ is the $\mathbf{A}$ matrix for the system in the normal form. Since $\mathbf{C}\,\Lambda\,\mathbf{C}^{-1} = \Lambda$, we have $\mathbf{V}\,\Lambda\,\mathbf{V}^{-1} = \mathbf{A}_N$ which proves the first part of our assertion.

3. The Method of Laplace Transform

This method applies to the case of multiple roots as well as to that of distinct roots.

Let $\mathbf{X}(s) = \mathcal{L}[\mathbf{x}(t)]$, where $\mathcal{L}$ is the Laplace transform operator, and where $\mathbf{x}(t)$ is translated along the time axis so that $t_0 = 0$. Then the equation $\dot{\mathbf{x}} = \mathbf{A}\,\mathbf{x}$, with $\mathbf{x}(0) = \mathbf{x}_0$, becomes

$$s\,\mathbf{X}(s) - \mathbf{x}_0 = \mathbf{A}\,\mathbf{X}(s) \tag{3-36}$$

thus

$$(s\mathbf{I} - \mathbf{A})\,\mathbf{X}(s) = \mathbf{x}_0, \qquad \mathbf{X}(s) = (s\mathbf{I} - \mathbf{A})^{-1}\mathbf{x}_0$$

Since

$$\mathbf{x}(t) = e^{\mathbf{A}t}\,\mathbf{x}_0$$

we have

$$\mathcal{L}[\Phi(t,0)] = \mathcal{L}[e^{\mathbf{A}t}] = (s\mathbf{I} - \mathbf{A})^{-1}$$

or

$$\Phi(t,0) = \mathcal{L}^{-1}\left[(s\mathbf{I} - \mathbf{A})^{-1}\right] \tag{3-37}$$

Thus to find $\Phi(t,0)$, one inverts the matrix $(s\mathbf{I} - \mathbf{A})$ and takes the inverse Laplace transform for each term of the matrix.

♦♦Example 3-7. Consider the system

$$G(p) = \frac{1}{p(p + \alpha)(p + \beta)}$$

In the normal form we have

$$\mathbf{A} = \begin{bmatrix} 0 & 1 & 0 \\ 0 & 0 & 1 \\ 0 & -\alpha\beta & -(\alpha + \beta) \end{bmatrix}, \quad \mathbf{b} = \begin{bmatrix} 0 \\ 0 \\ 1 \end{bmatrix}$$

Now the Vandermonde matrix is:

$$\mathbf{V} = \begin{bmatrix} 1 & 1 & 1 \\ 0 & -\alpha & -\beta \\ 0 & \alpha^2 & \beta^2 \end{bmatrix}$$

so that

$$\mathbf{V}^{-1} = \begin{bmatrix} 1 & \dfrac{\alpha+\beta}{\alpha\beta} & \dfrac{1}{\alpha\beta} \\ 0 & \dfrac{\beta}{\alpha(\alpha-\beta)} & \dfrac{1}{\alpha(\alpha-\beta)} \\ 0 & \dfrac{\alpha}{\beta(\beta-\alpha)} & \dfrac{1}{\beta(\beta-\alpha)} \end{bmatrix}$$

and the transition matrix $\Phi(t,0)$ is

$$\Phi(t,0) = \mathbf{V}e^{\Lambda t}\mathbf{V}^{-1} = \begin{bmatrix} 1 & \dfrac{\alpha+\beta}{\alpha\beta} + \dfrac{\beta e^{-\alpha t}}{\alpha(\alpha-\beta)} + \dfrac{\alpha e^{-\beta t}}{\beta(\beta-\alpha)} & \dfrac{1}{\alpha\beta} + \dfrac{e^{-\alpha t}}{\alpha(\alpha-\beta)} + \dfrac{e^{-\beta t}}{\beta(\beta-\alpha)} \\ 0 & \dfrac{\beta e^{-\alpha t}}{\beta-\alpha} + \dfrac{\alpha e^{-\beta t}}{\alpha-\beta} & \dfrac{e^{-\alpha t}}{\beta-\alpha} + \dfrac{e^{-\beta t}}{\alpha-\beta} \\ 0 & \dfrac{\alpha\beta}{\alpha-\beta}e^{-\alpha t} + \dfrac{\alpha\beta}{\beta-\alpha}e^{-\beta t} & \dfrac{\alpha e^{-\alpha t}}{\alpha-\beta} + \dfrac{\beta e^{-\beta t}}{\beta-\alpha} \end{bmatrix} \tag{3-38}$$

We can of course obtain the same result by means of the method of Laplace transform. Here

$$\mathbf{A} = \begin{bmatrix} 0 & 1 & 0 \\ 0 & 0 & 1 \\ 0 & -\alpha\beta & -(\alpha+\beta) \end{bmatrix}, \qquad (s\mathbf{I}-\mathbf{A}) = \begin{bmatrix} s & -1 & 0 \\ 0 & s & -1 \\ 0 & \alpha\beta & s+(\alpha+\beta) \end{bmatrix}$$

$$(s\mathbf{I}-\mathbf{A})^{-1} = \begin{bmatrix} \dfrac{1}{s} & \dfrac{s+(\alpha+\beta)}{s(s+\alpha)(s+\beta)} & \dfrac{1}{s(s+\alpha)(s+\beta)} \\ 0 & \dfrac{s+(\alpha+\beta)}{(s+\alpha)(s+\beta)} & \dfrac{1}{(s+\alpha)(s+\beta)} \\ 0 & \dfrac{-\alpha\beta}{(s+\alpha)(s+\beta)} & \dfrac{s}{(s+\alpha)(s+\beta)} \end{bmatrix}$$

$$= \begin{bmatrix} \dfrac{1}{s} & \dfrac{(\alpha+\beta)/\alpha\beta}{s} - \dfrac{\beta/[\alpha(\beta-\alpha)]}{s+\alpha} + \dfrac{\alpha/[\beta(\beta-\alpha)]}{s+\beta} & \dfrac{1/\alpha\beta}{s} + \dfrac{1/[\alpha(\alpha-\beta)]}{s+\alpha} + \dfrac{1/[\beta(\beta-\alpha)]}{s+\beta} \\ 0 & \dfrac{\beta/(\beta-\alpha)}{s+\alpha} + \dfrac{\alpha/(\alpha-\beta)}{s+\beta} & \dfrac{1/(\beta-\alpha)}{s+\alpha} + \dfrac{1/(\alpha-\beta)}{s+\beta} \\ 0 & \dfrac{\alpha\beta/(\alpha-\beta)}{s+\alpha} + \dfrac{\alpha\beta/(\beta-\alpha)}{s+\beta} & \dfrac{\alpha/(\alpha-\beta)}{s+\alpha} + \dfrac{\beta/(\beta-\alpha)}{s+\beta} \end{bmatrix}$$

By inspection, $\mathcal{L}^{-1}(sI - A)^{-1}$ will yield the same transition matrix as Eq. (3-38).◆◆

◆◆Example 3-8. For the system of Fig. 3-1, (i) find the transition matrix, (ii) find the transient response of the states for $r(t) \equiv 0$ and $x_1(0) = 4$, $x_2(0) = 2$, (iii) find the driven response of the system when starting at $t = 0$, $r(t) = \cos 2t$ and $x_1(0) = x_2(0) = 0$.

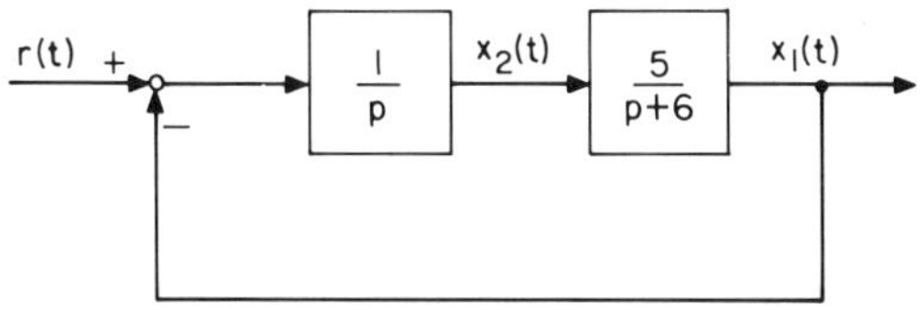

Fig. 3-1. The system of Example 3-8.

The system equations are

$$\dot{x}_1 = -6x_1 + 5x_2$$

$$\dot{x}_2 = -x_1 + r(t)$$

thus

$$A = \begin{bmatrix} -6 & 5 \\ -1 & 0 \end{bmatrix}, \quad b = \begin{bmatrix} 0 \\ 1 \end{bmatrix}$$

The system eigenvalues (poles) can be obtained from

$$|A - \lambda I| = \begin{vmatrix} -6-\lambda & 5 \\ -1 & -\lambda \end{vmatrix} = \lambda(\lambda + 6) + 5 = (\lambda + 1)(\lambda + 5)$$

hence

$$\lambda = -1, -5$$

To find the transition matrix, we first form the transforming matrix P by finding the eigenvectors. Forming $Az = \lambda z$ for $\lambda = -1$ and -5 respectively, we find the eigenvectors (to within a multiplicative constant) $\begin{bmatrix} 1 \\ 1 \end{bmatrix}$ and $\begin{bmatrix} 5 \\ 1 \end{bmatrix}$. Thus

$$P = \begin{bmatrix} 1 & 5 \\ 1 & 1 \end{bmatrix}, \quad P^{-1} = \frac{1}{4}\begin{bmatrix} -1 & 5 \\ 1 & -1 \end{bmatrix}$$

and we can verify that $\Lambda = P^{-1}AP$.

The transition matrix is formed by taking:

$$\Phi(t,0) = \mathbf{P}\begin{bmatrix} e^{-t} & 0 \\ 0 & e^{-5t} \end{bmatrix}\mathbf{P}^{-1} = \frac{1}{4}\begin{bmatrix} -e^{-t} + 5e^{-5t} & 5e^{-t} - 5e^{-5t} \\ -e^{-t} + e^{-5t} & 5e^{-t} - e^{-5t} \end{bmatrix}$$

With $r(t) \equiv 0$, $x_1(0) = 4$, and $x_2(0) = 2$, the transient behavior is given by

$$\mathbf{x}(t) = \Phi(t,0)\,\mathbf{x}(0) = \begin{bmatrix} \frac{3}{2}e^{-t} + \frac{5}{2}e^{-5t} \\ \frac{3}{2}e^{-t} + \frac{1}{2}e^{-5t} \end{bmatrix}$$

Finally, with $r(t) = \cos 2t$ and $x_1(0) = x_2(0) = 0$, the driven response starting at $t = 0$ is [from Eq. (3-22)]

$$\begin{bmatrix} x_1(t) \\ x_2(t) \end{bmatrix} = \int_0^t \Phi(t,\tau)\,\mathbf{b}(\tau)\,\mathbf{r}(\tau)\,d\tau$$

$$= \begin{bmatrix} \frac{1}{4}\int_0^t \left(5e^{-(t-\tau)} - 5e^{-5(t-\tau)}\right)\cos 2\tau\, d\tau \\ \frac{1}{4}\int_0^t \left(5e^{-(t-\tau)} - e^{-5(t-\tau)}\right)\cos 2\tau\, d\tau \end{bmatrix}$$

$$= \begin{bmatrix} \frac{1}{29}\left(12\sin 2t + \cos 2t - \frac{29}{4}e^{-t} + \frac{25}{4}e^{-5t}\right) \\ \frac{1}{29}\left(14\sin 2t + 6\cos 2t - \frac{29}{4}e^{-t} + \frac{5}{4}e^{-5t}\right) \end{bmatrix}$$ ♦♦

Before leaving this section, let us note that since for linear time-invariant systems $\Phi(t,t_0)$ is of the form $e^{\mathbf{A}(t-t_0)}$, it is not affected by a translation in time. Without loss of generality we can set $t_0 = 0$. We shall occasionally use the notation $\Phi(t)$ for the transition matrix of linear time-invariant systems.

3.5 The Transfer Function for Linear Time-Invariant Systems

Vector-matrix notation can also be useful for system representation in the transform domain. For a time-invariant multivariable system, we denote the Laplace transform of the inputs $u_1(t)$, $u_2(t), \ldots, u_r(t)$ in the traditional manner by $U_1(s), U_2(s), \ldots, U_r(s)$. This set of r variables in the transform domain can however be represented by an r-vector $\mathbf{U}(s)$. Similarly the state vector can be represented in the transform domain by an n-vector $\mathbf{X}(s)$ and the output vector by an m-vector $\mathbf{Y}(s)$. The relationship between these vectors can then be given by the transfer matrices $\mathbf{H}(s)$ and $\mathbf{G}(s)$ of dimensions $n \times r$ and $m \times r$ respectively through the following transfer equations:

$$\mathbf{X}(s) = \mathbf{H}(s)\mathbf{U}(s) \tag{3-39}$$

and

$$\mathbf{Y}(s) = \mathbf{G}(s)\mathbf{U}(s) \tag{3-40}$$

Let us recall that the transfer function between a given input and output is defined as the Laplace transform of the output response to a unit impulse input when all initial conditions and all the other inputs are 0. The entry $h_{ij}(s)$ of the matrix $\mathbf{H}(s)$ will then be the Laplace transform of the impulse response between the jth input and the ith state variable when all the other inputs are set to 0.

It is of interest to relate the system transfer function matrices $\mathbf{H}(s)$ and $\mathbf{G}(s)$ as defined by Eqs. (3-39) and (3-40) with the time-domain system matrices $\mathbf{A}$, $\mathbf{B}$, $\mathbf{C}$, and $\mathbf{D}$ of Eq. (2-8).

The reader can demonstrate to himself that practically all of the formulas for the Laplace transform in the scalar case carry directly over to the vector-matrix case without any change in form. Thus, consider the system $\dot{\mathbf{x}} = \mathbf{A}\mathbf{x} + \mathbf{B}\mathbf{u}$, $\mathbf{y} = \mathbf{C}\mathbf{x} + \mathbf{D}\mathbf{u}$. With zero initial conditions, taking the Laplace transform of both sides of the first equation:

$$s\mathbf{X}(s) = \mathbf{A}\,\mathbf{X}(s) + \mathbf{B}\,\mathbf{U}(s)$$

Rearranging:

$$[s\mathbf{I} - \mathbf{A}]\mathbf{X}(s) = \mathbf{B}\,\mathbf{U}(s)$$

Therefore,

$$\mathbf{X}(s) = [s\mathbf{I} - \mathbf{A}]^{-1}\mathbf{B}\,\mathbf{U}(s) \tag{3-41}$$

Also taking the Laplace transform of both sides of $\mathbf{y}(t) = \mathbf{C}\,\mathbf{x}(t) + \mathbf{D}\,\mathbf{u}(t)$ we obtain:

$$\mathbf{Y}(s) = \mathbf{C}\,\mathbf{X}(s) + \mathbf{D}\,\mathbf{U}(s) \tag{3-42}$$

and thus

$$\mathbf{Y}(s) = \left[\mathbf{C}[s\mathbf{I} - \mathbf{A}]^{-1}\mathbf{B} + \mathbf{D}\right]\mathbf{U}(s) \tag{3-43}$$

From Eqs. (3-39) through (3-43) we readily identify

$$\mathbf{H}(s) = [s\mathbf{I} - \mathbf{A}]^{-1}\mathbf{B} \tag{3-44}$$

and

$$\mathbf{G}(s) = \mathbf{C}[s\mathbf{I} - \mathbf{A}]^{-1}\mathbf{B} + \mathbf{D} \tag{3-45}$$

We see that Eqs. (3-44) and (3-45) give us a way to obtain the system transfer function from the system state equations.

♦♦Example 3-9. For the system of Example 2-4, we have

$$\mathbf{A} = \begin{bmatrix} \lambda_1 & 1 & 0 \\ 0 & \lambda_1 & 0 \\ 0 & 0 & \lambda_2 \end{bmatrix}, \quad \mathbf{B} = \mathbf{b} = \begin{bmatrix} 0 \\ 1 \\ 1 \end{bmatrix},$$

$$\mathbf{C} = \mathbf{c}^T = [c_1 \quad c_2 \quad c_3], \quad d = 0$$

then

$$G(s) = [c_1 \quad c_2 \quad c_3] \begin{bmatrix} (s-\lambda_1) & -1 & 0 \\ 0 & (s-\lambda_1) & 0 \\ 0 & 0 & (s-\lambda_2) \end{bmatrix}^{-1} \begin{bmatrix} 0 \\ 1 \\ 1 \end{bmatrix}$$

$$= [c_1 \quad c_2 \quad c_3] \begin{bmatrix} \dfrac{1}{(s-\lambda_1)} & \dfrac{1}{(s-\lambda_1)^2} & 0 \\ 0 & \dfrac{1}{(s-\lambda_1)} & 0 \\ 0 & 0 & \dfrac{1}{(s-\lambda_2)} \end{bmatrix} \begin{bmatrix} 0 \\ 1 \\ 1 \end{bmatrix}$$

$$= \frac{c_1}{(s-\lambda_1)^2} + \frac{c_2}{(s-\lambda_1)} + \frac{c_3}{(s-\lambda_2)}$$ ♦♦

♦♦Example 3-10. Consider now the system of Example 2-6. With the A, B, and C matrices given, we obtain (as displayed in the form of a partitioned matrix):

$$(s\mathbf{I} - \mathbf{A}) = \begin{bmatrix} s & -1 & 0 & 0 & 0 & 0 \\ \lambda_1\lambda_2 & s + (\lambda_1 + \lambda_2) & 0 & 0 & 0 & 0 \\ 0 & 0 & s + \lambda_3 & 0 & 0 & 0 \\ 0 & 0 & 0 & s + \lambda_4 & 0 & 0 \\ 0 & 0 & 0 & 0 & s & -1 \\ 0 & 0 & 0 & 0 & 0 & s + \lambda_5 \end{bmatrix}$$

thus

$$(s\mathbf{I} - \mathbf{A})^{-1} = \begin{bmatrix} \frac{s + \lambda_1 + \lambda_2}{(s + \lambda_1)(s + \lambda_2)} & \frac{1}{(s + \lambda_1)(s + \lambda_2)} & 0 & 0 & 0 & 0 \\ \frac{-\lambda_1\lambda_2}{(s + \lambda_1)(s + \lambda_2)} & \frac{s}{(s + \lambda_1)(s + \lambda_2)} & 0 & 0 & 0 & 0 \\ 0 & 0 & \frac{1}{s + \lambda_3} & 0 & 0 & 0 \\ 0 & 0 & 0 & \frac{1}{s + \lambda_4} & 0 & 0 \\ 0 & 0 & 0 & 0 & \frac{1}{s} & \frac{1}{s(s + \lambda_5)} \\ 0 & 0 & 0 & 0 & 0 & \frac{1}{s + \lambda_5} \end{bmatrix}$$

and

$$\mathbf{H}(s) = (s\mathbf{I} - \mathbf{A})^{-1}\mathbf{B} = \begin{bmatrix} \dfrac{k_1}{(s+\lambda_1)(s+\lambda_2)} & 0 \\ \dfrac{k_1 s}{(s+\lambda_1)(s+\lambda_2)} & 0 \\ \dfrac{k_2}{s+\lambda_3} & 0 \\ 0 & \dfrac{k_3}{s+\lambda_4} \\ 0 & \dfrac{k_4}{s(s+\lambda_5)} \\ 0 & \dfrac{k_4}{s+\lambda_5} \end{bmatrix}$$

therefore

$$\mathbf{G}(s) = \mathbf{C}[s\mathbf{I} - \mathbf{A}]^{-1}\mathbf{B} = \mathbf{C}\,\mathbf{H}(s)$$

$$= \begin{bmatrix} \dfrac{k_1}{(s+\lambda_1)(s+\lambda_2)} & \dfrac{k_3}{s+\lambda_4} \\ \dfrac{k_2 k_5}{s+\lambda_3} & 0 \\ \dfrac{k_2}{s+\lambda_3} & \dfrac{k_4}{s(s+\lambda_5)} \end{bmatrix}$$

The matrices $\mathbf{H}(s)$ and $\mathbf{G}(s)$ can also be obtained by inspection from Fig. 2-14.♦♦

3.6 Controllability and Observability of Linear Time-Invariant Systems

Control of a plant may be viewed as the technique of generating the control function $\mathbf{u}(t)$ in such a way that the output $\mathbf{y}(t)$ follows some desired time function. We now ask: what guarantees that $\mathbf{y}(t)$ can always be so controlled? This leads to the general question of the controllability of a plant.

◆◆**Definition 3-1.** A system $\dot{\mathbf{x}} = \mathbf{f}(\mathbf{x},\mathbf{u},t)$ is *completely controllable* if any initial state $\mathbf{x}(t_0)$ can be transferred to any final state $\mathbf{x}(t_1)$ by means of some $\mathbf{u}(t)$ over a *finite* interval $t_0 \le t \le t_1$.◆◆

The definition of complete controllability is straightforward, but so far the application of controllability is well exploited only for linear time-invariant systems.

Note that Definition 3-1 implies that each state of the plant must be influenced by at least one of the input components. This is best appreciated for a linear time-invariant plant in the canonical form.*

Consider first the case of a single input and a plant with distinct eigenvalues. The system equations are

$$\dot{x}_1 = \lambda_1 x_1 + b_1 u, \quad \dot{x}_2 = \lambda_2 x_2 + b_2 u, \ \ldots, \quad \dot{x}_n = \lambda_n x_n + b_n u \tag{3-46}$$

which may be represented as shown in Fig. 3-2.

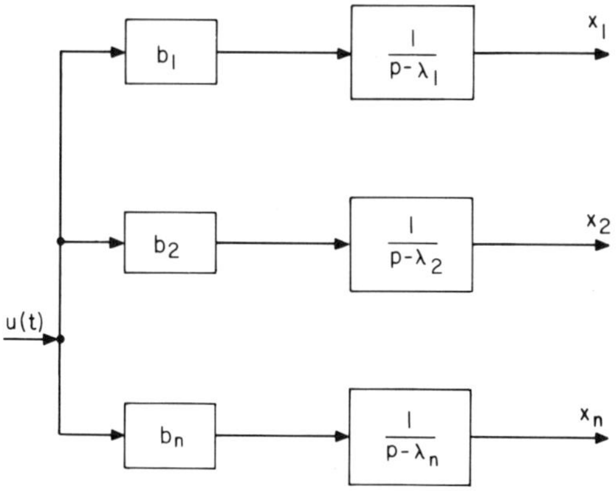

Fig. 3-2. A linear time-invariant system with a single input and with distinct eigenvalues in the canonical representation.

A given coordinate x_i would be influenced by the control variable u only if the corresponding gain b_i shown in Fig. 3-2 is nonzero. Since any choice of the system state can always be written as a linear combination of the system canonical states, it follows that if u can influence every state for a system in the canonical form, it can similarly influence every state for a system whose state equation is cast in any other form.

*See also [H12].

If none of the b_i's is 0, then it is readily seen that for the system (3-46), the requirements of complete controllability can be satisfied whatever the λ_i may be.

Note that the vanishing of the gain b_i in the above case signifies that the system transfer function has a 0 at λ_i. In other words there is a pole-zero cancellation at λ_i. Thus, noncontrollability of a plant is related to pole-zero cancellation.

Consider now the case of multiple roots. If the root λ_i has multiplicity m, then in the Jordan canonical form there is a set of m equations of the form:

$$\begin{aligned} \dot{x}_k &= \lambda_i x_k + x_{k+1} + b_k u \\ \dot{x}_{k+1} &= \lambda_i x_{k+1} + x_{k+2} + b_{k+1} u \\ &\vdots \\ \dot{x}_{k+m-1} &= \lambda_i x_{k+m-1} + b_{k+m-1} u \end{aligned} \tag{3-47}$$

Equation (3-47) can be represented as shown in Fig. 3-3.

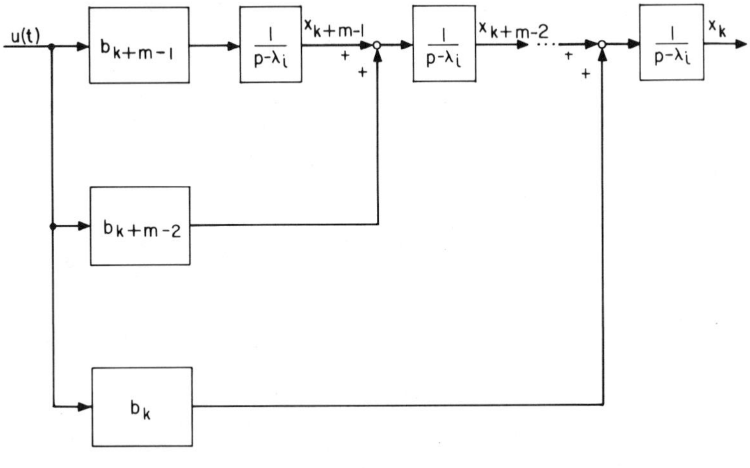

Fig. 3-3. Block diagram representation of the system of Eq. (3-47).

We see that if b_{k+m-1} is 0, we lose control of the state x_{k+m-1}. However, if the b_i's other than b_{k+m-1} are 0, we can still maintain control of each of the states over the main control path. Thus, the other b_i's are unimportant as far as controllability is concerned. In this manner we can say that a *linear, time-invariant system is completely controllable if: (1) for each simple pole* λ_i, *the corresponding* b_i *of (3-46) does not vanish, and (2) for each pole* λ_j *of multiplicity* m, *the coefficient* b_{k+m-1} *of (3-47) does not vanish.*

If there are multiple inputs so that $\mathbf{u}(t)$ is a vector, we see that a plant is completely controllable if each of its states is accessible by at least one component of the control $\mathbf{u}(t)$.*

The heuristic requirements stated above are included by the following theorem [K9]:

◆◆Theorem 3-4. The necessary and sufficient condition for the complete controllability of the linear time-invariant plant $\dot{\mathbf{x}} = \mathbf{A}\mathbf{x} + \mathbf{B}\mathbf{u}$ is that the $n \times nr$ matrix** $\mathbf{K} \triangleq \left[\mathbf{B} \mid \mathbf{A}\mathbf{B} \mid \mathbf{A}^2\mathbf{B} \mid \ldots \mid \mathbf{A}^{n-1}\mathbf{B}\right]$ has rank n. (See Appendix A.)◆◆

The necessity part of the theorem is not difficult to prove. As an example, for a single-input system with distinct roots, in the canonical form $\mathbf{A}$ is diagonal and so are $\mathbf{A}^2, \ldots, \mathbf{A}^n$. If any element of $\mathbf{b}$ is 0, say the kth, then we know the system is uncontrollable, and the $n \times n$ matrix $\mathbf{K} = \left[\mathbf{b} \mid \mathbf{A}\mathbf{b} \mid \mathbf{A}^2\mathbf{b} \mid \ldots \mid \mathbf{A}^{n-1}\mathbf{b}\right]$ will have the kth row composed entirely of 0s. Thus its rank is at most $n-1$ and hence does not fulfill the requirement of Theorem 3-4.

For a multiple-input system with distinct roots, if none of the input components influences the kth state, then in the canonical form the kth row of the matrix $\mathbf{B}$ will be composed of 0s. Thus in the $n \times nr$ matrix $\mathbf{K}$, the kth row will also be entirely filled with 0s. In this case, the determinant of any $n \times nr$ matrix $\mathbf{K}$ will vanish and thus the rank of $\mathbf{K}$ can again be at most $n-1$.

With more effort we can also demonstrate the necessary conditions for controllability for systems with repeated roots. (See Exercise 3-3.)

Proof of the sufficiency requires more ingenuity. Let us first note that to drive a system from a state $\mathbf{x}_0$ at t_0 to a state $\mathbf{x}_1$ at t_1, from Eq. (3-22), $\mathbf{u}(t)$ must be such that

$$\mathbf{x}_1 = \Phi(t_1, t_0)\mathbf{x}_0 + \int_{t_0}^{t_1} \Phi(t_1,\tau)\mathbf{B}(\tau)\mathbf{u}(\tau)\,d\tau$$

Now this $\mathbf{u}(t)$, defined over the interval $t_0 \le t \le t_1$, is the same as that which drives the system from the origin 0 to a state $\mathbf{x}_2 \triangleq \mathbf{x}_1 - \Phi(t_1, t_0)\mathbf{x}_0$ over the same interval. Conversely, if we define a state $\mathbf{x}_3$ such that $\mathbf{x}_1 \triangleq \Phi(t_1,t_0)\mathbf{x}_3$, then the above $\mathbf{u}(t)$ is also the same as that necessary to drive the state $\mathbf{x}_0 - \mathbf{x}_3$ to the origin over the interval $t_0 \le t \le t_1$. Thus the concept of controllability for linear time-invariant systems can be defined in the following equivalent ways:

*If each state component of a linear plant is influenced by every component of the control $\mathbf{u}(t)$, then the plant has additional desirable properties. This will be considered in Chap. 14 where we will extend the concept of controllability to time-varying linear systems.

**By the matrix $[\mathbf{B} \mid \mathbf{AB} \mid \mathbf{A}^2\mathbf{B} \mid \cdots \mid \mathbf{A}^{n-1}\mathbf{B}]$ is meant an $n \times rn$ matrix whose first r columns are filled by the matrix $\mathbf{B}$, the second r columns are filled by the matrix $\mathbf{AB}$ ... etc.

◆◆Definition 3-2 (Version A). A linear time-invariant system $\dot{\mathbf{x}} = \mathbf{A}\mathbf{x} + \mathbf{B}\mathbf{u}$ is completely controllable if the system can be transferred from the state 0 at a time $t = 0$ to any final state $\mathbf{x}(t_1) = \mathbf{x}_1$ by means of some $\mathbf{u}(t)$ over a finite interval $0 \le t \le T$.◆◆

◆◆Definition 3-2 (Version B). A linear time-invariant system $\dot{\mathbf{x}} = \mathbf{A}\mathbf{x} + \mathbf{B}\mathbf{u}$ is completely controllable if the system can be transferred from any initial state $\mathbf{x}_0$ at a time $t = 0$ to the origin 0 by means of some $\mathbf{u}(t)$ over a finite interval $0 \le t \le T$.◆◆

We can show the sufficiency of Theorem 3-4 for the case of a system with a single input by means of version A of Definition 3-2; for it implies that there is a $u(t)$ such that, at a time $t_1 > 0$, for an arbitrary $\mathbf{x}_1$:

$$\mathbf{x}_1 = \int_0^{t_1} \Phi(t_1, \tau)\,\mathbf{b}u(\tau)\,d\tau$$

$$= \int_0^{t_1} e^{\mathbf{A}(t_1-\tau)}\,\mathbf{b}u(\tau)\,d\tau = e^{\mathbf{A}t_1} \int_0^{t_1} e^{-\mathbf{A}\tau}\,\mathbf{b}u(\tau)\,d\tau \tag{3-48}$$

As a consequence of the Cayley-Hamilton theorem (see Appendix A),

$$e^{-\mathbf{A}t} = \sum_{j=0}^{n-1} \alpha_j(t)\,\mathbf{A}^j$$

Thus Eq. (3-48) can be written

$$\begin{aligned}\mathbf{x}_1 &= e^{\mathbf{A}t_1} \int_0^{t_1} \sum_{j=0}^{n-1} \alpha_j(\tau)\,\mathbf{A}^j\mathbf{b}u(\tau)\,d\tau \\ &= e^{\mathbf{A}t_1} \sum_{j=0}^{n-1} \left(\int_0^{t_1} \alpha_j(\tau)\,u(\tau)\,d\tau\right)\mathbf{A}^j\mathbf{b}\end{aligned} \tag{3-49}$$

As (3-49) must hold for any x_1, it means that the n vectors $\mathbf{b}, \mathbf{A}\mathbf{b}, \mathbf{A}^2\mathbf{b}, \ldots, \mathbf{A}^{n-1}\mathbf{b}$ must be linearly independent (see Appendix A) or a $u(t)$ will not be found to fulfill (3-49). But the condition that the above n vectors be linearly independent is exactly the same as the requirement that the matrix $\mathbf{K}$ of Theorem 3-4 has rank n.

For an arbitrary $n \times r$ matrix $\mathbf{B}$ the sufficiency of Theorem 3-4 can be shown in a similar way.

Closely related to the concept of controllability is that of observability. The property of observability dictates whether the value of system states in the past can be determined by observing the output alone. A definition pertaining to linear time-invariant system is:

♦♦**Definition 3-3.** A linear time-invariant system characterized by the equations $\dot{\mathbf{x}} = \mathbf{A}\,\mathbf{x} + \mathbf{B}\,\mathbf{u}$, $\mathbf{y} = \mathbf{C}\,\mathbf{x} + \mathbf{D}\,\mathbf{u}$ is *completely observable* if the initial state $\mathbf{x}(0)$ can be determined when (a) the matrices $\mathbf{A}$ and $\mathbf{C}$ and (b) the output $\mathbf{y}(t)$ over a finite time interval $[0,T]$ in response to initial conditions $\mathbf{x}(0)$ with $\mathbf{u}(t) \equiv 0$ are given.♦♦

In the case of a system in the canonical form with a single output, so that

$$y = \sum_{i=1}^{n} c_i x_i$$

a necessary and sufficient condition for complete observability is that each c_i must be nonzero. If a system in the canonical form has multiple outputs so that

$$y_j = \sum_{i=1}^{n} c_{ji} x_i, \quad j = 1, \ldots, m$$

a necessary and sufficient condition for complete observability is that each state should be coupled through a nonzero gain to at least one of the outputs, so that for each i, $i = 1, \ldots, n$, at least one of $c_{1i}, c_{2i}, \ldots, c_{mi}$ should be nonzero.

To parallel Theorem 3-4, we also have the following result.

♦♦**Theorem 3-5.** The necessary and sufficient condition for a linear time-invariant system $\dot{\mathbf{x}} = \mathbf{A}\,\mathbf{x} + \mathbf{B}\,\mathbf{u}$, $\mathbf{y} = \mathbf{C}\,\mathbf{x} + \mathbf{D}\,\mathbf{u}$ to be completely observable is that the $n \times nm$ matrix* $[\mathbf{C}^\dagger \mid \mathbf{A}^\dagger \mathbf{C}^\dagger \mid \mathbf{A}^{\dagger 2}\mathbf{C}^\dagger \mid \cdots \mid \mathbf{A}^{\dagger n-1}\mathbf{C}^\dagger]$ has rank n.♦♦

Before leaving the subject of controllability and observability of linear time-invariant plants we may remark that although useful, the definitions are given above are somewhat artificial. This is because the definition of controllability is dependent on the matrices $\mathbf{A}$ and $\mathbf{B}$ and that of observability is dependent on the matrices $\mathbf{A}$ and $\mathbf{C}$. But we have already demonstrated that these matrices are nonunique for a given system. Thus the same system can be observable but not controllable to one engineer, and controllable but unobservable to another.

♦♦**Example 3-11.** Consider a single-input, single-output system in the canonical form in which there is a pole-zero cancellation. If we select state variables in accordance with Eq. (2-19), one of the c_i in Eq. (2-20) is 0, the system is unobservable. However, if we let $x_i = \dfrac{c_i}{p - x_i}\,u$, then the system will be uncontrollable; but since y

*We use $\mathbf{A}^\dagger$ to denote the conjugate transpose of $\mathbf{A}$. (See Appendix A.)

is now

$$\sum_{i=1}^{n} x_i,$$

the system is observable.◆◆

From the above considerations we may be led to believe that the only system worth considering is one which is both completely controllable and completely observable. This is quite frequently, though not always, the case. Indeed in most practical systems the output is the only quantity being operated on and directly measured, and the system behavior is determined through the output. In this case, the underlying states are not always important. We will raise this point again in Chap. 10. Also in cases where $\mathbf{u}(t)$ is amplitude-limited, the concept of complete controllability does not imply practical controllability. This point will be pursued in Chap. 14.

3.7 Considerations for Linear Time-Varying Systems

So far we have dealt only with linear time-invariant systems, for which many results are already known in any case. We may inquire what systematic results exist in the case of the linear time-varying systems. In particular, can we always find the transition matrix for such systems in closed form? The answer is unfortunately in the negative. Indeed the state transition matrix viewpoint does little more than neatly arrange the classical time-domain results for differential systems. Only when a linear differential system has a closed-form solution classically, will it have a transition matrix expressible in a closed form.

Let us look at some known results:

Recalling the first-order linear time-varying system of Example 3-6 where the 1×1 transition matrix $\phi(t,t_0)$ is

$$\exp\left(\int_{t_0}^{t} a(\tau)\,d\tau\right)$$

we may conjecture that in the general case of a higher-order linear time-varying system in the form $\dot{\mathbf{x}} = \mathbf{A}(t)\mathbf{x}$, the transition matrix is of the form

$$\Phi(t,t_0) = \exp\left(\int_{t_0}^{t} \mathbf{A}(\tau)\,d\tau\right)$$

Though generally false, this conclusion is occasionally true. A case where it holds true (in addition to the obvious case where $A(t)$ is independent of t) is when $A(t)$ commutes with

$$\int_{t_0}^{t} A(\tau)\,d\tau$$

that is, [C5]

$$\left[\int_{t_0}^{t} A(\tau)d\tau\right] A(t) = A(t)\left[\int_{t_0}^{t} A(\tau)d\tau\right] \quad \text{for all} \quad t_0 \quad \text{and} \quad t \tag{3-50}$$

A special case of (3-50) is when $A(t)$ is a diagonal matrix.*

There is also a result of almost no practical interest: namely that in the general case of linear time-varying systems, the transition matrix can be obtained by means of repeated iteration through integration, resulting in what is known as a Neumann series. (See Exercise 3-5.)

It is of course clear that closed-form transition matrices can be found for many classically integrable linear time-varying systems. Let us consider a useful example:

♦♦Example 3-12. The Euler linear differential equation [I1] is of the general form:

$$a_0 t^n \frac{d^n x}{dt^n} + a_1 t^{n-1} \frac{d^{n-1}x}{dt^{n-1}} + \cdots + a_{n-1} t \frac{dx}{dt} + a_n x = f(t) \tag{3-51}$$

where $a_0, \ldots, a_n$ are constants. It can be transformed into a linear differential equation with constant coefficients by the substitution $t = e^\tau$ or $\tau = \ln t$, since then we have

$$\frac{dx}{dt} = \frac{dx}{d\tau}\frac{d\tau}{dt} = \frac{1}{t}\frac{dx}{d\tau}$$

$$\frac{d^2x}{dt^2} = \frac{d}{dt}\left(\frac{1}{t}\frac{dx}{d\tau}\right) = -\frac{1}{t^2}\frac{dx}{d\tau} + \frac{1}{t}\frac{d}{d\tau}\left(\frac{dx}{d\tau}\right)\frac{d\tau}{dt} \tag{3-52}$$

$$= \frac{1}{t^2}\left(\frac{d^2x}{d\tau^2} - \frac{dx}{d\tau}\right)$$

*A further special case of (3-50) is when $A(t)$ is such that $A(t_1)A(t_2) = A(t_2)A(t_1)$ for all t_1 and t_2; see [K16].

$$\vdots$$

$$\frac{d^n x}{dt^n} = \frac{1}{t^n}\frac{d}{d\tau}\left(\frac{d}{d\tau} - 1\right)\cdots\left(\frac{d}{d\tau} - (n-1)\right)x \qquad \text{(3-52) (cont'd)}$$

Substituting Eq. (3-52) into Eq. (3-51), we have a linear equation with constant coefficients. This will allow us to solve for the elements of the transition matrix in the variables $\tau - \tau_0$. On substituting $\tau = \ln t$ and manipulating terms, we can then obtain the transition matrix in terms of t.

Consider the equation

$$t^2\frac{d^2x}{dt^2} + 6t\frac{dx}{dt} + 6x = 0$$

In the τ-domain, it reduces to

$$\frac{d^2x}{d\tau^2} + 5\frac{dx}{d\tau} + 6x = 0$$

In the normal coordinates one readily finds that:

$$\Phi(\tau,\tau_0) = \begin{bmatrix} 3e^{-2(\tau-\tau_0)} - 2e^{-3(\tau-\tau_0)} & e^{-2(\tau-\tau_0)} - e^{-3(\tau-\tau_0)} \\ -6e^{-2(\tau-\tau_0)} + 6e^{-3(\tau-\tau_0)} & -2e^{-2(\tau-\tau_0)} + 3e^{-3(\tau-\tau_0)} \end{bmatrix}$$

This means that in the t-domain one actually has (on substituting $\tau = \ln t$):

$$\begin{bmatrix} x \\ t\dfrac{dx}{dt} \end{bmatrix} = \begin{bmatrix} 3\left(\dfrac{t_0}{t}\right)^2 - 2\left(\dfrac{t_0}{t}\right)^3 & \left(\dfrac{t_0}{t}\right)^2 - \left(\dfrac{t_0}{t}\right)^3 \\ -6\left(\dfrac{t_0}{t}\right)^2 + 6\left(\dfrac{t_0}{t}\right)^3 & -2\left(\dfrac{t_0}{t}\right)^2 + 3\left(\dfrac{t_0}{t}\right)^3 \end{bmatrix} \begin{bmatrix} x(t_0) \\ t_0\dfrac{dx}{dt}\Big|_{t=t_0} \end{bmatrix}$$

Thus in terms of the normal variables x and dx/dt, the transition matrix is evidently:

$$\Phi(t,t_0) = \begin{bmatrix} 3\left(\dfrac{t_0}{t}\right)^2 - 2\left(\dfrac{t_0}{t}\right)^3 & \dfrac{t_0^3}{t^2} - \dfrac{t_0^4}{t^3} \\ -6\dfrac{t_0^2}{t^3} + 6\dfrac{t_0^3}{t^4} & -2\left(\dfrac{t_0}{t}\right)^3 + 3\left(\dfrac{t_0}{t}\right)^4 \end{bmatrix}$$

Note that $\Phi(t_0, t_0) = \mathbf{I}$, which serves as a check on the result.♦♦

3.8 The Adjoint System

To a system described by the equation

$$\dot{\mathbf{x}} = \mathbf{A}(t)\mathbf{x} + \mathbf{B}(t)\mathbf{u} \tag{3-53}$$

there corresponds its *adjoint system*

$$\dot{\boldsymbol{\psi}} = -\mathbf{A}^{\dagger}(t)\boldsymbol{\psi} \tag{3-54}$$

where $\mathbf{A}^{\dagger}(t)$ is the conjugate transpose of $\mathbf{A}(t)$.

The adjoint system is useful both in providing solutions to a class of problems and in helping to understand linear differential systems. It is sometimes also helpful computationally. In Part III of this book we shall make important use of it.

To develop some of the properties of the adjoint system, let us consider the following.

♦♦Example 3-13. The adjoint system for the first-order time-invariant system $\dot{x} = ax + bu$ is $\dot{\psi} = -a\psi$. We note that it is exactly in the form of the unforced linear system $\dot{x} = ax$ except with a minus sign attached to the constant a. Since for the first-order system above, reversing time and running the system backward is the same as changing the sign of $\dot{x}$, we conclude that the adjoint system can produce the same effect as running the original unforced system backward.

We may inquire exactly what is meant by running a system backward in time. Intuitively if the response of a system with initial condition $x(t_0) = \alpha$ at $t = t_0$ is as shown in Fig. 3-4a (where T seconds later at $t = t_0 + T$, $x(t_0 + T) = \beta$), we expect that in the reverse time system the response to an initial condition of β units will be as shown in Fig. 3-4b (and in T seconds the response will be α units). This should hold for any values t_0 and T, or α and β.

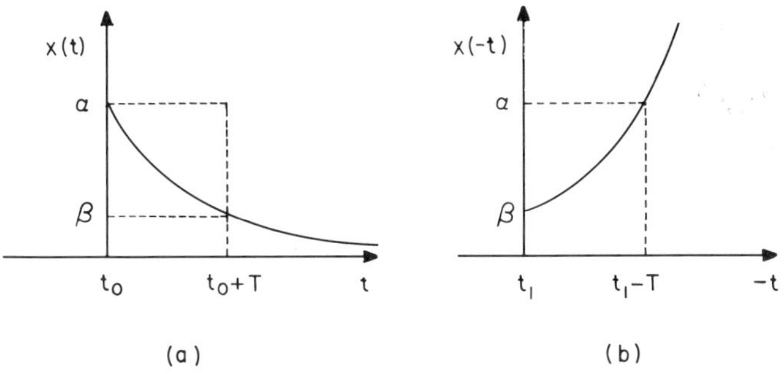

Fig. 3-4. a) The response of a first-order time-invariant system; b) The response of the system of Fig. 3-4a in reverse time.

We can translate the above intuitive picture into a condition on the system. If $\phi(t,t_0)$ and $\Psi(t,t_0)$ are the (one-dimensional) transition matrices for the forward and the backward systems respectively, the above amounts to saying that

$$\phi(t_1, t_0) = \Psi(t_0, t_1) \tag{3-55}$$

Thus in the first-order linear time-invariant system, we see that the adjoint system is exactly equivalent to the original unforced system "with time running backward" in the sense of Eq. (3-55).♦♦

In a time-varying linear system, the meaning of running time backward becomes more difficult to visualize. However, we can demonstrate that in the first-order case, if $\phi(t,t_0)$ is the transition matrix for the original system, and $\Psi(t,t_0)$ is the transition matrix for the adjoint system, Eq. (3-55) still holds.

♦♦Example 3-14. For the system $\dot{x} = tx$, the system solution is

$$x = x_0 \left[\exp\left(\frac{t^2 - t_0^2}{2}\right)\right]$$

whereas for the adjoint system $\dot{\psi} = -t\psi$, the solution is

$$\psi = \psi_0 \left[\exp\left(\frac{t_0^2 - t^2}{2}\right)\right]$$

Plotting the two responses, it is not immediately clear that one constitutes a reverse time system of the other. However, as

$$\phi(t,t_0) = \exp\left(\frac{t^2 - t_0^2}{2}\right)$$

and

$$\Psi(t,t_0) = \exp\left(\frac{t_0^2 - t^2}{2}\right)$$

we see that Eq. (3-55) still holds.♦♦

It turns out that even in the general higher order case, if Φ and Ψ denote the transition matrices for the original and adjoint systems respectively, we still have $\Psi^\dagger(t_1, t_0) = \Phi(t_0, t_1)$ for all t_0 and t_1. To show this, let us first define the transition matrix for the adjoint system, $\Psi(t_1, t_0)$, where

$$\frac{d}{dt}\Psi(t,t_0) = -\mathbf{A}^\dagger(t)\Psi(t,t_0), \qquad \Psi(t_0, t_0) = \mathbf{I} \tag{3-56}$$

Since

$$\begin{aligned}\frac{d}{dt}[\Psi^\dagger(t, t_0)\Phi(t, t_0)] &= \left[\frac{d}{dt}\Psi^\dagger(t, t_0)\right]\Phi(t,t_0) + \Psi^\dagger(t,t_0)\frac{d}{dt}\Phi(t,t_0) \\ &= [-\mathbf{A}^\dagger(t)\Psi(t,t_0)]^\dagger\,\Phi(t,t_0) + \Psi^\dagger(t,t_0)\mathbf{A}(t)\Phi(t,t_0) \\ &= -\Psi^\dagger(t,t_0)\mathbf{A}(t)\Phi(t,t_0) + \Psi^\dagger(t,t_0)\mathbf{A}(t)\Phi(t,t_0) = 0\end{aligned}$$

Thus,

$$\Psi^\dagger(t,t_0)\Phi(t,t_0) = \text{Constant} \tag{3-57}$$

Since at $t = t_0$, this product is equal to $\mathbf{I}$, then $\Psi^\dagger(t,t_0)\Phi(t,t_0) \equiv \mathbf{I}$ for any time t, and

$$\Psi^\dagger(t_1, t_0) = \Phi^{-1}(t_1, t_0) = \Phi(t_0, t_1) \qquad \text{for all} \quad t_0 \quad \text{and} \quad t_1 \tag{3-58}$$

So far we have developed the properties of the adjoint system when it is free running. However, since the transition matrix is closely related to the impulse response of a system, by Eq. (3-58) we expect that we may use the adjoint system to advantage even under input. As an illustrative example, consider:

◆◆Example 3-15. Consider a time-varying linear system, $\dot{\mathbf{x}} = \mathbf{A}(t)\mathbf{x} + \mathbf{b}(t)u$. Assume that the system is in normal form, so that

$$\mathbf{b}(t) = \begin{bmatrix} 0 \\ \vdots \\ 0 \\ b_n(t) \end{bmatrix}$$

Originally the system is at rest. At an unknown time t_0, an impulse in $u(t)$ is applied. In response to this impulse, the jth system state has been observed to reach its maximum value x_j' at a time t_1. Find the history of $x_j(t)$ in the interval $t_0 \le t \le t_1$.

Some reflection will indicate that all that is needed is to reconstruct the jth state $x_j(t)$ backwards from the point $x_j(t_1) = x_j'$.

Note that $x_j(t)$ depends on two parameters, t_0 (the time of application of the impulse) and t (the running time). We thus use the notation $x_j(t,t_0)$ for it. All we know is $x_j(t_1,t_0) = x_j'$. What is really needed is $x_j(t_1,t_0)$ as a function of t_0 for $t_0 < t_1$.

Let us denote the transition matrix $\Phi(t,t_0)$ for our system by the matrix $[\phi_{ij}]$. Similarly, the transition matrix $\Psi(t,\tau)$ of the adjoint system $\dot{\Psi} = -A^T(t)\Psi$ is denoted by the matrix $[\xi_{ij}]$. If $u(t)$ is an impulse applied at $t = t_0$, we have

$$x_j(t,t_0) = \phi_{jn}(t,t_0)\,b_n(t_0) \tag{3-59}$$

Consider, however, an impulse applied at the jth position of the adjoint system; that is, consider the response of ψ for the system $\dot{\psi} = -A^T(t)\psi + v(t)$, where $v(t)$ is a vector with an impulse $\mu(t_0)$ at the jth position and 0s elsewhere. The nth component of the vector ψ can immediately be written as $\psi_n = \xi_{nj}(t,t_0)$ which, by Eq. (3-58) becomes

$$\psi_n(t,t_0) = \phi_{jn}(t_0,t) \tag{3-60}$$

We see that by using the impulse response to the adjoint system, we have managed to invert the order of t_0 and t for ϕ_{jn}. This is exactly what is needed except for the fact that we need $\phi_{jn}(t_0,t)$ for $t_0 < t$, which is clearly unrealizable.

However, by reversing time in the adjoint system, (i.e., by substituting $\tau = t_1 - t$ and running the adjoint system backwards) under an impulse, we will evidently produce the desired result if we monitor $\psi_n(t_1 - \tau, t_1)$.*

Similarly if we generate $b_n(t)$ backwards to obtain $b_n(t_1 - \tau)$, then the product $\psi_n(t_1 - \tau, t_1)\,b_n(t_1 - \tau)$ will yield $x_j(t_1,t_0)$ as a function of t_0. ♦♦

Let us note that there are some definite problems associated with the use of the adjoint method particularly in simulation. First, for a stable system, it is clear that its adjoint system will be unstable and hence will be sensitive to noise and parameter errors. Second, for a nontrivial problem (for example, a multiple-input, multiple-output linear time-varying system), using the adjoint in a way similar to Example 3-15 will require a much more elaborate setup than the original system. In a way, we trade speed in running time with elaborateness in circuitry.

We will have occasion to use the adjoint system extensively when we deal with system optimization problems in Chaps. 13-17.

*This idea is developed more fully in [L1]. See pp. 239-247, 398-403.

3.9 Linear Systems That Cannot be Represented in the State Equation Form

There are a number of linear systems that cannot be characterized by ordinary differential equations of finite order. Typical of such systems are those which are governed by linear partial differential equations. For such systems, the state space techniques are inconvenient to use. However as these systems are linear, we can still characterize such systems by means of an impulse response $g(t)$ and write the system input-output relationship in terms of a superposition integral of the form

$$y(t) = y(t_0) + \int_0^t g(t - \tau)u(\tau)\,d\tau \tag{3-61}$$

where as usual $u(t)$ is the input and $y(t)$ is the output.

♦♦Example 3-16. For an idealized RC transmission line, let the normalized voltage at a distance x from one end and at a time t be given by the function $v(x,t)$; then it is known that the following linear partial differential equation holds

$$\frac{\partial^2 v(x,t)}{\partial x^2} = \frac{\partial v(x,t)}{\partial t} \tag{3-62}$$

For an input voltage time function (at the end $x = 0$) $v(0,t)$, the response at the point $x = x_1$ is given by

$$v(x_1,t) = v_0(x_1,t) + \int_0^t g(x_1,t - \tau)v(0,\tau)\,d\tau \tag{3-63}$$

which is essentially in the form of Eq. (3-61). In Eq. (3-63), $v_0(x_1,t)$ is the initial condition response of the system. Note that by Eq. (3-62), even when $v(0,t) \equiv 0$, $v(x_1,t)$ cannot be found unless an initial voltage distribution function along the entire transmission line $v(x,0)$ at the initial time $t = 0$ is given. In contrast, in the case of a differential system, we recall that only a finite number of initial conditions need to be specified. Since a voltage distribution function has infinite degree of freedom, we see that distributed parameter systems such as transmission lines can only be represented in a state space of infinite dimensions.

Where input-output relationship suffices we can, however, make use of the superposition integral (3-63). In particular, for system (3-62), it is possible to verify (see Exercise 3-15) that the initial condition response is given by

$$v_0(x,t) = \frac{1}{2\sqrt{\pi t}} \int_0^\infty \left(e^{-\frac{(\xi - x)^2}{4t}} - e^{-\frac{(\xi + x)^2}{4t}} \right) v(\xi,0)\, d\xi \tag{3-64}$$

whence the impulse response $g(x,t)$ is given by:

$$g(x,t) = \frac{x}{2\sqrt{\pi t^3}} e^{-\frac{x^2}{4t}} \quad (x \geq 0) \tag{3-65}$$

It is interesting to note in passing that for a fixed value of x, the system transfer function is no longer in ratios of polynomials in s. Specifically, we have

$$G(x,s) = \mathcal{L}[g(x,t)] = e^{-x\sqrt{s}} \tag{3-66}$$ ◆◆

3.10 Summary

This chapter considers several questions related to the solution of the system state equations. A solution of the state equation, when found, describes a trajectory in the state space of the system.

The most general sufficient condition that can be imposed on a system $\dot{\mathbf{x}} = \mathbf{f}(\mathbf{x},\mathbf{u},t)$ to guarantee a unique solution is that the Lipschitz condition (3-5) must be satisfied. For a linear system $\dot{\mathbf{x}} = \mathbf{A}(t)\mathbf{x} + \mathbf{B}(t)\mathbf{u}$, the fact that $\mathbf{A}(t)$ is Riemann-integrable is sufficient for the existence of a unique solution.

For a linear system, when the existence of a solution is assumed, the solution can be obtained as a function of the transition matrix $\Phi(t,t_0)$ by means of Eq. (3-16) or Eq. (3-22).

The transition matrix of a linear time-invariant system can in theory always be found, and any one of the methods of Sec. 3.4 can be used to this end. For linear time-varying systems, however, the transition matrix can only be found for isolated cases, some of which are discussed in Sec. 3.7.

The relationship between the vector-matrix state equation of a linear time-invariant system and its transfer function is discussed in Sec. 3.5.

Whether there is a control function $\mathbf{u}(t)$ which can drive a system $\dot{\mathbf{x}} = \mathbf{f}(\mathbf{x},\mathbf{u},t)$ from a given state to another touches on the question of controllability of the system. This question is fully answerable again only in the case of a linear time-invariant system. The basic question here is whether a given state component can be influenced by a given control component. The test of controllability of a linear time-invariant system can be reduced to a test of the rank of a matrix involving $\mathbf{A}$ and $\mathbf{B}$. (See Theorem 3-4.)

Whether the system initial state can be determined from a record of the system output $y(t)$ over a finite time interval touches on the question of observability of the system. Again, this question is completely answerable only for linear time-invariant systems, and Theorem 3-5 gives a necessary and sufficient condition.

To every linear system $\dot{x} = A(t)x$ there corresponds an adjoint system $\dot{\psi} = -A^{\dagger}(t)\psi$. The adjoint system is in some sense equivalent to running the associated linear system backward. It is useful sometimes as a computational aid and plays an important role in optimization problems. It is considered in Sec. 3.8.

There is no general way that the solution of a nonlinear system can be found except through numerical means. Even for linear systems, there are cases where the system is not amenable to state equation characterization.

3.11 Exercises

3-1 For the system $1/(p^2+1)$, select a set of state variables such that the elements of the A matrix are complex. Find the matrices A, P, and e^{At}. Find the adjoint system. Repeat with a set of state variables so chosen that the elements of A become real.

3-2 Show that the matrix $\Phi^{-1}(t,t_0)$ can be found from the matrix differential equation

$$\frac{d}{dt}\Phi^{-1}(t,t_0) = -\Phi^{-1}(t,t_0)A$$

with the initial condition $\Phi^{-1}(t_0,t_0) = I$ $\left[\text{hint: try } \frac{d}{dt}(\Phi^{-1}(t,t_0)\Phi(t,t_0)).\right]$

3-3 For a system with

$$A = \begin{bmatrix} \lambda_1 & 1 & 0 \\ 0 & \lambda_1 & 1 \\ 0 & 0 & \lambda_1 \end{bmatrix}, \quad b = \begin{bmatrix} b_1 \\ b_2 \\ b_3 \end{bmatrix}$$

show that the matrix $[b, Ab, \ldots, A^{n-1}b]$ is singular if b_3 is 0.

3-4 State the conditions that must be imposed such that for a linear autonomous system the origin is the only equilibrium state.

3-5 Show that in the general case of linear time-varying systems of the form $\dot{x} = A(t)x$, the transition matrix $\Phi(t,t_1)$ can be obtained by the Neumann series

$$\Phi(t,t_0) = I + \int_{t_0}^{t} A(\tau)\,d\tau + \int_{t_0}^{t} A(\tau_1)\int_{t_0}^{\tau_1} A(\tau_2)\,d\tau_2\,d\tau_1$$

$$+ \int_{t_0}^{t} A(\tau_1)\int_{t_0}^{\tau_1} A(\tau_2)\int_{t_0}^{\tau_2} A(\tau_3)\,d\tau_3\,d\tau_2\,d\tau_1 + \cdots$$

(Hint: differentiate both sides of the above expression with respect to t.)

3-6 When a system is driven by a standard input, e.g., a sine wave, it can be converted to a free system through the addition of more state variables. For example, a sine wave of radian frequency a may be considered to be the output of an autonomous system $1/(p^2+a^2)$ when the suitable initial condition is given. Thus by adding two more state variables, a driven system is converted to an autonomous system.

Use the above approach to find the response of the system $k/\big(p(p+a)\big)$ under the excitation $A \sin \omega t$ by finding the transition matrix of the enhanced system. Compare the labor involved with that from a straightforward application of Eq. (3-22).

3-7 For the linear system

$$\begin{bmatrix} \dot z_1 \\ \dot z_2 \end{bmatrix} = \begin{bmatrix} -1 & 0 \\ 1 & -2 \end{bmatrix}\begin{bmatrix} z_1 \\ z_2 \end{bmatrix} + \begin{bmatrix} 1 \\ 1 \end{bmatrix} u, \qquad y = z_1 + u$$

a) Obtain the transfer function $G(p)$ between the input u and the output y.
b) Obtain the state equations in the canonical form using the state variables x_1, x_2.
c) Obtain the state equations in the normal form, using the state variables y_1, y_2.
d) For the original state variables (z_1, z_2), as well as for the canonical state variables (x_1, x_2) and the normal state variables (y_1, y_2), investigate their complete controllability with respect to the input u and their complete observability with respect to the output y.

3-8 For the linear system given by

$$\begin{bmatrix} \dot x_1 \\ \dot x_2 \\ \dot x_3 \end{bmatrix} = \begin{bmatrix} 0 & 0 & 0 \\ 1 & -1 & 0 \\ 0 & -2 & -2 \end{bmatrix}\begin{bmatrix} x_1 \\ x_2 \\ x_3 \end{bmatrix} + \begin{bmatrix} 1 \\ 0 \\ 0 \end{bmatrix} u, \qquad y = [0,1,1]\begin{bmatrix} x_1 \\ x_2 \\ x_3 \end{bmatrix}$$

a) Find the transition matrix $\Phi(t,t_0)$.
b) Find the unit-impulse response $g(t)$ of the output y with respect to the input u.
c) Find the initial condition response $y(t)$ of this system (for zero input).
d) Determine whether the state is completely controllable with respect to the input u and completely observable with respect to the output y.

3-9 The functions $f_1(x), \ldots, f_4(x)$ all satisfy the conditions that $f(x) = +1$ for $|x| > 1$ and $f(x) = -1$ for $|x| < -1$. In the range $|x| \le 1$ they differ and are given by

$$f_1(x) = x, \; f_2(x) = 0, \; f_3(x) = x^3, \; f_4(x) = \sin^{-1} \frac{\pi}{2} x$$

For each determine whether the Lipschitz condition is satisfied globally. Find a Lipschitz constant where such is possible.

3-10 Find the transition matrix $\Phi(t,t_0)$ for the system of Fig. 3-5. Plot $x_1(t)$ when $u(t)$ is a unit impulse; do this for several values of t_0, the time when the impulse is applied.

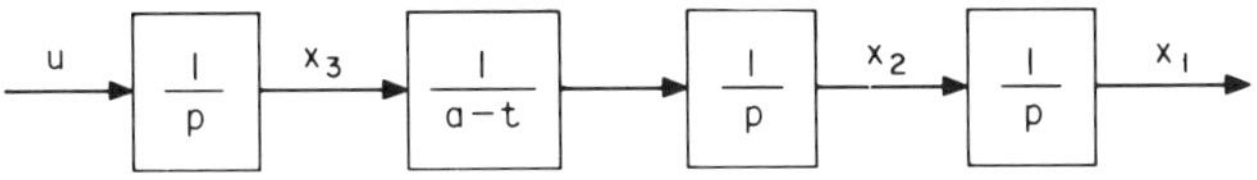

Fig. 3-5. The system considered in Exercise 3-10.

3-11 Show that for any constant square matrices A, $Ae^{At} = e^{At}A$.

3-12 Find the system given by Fig. 2-16. Find a transition matrix e^{At} if the nonlinear function $u(t) = f(e(t))$ is replaced by a constant gain k such that $u(t) = ke(t)$. Find the system response if:
a) $n(t) = 0$, $r(t)$ is a unit step.
b) $r(t) = 0$, $n(t)$ is a unit impulse.
c) $r(t)$ is an impulse at $t = 0$ and $n(t)$ is an impulse at $t = t_1 > 0$.

3-13 Prove that for a constant $n \times n$ matrix A, each element of the matrix $\Phi(s) = (sI - A)^{-1}$ is a rational function of s whose denominator is of degree n and whose numerator is always of degree less than n. (Hint: consult Appendix A.)

3-14 For the system given by $t^2\ddot{x} + 4t\dot{x} + 2x = u(t)$, let $x(t,t_0)$ be the impulse response of the system for $t \ge t_0$ when $u(t)$ is an impulse applied at t_0.
a) Find and plot $x(t,0)$, $x(t,2)$, $x(t,4)$, $x(t,6)$ as functions of t.
b) Obtain the plots for $x(2,t_0)$, $x(3,t_0)$ as functions of t_0 from the plots in (a).

3-15 Verify that Eqs. (3-63) and (3-65) satisfy (3-62). Prove Eq. (3-66).

3-16 For each of the following linear systems: (i) find the transition matrix, (ii) determine the response $y(t)$ to a unit impulse in $u(t)$, (iii) decide whether the system is controllable and whether the output is observable.

a) $\dot{x}_1 = -x_1 - u,\ \dot{x}_2 = x_1 + u;\ y = x_2$
b) $\dot{x}_1 = u,\ \dot{x}_2 = -x_1 - x_2;\ y = x_1 + x_2$
c) $\dot{x}_1 = -3x_1 + 5u,\ \dot{x}_2 = -8x_1 - 5x_2;\ y = x_1 + x_2$
d) $\dot{x}_1 = -5x_1 - 8u,\ \dot{x}_2 = 5x_1 + 3x_2 + 5u;\ y = x_2$

3-17 Show that for a time-invariant linear differential plant given by $\dot{\mathbf{x}} = \mathbf{A}\mathbf{x} + \mathbf{B}\mathbf{u}$, the transfer function matrix $\mathbf{H}(s)$ of Eq. (3-44) is invariant with the choice of the state coordinates.

3-18 State the conditions under which the transfer function matrix $\mathbf{H}(s)$ of Eq. (3-44) uniquely determines the system matrices $\mathbf{A}$ and $\mathbf{B}$ for a system in the normal form.

3-19 For the missile of Exercise 2-5, investigate the complete controllability of each of the following states:

a) the state (θ, ω, α)
b) the normal state $(a_N, \dot{a}_N, \ddot{a}_N)$
c) the canonical state.

Investigate the complete observability of the output $a_N(t)$ for each of the above cases. (The input is assumed to be $\delta(t)$ throughout.)

3.12 References

[D2], [O1], [S10], [T3], and [Z1] continue to be excellent references for the subject matter of this chapter. The reader will find it also stimulating to consult the mathematical texts [H14] and [S12], particularly Chaps. 1 and 2 of the former and Chaps. 1 through 4 of the latter. In addition [K12] is a useful reference on the mathematics of linear systems in general, including results in both the time and frequency domain. Chapter 8 of [K12] includes some results on the vector-matrix formulation of linear differential systems.

4

Second-Order Systems and the State Plane

The state space with only two dimensions, which we may call the state plane, is important for several reasons. First it allows easy visualization, since a trajectory on a plane can be readily traced or portrayed. Second, many practically important and dynamically complex systems can be reasonably well approximated by second-order systems and can be analyzed accordingly. Finally, because of its simplicity, many significant results and conclusions have been obtained and several important theorems concerning system phase trajectories have been formulated. Indeed, the particular two-dimensional state plane with the output and its rate of change as the coordinates is well known to the classical analyst as the phase plane, and system studied making use of the phase plane were carried out well before the turn of the century by mathematicians such as Poincaré.

The state plane, of course, has its limitations. The obvious one is that it is not applicable to systems that cannot be approximated by second-order systems. Besides this, the chief limitation is that only autonomous systems with unique solutions can be readily handled. When a system is driven by an input or when it is time varying to such an extent that there is no uniqueness, then the system trajectories will cross each other and, moreover, will depend on so many parameters that neither qualitative nor quantitative information can be derived by glancing at the state-plane portraits.*

*However, it should be mentioned that investigators have made fruitful use of state plane in investigating second-order time-invariant systems under simple inputs such as step or ramp. Indeed even some simple time-varying systems have been analyzed in the state plane.

In this chapter we review the potentiality of the phase plane. Beginning with an example, we proceed to study equilibrium states and equilibrium zones. We next consider state trajectories in a linear system. We then proceed to study limit cycles and multiple modes of behavior in nonlinear systems and we conclude the chapter by mentioning some standard methods of construction of state-plane portraits.

4.1 Some Examples of Trajectories in the State Plane

Let us first consider some second-order nonlinear control systems in order to become acquainted with the utility of the state plane.

♦♦Example 4-1. Consider the problem of one-dimensional attitude control of a satellite in its pitch plane. The goal is to point an antenna toward certain stellar objects in the plane (see Fig. 4-1). The attitude control is achieved by means of a pair of reaction jets; each is of the on-off type, capable of exerting either full torque on the satellite of magnitude T or zero torque. Let the stellar object be positioned at an angle θ relative to the axis of the telescope. Then the equation of motion of the satellite under the influence of the torque τ from the reaction jet will be

$$I\ddot{\theta} = \tau \tag{4-1}$$

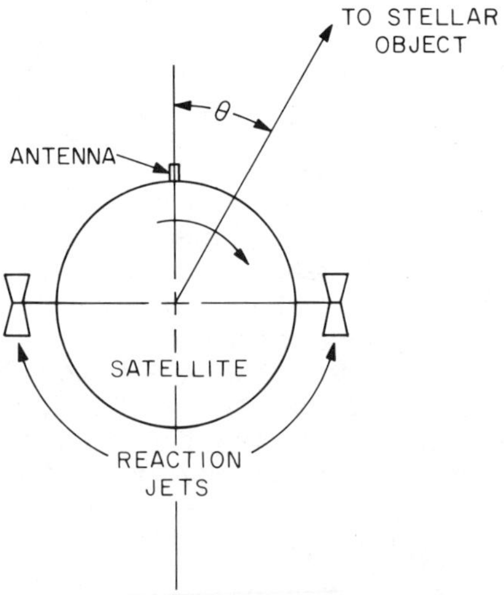

Fig. 4-1. A satellite whose pitch plane attitude is to be controlled such that the angle θ between the antenna and a stellar object is always zero.

where I is the moment of inertia of the satellite and where the torque τ can have the values $+IU$, $-IU$, or 0. Let $u = \tau/I$ and

$$x_1 = \theta,\ x_1(t_0) = x_{10},\ x_2 = \dot{\theta},\ x_2(t_0) = x_{20} \tag{4-2}$$

then, from Eq. (4-1), the equations of motion become

$$\dot{x}_1 = x_2,\ \dot{x}_2 = u \tag{4-3}$$

The block diagram of this system is shown in Fig. 4-2. Consider now the following cases.

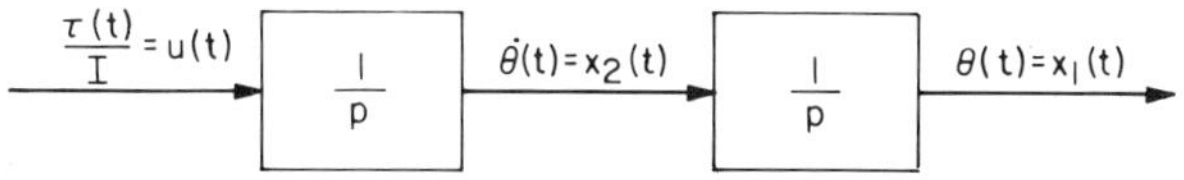

Fig. 4-2. Schematic representation of the satellite as a plant to be controlled.

Case 1. $u = 0$. Equation (4-3) becomes $\dot{x}_1 = x_2$, $\dot{x}_2 = 0$ which has the solution $x_2 = x_{20}$, $x_1 = x_{10} + x_{20}t$.

The trajectories on the state plane (phase plane), depending on the initial conditions, x_{10} and x_{20}, are shown in Fig. 4-3a.

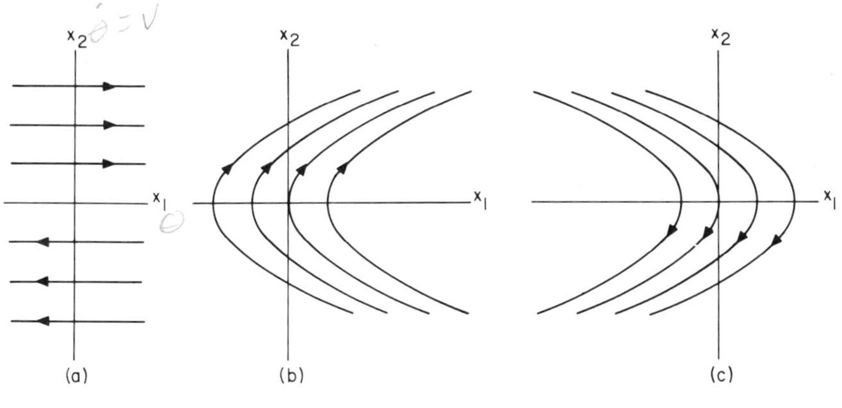

Fig. 4-3. Motion in the x_2 vs. x_1 plane shown for $u = 0$ in (a), for $u = +U$ in (b), and for $u = -U$ in (c).

The trajectories are straight lines, parallel to the x_1 axis. The trajectories above the x_1 axis proceed to the right, those below the x_1 axis proceed to the left. States on the x_1 axis will not move at all (since $x_2 = \dot{x}_1 = 0$). All this simply means that without any external torque, the satellite will rotate at its initial angular rate.

For this case, the equilibrium conditions occur whenever $\dot{x}_1 = \dot{x}_2 = 0$. This means that the entire x_1 axis is an equilibrium zone.

Case 2. $u = +U$. For $u = +U$, Eq. (4–3) can be integrated to yield

$$x_1 = x_{10} + x_{20}t + \frac{1}{2}Ut^2, \quad x_2 = x_{20} + Ut$$

where x_{10} and x_{20} are the initial conditions. Since the system trajectories may be viewed as curves with x_2 as a function of x_1, we can eliminate the time t. One way to do this is to consider

$$\frac{dx_1/dt}{dx_2/dt} = \frac{dx_1}{dx_2} = \frac{x_2}{U} \qquad \text{for} \qquad u = +U \tag{4–4}$$

Equation (4–4) may be integrated, yielding

$$\frac{x_2^2}{2} - Ux_1 = c \qquad \text{for} \qquad u = +U \tag{4–5}$$

where c is an integrating constant.

The trajectories are then parabolas curving to the right, as shown in Fig. 4–3*b*. Each parabola is seen to have the same shape.

From Fig. 4–3*b* we also see that there will be one and only one parabola which passes through the origin. If the initial conditions should be on the portion of that parabola that is below the x_1 axis, then by applying torque $+U$ until the origin is reached and then shut off the reaction jet, we will have achieved the objective of pointing the telescope on the stellar object. For other initial conditions, this cannot be done by using positive torque exclusively.

For this case of $u = +U$, it should be noted that there exists no equilibrium state in the entire state plane.

Case 3. $u = -U$. The same arguments as those for Case 2 $(u = +U)$ apply. Replacing $+U$ by $-U$ in Eqs. (4–4) and (4–5) yields

$$\frac{dx_1}{dx_2} = -\frac{x_2}{U} \qquad \text{for} \qquad u = -U \tag{4–6}$$

and its solution

$$\frac{x_2^2}{2} + Ux_1 = c \qquad \text{for} \qquad u = -U \tag{4–7}$$

where, again, c is an integrating constant. The state-plane portrait is a family of parabolas curving to the left shown in Fig. 4–3*c*.

Only those initial conditions that lie on the curve going through the origin in Fig. 4–3*c* can be driven to the origin with a (normalized) torque of $-U$. Here, too, there is no equilibrium state in the entire state plane.

Case 4. Suppose we connect a simple system as shown in Fig. 4-4. Here, we are feeding back the output signal $x_1(t)$ (or the attitude angle $\theta(t)$) and control the input signal $u(t)$ (or the reaction torque $\tau(t) = u(t)/I$) by the function

$$u(t) = -U \text{ sgn } x_1(t) \tag{4-8}$$

where

$$\text{sgn } x = \begin{cases} +1, & x > 0 \\ -1, & x < 0 \end{cases}$$

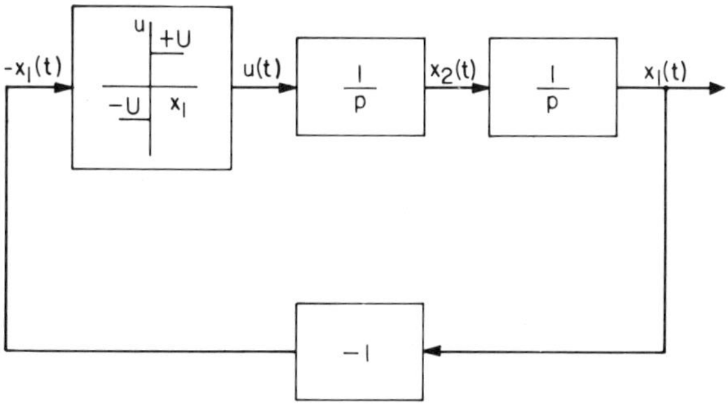

Fig. 4-4. A simple control system for the satellite.

Combining the trajectories of Figs. 4-3*b* and 4-3*c* and considering the constraint imposed by Eq. (4-8), we then obtain the state-plane portrait of this feedback system which is shown in Fig. 4-5.

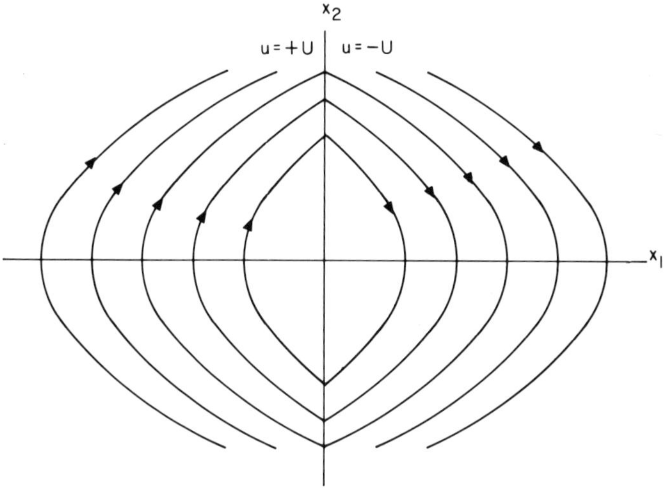

Fig. 4-5. State-plane portrait for the system of Fig. 4-4.

Each state-plane trajectory will be closed and its size will depend on the initial condition. The system will continue to recycle until all the fuel is consumed. Physically, when the state-plane trajectory is closed, the satellite will oscillate about the equilibrium position.

Oscillations occur more readily in nonlinear systems than in linear systems. The study of oscillatory motions plays an important role in nonlinear system analysis.

Case 5. The Use of Ideal Lead Compensation. It may be desired to quench the oscillation and, moreover, to design the control system such that x_1 and x_2 both eventually converge to the origin (i.e., the telescope eventually acquires the stellar object).

Suppose we wish to use a linear compensator in front of the on-off jets. Simple reasoning would indicate that a lead network is called for, so as to impart some "predictive" capability to the system.

To preserve the requirement that the system be second order, let us consider an ideal lead network of the form $p + a$. The resulting system is shown in Fig. 4-6.

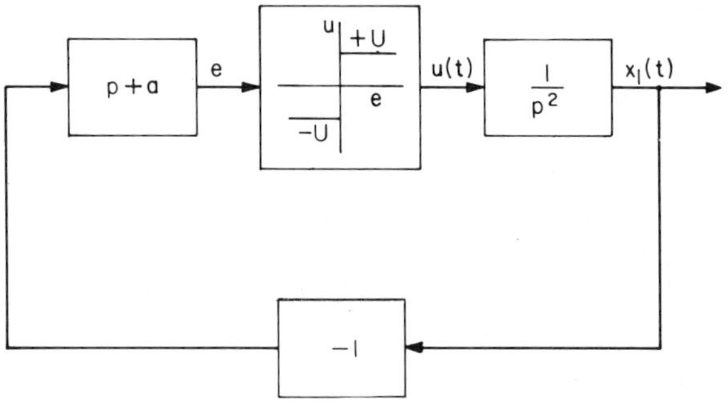

Fig. 4-6. A control system with a relay and an ideal lead network.

Now the switching function becomes

$$u(t) = -U \operatorname{sgn}(\dot{x}_1 + ax_1) = -U \operatorname{sgn}(x_2 + ax_1) \tag{4-9}$$

This means that the switching line, instead of being the x_2 axis, is now given by the straight line

$$x_2 + ax_1 = 0 \tag{4-10}$$

It is thus a line in the x_1, x_2 plane with a slope $-a$. The line lies in the second and fourth quadrant as shown in Fig. 4-7 if $a > 0$.

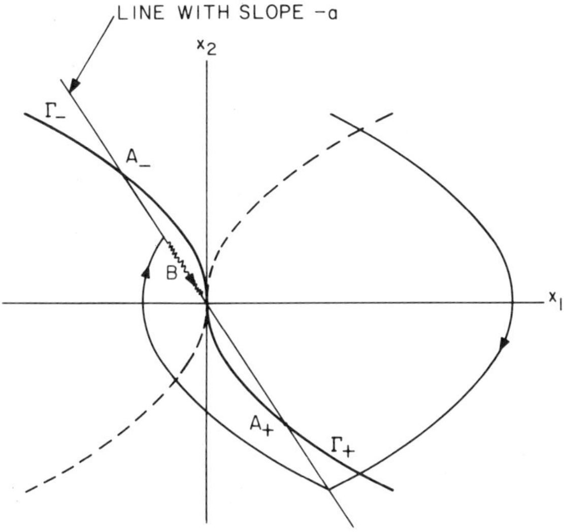

Fig. 4-7. A typical trajectory for the system of Fig. 4-6. The wavy line B indicates a possibility of chatter.

The system state trajectories can be found by integrating the set

$$\begin{aligned} \dot{x}_1 &= x_2, \quad \dot{x}_2 = -U \qquad \text{for} \qquad x_2 + ax_1 > 0 \\ \dot{x}_1 &= x_2, \quad \dot{x}_2 = +U \qquad \text{for} \qquad x_2 + ax_1 < 0 \end{aligned} \tag{4-11}$$

In each half of the state plane separated by the switching line, the system trajectories would still be the parabolas (4-5) and (4-7); thus the total system trajectory can be obtained by piecing together the various segments of the parabolas.

When we do this, we soon encounter a situation which is illustrated in Fig. 4-7. Consider the two parabolas passing through the origin and in particular those segments of the parabolas shown as Γ_+ and Γ_-. The switching line for $a > 0$ must necessarily intersect the segments at the points A_+ and A_- respectively. Beyond the points A_+ and A_-, the system trajectory under the driving function (4-9) will intersect Γ before the switch line. By the geometry of the situation, we see that the trajectory resulted from the reversal of the drive will bring it on a parabola passing much closer to the origin. This will continue until the system trajectory intersects the switch line at a point closer to the origin than the points A_+ or A_-. In this case, the trajectory will intersect the switch line before the segment Γ. Here, an instant after the relay is switched, the system trajectory will recross the switch line and the relay must switch back. Thus the relay will "chatter" while the system state stays on the line.* From physical consideration, the general trend of system motion even in the "chatter" case would be toward the origin along the switch line. Thus we fulfill our goal of achieving damping for the system, but in an inefficient way.

Case 6. An "Optimal" Scheme for Damping of System Motion. Suppose we wish to design a feedback element such that for every initial condition (x_{10}, x_{20}), the motion will approach the origin in an efficient manner. Again we assume that $u(t)$ can only take on the values $+U$, $-U$ or 0.

Superimposing the trajectories of Figs. 4-3b and 4-3c, we obtain the set of curves shown in Fig. 4-8. We note that the origin can be approached only by two possible trajectories, namely the paths Γ_+ and Γ_- of Fig. 4-7. These are also shown in Fig. 4-8.

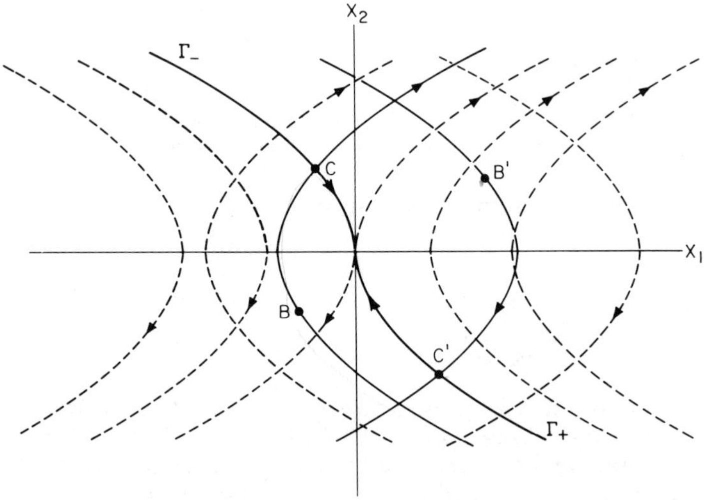

Fig. 4-8. An "optimal" control scheme should be such that sign reversals take place when the system trajectories intersect the switching curves Γ_+ and Γ_-.

Suppose we start at some arbitrary point in the state plane, say at point B of Fig. 4-8. The most feasible control strategy for bringing the state vector to the origin then would be to apply $u = +U$ which will move the state vector to point C on the path Γ_-.

*The frequency and amplitude of this "chatter" depend in practice on those higher order dynamics that were neglected. In a true second-order system, the chattering frequency would be infinite and its amplitude zero. Here the system state typically "slides" along the switching line.

At this instant, the control signal should be changed to $u = -U$ which will cause the state vector to move along the path Γ_-. As soon as the state vector has reached the origin, the control should be set to 0. The same strategy, except with reversed torques, should be used for a trajectory originating at a point such as B'.

It is quite clear from Fig. 4-8 that, whenever a state-plane trajectory approaches Γ_+ or Γ_-, a polarity reversal of the control signal u must take place, so that the trajectory can move along this line toward the origin. Thus the combination Γ_+ and Γ_- now constitutes the switching line. The following strategy will bring the state vector to the origin from any given initial condition:

When (x_{10}, x_{20}) lies to the left of the switching line, choose $u = +U$ until the trajectory hits the switching line. Then, make $u = -U$ until the origin is reached, at which time we set $u = 0$. If the initial state vector (x_{10}, x_{20}) lies to the right of the switching line, then the same strategy is used except for reversed polarities of u. The equation of the switching line follows from Eqs. (4-5) and (4-7) with $c = 0$. It is given by

$$Ux_{1s} + \frac{1}{2} \mid x_{2s} \mid x_{2s} = 0 \tag{4-12}$$

where (x_{1s}, x_{2s}) represents the set of state vectors along this switching line. The above control strategy is mathematically described by

$$u = -U \operatorname{sgn} \left[Ux_1 + \frac{1}{2} \mid x_2 \mid x_2 \right] = \begin{cases} +U, & x_1 < \dfrac{\mid x_2 \mid x_2}{2U} \\ -U, & x_1 > \dfrac{\mid x_2 \mid x_2}{2U} \end{cases} \tag{4-13}$$

With Eq. (4-13), Eq. (4-3) becomes

$$\dot{x}_1 = x_2, \quad \dot{x}_2 = -U \operatorname{sgn} \left[Ux_1 + \frac{1}{2} \mid x_2 \mid x_2 \right] \tag{4-14}$$

Note that the new feedback system has no input. Since it is also time invariant, it is an autonomous system. The block diagram of this feedback system is shown in Fig. 4-9.

If the torque level cannot exceed U, then it may be expected that the particular switching system, just devised, is in some sense a best system since at all times the maximum available torque level is used. As it turns out, the system is the optimum in the sense that it can take the system from any initial state to the origin in the minimum amount of time.◆◆

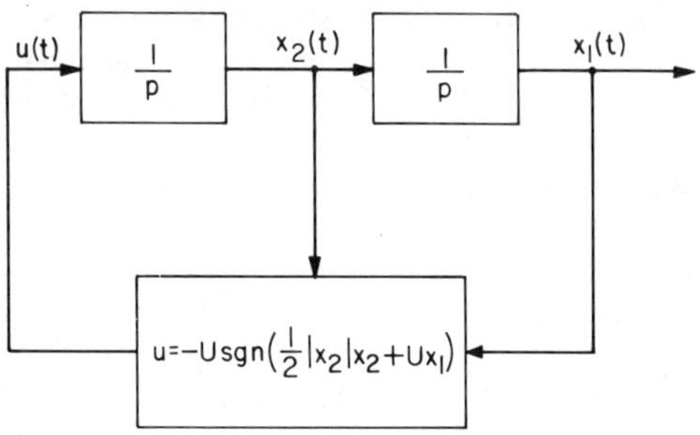

Fig. 4-9. A realization of the "optimal" control system.

Further discussion of this kind of optimum systems will be deferred until Chap. 12 and subsequent chapters.

4.2 Equilibrium States and Equilibrium Zones in Autonomous Systems

As has been indicated in Chap. 3, the equilibrium state(s) $\mathbf{x}_e$ of a system is defined by

$$\dot{\mathbf{x}} = 0 \quad \text{at} \quad \mathbf{x} = \mathbf{x}_e \tag{4-15}$$

For the second-order autonomous system

$$\dot{x}_1 = f_1(x_1, x_2), \qquad \dot{x}_2 = f_2(x_1, x_2) \tag{4-16}$$

the equilibrium state will be given by

$$f_1(x_{1e}, x_{2e}) = 0, \qquad f_2(x_{1e}, x_{2e}) = 0 \tag{4-17}$$

From Example 4-1, we have observed that in some cases every point on a line segment can be an equilibrium state, thus creating an equilibrium zone. In the example, this situation occurs only under a special set of circumstances, viz., $u = 0$. It is, however, important to point out that well-designed nonlinear control systems can have such zones. Let us consider two examples.

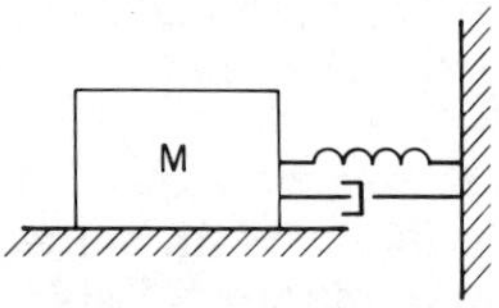

Fig. 4-10. A spring and dashpot system.

♦♦Example 4-2. The so-called *Coulomb friction* is a reasonable approximation of the friction force that acts on a heavy block when it is being pushed or pulled along a plank. The important characteristic of Coulomb friction is that it is a discontinuous function of velocity. Suppose an assembly such as is shown in Fig. 4-10 is caused to move; the equation of motion, assuming that the spring and dashpot have linear characteristics, will be of the form

$$\ddot{x} + a_1\dot{x} + a_2 x + f(\dot{x}) = 0, \qquad a_1, a_2 > 0 \tag{4-18}$$

The nonlinear function $f(\dot{x})$ is that characterizing the Coulomb friction. If sticking friction (stiction) is neglected, $f(\dot{x})$ can be ideally given by

$$f(\dot{x}) = \begin{cases} +c, & \dot{x} > 0 \\ -c, & \dot{x} < 0 \end{cases} \tag{4-19a}$$

where c is a constant. In this idealization $f(0)$ is not specified, but from physical reasoning, it must lie between $+c$ and $-c$, depending on the conditions. Thus

$$-c \leq f(0) \leq +c \tag{4-19b}$$

The equilibrium states in this case are clearly all those states where $a_2 x + f(0) = 0$. Since $-c < f(0) < +c$, the equilibrium states x_e must lie on the $\dot{x} = 0$ line somewhere between $x = +c/a_2$ and $x = -c/a_2$.

The above line segment possesses a certain stable property. Consider a system state that lies just above this line segment. By Eqs. (4-18) and (4-19) $\ddot{x} < 0$, and the force on the system state will be such as to decrease $\dot{x}$ and hence to drive it toward the line segment. On the other hand, a system state that is just below this line segment will be forced to move up and also toward the line segment. Using this line of reasoning we conclude that system states in the vicinity of the line segment $\dot{x} = 0$, and $-c/a_2 < x < +c/a_2$ will tend toward the line segment (see Exercise 4-1).♦♦

♦♦Example 4-3. Consider the system shown in Fig. 4-11. It consists of a linear block preceded by a nonlinear gain function $f(e)$ characterized by $f(e) = 0$ for $-\delta \leq e \leq +\delta$

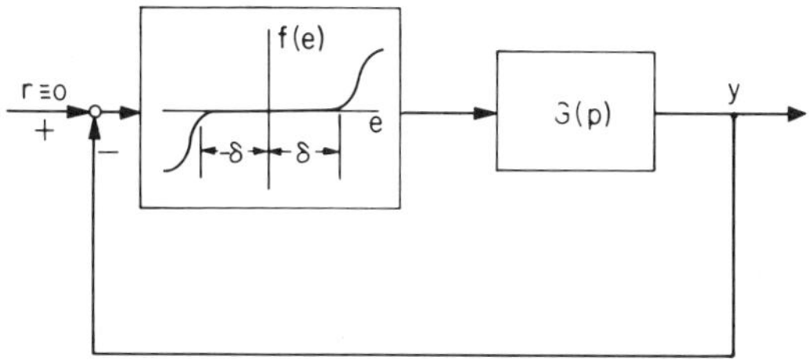

Fig. 4-11. The nonlinear system considered in Example 4-3.

If $G(p)$ is a second-order system with an integration, then in the normal form, the system state equations are

$$\dot{x}_1 = x_2, \quad \dot{x}_2 = -ax_2 + f(-x_1), \quad y = x_1 = -e$$

The equilibrium states are then all those states where $f(-x_1) = 0$. This occurs for $-\delta \leq x_1 \leq +\delta$ and $x_2 = 0$, which is again an entire line segment.♦♦

Note that by eliminating time in Eq. (4-16), we can obtain a differential equation involving only the state variables x_1 and x_2. By taking the ratio of the two equations in (4-16), we have

$$\frac{dx_2}{dx_1} = \frac{f_2(x_1, x_2)}{f_1(x_1, x_2)} \tag{4-20}$$

The derivative dx_2/dx_1 represents the tangent of the angle of the state-plane trajectory with respect to the x_1 axis. From Eqs. (4-17) and (4-20) we can deduce that at each equilibrium state (x_{1e}, x_{2e}), the direction of the state-plane trajectory is not defined; at every other point in the state plane, the direction is defined. Thus examining the behavior of system trajectories in the vicinity of an equilibrium state will prove profitable for determining the characteristics of that point. In the next section, we will first examine such behavior for a linear system.

4.3 Types of Equilibrium States for Autonomous Linear Second-Order Systems

For a linear autonomous system given by $\dot{\mathbf{x}} = \mathbf{A}\,\mathbf{x}$, the equilibrium states of the system are given by those states $\mathbf{x}_e$ satisfying $\mathbf{A}\,\mathbf{x}_e = 0$. From this we see that $\mathbf{x}_e = 0$ will be the only solution of the above equation provided that the determinant of $\mathbf{A}$ is nonzero. Hence we have:

♦♦Theorem 4-1. The origin of a linear autonomous system $\dot{\mathbf{x}} = \mathbf{A}\,\mathbf{x}$ is the only equilibrium state provided that $|\mathbf{A}| \neq 0$.♦♦

In particular if all the eigenvalues of the system are different from 0, then the origin is the only equilibrium state (why?). Thus the behavior of system phase trajectories in the vicinity of the equilibrium states is here reduced to examining their behavior about the origin. In fact, in these cases the behavior of the linear system trajectories throughout the state plane can be ascertained, at least qualitatively, by examining the behavior of the system trajectories in the vicinity of the origin.

It will be clear that for linear autonomous systems the examination of the system state-plane trajectory can best be done in the canonical form representation, since in this form, each of the system dominant modes are separated or uncoupled, and the resultant relaxation behavior can readily be deduced.

State-plane coordinates, however, are usually taken to be the normal coordinates, involving the output y and the output rate $\dot{y}$. Now the transformation between the normal set of coordinates and the canonical set of coordinates is a linear one* (in particular if the λ's are distinct, the transformation matrix is the Vandermonde matrix, as has been shown in Chap. 3) and, moreover, the origin in the normal system is also the origin in the canonical system. It is then reasonable to expect that the dominant features of a state-plane trajectory about the origin will be preserved as we go from one set of coordinates to another, and only the shape of the trajectory will be distorted. Thus without loss of generality, we can study the trajectories of a second-order linear system about the singular point 0 in the canonical set of coordinates. In the canonical form, with distinct roots, the system equations are

$$\begin{aligned} \dot{x}_1 &= \lambda_1 x_1, \quad & x_1(0) &= x_{10}, \\ \dot{x}_2 &= \lambda_2 x_2, \quad & x_2(0) &= x_{20} \end{aligned} \tag{4-21}$$

The solution of (4-21) is

$$x_1(t) = x_{10} e^{\lambda_1 t}, \quad x_2(t) = x_{20} e^{\lambda_2 t} \tag{4-22}$$

We shall now study the following cases:

Case 1. Both Eigenvalues are Real, Nonzero, and of the Same Sign. From (4-21), we obtain

$$\frac{dx_2}{dx_1} = \frac{\lambda_2}{\lambda_1} \frac{x_2}{x_1} \tag{4-23}$$

yielding

$$x_2 = c x_1^{\lambda_2/\lambda_1} \tag{4-24}$$

where c is an arbitrary constant.

Equation (4-24) indicates the form of the state-space trajectories. This is shown in Fig. 4-12a for the case $0 > \lambda_2 > \lambda_1$ and in Fig. 4-12b for $0 > \lambda_1 > \lambda_2$.

The singular points for the cases considered in Fig. 4-12 are called *nodes*. They are stable as shown with the λ's negative. When the λ's are positive, the nodes become unstable and the state

*Such transformation, however, is in general not an orthogonal one, and hence is not equivalent to a simple rotation of axes. See Appendix A.

portraits will retain the character of Fig. 4-12 but with the direction reversed.

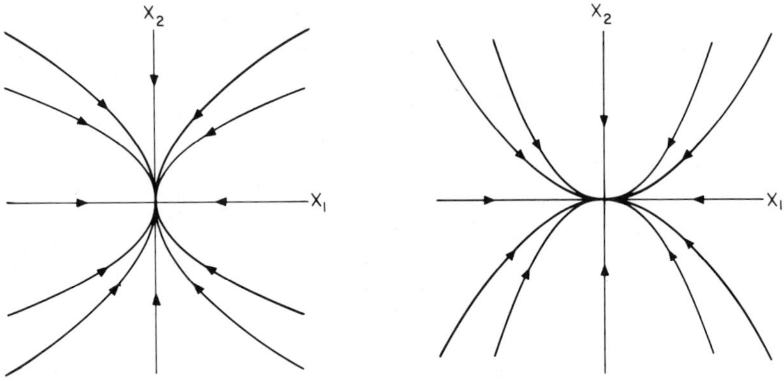

(a) (b)

Fig. 4-12. The state-plane trajectories in the canonical coordinates for a second-order time-invariant linear system whose eigenvalues are λ_1 and λ_2. The case $0 > \lambda_2 > \lambda_1$ is shown in (a) and the case $0 > \lambda_1 > \lambda_2$ is shown in (b).

Case 2. Both Eigenvalues are Real, Nonzero, and of Different Sign. For this case, it follows from (4-22) or from (4-24) that the state-plane portrait will have the form shown in Fig. 4-13. This type of singular point will be called a *saddle point* denoting the fact that all motion approaching this point will eventually be deflected away from it. Needless to say, a saddle point is unstable.

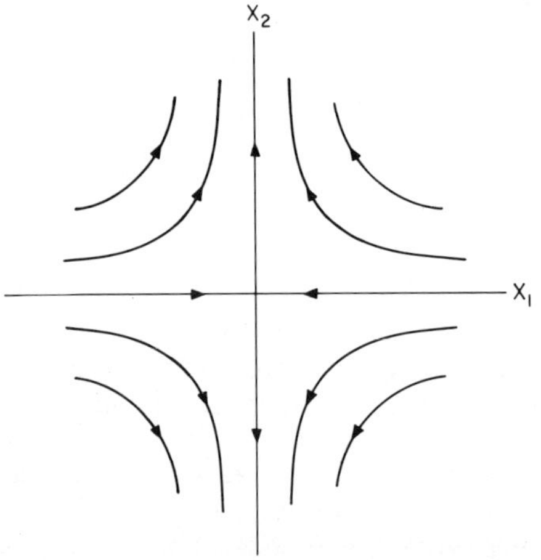

Fig. 4-13. The state-plane trajectories in the canonical coordinates for a second-order time-invariant linear system whose eigenvalues λ_1, λ_2 are such that $\lambda_2 > 0 > \lambda_1$.

Case 3. The Eigenvalues are Complex Conjugates. Here, if we use the canonical representation, then the equations

$$\dot{x}_1 = (\alpha + j\beta)\, x_1, \qquad \dot{x}_2 = (\alpha - j\beta)\, x_2 \tag{4–25}$$

have the solutions:

$$x_1 = x_{10}e^{\alpha t}\, e^{j\beta t} = x_{10}e^{\alpha t}\, [\cos \beta t + j \sin \beta t]$$

$$x_2 = x_{20}e^{\alpha t}\, e^{-j\beta t} = x_{20}e^{\alpha t}\, [\cos \beta t - j \sin \beta t]$$

Thus, the canonical coordinates x_1 and x_2 are conjugate couples. For this case, as the coordinates are given by complex numbers, the state-space portrait is not easily visualized. It will then be convenient to make a further transformation. Let

$$x_1 = z_1 + jz_2, \quad x_2 = z_1 - jz_2 \tag{4–26}$$

both z_1 and z_2 are assumed to be real; solving for them, we obtain

$$\begin{aligned} z_1 &= \frac{1}{2}(x_1 + x_2) = z_{10}\, e^{\alpha t} \cos \beta t \\ z_2 &= \frac{1}{2j}(x_1 - x_2) = -z_{20}\, e^{\alpha t} \sin \beta t \end{aligned} \tag{4–27}$$

Considering the complex plane with coordinates z_1 and jz_2, we realize that the solution

$$x_1(t) = z_1(t) + jz_2(t) = x_{10}e^{\alpha t}\, e^{j\beta t}$$

$$x_1(0) = x_{10} = z_{10} + jz_{20}$$

yields a logarithmic spiral in the z_1, z_2 plane. When $\alpha < 0$, this spiral will converge toward the origin and the state-plane portrait will be as shown in Fig. 4–14a. If $\alpha > 0$, then this spiral will diverge from the origin as is shown in Fig. 4–14b. For $\alpha = 0$, the state-plane trajectories will be circles centered about the origin as shown in Fig. 4–14c.

The equilibrium state for $\alpha < 0$ is called a *stable focus*, that for $\alpha > 0$ is called an *unstable focus*, and that for $\alpha = 0$ is called a *vortex* or *center*.

In the case $\alpha = 0$, the motion is periodic and the period of traversing any of the closed circular paths is the same and is equal to $2\pi/\beta$.

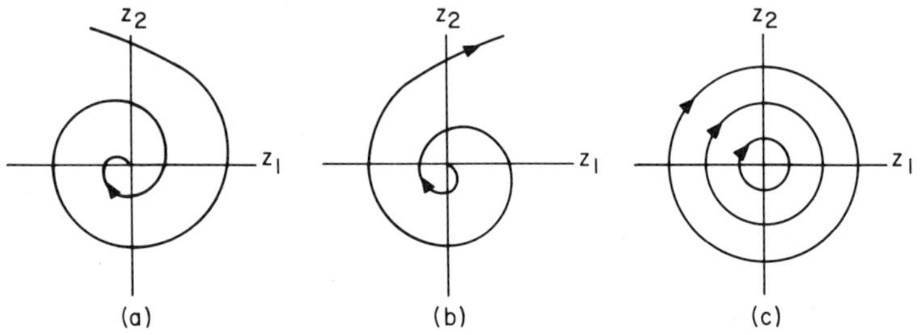

Fig. 4-14. The state-plane trajectories of the system of Eq. (4-27) with the case $\alpha < 0$ shown in (a), $\alpha > 0$ shown in (b), and $\alpha = 0$ shown in (c).

Case 4. Nonzero Repeated Roots. For this case, from the discussion of Chap. 2, the A matrix can be taken in the Jordan canonical form, i.e., the motion is given by

$$\begin{bmatrix} \dot{x}_1 \\ \dot{x}_2 \end{bmatrix} = \begin{bmatrix} \lambda & k \\ 0 & \lambda \end{bmatrix} \begin{bmatrix} x_1 \\ x_2 \end{bmatrix}, \quad \begin{bmatrix} x_1(0) \\ x_2(0) \end{bmatrix} = \begin{bmatrix} x_{10} \\ x_{20} \end{bmatrix} \tag{4-28}$$

where k is a constant which can be 0. The solution is then

$$x_1(t) = kx_{20}te^{\lambda t} + x_{10}e^{\lambda t}, \quad x_2(t) = x_{20}e^{\lambda t} \tag{4-29}$$

From Eq. (4-28), the first-order differential equation can also be obtained for the state-plane trajectory,

$$\frac{dx_2}{dx_1} = \frac{\lambda x_2}{\lambda x_1 + kx_2} = \frac{1}{k/\lambda + x_1/x_2} \tag{4-30}$$

Equation (4-30) can be solved graphically (see Sec. 4.5) yielding trajectories in the form shown in Fig. 4-15a or 4-15b, depending on the sign of the repeated root.

Here, as in Case 1, the equilibrium states are called *nodes*.

Case 5. One or Both Eigenvalues Are Zero. When one or both roots are zero, the state-plane portraits are in some sense degenerate and there will be equilibrium states other than the origin. Two situations can be listed:

1) *One eigenvalue is zero, the other is nonzero*. Then, Eq. (4-21) becomes

$$\dot{x}_1 = 0, \qquad \dot{x}_2 = \lambda x_2$$

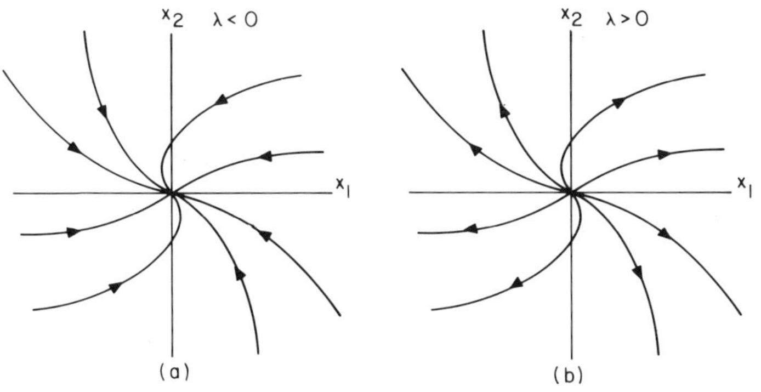

Fig. 4-15. The state-plane trajectories of the system of Eq. (4-28) with the case of $\lambda < 0$ shown in (a), and $\lambda > 0$ in (b).

Thus, every state $(x_1, x_2) = (c, 0)$ is an equilibrium state where c is an arbitrary constant.

2) *Both eigenvalues are zero.* Here, the canonical form (4-28) applies for $\lambda = 0$, i.e., we have

$$\dot{x}_1 = kx_2, \quad \dot{x}_2 = 0$$

which has the solution

$$x_1(t) = x_{10} + kx_{20}t, \qquad x_2(t) = x_{20}$$

Thus, every state $(x_1, x_2) = (c, 0)$ is an equilibrium state where, again, c is an arbitrary constant. In addition, if $k = 0$, we have $\dot{x}_1 = 0$, $x_2 = 0$, and every point in the state plane becomes an equilibrium state.

The state-plane trajectories for these cases are shown in Fig. 4-16. Note that in every case, every point on the x_1 axis is an equilibrium state.

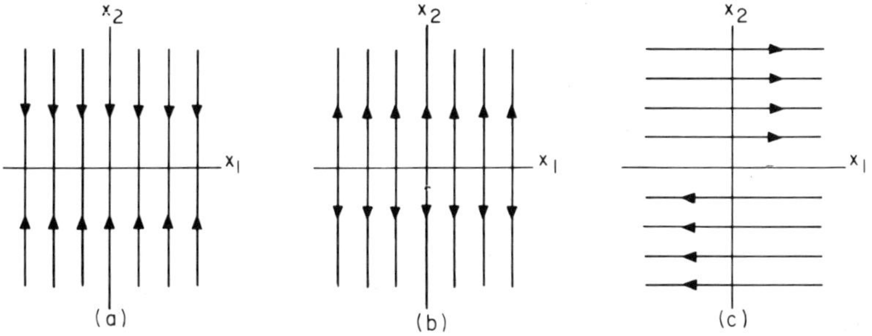

Fig. 4-16. The state-plane trajectories in the canonical coordinates for a second-order time-invariant plant with the case $\lambda_1 = 0$, $\lambda_2 < 0$ shown in (a), $\lambda_1 = 0$, $\lambda_2 > 0$ shown in (b), $\lambda_1 = \lambda_2 = 0$ shown in (c).

Having established the trajectories in the canonical set of coordinates, we need to transform from the canonical set of coordinates to the normal set of coordinates. As has been indicated, the matrix of transformation is not an orthogonal one.

As an example, consider a case where the poles are distinct and real, then the coordinates of the normal system

$$\begin{bmatrix} y_1 \\ y_2 \end{bmatrix}$$

can be obtained from the canonical system

$$\begin{bmatrix} x_1 \\ x_2 \end{bmatrix}$$

through the transformation

$$\begin{bmatrix} y_1 \\ y_2 \end{bmatrix} = \begin{bmatrix} 1 & 1 \\ \lambda_1 & \lambda_2 \end{bmatrix} \begin{bmatrix} x_1 \\ x_2 \end{bmatrix} \tag{4-31}$$

Note from Eq. (4-31), that the line $x_1 = 0$ is transformed into a line $y_2 = \lambda_2 y_1$, whereas the line $x_2 = 0$ is transformed into the line $y_2 = \lambda_1 y_1$. In general, these lines are no longer orthogonal. Nevertheless, the general character of the state-plane portrait will be preserved with respect to these lines. This fact is particularly useful in permitting us to construct nodes and saddle points in the state plane with normal coordinates. Suppose the origin is a stable node. This means the λ's are real and negative. Let $0 > \lambda_1 > \lambda_2$. In the canonical coordinates, as shown in Fig. 4-12a, all trajectories ultimately are tangent to the x_2 axis. We can convince ourselves that in this case, when the trajectories are transformed to the normal coordinates, they are all tangent to the image of the x_2 axis (or the $x_1 = 0$ line), namely $y_2 = \lambda_2 y_1$. Moreover, no trajectory crosses either the $x_1 = 0$ or $x_2 = 0$ lines. This condition must also be preserved. Synthesizing these facts, we arrive at a state-plane portrait of Fig. 4-17a as the normal-coordinate image of Fig. 4-12a.

In the case of a saddle point [Fig. (4-13)], where $\lambda_1 < 0$ and $\lambda_2 > 0$, we note that the x_1 and x_2 axes are the asymptotes for the hyperbolic trajectories. This must be preserved under the transformation (4-31) as must the sense of approach of the trajectories to these asymptotes. Hence the state-plane portrait of Fig. 4-17b must hold in the normal coordinates.

When the λ's are complex conjugates, it is easy to see that the state-plane portraits for the normal coordinates will be as shown in Fig. 4-17c (for the case of λ having negative real parts). Similarly, when the λ's are purely imaginary, the portraits for the normal coordinates will be as shown in Fig. 4-17d.

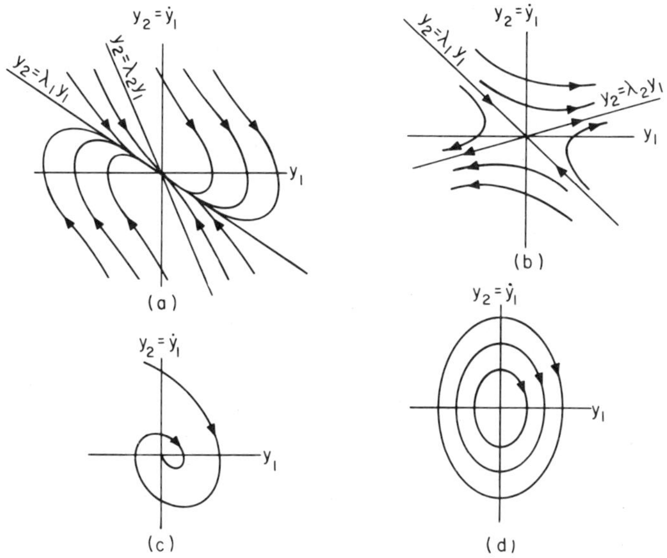

Fig. 4-17. The state-plane portraits in the normal coordinates; (a) for $\lambda_1 < 0$, $\lambda_2 < 0$, (b) for $\lambda_1 < 0$, $\lambda_2 > 0$, (c) for λ's which are complex and negative real parts, (d) for the λ's which are purely imaginary.

The importance of studying the behavior of linear systems about the equilibrium state 0 is that in many cases the local or in-the-small behavior of a nonlinear system about an equilibrium state can be deduced by linearization about that equilibrium state and the character of the resultant linear set of equations can be examined. This point will be made clear in Chap. 5.

4.4 Limit Cycles and Multiple Modes of Behavior in Nonlinear Autonomous Systems

The linear autonomous systems which are not degenerate boast the characteristics that (1) they have only a single equilibrium state and (2) their behavior about the equilibrium state completely determines the qualitative behavior in the entire state plane. The same unfortunately does not apply to the nonlinear autonomous systems. We indicate two of the possible modes of such "anomalous" behaviors in nonlinear autonomous systems in this section, namely, limit cycles and multiple modes of behavior.

In linear second-order autonomous systems, oscillations can take place for only particular combinations of system parameters. Slight changes in system parameters will destroy the oscillation. When oscillations occur, the resulting state space trajectories will be closed curves surrounding the origin such as those shown in Fig. 4-17d. The size of the closed curve, and hence the amplitude of the oscillation, is not fixed and changes directly with the size of the initial conditions.

In nonlinear systems, oscillations of the above type can also occur. What is more interesting is that there can be oscillations that are independent of the size of the initial conditions. These are the oscillations of the limit-cycle type which is the key for any practical oscillators. A further property of limit-cycle type oscillations is that the oscillation is usually much less sensitive to system parameter variations. In particular, there usually exist finite ranges of parameter values over which the oscillation can be sustained.

A limit cycle of a system may be loosely defined as a closed-curve $\mathcal{C}$ in state space with one of the following properties:

1) All system trajectories in the vicinity of $\mathcal{C}$ ultimately tend toward $\mathcal{C}$ as $t \to \infty$. (See Fig. 4-18a.)
2) All system trajectories in the vicinity of $\mathcal{C}$ starting from points arbitrarily close to $\mathcal{C}$ will tend away from $\mathcal{C}$ as $t \to \infty$. (See Fig. 4-18b.)
3) All system trajectories in the vicinity of $\mathcal{C}$ fall into two mutually exclusive families, from one class all trajectories tend toward $\mathcal{C}$ as $t \to \infty$, from the other class all trajectories tend away from $\mathcal{C}$ as $t \to \infty$. (See Fig. 4-18c.)

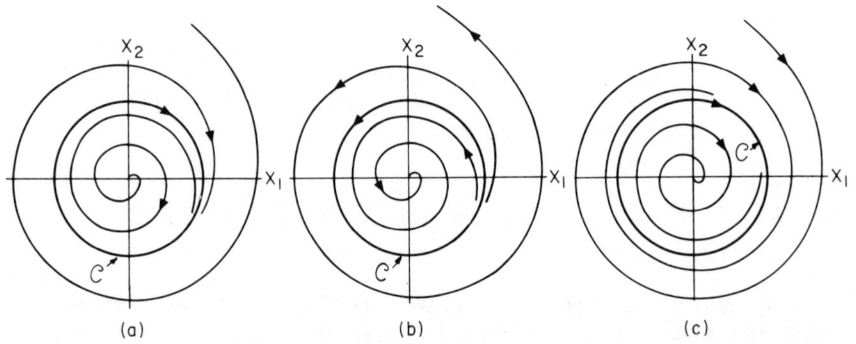

Fig. 4-18. (a) A stable limit cycle $\mathcal{C}$, (b) An unstable limit cycle $\mathcal{C}$, (c) A semi-stable limit cycle $\mathcal{C}$.

Classically, a limit cycle of class (1) is called a *stable limit cycle*; one of class (2) is called an *unstable limit cycle*, and one of class (3) is called a *semistable limit cycle*. As we shall demonstrate in the next chapter, the word "stable" alone is insufficient to characterize the type of stability being postulated. The concept of "orbital asymptotic stability" must be invoked.

A limit cycle in an autonomous second-order system is particularly easy to visualize.

◆◆Example 4-4. The system

$$\frac{dx}{dt} = y - x(x^2 + y^2 - 1), \qquad \frac{dy}{dt} = -x - y(x^2 + y^2 - 1) \tag{4-32}$$

has a stable limit cycle which is the unit circle. To see this, transform to the polar coordinate to obtain

$$\frac{dr}{dt} = -r(r^2 - 1), \qquad \frac{d\theta}{dt} = -1$$

When $r < 1$, the forces acting on the system will be such as to increase r; when $r > 1$ the forces acting on the system will reduce r, and when $r \equiv 1$, there is no force on the system and the curve $r = 1$, $\theta = \theta_0 + t$ can be maintained indefinitely.

Similarly, we can show that the system

$$\frac{dx}{dt} = y + x(x^2 + y^2 - 1), \qquad \frac{dy}{dt} = -x + y(x^2 + y^2 - 1) \tag{4-33}$$

has an unstable limit cycle.

The system

$$\frac{dx}{dt} = y - x(x^2 + y^2 - 1)^2, \qquad \frac{dy}{dt} = -x - y(x^2 + y^2 - 1)^2 \tag{4-34}$$

can be shown to have a semistable limit cycle.◆◆

In addition to limit cycles, a nonlinear system can have multiple modes of behavior. This manifests itself either in a system having a multiple of isolated equilibrium states or, in some cases, in systems having different modes of behavior in different regions surrounding the same equilibrium state.

When the latter case occurs, the limiting system trajectory separating the regions of different modes of system behavior is known as a *separatrix*.

The following nontrivial example is particularly illustrative as it exhibits some unusual multiple modes of behavior.

◆◆Example 4-5 [J4]. Consider a series generator—series motor drive of Fig. 4-19. Such a drive when properly designed exhibits relative independence of motor speed with respect to the load.

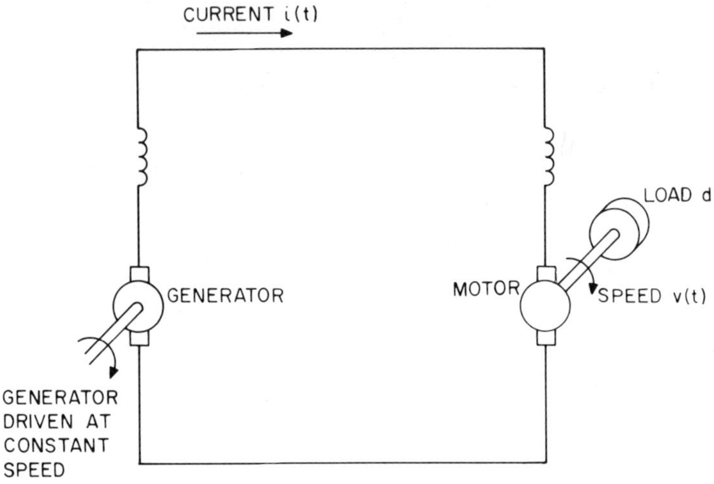

Fig. 4-19. The series generator— series motor drive of Example 4-5.

Let us assume that (1) the magnetizing curves of both machines have the form of Fig. 4–20, (2) both machines saturate at the same current level (but not necessarily at the same saturation flux), and (3) the generator is driven with constant speed.

The normalized equations of motion of this system are:

$$ai(t) + T\frac{di(t)}{dt} = [M - \xi v(t)]\,\psi(t) - T_E\frac{d\psi(t)}{dt}$$

$$\psi(t)\,i(t) = d + bv(t) + T_J\frac{dv(t)}{dt}$$

$$\psi(t) = \psi(i(t)) \tag{4–35}$$

where $i(t)$, $v(t)$, and $\psi(t)$ are normalized system variables with the following meanings: $i(t)$—circuit current, $v(t)$—motor speed, $\psi(t) = \psi(i(t))$—magnetic flux. The relationship of $\psi(i(t))$ with the circuit current $i(t)$ is shown in Fig. 4–20.

The remaining quantities are the parameters of this normalized system. In particular, d represents the constant-load component of the motor type and b represents the load-torque component proportional to angular speed.

The set (4–35) is a highly nonlinear second-order system and its behavior for different combinations of the values of the system parameters is quite complex [J4]. For the time being, we are only interested in some of its special modes of behavior.

For the special set of parameter values: $\xi = 1$, $\psi_{max} = 1.5$, $M = 1$, $T_m = T_g = 1$, $a = 0.2$, $T_J = 50$ msec, $T = 30$ msec, $T_F = 60$ msec, $b = 5$, $d = 0$, the relations for the system equilibrium states are given by

$$0.2i = (1 - v)\psi, \qquad \psi i = 5v \tag{4-36}$$

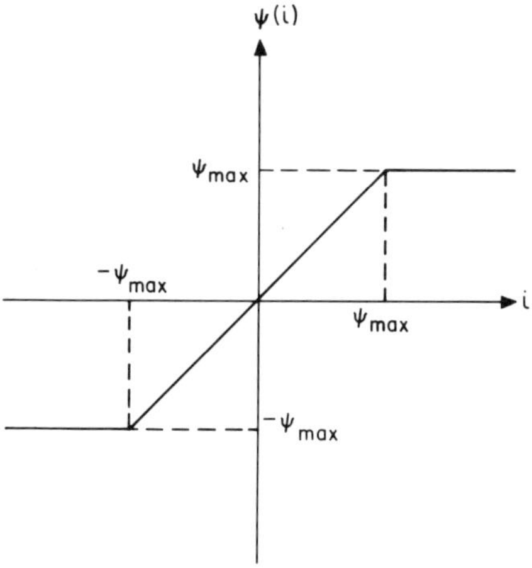

Fig. 4-20. The magnetizing curves of both the generator and the motor of Example 4-5.

When we solve (4-36) using the magnetization curve of Fig. 4-20 with the value $\psi_{max} = 1.5$, we obtain three equilibrium states. The first is located at the origin $i = 0$, $v = 0$. The second and third are the pair $i = \pm 2.31$, $v = 0.692$.

The state-plane portrait as obtained on the analog computer is as shown in Fig. 4-21. It is seen that the first equilibrium state looks somewhat like a saddle point, whereas the second and third look like stable foci.

Interestingly enough, if we set $b = 0$ and $d = 1$ while keeping the remaining values the same as those given above, the first equilibrium state disappears from the finite part of the state plane (it actually has gone to $i = 0$, $v = -\infty$), while the second and third ones now are located at $i = \pm 1.00$, $v = 0.8$. The state-plane portrait becomes that of Fig. 4-22. A rather unusual situation occurs; in the immediate neighborhoods of the last two equilibrium states there are regions with closed curves. However, beyond these regions all curves spiral inward toward a pair of limit-cycle-like curves. These "limit cycles" thus form *separatrices* which separate the state plane into different regions with difficult modes of state trajectory behavior. ◆◆

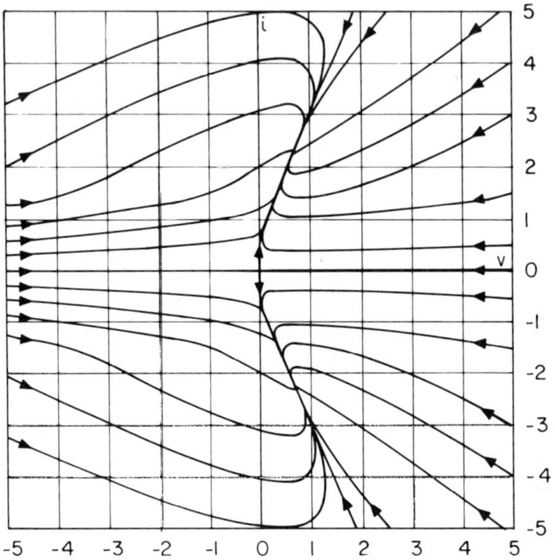

Fig. 4-21. The $i(t)$ vs. $v(t)$ state-plane portrait for the system of Example 4-5 with $\xi = 1$, $\psi_{max} = 1.5$, $M = 1$, $T_m = T_g = 1$, $a = 0.2$, $T_J = 50$ msec, $T = 30$ msec, $T_E = 60$ msec, $b = 5$, and $d = 0$.

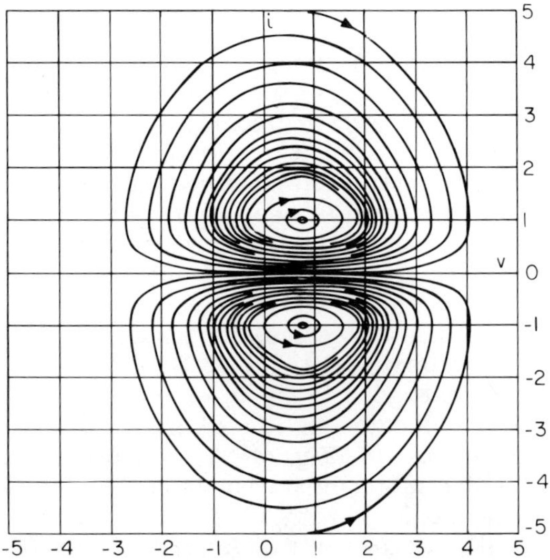

Fig. 4-22. The $i(t)$ vs. $v(t)$ state-plane portrait for the system of Example 4-5 with the same parameter values as those for Fig. 4-21 except that $b = 0$ and $d = 1$.

4.5 State-Plane Trajectories for Conservative Systems

The class of second-order systems of the form $\ddot{x} + f(x) = 0$ is known as that of conservative systems. It is so-named because $\dot{x}$, which generally represents a measure of damping or energy dissipation in the system, is missing. For this class of systems therefore, energy is conserved. To see this, we write the system equations in the form $\dot{x}_1 = x_2$, $\dot{x}_2 = -f(x_1)$, or alternately

$$\frac{dx_2}{dx_1} = \frac{-f(x_1)}{x_2} \tag{4-37}$$

Equation (4–37) can be integrated to yield

$$\frac{x_2^2}{2} + \int_{x_{10}}^{x_1} f(x)dx = E \tag{4-38}$$

where E is the integrating constant.

The first term of Eq. (4–38) is seen to be a measure of the kinetic energy of the system, while the second term is a measure of the potential energy. x_{10} is the equilibrium state in x_1 with reference to which the potential energy is measured. The value of the constant E is thus a measure of the total energy; it is seen to be dependent on the initial condition. For each given value of E, Eq. (4–38) gives the trajectory for the system.

The state-plane trajectories for a conservative system can be plotted by inspection. To appreciate this, it is instructive first to plot the function

$$P(x_1) = \int_{x_{10}}^{x_1} f(x)\,dx$$

vs. x_1. Then rewriting Eq. (4–38) in the form

$$x_2 = \pm\left[E - P\left(x_1\right)\right]^{1/2}$$

we see that for each given value of E, we can obtain the trajectory x_2 vs. x_1. For example, suppose the $P(x_1)$ vs. x_1 plot is given by Fig. 4–23a, where $P_{\min}$ marks the minimum value of P. A first point to note is that a value of total energy E less than $P_{\min}$ is impossible, and no real trajectory can result. When $E = P_{\min}$, the only possible value of x_2 is 0, hence the minimum value of x_1 at which $P(x_1) = P_{\min}$ is an equilibrium state of the system with $x_2 = 0$. In Fig. 4–23b this point is marked as x_{1e}.

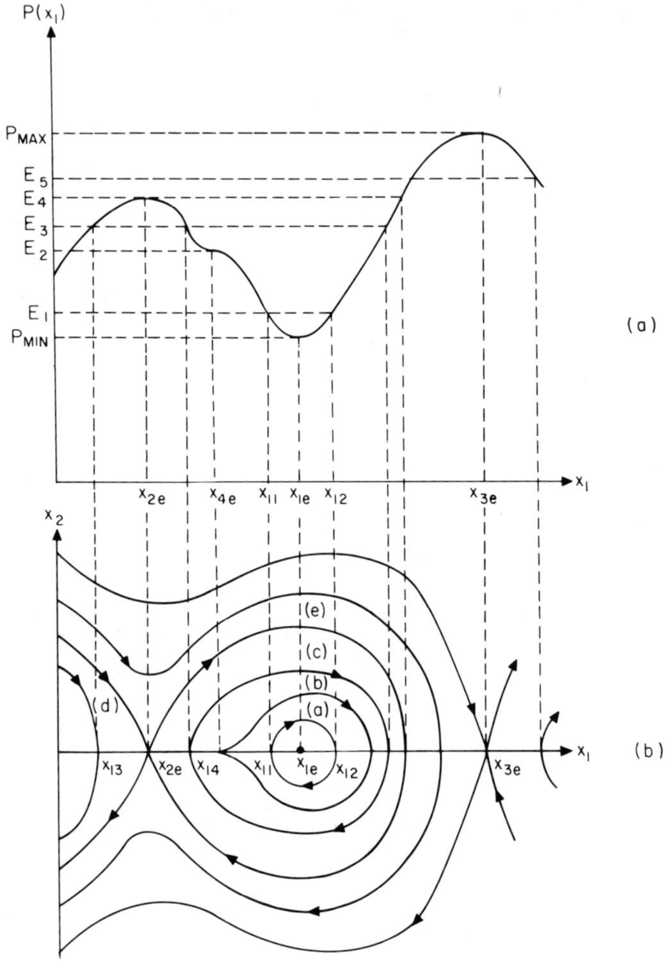

Fig. 4-23. The graphical construction of the state-plane portrait of a typical conservative system whose $P(x_1)$ characteristic is shown in part (a) of this figure.

When E is slightly greater than P_{min}, a possible system trajectory exists because positive kinetic energy is now implied. Since the kinetic energy is proportional to x_2^2, the system trajectory for a total energy such as given by $E = E_1$ in Fig. 4-23a must yield closed curves that are symmetric with respect to the x_1 axis as given by the curve (a) in Fig. 4-23b. Note that there are now two values of x_1 such that $P(x_1) = E_1$. These two values, shown as x_{11} and x_{12}, represent the limits of excursions in x_1 that are possible when the total energy has the value E_1. (Since $\dot{x}_1 = x_2$, the sense of the closed trajectory must be as indicated.) Reasoning this way we see that a minimum point of potential energy must yield an equilibrium state that resembles a center.

Suppose now $P(x_1) = E_4$, where $E_4 > E_1$ gives a local maximum in $P(x)$, as shown in Fig. 4–23. The state x_{2e} where $P(x_{2e}) = E_4$ is seen to be another equilibrium state for the system; however, when E is slightly less than E_4 say E_3, we can quickly infer that the state portrait about the equilibrium state $x_1 = x_{2e}$, $x_2 = 0$ must be as shown in curves (c) and (d) in Fig. 4–23b. This is because the interval between the two values of x_1 where $P(x_1) = E_3$, given as x_{13} and x_{14}, cannot have real trajectories passing through it. Thus the state $(x_{2e}, 0)$ resembles a saddle point. The trajectory that passes through $(x_{2e}, 0)$ is shown as the curve (e).

Reasoning in the above manner, we can show in addition that a point of inflection in $P(x_1)$ with zero slope (shown as $P(x_1) = E_2$) is again an equilibrium state with the state trajectory shown as curve (b) passing through it. Indeed, once the significance of the $P(x_1)$ plot for a conservative system is appreciated, the phase trajectory relative to it can be quickly plotted. (The reader should attempt to verify the shapes of the other curves of Fig. 4–23b.)

We can summarize the results of this section in the form of a theorem:

◆◆Theorem 4-2 (Lagrange). For a second-order conservative system $\dot{x}_1 = x_2$, $\dot{x}_2 = -f(x_1)$, the equilibrium states occur at each point at which the potential energy

$$P(x_1) = \int_{x_{10}}^{x_1} f(x)\,dx$$

attains a local minimum, a local maximum, or an inflection point with zero slope. The system trajectories will not diverge from the neighborhood of an equilibrium state only if it corresponds to a local minimum of the potential energy.◆◆

We may loosely state that only an equilibrium state corresponding to a local minimum in P is stable, the others are unstable. While this is intuitively true, we will need the material of the next chapter to make the statement completely meaningful.

4.6 The Construction of the State-Plane Trajectories

As linear autonomous second-order systems can always be solved, the state-plane trajectories can always be plotted directly from the solutions. For general second-order nonlinear autonomous systems that are not conservative, other ways must be devised.

Consider a system of the form

$$\dot{x}_1 = f_1(x_1, x_2) \qquad \dot{x}_2 = f_2(x_1, x_2) \tag{4-39}$$

We briefly study some methods for the construction of state-plane trajectories below:

1. Solution of the Differential Equations

If it is possible to solve Eq. (4-39) directly, then the state trajectory can be constructed parametrically. This method as such requires no further comment. Sometimes however, the set of second-order differential equations can be more fruitfully integrated as a first-order differential equation through the elimination of the time variable, viz.,

$$\frac{dx_2}{dx_1} = \frac{f_2(x_1, x_2)}{f_1(x_1, x_2)} \tag{4-40}$$

If Eq. (4-40) can be integrated, it directly yields the analytical expression for state-plane trajectories in terms of the state coordinates.

2. Solutions by Analog or Digital Computation

If the system differential equations cannot be easily solved, then modern analog or digital computers, if available, would probably be resorted to by the engineer today. An analog computer and X–Y plotter, for example, can be a most versatile combination.

Even if the engineer does have access to a computer, he can still make errors in the process of programming. The methods to be described below can frequently be used to make quick checks of the correctness of the machine solutions.

3. The Method of Isocline

Consider the system (4-39); let

$$m(x_1, x_2) \triangleq \frac{dx_2}{dx_1} = \frac{f_2(x_1, x_2)}{f_1(x_1, x_2)} \tag{4-41}$$

As defined, $m(x_1, x_2)$ gives the slope of the local tangent of the trajectory passing through the point x_1, x_2. The idea of the method of isoclines is then to construct a suitable field of local tangents m, assuming that the tangent is constant over a *small region* near the point. From this, the system trajectories can be constructed.

The simplest way to construct the field of local tangents is first to find the lines of constant m. To show this, we consider the example below:

♦♦Example 4-6. The Dutch mathematician Balthasar Van der Pol, in studying a certain class of oscillators, found that their action can be represented by the equation

$$\dot{x}_1 = x_2, \quad \dot{x}_2 = -\mu\left(x_1^2-1\right)x_2 - x_1 \tag{4-42}$$

Equation (4-42) is now known as Van der Pol's equation.

For this system

$$m = \frac{dx_2}{dx_1} = -\mu\left(x_1^2 - 1\right) - \frac{x_1}{x_2}$$

or, solving for x_2,

$$x_2 = \frac{x_1}{\mu\left(1 - x_1^2\right) - m}$$

Assume now that $\mu = 0.2$; then, the locus for $m = 0$ will be the curve $x_2 = x_1/\left[0.2(1 - x_1{}^2)\right]$. The procedure is then to plot the curve on the state plane. All along this curve we indicate the fact that all trajectories must cross it with a local slope of 0 by small horizontal lines in Fig. 4-24.

The locus for $m = -1$ will be the line $x_2 = x_1/(1.2 - 0.2\,x_1{}^2)$. Along this curve we draw short lines with slope of -1.

Continuing this process, we obtain the field as shown in Fig. 4-24. A trajectory starting from near the origin will be seen to spiral out, but eventually will appear to approach a closed trajectory, or a limit cycle. A trajectory starting outside this limit cycle will also approach the limit cycle. Thus for the particular choice of μ the system would seem to have a stable limit cycle. We shall have occasion to discuss this system again in the next chapter. ♦♦

4. The Delta Method

This method is suitable to obtain a particular state trajectory. Let the system be represented by the equations:

$$\dot{x}_1 = x_2, \quad \dot{x}_2 = -f(x_1, x_2) \tag{4-43}$$

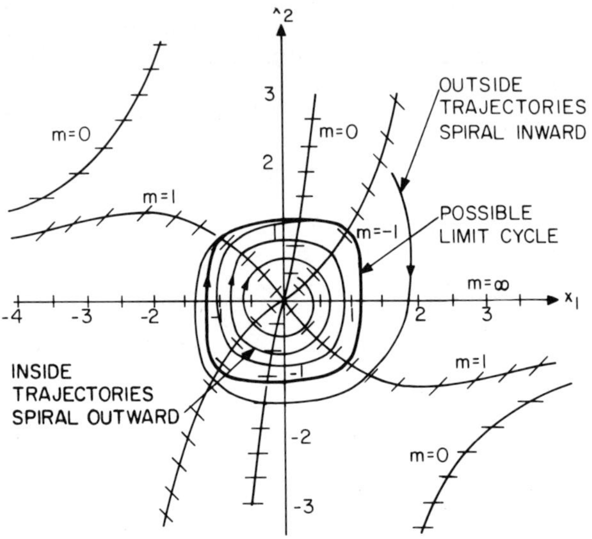

Fig. 4-24. The graphical construction of the state-plane portrait of the system of Example 4-6 by the isocline method.

Adding and subtracting the term $\omega_0^2 x_1$ in the second equation, we obtain

$$\dot{x}_1 = x_2, \quad \dot{x}_2 = -\omega_0^2 x_1 - \delta(x_1 x_2) \qquad \textbf{(4-44)}$$

where

$$\delta(x_1, x_2) \stackrel{\Delta}{=} f(x_1, x_2) - \omega_0^2 x_1 \qquad \textbf{(4-45)}$$

Again we make the assumption that $\delta(x_1, x_2)$ is a constant over a small region about the point x_1, x_2 in the state plane.

Then

$$\frac{dx_2}{dx_1} = -\frac{\omega_0^2 x_1 + \delta(x_1, x_2)}{x_2} \qquad \textbf{(4-46)}$$

which, when integrated, yields (on treating δ as a constant)

$$\frac{x_2^2}{2} + \frac{\omega_0^2 x_1^2}{2} + \delta(x_1, x_2)\, x_1 = \text{constant.}$$

The above equation can be cast into the form

$$x_2^2 + \left[\omega_0 x_1 + \frac{\delta(x_1, x_2)}{\omega_0}\right]^2 = R^2 \tag{4-47}$$

which indicates that through a given point $(\omega_0 x_1, x_2)$ of the state plane with $\omega_0 x_1$ and x_2 as the coordinates, for some arbitrary ω_0, the local trajectory can be approximated by an arc of a circle with the point

$$\left[-\frac{\delta(x_1, x_2)}{\omega_0^2}, 0\right]$$

as the center.

If a change of scale is carried out such that the new state-plane coordinates become x_2 vs. $\omega_0 x_1$, then through each point of the new phase $(\omega_0 x_1, x_2)$ the state trajectory may be approximated by the arc of a circle with the point $(-\delta/\omega_0, 0)$ as center. Continuing this process as illustrated in Fig. 4-25, will result in an approximate state-plane trajectory in the x_2 vs. $\omega_0 x_1$ state plane.

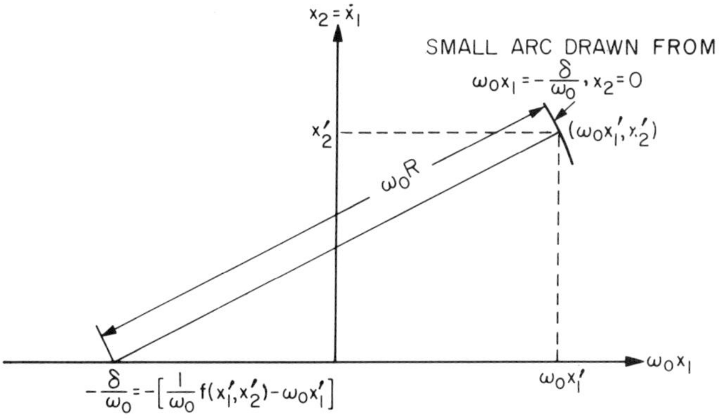

Fig. 4-25. The delta method of graphical construction of state-plane trajectories.

5. Pell's Method

The method of Pell [P3] is convenient for constructing particular trajectories of second-order autonomous systems that can be cast into the special form* $\ddot{x} + g(\dot{x}) + f(x) = 0$. For this class of

*The method can be extended to second-order systems of more general forms. See [R1] and [W1].

systems, letting $x_1 = x$, $x_2 = \dot{x}_1$, we can write

$$\frac{dx_2}{dx_1} = \frac{-g(x_2) - f(x_1)}{x_2} \tag{4-48}$$

The goal as usual is to find the slope dx_2/dx_1 at a given point (x_1, x_2). By drawing a small segment at the point with the given slope to approximate the trajectory we can proceed to a new point and repeat the process.

To find dx_2/dx_1, we employ the following procedure:

1) Using the $-x_1$ axis as coordinates for $g(x_2)$, plot $g(x_2)$ vs. x_2, and using the $-x_2$ axis as coordinates for $f(x_1)$, plot $f(x_1)$ vs. x_1. (Such as is shown in Fig. 4-26.)

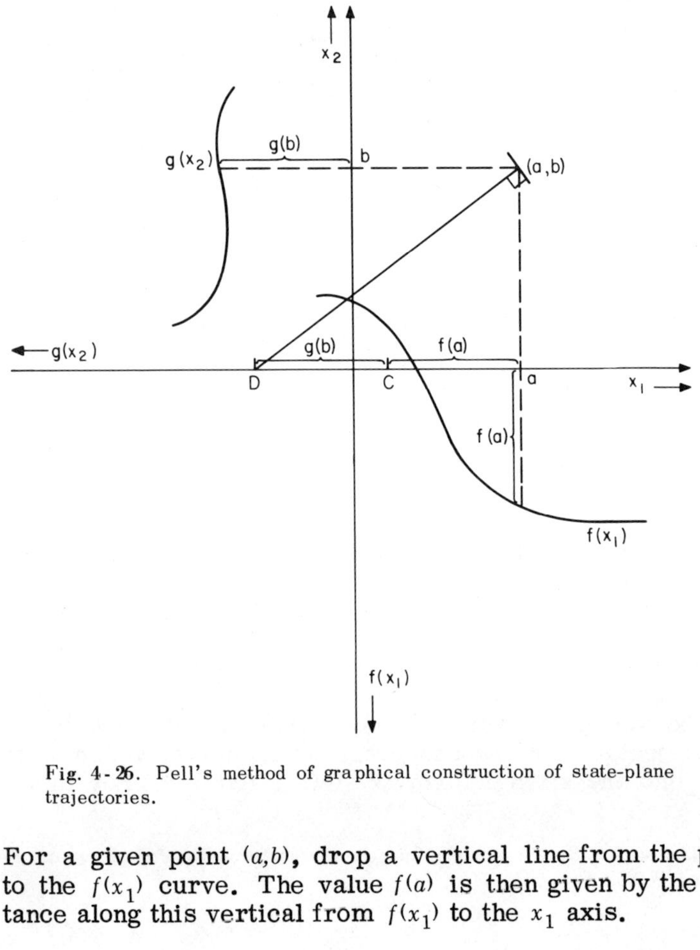

Fig. 4-26. Pell's method of graphical construction of state-plane trajectories.

2) For a given point (a,b), drop a vertical line from the point to the $f(x_1)$ curve. The value $f(a)$ is then given by the distance along this vertical from $f(x_1)$ to the x_1 axis.

3) Lay off a distance $|f(a)|$ along the x_1 axis from point a. Do this in the negative direction if $f(a)$ is positive and vice versa. This produces the point C in Fig. 4–26.
4) From the point C, lay off the distance $|g(b)|$ along the x_1 axis. Again if $g(b)$ is positive, then the distance must be laid off in the negative direction and vice versa. This results in the point D in Fig. 4–26.
5) From the point D construct a line to the point (a,b). A small segment through (a,b) perpendicular to this line is then the approximating segment of the system trajectory sought for.

The reason why the segment can be so constructed is seen from the fact that the slope of the line from D to (a, b) is given by $x_2/[f(x_1) + g(x_2)]$. Thus a line segment perpendicular to this line must have a slope that is its negative reciprocal, which is precisely that given by the rhs of Eq. (4–48).

4.7 Construction for Time from State-Plane Trajectories

Since state-plane trajectories are essentially plotted by eliminating time, it will be instructive to inquire how time can be inferred from the trajectory. We consider here three methods which are applicable to the system

$$\ddot{x} = f(x,\dot{x}) \tag{4–49}$$

1) We can integrate:

$$\int_{x(t_0)}^{x(t_1)} \frac{1}{\dot{x}}\, dx = t_1 - t_0 \tag{4–50}$$

This is almost self-explanatory. Graphically this can be illustrated as shown in Fig. 4–27*a*.
2) We can integrate:

$$\int_{\dot{x}(t_0)}^{\dot{x}(t_1)} \frac{d\dot{x}}{f(x,\dot{x})} = \int_{x(t_0)}^{x(t_1)} \frac{dt}{d\dot{x}}\, d\dot{x} = t_1 - t_0 \tag{4–51}$$

Thus graphically, we can plot $1/f(\dot{x}, x)$ vs. $\dot{x}$ and find the area under the curve as per Fig. 4–27*b*.
3) We can make angular measurements from trajectories. This is based on the delta method, from which we recall [see Eq. (4–44)] that for a small arc from the point $-\delta/\omega_0$, we have:

$$\ddot{x} + \omega_0^2 x + \delta = 0 \tag{4–52}$$

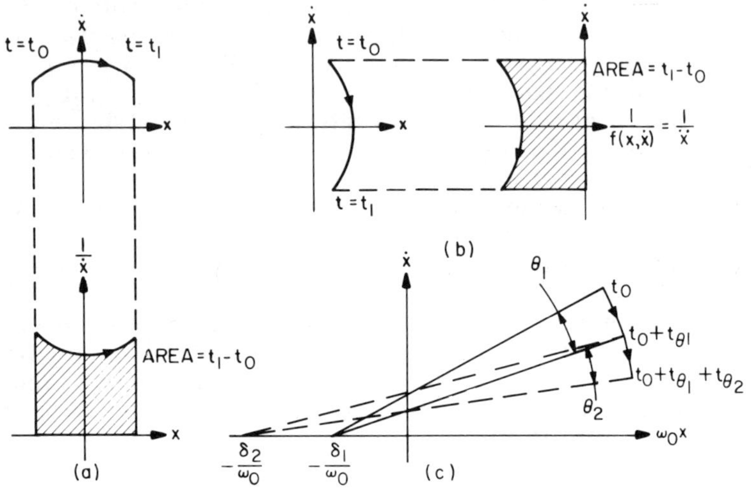

Fig. 4-27. Graphical constructions to find time for trajectories plotted in the $\dot{x}$ vs. x coordinates by using (a) Eq. (4-50), (b) Eq. (4-51), (c) by using angular measurements based on Eq. (4-52).

Then for an arc over an angle θ, the rate of travel of the phase point, by integrating the above, is approximately $\omega_0 t$.

Or, for a small arc θ, as $\omega_0 t_\theta = \theta$, we therefore have $t_\theta = \theta/\omega_0$, where t_θ is approximately the time required to traverse the arc of angle θ. This is illustrated in Fig. 4-27c.

If a trajectory can be broken up into m circular arc segments of angles $\theta_1, \theta_2, \ldots, \theta_m$, (see Fig. 4-27$c$), then, the total elapsed time of this trajectory is seen to be

$$\left(\sum_{i=1}^{m} \theta_i\right) \Big/ \omega_0$$

4.8 Summary

Almost all practical time-invariant systems which can be represented by second-order differential equations can be fruitfully displayed in the state plane. A large number of techniques have been evolved over the years toward finding the system trajectories and characterizing their behaviors.

The state-plane portraits of a linear autonomous second-order system are particularly simple to sketch (Sec. 4.3). A factor in this regard is that under fairly general conditions (Theorem 4-1) the origin is the only equilibrium state. Understanding the behavior of linear systems near the origin will benefit us when we attempt to linearize a nonlinear system, as will be discussed in the next chapter.

A nonlinear autonomous second-order system is marked by the possible existence of limit cycles, multiple equilibrium states, equilibrium zones, and multiple modes of behavior (Sec. 4.4). General methods for constructing the state-plane portraits only exist for the class known as conservative systems (Sec. 4.5).

There are however, many methods which can permit rapid construction of approximate state-trajectories through the piecing together of small line segments in the state plane (Sec. 4.6).

The independent variable, time, usually does not explicitly appear on state trajectories. However, given a state trajectory plotted to scale, time can readily be estimated (Sec. 4.7).

The limitations of the state plane methods are clear. The methods are not useful for high-order systems or for systems that are not autonomous.

4.9 Exercises

4-1 The system given by $\ddot{\theta} + \omega_n^2\theta = -B \operatorname{sgn} \dot{\theta}$ describes a system with Coulomb friction. Develop the state trajectories for the system.

4-2 Construct the state-plane trajectories for the following systems in the normal coordinates

a) $\ddot{x} + \dot{x}x + x = 0$

b) $\ddot{x} + \dot{x}^2 + x = 0$

Give physical explanation of the result.

4-3 By the method of isocline, sketch the state-plane trajectories for a second-order linear autonomous system with a double root on the negative real axis. Use the canonical variables such that

$$\begin{bmatrix} \dot{x}_1 \\ \dot{x}_2 \end{bmatrix} = \begin{bmatrix} \lambda & k \\ 0 & \lambda \end{bmatrix} \begin{bmatrix} x_1 \\ x_2 \end{bmatrix}$$

where k is a real constant and $\lambda < 0$. What is the effect of k on the shape of the state-plane portrait and what is its physical significance? In particular, consider the case $k = 0$. What would the system differential equation be in this case?

4-4 (Perron) For the system

$$\dot{x} = x - 4y\sqrt{|xy|}$$

$$\dot{y} = -y + 4x\sqrt{|xy|}$$

where only the positive square root is to be taken

a) Find all the equilibrium states.

b) Plot the state-plane trajectories.

4-5 Consider putting a network of the form $(p - 1)$ ahead of the relay in the satellite attitude control system considered in Sec. 4.1. Construct

a) the switching line for the problem,

b) trace some typical state trajectories.

4-6 (Nelson) An important point that has not been considered in the satellite attitude control system of Sec. 4.1 is that in addition to the equilibrium point $\theta = 0$, $\dot{\theta} = 0$, any point $\theta = 2n\pi, \dot{\theta} = 0, (n = 1, \ldots)$ represents the same point. Discuss in detail how this fact alters the result of Case 6 of Example 4-1.

4-7 (Kalman) Consider the system of Fig. 4-28. Find the state-plane portraits in the $\dot{e}$ vs. e plane.

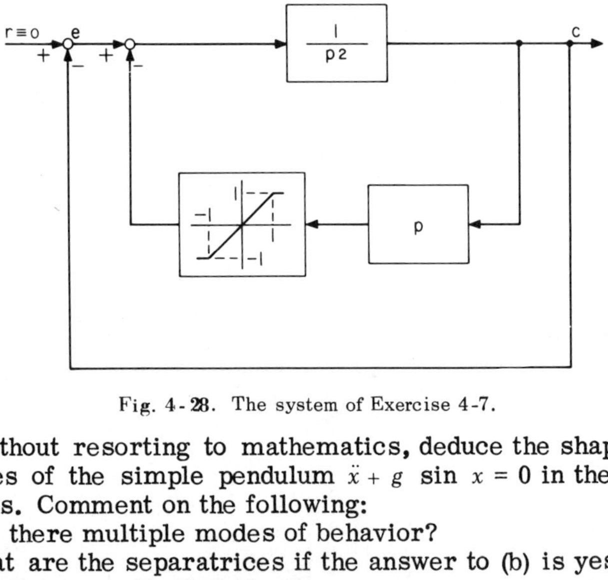

Fig. 4-28. The system of Exercise 4-7.

4-8 Without resorting to mathematics, deduce the shape of the trajectories of the simple pendulum $\ddot{x} + g \sin x = 0$ in the normal coordinates. Comment on the following:

a) Are there multiple modes of behavior?

b) What are the separatrices if the answer to (b) is yes?

c) Are there any limit cycles?

4-9 For the system of Fig. 4-29, find the normal state trajectories if $0 < a < b < c$, $K > 0$.

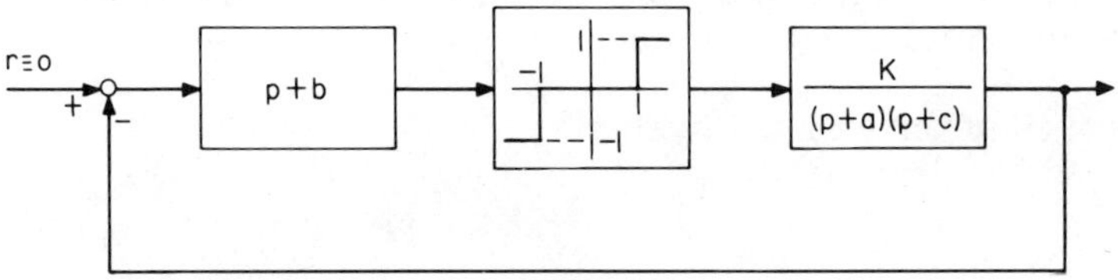

Fig. 4-29. The system of Exercise 4-9.

4–10 For the system $y(p)/u(p) = (p+4.5)/(p^2+p+9)$ with $u(t) = \pm U$, where U is a constant,

a) Obtain the state-plane portraits using the normal coordinates for both $u = +U$ and $u = -U$. What are the equilibrium states for each case?

b) What happens to the state vector $(y, \dot{y})$ at the instant t_1 when the input is switched from $u = +U$ to $u = -U$? Draw a typical trajectory for the case where $u(t) = +U$ for $0 < t < t_1$ and $u(t) = -U$ for $t_1 \le t$.

c) Choose a state vector (z_1, z_2) with $z_1 = y$ such that the state equation contains u but not $\dot{u}$. Repeat (a) and (b) for this set of equations.

4–11 For the following first-order systems, sketch the system trajectories in the x vs. t plane:

a) $\dot{x} = \sin x$

b) $\dot{x} = \sin^2 x$

c) $\dot{x} = x(x-1)(x+2)$

d) $$\dot{x} = \begin{cases} x^{3/2}, & 0 \le x \le 1 \\ (x-2)^2, & 1 \le x \le 2 \\ 0, & \text{otherwise} \end{cases}$$

4–12 By finding the equation of the trajectories for $dr/d\theta$ in the polar coordinates, show that the system

$$\dot{x} = y + x(x^2 + y^2 - 1)\sin\frac{1}{x^2+y^2-1}$$

$$\dot{y} = -x + y(x^2 + y^2 - 1)\sin\frac{1}{x^2+y^2-1}$$

has infinitely many limit cycles.

4–13 For a conservative system $\ddot{x} + f(x) = 0$, find an expression for the velocity of the trajectory in the canonical coordinates in terms of x and $\dot{x}$.

4–14 The equation $t^2\ddot{x} + t\dot{x} + (t^2 - n^2)x = 0$ is known as *Bessel's equation*. Determine

a) Is the system (i) linear? (ii) autonomous?

b) Find the equilibrium states.

c) Can you conveniently sketch state trajectories for the system?

4-15 For the linear system $\ddot{x} + 2a\dot{x} + bx = 0$, sketch in the a vs. b plane regions of stability and instability of the origin. Indicate the character of the origin as an equilibrium state in the various regions. Indicate also the character of the equilibrium state on these lines.

4-16 (The Lancaster Equation) In certain battle situations it was found that courage was hardly the dominant characteristic. Each side is conveniently hidden from the other and each fires into the area the other is believed to be occupying. In such a battle, the loss rate on each side is proportional both to the number of men on the other side and to the number of men in the area under fire. Assume that the number of men on each side is large so that they can be represented by continuous variables x_1 and x_2, then x_1 and x_2 can be represented by the differential equations

$$\dot{x}_1 = -k_1 x_1 x_2, \qquad \dot{x}_2 = -k_2 x_1 x_2$$

a) If $k_1 > k_2$, and $x_1, x_2 \geq 0$ with $k_1, k_2 > 0$ find a rule for x_1 to annihilate x_2 and vice versa.
b) To generalize, assume x_1 and x_2 can become negative as well; find the equilibrium points of the system and comment on their stability.

4-17 For the feedback system $-e(t) = [1/(p(p+1))]\,u(t)$, where

$$u(t) = \begin{cases} 1, & e > 2 \\ 0, & |e| \leq 2 \\ -1, & e < 2 \end{cases}$$

obtain the system trajectories in the $\dot{e}$ vs. e plane and indicate the equilibrium points of the system. Comment on the stability of the equilibrium points.

4.10 References

The well-written text [A3] did much originally to stimulate interest on nonlinear systems analysis in this country. It remains to this date one of the best books on the classical techniques of Poincare and others. Chapters 1 through 3, treating phase-plane and related topics, are particularly worth reading. A large number of examples are provided. More up-to-date is the book [B22]; it too is characterized by a wealth of examples. (See in particular pp. 1-71.)

One of the best books on nonlinear control system as of 1961 was [G8]. For some interesting phase-plane plots of nonlinear second-order control systems (not necessarily autonomous) read pp. 315–345 and 370–393. In addition see Chap. 7. The reader will also find it stimulating to consult [K22], which treats graphically a class of third-order systems. [K22] also features a comprehensive bibliography of 735 entries on nonlinear system analysis including papers published through 1957.

For books that treat the topics of the present chapter in a more mathematical vein, see Chap. 2 of [P7], Chap. 16 of [C5], and Chaps. 2–4 of [S7].

PART II

SYSTEM STABILITY ANALYSIS

5

Linearization and Stability in the Small

5.1 The Concept of Stability

In linear time-invariant systems, stability is relatively simple to determine. A number of necessary and sufficient conditions have been established which yield unequivocal information concerning the system stability; these conditions include the well-known Routh and Hurwitz criteria.

If we confine our discussion to linear time-invariant systems having only poles with nonzero real parts, then, as we have learned, when the input is zero, the origin is the only equilibrium state of the system. For such systems, the following two notions of system stability (and instability) turn out to be the same:

1) A system is stable (unstable) if with zero input, and with arbitrary initial conditions, the resulting trajectory tends toward the origin (the resulting trajectory goes to infinity).
2) A system is stable (unstable) if with bounded input, the system output is bounded (unbounded).

The first notion of stability generally concerns a free system relative to its transient behavior and the second notion concerns a system under the influence of an input. Since these two definitions are essentially equivalent in a linear time-invariant system, it has not been necessary to probe too deeply into the question of stability when the analyst investigates systems that are primarily linear.

In nonlinear systems, unfortunately there is generally no clear-cut correspondence between these two definitions of stability. The free (transient) behavior of the system can differ greatly from the driven behavior of the system.

◆◆Example 5-1. Consider the nonlinear first order system $\dot{x}(t) = ax(t)/[u(t) - 1]$ (why is this system nonlinear?), where the constant a is positive. With $u(t) \equiv 0$, the system is clearly stable. However. with $u(t) \neq 0$, any time that $u(t) = 1$, $x(t)$ becomes unbounded. Indeed, if $u(t)$ is a constant greater than unity, $x(t)$ will also be unbounded. Thus, there is no guarantee that $x(t)$ will be bounded whenever $u(t)$ is bounded. ◆◆

As may be expected, it is a much simpler matter to discuss the stability of nonlinear systems in the sense of the first notion above, i.e., when the system has no input. Many of the important results obtained thus far concern systems of this class. We shall thus confine ourselves to this definition of stability in the present chapter.

In nonlinear systems, the concept of stability even in the context of the first notion is still a rather elusive one. As we have seen from considering the Van der Pol system, it is possible for a system to be unstable *locally* about an equilibrium state, but that all system trajectories eventually settle into a limit cycle. If such a limit cycle is sufficiently small, the system behavior may be practically acceptable in the large signal sense. Thus the system may be considered to be unstable for small deviations about the origin but practically stable for large deviations.

Again, in a nonlinear system with multiple equilibrium states, it is possible for all system trajectories to lead away from a given singular point, but some of these trajectories can tend to other singular points as time progresses. This is generally the case, for example, for simple oscillators where part of the circuit has "negative resistance" manifestations.

Considering the gist of our remarks so far, we can now make the following observations:

First, unlike linear systems, it would appear that it is simpler to speak of system stability relative to an equilibrium state rather than to speak generally about "the stability of a system."

Second, even in the case of a free system, stability information derived when viewing the system phase trajectory in some neighborhood about an equilibrium state cannot be used to infer stability in the entire state space. In other words, local stability does not imply stability in the overall state space and the two concepts should be considered separately.

Third, even locally, a distinction should be made between two possible cases when investigating the stability of an equilibrium state. The first is boundedness in the sense that the system state, is started initially in some suitably restricted zone, will henceforth never leave some other well-defined zone. The second is asymptoticity in the sense that all trajectories will eventually tend toward the equilibrium state in question.

In this and the following chapter, we will be discussing in detail most of the points raised above.

5.2 Stability in the Small (Lyapunov Stability) for Nonlinear Autonomous Systems

The basic idea of stability as formulated by the Russian mathematician A. M. Lyapunov has to do with the boundedness of the free response of a system in a special sense. We shall first consider it in relation to an autonomous system.*

In the state space, an ϵ neighborhood of an equilibrium state x_e is given by the n-dimensional sphere $\|x - x_e\| < \epsilon$. We say that an equilibrium state is stable (or stable in the small) if the system state can be made to stay forever within an ϵ neighborhood, *however small* ϵ *may be*, by starting it *anywhere* within an appropriately chosen (and usually smaller) δ neighborhood. In other words an equilibrium state of a system is stable if, when the system state is perturbed slightly from this state, the subsequent motion will remain in a neighborhood of the equilibrium state, the size of this neighborhood being dependent only on the magnitude of the perturbation. To be more precise, let $x = x_0$ at the initial time $t = t_0$, then we have:

◆◆Definition 5-1. Lyapunov Stability [L18]: An equilibrium state x_e of an autonomous dynamic system is stable (or stable in the sense of Lyapunov) if for every $\epsilon > 0$, there exists a $\delta > 0$, where δ depends only on ϵ, such that $\|x_0 - x_e\| < \delta$ results in $\|x(t;x_0) - x_e\| < \epsilon$ for all $t > t_0$.◆◆

It is instructive to paraphrase the ϵ and δ type of definition above in a challenge-answer form. For a designer to demonstrate that his system is stable in the sense of Lyapunov, then, for any value of ϵ that a challenger may care to designate, the designer must produce a value δ so that a system state initially in the δ neighborhood of the equilibrium state x_e will never leave the ϵ neighborhood. This is illustrated in Fig. 5-1.

◆◆Example 5-2. The origin of a time-invariant second-order linear system with a pair of purely imaginary roots is stable in the sense of Lyapunov, since the resulting free motion is a closed curve in the state plane whose maximum distance from the origin is determined entirely by the initial condition, and in particular is determined by the value of the minimum distance from the closed curve to the origin. Thus if a value of ϵ, say ϵ_1, is given as a challenge, we can first find that closed free trajectory of the system whose *maximum* distance to the origin is ϵ_1, and then pick a value of δ which is less than the *minimum* distance from that curve to the origin. The δ so chosen will satisfy the conditions that guarantee stability. ◆◆

◆◆Example 5-3. The equilibrium state within the limit cycle in the Van der Pol equation considered in the previous chapter is

*The type of stability defined in this section is applicable to any free systems, but is most useful for autonomous systems. See Sec. 5.6.

not Lyapunov stable since, for any ϵ which is less than the maximum distance from the origin of the limit cycle, a value of δ cannot be produced to satisfy the condition of the definition.♦♦

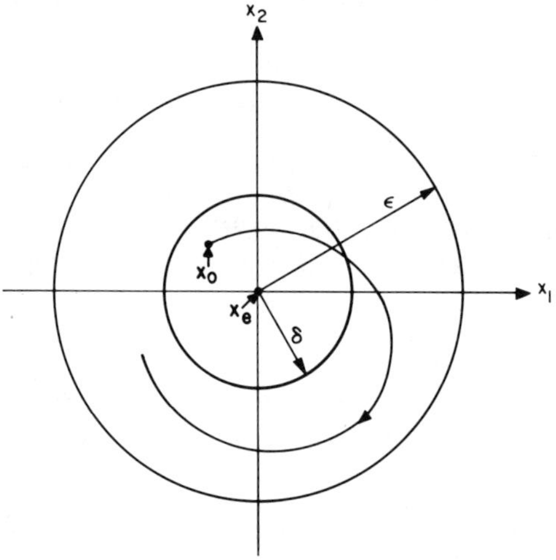

Fig. 5-1. Lyapunov stability: An equilibrium state $\mathbf{x}_e$ is stable if for every $\epsilon > 0$, however small, there is a $\delta > 0$ such that a trajectory started within the δ neighborhood of $\mathbf{x}_e$ remains henceforth in the ϵ neighborhood of $\mathbf{x}_e$.

Equilibrium states similar to a stable focus or node toward which all the system trajectories in the neighborhood converge merit a separate definition. This is the concept of asymptotic stability, which, as we shall see from the following definition, is also an in-the-small concept.

♦♦Definition 5-2. An equilibrium state x_e of a free dynamic system is asymptotically stable if

1) it is stable, and
2) there is a number δ_a such that every motion starting in δ_a neighborhood of x_e converges to x_e as $t \rightarrow \infty$.♦♦

If property (2) above is observed but not property (1), the equilibrium state is said to be quasi-asymptotically stable.

Note that as defined, an equilibrium state must first be stable before it can qualify to be asymptotically stable. This is to prevent a system trajectory from straying arbitrarily far from the equilibrium state before converging toward it. Note also that the definition requires only that those trajectories starting very close to x_e tend toward x_e as $t \rightarrow \infty$. This is shown in Fig. 5-2.

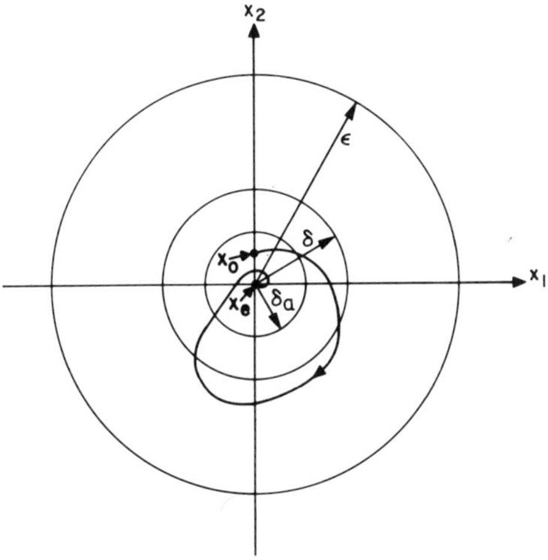

Fig. 5-2. Asymptotic stability: An equilibrium state $\mathbf{x}_e$ is asymptotically stable if, in addition to being stable, there is further a δ_a such that trajectories started within the δ_a neighborhood of $\mathbf{x}_e$ will converge to $\mathbf{x}_e$ as $t \to \infty$.

Lyapunov also gave a definition of instability:

◆◆Definition 5-3. An equilibrium state x_e of a free dynamic system is unstable if there exists an ϵ such that no δ can be found to satisfy the conditions of Definition 5-1.◆◆

This is reasonably intuitive. Note, however, that this definition of instability only guarantees that the system trajectory will leave some ϵ neighborhood about x_e; it does not necessarily mean that the system trajectory will stray arbitrarily far from x_e. Thus the origin of the Van der Pol equation is unstable, no matter how small the limit cycle is.

It cannot be stressed enough that the concepts of Lyapunov stability and asymptotic stability are *local* concepts in that they apply to stability behavior *in the small* or in a small neighborhood about the origin. Note that as worded, the size of the ϵ is unimportant, it is the size of δ which is the determining factor. If a δ_1 is found to satisfy the stipulations of the definition for a given ϵ_1, then that same δ_1 would surely satisfy the definitions relative to any $\epsilon > \epsilon_1$. A mean challenger would therefore select only small ϵ's, and it is up to the designer to produce the δ appropriate to these small ϵ's.*

*From the definition it is also clear that a δ appropriate for a given ϵ must be smaller or equal to the given ϵ.

In the sequel we shall use the terms "stability in the small" and "asymptotic stability in the small" interchangeably with Lyapunov stability and asymptotic stability respectively.

We should note that relative to any distinct equilibrium state x_e, by a simple change of variables $x - x_e$, the study of system trajectory about a given singular point can be transformed to a study of an equivalent system about the origin 0. Without much loss in generality then, we shall henceforth (unless otherwise noted) consider only the stability of systems where the origin is an equilibrium state.

Let us consider some examples.

♦♦Example 5-4. Consider the system shown in Fig. 5-3. The state-plane portrait in the $\dot{e}$ vs. e plane is shown in Fig. 5-4. For this system, all trajectories originating in the region:

$$\sqrt{e^2 + \dot{e}^2} \leq 1 \tag{5-1}$$

will tend to the origin. Moreover, it is quite clear that for any value of ϵ, a δ can be found to fulfill the Lyapunov stability conditions. Thus the origin is asymptotically stable.

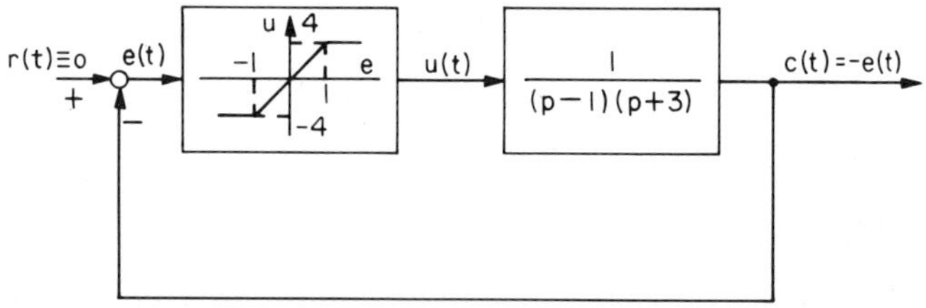

Fig. 5-3. The system of Example 5-4.

Note however, that the trajectories originating from a region outside the circle described by Eq. (5-1) may well tend toward infinity as shown in Fig. 5-4. Then the system origin is not stable *in the large*. This fact cannot be inferred from examining the local behavior of trajectories in the vicinity of an equilibrium state. It turns out that these divergent trajectories arise because the system, in addition to the origin, also has other equilibrium states which are unstable. This will become clear in a more detailed analysis of the same system in Sec. 5.4.♦♦

We see from the foregoing that local stability analysis is not without danger. Unfortunately, local stability is the only mode for stability that can be investigated using the technique of linearization, which is a prevalent engineering approach. In the following sections, we will analyze this approach, its relation to stability analysis, and its generalized formulation.

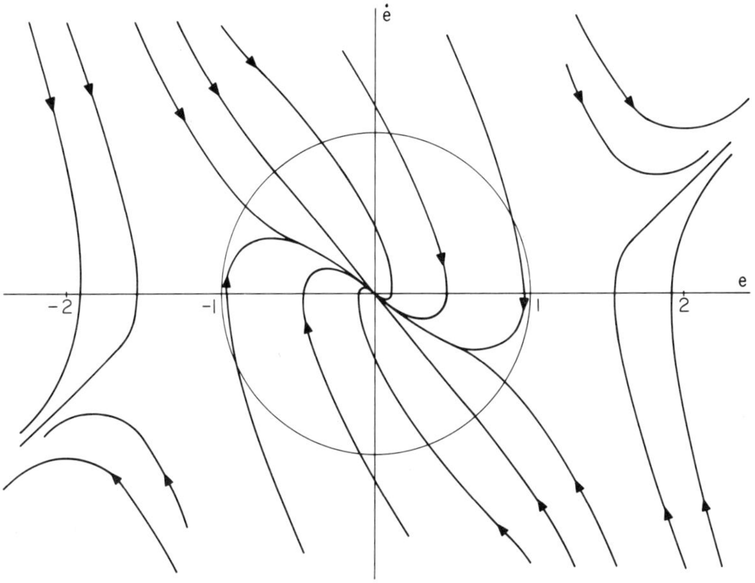

Fig. 5-4. Partial state-plane portrait for the system of Example 5-4.

The important question of stability in the large is discussed in Sec. 5.9 and presented in detail in Chaps. 9, 10, and 11.

5.3 The Method of Local Linearization

Knowingly or unknowingly, each engineer has applied the method of local linearization to problems of design and anlaysis. In designing a vacuum tube or transistor amplifier, for example, it is customary to linearize about the operating point and to determine parameters such as the amplification factor. The method is also known as *perturbation analysis*.

In this section, we will give a systematic and generalized formulation of this method. The use of this method leads to the application of Lyapunov's First Method, which will be presented in the next section.

To fix ideas, it is instructive to consider initially a first-order example.

♦♦Example 5-5. For the system $\dot{x} = -\sin x$, the equilibrium states are at $x = n\pi$, $n = 0, 1, \ldots$. Integration yields directly the solution

$$\tan \frac{x}{2} = \left(\tan \frac{x_0}{2}\right) e^{-(t - t_0)}$$

which indicates that the states $x_e = 2m\pi$, $m = 0,1,\ldots$ are stable while the states $x_e = (2m+1)\pi$, $m = 0,1\ldots$ are unstable. This result, of course, can also be inferred by inspection.

Let us nevertheless try to linearize the system about the origin and let us proceed in such a way as to spotlight the steps necessary to achieve linearization.

Suppose at $t = t_0$, the state $x(t)$ is perturbed from the equilibrium state x_e by a small amount $\delta x(t)$. We have

$$x(t) = x_e + \delta x(t) \qquad \text{for} \qquad t > t_0 \tag{5-2}$$

This means the system equation is now

$$\frac{d}{dt}(x_e + \delta x) = -\sin(x_e + \delta x) \tag{5-3}$$

The right-hand side (rhs) of Eq. (5-3) can be expanded in a Taylor series about the state x_e, to yield

$$\frac{d}{dt}(x_e + \delta x) = -\sin x_e + \frac{d}{dx}(-\sin x)\bigg|_{x=x_e} \delta x + \ldots$$

$$= -\sin x_e - \cos x_e \delta x + \ldots \tag{5-4}$$

where terms in $(\delta x)^2$ or higher are not explicitly written.

It is reasonable to expect that when δx is sufficiently small, the behavior of the system about x_e can be adequately given by using Eq. (5-4) but neglecting the higher order terms. That is,

$$\frac{d}{dt}(x_e + \delta x) \cong -\sin x_e - \cos x_e \delta x \tag{5-5}$$

Subtracting from Eq. (5-5) the trivial solution $(d/dt)\, x_e = -\sin x_e$ which must hold at the equilibrium state, we obtain

$$\frac{d}{dt}\delta x \triangleq \delta\dot{x} \cong -\cos x_e \delta x \tag{5-6}$$

which is the linearized equation of motion of the perturbed variable δx. Note that at $x_e = 0$ or $2m\pi$, $m = 1,\ldots,$ Eq. (5-6) becomes $\delta\dot{x} = -\delta x$, and asymptotic stability is indicated because $\lim_{t\to\infty} \delta x = 0$. However, at $x_e = (2m+1)\pi$, Eq. (5-6) becomes $\delta\dot{x} = \delta x$ and we have a divergent response, indicating that the latter equilibrium states are unstable.

Thus in this case, linearization does not alter the stability conclusion. ◆◆

We can readily extend the above linearization procedure to nth-order systems under constants inputs. Consider the time-invariant nonlinear system

$$\dot{\mathbf{x}} = \mathbf{f}(\mathbf{x},\mathbf{u}) \tag{5-7}$$

where the function $\mathbf{f}(\mathbf{x},\mathbf{u})$ is assumed to be continuously differentiable with respect to each component of $\mathbf{x}$ and $\mathbf{u}$.

When the control function $\mathbf{u}$ is identically 0 or is a constant vector $\mathbf{u}_0$, the equilibrium states are those $\mathbf{x}_e$'s where

$$0 = \mathbf{f}(\mathbf{x}_e, \mathbf{u}_0) \tag{5-8}$$

is satisfied. Let

$$\begin{aligned} \mathbf{x}(t) &= \mathbf{x}_e + \delta\mathbf{x}(t), \quad \mathbf{u}(t) = \mathbf{u}_0 + \delta\mathbf{u}(t) \\ \dot{\mathbf{x}}(t) &= \dot{\mathbf{x}}_e + \delta\dot{\mathbf{x}}(t), \quad \delta\dot{\mathbf{x}}(t) \triangleq \frac{d}{dt}\,\delta\mathbf{x}(t) \end{aligned} \tag{5-9}$$

where $\delta\mathbf{x}(t)$ and $\delta\mathbf{u}(t)$ are perturbations on $\mathbf{x}_e$ and $\mathbf{u}_0$ respectively and $\delta\dot{\mathbf{x}}(t)$ is the time derivative of $\delta\mathbf{x}(t)$.

Substituting (5-9) into the original system equation (5-7) and subtracting (5-8) we have the perturbed system equation:

$$\delta\dot{\mathbf{x}}(t) = \mathbf{f}\big(\mathbf{x}_e + \delta\mathbf{x}(t), \mathbf{u}_0 + \delta\mathbf{u}(t)\big) \tag{5-10}$$

Since $\mathbf{f}$ is assumed to be continuously differentiable with respect to its arguments, Eq. (5-10) can be put in the form

$$\delta\dot{\mathbf{x}} = \frac{\partial\mathbf{f}}{\partial\mathbf{x}}(\mathbf{x}_e, \mathbf{u}_0)\,\delta\mathbf{x} + \frac{\partial\mathbf{f}}{\partial\mathbf{u}}(\mathbf{x}_e, \mathbf{u}_0)\,\delta\mathbf{u} + \mathbf{h}(\mathbf{x}_e, \mathbf{u}_0, \delta\mathbf{x}, \delta\mathbf{u}) \tag{5-11}$$

where $\partial\mathbf{f}(\mathbf{x}_e, \mathbf{u}_0)/\partial\mathbf{x}$ and $\partial\mathbf{f}(\mathbf{x}_e, \mathbf{u}_0)/\partial\mathbf{u}$ are the following Jacobian matrices:

$$\frac{\partial\mathbf{f}}{\partial\mathbf{x}}(\mathbf{x}_e, \mathbf{u}_0) \triangleq \begin{bmatrix} \dfrac{\partial f_1}{\partial x_1} & \dfrac{\partial f_1}{\partial x_2} & \cdots & \dfrac{\partial f_1}{\partial x_n} \\ \vdots & & & \\ \dfrac{\partial f_n}{\partial x_1} & & \cdots & \dfrac{\partial f_n}{\partial x_n} \end{bmatrix} \text{evaluated at } \mathbf{x} = \mathbf{x}_e,\ \mathbf{u} = \mathbf{u}_0 \tag{5-12a}$$

$$\frac{\partial \mathbf{f}}{\partial \mathbf{u}}(\mathbf{x}_e, \mathbf{u}_0) \triangleq \begin{bmatrix} \frac{\partial f_1}{\partial u_1} & \frac{\partial f_1}{\partial u_2} & \cdots & \frac{\partial f_1}{\partial x_r} \\ \vdots & & & \\ \frac{\partial f_n}{\partial u_1} & & \cdots & \frac{\partial f_n}{\partial u_r} \end{bmatrix} \quad \text{evaluated at } \mathbf{u} = \mathbf{u}_0,\ \mathbf{x} = \mathbf{x}_e \tag{5-12b}$$

and $\mathbf{h}(\mathbf{x}_e, \mathbf{u}_0, \delta\mathbf{x}, \delta\mathbf{u})$, abbreviated to $\mathbf{h}(\delta\mathbf{x}, \delta\mathbf{u})$, contains the remainder terms.

We now assume that as $\delta\mathbf{x}$ and $\delta\mathbf{u}$ go to 0, $\mathbf{h}$ approaches 0 faster than the linear terms on the rhs of Eq. (5-11). Specifically, assume that*

$$\lim_{\substack{\|\delta\mathbf{x}\| \to 0 \\ \|\delta\mathbf{u}\| \to 0}} \frac{\mathbf{h}(\delta\mathbf{x}, \delta\mathbf{u})}{\|\delta\mathbf{x}\|} = \lim_{\substack{\|\delta\mathbf{x}\| \to 0 \\ \|\delta\mathbf{u}\| \to 0}} \frac{\mathbf{h}(\delta\mathbf{x}, \delta\mathbf{u})}{\|\delta\mathbf{u}\|} = 0 \tag{5-13}$$

then in a sufficiently small region about $\mathbf{x}_e$ and for sufficiently small values of $\|\delta\mathbf{u}\|$, the behavior of the perturbed system can be approximated by the *locally linearized equation*:

$$\delta\dot{\mathbf{x}} = \frac{\partial \mathbf{f}}{\partial \mathbf{x}}(\mathbf{x}_e, \mathbf{u}_0)\,\delta\mathbf{x} + \frac{\partial \mathbf{f}}{\partial \mathbf{u}}(\mathbf{x}_e, \mathbf{u}_0)\,\delta\mathbf{u} \tag{5-14}$$

As has been indicated, the fact that this set is now linear and time invariant makes it much simpler to study from an analytical point of view. Any of the methods that have been devised for linear systems can now be attempted. Let us consider an example:

◆◆Example 5-6. Linearized equations for a missile. Fig. 2-15 showed a simplified fin-controlled missile moving in a plane after the termination of thrust. We are now prepared to derive the linearized equation of motion for the missile. The overall missile equations of motion are:

$$I\ddot{\theta} = AlQC_M(\alpha, \delta) \tag{5-15a}$$

$$mV\dot{\gamma} = AQC_L(\alpha, \delta) \tag{5-15b}$$

$$mga_N = AQC_N(\alpha, \delta) \tag{5-15c}$$

*If $\mathbf{f}(\mathbf{x},\mathbf{u})$ can be expanded in a Taylor series about $\mathbf{x}_e$ and $\mathbf{u}_0$, then $\mathbf{h}(\delta\mathbf{x},\delta\mathbf{u})$ represents all the terms in the second power in $\delta\mathbf{x}$ and $\delta\mathbf{u}$ and higher. In this case Eq. (5-13) is clearly satisfied.

where it will be recognized that the first equation is a moment equation, the second is a force equation in a direction normal to the missile velocity vector, and the third is a lateral force equation. The symbols, in addition to those given in Exercise 2-5, are defined below:

C_M, C_L, C_N: dimensionless coefficients of moment, of lift force (normal to the velocity vector), and of normal force (normal to missile axis) respectively. They are generally given as curves plotted as functions of the variables α and δ as taken from empirical or wind tunnel data. Figure 5-5 shows typical curves for C_M, C_N, and C_L

A, l: a reference area and a reference length respectively. They provide the normalizing factors for the coefficients C_M, C_L and C_N. For our purpose they may be set to unity.

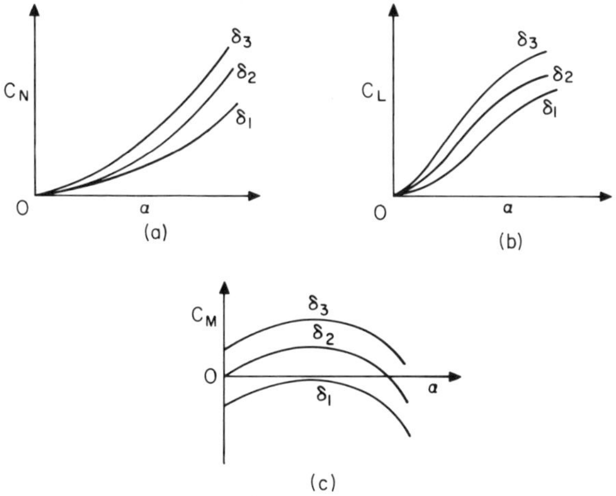

Fig. 5-5. Typical aerodynamic curves for the missile of Example 5-6.

The equations given are sufficient to provide answers concerning the missile dynamics. In particular, let us attempt to find the effect of a small deflection of the control fin of the missile on the rate of change of the attitude angle $\dot{\theta}$ and on the lateral acceleration a_N.

Since $\theta = \alpha + \gamma$, let us choose $\dot{\theta}$ and α as the two state variables. From the first two equations then, we have:

$$\frac{d}{dt}\dot{\theta} = \frac{Q}{I} C_M(\alpha, \delta), \qquad \frac{d}{dt}\alpha = -\frac{Q}{mV} C_L(\alpha, \delta) + \dot{\theta} \tag{5-16}$$

In aerospace language, a trim condition is that set of values α_T, δ_T, and $\dot{\theta}_T$ such that the left-hand side (lhs) of the equations vanish:

$$0 = \frac{Q}{I} C_M(\alpha_T, \delta_T), \quad 0 = -\frac{Q}{mV} C_L(\alpha_T, \delta_T) + \dot{\theta}_T \tag{5-17}$$

The set α_T, δ_T, and $\dot{\theta}_T$ thus constitutes an equilibrium state* for our system. In particular, from physical reasoning, the set $\alpha_T = \delta_T = \dot{\theta}_T = 0$ must constitute an equilibrium state.

To study the system behavior about $\alpha_T = \delta_T = \dot{\theta}_T = 0$, we have $\delta\dot{\theta} = \dot{\theta}$, $\delta\alpha = \alpha$, etc., and the local linearization equations then become:

$$\frac{d}{dt}\dot{\theta} = \frac{Q}{I}\left[\left.\frac{\partial C_M}{\partial \alpha}\right|_{\alpha=0} \alpha + \left.\frac{\partial C_M}{\partial \delta}\right|_{\delta=0} \delta\right]$$

$$\frac{d}{dt}\alpha = -\frac{Q}{mV}\left[\left.\frac{\partial C_L}{\partial \alpha}\right|_{\alpha=0} \alpha + \left.\frac{\partial C_L}{\partial \delta}\right|_{\delta=0} \delta\right] + \dot{\theta} \tag{5-18}$$

Consistent with aerospace practice, let

$$C_{M\alpha} \triangleq \left.\frac{\partial C_M}{\partial \alpha}\right|_{\alpha=0}, \quad C_{M\delta} \triangleq \left.\frac{\partial C_M}{\partial \delta}\right|_{\delta=0}, \quad C_{L\alpha} \triangleq \left.\frac{\partial C_L}{\partial \alpha}\right|_{\alpha=0}, \quad C_{L\delta} \triangleq \left.\frac{\partial C_L}{\partial \delta}\right|_{\delta=0} \tag{5-19}$$

Then we have

$$\frac{d}{dt}\dot{\theta} = \frac{Q}{I}(C_{M\alpha}\alpha + C_{M\delta}\delta), \quad \frac{d}{dt}\alpha = -\frac{Q}{mV} C_{L\alpha}\alpha - \frac{Q}{mV} C_{L\delta}\delta + \dot{\theta} \tag{5-20}$$

which allows the solving of the two quantities α and $\dot{\theta}$ in terms of δ.

If the achieved lateral acceleration is to be used as an output quantity, then (5-15*c*) can be used. Linearizing locally about $\alpha_T = 0$, $\delta_T = 0$, $\dot{\theta}_T = 0$, gives

$$mga_N = Q(C_{N\alpha}\alpha + C_{N\delta}\delta) \tag{5-21}$$

*The reader should recognize that in this simplified problem we are considering the missile as flying in a homogeneous medium. Otherwise, the equilibrium state can be time varying and the situation will be much more complicated.

where as before

$$C_{N\alpha} \triangleq \left.\frac{\partial C_N}{\partial \alpha}\right|_{\alpha=0}, \quad C_{N\delta} \triangleq \left.\frac{\partial C_N}{\partial \delta}\right|_{\delta=0} \tag{5-22}$$

The partial derivative is usually directly measured off the curves plotted from the wind-tunnel data.

Equations (5-20) and (5-21) constitute the small-signal linearized equations of motion of the missile. ◆◆

5.4 Lyapunov's First Method for Equilibrium States

The so-called Lyapunov's First Method is actually a theorem stating the conditions under which system stability information can be inferred by examining the simplified equations obtained through local linearization. The theorem is advanced in the first part of the now famous dissertation completed in 1892 by the Russian mathematician A. M. Lyapunov [L18].

The theorem as usually stated applied to autonomous systems only. Before considering the first method then, it is well to pause and consider the role that the input plays in stability analysis.

When the input $\mathbf{u}$ in a system $\dot{\mathbf{x}} = \mathbf{f}(\mathbf{x},\mathbf{u})$ is a constant, then it is no more than a constant of the function $\mathbf{f}(\mathbf{x},\mathbf{u})$. In this case the system with input is the same as an equivalent system without input (with $\mathbf{u}$ being treated as a constant vector) but with an equilibrium state that is different from that of the first system. Specifically in the system $\dot{\mathbf{x}} = \mathbf{f}(\mathbf{x},\mathbf{u})$, for $\mathbf{u} = \mathbf{k}$ (a constant), the behavior of the system will be equivalent to the autonomous system $\mathbf{x} = \mathbf{f}(\mathbf{x},\mathbf{k})$ with the equilibrium state $\mathbf{x}_e$ defined by $\mathbf{f}(\mathbf{x}_e,\mathbf{k}) = \mathbf{0}$. This is clear in a linear system of the form $\dot{\mathbf{x}} = \mathbf{A}\,\mathbf{x} + \mathbf{B}\,\mathbf{u}$, where for constant inputs, when $\mathbf{A}^{-1}$ exists, the equilibrium state for the equivalent system is simply

$$\mathbf{x}_e = -\mathbf{A}^{-1}\mathbf{B}\mathbf{k}$$

For a $\mathbf{u}(t)$ that is time varying, it is not possible in general to find a transformation such that a single, fixed equilibrium state pertains. Therefore the Lyapunov stability concepts cannot be readily applied to systems with general inputs. Sometimes, however, a particular solution may be known. In that case, it is possible to study the stability of that particular solution. This will be the subject of the next section. For the time being, since stability criteria can be readily applied only to time invariant systems, we will concern ourselves only with autonomous systems or time invariant systems with constant inputs.

Relative to the above class of systems, Lyapunov's First Method states that:

♦♦Theorem 5-1. For an autonomous system $\dot{x} = f(x)$, let $\delta\dot{x} = (\partial f(x_e)/\partial x)\delta x + h(x_e, \delta x)$ be the equation of the perturbed system about an equilibrium state x_e. If

$$\lim_{\|\delta x\| \to 0} \frac{h(x_e, \delta x)}{\|\delta x\|} = 0 \tag{5-23}$$

then:

1) if the linearized system $\delta\dot{x} = (\partial f(x_e)/\partial x)\delta x$ has only eigenvalues with negative real parts, x_e is asymptotically stable;
2) if the linearized system has one or more eigenvalues with positive real parts, x_e is unstable;
3) if the linearized system has one or more eigenvalues with zero real parts and the remaining eigenvalues have negative real parts, the stability of x_e cannot be ascertained by studying the linearized system alone, even in the small.* ♦♦

The proof of the theorem will be deferred to Chap. 9 where Lyapunov's Second Method is introduced.

From these theorems, we may also expect that locally, about the equilibrium state, the state portrait will be similar to that of the linearized system. In particular, for second-order nonlinear systems, the local state trajectories about the equilibrium state can be predicted by the linearized system provided that the linearized system has no eigenvalues lying on the imaginary axis. The character of the equilibrium state will be similar to those discussed in the preceding chapter, depending on the location of the poles of the linearized equation.

Let us consider some examples.

♦♦Example 5-7. Let us reconsider the system of Example 5-4 (Fig. 5-3). The state equations are:

$$x_1 \triangleq e, \; x_2 \triangleq \dot{e}, \; \dot{x}_1 = x_2, \; \dot{x}_2 = -2x_2 + 3x_1 - f(x_1), \tag{5-24}$$

$$f(x_1) = \begin{cases} 4, & x_1 \geq 1 \\ 4x_1, & -1 \leq x_1 \leq 1 \\ -4, & x_1 \leq -1 \end{cases}$$

*These cases are referred to as *critical cases* in the literature.

We see that there are three equilibrium states for this system:

$$\begin{bmatrix} x_{1e} \\ x_{2e} \end{bmatrix} = \begin{bmatrix} -\frac{4}{3} \\ 0 \end{bmatrix}, \quad \begin{bmatrix} x_{1e} \\ x_{2e} \end{bmatrix} = \begin{bmatrix} 0 \\ 0 \end{bmatrix}, \quad \begin{bmatrix} x_{1e} \\ x_{2e} \end{bmatrix} = \begin{bmatrix} \frac{4}{3} \\ 0 \end{bmatrix} \tag{5-25}$$

To obtain the linearized system about each equilibrium state, let

$$\delta x_1 = x_1 - x_{1e}, \quad \delta x_2 = x_2 - x_{2e} \tag{5-26}$$

Consider first the equilibrium state $x_{1e} = 0$, $x_{2e} = 0$.

For this state, Eqs. (5-24) and (5-26) yield

$$\delta \dot{x}_1 = \delta x_2, \qquad \delta \dot{x}_2 = -2\,\delta x_2 - \delta x_1 \tag{5-27}$$

The characteristic equation of this linearized system is

$$\lambda^2 + 2\lambda + 1 = (\lambda + 1)^2 = 0$$

with the double root $\lambda = -1$. Thus (see Chap. 4), this equilibrium state is a stable node. A phase-plane trajectory originating from an infinitesimally small distance from the origin will travel toward the origin. This can be seen in Fig. 5-4.

Consider now the equilibrium state $x_{1e} = 4/3$, $x_{2e} = 0$. For this state, linearization yields

$$\delta \dot{x}_1 = \delta x_2, \qquad \delta \dot{x}_2 = -2\delta x_2 + 3\delta x_1 \tag{5-28}$$

The characteristic equation for this linearized system is

$$\lambda^2 + 2\lambda - 3 = (\lambda - 1)(\lambda + 3) = 0$$

yielding roots $\lambda = +1$ and $\lambda = -3$. Thus, this equilibrium state is a saddle point and therefore unstable.

In the same way as shown above, we can demonstrate that the equilibrium state $(x_{1e}, x_{2e}) = (-4/3, 0)$ will also be represented as a saddle point in the phase plane and thus will also be unstable in the sense of Lyapunov. (See Exercise (5-17.)◆◆

◆◆Example 5-8. Let us now reconsider the in-the-small stability characteristics of the missile of Example 5-6. We shall assume that Eq. (5-23) holds.

From Eqs. (5-20), we write

$$\begin{bmatrix} p & -\frac{Q}{I} C_{M\alpha} \\ -1 & p + \frac{Q}{mV} C_{L\alpha} \end{bmatrix} \begin{bmatrix} \dot{\theta} \\ \alpha \end{bmatrix} = \begin{bmatrix} \frac{Q}{I} C_{M\delta} \\ -\frac{Q}{mV} C_{L\delta} \end{bmatrix} \delta \tag{5-29}$$

Inverting (5-29), we obtain

$$\dot{\theta} = \frac{A_\delta Q(p + a_2)\delta}{p^2 + a_1 p + a_0} \qquad (5\text{-}30a)$$

$$\alpha = \frac{B_\delta Q(p + b_2)\delta}{p^2 + a_1 p + a_0} \qquad (5\text{-}30b)$$

where

$$A_\delta = \frac{C_{M\delta}}{I}, \quad B_\delta = -\frac{1}{mV} C_{L\delta}, \quad a_0 = -\frac{Q}{I} C_{M\alpha}, \quad a_1 = \frac{1}{mV} C_{L\alpha},$$

$$a_2 = \frac{1}{mV} C_{L\alpha}\left[1 - \frac{C_{M\alpha} C_{L\delta}}{C_{M\delta} C_{L\alpha}}\right], \quad b_2 = -\frac{mV}{I}\frac{C_{M\delta}}{C_{L\delta}}$$

Equations (5-30a) and (5-30b) permit us to examine the stability in the small of the missile about the equilibrium state (trim condition) $\alpha_T = \delta_T = \dot{\theta}_T = 0$. The theoretical legitimacy is provided by Lyapunov's First Method.

The characteristic equation of the uncontrolled missile from (5-30) is

$$\lambda^2 + a_1\lambda + a_0 = 0 \qquad (5\text{-}31)$$

The missile is then inherently asymptotically stable in the small if both a_1 and a_0 are positive. This turns out to be a basic design factor for a fin-controlled missile. Physically the fact that a_0 and a_1 are both positive will mean that the center of pressure (i.e., the point through which the net force on the missile must act in order to produce the achieved moment on the missile) lies behind the center of mass of the missile. The missile in this case is said to be statically stable.

On the other hand, if either a_0 or a_1 (or both) is negative, the center of pressure of the missile lies ahead of the center of mass of the missile and the missile is said to be statically unstable.

From the point of view of autopilot design, the uncontrolled missile considered so far constitutes the plant to be controlled. An autopilot is usually designed around it to improve the stability margin and to achieve the required performance. The static stability or instability of the missile then determines whether the plant to be controlled is inherently stable or unstable.♦♦

♦♦**Example 5-9.** Let us now examine the stability of the equilibrium states of the series generator–series motor combination of *Example 4-5.*

The normalized equations of motion are given by Eq. (4-35):

$$ai(t) + T\frac{di(t)}{dt} = \left[M - \xi v(t)\right]\psi(t) - T_E\frac{d\psi(t)}{dt}$$

$$\psi(t)\,i(t) = d + bv(t) + T_J\frac{dv(t)}{dt}$$

$$\psi(t) = \psi\left(i(t)\right) \tag{5-32}$$

Setting di/dt, $d\psi/dt$, and dv/dt to 0, we obtain for the equilibrium state i_e, ψ_e, v_e:

$$ai_e = (M - \xi v_e)\psi_e, \quad \psi_e i_e = d + bv_e, \quad \psi_e = \psi_e(i_e) \tag{5-33}$$

Defining the quantity:

$$\gamma \triangleq d + \frac{b}{\xi}(M - a) \tag{5-34}$$

we obtain for the possible regions of the magnetization curve (see Fig. 4-20) the following sets of equilibrium states:

$$\begin{bmatrix} v_e \\ i_e \end{bmatrix} = \begin{bmatrix} \frac{1}{\xi}(M - a) \\ \sqrt{\gamma} \end{bmatrix}, \begin{bmatrix} \frac{1}{\xi}(M - a) \\ -\sqrt{\gamma} \end{bmatrix}, \text{ and } \begin{bmatrix} -\frac{d}{b} \\ 0 \end{bmatrix} \quad \text{if} \quad 0 \le \gamma < \psi^2_{\max} \tag{5-35a}$$

$$\begin{bmatrix} v_e \\ i_e \end{bmatrix} = \begin{bmatrix} -\frac{d}{b} \\ 0 \end{bmatrix} \quad \text{if} \quad \gamma \le 0 \tag{5-35b}$$

$$\begin{bmatrix} v_e \\ i_e \end{bmatrix} = \begin{bmatrix} \dfrac{\psi^2_{\max} M - ad}{ab + \xi\psi^2_{\max}} \\ \pm\dfrac{bM + \xi d}{ab + \xi\psi^2_{\max}}\psi_{\max} \end{bmatrix}, \text{ and } \begin{bmatrix} -\frac{d}{b} \\ 0 \end{bmatrix} \quad \text{if} \quad \gamma \ge \psi^2_{\max} \tag{5-35c}$$

It is thus seen that for $0 \le \gamma < \psi^2_{\max}$, the steady-state motor speed v_e is independent of the load torque.* This represents the

*The steady-state motor torque is given by $d + bv_e$.

prime desirable feature of the series generator-series motor drive. The range $\gamma < 0$ represents operation of the drive for which the steady state becomes "open circuited." When $\gamma \geq \psi_{max}^2$, or when the saturation region of the magnetization curve is reached, then the steady-state motor speed is dependent on the load parameters d and b.

We conclude that if the design is to be meaningful, then for the possible range of load parameters b and d, the condition $0 < \gamma < \psi_{max}^2$ should be met. If this condition holds, then the system will have the three equilibrium points of Eq. (5-35a).

We can proceed to study the stability of these equilibrium states in the small. Here $i_e^2 = \psi_e^2 < \psi_{max}^2$. Let

$$i = i_e + \delta i, \qquad \psi = i_e + \delta\psi, \qquad v = v_e + \delta v \tag{5-36}$$

Note that for $i_e^2 < \psi_{max}^2$ and for small $\delta\psi$, we are constrained by the magnetization curve to $\delta\psi = \delta i$. Using this fact when we substitute (5-35a) into (5-32) and ignoring products of small quantities, we have the small-signal linearized equations

$$\begin{bmatrix} (T + T_E)p & \xi i_e \\ -2\,i_e & (b + T_J p) \end{bmatrix} \begin{bmatrix} \delta i \\ \delta v \end{bmatrix} = \begin{bmatrix} 0 \\ 0 \end{bmatrix} \tag{5-37a}$$

with

$$i_e = \pm\sqrt{d + \frac{b}{\xi}(M - a)} \neq 0, \qquad v_e = \frac{1}{\xi}(M - a)$$

and

$$\begin{bmatrix} \left[-\dfrac{\xi}{b}\left(d + \dfrac{b}{\xi}(M - a)\right) + (T + T_E)p\right] & 0 \\ 0 & (b + T_J p) \end{bmatrix} \begin{bmatrix} \delta i \\ \delta v \end{bmatrix} = \begin{bmatrix} 0 \\ 0 \end{bmatrix} \tag{5-37b}$$

with

$$i_e = 0, \quad v_e = -\frac{d}{b}$$

where p is the operator d/dt as before.

The characteristic equations corresponding to (5-37a) and (5-37b) respectively are:

$$p^2 + \frac{b}{T_J}\,p + \frac{2\,\xi\gamma}{T_J(T + T_E)} = 0 \tag{5-38a}$$

$$\left(p - \frac{\zeta\gamma}{T + T_E}\right)\left(p + \frac{b}{T_J}\right) = 0 \qquad (5\text{-}38b)$$

Since ξ, T, and T_J all > 0, Eqs. (5-38a) and (5-38b) indicate that if $0 < \gamma < \psi^2_{max}$, there are two symmetical equilibrium states at $i_e = \pm\sqrt{\gamma}$, $v_e = 1/\xi(M - a)$. Each of these is:

1) a stable node if $b^2(T + T_E) \geq 8T_J\zeta\gamma$,
2) a stable focus if $b^2(T + T_E) < 8T_J\zeta\gamma$, and
3) a vortex point if $b(T + T_E) = 0$.

Also, Eq. (5-37b) indicates that there is a single saddle point at $i_e = 0$, $v_e = -d/b$. Moreover, from (5-35b) and (5-38), if $\gamma < 0$, then there is a stable node at $i_e = 0$ and $v_e = -d/b$.◆◆

For an example of a system whose linearized equation has an eigenvalue with 0 real part and whose stability character cannot be determined by considering the linearized equation alone, consider:

◆◆Example 5-10. The first-order system,

$$\dot{x} = kx^m, \quad m = 2,3, \ldots$$

has a linearized equation which is the trivial equation $\delta\dot{x} = 0$. The equation indicates that all the points along the x axis are equilibrium states, and that there will be no motion of the system state. But here the eigenvalue of the linearized equation is 0 and Lyapunov's First Method does not apply. It is easy to see by elementary integration that the origin of this system $\dot{x} = kx^m$, $m > 1$ is (asymptotically) stable if and only if $k < 0$ and m is odd, and it is unstable if either m is even, or m is odd but $k > 0$. Thus the true motion of the system cannot be inferred through linearization.◆◆

The major pitfall in linearization is that even for those cases where Lyapunov's First Method does apply, we can only obtain in-the-small information concerning the system behavior in some unspecified region about an equilibrium state. Engineering judgment, and sometimes simulation and other means, must be used to determine the extent of the safe region in which linearization yields the correct information.

5.5 Local Linearization about a Trajectory—Sensitivity and Error Analysis

The procedure of local linearization about an equilibrium point outlined above can be readily generalized. In particular we can linearize about a given solution or trajectory of a system Such a procedure is very useful, for example, in a space navigation problem in which a nominal trajectory for a spaceship has been found. By linearizing about the nominal trajectory the necessary control signals can be determined which will allow the space ship to stay close to the nominal trajectory. At the same time, the resulting linearized set of equations will show how error in initial conditions and parameter values propagate; further, the sensitivity coefficients for the problem can be determined.

The procedure is not without its problems. First, *the resulting linear equations will in general be time varying*, so that closed-form solutions will not be available and computers will usually be required to find the transition matrix and other relevant parameters. Second, the available theoretical results for linear time-varying systems are rather restrictive and difficult to apply, and will require the notion of uniform asymptotic stability. Third, more than ever in this case of time-varying systems we must constantly ask how small is "small enough?" and how far may a variable deviate and still remain in the range of validity of the linearized equations? When in doubt, the linearized solutions must constantly be compared with the numerical solution of the actual nonlinear system if one is available.

To develop the approach, consider a general time-varying nonlinear system

$$\dot{\mathbf{x}} = \mathbf{f}(\mathbf{x}, \mathbf{u}, t) \tag{5-39}$$

Suppose we have managed to find a particular solution for the system $\mathbf{x}_1(\mathbf{u}_1(t), t; \mathbf{x}_0, t_0)$—to be labeled $\mathbf{x}_1(t)$ henceforth. This particular solution, which results from the application of the specific control function $\mathbf{u}_1(t)$, can be expressed either numerically or in a closed form. Let us consider now the effects of small perturbation in either $\mathbf{x}$ or $\mathbf{u}$ (or both) on the system motion. Again let

$$\mathbf{x}(t) = \mathbf{x}_1(t) + \delta\mathbf{x}(t), \quad \mathbf{u}(t) = \mathbf{u}_1(t) + \delta\mathbf{u}(t), \quad \dot{\mathbf{x}}(t) = \dot{\mathbf{x}}_1(t) + \delta\dot{\mathbf{x}}(t) \tag{5-40}$$

and make the assumption that $\mathbf{f}(\mathbf{x},\mathbf{u},t)$ is continuously differentiable with respect to $\mathbf{x}$ and $\mathbf{u}$. Then from

$$\dot{\mathbf{x}}_1(t) + \delta\dot{\mathbf{x}}(t) = \mathbf{f}(\mathbf{x}_1 + \delta\mathbf{x}, \mathbf{u}_1 + \delta\mathbf{u}, t) \tag{5-41}$$

by expanding the rhs to the first power in $\delta\mathbf{x}$ and $\delta\mathbf{u}$ and subtracting the nominal solution

$$\dot{\mathbf{x}}_1(t) = \mathbf{f}(\mathbf{x}_1(t), \mathbf{u}_1(t), t)$$

we obtain

$$\delta\dot{\mathbf{x}} = \frac{\partial \mathbf{f}}{\partial \mathbf{x}}(\mathbf{x}_1, \mathbf{u}_1, t)\,\delta\mathbf{x} + \frac{\partial \mathbf{f}}{\partial \mathbf{u}}(\mathbf{x}_1, \mathbf{u}_1, t)\,\delta\mathbf{u} + \mathbf{h}(\mathbf{x}_1, \mathbf{u}_1, \delta\mathbf{x}, \delta\mathbf{u}, t) \tag{5-42}$$

where

$$\frac{\partial \mathbf{f}}{\partial \mathbf{x}}(\mathbf{x}_1, \mathbf{u}_1, t) \quad \text{and} \quad \frac{\partial \mathbf{f}}{\partial \mathbf{u}}(\mathbf{x}_1, \mathbf{u}_1, t)$$

are the following Jacobian matrices:

$$\frac{\partial \mathbf{f}}{\partial \mathbf{x}}(\mathbf{x}_1, \mathbf{u}_1, t) = \begin{bmatrix} \dfrac{\partial f_1}{\partial x_1} & \cdots & \dfrac{\partial f_1}{\partial x_n} \\ \vdots & & \vdots \\ \dfrac{\partial f_n}{\partial x_1} & \cdots & \dfrac{\partial f_n}{\partial x_n} \end{bmatrix} \quad \begin{array}{l} \text{evaluated along} \\ \mathbf{x}(t) = \mathbf{x}_1(t) \\ \mathbf{u}(t) = \mathbf{u}_1(t) \end{array} \tag{5-43}$$

$$\frac{\partial \mathbf{f}}{\partial \mathbf{u}}(\mathbf{x}_1, \mathbf{u}_1, t) = \begin{bmatrix} \dfrac{\partial f_1}{\partial u_1} & \cdots & \dfrac{\partial f_1}{\partial u_r} \\ \vdots & & \vdots \\ \dfrac{\partial f_n}{\partial u_1} & \cdots & \dfrac{\partial f_n}{\partial u_r} \end{bmatrix} \quad \begin{array}{l} \text{evaluated along} \\ \mathbf{x}(t) = \mathbf{x}_1(t) \\ \mathbf{u}(t) = \mathbf{u}_1(t) \end{array} \tag{5-44}$$

and $\mathbf{h}(\mathbf{x}_1, \mathbf{u}_1, \delta\mathbf{x}, \delta\mathbf{u}, t)$, abbreviated to $\mathbf{h}(\delta\mathbf{x}, \delta\mathbf{u}, t)$, is again the remainder term.

We note that the Jacobian matrices $\partial\mathbf{f}(\mathbf{x}_1, \mathbf{u}_1, t)/\partial\mathbf{x}$ and $\partial\mathbf{f}(\mathbf{x}_1, \mathbf{u}_1, t)/\partial\mathbf{u}$ evaluated along the trajectory $\mathbf{x}(t) = \mathbf{x}_1(t)$ and $\mathbf{u}(t) = \mathbf{u}_1(t)$, are no longer dependent on $\mathbf{x}(t)$ and $\mathbf{u}(t)$ but are, however, functions of time t.* Let us therefore use the notation

$$\frac{\partial \mathbf{f}}{\partial \mathbf{x}}(t) \triangleq \frac{\partial \mathbf{f}}{\partial \mathbf{x}}(\mathbf{x}_1, \mathbf{u}_1, t), \quad \frac{\partial \mathbf{f}}{\partial \mathbf{u}}(t) \triangleq \frac{\partial \mathbf{f}}{\partial \mathbf{u}}(\mathbf{x}_1, \mathbf{u}_1, t) \tag{5-45}$$

*The relevant Jacobian matrices are not functions of time if (i) the system is time invariant, and (ii) the particular solution $\mathbf{x}_1(t)$ is not an explicit function of time. Note that in this light the material in Sec. 5.3 can be considered as the special case of linearizing a time invariant set of equations about the particular solution $\mathbf{x}_1(t) \equiv \mathbf{x}_e$.

Then (5-42) becomes

$$\delta\dot{\mathbf{x}} = \frac{\partial \mathbf{f}}{\partial \mathbf{x}}(t)\,\delta\mathbf{x} + \frac{\partial \mathbf{f}}{\partial \mathbf{u}}(t)\,\delta\mathbf{u} + \mathbf{h}(\delta\mathbf{x}, \delta\mathbf{u}, t)$$

Suppose now $\mathbf{h}$ is such that

$$\lim_{\substack{\|\delta\mathbf{x}\| \to 0 \\ \|\delta\mathbf{u}\| \to 0}} \frac{\mathbf{h}(\delta\mathbf{x}, \delta\mathbf{u}, t)}{\|\delta\mathbf{x}\|} = \lim_{\substack{\|\delta\mathbf{x}\| \to 0 \\ \|\delta\mathbf{u}\| \to 0}} \frac{\mathbf{h}(\delta\mathbf{x}, \delta\mathbf{u}, t)}{\|\delta\mathbf{u}\|} = 0 \tag{5-46}$$

is observed for all t, then the system behavior within the small region about the solution $\mathbf{x}_1(t)$ for sufficiently small $\delta\mathbf{u}$ is expected to be adequately represented in many cases by the local linearized equation

$$\delta\dot{\mathbf{x}} = \frac{\partial \mathbf{f}}{\partial \mathbf{x}}(t)\,\delta\mathbf{x} + \frac{\partial \mathbf{f}}{\partial \mathbf{u}}(t)\,\delta\mathbf{u} \tag{5-47}$$

The approaches given in Chap. 3 can be invoked to solve the time-varying linear equation (5-47). In particular one can exhibit the general solution of (5-47) by means of Eq. (3-22) of Chap. 3

$$\delta\mathbf{x}(t) = \boldsymbol{\Phi}(t, t_0)\,\delta\mathbf{x}(t_0) + \int_{t_0}^{t} \boldsymbol{\Phi}(t,\tau)\,\frac{\partial \mathbf{f}}{\partial \mathbf{u}}(\tau)\,\delta\mathbf{u}(\tau)\,d\tau \tag{5-48}$$

where as before $\boldsymbol{\Phi}(t, t_0)$ is the transition matrix of the system (5-46) and it satisfies the matrix differential equation

$$\frac{d\boldsymbol{\Phi}(t, t_0)}{dt} = \frac{\partial \mathbf{f}}{\partial \mathbf{x}}(t)\,\boldsymbol{\Phi}(t, t_0), \qquad \boldsymbol{\Phi}(t_0, t_0) = \mathbf{I} \tag{5-49}$$

When put into the form (5-48), some further properties of the transition matrix can be seen when viewed in the present context. First at any time t_1, we have

$$\delta\mathbf{x}(t_1) = \boldsymbol{\Phi}(t_1, t_0)\,\delta\mathbf{x}(t_0) + \int_{t_0}^{t_1} \boldsymbol{\Phi}(t_1, \tau)\,\frac{\partial \mathbf{f}}{\partial \mathbf{u}}(\tau)\,\delta\mathbf{u}(\tau)\,d\tau \tag{5-50}$$

Now only the first term of the rhs depends on $\delta\mathbf{x}(t_0)$, in particular, a one-unit perturbation in the ith component of $\delta\mathbf{x}(t_0)$ will result in a change in the jth component of $\delta\mathbf{x}(t_1)$ of magnitude $\phi_{ji}(t_1, t_0)$. Thus *the transition matrix* $\boldsymbol{\Phi}(t_1,t_0)$ *can also be viewed as a sensitivity matrix relating a perturbation* $\delta\mathbf{x}$ *at time* t_0 *to a change in* $\delta\mathbf{x}$ *at the time* t_1 *providing that* $\delta\mathbf{u}$ *is held fixed.*

Also the integral

$$\int_{t_0}^{t_1} \Phi(t_1, \tau) \frac{\partial \mathrm{f}}{\partial \mathrm{u}}(\tau)\, \delta \mathrm{u}(\tau)\, d\tau \tag{5-51}$$

yields a sensitivity matrix which gives changes in $\delta \mathrm{x}$ due solely to changes in $\delta \mathrm{u}(t)$. For example, a unit impulse change in the ith component of $\delta \mathrm{u}$ at some time t_2 will result in a change in the jth component of $\delta \mathrm{x}(t_1)$ of $\sum_{k=1}^{n} \phi_{jk}(t_1, t_2)\, [\partial \mathrm{f}(t_2)/\partial \mathrm{u}]_{ki}$ units. A unit step change in the ith component of $\delta \mathrm{u}$ at time t_2 will result in a change in the jth component of $\delta \mathrm{x}(t_1)$ of $\int_{t_2}^{t_1} \Phi(t_1, \tau)\, [\partial \mathrm{f}(t)/\partial \mathrm{u}]_{ki}\, d\tau$ units, where $[\partial \mathrm{f}(t)/\partial \mathrm{u}]_{ki}$ is the ki entry of the matrix $\partial \mathrm{f}(t)/\partial \mathrm{u}$.

In regard to small perturbations, we may point out that the effect of changes in system parameters can also be similarly handled. Consider a system characterized by the equation

$$\dot{\mathrm{x}} = \mathrm{f}\big(\mathrm{x}, \mathrm{p}(t), t\big) \tag{5-52}$$

where $\mathrm{p}(t)$ is a set of parameters (such as gain, time constants, etc.) whose effect we wish to estimate. If f can be continuously differentiated with respect to p as well as to x, we can again expand Eq. (5-52) to obtain the perturbed equation in $\delta \mathrm{x}$ and $\delta \mathrm{p}$ about any particular solution

$$\delta \dot{\mathrm{x}} = \frac{\partial \mathrm{f}}{\partial \mathrm{x}}(t)\, \delta \mathrm{x} + \frac{\partial \mathrm{f}}{\partial \mathrm{p}}(t)\, \delta \mathrm{p} + \mathrm{h}(\delta \mathrm{x}, \delta \mathrm{p}) \tag{5-53}$$

where as before, $\partial \mathrm{f}(t)/\partial \mathrm{x}$ and $\partial \mathrm{f}(t)/\partial \mathrm{p}$ are the appropriate Jacobian matrices evaluated about the nominal trajectory.

Then in the small, we can approximate Eq. (5-52) by the linear part of Eq. (5-53). We may note incidentally that, in the linearized version, the parameter perturbations $\delta \mathrm{p}$ appear as driving functions for the system.

◆◆Example 5-11. The equations of motion of an artificial satellite with applied control torque (e.g., of the jet type) in terms of the component of its angular rates in the principle axes of the satellite are given by the Euler dynamical equations:

$$\dot{\omega}_1 = -\frac{(I_3 - I_2)}{I_1}\, \omega_2 \omega_3 + \frac{u_1(t)}{I_1}, \quad \dot{\omega}_2 = -\frac{(I_1 - I_3)}{I_2}\, \omega_3 \omega_1 + \frac{u_2(t)}{I_2}$$

$$\dot{\omega}_3 = -\frac{(I_2 - I_1)}{I_3}\, \omega_1 \omega_2 + \frac{u_3(t)}{I_3} \tag{5-54}$$

where I_i, ω_i, $u_i (i = 1, 2, 3)$ are respectively the moment of inertia, the component of angular rate, and applied torque, all with respect to the ith principal axis of the satellite.

When $I_1 = I_2 = I$, it is seen from (5-54) that a solution for $u_1(t) = u_2(t) = u_3(t) \equiv 0$ is:

$$\begin{bmatrix} \omega_1 \\ \omega_2 \\ \omega_3 \end{bmatrix} = \begin{bmatrix} \omega_0 \sin(\beta t + \alpha) \\ \omega_0 \cos(\beta t + \alpha) \\ \omega_{30} \end{bmatrix} \tag{5-55}$$

where ω_0, ω_{30}, α and β are all constants with

$$\beta = \frac{I_1 - I_3}{I_1}\omega_{30}, \quad \alpha = \tan^{-1}\frac{\omega_{10}}{\omega_{20}}, \quad \omega_0 = \sqrt{\omega_{10}^2 + \omega_{20}^2}$$

$$\omega_{10} = \omega_1(0), \quad \omega_{20} = \omega_2(0), \quad \omega_{30} = \omega_3(0)$$

The linearized equation of motion of (5-54) along the trajectory (5-55) becomes

$$\delta\dot{\omega}_1 = \beta\delta\omega_2 + k\cos(\beta t + \alpha)\,\delta\omega_3 + \frac{\delta u_1(t)}{I}$$

$$\delta\dot{\omega}_2 = -\beta\delta\omega_1 - k\sin(\beta t + \alpha)\,\delta\omega_3 + \frac{\delta u_2(t)}{I} \tag{5-56}$$

$$\delta\dot{\omega}_3 = \frac{\delta u_3(t)}{I_3}$$

where $k = \omega_0(I - I_3)/I$. With δu_3 and $\delta\omega_3$ set to 0, the effects of δu_1 and δu_2 can be assessed by simply considering the first two equation of (5-56) alone since they are uncoupled from the third equation. Indeed, in this particular case, the resulting linearized equations will be exact since leaving ω_3 unperturbed will not only uncouple the Eqs. (5-54) but render them linear as well. A linearized version of an originally linear equation clearly will be the same as the original equation.◆◆

◆◆Example 5-12. For the system of Example 5-11, let us consider the effect of a finite $\delta\omega_{30}$ imposed at $t = 0$ (which is equivalent to analyzing the effect of an impulse in $\delta u_3(t)$). Here, with $\delta u_1 = \delta u_2 = 0$, the effect of $\delta\omega_3$ can be treated as driving functions for the first two equations and (5-56) can be solved in closed form. In particular, for the first two equations, we have

$$\mathbf{A} = \begin{bmatrix} 0 & \beta \\ -\beta & 0 \end{bmatrix}, \quad \mathbf{b} = \begin{bmatrix} k\cos(\beta t + \alpha) \\ -k\sin(\beta t + \alpha) \end{bmatrix}$$

whence

$$\boldsymbol{\Phi}(t, \tau) = \begin{bmatrix} \cos\beta(t - \tau) & \sin\beta(t - \tau) \\ -\sin\beta(t - \tau) & \cos\beta(t - \tau) \end{bmatrix}$$

and

$$\begin{bmatrix} \delta\omega_1 \\ \delta\omega_2 \end{bmatrix} = k\delta\omega_{30}\int_0^t \begin{bmatrix} \cos\beta(t - \tau) & \sin\beta(t - \tau) \\ -\sin\beta(t - \tau) & \cos\beta(t - \tau) \end{bmatrix} \begin{bmatrix} \cos(\beta\tau + \alpha) \\ -\sin(\beta\tau + \alpha) \end{bmatrix} d\tau$$

From this we obtain

$$\delta\omega_1 = k\delta\omega_{30}\big(\cos(\beta t + \alpha)\big)\,t, \qquad \delta\omega_2 = -k\delta\omega_{30}\big(\sin(\beta t + \alpha)\big)\,t \tag{5-57}$$

We see that both $\delta\omega_1$ and $\delta\omega_2$ increase without bound, which appears to imply that ω_1 and ω_2 will also increase without bound. This is of course quite impossible since, for example, the angular momentum after the impulse must be conserved at all times. Knowing the form of the solution and the fact that the system is a conservative one after the impulse, we can deduce for what length of time the linear approximation yield a reasonable answer to the problem (see Exercise 5-18).◆◆

◆◆Example 5-13. For the system of the previous two examples, let us now see the effect of a perturbation on the parameter I_1, starting at $t = 0$, i.e., $I_1 = I + \delta I_1$, with $I_2 = I$ and I_3 remaining unperturbed.

The linearized equation corresponding to (5-53) becomes (on setting $\delta u_1 = \delta u_2 = \delta u_3 = 0$):

$$\begin{aligned} \delta\dot{\omega}_1 &= \beta\delta\omega_2 + k\cos(\beta t + \alpha)\,\delta\omega_3 - \frac{k}{I}\,\omega_{30}\cos(\beta t + \alpha)\,\delta I_1 \\ \delta\dot{\omega}_2 &= -\beta\delta\omega_1 - k\sin(\beta t + \alpha)\,\delta\omega_3 - \frac{\omega_0}{I}\,\omega_{30}\sin(\beta t + \alpha)\,\delta I_1 \\ \delta\dot{\omega}_3 &= \frac{1}{I_3}\,\omega_0^2\sin(\beta t + \alpha)\cos(\beta t + \alpha)\,\delta I_1 = \frac{\omega_0^2}{2I_3}\,\sin\big(2(\beta t + \alpha)\big)\,\delta I_1 \end{aligned} \tag{5-58}$$

We can find the linearized solution by first solving for $\delta\omega_3$ in the third equation of (5-58). We substitute that value into the first two equations to find $\delta\omega_1$ and $\delta\omega_2$. The steps are mechanical and will be left to the reader. We may note, however, from the third equation that when I_1 is changed by δI_1 so that the satellite is no longer dynamically symmetric (i.e., $I_1 \neq I_2$) an oscillation of frequency 2β now appears in $\delta\omega_3$. This checks the result of the so-called Poinsot [G7] construction for the general force free motion of an unsymmetric satellite.

According to the linearized model, $\delta\omega_1$ and $\delta\omega_2$ will again diverge, which is physically impossible.◆◆

5.6 The Stability of a System Trajectory—The Concept of Uniform Asymptotic Stability

The concept of the stability in the small of a trajectory of a system is not difficult to formulate. We can merely extend the idea of Lyapunov stability and asymptotic stability as has been previously discussed.

As in the case of Sec. 5.5, let $x_1(u_1(t), t; x_0, t_0)$ be the particular system trajectory under consideration. The notation implies that it is the trajectory in state space generated by the input $u_1(t)$ acting on the system (5–39) starting from an initial state $x(t_0) = x_0$. Now holding $u_1(t)$ fixed,* we can consider the effect of a perturbation $\delta x(t_0) = \delta x_0$ on the initial system state. Let $x(u_1(t), t, x_0 + \delta x_0, t_0)$ be the resultant perturbed trajectory, then the concepts of Lyapunov stability and asymptotic stability can be formulated in the following way:

◆◆Definition 5-4. A system trajectory $x_1(u_1(t), t; x_0, t_0)$ is stable (or stable in the sense of Lyapunov) if for every $\epsilon > 0$, there exists a $\delta > 0$ where δ depends on ϵ *and possibly on* t_0 such that for any perturbed trajectory $x(u_1(t), t; x_0 + \delta x_0, t_0)$, $\|\delta x_0\| < \delta$ will result in $\|x_1(t) - x(t)\| < \epsilon$ for all $t > t_0$.◆◆

◆◆Definition 5-5. A trajectory $x_1(u_1(t), t; x_0, t_0)$ is asymptotically stable if:

1) it is stable, and
2) there exists a δ_a depending possibly on t_0 such that $\|\delta x_0\| < \delta_a$ will result in $\|\delta x(t)\| = \|x_1(t) - x(t)\| \to 0$ as $t \to \infty$.◆◆

◆◆Definition 5-6. A trajectory $x_1(u_1(t), t; x_0, t_0)$ is unstable if there is an ϵ such that no δ can be found to satisfy the condition of Definition 5-4.◆◆

The above extensions have been straightforward, but in a misleading way. Let us pinpoint at least two inadequacies by means of the following examples:

* This is necessary since Lyapunov's definition does not admit an input.

♦♦Example 5-14. It is clear that any limit cycle can at most be stable but cannot be asymptotically stable. For this, consider a perturbation $\delta \mathbf{x}$ along the limit cycle. This perturbs a trajectory in the limit cycle into another one in the same limit cycle. It is obvious from the definition of the limit cycle that $\delta \mathbf{x}$ cannot go to 0. Hence any limit cycle cannot be asymptotically stable.♦♦

♦♦Example 5-15. Many conservative systems whose period of oscillation is a function of the distance from an equilibrium point $\|\mathbf{x} - \mathbf{x}_e\|$ will by definition have trajectories that are unstable, even though from a less stringent viewpoint the trajectories have obvious "stable" manifestations.

Consider a satellite in a spherical orbit at a radial distance R from an inverse-square force center. Now let the satellite's position and velocity be perturbed such that a circular orbit at a radial distance $R + \delta R$ results. By choosing perturbations that are small, δR can be made arbitrarily small. Thus either from the orbit or from the appropriate state-space closed trajectories, we may jump to the conslusion that a circular orbit is stable in the sense of Lyapunov. However, let us consider the angular rate of the motion. A circular orbit may be viewed as one over which at every moment the centrifugal force is balanced by the force of gravitational attraction. Thus we have

$$m\omega^2 R = m \frac{k}{R^2}$$

where m is the mass of the satellite, k is the gravitational constant, and ω is the angular rate of motion of the satellite. We see that ω is proportional to $R^{-3/2}$, therefore the two orbits will be traversed at different periods. As time progresses, the distance between the perturbed satellite and the reference satellite increases to as much as $2R$. This will happen irrespective of how small the value of δR may be. Thus a satellite orbit is unstable in the sense of Lyapunov. Similarly, we can show that the angular motion of a simple pendulum about any trajectory (except the trivial one) is unstable in the sense of Lyapunov.♦♦

The two foregoing examples show that the ideas of Lyapunov stability and asymptotic stability are sometimes too stringent when applied to trajectories. This stringency can be relaxed when we introduce the notion of orbital stability in the next section. On the other hand, we can also show that for certain time-varying and/or nonlinear systems, the requirements of Lyapunov stability and asymptotic stability are not stringent enough.

♦♦Example 5-16. Consider the time-varying linear system $\dot{x} + (1/t)x = 0$, which is similar to a first-order Euler linear differential equation considered in Example 3-12. Elementary integration gives the solution

$$x(t) = \frac{t_0}{t} x(t_0)$$

It is seen that $x(t)$ for $t > t_0$ is always smaller than $x(t_0)$ and moreover $x(t) \to 0$ as $t \to \infty$; thus the origin of the system is asymptotically stable. However, when we consider the system rate of convergence, we will note that for ever larger values of t_0 the rate of convergence becomes ever smaller. (For example, if $t_0 = 1$, then in 9 seconds $x(t)$ will have to do down to 0.1 $x(t_0)$. However, if $t_0 = 1{,}000$, it will take 9,000 seconds to achieve the same end.) We see that practically speaking, asymptotic stability here is no more useful than mere stability.◆◆

By inspection we see that systems governed by an Euler linear differential equation will display the above behavior if the origin is asymptotically stable.

In addition to convergence rates that vary with t_0, sometimes a time-varing system, in response to a perturbation δx, can exhibit response peaks that grow indefinitely with t_0 and hence cannot be bounded by a single number that holds for all t_0. This means the number δ in the definition for Lyapunov stability must be a function of t_0.

◆◆Example 5-17. (Massera): Consider the time-varying linear system $\dot{x} = (6t \sin t - 2t)x$; on integrating, the general solution, for $t_0 > 0$ is

$$x(t) = x(t_0) \exp\left(6 \sin t - 6t \cos t - t^2 - 6 \sin t_0 + 6t_0 \cos t_0 + t_0^2\right)$$

Letting $T = t - t_0$, the ratio $x(t)/x(t_0)$ is bounded by $\exp[12 + T(6 - T)]$ for $T > 6$ and hence approaches 0 as $T \to \infty$. However, if t_0 is taken to be $2n\pi$, then $x_0 = x(2n\pi)$ and

$$\frac{x\big((2n + 1)\pi\big)}{x_0} = \exp[(4n + 1)(6 - \pi)\pi]$$

As $n \to \infty$, this ratio goes to ∞, implying that as the perturbation occurs ever later in time, the "peak overshoot" in the response to the perturbation will increase without bound.◆◆

From Examples 5-16 and 5-17, we see that for time-varying systems it is necessary to define new notions of stability such that the system convergence and other behaviors are independent of the time t_0 at which a perturbation is carried out. These notions are supplied by uniform stability and uniform asymptotic stability.

When we say that a perturbed trajectory is such that $\|\delta \mathrm{x}(t)\| \to 0$ uniformly in $\delta \mathrm{x}_0$, we mean that there is a finite bound (depending on $\|\delta \mathrm{x}_0\|$) in the convergence time for $\|\delta \mathrm{x}\|$ to become smaller or equal to any given value which applied for all possible $\delta \mathrm{x}_0$. Thus the convergence is only a function of the magnitude (or norm) of $\delta \mathrm{x}_0$ and not a function of the sense or direction of $\delta \mathrm{x}_0$ from the origin $\delta \mathrm{x} = 0$. A linear system that is asymptotically stable can be viewed in the following way: For every number μ, there *always* exists another number T, depending on μ, $\delta \mathrm{x}_0$, and t_0, such that all trajectories $\delta x(t)$ with δx_0 inside a sphere of radius $\delta_a(t_0)$ centered at the origin will at time $t_0 + T$, *and afterwards*, be μ units from the origin or closer. Here the convergence time T will in fact, not be dependent on the exact value of δx_0 but is dependent on the maximum magnitude of δx_0, namely δ_a; thus we can write it as $T(\mu, \delta_a(t_0), t_0)$. For the same value of μ, for linear systems, if $\delta_a' > \delta_a$, then $T(\mu, \delta_a', t_0) > T(\mu, \delta_a, t_0)$. The trajectory of a linear asymptotically stable system thus goes to the origin uniformly in x_0 (see Chap. 11). In the case of a nonlinear system, it is possible for a system to be asymptotically stable yet whose trajectory does not go to the origin uniformly in δx_0. There may, for example, be particular directions (or hyperplanes) such that $T(\mu, \delta x_0, t_0) \to \infty$ when the δx_0 taken approaches these preferred directions or hyperplanes (i.e., rate of convergence is a function of direction from the origin of δx_0 and, in particular, there are directions in which the rate of convergence approaches 0).* In these cases, the upper bound in T does not exist whatever the size of the neighborhood δ_a.

The expression $\|\delta x(t)\| \to 0$ uniformly in x_0 therefore means that the convergence is only a function of the norm of the initial state $\|x_0\|$. Thus the convergence time T, as defined above, is only a function of δ_a, which bounds $\|x_0\|$.

The expression $\|\delta x(t)\| \to 0$ uniformly in t_0 means that the convergence is not a function of the initial time. Thus we require that T be independent of t_0. Those systems whose convergence rate decreases to 0 as $t_0 \to \infty$, such as that of Example 5-16, then do not go to the origin uniformly in t_0.

With these preliminaries, we can now define the following terms:

◆◆Definition 5-7. A trajectory $x_1(u_1(t), t; x_0, t_0)$ is uniformly stable if it is stable (see Definition 5-4) in such a way that δ does not depend on t_0.◆◆

◆◆Definition 5-8. A trajectory $x_1(u_1(t), t; x_0, t_0)$ is equi-asymptotically stable if

1) it is stable, and
2) all perturbed motions with $\|\delta x_0\| < \delta_a$ are such that $\|\delta x\| \to 0$ uniformly in δx_0.◆◆

◆◆Definition 5-9. A trajectory $x_1(u_1(t), t; x_0, t_0)$ is uniformly asymptotically stable if

1) it is uniformly stable, and
2) all perturbed motions with $\|\delta x_0\| < \delta_a$ are such that $\|\delta x\| \to 0$ uniformly both in δx_0 and t_0. ◆◆

We may note that a linear time-invariant system which is asymptotically stable goes to the origin in a manner which can be bounded from above by a decaying exponential function (see Chap.

*For an example, see [K8].

11) and is therefore uniformly asymptotically stable.* However, note that the asymptotically stable, linear time invariant system is special in that if a $T(\mu)$ is found along any one direction in the δ_a neighborhood, it applies to all other directions as well. Further, if a $T(\mu)$ is found for a particular t_0, it applies for all other t_0. These are not necessary for a general uniformly asymptotically stable system.

Utilizing the concept of uniform asymptotic stability, we can make use of the following theorem which relates the stability of a particular trajectory of a nonlinear time-varying system to the stability of the local linearized system.

◆◆Theorem 5-2. [K8] Consider a time-varying nonlinear system of the form (5-39) which can be expanded in terms of the perturbation variables (about a particular trajectory $x_1(t)$ under a particular control $u_1(t)$) into the form

$$\delta\dot{\mathbf{x}} = \frac{\partial \mathbf{f}}{\partial \mathbf{x}}(\mathbf{x}_1, \mathbf{u}_1, t)\,\delta\mathbf{x} + \mathbf{h}(\delta\mathbf{x}, t)$$

where $\mathbf{h}(\delta\mathbf{x}, t)$ contains terms that are higher than the first degree. Assume $\|\mathbf{h}(\delta\mathbf{x}, t)\| / \|\delta\mathbf{x}\| \to 0$ *uniformly* in t as $\|\delta\mathbf{x}\| \to 0$, then uniform asymptotic stability of the origin for the linearized system $\delta\dot{\mathbf{x}} = [(\partial\mathbf{f}(\mathbf{x}, \mathbf{u}, t)/\partial\mathbf{x})]\,\delta\mathbf{x}$ implies that the trajectory $\mathbf{x}_1(t)$ is also uniformly asymptotically stable.**◆◆

A proof of this theorem will be given in Chap. 11.

The question now is how to establish uniform asymptotic stability for a time-varying linear system. We are not yet prepared to consider this question in its generality. A possible approach is to make use of Lyapunov's Second Method, which will be discussed in Chap. 9.

While Theorem 5-2 is quite general, it only states a sufficient condition. In some systems such as aircrafts or missiles, the Jacobian matrix $\partial\mathbf{f}(t)/\partial\mathbf{x}$ for the linearized approximate system varies smoothly and relatively slowly with time. Here the designers have been very successful in designing autopilots by "freezing time"; i.e., at each instant, consider the time-varying parameters as being fixed at the current value and treat the linearized system as time invariant. An autopilot is evolved after examining a series of such frozen-time regimes.

The above procedure is certainly not to be recommended for all systems, but it has been generally found that for many practical systems if

1) the coefficients of the linearized system vary slowly compared to the response time of the system, or if the coefficients vary monotonically, and

*Indeed all asymptotically stable time invariant systems are clearly uniformly asymptotically stable.

**Bellman has an interesting counterexample to show that mere asymptotic stability of the linearized system is not enough. See [B6] p. 87.

2) the system eigenvalues are not close to the imaginary axis,

the in-the-small stability behavior of the system can be closely approximated by its linearized, frozen-time model. However, be on guard if the elements of the Jacobian matrix in the linearized equation are periodic, or if the system eigenvalues are near the imaginary axis, as the following example shows.*

♦♦Example 5-18. The following example was attributed to Vinogradov of Russia [R3]. Consider the system $\dot{\mathbf{x}} = \mathbf{A}(t)\mathbf{x}$ with

$$\mathbf{A}(t) = \begin{bmatrix} -1 - 9\cos^2 6t + 12\sin 6t\cos 6t & 12\cos^2 6t + 9\sin 6t\cos 6t \\ -12\sin^2 6t + 9\sin 6t\cos 6t & -1 - 9\sin^2 6t - 12\sin 6t\cos 6t \end{bmatrix}$$

By solving for the determinant $|\mathbf{A} - \lambda\mathbf{I}|$, we find that the elements of $\mathbf{A}(t)$ have been so contrived that the eigenvalues are constant and have the values $\lambda = -1, -10$ for all t. One may thus blithely conclude that the system origin is asymptotically stable. However, the closed-form system solution is (as we may readily verify),

$$x_1 = a_1 e^{2t}(\cos 6t + 2\sin 6t) + a_2 e^{-13t}(\sin 6t - 2\cos 6t)$$

$$x_2 = a_1 e^{2t}(2\cos 6t - \sin 6t) + a_2 e^{-13t}(2\sin 6t + \cos 6t)$$

The presence of the e^{2t} term means that the system is actually unstable. ♦♦

It is sometimes convenient to display the exact equation of motion or the exact equation of propagation of the perturbation variable $\delta\mathbf{x}$. Using the variables as defined in (5-40), we write

$$\delta\dot{\mathbf{x}} = \dot{\mathbf{x}} - \dot{\mathbf{x}}_1 = \mathbf{f}(\delta\mathbf{x} + \mathbf{x}_1, \mathbf{u}_1, t) - \mathbf{f}(\mathbf{x}_1, \mathbf{u}_1, t) \tag{5-59}$$

Since $\mathbf{x}_1$ and $\mathbf{u}_1$ are assumed to be known, the rhs of (5-59) is a function of $\delta\mathbf{x}$ and t only. We can then write

$$\delta\dot{\mathbf{x}} = \mathbf{g}(\delta\mathbf{x}, t) \tag{5-60}$$

with

$$\mathbf{g}(\delta\mathbf{x}, t) = \mathbf{f}(\delta\mathbf{x} + \mathbf{x}_1, \mathbf{u}_1, t) - \mathbf{f}(\mathbf{x}_1, \mathbf{u}_1, t) \tag{5-61}$$

Equation (5-60) is the (exact) equation of the propagation of the perturbation $\delta\mathbf{x}$ with time. Note that from (5-61),

$$\mathbf{g}(0, t) = 0 \tag{5-62}$$

*See also Exercise 5-22.

so that $\delta x \equiv 0$ is an equilibrium state for the system (5-60) at all time.

The stability in the small about a trajectory is then seen to be reducible to the stability of the perturbation variable δx about the origin in accordance with equations (5-60) and (5-61). In particular, a trajectory is uniformly asymptotically stable if the origin of its corresponding equation of motion of perturbation is uniformly asymptotically stable.

◆◆Example 5-19. In the case of the satellite of Example 5-11, applying Eq. (5-61) to (5-54), we obtain

$$\delta\dot{\omega}_1 = -\frac{(I_3 - I_2)}{I_1}(\omega_{20}\,\delta\omega_3 + \omega_{30}\,\delta\omega_2 + \delta\omega_2\,\delta\omega_3)$$

$$\delta\dot{\omega}_2 = -\frac{(I_1 - I_3)}{I_2}(\omega_{10}\,\delta\omega_3 + \omega_{30}\,\delta\omega_1 + \delta\omega_1\,\delta\omega_3)$$

$$\delta\dot{\omega}_3 = -\frac{(I_2 - I_1)}{I_3}(\omega_{20}\,\delta\omega_1 + \omega_{10}\,\delta\omega_2 + \delta\omega_1\,\delta\omega_2)$$

where $\omega_{10}, \omega_{20}, \omega_{30}$ are the known solutions about which we are taking the perturbations in the ω's. The $u(t)$'s in (5-54) are assumed to be unperturbed.◆◆

5.7 Orbital Stability and the Stability of Equilibrium Zones

The definition of the stability of trajectories in the previous section is somewhat unsatisfactory especially when applied to closed trajectories in the state space, because of the stringent requirement that neighboring trajectories must have the same period in order to qualify as being stable.

A more useful notion is *orbital stability*, which is concerned only with stability relative to a closed trajectory as an entity in itself and is not concerned with any specific reference point traveling along the trajectory.

Let $\rho(x, \mathcal{C})$ be the *minimum* Euclidean distance from a point x to a closed curve $\mathcal{C}$, then we have:

◆◆Definition 5-10. A closed trajectory $\mathcal{C}$ of a system $\dot{x} = f(x, t)$ is orbitally stable if given any $\epsilon > 0$ there is a $\delta(\epsilon, t_0) > 0$ such that every solution of the system $x(t)$ with $\rho(x(t_0), \mathcal{C}) < \delta$ satisfies $\rho(x(t), \mathcal{C}) < \epsilon$ for all $t > t_0$.◆◆

In addition we have:

◆◆Definition 5-11. A closed trajectory $\mathcal{C}$ of a system $\dot{x} = f(x, t)$ is orbitally asymptotically stable if it is

1) orbitally stable, and
2) for all trajectories that are sufficiently close to $\mathcal{C}$, $\rho(x(t), \mathcal{C}) \to 0$ as $t \to \infty$.◆◆

The above ideas can also be extended to define the stability of an equilibrium zone. Note that a system trajectory starting either in an equilibrium zone or on a closed trajectory will remain in the zone or the trajectory for all t. Mathematically, the equilibrium zone and the closed trajectory constitute *invariant sets* which are defined as:

◆◆Definition 5-12. An invariant set $\mathfrak{M}$ of a system is the set of points with the property that if the state of the system at t_0, $x(t_0)$, is in $\mathfrak{M}$, then $x(t)$ remains in $\mathfrak{M}$ for $-\infty \leq t \leq \infty$.◆◆

Using the above notion, Zubov [Z4] succeeded in providing definitions for the stability of an invariant set as follows: Let $\mathfrak{M}$ be the invariant set whose stability we wish to establish, let $\rho(x, \mathfrak{M})$ be the *minimum* distance from a point x to the invariant set $\mathfrak{M}$, then:

◆◆Definition 5-13. An invariant set $\mathfrak{M}$ is a stable relative to a free system $\dot{x} = f(x, t)$ if for any given $\epsilon > 0$ a $\delta > 0$ can be found such that if $\rho(x(t_0), \mathfrak{M}) < \delta$ then $\rho(x(t), \mathfrak{M}) < \epsilon$ for all $t > t_0$.◆◆

◆◆Definition 5-14. An invariant set $\mathfrak{M}$ is asymptotically stable if:

1) it is stable, and
2) $\lim_{t \to \infty} \rho(x(t), \mathfrak{M}) = 0$ ◆◆

◆◆Example 5-20. By Definition 5-10, we now see that the satellite in Example 5-15 is orbitally stable. Similarly, a simple pendulum is orbitally stable. The closed trajectories of both of these systems, as we recall, were found to be unstable in the sense of Lyapunov.◆◆

It is possible to use linearization to infer orbital stability of a trajectory. Since to indicate the relevant results requires some additional concepts, these results will be deferred until Chap. 11.

We may note that the classical definition of a stable limit cycle as given in Chap. 4 concerns only orbital asymptotic stability. In the next section we list some useful results concerning the orbital asymptotic stability of limit cycles for second-order systems.

5.8 Theorems on Limit Cycles and Their Orbital Stability for Second-Order Systems

There are very few general theorems on the existence of limit cycles. The bulk of those extant apply only to second-order time-invariant systems and have been known for a long time. Of these, we will consider four important ones.

The first theorem to be stated is due to Poincaré, who observed that there is a certain fixed relationship between a limit cycle and the type of singularities that it encloses.

Let N denote the number of nodes, centers, and foci enclosed by a limit cycle, and let S denote the number of saddle points enclosed by a limit cycle; then we have:

◆◆Theorem 5-3. (Poincaré) For a second-order system, if a limit cycle exists, then $N - S = 1$.* ◆◆

The reader can convince himself of the truth of this theorem by making a number of sketches in the phase plane. For a more detailed proof he is referred to the book by Coddington and Levinson [C5].

The next theorem is due to Bendixson [B8] and is sometimes referred to as the first theorem of Bendixson. It gives a sufficient condition for the *nonexistence* of a limit cycle.

◆◆Theorem 5-4. (Bendixson) For the second-order system

$$\dot{x}_1 = f_1(x_1, x_2), \qquad \dot{x}_2 = f_2(x_1, x_2)$$

where f_1 and f_2 possess first partial derivatives with respect to x_1 and x_2, no limit cycle can exist in a region $\mathcal{R}$ of the phase plane in which $\partial f_1/\partial x_1 + \partial f_2/\partial x_2$ does not vanish and does not change sign.◆◆

Proof: Along any trajectory in the phase plane, the relation

$$\frac{dx_2}{dx_1} = \frac{f_2}{f_1} \tag{5-63}$$

will be observed, which can be written as

$$f_2\,dx_1 - f_1\,dx_2 = 0 \tag{5-64}$$

In particular (5-63) and (5-64) will be observed along an entire limit cycle.

Let us assume a limit cycle exists and let us consider a line integral of (5-64) over the closed curve of the assumed limit cycle:

$$\oint_{\mathcal{C}} (f_1\,dx_2 - f_2\,dx_1) = 0 \tag{5-65}$$

where $\mathcal{C}$ denotes the limit cycle.

We now recall from vector analysis Stokes' Theorem** which relates a line integral over a closed curve to an area integral over

*The numbers N and S can be defined relative to any closed curve in a phase plane and not simply in terms of a limit cycle. The difference $N - S$ is sometimes referred to as the index of Poincaré.

**This is also known as Gauss's Theorem.

the area bounded by the curve. It can be written as

$$\int_{\mathcal{C}} (f_1\, dx_2 - f_2\, dx_1) = \int_{\mathcal{R}}\!\int \left(\frac{\partial f_1}{\partial x_1} + \frac{\partial f_2}{\partial x_2}\right) dx_1\, dx_2 \qquad (5\text{-}66)$$

where the integration in the rhs is understood to be taken over an area bounded by the closed curve (the limit cycle).

By Eq. (5-65), the rhs of Eq. (5-66) must vanish, but this is impossible if the integrand $\partial f_1/\partial x_1 + \partial f_2/\partial x_2$ neither vanishes nor changes sign. This contradicts the original assumption that a limit cycle exists; thus the assumption is false, and the theorem is proved by contradiction.

Our third theorem is also due to Bendixson and is sometimes referred to as the second theorm of Bendixson:

◆◆Theorem 5-5. (Bendixson) If a trajectory of a second-order autonomous system remains inside a finite region $\mathcal{R}$ and does not approach an equilibrium state, then it must either be an orbitally asymptotically stable limit cycle itself or it must tend to an orbitally asymptotically stable limit cycle.◆◆

This theorem seems to be rather obvious, but its proof turns out to be quite involved and will be omitted.*

The foregoing theorems on limit cycles can in some cases be used to advantage for second-order systems. This we do through another example:

◆◆Example 5-21. For a vacuum tube oscillator shown in Fig. 5-6*a* the following relation holds

$$e_g = Mpi_L = Mp\frac{i_b}{LCp^2 + RCp + 1} \qquad (5\text{-}67)$$

where $p = d/dt$. Let

$$x_1 = \frac{e_g}{e_0}, \qquad i_b = \frac{\sqrt{LC}}{M}\, e_0 f(x_1) \qquad (5\text{-}68)$$

where e_0 is a constant and $f(x_1)$ is the nonlinear characteristic of Fig. 5-6*b*.** Then Eq. (5-67) becomes

$$x_1 = \frac{\omega_0 p f(x_1)}{p^2 + 2\omega_0\xi_0 p + \omega_0^2} \qquad (5\text{-}69)$$

* See [B8].

** Note that $f(0) \neq 0$.

where

$$\omega_0^2 = \frac{1}{LC}, \quad \xi_0 = \frac{R}{2}\sqrt{\frac{C}{L}} \tag{5-70}$$

Let it be desired to carry out the following:

1) Examine the existence and stability of the singular points.
2) Establish the condition on the gain K that is *necessary* for the existence of a limit cycle.
3) Find a necessary and sufficient condition on K for existence of a limit cycle.

The system in block diagram form is shown in Fig. 5–6*c*.

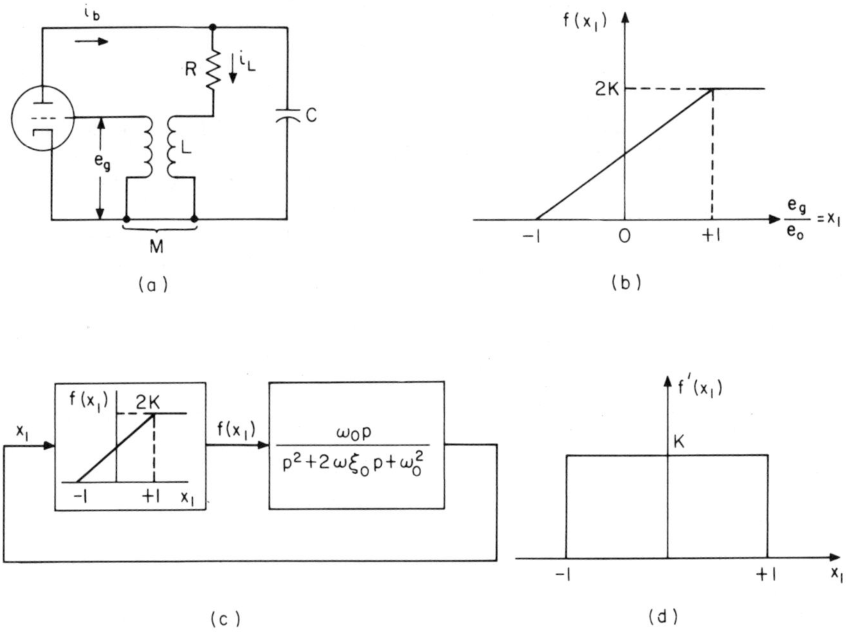

Fig. 5-6. a) A vacuum tube oscillator; b) The tube characteristics showing $f(x_1) = (Mi_b/\sqrt{LC})e_0$ plotted against $x_1 = e_g/e_0$; c) The block diagram of the oscillator of Fig. 5-6*a*; d) The function $f'(x_1) = df(x_1)/dx_1$ plotted against x_1.

Inspecting the system, one sees that first, due to the differentiator in the linear portion of the system, the "quiescent current" $f(0)$ will not give rise to a dc component in the output. Thus we expect the origin, $x_1 = \dot{x} = 0$, to be an equilibrium state. Because of the positive feedback, moreover, we expect it to be unstable.

The set of differential equations of the system follows from Eq. (5-69) and is

$$\dot{x}_1 = x_2, \quad \dot{x}_2 = -2\omega_0 \xi_0 x_2 - \omega_0^2 x_1 + \omega_0 \frac{d}{dt} f(x_1) \qquad (5\text{-}71)$$

Observe that

$$\frac{d}{dt} f(x_1) = \frac{df(x_1)}{dx_1} \dot{x}_1 = \frac{df(x_1)}{dx_1} x_2 = f'(x_1) x_2 \qquad (5\text{-}72)$$

where

$$f'(x_1) = \frac{df(x_1)}{dx_1} \qquad (5\text{-}73)$$

The characteristics of $f'(x_1)$ vs. x_1 are plotted in Fig. 5-6*d*. From Figs. 5-6*b* or 5-6*d* we have:

$$f'(x_1) = \begin{cases} 0, & |x_1| > 1 \\ K, & |x_1| \le 1 \end{cases} \qquad (5\text{-}74)$$

With Eqs. (5-72) and (5-73), Eq. (5-71) becomes

$$\dot{x}_1 = x_2, \quad \dot{x}_2 = -\left(2\xi_0 - f'(x_1)\right)\omega_0 x_2 - \omega_0^2 x_1 \qquad (5\text{-}75)$$

or

$$\dot{x}_1 = x_2, \quad \dot{x}_2 = -g(x_1)\omega_0 x_2 - \omega_0^2 x_1 \qquad (5\text{-}76)$$

where

$$g(x_1) = \begin{cases} 2\xi_0, & |x_1| > 1 \\ 2\xi_0 - K, & |x_1| \le 1 \end{cases} \qquad (5\text{-}77)$$

Setting $\dot{x}_1 = 0, \ \dot{x}_2 = 0$ in (5-76) yields

$$\begin{bmatrix} x_{1e} \\ x_{2e} \end{bmatrix} = \begin{bmatrix} 0 \\ 0 \end{bmatrix} \qquad (5\text{-}78)$$

as the only equilibrium state.

The system is linear for $|x_1| \leq 1$. Thus, we have the characteristic equation (for small signals about $x_e = 0$):

$$\begin{vmatrix} p & -1 \\ \omega_0^2 & p + (2\xi_0 - K)\omega_0 \end{vmatrix} = p^2 + \omega_0(2\xi_0 - K)p + \omega_0^2 = 0 \tag{5-79}$$

From Eq. (5-79) it follows that the equilibrium state 0 is

$$\begin{array}{ll} \text{asymptotically stable, if } K < 2\xi_0 \\ \text{unstable} \qquad\qquad\qquad\text{, if } K > 2\xi_0 \end{array} \tag{5-80}$$

Since the system is linear whenever $|x_1| \leq 1$, it is also clear that when $K = 2\xi_0$ the origin is stable in the sense of Lyapunov. Part 1 of the problem is thus answered.

Equation (5-76) may be written as

$$\dot{x}_1 = f_1(x_2), \quad \dot{x}_2 = f_2(x_1, x_2) \tag{5-81}$$

where

$$f_1(x_2) = x_2, \quad f_2(x_1, x_2) = -g(x_1)\omega_0 x_2 - \omega_0^2 x_1 \tag{5-82}$$

Using (5-77) and (5-82), we have,

$$\frac{\partial f_1}{\partial x_1} + \frac{\partial f_2}{\partial x_2} = -g(x_1)\omega_0 = \begin{cases} -2\xi_0\omega_0 & |x_1| > 1 \\ -(2\xi_0 - K)\omega_0 & |x_1| \leq 1 \end{cases} \tag{5-83}$$

Therefore, by Bendixson's First Theorem, we conclude that a necessary condition for the existence of a limit cycle is

$$K > 2\xi_0 \tag{5-84}$$

Part (2) of the problem is thus answered.

Note from conditions (5-80) and (5-84) that $K > 2\xi_0$ is not only necessary for the existence of a limit cycle but also necessary and sufficient for instability of the equilibrium state (here the origin). We will now show that this condition is also sufficient for existence of a limit cycle.

Note first that when $K > 2\xi_0$, the origin is either an unstable focus or an unstable node. Since the origin is the only equilibrium state, the Poincaré index is 1, and thus it is possible to have a limit cycle. Next note that, for $K > 2\xi_0$, since the origin is now an unstable equilibrium state, any trajectory starting near the origin will diverge from the origin. The trajectory may either go into a limit cycle or toward infinity. If the trajectory does not leave the finite region of the phase plane then it must go into a stable limit cycle by Bendixson's Second Theorem. It thus remains to be shown that for $K > 2\xi_0$ the trajectory cannot leave the finite region of the phase plane.

From Eqs. (5-76) and (5-77), we note that for $|x_1| > 1$, all motion is asymptotically stable with respect to the "virtual equilibrium state"* $(x_{1e}, x_{2e}) = (0,0)$. Thus, the trajectory will stay within the finite region of the phase plane. This, as we have explained above, means that any trajectory must asymptotically approach a stable limit cycle if $K > 2\xi_0$. Thus the condition $K > 2\xi_0$ is necessary and sufficient for the existence of a limit cycle.◆◆

A final theorem is attributed to Poincaré [C6].

◆◆Theorem 5-6. A closed path $\mathcal{C}$ of a second-order autonomous system $\dot{x}_1 = f_1(x_1, x_2)$, $\dot{x}_2 = f_2(x_1, x_2)$ is orbitally asymptotically stable if the line integral

$$\int_{\mathcal{C}} \left(\frac{\partial f_1}{\partial x_1} + \frac{\partial f_2}{\partial x_2} \right) dt$$

yields a negative number.◆◆

The proof of Theorem 5-6 requires the concept of the characteristic exponent and will be omitted.

5.9 Introduction to Stability in the Large–The Conjectures of Aizerman and Kalman

Thus far we have only been concerned with in-the-small stability properties. Such properties are relatively easy to analyze. However, the region of validity of the various types of in-the-small stability is generally not known without further analysis. In other words, the real extent of the δ neighborhood (or the δ_a neighborhood in the case of asymptotic stability) in the stability definitions is not specified *a priori*. Thus in some cases these neighborhoods may be too small to be of any use practically. On the other hand, in some other cases, they may be much larger than a designer had dared to hope, thus giving rise to systems that are too conservatively designed. (See Exercise 5-5.)

*A "virtual equilibrium state" is an equilibrium state that lies outside the region for which it is valid. For example, here the virtual equilibrium state for the region $|x_1| > 1$ is $(x_{1e}, x_{2e}) = (0,0)$ which lies outside the region $|x_1| > 1$. In this particular example, it happens that $(x_{1e}, x_{2e}) = (0,0)$ is also the equilibrium state for the region $|x_1| < 1$ in which it lies. However, in general, virtual equilibrium states are usually different from the equilibrium states of the system. See [K5].

The in-the-large stability properties are more suitable for engineering purposes since a region of convergence $\mathfrak{R}$ is defined in advance.

◆◆Definition 5-15. An equilibrium state x_e of a free system is asymptotically stable in the large with respect to a bounded region $\mathfrak{R}$ if:

1) x_e is stable, and
2) every trajectory of the system starting in $\mathfrak{R}$ tends to x_e as $t \to \infty$.◆◆

When the region $\mathfrak{R}$ is the entire state space, we have *global asymptotic stability*.*

◆◆Definition 5-16. An equilibrium state x_e of a free dynamic system is globally asymptotically stable if

1) x_e is stable, and
2) every trajectory of the system converges to x_e as $t \to \infty$.◆◆

It is clear that we can define, in the same vein, concepts such as "global equi-asymptotic stability," "uniform asymptotic stability in the large," "global orbital asymptotic stability." These straightforward extensions in the stability definitions will be omitted here (although the names will occasionally be invoked).

Unfortunately, there are thus far very few general results on asymptotic stability in the large and global asymptotic stability.** There is nothing corresponding to Lyapunov's First Method which can guide us.

One may suppose, however, that if sufficient restrictions were to be imposed on the system to be investigated, some general theorem could perhaps be formulated. In 1949, M. A. Aizerman of Russia considered the system of the form of Fig. 5-7. The system is linear except for a nonlinear gain element $f(e)$. The restriction on this nonlinear element is that the $f(e)$ vs. e curve always lies between two straight-line segments $k_1 e$, $k_2 e$, i.e.,

$$f(0) = 0, \quad 0 \leq k_1 \leq \frac{f(e)}{e} \leq k_2 \tag{5-85}$$

If $f(e)$ is replaced by a linear gain $u = ke$, then the resulting system is linear. Suppose that this linear feedback system is stable for every k such that $k_1 \leq k \leq k_2$. An interesting question then arises: Is it now possible to state that the original nonlinear

* The usage of the terms "asymptotic stability in the large" and "global asymptotic stability" have not been standardized. Some writers even consider them to be synonymous.

** Some special methods due to Lyapunov and Popov useful in investigating these modes of stability will be introduced in Chaps. 9 and 10.

system is globally asymptotically stable for all $f(e)$ obeying (5–85)?

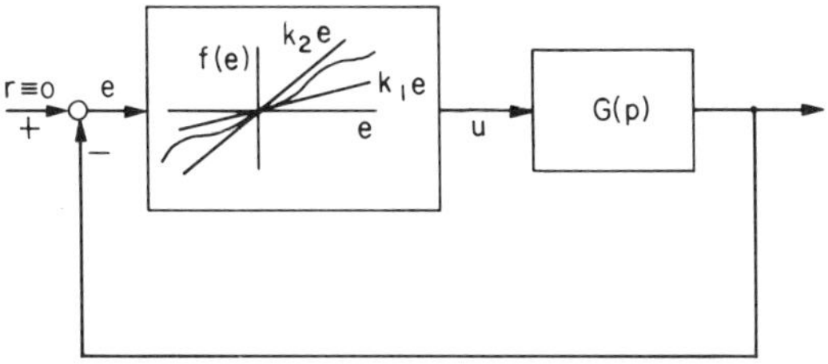

Fig. 5-7. A system in a form for the application of Aizerman's conjecture. The nonlinearity $f(e)$ satisfies the condition given by Eq. (5-85).

M. A. Aizerman conjectured in 1949 that the answer to the above question would be "yes."

Let us note that (5–85) and the fact that k_1 and k_2 represent the stability limits of a linear "comparison" system imply that the Aizerman system is stable in the small.* The conjecture then is an effort to extrapolate asymptotic stability in the small to global asymptotic stability for the special class of nonlinear systems which we call the Aizerman systems. To be specific, if the Aizerman conjectures were true, it is implied that for the class of systems under consideration, the stability question can be completely inferred from an examination of the overall slope $f(e)/e$ of the nonlinear gain.

But the Aizerman conjecture turns out to be false [P6], [D5], [F1], [W6].

A more stringent conjecture than Aizerman's is the Kalman conjecture [K5]. In the context of the system of Fig. 5–7, this conjecture can be stated as follows: Let the slope of the function $f(e)$ lie between two bounds k_1' and k_2', i.e.,

$$k_1' \le \frac{d}{de} f(e) \overset{\Delta}{=} f'(e) < k_2' \tag{5–86}$$

If the linear system with $f(e) = ke$ is stable for every k in $k_1' \le k \le k_2'$, then the nonlinear system is globally asymptotically stable for every $f(e)$ satisfying Eq. (5–86).

It is clear from Eqs. (5–85) and (5–86) that for the same $f(e)$, the bounds k_1, k_2, k_1' and k_2' must be related by $k_1' \le k_1 \le k_2 \le k_2'$. This means that, if the conditions for the Kalman conjecture are

*Except for critical cases where (5-85) should be written with strict inequality for at least one of the limits.

fulfilled, then the conditions for Aizerman's conjecture are automatically fulfilled. The converse, however, is not true.

Due to its conservative nature, one would expect Kalman's conjecture to hold in general. Recent results have shown, however, that the Kalman conjecture is also false. In particular, R. E. Fitts [F1] has considered a system of the form of Fig. 5-7, with

$$G(p) = \frac{p^2}{[(p + 0.5)^2 + 0.9^2]\,[(p + 0.5)^2 + 1.1^2]}, \qquad f(e) = e^3 \qquad \text{(5-87)*}$$

The linear system with $f(e) = ke$ will be stable for every k in $-0.7124 \leq k < \infty$. (Show this.) Thus, for $f(e) = e^3$, both the conditions for the Aizerman conjecture, (5-85), and for the Kalman conjecture, (5-86), are satisfied for every finite e. However, Fitts observed that an analog computer simulation of this system exhibited self oscillation.** Hence, Kalman's and Aizerman's conjectures do not hold. Willems [W6] showed an analytical procedure to disprove the conjectures.

We should note, however, that the two conjectures have been proved wrong only in systems that are in some sense extraordinary. In fact, for the linear feedback system with $G(p)$ given by (5-87) and $f(e) = ke$, we can show that the roots of the characteristic equation $1 + kG(\lambda) = 0$ will asymptotically approach the imaginary axis in the λ plane as $k \to \infty$. Intuitively, this would indicate that the stability becomes marginal for large values of k. For the nonlinear function $f(e) = e^3$ considered by Fitts, this will correspond to marginal stability for only large values of $|e|$. Indeed, Fitts' experimental results have confirmed this, as his system would oscillate only after initial excitation by a sufficiently large disturbance.

Heuristically speaking, it appears that the degree of justification of both the Aizerman and Kalman conjectures is related to the degree of stability*** of the linear feedback system with $f(e) = ke$ for the entire range of k corresponding to either (5-85) or (5-86).

From an engineering point of view, then, both Aizerman's conjecture and the more reliable though more restrictive Kalman conjecture can be excellent rules of thumb.

One further physical fact is worth noting. In almost all cases where Aizerman's and Kalman's conjectures fail to hold, the

* The function $G(p)$ in (5-87) represents a special case of two or more general classes of linear elements considered in Fitts' paper.

** Fitts also demonstrated the plausibility of self-oscillation by an approximate analysis using the dual-input describing function method (see Chap. 7). Dual-input describing function also forms the basis of the procedure by Willems.

*** The degree of stability of this linear system is measured by the smallest distance (to the left) from the imaginary axis of the roots of the characteristic equation $kG(\lambda) + 1 = 0$ for the entire range of k considered.

resultant mode of instability is always one of self-oscillation. Indeed in most physical systems, saturation ultimately limits the amplitudes of all signals and thus self-oscillation is generally the sole manifestation of instability.

Since at present there is no general way to determine global asymptotic stability in a system and since the most common mode of instability in practical systems is self-oscillation, it becomes meaningful to lower our sights and look into ways to establish whether a limit cycle can exist in a system. This topic will concern us for the next three chapters.

5.10 Summary

For nonlinear systems, because of the many possible modes of behavior, it is necessary to devote some care to the definition of stability for the systems.

For systems with isolated equilibrium states, it is most meaningful to define the stability of a system relative to each of the equilibrium states.

Lyapunov's concepts of stability (Definition 5-1) and asymptotic stability (Definition 5-2) concern the stability behavior of a system in a neighborhood of an equilibrium state. They are concerned with stability in the small. The exact region of stability is not given *a priori*.

For autonomous systems, stability in the small of an isolated equilibrium state can be determined through linearization about the state, provided that (1) linearization is possible, and (2) the linearized equation does not have one or more eigenvalues with zero real parts (with the remaining eigenvalues having negative real parts). Our ability to do this is guaranteed by Lyapunov's First Method (Theorem 5-1).

It is possible to linearize about a particular trajectory of a system. In general this procedure results in a time-varying linear equation.

When the system equation is time-varying, the stability concepts must be further refined. This is because it is possible for a system's convergence time to change with the time of application of the initial condition in such a way that it ultimately becomes unbounded (Example 5-15). Similarly, it is possible for a system's initial condition response to exhibit peaks that become ultimately unbounded (Example 5-16). By imposing the requirement of uniform asymptotic stability (Definition 5-9), both of the above eventualities are precluded.

In order to infer uniform asymptotic stability of a system trajectory, it is necessary that the linearized equation about the trajectory also be uniformly asymptotically stable (Theorem 5-2).

Relative to a trajectory, particularly a closed trajectory, the Lyapunov concepts of asymptotic stability are sometimes too stringent. No limit cycle, for example, can be asymptotically stable. For this, the concept of orbital asymptotic stability (Definition 5-10) is more useful. This concept can be extended to apply to other trajectories or to an equilibrium zone (Definition 5-14).

In Sec. 5.8 some theorems concerning the existence and the orbital asymptotic stability of limit cycles in second-order time-invariant systems are given.

The chapter ends with a glimpse into the problems associated with determining the asymptotic stability in the large and global asymptotic stability in systems. The definitions of these two types of stability are given by Definitions 5-15 and 5-16. Conjectures by Aizerman and Kalman have been advanced. These conjectures seek to relate global asymptotic stability of a certain class of nonlinear control systems with the stability of a linear system. These conjectures have been proven wrong in general; however, as they usually only fail in extraordinary situations, they can sometimes provide useful rules of thumb for an engineer.

One of the most common modes of instability in nonlinear systems is self-oscillation, which will be discussed in the next three chapters.

5.11 Exercises

5-1 The system $\dot{y} = y^2 - u$, $y(0) = 0$ has a particular solution $y_1(t) = (1-e^{2t})/(1+e^{2t})$ for $u = +1$.

a) Find the linearized equation of the system about this solution.
b) If $u = 0$, can local linearization about the equilibrium state $y = 0$ yield stability information in the small?
c) The system $\dot{y} = y^2$ does not obey a global Lipschitz condition. Show that for this system it is possible for $y(t)$ to go infinity as t approaches some finite time t_0. This behavior is called "finite escape time" and occurs only for nonlinear systems.

5-2 Consider the system of Fig. 5-8.

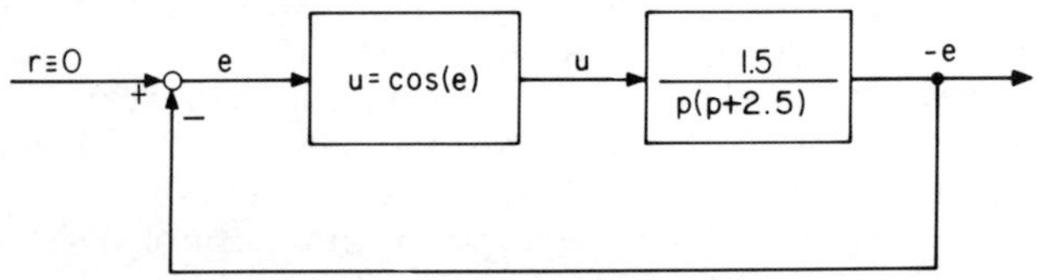

Fig. 5-8. The system of Exercise 5-2.

a) Write the equations in terms of e and $\dot{e}$.
b) Find all equilibrium states of the system and determine their stability.

5-3 Consider the system of Fig. 5-9.

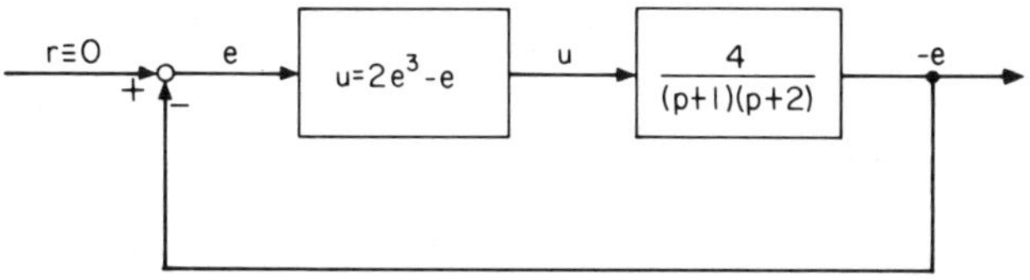

Fig. 5-9. The system of Exercise 5-3.

a) Write the state equations in terms of e and $\dot{e}$.
b) Find all the equilibrium states of the system and determine their stability.

5-4 The radial motion of a vehicle about a power law attractive central force field is given by

$$\left(\ddot{r} - \frac{L^2}{m^2 r^3}\right) = -\frac{k}{r^n}$$

where r is the radius of the vehicle from the force center, m is the mass of the vehicle, and L is its angular momentum. m, k, L, and n are constants with n a positive integer.

a) Find the condition on r such that the vehicle describes a circular orbit.
b) Show that $n < 3$ is a necessary condition for the circular orbit not to be orbitally unstable.

5-5 (Malkin) This exercise is designed to show that the desirability of asymptotic stability should not be taken as an edict. In some cases, the region of stability is too small for practical interest. On the other hand, a system may have an unstable equilibrium state but yet in a larger sense be stable.

a) Show by physical reasoning that the origin of the system given by $\dot{x} = -0.01x + x^3$ is asymptotically stable. Show also that whenever $|x_0| > 0.1$, the system solution increases without bound.
b) Show that the origin of the system $\dot{x} = 0.01x - x^3$ is unstable. Show also that whatever the value of x_0, the system solution converges to the values of $+0.1$ or -0.1. Plot typical trajectories of the system on the x vs. t plane.

5-6 A cannon fires a unit mass projectile with velocity V_0 at an elevation angle θ into resistanceless air over a flat earth. A gravitation acceleration of g units acts on the projectile throughout the flight.

a) Find the transition matrix for the problem
b) Find the sensitivity coefficient for the change in range per unit change in the elevation angle θ.
c) Find the sensitivity coefficient for the change in range per unit change in the gravitational acceleration g.

5-7 Over the time interval $0 < t_0 \leq t$, is the origin of the system $\dot{x} + [1 + (1/t)]x = 0$

a) stable?
b) asymptotically stable?
c) equi-asymptotically stable?
d) uniformly stable?

Explain. What happens when $t_0 < 0$?

5-8 Over the time interval $0 < t_0 \leq t$, is the origin of the system $\dot{x} + x/(1 + t) = 0$

a) stable?
b) asymptotically stable?
c) equi-asymptotically stable?
d) uniformly asymptotically stable?

Explain.

5-9 For the satellite of Example 5-11, if $I_1 > I_2 > I_3$

a) find the equilibrium state(s) of the system if $\mathbf{u} \equiv \mathbf{0}$, and
b) investigate the stability of the equilibrium state(s).

5-10 Show that the system

$$\dot{x}_1 = \frac{3x_1\sqrt{x_1^2 + x_2^2} - (x_1 + x_2)\left(x_1^2 + x_2^2\right) + x_1^2}{x_1^2 + x_2^2}$$

$$\dot{x}_2 = \frac{3x_2\sqrt{x_1^2 + x_2^2} + (x_1 - x_2)\left(x_1^2 + x_2^2\right) + x_1x_2}{x_1^2 + x_2^2}$$

has at least one limit cycle in $1 < x_1^2 + x_2^2 < 5$.

5-11 Using the Poincaré index (see Theorem 5-3), determine whether each of the following systems has limit cycles.

a) $\dot{x} = 2x^2 - y^2, \quad \dot{y} = 1 - x^2 + y^2$
b) $\dot{x} = x(1 + x) + 4y, \quad \dot{y} = x\left(1 + \dfrac{x}{4}\right) + y$

5-12 For the system $\dot{x} = x^3 + xy^2 - x, \; \dot{y} = x^2y + y^3 - y$

a) Find the equilibrium states.
b) Show that the system has no closed trajectories.
c) Show that the system is unstable outside the unit circle $x^2 + y^2 = 1$.

5-13 This problem and the next are designed to show that an asymptotically stable linear time-invariant differential system is also globally uniformly asymptotically stable. Moreover, the initial condition response of such a system can always be bounded by a decaying exponential.

Prove the following theorem:

◆◆Theorem 5-7. Let all eigenvalues $\lambda_i (i = 1, \ldots, n)$ of a constant system matrix $\mathbf{A}$ lie in $\Re e\ \lambda_i < \alpha$, then each element $\phi_{ij}(t, 0)$ of the transition matrix $\mathbf{\Phi}(t, 0) = \mathcal{L}^{-1}[(s\mathbf{I} - \mathbf{A})^{-1}]$ will be bounded as $|\phi_{ij}(t, 0)| \le K_{ij}e^{-\alpha t}$. Also, the time derivative of the element will be bounded as $|\dot{\phi}_{ij}(t,0)| \le K'_{ij}e^{-\alpha t}$.◆◆

5-14 Let the norm of a matrix $\mathbf{A}$ be defined as

$$||\mathbf{A}|| \triangleq \left(\sum_{i=1}^{n} \sum_{j=1}^{n} \left(a_{ij}\right)^2\right)^{1/2}$$

prove the following theorem:

◆◆Theorem 5-8. Let all eigenvalues $\lambda_i, (i = 1, \ldots, n)$ of a constant system matrix $\mathbf{A}$ lie in $\Re e\ \lambda_i < \alpha$, then there exists positive numbers M and M' such that

$$||\mathbf{\Phi}(t, 0)|| \le Me^{-\alpha t}, \qquad ||\dot{\mathbf{\Phi}}(t, 0)|| \le M'e^{-\alpha t}$$ ◆◆

(Hint: Use Theorem 5-7 as given in Exercise 5-13.)

5-15 (Volterra's Equations) Consider the equations

$$\dot{x}_1 = -k_1x_1x_2 - k_3x_1, \qquad \dot{x}_2 = -k_2x_1x_2 - k_4x_2$$

where k_1, k_2, k_3, and k_4 are all possible constants.

a) Find the equilibrium states and determine their stability.
b) Note that these equations include the Lancaster equations (Exercise 4-16) as a special case. They can also be given a battle or competitive interpretation. Find a general condition on $x(t_0)$ as a function on the k's such that $x_1 \to 0$ as $t \to \infty$ or $x_2 \to 0$ or $t \to \infty$.

5-16 A phase-locked loop for communications application is given by $\ddot{x} + (a + b \cos x)\dot{x} + c \sin x = 0$. Assume that $a > b > 0$ and $c > 0$; is the origin of the system stable in the small? Using phase-plane construction, find the region in state space for which the origin is asymptotically stable.

5-17 Complete Fig. 5-4 in the vicinity of the other two equilibrium states $e = 4/3$, $\dot{e} = 0$ and $e = -4/3$, $\dot{e} = 0$.

5-18 Find an exact solution to the problem of Example 5-12 and compare with the linearized solution given in the example.

5-19 A single lane traffic situation can be described by the following equation:

$$\frac{dy(t)}{dt} = V - A \exp\left(\frac{-\alpha}{y(t - T)}\right)$$

where y is the relative distance between two cars, V is the (constant) velocity of the lead car, and A, T and α are real positive constants.

a) What kind of information in terms of initial conditions is needed in order to uniquely define the solution $y(t)$ for all $t \geq 0$? Explain.
b) Obtain the equilibrium value Y. Also, obtain the ranges for V/A in $0 \leq V/A \leq \infty$ for which a positive equilibrium value $Y > 0$ can exist.
c) Show that an equilibrium Y is asymptotically stable if and only if

$$\frac{\alpha TV}{Y^2} < \frac{\pi}{2}$$

5-20 Consider the linear time-invariant system given by

$$\begin{bmatrix} \dot{x}_1 \\ \dot{x}_2 \\ \dot{x}_3 \end{bmatrix} = \begin{bmatrix} -3 & 0 & 0 \\ -1 & -1 & 0 \\ -1 & 0 & 1 \end{bmatrix} \begin{bmatrix} x_1 \\ x_2 \\ x_3 \end{bmatrix} + \begin{bmatrix} 4 \\ 1 \\ 1 \end{bmatrix} u, \qquad y = x_3 - x_2$$

a) Is the system controllable? Is the output observable?

b) Discuss the stability of the origin 0 when $u = 0$.
c) Discuss the stability of the origin 0 when a feedback $u = ky$ is applied.

5-21 Show that the origin of any linear time-invariant system whose transfer function $G(s)$ has a pole-zero cancellation in the right-half plane cannot be made stable by linear feedback around the plant.

5-22 (Baker and Bergen) Consider the single-loop time-varying control system $\ddot{y}(t) + 2\dot{y}(t) + y(t) = -k(t)y(t)$

a) Sketch the block diagram for the system
b) Show that the system is stable if $k(t) \equiv 100$ or $k(t) \equiv 0$
c) Show that if

$$k(t) = \begin{cases} 100, & i \leq t \leq i + \tau \quad (i = 1,2,\ldots) \\ 0, & \text{elsewhere} \end{cases}$$

then $y(t)$ will become unbounded for $\tau = 0.17$ if the initial conditions were $y(0) = 0$, $\dot{y}(0) = 1$.

Comment on the significance of this exercise.

5.12 References

The original reference of Lyapunov's definition of stability and Lyapunov's first method can be found in [L18].

The other results of this chapter are well scattered in the literature. Many topics are also considered in works treating the second method of Lyapunov, which will be discussed in Chap. 9. One of the best tutorial works in this direction is [K8], which includes excellent discussions on the various definitions of stability and the result of linearization of time-varying nonlinear systems.

An illuminating work on the mathematical aspect of stability is [C6].

6

Equivalent Linearization and the Describing Function

We propose now to look at the subject of stability analysis from a more pragmatic point of view. The important point to raise here is that the engineer is frequently compelled to tread where there is little or no theoretical foundation. Indeed, the demands of science and engineering seldom wait for the definitive pronouncements from the theoretician. The engineer must exercise judgment in such cases.

Chapter 5 has shown that a practical approach is the analysis of the local stability of isolated equilibrium states of an autonomous system. When the system is time varying, the theoretical basis immediately becomes incomplete.

But a much more important question is stability in the large. In practical systems, because of saturation, this frequently reduces to the question: Can the system go into an uncontrolled oscillation? This means a system must be examined to determine whether a stable limit cycle exists for large signals. If it does, the system is unstable in the large. Often then, the engineer can bypass the difficult problem of determining stability in the large by discovering whether the system can go into a limit cycle.

Unfortunately, exact methods even for establishing the existence of limit cycles are rare, and where they do exist, the methods are difficult to apply; thus quite frequently approximate methods are used. Those methods that have proved to be the most successful are quite naturally those which have been salted with engineering wisdom.

A common characteristic of approximate methods is that there are no clear-cut conditions that guarantee that the methods will work. Indeed, occasionally counterexamples can be found which show that the methods fail. The test for a good approximate method, of course, is that the conditions under which the method fail are pathological or unlikely to occur in practice.

In this chapter, we investigate the sinusoidal describing function method, which is probably the most versatile approximate method at the disposal of the control engineer. The method is most useful in finding conditions under which a system can go into self-oscillation. It can also be applied to the investigation of forced oscillations, and in particular, it can be used to establish the condition for the existence of jump-type phenomenon.

In presenting the method, we make use of an approach which will be invoked again on many occasions in future chapters. The approach consists in assuming, at a certain point in the closed-loop system, a solution of a particular form. By tracing the effect of this solution around the loop, we can establish the conditions that must be satisfied to sustain this solution.

In certain favorable cases, the *exact* conditions for the existence of the assumed solution can be established in terms of the system parameters. More often than not, however, the exact solution turns out to be difficult to find, and approximations must be made. The specific approximation involved in the describing function method or, more generally, the equivalent linearization method is to cast the nonlinear element into one with certain linear manifestations.

It is important to appreciate the *spirit* of the method of equivalent linearization since it possesses much practical potentiality which has not been fully explored. In our presentation, we depart somewhat from the standard approach and hope to shed new light on the subject.

In Secs. 6.6 and 6.7 we present the concept of amplitude-dependent gain margin, which is useful in prescribing the stability margin of large-scaled systems. Under this concept, nonlinear shaping and compensation of large-scaled systems can be readily applied. It is further shown that the data for the amplitude-dependent gain margin can be obtained by means of an oscillating test. This test, simple to apply, represents an interesting extension of the idea inherent in the equivalent linearization method. It is an approach which the authors have employed with success in practical applications.

In the final section some comments are made on cases where the describing function approach fails. It is seen that in most of these cases the usual assumptions needed to render the describing function approach plausible are generally violated.

6.1 An Example

To savor the spirit of equivalent linearization, we shall begin with an example.

◆◆Example 6-1. Consider a system that obeys Van der Pol's equation

$$\ddot{x} + \mu(x^2 - 1)\dot{x} + x = 0 \tag{6-1}$$

Let us attempt to determine the possible existence of a limit cycle in the system. If one does exist, we will attempt to determine its approximate period and amplitude of oscillation. The system state equation, using $x_1 = x$, $x_2 = \dot{x}$, is:

$$\dot{x}_1 = x_2, \quad \dot{x}_2 = -\mu\left(x_1^{\,2} - 1\right)x_2 - x_1 \tag{6-2}$$

To begin, it is well to inspect Eq. (6-1) or (6-2). In (6-1), consider the term $\mu(x^2 - 1)\dot{x}$ which provides the damping. For $\mu > 0$, in the region $x^2 \ll 1$, $\dot{x} \neq 0$, it is seen that the damping term has a negative sign. This implies an unstable second-order system. Since it is clear that the origin $x = 0$, $\dot{x} = 0$ is the only equilibrium state, in this case, we would expect the origin to be unstable in the small. On the other hand for $x^2 \gg 1$, $\dot{x} \neq 0$, the damping term is large and positive if $\mu > 0$, and the system is strongly stable. Thus if we go sufficiently far from the origin, the system will behave very much as if the origin were stable. This is the type of situation that strongly indicates the possible existence of a stable limit cycle for $\mu > 0$. (By the same reasoning, it is clear that for $\mu < 0$, the origin will be stable in the small and unstable in the large, thus indicating the existence of an unstable limit cycle.)

We can also make a rough estimation of the "size" of the limit cycle. From Eq. (6-2) we can see that it probably occurs in the vicinity of $x_1^{\,2} = 1$. Indeed if we picture the limit cycle as resulting from a tug-of-war between a stable and unstable region of phase plane we expect $x_1^{\,2}$ to oscillate above and below the value of 1.

Having made the above quick estimates we can apply more detailed analysis. From Eq. (6-2) we see that the only singular point is the origin of the system $x_e = 0$.

Letting $x_1 - x_{1e} = \delta x_1$ and $x_2 - x_{2e} = \delta x_2$, we obtain the local linearized equations:

$$\begin{bmatrix} \delta\dot{x}_1 \\ \delta\dot{x}_2 \end{bmatrix} = \begin{bmatrix} 0 & 1 \\ -1 & \mu \end{bmatrix} \begin{bmatrix} \delta x_1 \\ \delta x_2 \end{bmatrix} \tag{6-3}$$

The characteristic equation is immediately found to be

$$\lambda^2 - \mu\lambda + 1 = 0 \tag{6-4}$$

and thus the characteristic roots are

$$\lambda = \frac{\mu}{2} \pm \sqrt{\frac{\mu^2}{4} - 1} \tag{6-5}$$

Thus the system is unstable in the small if $\mu > 0$. In particular for $\mu^2/4 < 1$, the origin is an unstable focus; and for $\mu^2/4 \geq 1$, the origin is an unstable node.

We may ask where the trajectories go. In the case of a general system there are three possibilities as to where a trajectory emerging from an unstable equilibrium state can go. First, it can go to another equilibrium state; second, it can go to infinity; and third, it can tend to a limit cycle. Since our system possesses only one equilibrium state, the first possibility cannot occur. Of the second and third possibilities, we strongly suspect the occurrence of the latter on the strength of our quick calculation. To see whether we are correct, we can make use of an approximation method. To do this consider the block diagram of the system (6-1) shown in Fig. 6-1, where the dotted box contains all the nonlinearities of the system. The remaining portion of the system is seen to be a linear block. The linear block is unstable, although in terms of frequency response, it possesses low-pass characteristics.

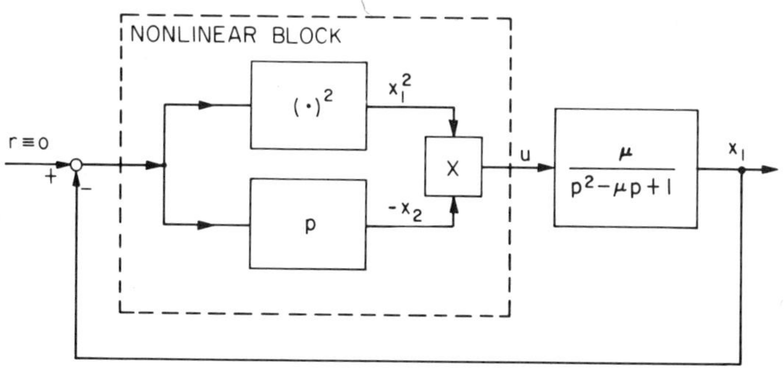

Fig. 6-1. A block diagram of a system obeying Van der Pol's equation (Eq. (6-2)).

Let us assume that x_1 is a sinusoidal oscillation. In going through the nonlinear block, there will be harmonics generated. However, if such harmonics are sufficiently attenuated through the linear part, then only the fundamental component will be left. If the resulting amplitude of the fundamental in returning matches that of the assumed amplitude of oscillation for x_1, then there will be a distinct possibility for self-oscillation.

Consider the nonlinear block of Fig. 6-1 with input $-x_1$. Let its output be denoted by u. Let us assume that x_1 is of the form

$$x_1 = \hat{x}_1 \sin \omega t = x_{1p}(t) \tag{6-6}$$*

Then

$$\dot{x}_1 = \hat{x}_1 \omega \cos \omega t = x_2$$

and

$$\begin{aligned} u &= -x_1{}^2 \dot{x}_1 = -\hat{x}_1{}^2 (\sin^2 \omega t)(\hat{x}_1 \omega \cos \omega t) \\ &= -\hat{x}_1{}^3 \omega \left(\frac{1}{2} - \frac{1}{2}\cos 2\omega t\right) \cos \omega t = -\frac{\hat{x}_1{}^3 \omega}{4}(\cos \omega t - \cos 3\omega t) \end{aligned} \tag{6-7}$$

which is the output. We see that the output possesses a third harmonic term.

Assuming now that the 3ω term is sufficiently attenuated by the linear element, we have the approximate relation

$$u \simeq -\frac{x_1{}^3}{4} \omega \cos \omega t = -\frac{\hat{x}_1{}^2}{4} \frac{d}{dt} (\hat{x}_1 \sin \omega t) = -\frac{\hat{x}_1{}^2}{4} p x_1 \tag{6-8}$$

Thus under the assumption that the third harmonic component can be neglected, the nonlinear block may now be approximated by an equivalent block given by Eq. (6-8). It may be viewed as a differentiator with a gain that is proportional to $\hat{x}_1{}^2$.

With the understanding that $\hat{x}_1$ is an unknown to be ultimately solved for, the original nonlinear system can now be viewed as an equivalent linear one boasting a gain that depends on the amplitude $\hat{x}_1$. Our object then is to investigate under what condition this equivalent linear system can sustain an oscillation of the form $\hat{x}_1 \sin \omega t$ at the point x_1.

The open-loop transfer function for the equivalent linear system is

$$\frac{\mu \hat{x}_1{}^2 p/4}{p^2 - \mu p + 1} \tag{6-9}$$

The characteristic equation for the closed-loop system is then

$$\frac{1}{4} \mu \hat{x}_1{}^2 \lambda + \lambda^2 - \mu \lambda + 1 = 0 \tag{6-10}$$

Solving for λ gives

$$\lambda = -\frac{1}{2}\left(\frac{1}{4}\hat{x}_1{}^2 - 1\right)\mu \pm \sqrt{\frac{1}{4}\mu^2 \left(\frac{1}{4}\hat{x}_1{}^2 - 1\right)^2 - 1} \tag{6-11}$$

*We use $\hat{x}$ to denote the amplitude of a sinusoidal signal $x(t)$. We use the subscript p to designate a periodic wave where this need arises.

The eigenvalue must be imaginary for $x = \hat{x}_1 \sin \omega t$ to be regenerated around the loop. This occurs when $\frac{1}{4}\hat{x}_1^2 = 1$ or $\hat{x}_1 = 2$. For $\hat{x}_1 = 2$ we have $\lambda = \pm\sqrt{-1} = \pm j$; thus $\omega = 1$. We have therefore established that there exist an oscillation of amplitude 2 and frequency 1 sec^{-1}.

The intriguing aspect of our approximate approach is that it yields results in $\hat{x}$ and ω neither of which depends on μ. At first sight, this seems crude; however, Figs. 6-2 and 6-3 show the results of an analog simulation of the limit cycle of Van der Pol's equation for four values of μ ($\mu = 0, 1, 2, 8$) along with the associated plots of $x_1(t)$ and $u(t)$. For each case we see that the approximation over a reasonable range of μ is remarkably good. We can explain this to some extent by attempting to assess the error incurred in making the sinusoidal approximation Eq. (6-6).

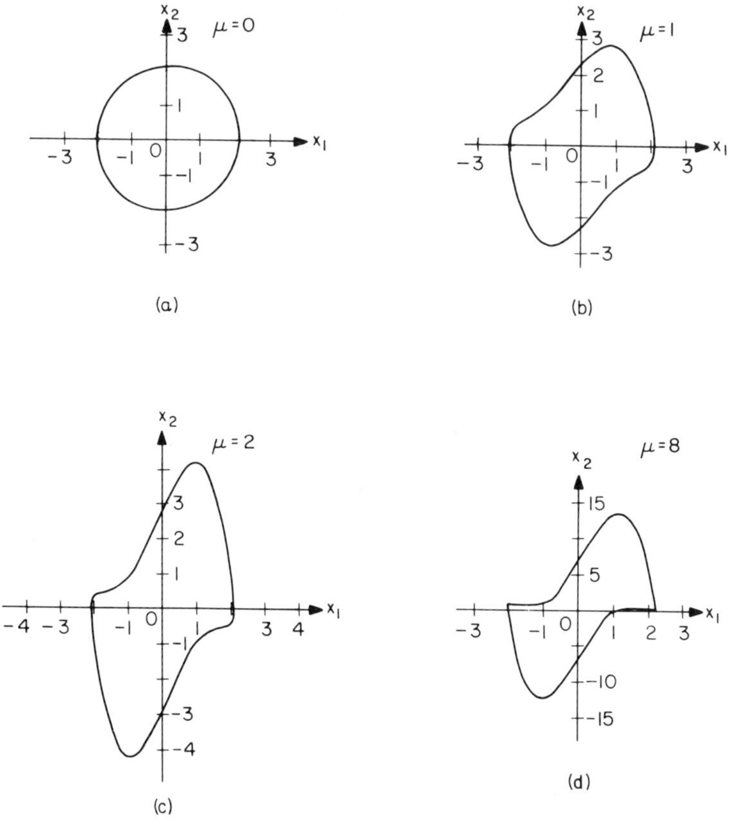

Fig. 6-2. The limit cycle of Van der Pol's equation (Eq. (6-12)) for four values of μ.

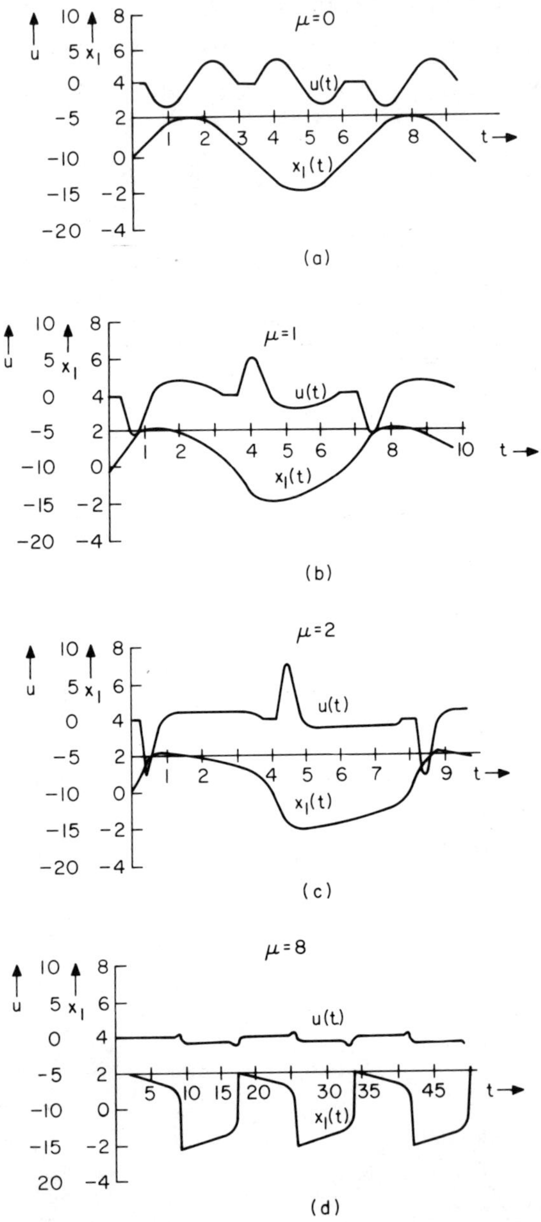

Fig. 6-3. $x_1(t)$ and $u(t)$ of the system of Fig. 6-1 for four values of μ.

From Eq. (6-7) it is seen that a third harmonic of the same amplitude as the fundamental is produced. In passing through the linear block with the transfer function $\mu/(p^2 - \mu p + 1)$ of Fig. 6-1 it is seen that the fundamental component is unchanged whereas the third harmonic is attenuated by a factor $\mu/\sqrt{64 + (3\mu)^2}$. For $\mu = 1$ then, the third harmonic is attenuated by more than 18 dB whereas the fundamental is unattenuated. Thus on returning to the input of the nonlinear block of Fig. 6-1, the amplitude of the third harmonic is almost an order of magnitude less than that of the fundamental. For $\mu < 1$ we expect the approximation to be even better; whereas, for $\mu \gg 1$ we expect the approximation to be poorer. These are corroborated by the experimental evidences cited.

Due to the fact that the third harmonic is present, we should expect that the waveform at the point x_1 will not necessarily be sinusoidal. Again by our previous reasoning, we expect that as $\mu \to 0$ the waveform should approach a sinusoid and as $\mu \to \infty$ the waveform should depart drastically from a sinusoid. This is again borne out by Figs. 6-2 and 6-3.

A final question that we can ask now is: Is this approximate limit cycle orbitally asymptotically stable? This question can be settled by examining Eq. (6-11). Let us suppose that $\hat{x}_1$ is increased to a value higher than 2, then Eq. (6-11) tells us that λ now has a negative real part. This renders the closed-loop system stable and the amplitude of oscillation $\hat{x}_1$ will then exponentially decrease. On the other hand if $\hat{x}_1$ is decreased to a value slightly less than two, Eq. (6-11) indicates that the system will become unstable and hence α will be increased. Thus judging from our approximated solution, the limit cycle is orbitally asymptotically stable.

The aforementioned procedure of determining the stability of a limit cycle is tantamount to an analysis using a root-locus of the system plotted as a function of $\hat{x}_1$. Since a self-oscillation of the form $x_1 = \hat{x}_1 \sin \omega t$ is assumed, clearly only the portion of the root loci near the points at which they cross the imaginary axis will be of any significance. The root locus of the linearized system

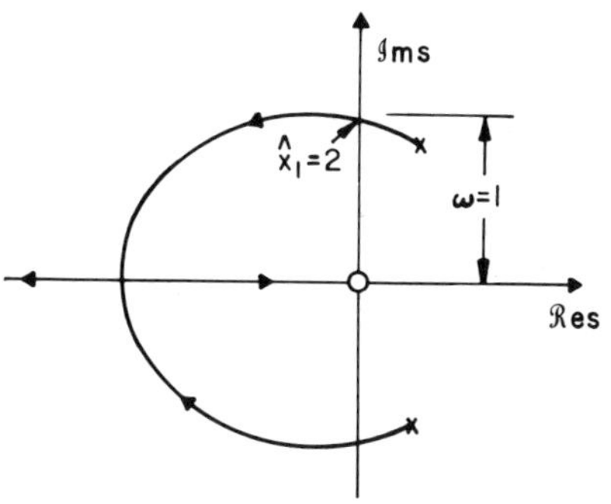

Fig. 6-4. The root locus plot of the linearized version of Van der Pol's equation.

as a function of $\hat{x}_1$ is shown in Fig. 6-4. By exactly the same argument as that in the previous paragraph the stability of the limit cycle can be ascertained.♦♦

Indeed, upon carrying out the equivalent linearization procedure, other linear techniques such as the Nyquist diagram or the Bode plot can also be readily used. This we shall make clearer in the next section.

6.2 The Method of Equivalent Gains

Example 6-1 exposed us to the method of equivalent linearization. The idea of equivalent linearization has its classical origin. Magnus [M1] for example, has shown that it is directly related to many classical approaches to nonlinear analysis, among them are the method of Ritz and Galerkin, the method of variation of parameters, the method of perturbation, and the method of harmonic balance.* It is further interesting to observe that equivalent linearization or the sinusoidal describing function method was first applied to control system analysis independently in the period from 1947 to 1950, by at least five different investigators in five different countries.**

In this section we are ready to examine the basic tenet of the idea of sinusoidal equivalent linearization or describing function from the point of view of balancing of the first harmonics. In a later section we will try to look at it from another point of view, namely that of minimization of the mean-squared error.

Consider the autonomous system S of Fig. 6-5, where it is assumed that all the system nonlinearies can be grouped into a block labeled $\mathfrak{N}$. The remaining portion of the system is then, by assumption, linear as well as *time invariant*.***

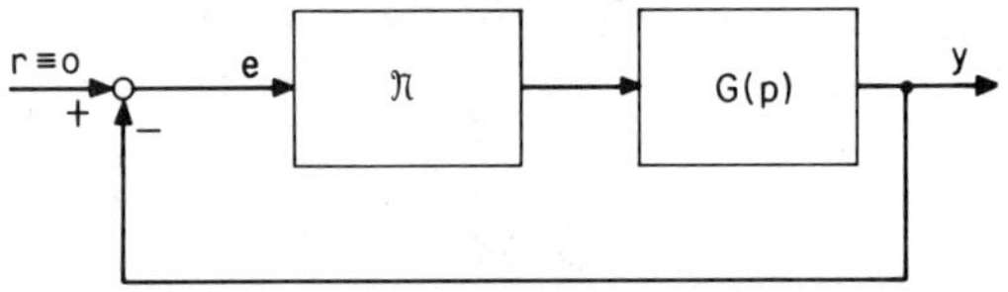

Fig. 6-5. An autonomous system S.

*For careful discussions of some of these methods and their uses, see, e.g., [C7] and [M13].

**See [K18], [D12], [G6], [T7], and [O3].

***Since we will have frequent occasions to use systems of the configuration of Fig. 6-5, this configuration will be referred to as the *standard form* in the sequel. It is important to recognize that while the configuration of Fig. 6-5 is single-loop in form, any single-output multiple loop system whose components are all linear and time-invariant, except for an isolated nonlinear block, can usually be manipulated into the single-loop form of Fig. 6-5.

From the example of the previous section, we see that the approach hinges on the following steps: (1) a pure sinusoidal oscillation is assumed at the point e, and (2) conditions under which the oscillation can be sustained are established. The last step is done by *disregarding the effects of all the harmonics as generated by the nonlinearity. However, the characteristics of the nonlinearity in transmitting the amplitude and the phase of the fundamental component are retained.*

The above is tantamount to replacing the nonlinear element $\mathfrak{N}$, generally assumed to be time invariant, by another nonlinear time-invariant element $\mathfrak{N}'$ with the property that it operates on any sinusoidal input $e(t) = \hat{e} \sin \omega t$ by passing its fundamental frequency in exactly the same manner as the $\mathfrak{N}$; but whatever the input frequency ω, $\mathfrak{N}'$ generates no higher harmonics. Having replaced $\mathfrak{N}$ by $\mathfrak{N}'$, we proceed to analyze the resulting system S' *exactly* by establishing conditions under which an assumed oscillation $e(t) = \hat{e} \sin \omega t$ can be sustained.

It is clear that at each assumed amplitude $\hat{e}$ of $e(t)$ and at each assumed frequency ω, $\mathfrak{N}'$ is completely specified by a complex gain $N(\hat{e}, \omega) = |N(\hat{e}, \omega)| e^{j\phi}$, where as usual the real number $|N(\hat{e}, \omega)|$ gives the gain (attenuation) of the amplitude $\hat{e}$ as it passes through $\mathfrak{N}'$ and the real number $\phi = \tan^{-1}[\mathfrak{Im}\, N(\hat{e}, \omega)/\mathfrak{Re}\, N(\hat{e}, \omega)]$ gives the phase shift of the input sine wave as it passes through $\mathfrak{N}'$. Thus under the input $e(t) = \hat{e} \sin \omega t$, the output of $\mathfrak{N}'$ is now

$$u(t) = \hat{e} |N(\hat{e}, \omega)| \sin(\omega t + \phi) \tag{6-12}$$

To establish the condition under which the system S' can sustain the oscillation $e(t) = \hat{e} \sin \omega t$, the values of $\hat{e}$ and ω at which the "loop gain" of the system S' becomes -1 must be found. This is the condition

$$N(\hat{e}, \omega) G(j\omega) = -1 \tag{6-13}$$

where $G(s)$ is the system transfer function of the linear block $G(p)$.

Note that with respect to the general nonlinearity $\mathfrak{N}$, it is not meaningful to speak of its gain and phase relative to a sine-wave input, but with respect to the nonlinearity $\mathfrak{N}'$ it is. Moreover, since $N(\hat{e}, \omega)$ for a given $\mathfrak{N}'$ can be calculated, condition (6-13) can be established by various means. We may in particular extemporize from well-known linear techniques:

1) Fixing $\hat{e}$ we can plot a "Nyquist diagram" of $N(\hat{e}, \omega) G(j\omega)$ with ω as the parameter. Plot a family of such Nyquist diagrams for various $\hat{e}$. That value of $\hat{e}$ for the plot which passes the -1 point and that ω at which the plot passes the -1 point then yield the necessary amplitude and frequency

for self-sustained oscillation at the point $e(t)$. (See Fig. 6-6.) Note that we only need to construct the plots near the -1 point. With some practice the values of $\hat{e}$ and ω that bring about oscillation can be obtained by a very few trials.

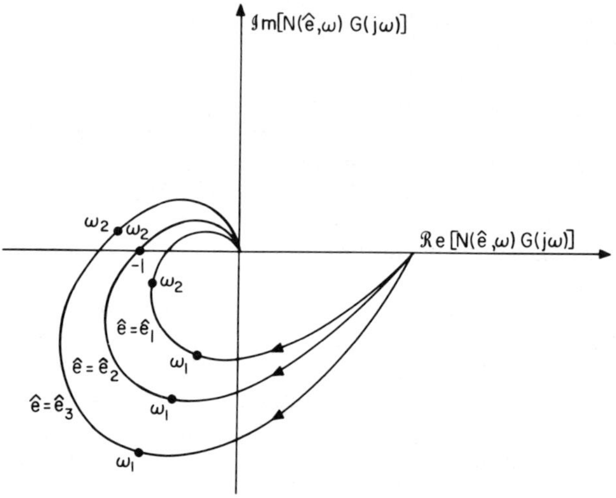

Fig. 6-6. Typical plots of $N(\hat{e},\omega)G(j\omega)$ as a function of ω for various values of $\hat{e}$. The curve that passes through the -1 point yields $\hat{e}$ and ω for self-oscillation.

2) The same idea as above can obviously be applied to a family of "Bode plots" of $N(\hat{e},\omega)G(j\omega)$. The value of $\hat{e}$ and ω at which the "gain crossover point" becomes unity can then be found.
3) Under certain circumstances (in particular when $N(\hat{e},\omega)$ is real), the root locus plot of $NG(s)$ may be used to advantage. The value of N which causes the poles of $NG(s)$ to cross the imaginary axis can be found.

Relative to technique (1) above, it is sometimes more convenient to write Eq. (6-13) as

$$G(j\omega) = -\frac{1}{N(\hat{e},\omega)} \tag{6-14}$$

and plot the rhs and lhs of the Eq. (6-14) separately on the $G(j\omega)$ (Nyquist) plane. The lhs yields the conventional Nyquist diagram for the linear part $G(p)$ while the rhs yields a two-parameter family of curves. There will, in general, be a number of intersections between the lhs and rhs curves. We first attempt to find those intersection points at which the ω values correspond. These yield the possible frequencies of oscillation. The values of $\hat{e}$ of the rhs which result in these points are then the possible amplitudes of oscillation.

The above method is useful for simple cases of $N(\hat{e}, \omega)$. Some writers, however, treat it as if it were the only possible way to establish self-oscillation; this is not justifiable.

Thus far we have only obtained an exact analysis of the conditions for self-oscillation of the system S'. The key to the equivalent gain or describing function approach lies in making the assumption: *the exact conditions for self-oscillation for the system S' constitute the approximate conditions for self-oscillation for the system S.* In particular the complex quantity $N(\hat{e}, \omega)$ is called the *equivalent gain* or the *describing function* of the nonlinearity $\mathfrak{N}$.

Indeed, because of the fact that a nonlinearity is replaced by a quantity describable in terms of "gain" and "phase," the procedure is popularly called "equivalent linearization." This appellation, however, is not particularly apt since neither additivity nor homogeneity is observed through the equivalent gain $N(\hat{e}, \omega)$.*

Let us consider some examples for the finding of the equivalent gain.

◆◆Example 6-2. Find the sinusoidal describing function of a saturation element given by:

$$f(e) = \begin{cases} \dfrac{A}{B}e, & -B < e < B \\ A, & B \le e \\ -A, & -B \ge e \end{cases} \tag{6-15}$$

Let the input sinusoidal wave be denoted as $\hat{e}\sin\omega t$; we note that when $\hat{e}$ is less than B, we are essentially operating in the linear region and the equivalent gain, as may be expected, will be simply A/B. When $\hat{e}$ exceeds B, the output wave is no longer A/B times the input wave but will be clipped at level A. As $\hat{e}$ is further increased in amplitude, the output wave will approach a square wave with a fixed amplitude A. The fundamental of a square wave with a period $2\pi/\omega$ and amplitude A is $4A/\pi$, which occurs as $\hat{e} \to \infty$. The equivalent gain is thus $4A/\pi\hat{e}$ which approaches zero. Between the values A/B and 0, we expect a continuous variation in the equivalent gain such as pictured in Fig. 6-7.

Note that from just the simple consideration above we expect no frequency dependence in the equivalent gain since the situation

*For that matter, the term "equivalent gain" is itself not very appropriate.

is unaltered as the input frequency ω is changed. Moreover, from the symmetry of the waveshape we also expect no phase shift.

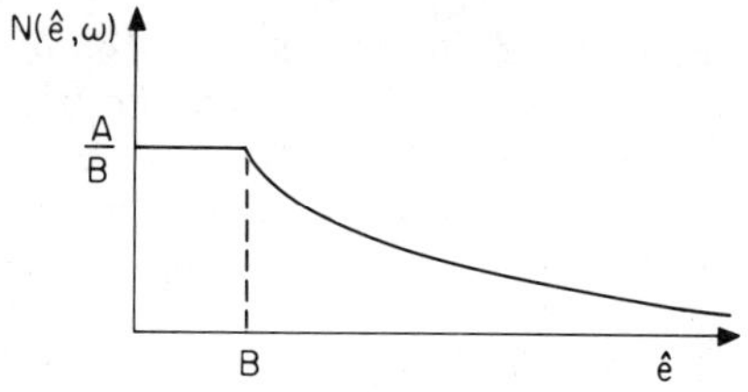

Fig. 6-7. The sinusoidal describing function for the limiter of Eq. (6-15).

For an input $e = \hat{e}\sin\omega t$, the output $u(t)$ is:

$$u(t) = \begin{cases} \dfrac{A}{B}\hat{e}\sin\omega t\,, & n\pi - \sin^{-1}\dfrac{B}{\hat{e}} < \omega t < n\pi + \sin^{-1}\dfrac{B}{\hat{e}} \\ A\,, & 2n\pi + \sin^{-1}\dfrac{B}{\hat{e}} \le \omega t \le (2n+1)\pi - \sin^{-1}\dfrac{B}{\hat{e}} \\ -A\,, & (2n-1)\pi + \sin^{-1}\dfrac{B}{\hat{e}} \le \omega t \le 2n\pi - \sin^{-1}\dfrac{B}{\hat{e}} \end{cases}$$

$$n = 0, \pm 1, \pm 2, \cdots \qquad (6\text{-}16)$$

To find the describing function, we need to find the fundamental component of the Fourier series expansion of $u(t)$. Let

$$u(t) = \alpha_1 \sin\omega t + \alpha_2 \sin 2\omega t + \cdots + \beta_0 + \beta_1\cos\omega t + \beta_2\cos 2\omega t + \cdots \qquad (6\text{-}17)$$

Since $f(e)$ displays odd symmetry, we immediately have

$$\beta_n = 0\,, \quad n = 0, \ldots$$
$$\alpha_{2m} = 0\,, \quad m = 1, \ldots \qquad (6\text{-}18)$$

We are only interested in α_1, whence

$$\alpha_1 = \frac{1}{\pi}\int_0^{2\pi} u(t)\sin\omega t\, d\omega t \qquad (6\text{-}19)$$

On integrating and using (6-16), we obtain

$$\alpha_1 = \frac{A\hat{e}}{B\pi}\left\{2\sin^{-1}\left(\frac{B}{\hat{e}}\right) - \sin\left[2\sin^{-1}\left(\frac{B}{\hat{e}}\right)\right]\right\} + \frac{4A}{\pi}\cos\left[\sin^{-1}\left(\frac{B}{\hat{e}}\right)\right] \qquad (6\text{-}20)$$

The describing function of the characteristic of Eq. (6-15) is then $\alpha_1/\hat{e}$ or

$$N(\hat{e}, \omega) = N(\hat{e})$$

$$= \frac{A}{B\pi}\left\{2 \sin^{-1}\left(\frac{B}{\hat{e}}\right) - \sin 2\left[\sin^{-1}\left(\frac{B}{\hat{e}}\right)\right]\right\} + \frac{4A}{\hat{e}\pi} \cos\left[\sin^{-1}\left(\frac{B}{\hat{e}}\right)\right] \tag{6-21}$$

which is seen to be real and independent of the input frequency ω.

If we hold A fixed while letting $B \to 0$ in Eq. (6-21), we obtain (on employing L'Hospital's rule to resolve a resulting 0/0 term):

$$N(\hat{e}) = \frac{4A}{\hat{e}\pi} \tag{6-22}$$

Since with $B \to 0$ in (6-15) we obtain the characteristics of an ideal relay, we see that an ideal relay of amplitude A will have a describing function (6-22).◆◆

◆◆Example 6-3. Consider again Example 5-21. Determine the existence and stability of a limit cycle for the system using the following set of parameters: $\omega_0 = 10$ rad/sec, $\xi_0 = 0.105$, $K = 1.0$.

Let

$$f(x_1) = K + n(x_1) \tag{6-23}$$

where we create the symmetrical characteristic

$$n(x_1) = \begin{cases} K, & x_1 \leq 1 \\ Kx_1, & |x_1| < 1 \\ -K, & x_1 \leq 1 \end{cases} \tag{6-24}$$

Assume now:

$$x_1(t) \simeq \hat{x}_1 \sin \omega t = x_{1_p}(t) \tag{6-25}$$

The sinusoidal describing function for the characteristic $n(x_1)$ is, according to Eq. (6-21)

$$N(\hat{x}_1) = \frac{K}{\pi}\left\{2 \sin^{-1}\left(\frac{1}{\hat{x}_1}\right) - \sin\left[2 \sin^{-1}\left(\frac{1}{\hat{x}_1}\right)\right] + \frac{4}{\hat{x}_1} \cos\left[\sin^{-1}\left(\frac{1}{\hat{x}_1}\right)\right]\right\}$$

$$= \frac{2K}{\pi}\left[\sin^{-1}\left(\frac{1}{\hat{x}_1}\right) + \frac{1}{\hat{x}_1}\sqrt{1 - \left(\frac{1}{\hat{x}_1}\right)^2}\,\right] \tag{6-26}$$

From Eq. (5-69) we have

$$x_1(t) = \frac{\omega_0 pf\left(x_1(t)\right)}{p^2 + 2\omega_0\xi_0 p + \omega_0^2}$$

Now

$$pf\left(x_1(t)\right) = \frac{d}{dt} f\left(x_1(t)\right) = \frac{d}{dt}\left[K + n\left(x_1(t)\right)\right] = pn\left(x_1(t)\right) \qquad \text{(6-27)}$$

Replacing $n(x_1)$ by its equivalent-gain term $N(\hat{x}_1)x_{1p}$ we have:

$$x_{1p}(t) = \frac{\omega_0 N(\hat{x}_1)p}{p^2 + 2\omega_0\xi_0 p + \omega_0^2}\, x_{1p}(t) \qquad \text{(6-28)}$$

The equivalent system (6-28) has the characteristic equation

$$\lambda^2 + \left[2\xi_0 - N(\hat{x}_1)\right]\omega_0\lambda + \omega_0^2 = 0 \qquad \text{(6-29)}$$

Thus the system can have imaginary roots at $\lambda = \pm j\omega_0$ if $N(\hat{x}_1) = 2\xi_0$. By the describing function method, then, there apparently exists a limit cycle with an amplitude $\hat{x}_{10}$ given by the relation

$$N(\hat{x}_{10}) = 2\xi_0 \qquad \text{(6-30)}$$

It is interesting to note that the condition $K > 2\xi_0$ has to be satisfied in order that the describing function method can yield a solution to the assumed oscillation. We had previously shown in Example 5-21 that this condition is both necessary and sufficient for the existence of a limit cycle. Thus in this particular case, the condition for the existence of a limit cycle as inferred from the describing function analysis is correct and exact.

To determine the stability of the limit cycle, note from Fig. 6-7 that the equivalent gain $N(\hat{x}_1)$ for a saturation nonlinearity decreases with increasing amplitude $\hat{x}_1$. From Eq. (6-29), if for any reason $N(\hat{x}_1)$ should decrease from $N(\hat{x}_{10})$, which implies that $\hat{x}_1$ is increasing from $\hat{x}_{10}$, the system becomes stable. This will tend to decrease $\hat{x}_1$ toward $\hat{x}_{10}$. The same line of reasoning will show that as $\hat{x}_1$ tries to decrease, it will cause the system to become unstable. This will tend to increase the magnitude of $\hat{x}_1$ toward that of $\hat{x}_{10}$. Thus the limit cycle is orbitally asymptotically stable.

For the numerical values given, we have

$$2\xi_0 = 0.21 = N(\hat{x}_{10}) = \frac{1}{\pi}\left\{2\sin^{-1}\left(\frac{1}{\hat{x}_{10}}\right) - \sin 2\sin^{-1}\left(\frac{1}{\hat{x}_{10}}\right) + \frac{4}{\hat{x}_{10}}\cos\sin^{-1}\left(\frac{1}{\hat{x}_{10}}\right)\right\}$$

Solving graphically, we obtain $\hat{x}_{10} = 6.00$.♦♦

A characteristic of the form (6–15) with $A = B = 1$ will be called the unit limiter and labeled $l(e)$. This characteristic is quite useful since other limiters and nonlinear characteristics can be given in terms of $l(e)$. (See, e.g., Exercise 6–3.) By Eq. (6–26) we see that the describing function for $l(e)$, labeled $N_l(\hat{e})$, is given by

$$N_l(\hat{e}) = \frac{2}{\pi}\left[\sin^{-1}\left(\frac{1}{\hat{e}}\right) + \frac{1}{\hat{e}}\sqrt{1 - \frac{1}{(\hat{e})^2}}\right] \tag{6-31}$$

The numerical values for $N_l(\hat{e})$ have been tabulated by Magnus to five decimal places. They are reproduced in Table 6–1. In addition, the describing functions for some common memoryless nonlinearities, again due to Magnus, are given in Table 6–2 (numbers 1 through 19).

6.3 The Describing Function for Nonlinear Elements with Memory

Thus far we have only considered the describing function for simple zero-memory nonlinearities. By a zero-memory element we mean an element whose output value bears an instantaneous one-to-one relationship with each input value. For such an element, the input-output characteristic can be given by a plot such as shown in Fig. 6–8a.

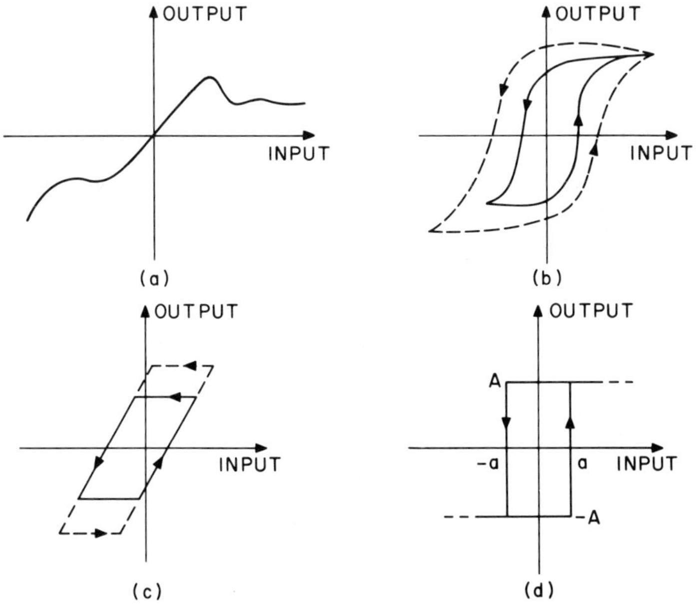

Fig. 6-8. (a) A zero-memory nonlinearity; (b) A hysteresis nonlinearity; (c) A backlash nonlinearity; (d) A relay with hysteresis.

TABLE 6-1*

Numerical Values of the Sinusoidal Describing Function for the Unit Limiter $N_l(\hat{x})$** (Magnus)

$\hat{x}$	0	1	2	3	4	5	6	7	8	9
				Range $1 \le \hat{x} \le 20$, step width 0.1						
1	1.00000	0.96755	0.92037	0.87163	0.82474	0.78090	0.74040	0.70319	0.66906	0.63775
2	0.60900	0.58254	0.55815	0.53561	0.51474	0.49537	0.47735	0.46055	0.44487	0.43018
3	0.41642	0.40348	0.39131	0.37984	0.36901	0.35877	0.34907	0.33988	0.33115	0.32286
4	0.31496	0.30744	0.30026	0.29341	0.28686	0.28059	0.27459	0.26884	0.26333	0.25803
5	0.25294	0.24804	0.24333	0.23880	0.23443	0.23022	0.22615	0.22222	0.21843	0.21476
6	0.21122	0.20779	0.20447	0.20125	0.19813	0.19511	0.19217	0.18933	0.18656	0.18388
7	0.18127	0.17873	0.17627	0.17387	0.17153	0.16926	0.16704	0.16489	0.16279	0.16074
8	0.15874	0.15679	0.15489	0.15303	0.15122	0.14945	0.14772	0.14603	0.14437	0.14276
9	0.14118	0.13963	0.13812	0.13664	0.13519	0.13378	0.13239	0.13103	0.12969	0.12839
10	0.12711	0.12586	0.12463	0.12342	0.12224	0.12108	0.11994	0.11882	0.11772	0.11665
11	0.11559	0.11455	0.11353	0.11253	0.11154	0.11058	0.10962	0.10869	0.10777	0.10687
12	0.10598	0.10511	0.10425	0.10340	0.10257	0.10175	0.10094	0.10015	0.09937	0.09860
13	0.09784	0.09710	0.09636	0.09564	0.09493	0.09423	0.09353	0.09285	0.09218	0.09152
14	0.09087	0.09022	0.08959	0.08896	0.08835	0.08774	0.08714	0.08655	0.08596	0.08539
15	0.08482	0.08426	0.08370	0.08316	0.08262	0.08209	0.08156	0.08104	0.08053	0.08002
16	0.07952	0.07903	0.07854	0.07806	0.07759	0.07712	0.07665	0.07620	0.07574	0.07529
17	0.07485	0.07441	0.07398	0.07356	0.07313	0.07272	0.07230	0.07190	0.07149	0.07109
18	0.07070	0.07031	0.06892	0.06954	0.06916	0.06879	0.06842	0.06805	0.06769	0.06733
19	0.06698	0.06663	0.06628	0.06594	0.06560	0.06526	0.06493	0.06460	0.06428	0.06395

Range $20 \leq \hat{x} \leq 1.00$, step width 1

20	0.06363	0.06061	0.05785	0.05534	0.05303	0.05092	0.04896	0.04715	0.04546	0.04389
30	0.04243	0.04106	0.03978	0.03858	0.03744	0.03637	0.03537	0.03441	0.03350	0.03264
40	0.03183	0.03105	0.03031	0.02961	0.02893	0.02829	0.02768	0.02709	0.02652	0.02598
50	0.02546	0.02496	0.02448	0.02402	0.02358	0.02315	0.02273	0.02233	0.02195	0.02158
60	0.02122	0.02087	0.02053	0.02021	0.01989	0.01959	0.01929	0.01900	0.01872	0.01845
70	0.01819	0.01793	0.01768	0.01744	0.01720	0.01697	0.01675	0.01653	0.01632	0.01612
80	0.01591	0.01572	0.01553	0.01534	0.01516	0.01498	0.01480	0.01463	0.01447	0.01430
90	0.01415	0.01399	0.01384	0.01369	0.01354	0.01340	0.01326	0.01313	0.01299	0.01286
100	0.01273	...	...	...	...	...	...	...	...	...

* See footnote to Table 6-2, page 204.

$$^{**}N_l(\hat{x}) = \frac{2}{\pi}\left[\sin^{-1}\left(\frac{1}{\hat{x}}\right) + \frac{1}{\hat{x}}\sqrt{1 - \left(\frac{1}{\hat{x}}\right)^2}\right]$$

TABLE 6-2*

The Sinusoidal Describing Function for Some Common Nonlinearities

(Input $\hat{x} \sin \omega t$ to a nonlinearity $f(x)$ or $\mathcal{F}[x(t)]$, describing function given by $N(\hat{x})$)

Number	$f(x)$ or $\mathcal{F}[x(t)]$	$\mathcal{R}e\, N(\hat{x})$	$\mathcal{I}m\, N(\hat{x})$
1	constant	0	0
2	x^{2n} $(n = 1,2,3,\ldots)$	0	0
3	x	1	0
4	x^3	$\frac{3}{4}\hat{x}^2$	0
5	x^5	$\frac{5}{8}\hat{x}^4$	0
6	x^{2n-1} $(n = 1,2,3,\ldots)$	$\frac{2n-1}{2n}\frac{2n-3}{2n-2}\frac{2n-5}{2n-4}\cdots\frac{3}{4}x^{2n-2}$	0
7	$x\|x\|$	$\frac{8}{3\pi}\hat{x}$	0
8	$x^3\|x\|$	$\frac{32}{15\pi}\hat{x}^3$	0
9	$x^{2n-1}\|x\|$ $(n = 1,2,3,\ldots)$	$\frac{4}{\pi}\frac{2n}{2n+1}\frac{2n-2}{2n-1}\frac{2n-4}{2n-3}\cdots\frac{2}{3}\hat{x}^{2n-1}$	0

10	$\sin x$	$\frac{2}{\hat{x}} J_1(\hat{x}) = 1 - \frac{1}{8}\hat{x}^2 + \frac{1}{192}\hat{x}^4 - \frac{1}{9216}\hat{x}^6 + \frac{1}{737{,}280}\hat{x}^8 \ldots$ $J_1(x)$ is Bassel's function of the first kind of order 1	0
11**	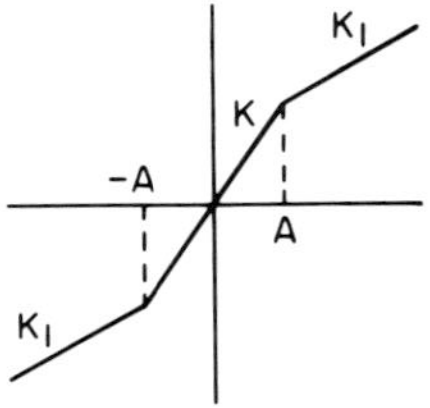	K for $\frac{\hat{x}}{A} \leq 1$ $K_1 + (K - K_1)N_l\left(\frac{\hat{x}}{A}\right)$ for $\frac{\hat{x}}{A} \geq 1$	0
12	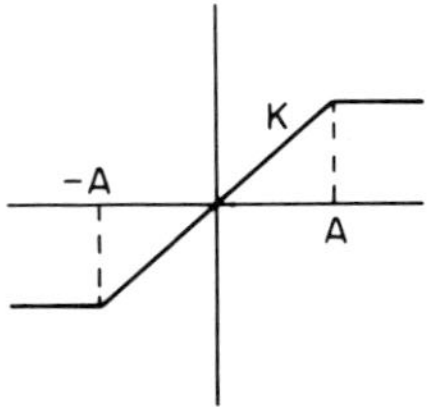	K for $\frac{\hat{x}}{A} \leq 1$ $KN_l\left(\frac{\hat{x}}{A}\right)$ for $\frac{\hat{x}}{A} \geq 1$	0
13	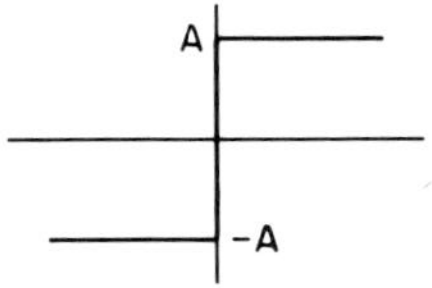	$\frac{4A}{\pi\hat{x}}$	0

TABLE 6-2 (Cont'd.)

Number	$f(x)$ or $\mathcal{F}[x(t)]$	$\mathcal{R}e\, N(\hat{x})$	$\mathcal{I}m\, N(\hat{x})$
14	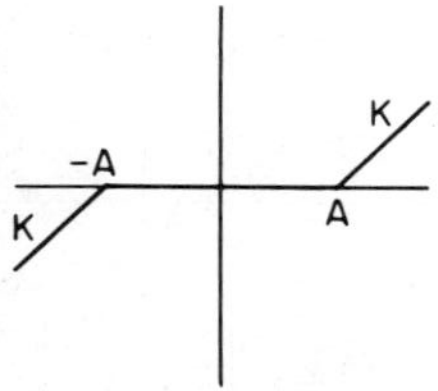	0 for $\frac{\hat{x}}{A} \leq 1$ $K\left[1 - N_l\left(\frac{\hat{x}}{A}\right)\right]$ for $\frac{\hat{x}}{A} \geq 1$	0
15	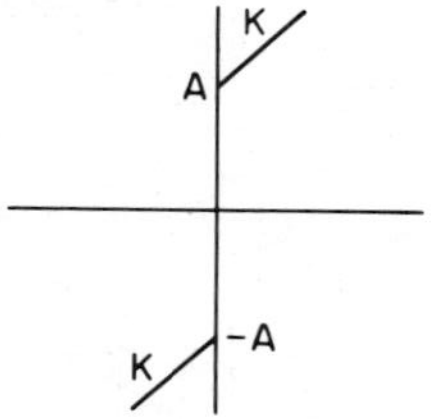	$K + \frac{4A}{\pi\hat{x}}$	0
16	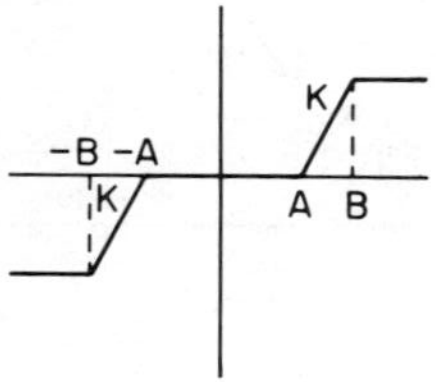	$K\left[1 - N_l\left(\frac{\hat{x}}{A}\right)\right]$ for $1 \leq \frac{\hat{x}}{A} \leq \frac{B}{A}$ $K\left[N_l\left(\frac{\hat{x}}{B}\right) - N_l\left(\frac{\hat{x}}{A}\right)\right]$ for $\frac{\hat{x}}{A} \geq \frac{B}{A}$	0

17	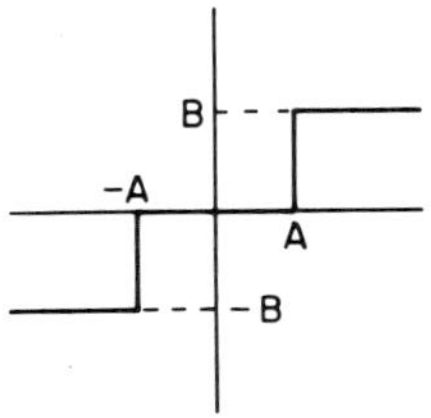	0 for $\hat{x} \leq A$ $\frac{4B}{\pi\hat{x}}\sqrt{1-\left(\frac{A}{\hat{x}}\right)^2}$ for $\hat{x} \geq A$	0
18	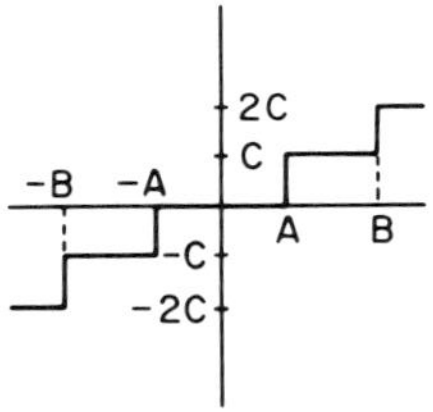	0 for $\hat{x} \leq A$ $\frac{4C}{\pi\hat{x}}\sqrt{1-\left(\frac{A}{\hat{x}}\right)^2}$ for $A \leq \hat{x} \leq B$ $\frac{4C}{\pi\hat{x}}\left[\sqrt{1-\left(\frac{A}{\hat{x}}\right)^2}+\sqrt{1-\left(\frac{A}{\hat{x}}\right)^2}\right]$ for $\hat{x} \geq B$	0
19	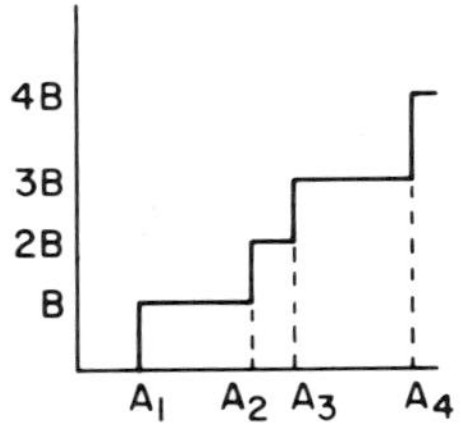	$\frac{4B}{\pi\hat{x}}\sum_{i=1}^{n}\sqrt{1-\left(\frac{A_i}{\hat{x}}\right)^2}$ for $\hat{x} \geq A_i$	0

TABLE 6-2 (Cont'd.)

Number	$f(x)$ or $\mathcal{F}[x(t)]$	$\mathcal{R}e\, N(\hat{x})$	$\mathcal{I}m\, N(\hat{x})$
20	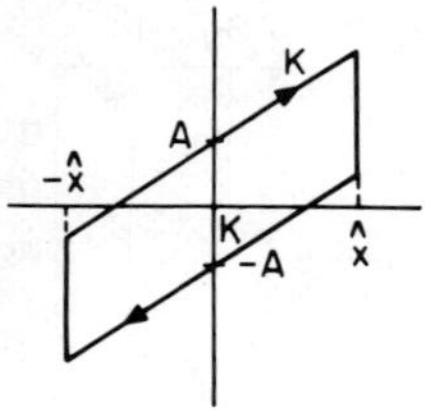	K	$\dfrac{4A}{\pi\hat{x}}$
21	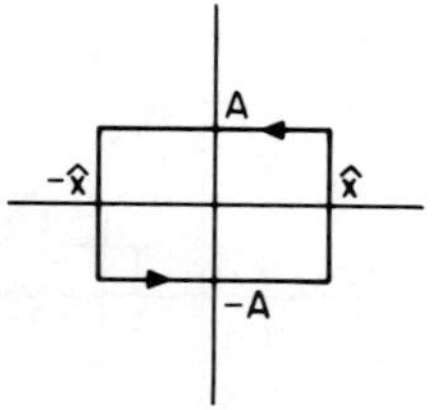	0	$-\dfrac{4A}{\pi\hat{x}}$
22	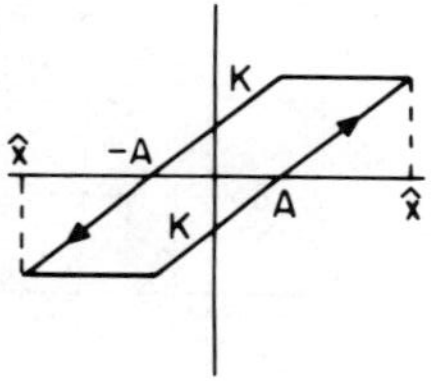	$0 \quad$ for $\dfrac{\hat{x}}{A} \le 1$ $\dfrac{K}{2}\left[1 - N_l\left(\dfrac{\hat{x}/A}{2 - \hat{x}/A}\right)\right] \quad$ for $\dfrac{\hat{x}}{A} \ge 1$	$0 \quad$ for $\hat{x} \le A$ $\dfrac{4KA(A - \hat{x})}{\pi\hat{x}^2} \quad$ for $\hat{x} \ge A$

23	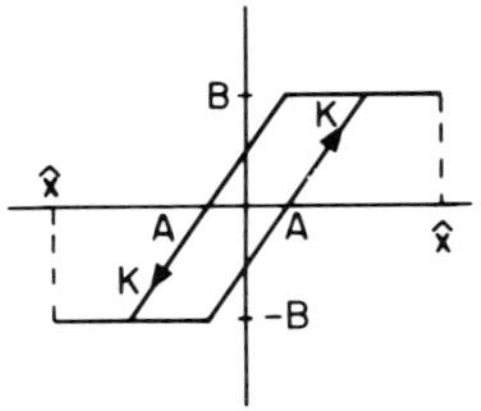	0 for $\frac{\hat{x}}{A} \le 1$ $\frac{K}{2}\left[1 - N_l\left(\frac{\hat{x}/A}{2 - \hat{x}/A}\right)\right]$ for $1 \le \frac{\hat{x}}{A} \le \frac{B}{A}$ $\frac{K}{2}\left[N_l\left(\frac{\hat{x}}{B}\right) - N_l\left(\frac{\hat{x}/A}{2 - B/A}\right)\right]$ for $\hat{x} \ge B$	0 for $\hat{x} \le A$ $\frac{4KA(A - \hat{x})}{\pi \hat{x}^2}$ for $A \le \hat{x} \le B$ $\frac{4KA(A - B)}{\pi \hat{x}^2}$ for $\hat{x} \ge B$
24	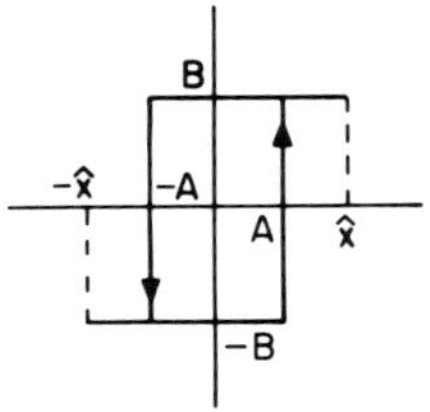	0 for $\hat{x} \le A$ $\frac{4B}{\pi \hat{x}}\sqrt{1 - \left(\frac{A}{\hat{x}}\right)^2}$ for $\hat{x} \ge A$	0 for $\hat{x} \le A$ $-\frac{4AB}{\pi \hat{x}^2}$ for $\hat{x} \ge A$
25	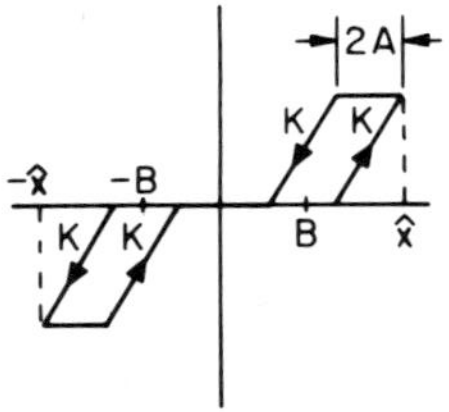	0 for $\hat{x} \le A + B$ $\frac{K}{2}\left[1 - N_l\left(\frac{\hat{x}}{A + B}\right) - N_l\left(\frac{\hat{x}}{\hat{x} - 2A}\right) - N_l\left(\frac{\hat{x}}{B - A}\right)\right]$ for $\hat{x} \ge A + B$	0 for $\hat{x} \le A + B$ $\frac{4KA(A + B - \hat{x})}{\pi \hat{x}^2}$ for $\hat{x} \ge A + B$

TABLE 6-2 (Cont'd.)

Number	$f(x)$ or $\mathfrak{F}[x(t)]$	$\mathfrak{Re}\, N(\hat{x})$	$\mathfrak{Im}\, N(\hat{x})$
26	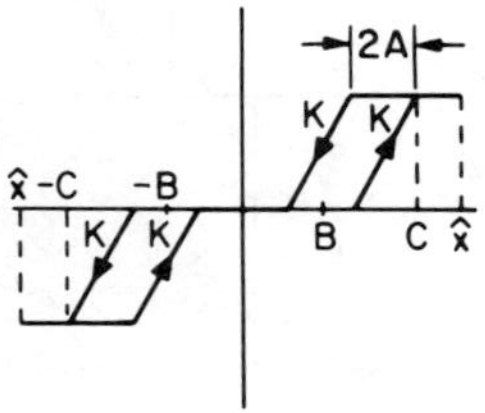	0 for $\hat{x} \leq A + B$ $\frac{K}{2}\left[1 - N_l\left(\frac{\hat{x}}{A+B}\right) + N_l\left(\frac{\hat{x}}{\hat{x}-2A}\right) - N_l\left(\frac{\hat{x}}{B-A}\right)\right]$ for $A+B \leq \hat{x} \leq C$ $\frac{K}{2}\left[N_l\left(\frac{\hat{x}}{C}\right) - N_l\left(\frac{\hat{x}}{A+B}\right) + l\left(\frac{\hat{x}}{C-2A}\right) - N_l\left(\frac{\hat{x}}{B-A}\right)\right]$ for $\hat{x} \geq C$	0 for $\hat{x} \leq A + B$ $\frac{4KA(A+B-\hat{x})}{\pi\hat{x}^2}$ for $A + B \leq \hat{x} \leq C$ $\frac{4KA(A+B-C)}{\pi\hat{x}^2}$ for $\hat{x} \geq C$
27	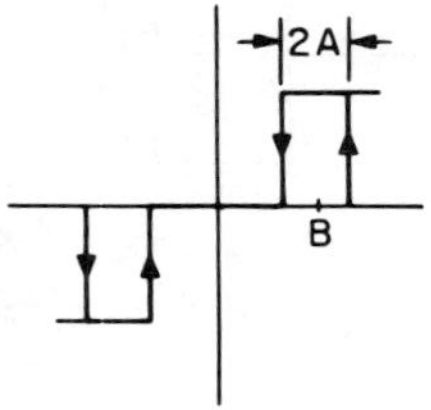	0 for $\hat{x} \leq A + B$ $\frac{2C}{\pi\hat{x}}\left[\sqrt{1-\left(\frac{B-A}{\hat{x}}\right)^2} + \sqrt{1-\left(\frac{B+A}{\hat{x}}\right)^2}\right]$ for $\hat{x} \geq A + B$	0 for $\hat{x} \leq A + B$ $-\frac{4AC}{\pi\hat{x}^2}$ for $\hat{x} \geq A + B$

*Tables 6-1 and 6-2 printed with the kind permission of Dr. Kurt Magnus. They are adapted from his paper "Über ein Verfahren zur Untersuchung nichtlinearer Schwingungs – und Regelungs-Systeme," VDI-Forschungsheft 451, 1955. This paper has been translated by Langley Research Center, NASA, in October 1958 under the title "On a Method of Investigation Nonlinear Systems of Oscillations and of Servomechanisms."

**In the figures the letter K over a line segment indicates its slope.

Quite frequently elements encountered in control systems are only describable by memory-type elements, i.e., elements whose input-output characteristics are not unique in a static sense but are unique if initial pairs of input-output values plus the entire histories of the inputs are specified. Examples of this type of elements are the hysteresis element, the backlash element, and the relay element with hysteresis. These are shown in Figs. 6-8b, 6-8c, and 6-8d for a specific input periodic wave of a given amplitude. For a larger amplitude, the excursion will become those shown in the dotted line. For the relay with hysteresis, it happens that its characteristic is unchanged when the input periodic wave amplitude is changed.

Since the output for a memory-type device depends on the entire input history, the input-output relationship for the memory-type device can only be represented mathematically by a *functional*, which may be defined as a function of a function, i.e., it yields a value (the output) for a given *function* (the input history). If the input and output as functions of time are denoted as $x(t)$ and $y(t)$ respectively, we shall use the following notation to denote a functional:

$$y(t) = \mathcal{F}[x(t)] \tag{6-32}$$

We will further employ the block diagram of Fig. 6-9 with the understanding that the input-output relationship is given by Eq. (6-32).

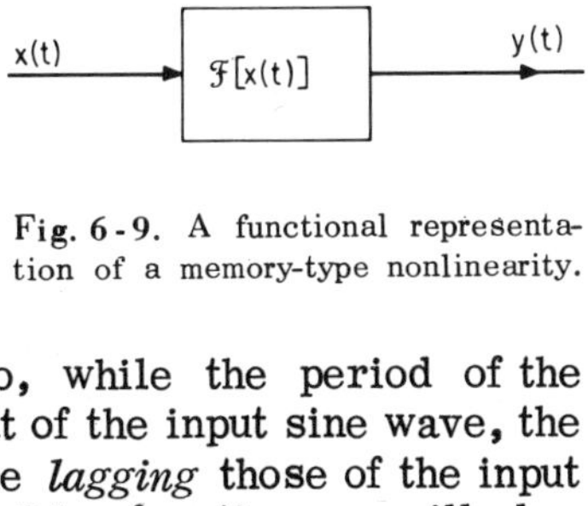

Fig. 6-9. A functional representation of a memory-type nonlinearity.

♦♦Example 6-4. Consider the relay with hysteresis of Fig. 6-8d. For a sinusoidal input, the output is seen to be a square wave whenever the input amplitude exceeds the "half-width" a of the hysteresis characteristic (see Fig. 6-10). Also, while the period of the square wave remains the same as that of the input sine wave, the zero crossings of the square wave are *lagging* those of the input sine wave. This indicates that the describing function now will also include a phase shift, in particular a lagging phase shift.

To be more specific, we note that when the input amplitude just exceeds a, the output fundamental will lag the input by 90°. This lag however, will *decrease* as the input amplitude increases. When the input amplitude becomes very large compared to a, the phase-lag approaches zero. On the other hand, by inspection, we see that the amplitude characteristic of the output fundamental depends on the input amplitude in much the same way as an ideal relay, which is obtained from the relay with hysteresis by letting the "hysteresis half-width" a go to zero.♦♦

To obtain an analytical expression for the describing function, we as usual assume a sinusoidal input and carry out a Fourier

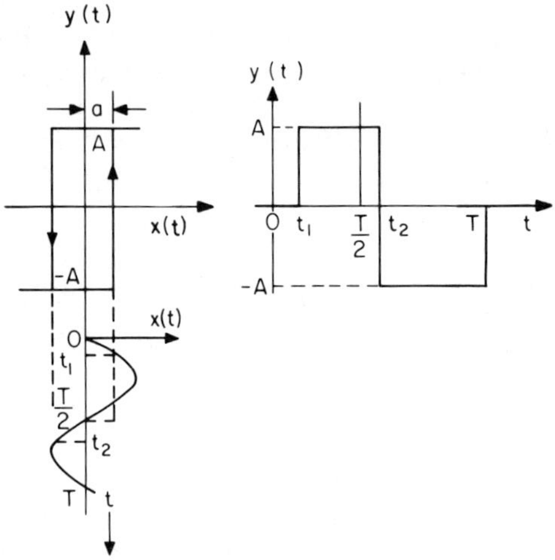

Fig. 6-10. Input-output relationship of a relay with hysteresis for a sinusoidal input.

series expansion of the output. Only the fundamental component needs to be found.

♦♦Example 6-5. For the nonlinear characteristic of Fig. 6-8d, assume that the output is initially at $-A$; then for an input $\hat{e}$ sin ωt we have, over one cycle, $0 \leq \omega t \leq 2\pi$:

$$u(t) = \begin{cases} -A, & -\pi + \sin^{-1}\dfrac{a}{\hat{e}} < \omega t < \sin^{-1}\dfrac{a}{\hat{e}} \\ +A, & \sin^{-1}\dfrac{a}{\hat{e}} < \omega t < \pi + \sin^{-1}\dfrac{a}{e} \end{cases}$$

Expanding $u(t)$ in a Fourier series: $u(t) = \alpha_1 \sin\omega t + \beta_1 \cos\omega t + \cdots$ we have

$$\alpha_1 = \frac{A}{\pi}\left[-\int_{-\pi+\sin^{-1}(a/\hat{e})}^{\sin^{-1}(a/\hat{e})} \sin\omega t \, d\omega t + \int_{\sin^{-1}(a/\hat{e})}^{\pi+\sin^{-1}(a/\hat{e})} \sin\omega t \, d\omega t\right]$$

$$= \frac{4A}{\pi}\sqrt{1 - \frac{a^2}{\hat{e}^2}}$$

$$\beta_1 = \frac{A}{\pi}\left[-\int_{-\pi+\sin^{-1}(a/\hat{e})}^{\sin^{-1}(a/\hat{e})} \cos\omega t\, dt + \int_{\sin^{-1}(a/\hat{e})}^{\pi+\sin^{-1}(a/\hat{e})} \cos\omega t\, d\omega t\right]$$

$$= -\frac{4Aa}{\pi\hat{e}}$$

These hold whenever $\hat{e} > A$.

Thus the amplitude of the fundamental component of the output is

$$\sqrt{\alpha_1^{\,2} + \beta_1^{\,2}} = \frac{4A}{\pi}$$

and the phase of the fundamental component of the output is

$$\tan^{-1}\frac{\beta_1}{\alpha_1} = \tan^{-1}\frac{a}{\sqrt{\hat{e} - a^2}} = -\sin^{-1}\frac{a}{\hat{e}}$$

The describing function in a phasor form is then

$$N(\hat{e}) = \frac{4A}{\pi\hat{e}} \angle -\sin^{-1}\frac{a}{\hat{e}}$$ ◆◆

The fact that a memory element has a describing function whose phase shift decreases with increasing amplitude is fairly general. The reader can prove this to himself by considering some other memory element. Also, the gain characteristic can frequently be obtained by letting the hysteresis portion of the nonlinearity go to zero. We must, however, be careful in reaching conclusions about the *sign* of the phase shift, since this generally depends on whether the memory element is "passive" or "active."

To make this point clear, we first consider what is meant by the terms passive and active.

A memory element is *passive* if, over one cycle of the input, the characteristic is traversed in such a way that a nonzero area is encircled in a counterclockwise direction. (See Fig. 6-11a.) A memory element is *active*, if over one cycle of the input, the characteristic is traversed in such a way that a nonzero area is encircled in a clockwise direction. (See Fig. 6-11b.)

Relative to the above definitions, it is a simple matter to show that a passive memory element always gives rise to lagging phase shift and an active memory element always gives rise to leading phase shift.

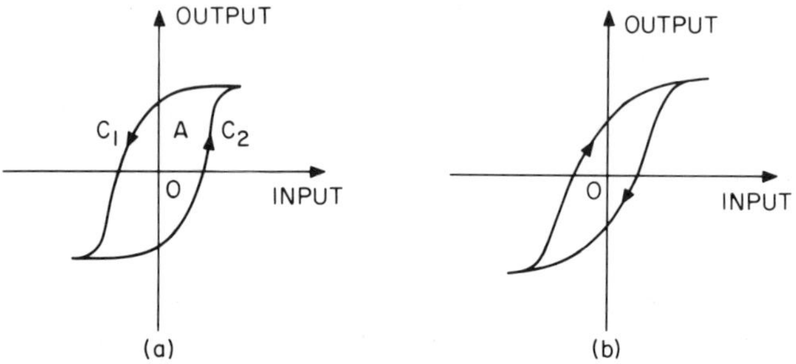

Fig. 6-11. (a) A passive memory element; (b) An active memory element.

We have shown that some zero-memory nonlinearities do not cause phase shift in the describing function sense whereas some memory-type nonlinearities do cause phase shift in this sense. It turns out that any zero-memory nonlinearity yields only a real describing function (and therefore gives no phase shift). This we can state as a theorem in the following way:

♦♦Theorem 6-1. The sinusoidal describing function for a zero-memory-type nonlinearity is always real.♦♦

Proof: Let us assume a general type of nonlinearity (such as that shown in Fig. 6-11a) $x(t) = x_p(t) = \hat{x}\sin\omega t$, then $u(t)$ can be given by a Fourier series, $u(t) = \alpha_1 \sin\omega t + \beta_1 \cos\omega t + \cdots$.

By definition, the describing function is given by:

$$N(\hat{x}) \triangleq \frac{\alpha_1}{\hat{x}} + j\frac{\beta_1}{\hat{x}} \tag{6-33}$$

where

$$\alpha_1 \triangleq \frac{1}{\pi}\int_0^{2\pi} \mathcal{F}[x_p(t)] \sin\omega t \, d(\omega t) \tag{6-34a}$$

$$\beta_1 = \frac{1}{\pi}\int_0^{2\pi} \mathcal{F}[x_p(t)] \cos\omega t \, d(\omega t) \tag{6-34b}$$

Since $dx_p(t)/d\omega t = \hat{x}\cos\omega t$, Eq. (6-34b) can be written as:

$$\beta_1 = \frac{1}{\hat{x}\pi}\left[\int_{C_1} \mathcal{F}[x_p(t)]\, dx_p(t) + \int_{C_2} \mathcal{F}[x_p(t)]\, dx_p(t)\right]$$

$$= \frac{1}{\hat{x}\pi}\left[\int_{C_1+C_2} \mathcal{F}[x_p(t)]\, dx_p(t)\right] \tag{6-35}$$

where the curves C_1 and C_2 are as shown in Fig. 6-11a.

The term under the bracket in (6-35) is simply seen to be the area A enclosed by the curves C_1 and C_2. Thus we have:

$$\beta_1 = \frac{A}{\pi\hat{x}} \quad \text{or} \quad \mathfrak{Im}\, N(\hat{x}) = \frac{A}{\pi\hat{x}^2} \tag{6-36}$$

Thus the imaginary or the phase-dependent part of $N(\hat{x})$ is proportional to the area enclosed by the hysteresis characteristic. For a zero-memory element, it follows that $\mathfrak{Im}\, N(\hat{x}) = 0$. This proves the theorem.

Note that generally the area A under a passive memory-type nonlinear device is a measure of the energy dissipated during each cycle. Looked at from another direction, we can often achieve damping in a system by introducing a passive memory-type element.

The describing function of some of the common nonlinearities with memory are given in Table 6-2 (numbers 20-27).

6.4 A General Formulation of the Describing Function Method for Zero-Memory Nonlinearities

Our formulation of the describing function thus far applies only to the sinusoidal input. We now consider alternate formulation of equivalent gains which can be applied to a larger class of inputs.

An intuitively appealing and analytically tractable procedure is that of defining the equivalent gain as one that minimizes the mean-square output error for a given input. Using this definition, other periodic inputs, even random inputs, can be treated. An added advantage of this procedure is that when applied to the sinusoidal input case, the usual sinusoidal describing function results. This is an immediate consequence of the orthogonality of the Fourier components. Finally, the approach can be readily extended to cases with more than a single input.

Consider a set of memoryless nonlinear elements of the following form:

$$\mathrm{y} = \mathrm{f}(\mathrm{x}) \tag{6-37}$$

Assuming that the input $\mathrm{x}(t)$ is of a specific form $\mathrm{x}(t) = \mathrm{x}_1(t)$ (e.g., $\mathrm{x}_1(t)$ can be a periodic function $\mathrm{x}_p(t)$), we wish to seek an equivalent set of gains which yields

$$\mathrm{y}_1(t) = \mathrm{N}(\mathrm{x}_1)\mathrm{x}_1 \tag{6-38}$$

where the equivalent gain matrix N, which is in general a function of some parameter of $\mathrm{x}_1(t)$, is chosen such as to minimize the mean-square error between the actual output $f(x_1)$ and the approximate output (6-38). Thus, if

$$\varepsilon(t) \triangleq f(x_1) - N(x_1)x_1 \tag{6-39}$$

then $N(x_1)$ is to be chosen such as to minimize the norm of the mean-square error:

$$\overline{\|\varepsilon(t)\|^2} \triangleq \lim_{T\to\infty} \frac{1}{2T}\int_{-T}^{T} \|\varepsilon(t)\|^2\, dt \tag{6-40}$$

This procedure is schematically illustrated in Fig. 6-12. Now,

$$\overline{\|\varepsilon\|^2} = \overline{\sum_{i=1}^{n}\left[f_i(x_1) - \sum_{j=1}^{n} N_{ij}(x_1)x_{1j}\right]^2} = \overline{(f - N x_1)^T(f - N x_1)} \tag{6-41}$$

$$= \overline{f^T f} - \left(\overline{f^T N x_1} + \overline{x_1^T N^T f}\right) + \overline{x_1^T N^T N x_1}$$

where the meaning of the overscored quantities are clear in view of Eq. (6-40).

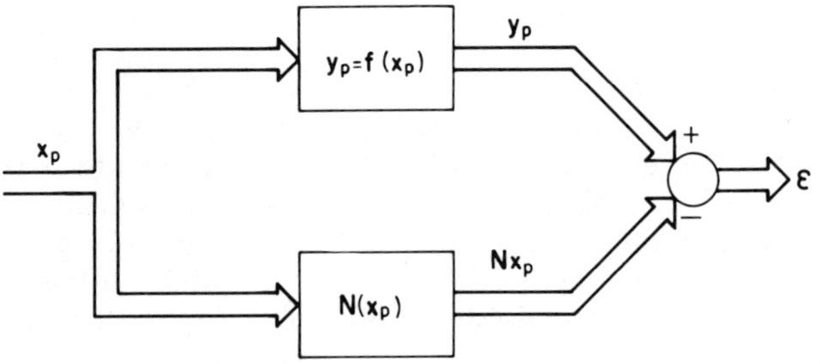

Fig. 6-12. Block diagram representation of the interpretation of the (vector) describing function as one which minimizes the mean-square outout error for a given input. Here N is to be chosen to minimize Eq. (6-41) where ε is the output shown.

The minimizing of $\overline{\|\varepsilon\|^2}$ with respect to N_{ij} can be carried out by taking $\partial\,\overline{\|\varepsilon\|^2}/\partial N_{ij}$ and setting the quantity equal to zero. This yields:

$$-\overline{2f_i x_{1_j}} + \overline{\left(2\sum_{k=1}^{n} N_{ik}x_{1_k}\right)x_{1_j}} = 0 \tag{6-42}$$

Hence,

$$\sum_{k=1}^{n} N_{ik} \overline{x_{1_k} x_{1_j}} = \overline{f_i x_{1_j}} \quad (i, j = 1, \ldots, n) \tag{6-43}$$

Since the quantities $\overline{x_{1_k} x_{1_j}}$ and $\overline{f_i x_{1_j}}$ can be computed, then using Eq. (6-43), the describing function N_{ik} can be found.

♦♦Example 6-6. Consider the case of a single nonlinearity. Here N is 1×1 and Eq. (6-43) becomes

$$N \overline{x_1^2} = \overline{fx_1} \qquad \text{or} \qquad N = \frac{\overline{fx_1}}{\overline{x_1^2}} \tag{6-44}$$

If x_1 is the sinusoidal input, then $x_1 = \hat{x} \sin \omega t$. To evaluate N from (6-44) we have

$$\overline{fx_1} = \frac{\hat{x}}{2\pi} \int_0^{2\pi} [f(\hat{x} \sin \omega t)] \sin \omega t \, (d\omega t)$$

and

$$\overline{x_1^2} = \frac{\hat{x}^2}{2}$$

Thus

$$N(\hat{x}) = \frac{1}{\pi \hat{x}} \int_0^{2\pi} [f(\hat{x} \sin \omega t)] \sin \omega t \, (d\omega t) \tag{6-45}$$

which is seen to be the describing function as discussed in the previous section.♦♦

We have thus shown that *the describing function results when we attempt to minimize the mean-squared error for a sinusoidal input*.

♦♦Example 6-7. Consider the case of a nonlinear element with two inputs x_{11} and x_{12} and one output. We have here:

$$\varepsilon^2 = \overline{\left(N_{11}x_{11} + N_{12}x_{12} - f(x_{11}, x_{12})\right)^2}$$

$$= N_{11}^2 \overline{x_{11}^2} + N_{12}^2 \overline{x_{12}^2} + \overline{f^2} + 2N_{11}N_{12} \overline{x_{11}x_{12}}$$

$$-2N_{11} \overline{x_{11}f} - 2N_{12} \overline{x_{12}f}$$

To minimize, we set $\overline{\partial\varepsilon^2}/\partial N_{11}$ and $\overline{\partial\varepsilon^2}/\partial N_{12}$ equal to 0. This yields

$$N_{11}\,\overline{x_{11}^2} + N_{12}\,\overline{x_{11}x_{12}} = \overline{x_{11}f} \tag{6-46a}$$

$$N_{11}\,\overline{x_{11}x_{12}} + N_{12}\,\overline{x_{12}^2} = \overline{x_{12}f} \tag{6-46b}$$

When $x_{11} = \alpha \sin(\omega t + \phi_1)$ and $x_{12} = \beta \sin(\omega t + \phi_2)$, then

$$\overline{x_{11}^2} = \frac{\alpha^2}{2}, \qquad \overline{x_{12}^2} = \frac{\beta^2}{2}, \qquad \overline{x_{11}x_{12}} = \frac{\alpha\beta}{2}\cos(\phi_1 - \phi_2) \tag{6-47}$$

Also

$$\overline{x_{11}f} = \frac{\alpha}{2\pi}\int_0^{2\pi}\left[f\Big(\alpha\sin(\omega t + \phi_1), \beta\sin(\omega t + \phi_2)\Big)\right]\sin(\omega t + \phi_1)\,d\omega t \tag{6-48a}$$

$$\overline{x_{12}f} = \frac{\beta}{2\pi}\int_0^{2\pi}\left[f\Big(\alpha\sin(\omega t + \phi_1), \beta\sin(\omega t + \phi_2)\Big)\right]\sin(\omega t + \phi_2)\,d\omega t \tag{6-48b}$$

Substituting (6-47) and (6-48) into (6-46), the describing functions N_{11} and N_{12} can be solved for.

We have already encountered an example of a nonlinearity with two inputs in the Van der Pol equation of Sec. 6.1 which could be represented in the form of a feedback system with a nonlinear term given by

$$f(x_1, x_2) = \mu x_1^2 x_2, \qquad \dot{x}_1 = x_2$$

Thus,

$$f(x_{11}, x_{12}) = -\frac{\mu\alpha^2\beta}{2}\Big[\sin(\omega t + \phi_2) + \tfrac{1}{2}\sin(\omega t + 2\phi_1 - \phi_2)$$

$$-\tfrac{1}{2}\sin(3\omega t + 2\phi_1 + \phi_2)\Big]$$

without loss of generality, we can set $\phi_1 = 0$ to obtain

$$\overline{x_{11}f} = -\frac{3}{8}\mu\alpha^3\beta\cos\phi_2$$

$$\overline{x_{12}f} = -\frac{\mu\alpha^2\beta^2}{4}\left(1 + \frac{1}{2}\cos 2\phi_2\right) \tag{6-49}$$

Since $x_2 = \dot{x}_1$, then $\phi_2 = \pi/2$. In view of this, substituting (6–47) and (6–49) into (6–46) results in $N_{11} = 0$ and $N_{22} = -\mu(a^2/4)$, which agree with the results in Sec. 6.1 with $x = \hat{x}_1$.◆◆

◆◆Example 6-8. The possible modes of periodic oscillations in the series motor—series generator combination, which has engaged our attention in Example 4–5 as well as in Example 5–8, can now be studied.

The normalized equations of the system (Eq. (5–32)) are represented by the block diagram of Fig. 6–13. No less than three nonlinearities are shown there.

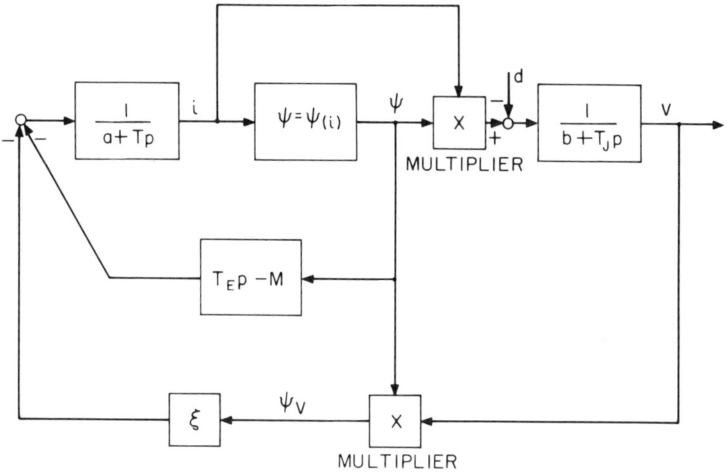

Fig. 6-13. The block diagram of the series motor—series generator system of Example 6-8.

Let us assume that the higher harmonic terms generated by the three nonlinearities will be sufficiently attenuated in the linear parts of the system, so that we can assume for periodic oscillation in the system

$$\begin{aligned} i &= i_0 + \hat{i} \sin \omega t \\ v &= v_0 + \hat{v} \sin(\omega t + \phi) \end{aligned} \tag{6–50}$$

For the input-output relations of the two nonlinear terms $\psi(i)$ and $i\psi(i)$, we will then attempt to find $N_{11}(i_0, \hat{i})$, $N_{21}(i_0, \hat{i})$, $N_{10}(i_0, \hat{i})$, and $N_{20}(i_0, \hat{i})$ such that:

$$\begin{aligned} \psi(i) &= \psi_0 + \hat{\psi} \sin \omega t + \cdots \\ &= N_{10}(i_0, \hat{i})\, i_0 + N_{11}(i_0, \hat{i})\, \hat{i} \sin \omega t + \cdots \end{aligned} \tag{6–51}$$

and

$$\psi(i)\,i = N_{20}(i_0, \hat{i})\,i_0 + N_{21}(i_0, \hat{i})\,\hat{i}\sin\omega t + \cdots \tag{6-52}$$

where ... indicates the higher harmonics terms.

The third nonlinearity is the product ψv. By (6-50) and (6-51), we have

$$\begin{aligned}\psi(i)\,v &= (\psi_0 + \hat{\psi}\sin\omega t)\Big(v_0 + \hat{v}\sin(\omega t + \phi)\Big) + \cdots \\ &= \psi_0 v_0 + \frac{\hat{\psi}\hat{v}}{2}\cos\phi + v_0\hat{\psi}\sin\omega t + \psi_0\hat{v}\sin(\omega t + \phi) + \cdots \\ &= N_{10}i_0v_0 + \tfrac{1}{2}N_{11}\hat{i}\hat{v}\cos\phi + v_0N_{11}\hat{i}\sin\omega t + N_{10}i_0\hat{v}\sin(\omega t + \phi) + \cdots\end{aligned} \tag{6-53}$$

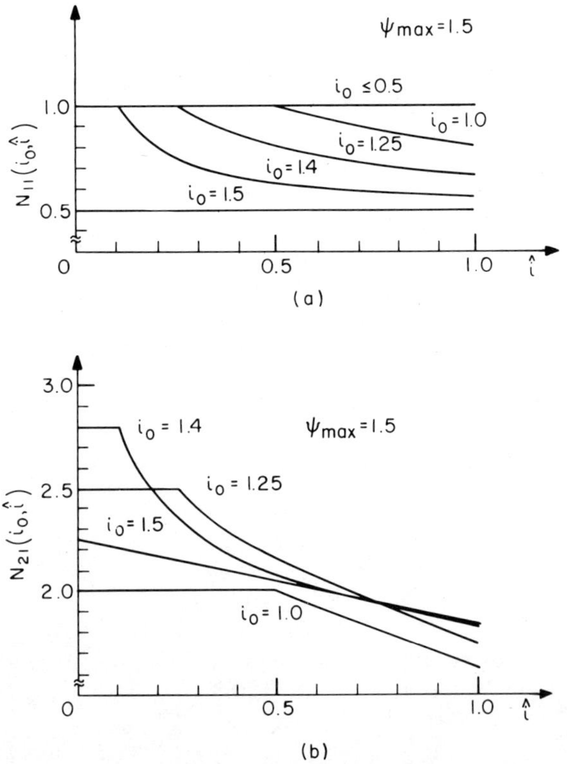

Fig. 6-14. The describing functions $N_{11}(i_0, \hat{i})$, and $N_{21}(i_0, \hat{i})$ for the system of Example 6-8.

The ac equivalent gains $N_{11}(i_0, \hat{i})$ and $N_{21}(i_0, \hat{i})$ can be obtained for the idealized magnetization curve of Fig. 4-20. They are:

$$N_{11}(i_0, \hat{i}) = 1 + \frac{\sin 2\alpha}{2\pi} - \frac{\alpha}{\pi} \tag{6-54a}$$

$$N_{21}(i_0, \hat{i}) = i_0(1 + N_{11}) + \frac{\hat{i}}{\pi}\left(\alpha \cos\alpha - \frac{5}{4}\sin\alpha + \frac{1}{12}\sin 3\alpha\right) \tag{6-54b}$$

where

$$\alpha = \begin{cases} \cos^{-1}\dfrac{\psi_{max} - |i_0|}{\hat{i}}, & \psi_{max} - |i_0| \le \hat{i} \\ 0, & \psi_{max} - |i_0| > \hat{i} \end{cases} \tag{6-55}$$

The curves of N_{11} and N_{21} vs. $\hat{i}$ for various values of i_0 are shown in Fig. 6-14.

It is convenient to consider the dc term and the ac term separately as they must separately reach equilibrium within the loop. For this purpose, we can redraw Fig. 6-13 (in view of Eqs. (6-51) to (6-53) into the form of Fig. 6-15a and 6-15b. (Show this.)

For $\hat{i} = 0$, the dc terms are given in (5-35). Consider only the case $|i_{dc}| = |i_0| < \psi_{max}$, we have:

$$\begin{aligned} &i_{dc} = \psi_{dc} = i_0 = \pm\sqrt{\gamma}, \quad N_{10}(i_0, 0) = 1, \\ &N_{20}(i_0, 0) = i_0, \quad v_{dc} = v_0 = \frac{1}{\xi}(M - a) \end{aligned} \tag{6-56}$$

In the presence of self-oscillation, the dc values will shift slightly in order to come to equilibrium again in accordance with Fig. 6-15*a*. This shift of dc value will, in turn, cause a shift in the ac gains. In this example however, for typical numerical values, the effect of the dc shift turns out to be unimportant in the calculation for the amplitude and frequency of self-oscillation and hence will neglected. In the next chapter we will consider ways to handle dc and ac terms simultaneously.

In view of the above, we now assume that (6-56) will also hold for $\hat{i} \neq 0$. With this assumption, taking into account only the fundamental component terms in Eqs. (6-51) to (6-53), it follows on using (6-56) that

$$\begin{bmatrix} [a(1 - N_{11}) + (T + N_{11}T_E)p] & \xi i_0 \\ -N_{21} & (b + T_J p) \end{bmatrix} \begin{bmatrix} \hat{i}\sin\omega t \\ \hat{v}\sin(\omega t + \phi) \end{bmatrix} = \begin{bmatrix} 0 \\ 0 \end{bmatrix} \tag{6-57*}$$

*Note that if $\hat{i} \to 0$ and $\hat{v} \to 0$, then (6-57) becomes identical to (5-37) if we replace $\hat{i}\sin\omega t$ with δi and $\hat{v}\sin(\omega t + \phi)$ with δv. The reader may try to explain to his own satisfaction why this is so.

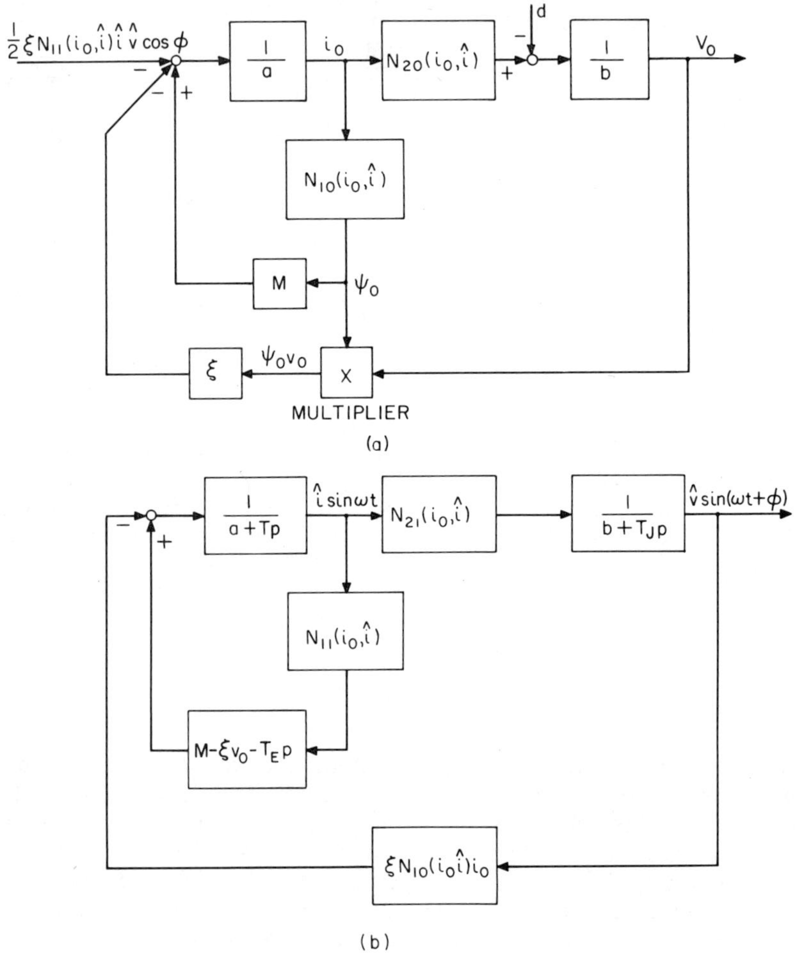

Fig. 6-15. (a) The block diagram for the dc term for the system of Example 6-8 under the describing function assumption; (b) The block diagram for the ac term for the system of Example 6-8 under the describing function assumption.

Equation (6–57) is obtained under the assumption of periodic oscillation. In order to verify this, we must show that the characteristic equation (6–57) has imaginary solutions. The characteristic equation (6–57) is:

$$T_J(T + N_{11}T_E)\lambda^2 + \left[b(T + N_{11}T_E) + a(1 - N_{11})T_J\right]\lambda + ab(1 - N_{11}) + \xi i_0 N_{21} = 0 \quad \textbf{(6–58)}$$

The roots of (6-58) are given by

$$\lambda = \frac{b(T+N_{11}T_E)+a(1-N_{11})T_J}{2T_J(T+N_{11}T_E)}\left\{-1 \pm \left[1-\frac{4T_J(T+N_{11}T_E)[ab(1-N_{11})+\xi i_0 N_{21}]}{[b(T+N_{11}T_E)+a(1-N_{11})T_J]^2}\right]^{\frac{1}{2}}\right\} \tag{6-59}$$

Physically, we must have $\xi \geq 1$, $a \geq 0$, $b \geq 0$, $T_J \geq 0$, $T \geq 0$, and $T_E \geq 0$. Furthermore, from (6-54), we have $0 \leq N_{11} \leq 1$ and $N_{21} i_0 > 0$. Therefore, the following always holds

$$\begin{aligned} b(T + N_{11}) + a(1 - N_{11})T_J &\geq 0 \\ ab(1 - N_{11}) + \xi i_0 N_{21} &> 0 \end{aligned} \tag{6-60}$$

From (6-59) and (6-60), it is clear that the roots of the characteristic equation can have only zero or negative real parts. A periodic solution is possible within our approximation only if the roots have zero real parts or if:

$$b(T + N_{11}T_E) + a(1 - N_{11})T_J = 0 \tag{6-61}$$

This will be so if the constant b vanishes, and at the same time $N_{11} = 1$.

Consider now when $b = 0$. First of all by (6-54), there is a range of small values of $\hat{i}$ for which $N_{11} = 1$ is satisfied. This indicates that within this range of $\hat{i}$, the system trajectory will execute vortex type motion about the equilibrium point ($i_e = i_0$, $v_e = v_0$). Outside of this range, however, when $\hat{i} > \psi_s - i_0$, we have $N_{11} < 1$. This means that $\Re e\,\lambda < 0$ for the characteristic roots and thus for large amplitudes the trajectories will spiral inward. Clearly there will be separatrices separating the vortex-type motion from the inward spiraling motion. The above explains the interesting state-plane portrait of Fig. 4-22.

If $b \neq 0$, then (6-59) indicates that $\Re e\,\lambda < 0$, which points to stable motion. However, strictly speaking, the describing function analysis is valid only for imaginary roots; we will not attempt to interpret results in this case. A typical result is as shown in Fig. 4-21.

For other possible modes of operation, the reader is referred to the reference [J4].♦♦

6.5 The Describing Function for Closed-Loop Nonlinear Systems and the Jump Phenomenon

The describing function approach can be extended to study the behavior of a closed-loop nonlinear system under a specified excitation. This step is, however, not without its hazards, for the analyst must now reckon with several modes of anomalous behavior that are possible with nonlinear closed-loop systems under a forcing function. To be more specific, consider a closed-loop nonlinear system under a sinusoidal forcing function. The possible modes of behavior are:

1) The system undergoes self-oscillation in spite of the driving function.
2) The system output is a periodic function whose period is a *multiple* of the input period, i.e., the system undergoes a *subharmonic oscillation*.
3) The system output is a periodic function whose period is a *submultiple* of the input period, i.e., the system undergoes a *harmonic oscillation*.
4) The system goes into an *almost periodic oscillation*.*
5) The system output is a periodic function whose period is the same as that of the input.

For most control systems, only case (5) yields a desired type of response. Cases (1)-(4) then represent anomalous system behaviors whose characteristics a system designer needs to know in order to prevent them from occurring.

Generally speaking cases (1)-(4) occur only when the system in question is at the verge of self-oscillation even without input. Case (2), for example, can occur if the system self-oscillation period is close to a multiple of the input period; whereas case (3) can occur if the system self-oscillation period is close to a submultiple of the input period. Case (1), of course, can occur only when the system is inherently oscillatory.

A closed-loop system consisting of a linear plant and a simple nonlinearity can be at the verge of oscillation for two reasons. A plant that is third order or higher can exhibit oscillatory tendencies because of the nonlinearity in the loop or because the linear plant has a resonance peak at a particular frequency. If a designer guards against these two possibilities, then he can generally assure that the system output period matches that of the input.

Even when the input and output are of the same periodicity, however, there is still a further mode of anomalous behavior that can occur in a nonlinear system. This is the phenomenon of jump resonance.

***Almost periodic oscillation* occurs for example in a system near the verge of self-oscillation when the period of the input and the period of the system self-oscillation are not commensurate with each other; thus the modulated output wave does not have a distinct period although on casual inspection the waveform appears to be periodic. See, e.g., [H8].

If $\hat{y}$ is the amplitude of the fundamental component of the output waveform, $\hat{r}$ is the amplitude of the input sinusoidal wave and ω is the input frequency, then, typically, the jump resonance phenomenon manifests itself in the manner shown in Fig. 6-16. When ω is fixed and $\hat{r}$ is slowly increased, the ratio $\hat{y}/\hat{r}$ varies smoothly until a value $\hat{r}_2$ is reached, then suddenly a jump in the $\hat{y}/\hat{r}$ ratio is observed. This same phenomenon is usually also observed in the phase lag between the input and the output wave.

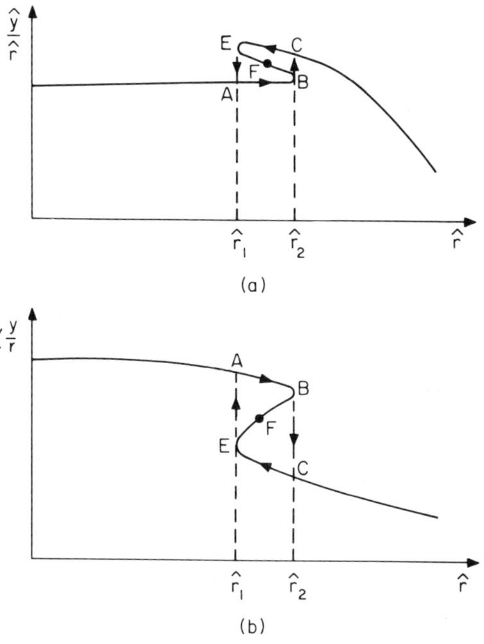

Fig. 6-16. A typical jump phenomenon in a nonlinear system.

When $\hat{r}$ is decreased from a value above $\hat{r}_2$, there is another jump taking place at a point $\hat{r}_1$. Usually $\hat{r}_1$ is less than $\hat{r}_2$. The jump resonance phenomenon can also manifest itself at a fixed value of $\hat{r}$ when the input frequency is slowly increased. The $|\hat{y}/\hat{r}|$ vs. ω and $\angle y/r$ vs. ω characteristics are similar to those of the $\hat{y}/\hat{r}$ vs. $\hat{r}$ and $\angle y/r$ vs. $\hat{r}$ of Fig. 6-16.

The phenomenon of jump resonance can, in many cases, be investigated by the use of the describing function, provided of course that sufficient precautions are taken to prevent the occurrence of the four phenomena (1)-(4), about which the describing function approach as such can yield no useful information.

In this section, we shall consider the particular case of a system containing a saturation type nonlinearity. By means of a geometrical construction, some rather interesting conclusions concerning the jump resonance in the system can be made.

Let the system be that represented by Fig. 6-17; with $r(t) = \hat{r} \sin \omega t$, and let the unit limiter $l(e)$ as defined in Sec. 6.2 be the nonlinearity $\mathfrak{N}$. Let us further assume that:

1) No subharmonics are generated by the system.
2) $G(j\omega)$ is stable and exhibits a low-pass characteristic so that the higher frequencies are uniformly more attenuated than the lower frequencies.
3) With no input, the system is closed-loop stable.

Under these assumptions, the describing function should provide fairly accurate prediction of the system forced-oscillation response.

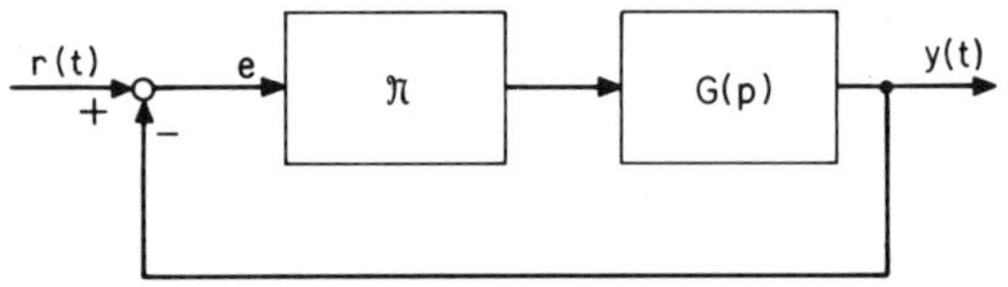

Fig. 6-17. A simple, single-loop system for investigating the jump phenomenon.

Let the sinusoidal input be $r(t) = \hat{r} \sin(\omega t + \theta)$ and let the fundamental components of the steady-state responses $e(t)$ and $y(t)$ be given by $\hat{e} \sin(\omega t + \delta)$ and $\hat{y} \sin(\omega t + \phi)$ respectively.

Relative to the system under consideration, the following approach due to J. C. Lozier [L16] is useful in helping us to visualize the mechanism of the jump phenomenon.

Regard the three sine waves $\hat{r} \sin(\omega t + \theta)$, $\hat{e} \sin(\omega t + \delta)$, and $\hat{y} \sin(\omega t + \phi)$ as the phasors $\overline{R}(\omega)$, $\overline{E}(\omega)$, and $\overline{Y}(\omega)$ respectively. If the describing function assumption holds, we have, at the loop summing junction:

$$\overline{R}(\omega) = \overline{E}(\omega) + \overline{Y}(\omega) \tag{6-62}$$

Let us immediately note that if $E(\omega)$ is chosen as the reference phasor then with $\delta = 0$, $\overline{E}$ lies parallel with the real axis. The determination of the existence of jump resonance can now be reduced to a simple geometrical problem on the $G(j\omega)$ (Nyquist) plane. If $\delta = 0$, then the phase angle of $\overline{Y}$ will be given by the phase angle of $G(j\omega)$. Using a standard notation, we have:

$$\angle \overline{Y} = \angle G(j\omega) \tag{6-63}$$

Consider now the geometric picture that pertains when $\hat{e}$ changes in value. At $\hat{e} = 1$, the saturation value is just reached.

Here the magnitude of $\overline{Y}$ is also given by the magnitude of $G(j\omega)$. When Eq. (6–62) is used, the phasor triangle of Fig. 6–18a will hold (shown with a dashed base line). This triangle is readily constructed on the $G(j\omega)$ plane and we directly make use of the Nyquist plot of $G(j\omega)$.

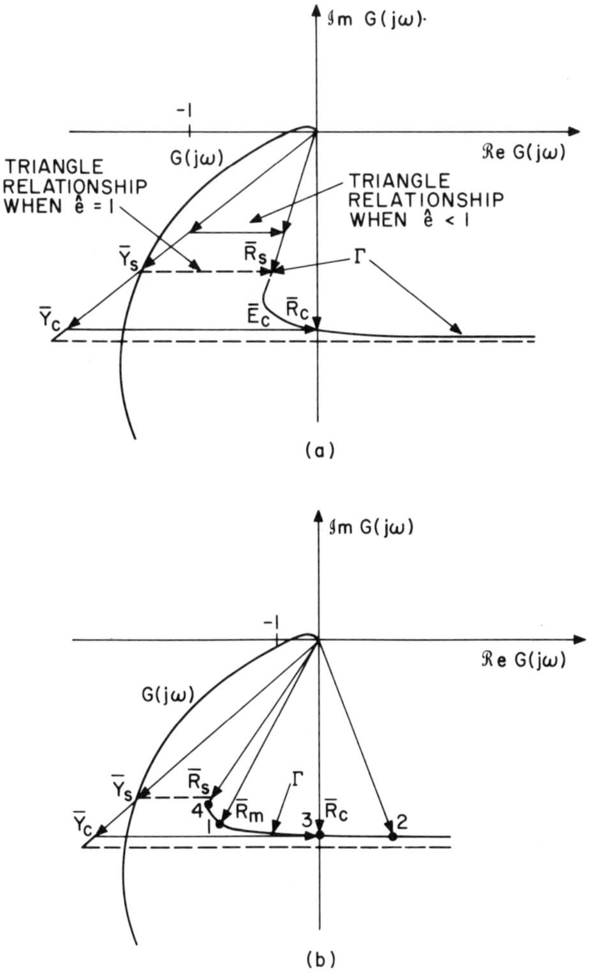

Fig. 6-18. The triangle construction of Lozier in the $G(j\omega)$ plane. It can be used to determine the possibility of a jump phenomenon for a system with a limiter.

For $\hat{e} < 1$, the system operates in the linear region, here a triangle similar to but smaller than the case for $\hat{e} = 1$ will obtain. (See Fig. 6–18a.)

When $\hat{e} > 1$, the system saturates periodically. Using the describing function approximation, we have

$$\overline{R}(\omega) = \overline{E}(\omega) + N(\hat{e})\hat{e}\overline{G}(j\omega) \tag{6-64}$$

where $N(\hat{e})$ is the describing function of the saturation nonlinearity. From Sec. 6.2 for the unit limiter we have:

$$N(\hat{e}) = \frac{2}{\pi}\left[\sin^{-1}\frac{1}{\hat{e}} + \frac{1}{\hat{e}}\sqrt{1 - \left(\frac{1}{\hat{e}}\right)^2}\,\right] \tag{6-65}$$

By Eq. (6-64), which is in essence a statement of balance of the fundamental component at the error junction, we see that it is convenient to study the problem with $\hat{e}$ as the variable. Thus we label $\overline{R}$ as $\overline{R}(\omega, \hat{e})$.

Using Eqs. (6-64) and (6-65), the locus of $\overline{R}(\omega, \hat{e})$ for a given ω and for $1 \leq \hat{e} < \infty$ can be constructed. This locus is labeled as Γ on Fig. 6-18a. Since $N(\hat{e})\hat{e}$ is a monotonically increasing function with an upper bound of $4/\pi$, the locus Γ must assume the shape as depicted.

We note that for a given system of the form of Fig. 6-17 under a sinusoidal input, for each value of ω, a locus Γ can be plotted. We can now show that by studying geometrically the corresponding locus Γ, we can ascertain the existence of jump phenomenon for the particular value of ω.

For the particular case shown in Fig. 6-18a, let us designate the value of $\overline{R}(\omega, 1)$ as $\overline{R}_s$, and the point where Γ crosses the imaginary axis as $\overline{R}_c$. Let us first study the effect of increasing the input sinusoidal amplitude $\hat{r}$ continuously.

If $\overline{R}_s > \overline{R}_c$, then there will be a value of $\overline{R}$, denoted $\overline{R}_m$, which lies on the segment of Γ between $\overline{R}_s$ and $\overline{R}_c$ with the property that its magnitude is the largest of all the $\overline{R}$'s over this segment. If $\hat{r}$ is increased incrementally beyond $|\overline{R}_m|$, Eq. (6-65) can only be satisfied by a discontinuous change in the *direction* of the vector $\overline{R}$ from point 1 to point 2 in Fig. 6-18b. However, such a jump in direction of $\overline{R}$ will bring about a jump in the *magnitude* of $\overline{Y}$ and $\overline{E}$. The result, both in amplitude and in phase, will be the same as that of the jump ABC depicted in Fig. 6-16. We thus see that under the above circumstances, the system operating point cannot lie between $\overline{R}_m$ and $\overline{R}_c$.

Consider now when $\hat{r}$ is decreased from an initial value larger than $|\overline{R}_m|$. From Fig. 6-18b we can see that all the points of the curve Γ to the right of the value $\overline{R}_c$ are possible operating points for the system. But since $\overline{R}_c$ is now locally a minimum, as R falls to the value of $\overline{R}_c$, the vector $\overline{R}$ must change discontinuously in *direction* from point 3 to point 4. $\overline{Y}$ and $\overline{E}$ must again suffer a jump in magnitude. This results in the jump CEA of Fig. 6-16.

Notice that points on the segment BFE on both the amplitude and phase plots of Fig. 6-16 represent possible operating points from a consideration of the curve Γ but actually they cannot exist physically from the foregoing analysis. They represent unstable operating points of the system.

When we study the resultant geometric picture, some interesting conclusions can be made (see Exercise 6-10):*

1) The jump phenomenon in the $\hat{y}/\hat{r}$ vs. $\hat{r}$ characteristics for a given ω will occur if and only if $\Re e\, \overline{R}_s < 0$ and $\overline{R}_m$ exists.
2) If $\Re e\, G(j\omega) > -1$ for all ω, then no jump resonance will occur.
3) A sufficient condition for the occurrence of jump resonance at some frequency ω_1 is that $G(j\omega_1)$ falls in the region B of Fig. 6-19, which lies to the left of the two straight lines labeled Λ. When this condition on $G(j\omega_1)$ is met, jump resonance can occur due to disturbances within the system even if the system initially operates in the linear range.

Indeed, conclusions (1) and (2) spell out the necessary and sufficient condition for jump resonance clearly enough that a boundary can be found once and for all, demarcating areas on the $G(j\omega)$ plane where jump will occur from that where jump cannot occur. This boundary can either be found graphically or numerically by means of a computer. It is shown as the curve Ω in Fig. 6-19.

Since the jump phenomenon is generally considered to be undesirable in a control system, the locus Ω imposes a restriction on the Nyquist diagram of the linear plant $G(p)$. For all ω, it is desirable that the plot $G(j\omega)$ always stay to the right of the locus Ω.

We may note incidentally that to the right of the locus Ω, and to every point on the Nyquist plane there corresponds a unique value of $\hat{y}/\hat{r}$ for a given value of R. This simply means that as long as $G(j\omega)$ stays to the right of Ω, the *closed-loop* system of Fig. 6-17 under a sinusoidal input possesses a unique describing function between the input r and output y. This describing function can again be calculated using the triangle approach of this section. Notice that this describing function, in addition to being dependent on the amplitude R, is also *frequency dependent* and complex. (See Exercise 6-11.) Indeed, a closed-loop system which is linear except for a zero-memory nonlinear element will generally yield a complex describing function that is frequency dependent.

The insight gained from a consideration of the special case of this section can be used to study systems with other nonlinearities and to construct the Ω locus for these systems.** For extensions

*Provided of course that assumptions necessary for the describing function approach to be applicable are satisfied. These assumptions are implied throughout the discussion of this section.

**In Chapt. 11 we will indicate that the Ω locus obtained using describing function is always less conservative than those obtained using exact methods.

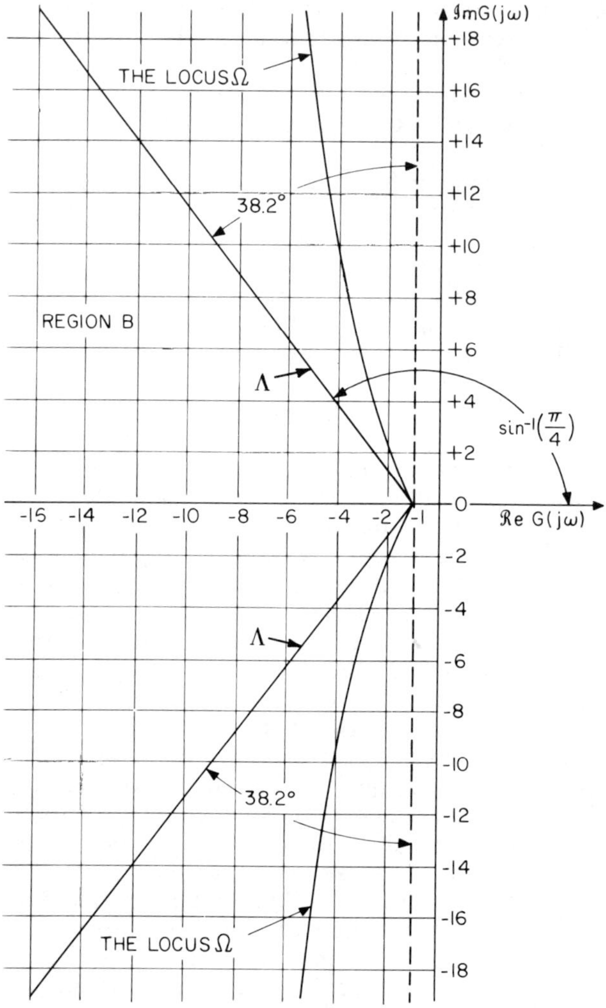

Fig. 6-19. Two loci relevant to the determining of jump phenomenon for a closed-loop system with a unit-limiter under sinusoidal input. If the Nyquist plot of the linear portion of the system $G(j\omega)$ lies to the right of the locus Ω, the describing function approach will lead to the conclusion that no jump phenomenon can occur. If the Nyquist plot of $G(j\omega)$ lies inside the region B bounded by the two lines labeled Λ, then jump can occur for some value of ω.

of the ideas contained in this section to other nonlinearities, the reader is referred to articles by Hatanaka [H7], and Fukuma and Matsubara [F5].

6.6 The Amplitude-Dependent Gain Margin and Its Application to Nonlinear Stabilization

In this section, we shall present an example which illustrates the ideas discussed in the previous sections and is typical for a large class of practical control systems. We shall consider the actuator-controlled feedback system shown in Fig. 6-20.

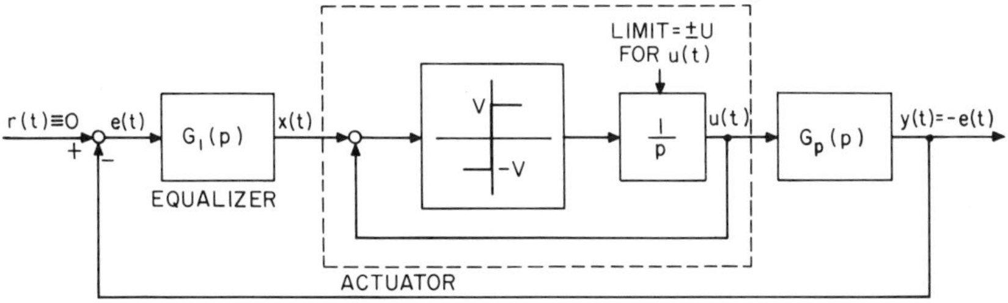

Fig. 6-20. An actuator-controlled feedback system.

Nonlinear actuators are among some of the worst contributors to anomalous system behavior. Often the user of an actuator is misled by its rather optimistic specifications. The gain-bandwidth figures given for actuators are often measured at very small amplitudes. The system engineer who uses these figures as a basis for a design of a control system may find out later that, though his system is stable at small signals, any appreciable transient (e.g., due to an input command) will cause it to become unstable and/or to go into undesirable oscillations. Even if this does not happen, the true system performance is likely to differ considerably from the intended one. We shall show here and in the next section how this comes about and what considerations the designer can take to remedy the situation.

Generally speaking, in a well-designed control system, both position and velocity of the actuator will "hit the limits" as often as possible, thereby making maximum use of the available control power. This then means that in any realistic control situation, i.e., for appreciable control signal amplitudes, the actuator will be characterized mainly by its limits of position and velocity; in a hydraulic actuator, for example, these limits correspond to piston length and maximum fluid flow respectively.

For any appreciable signal, a good approximation for the behavior of some actuators can be given in terms of the model shown in dotted block on Fig. 6-20.* For the particular actuator

*Note that as indicated in Fig. 6-20, not only is the actuator output limited to $\pm U$, but the actuator output velocity is also limited to $\pm V$.

model of Fig. 6-21a, the describing function is illustrated in Fig. 6-21b.* (See also Exercise 6-12.)

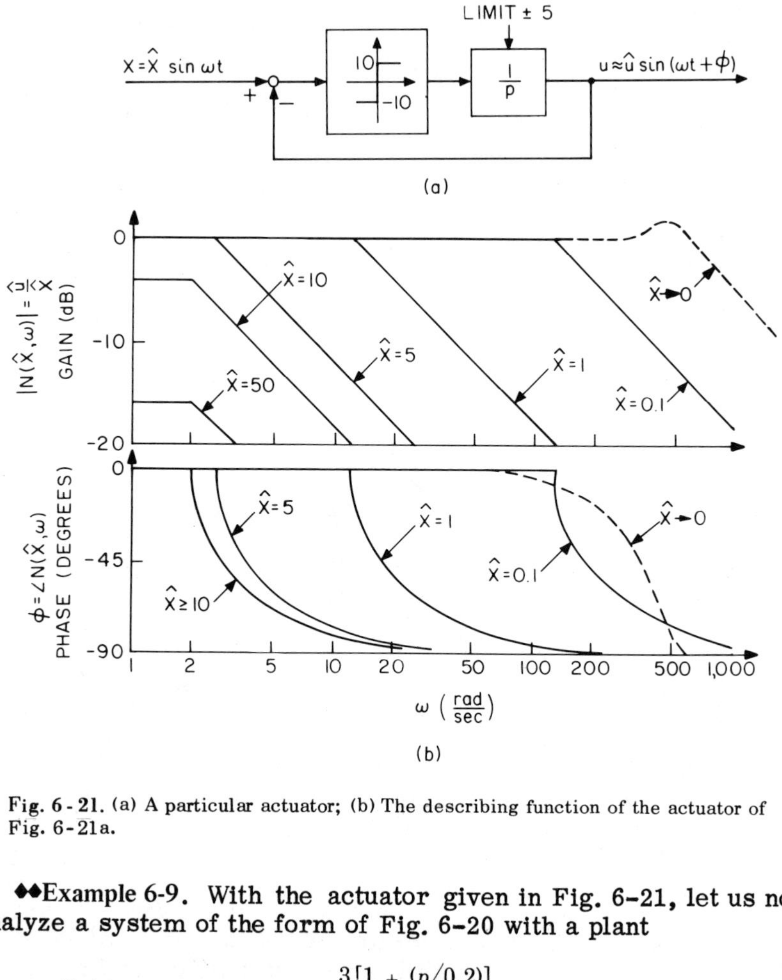

Fig. 6-21. (a) A particular actuator; (b) The describing function of the actuator of Fig. 6-21a.

◆◆Example 6-9. With the actuator given in Fig. 6-21, let us now analyze a system of the form of Fig. 6-20 with a plant

$$G_p(p) = \frac{3[1 + (p/0.2)]}{[1 + (p/45) + (p^2/9)][1 + (p/60)][1 + (p/300)]} \tag{6-66}$$

Let us now see what happens if we design a control system on the basis of small-signal performance. For small signals, the actuator behaves like a linear unity gain element. When we assume

*The dotted curves in Fig. 6-21b represent closed-loop responses for a typical actuator, valid for small signals. For appreciable amplitude values, however, the response curves of the true actuator will be closer to those of the (large-signal) model considered here.

small signals, we can design an equalizer network that yields satisfactory closed-loop performance. A possible equalizer is given by

$$G_1(p) = 10.53\left[\frac{1 + (p/6)}{1 + (p/0.1)}\right] \tag{6-67}$$

The total effective open-loop transfer function for small signals is then given by $G(s) \triangleq G_p(s)G_1(s)$.

The total open-loop frequency response, which includes that of the actuator, will be given by $N(\hat{x}, \omega)\,G(j\omega)$. This is presented in Fig. 6-22. From the figure we see that for small amplitudes $\hat{x}$, the design is satisfactory.

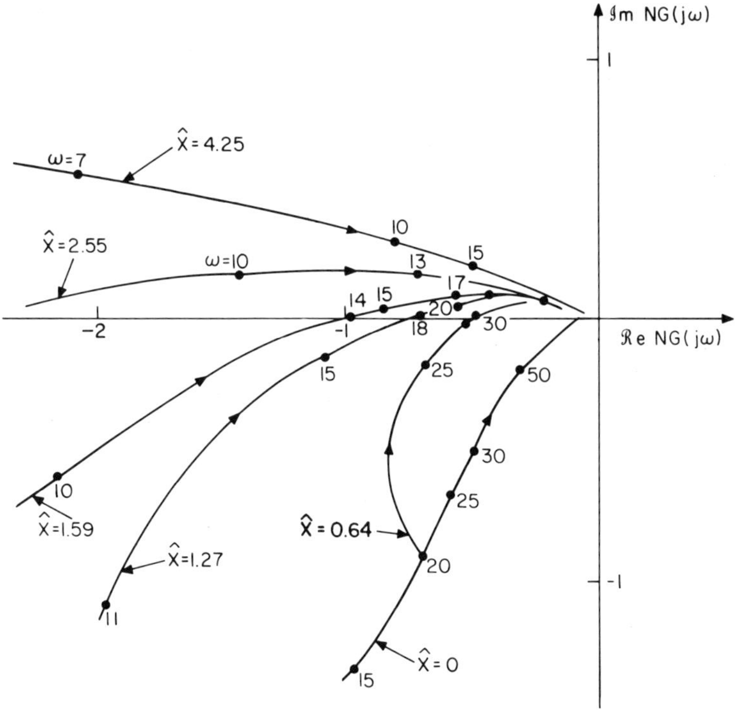

Fig. 6-22. The Nyquist plots of the function $N(\hat{x}, \omega)\,G(j\omega)$ for the system of Example 6-9.

However, rapid degradation of performance takes place as the amplitudes increase. In fact unstable self-oscillation can occur at an amplitude $\hat{x} = 1.6$ and a frequency $\omega_0 = 14$ rad/sec. The describing function analysis thus tells us that, though the system is stable for small signals, it can become unstable under large signals.

Among the possible remedies for large-signal instability of a system of the above type are the following:

1) Reduce the open-loop gain such that the frequency loci for all $\hat{x}$ cross the negative real axis in Fig. 6-22 to the right of the -1 point.
2) Design a linear filter such as to achieve the same result as in (1).
3) Insert a limiter into the loop such as to keep the amplitude $\hat{x}$ below its critical value.

The frequency response curves in Fig. 6-22 suggest that remedies (1) or (2) may stabilize the system, but at the cost of very sluggish response for smaller signals and poor steady-state control performance. Remedy (3) or a combination of remedies (1) and (3), however, can offer a simple and effective means of stabilization, without affecting the satisfactory performance at lower signal levels. This is best explained in terms of the amplitude-dependent gain margin which will now be introduced.

We recall that for a linear feedback system, an effective stability measure is given by its gain margin, which is the value of the open-loop gain increase required to render the closed-loop system unstable. This concept can be extended to nonlinear feedback systems by defining the *amplitude-dependent gain margin as the gain increase required to cause self-oscillation of the closed loop at a given amplitude of one of the system signals.**

For the example of the system considered in this section, the amplitude-dependent gain margin, K_c, can be obtained from the frequency-response curves of Fig. 6-22. For each given amplitude $\hat{x}$, K_c is the quantity $1/|N_A(\hat{x}, \omega)\, G_1(j\omega)\, G_p(j\omega)|$, at the frequency where the total open-loop phase shift is $-180°$, i.e.,

$$K_c(\hat{x}) = \frac{1}{|N_A(\hat{x}, \omega)\, G_1(j\omega_0)\, G_p(j\omega_0)|} \tag{6-68a}$$

where ω_0 is defined by

$$\underline{/N_A(\hat{x}, \omega_0)\, G_1(j\omega_0)\, G_p(j\omega_0)} = -180° \tag{6-68b}$$

The result for the system under consideration is presented in Fig. 6-23, which shows the gain margin $K_c = K_c(\hat{x})$ as a function of amplitude $\hat{x}$. Also indicated are values of the phase crossover frequency ω_0 (where the open-loop phase shift is $-180°$) for various values of amplitude $\hat{x}$. Note that for $\hat{x} \geq 1.6$, the gain margin in dB's becomes negative, which indicates instability for large signals.

*The definition of the amplitude-dependent gain margin is of course based on the same assumption that is basic to the stability interpretation of the describing function method.

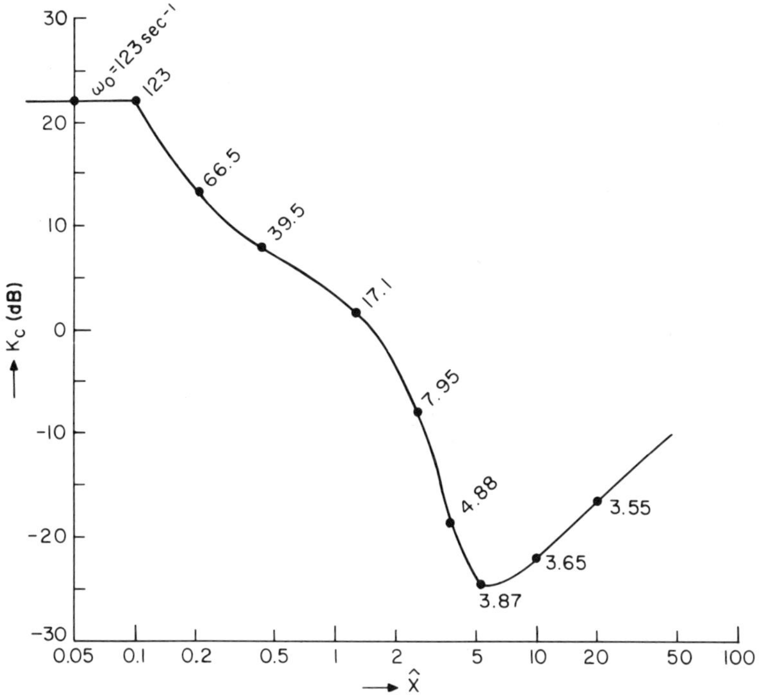

Fig. 6-23. The amplitude-dependent gain margin $K_c(\hat{x})$ for the system of Example 6-9.

From Fig. 6-23, we may also obtain similar curves showing the gain margin vs. the amplitude of some other signal in the system. For example, we may be interested in the amplitude $\hat{y}$ of the system output. The relation between $\hat{x}$ and $\hat{y}$ is now

$$\hat{y} = |N_A(\hat{x}, \omega_0)\, G_p(j\omega_0)|\, \hat{x} = \frac{\hat{x}}{K_c(\hat{x})\, |G_1(j\omega_0)|} \tag{6-69}$$

where $G_1(p)$ is given by Eq. (6-67). The curve $K_c = K_c(\hat{y})$, shown in solid line in Fig. 6-24, can thus be obtained from the curve $K_c = K_c(\hat{x})$ of Fig. 6-23.

We are now ready to consider the stabilization of the system by inserting a nonlinear element into the error path of the system. The system configuration with a nonlinear compensation is shown in Fig. 6-25. The effect of the nonlinear compensating function $e = f(e_1)$ is analyzed by superimposing its equivalent gain, $N(\hat{e}_1) = N(\hat{y})$, on the gain margin curve $K_c(\hat{y})$ for the system without the nonlinear element. (See Fig. 6-26.) Since $K_c(\hat{y})$ represents the gain increase required to cause oscillatory motion of the system without $f(e_1)$, the nonlinear element will have the effect of reducing the gain

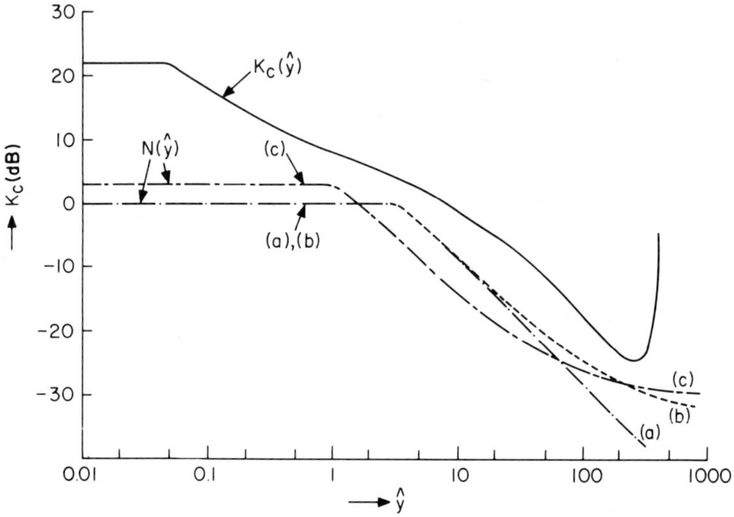

Fig. 6-24. The gain margin $K_c(\hat{y})$ and the describing functions of several nonlinear compensators plotted as functions of the output fundamental amplitude $\hat{y}$.

margin by the amount of its equivalent gain. Thus, as illustrated in Fig. 6-26, the gain margin of the system with $f(e_1)$ will be given by

$$K_c'(\hat{y}) = \frac{K_c(\hat{y})}{N(\hat{y})}$$

or

$$K_c'(\hat{y})\Big|_{db} = K_c(\hat{y})\Big|_{db} - N(\hat{y})\Big|_{db} \tag{6-70}$$

The objective of nonlinear stabilization thus is to find a nonlinear function $e = f(e_1)$ such that its describing function $N(\hat{e}_1) = N(\hat{y})$ will lie safely below the $K_c(\hat{y})$ curve. On the other hand, $N(\hat{y})$ should not be too far below the K_c curve in order to maintain the necessary gain for effective control.

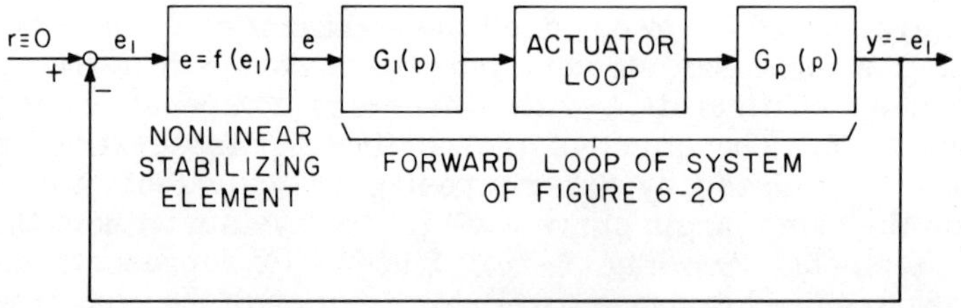

Fig. 6-25. Nonlinear compensation of an actuator-controlled system.

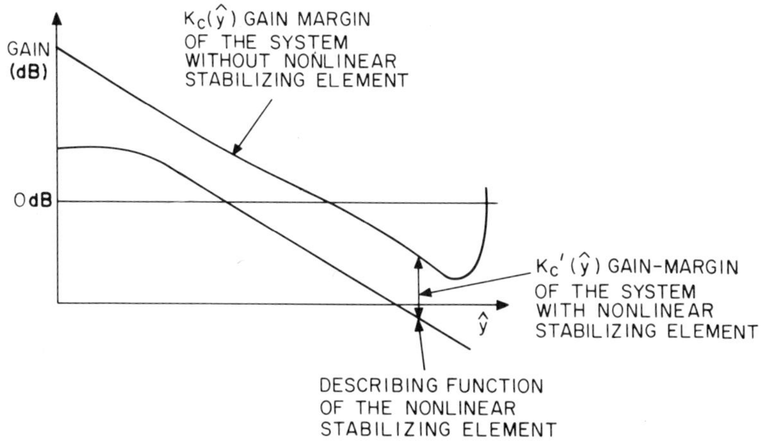

Fig. 6-26. The gain margin of a system with nonlinear stabilizing element is equal to the difference (in dB) between the gain margin of the system without the nonlinear stabilizing element and the describing function of the nonlinear stabilizing element.

For the example discussed in this section, three particular nonlinear functions, shown in Fig. 6-27, are considered. Their describing functions are shown in Fig. 6-24 by the curves (a), (b), and (c). All three describing functions lie below the $K_c(\hat{y})$ curve by a reasonably safe margin.

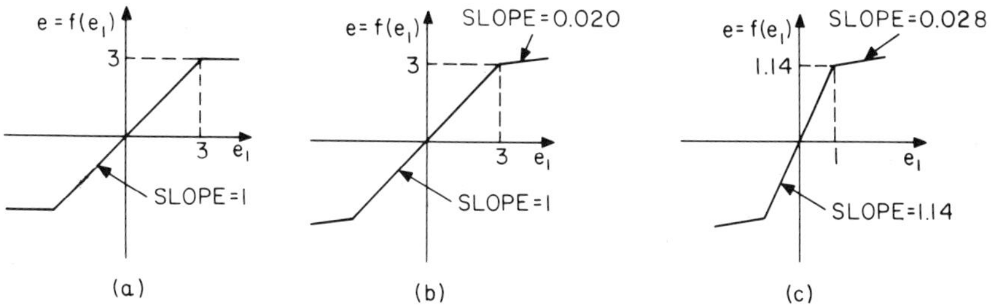

Fig. 6-27. Three possible nonlinear stabilizing elements for the system of Example 6-9. The describing functions of these elements are shown in Fig. 6-24.

We can see in Fig. 6-24 that the simple limiter (a) already offers a satisfactory solution. For higher amplitudes, the open-loop gain can be increased by replacing the limiter (a) by the element (b). Element (c) will permit higher open-loop gain at low amplitudes at the expense of lower loop gain at higher amplitudes. Thus, element (b) is better if the system is to operate predominantly at large signals, and element (c) is better if the signals are predominantly small.♦♦

We must realize that the above interpretation of our curves is intuitive, as is the transient interpretation of any describing function analysis. Quantitative transient response data must come from a test or simulation of the system. However, the procedure is pragmatic and highly reasonable. It has been used by the authors with much success in dealing with rather complex systems encountered in the industry. However, much work in this area, analytical or practical, can yet be done.

The major work in the approach outlined here lies in obtaining the amplitude-dependent gain margin curve from the system. In the next section we will show how this curve can be obtained easily through the use of an oscillating test.

6.7 Testing and Stabilization of Large-Scale Control Systems

It is an unfortunate fact in control system design that, as the order of a system goes into the tens or higher, the utility of most of the methods comes to an end. The designer generally has only the recourse to make the system as linear as possible and provide himself with plenty of margins.

The one method that theoretically can still be readily used for higher order systems is the method of equivalent linearization. We say theoretically because in higher order systems the probability of the existence of anomalous behavior within the system increases and the danger of obtaining wrong answers using equivalent linearization also increases.

One of the most important points to check in a large-scaled system is its behavior in a self-oscillation mode. Most large-scaled control systems can be made to oscillate.* By observing the amplitude, frequency, and, sometimes, the wave shape of this oscillation, much can be inferred concerning the system.

An obvious test to determine the existence of anomalous behavior which can be applied to a system (or its simulation thereof) is to raise one of its gains, say K, from its nominal designed value K_0 to a point K_1 where the system begins to self-oscillate. When the self-oscillation is well established, lower the gain slowly. Usually the value of the gain at which the oscillation ceases, K_2, is well below K_1. Sometimes, however, it may happen that K_2 is even lower than K_0. This means that at the nominal design, the system is stable in the small but unstable in the large and any significant distrubance may send the system into oscillation. This is then a sure sign of an ill-designed system. An example of such a system

*It is probably not desirable to carry out this test on the actual system itself. Frequently however, a simulation of the system is available for the oscillating test.

is that considered in the last section. Needless to say, when there is a jump-type anomaly in a minor loop of the system (see Sec. 6.5), then the changes in the system behavior may be even more drastic.

The simple test given above does not offer a complete picture of system stability or instability. The oscillating amplitude and frequency are likely to depend on the saturation value* of the linear gain element K unless the saturation value is high enough that some element in the system goes into saturation first. Since we have shown that system stability can be conveniently expressed in terms of the amplitude-dependent gain margin over the entire range of possible amplitudes, we now present a simple method by which the amplitude-dependent gain margin can be measured directly on a system or a simulation of the system.

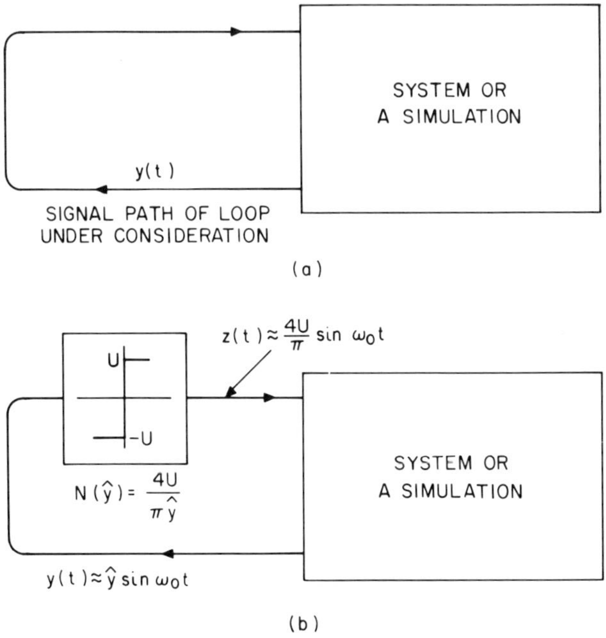

Fig. 6-28. Implementation of the oscillating test for a complex system.

Consider a complex control system with a signal path of one of the loops exposed for measurement. (See Fig. 6-28a.) Let us place an ideal relay of output-level U into this path. (See Fig. 6-28b.) This is almost certain to cause oscillation of the system in a simple

*Every realistic gain element must have some saturation value.

periodic manner.* Making the same assumptions as in the describing function analysis, we take the relay input to be of the form $\hat{y}$ sin $\omega_0 t$.** The equivalent gain of the relay for the amplitude $\hat{y}$ represents the gain increase needed in the given loop to cause self-oscillation of amplitude $\hat{y}$. Hence, the *equivalent gain of the relay equals $K_c(\hat{y})$, the gain margin of the loop with respect to the oscillating amplitude* $\hat{y}$.

Since the equivalent gain of the relay is simply $4U/\pi\hat{y}$, then a plot of this quantity vs. $\hat{y}$, for various values of relay-levels U, will yield the desired gain margin curve. Thus, the test, which we shall call the *oscillating test*, involves taking data on oscillating amplitudes $\hat{y}$ vs. relay levels U. From these data, we can obtain the equivalent relay gain versus amplitude, or $K_c(\hat{y}) = 4U/\pi\hat{y}$ vs. $\hat{y}$. Thus, a curve such as the $K_c(\hat{y})$ curve in Fig. 6-26 can be obtained directly from the oscillating test. From this curve we can then determine directly any nonlinear stabilizing element that may be required. A typical plot of $\hat{y}$ vs. U may be as shown in Fig. 6-29.

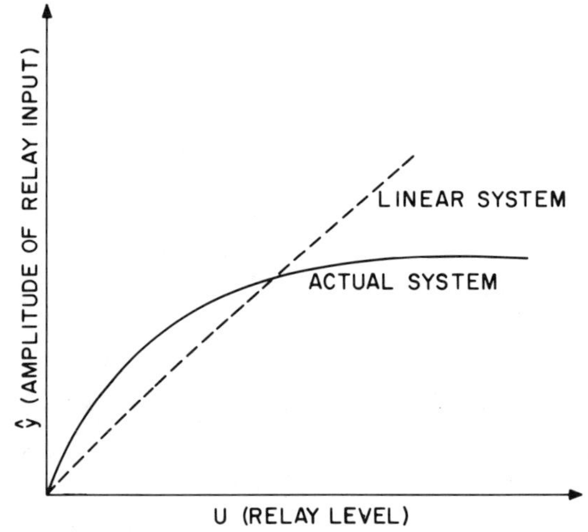

Fig. 6-29. A typical $\hat{y}$ vs. U characteristic obtained from an oscillating test. From this the gain margin $K_c(\hat{y}) = 4U/\pi\hat{y}$ can be constructed.

In carrying out the oscillating test, we can also readily record the frequency of self-oscillation, ω_0, for each amplitude $\hat{y}$, during the oscillating test. In a linear system, the frequency ω_0, representing the phase-crossover frequency at which the open-loop

*See Chap. 8 for a discussion of relay control systems.

**The signal $y(t)$ during oscillation is usually recorded experimentally in order to verify how reasonable the assumption $y(t) = \hat{y}$ sin ωt is.

phase shift is 180° (for all amplitudes), provides a rough measure of the bandwidth for the closed-loop system.* Extending this concept to nonlinear systems, we may speak of "crossover frequency," ω_0, as that frequency where the phase shift of the fundamental component of the open-loop equivalent transfer-function is −180°. In this case, the crossover frequency is a function of amplitude. The crossover frequency can also be readily obtained when we carry out the oscillating test. For the system of Fig. 6-20, for example, the f_0 vs. $\hat{y}$ curve is obtained as shown in Fig. 6-30.

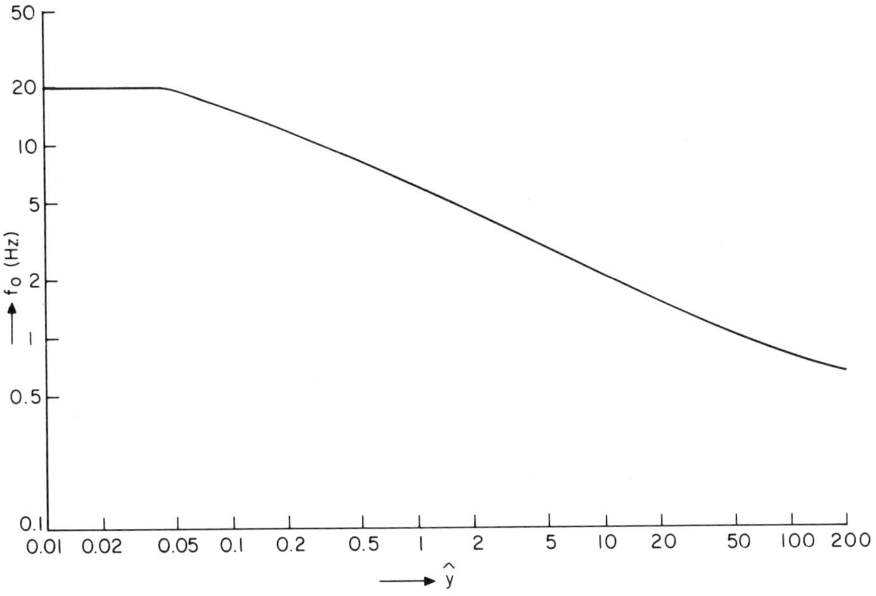

Fig. 6-30. A plot of the fundamental frequency of self-oscillation f_0 vs. $\hat{y}$, as obtained from the oscillating test. f_0 provides a measure of the "turnabout time" of the system.

At this point, a word of caution is in order. It is not possible to find any precise interpretation for the curve $f_0 = f_0(\hat{y})$. In particular it is not advisable to interpret $f_0(\hat{y})$ in terms of "bandwidth for various amplitudes." The curve, however, can help to shed some light on the transient performance of the system. For example, we may interpret $1/2f_0$ as a measure of "turnabout time," i.e., the time it takes to reverse the output signal at a given level that corresponds to the value of $\hat{y}$. However, any precise statement on

*We must be careful in relating the phase-crossover frequency f_0 with the closed-loop bandwidth. The values for these two frequencies are not always close together.

the transient response of the system must come from a transient response test itself on the system or its simulation.

The oscillating test yields roughly the same information that one obtains from the describing function method. It is expected to be effective, provided the filtering assumption concerning the higher harmonics generated by the nonlinearities is fulfilled. This assumption, however, may not be true for all the points in the system where signals are fed into the various nonlinear elements. In fact, the gain-phase characteristic (for the fundamental frequency component) of a nonlinear subsystem may be influenced by the presence of higher harmonic terms in its input signal. Both physical insight and appropriate measurement of the signals involved during the test can help in assessing the possible effects of these higher harmonics.

The oscillating test will provide gain margins with respect to oscillatory types of instability, but it will not yield any information on nonoscillatory types of instability. To this extent, the result is identical to that obtained from the describing function method. However, the oscillating test will not yield any oscillating condition that corresponds to an unstable oscillation For most practical cases, this is not an undue disadvantage. In any case, the availability of the system or its simulation makes it possible to make suitable checks on the conclusions reached from the oscillating test.

6.8 Problems for Which the Describing Function Approach Fails

We have mentioned that the describing function, being inexact, can fail in certain cases. Let us give some brief consideration to situations where the method does not yield the correct solution.

It can be readily shown that for nonlinearities without memory, the cases in which the describing function method holds are about as comprehensive as the cases where the Aizerman's conjecture holds. Specifically it is easy to show that (see Exercise 6-15) for all those cases where the Aizerman conjecture fails to hold because of the existence of limit cycles, the describing function method will fail also. Thus, for example, describing function will not be able to predict the existence of a limit cycle for the system of Eq. (5-87). Indeed all of the systems that prove to be counter examples to the Aizerman's conjecture in references [P6], [D5], and [F1] also constitute counter examples to the describing function.

Since describing function also can be used for systems with memory type nonlinearities, it is clearly valid for more cases than Aizerman's conjecture.

We note, however, that for most of the cases where Aizerman's conjecture and describing function fail the $G(j\omega)$ characteristic of linear plant usually has high resonant peaks. These are the very cases where engineers have traditionally been warned to be wary of the results indicated by describing function.

It is quite possible to give physical rationale as to why describing function fail in the indicated cases (see Exercise 6-16). Our understanding of the mechanism of failure is further strengthened when we study dual-input describing functions in the next chapter.

6.9 Summary

The describing function and related methods constitute powerful tools in the analysis and design of a large class of practical control systems, particularly those of higher order.

The methods are useful in predicting the existence and stability of large-signal oscillations of the limit-cycle type in a free nonlinear system.

The methods are approximate and generally require that the harmonics generated by the nonlinearities in a closed-loop control system do not materially affect the operating condition of the system. Under these conditions, the harmonics are neglected and only the fundamental component of an assumed oscillating frequency is taken into account. Then, on writing down the necessary conditions for self-oscillation we can solve, either analytically or graphically, for the amplitude and frequency of the system self-oscillation, if such exists.

Conventionally, the methods are applied to a system with well-defined linear and nonlinear parts (Fig. 6-5). Here when the nonlinearity is sufficiently simple (e.g., a simple piecewise linear zero-memory element or a simple element with hysteresis), the describing function can be found with reasonable ease (see Table 6-2) and methods related to the linear techniques making use of the Nyquist or the Bode plots of the linear element can then be used to determine the conditions for self-oscillation.

But the greatest utility of the describing function approach lies in its ability to handle more complicated systems or problems. First, it is useful in determining whether a system of the form of Fig. 6-5 will exhibit jump resonance under sinusoidal excitation. The mechanism of the jump phenomenon is a closed-loop system boasting a limiter is explained through a phasor approach first used by Lozier [L16] in Sec. 6.5.

Second, the describing function method permits us to obtain the stability margins of a nonlinear system for both small and large signals through an *amplitude-dependent gain margin*. This can be obtained for a free closed-loop nonlinear system consisting of one or more inner loops such as nonlinear actuator loops. The use of the amplitude dependent gain margin opens up several possibilities in nonlinear compensation, as is shown in a detailed example given in Sec. 6.6.

To obtain the amplitude-dependent gain margin in the orthodox manner can be a laborious process. In Sec. 6.7, an effective procedure that can be used to obtain the margin quickly for a high-order system is described. The procedure has been used with success by the authors in industry.

The possibilities in the uses of the methods related to the describing function approach do not appear to have been exhausted.

6.10 Exercises

6-1 Consider the system $m\ddot{x} + kx\,|x| = 0$

a) Obtain the general solutions in the state plane. (Note that the system is conservative.)
b) Use the describing function method to determine if self-oscillation is possible; if it is, find the period and amplitude of oscillation.
c) The period of the solution can be obtained by direct integration. Check the result of (b) with the exact value.

6-2 Derive the describing function for the nonlinearities numbers 6, 11, and 23 in Table 6-2.

6-3 Discuss how a system of the form of Fig. 6-5 with the nonlinearity an arbitrary limiter

$$n = \begin{cases} Kx\,, & |x| \le a \\ Ka\,, & x > a \\ -Ka\,, & x < -a \end{cases}$$

can be transformed so that the describing function for the unit limiter, as given in Table 6-2, can be used.

6-4 Consider a system of the form of Fig. 6-5 with the nonlinearity an ideal relay of amplitude U and with

$$G(p) = \frac{B[1 - (p/b)]}{p(p + a)}$$

a) Investigate the existence and in-the-small stability of all possible equilibrium states.

b) Investigate the existence and stability of all possible limit cycles using the technique of equivalent linearization.
c) Identify equilibrium states and the amplitude(s) and frequency(ies) of limit cycle(s) for the following set of parameters: $U = 2$, $B = 10\ \text{sec}^{-2}$, $b = 25\ \text{sec}^{-1}$, $a = 1\ \text{sec}^{-1}$.
d) For a constant input $r(t) = R$, what is the average value of the output $x(t)$ of the system in the steady state?

6-5 Consider an nth-order linear time-invariant system with n pairs of nonrepeating, purely imaginary poles. Let these roots be incommensurable with each other; i.e., if the poles are given by $p = \pm jp_1, \pm jp_2, \ldots,$ then the ratio p_i/p_k, $i \neq k$, cannot be given as a ratio of integers. Discuss the resulting free motion in any state space appropriate for the system. Is it stable? Orbitally stable? Periodic? Bounded?

6-6 For the system of Example 6-3, solve graphically for the amplitude and frequency of self-oscillation in the system by plotting the Nyquist plot of the linear portion of the system against the function $-1/N(\hat{x}_1)$. (See Sec. 6.2), especially the discussion pertaining to Eq. (6-14).)

6-7 For a system of the form of Fig. 6-5 with a nonlinearity that is the "backlash characteristic" (nonlinearity 22 in Table 6-2) and with

$$G(p) = \frac{40}{p(p + 1)(p + 4)}$$

a) Using equivalent linearization, determine the range of the slope K of the backlash characteristic for which no self-oscillations can exist. State the assumptions made.
b) For the range of K for which self-oscillations can exist, plot curves showing the frequency of self-oscillation ω_0 and the relative amplitude of self-oscillation $\hat{e}/A$, both as functions of K (in dB).
c) Describe what happens physically when the value of K lies below and above the range of self-oscillations.
d) Determine the system equilibrium points and their stability for the three ranges of K. (Suggestion: use the Nichols chart for the describing function analysis.)

6-8 The describing function is based on the assumption that the higher harmonics generated by the nonlinear element are filtered out by the linear elements in the control loop. To illustrate that the method occasionally is effective even if the above assumption is not met, consider a system of the form of Fig. 6-5 having as nonlinearity the backlash with saturation characteristic (No. 23 in Table 6-2) with $K = 1$, $B = 4$. For $G(p)$ we have a transportation lag of the form $2e^{-p}$.

a) On the basis of describing function analysis, obtain the range of A for which no self-oscillations exist.
b) Show by physical reasoning that all motion will tend toward an equilibrium zone in e if $A > 1$. Identify this zone. (Hint: use $e(t) = e_0$ for $0 \leq t < 1$.)
c) Compare the approximate result of (a) and the exact result of (b) and discuss how the information obtained by the describing function analysis is to be interpreted.

6-9 A linear distributed parameter plant driven by an actuator is shown in Fig. 6-31.

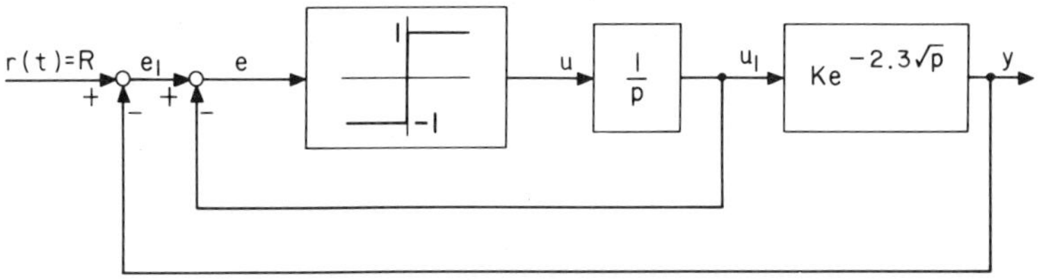

Fig. 6-31. The system of Exercise 6-9.

a) For $R = 0$ and $K = 100$, investigate the existence and stability of self oscillation of the system by means of describing function analysis. Determine the oscillating frequency ω_0 and the *output* amplitude of oscillation $\hat{y}_0$.
b) Using physical reasoning show that the result of (a) is not changed for a constant system input $R \neq 0$. Obtain the average output value Y in terms of R during periodic steady state.
c) Determine the gain K such that it lies 6 dB below the critical gain.
d) Discuss the possible advantages and disadvantages of the oscillating system with $K = 100$ and compare with the non-oscillating system obtained in (c), in terms of transient and steady-state response to an input $r(t)$. (No calculation is required here.)

6-10 Using the triangle construction of Sec. 6.5, prove assertions (1), (2), and (3) on page 223. Show that the region B is given by the boundaries shown in Fig. 6-19.

6-11 For a system of the form of Fig. 6-5 with the unit limiter as the nonlinearity and with $G(p) = 1/[s(s+1)]$, obtain and plot the *closed-loop* describing functions $|\hat{y}/\hat{r}|$ vs. $\hat{r}$ (on log-log paper) and $\underline{/y/r}$ vs. $\hat{r}$ (on semilog paper) for the following values of ω: $\omega =$ 0.2, 1, 3, 5. (Hint: Use the geometric construction of Sec. 6.5.)

6-12 For the actuator model in the system of Fig. 6-20, show that the closed-loop describing function can be approximately expressed as $N(\hat{x}, \omega) = N_1(\hat{x})N_2(\hat{y}, \omega)$, where

$$\hat{y} = \hat{x}N_1(\hat{x}); \qquad N_1(\hat{x}) = \begin{cases} 1, & \hat{x} \le U \\ \dfrac{2}{\pi}\left[\sin^{-1}\left(\dfrac{U}{\hat{x}}\right) + \dfrac{U}{\hat{x}}\sqrt{1 - \left(\dfrac{U}{\hat{x}}\right)^2}\,\right], & \hat{x} \ge U \end{cases}$$

$$|N_2(\hat{y}, \omega)| = \begin{cases} 1, & \omega\hat{y} \le \dfrac{4V}{\pi} \\ \dfrac{4V/\pi}{\omega\hat{y}}, & \omega\hat{y} \ge \dfrac{4V}{\pi} \end{cases}; \qquad \angle N_2(\hat{y}, \omega) = -\cos^{-1}|N_2(\hat{y}, \omega)|$$

6-13 Show by the describing function method that the Volterra equation of Exercise 5-15 does not have a limit cycle.

6-14 For the system of Fig. 6-32:

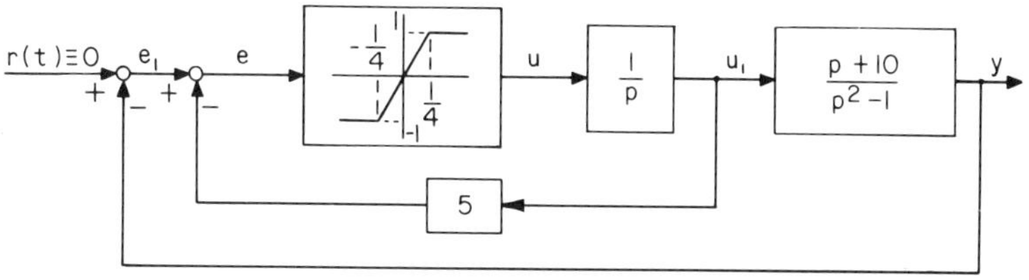

Fig. 6-32. The system of Exercise 6-14.

Investigate by describing function analysis the existence of periodic oscillations. Determine the stability of the oscillations if they exist. Find also the output amplitudes $\hat{y}$ and the frequencies of such oscillations.

6-15 Suppose there is a system in the standard form of Fig. 6-5 with a nonlinearity such that the Aizerman conjecture holds (see Sec. 5.9), show that describing function analysis will not be able to disclose the existence of a limit cycle for the system.

6-16 For the system of Eq. (5-87), give a discussion of why from physical reasoning, the describing function approach may fail.

6.11 References

The best exposition on describing function that we find in texts thus far is probably in Chap. 9 of [G3]; in many ways, the approach is complementary to ours. The reader should also consult Chap. 6, particularly Secs. 6.6 through 6.11.

Chapters 4 and 5 of [G8] present a refreshingly individualist approach to describing function.

Reference [L16], published in 1956, opens the way for intelligent discussion of the jump phenomenon. The approach in [L16] is generalized to other zero-memory nonlinearities in [H7] and to nonlinearities with memory in [F5].

7

The Dual-Input Describing Function and the Oscillating Servo

In Chap. 6, we have considered the general method of analyzing the conditions for the existence and stability of self-oscillation in an autonomous system. A balanced condition for the fundamental component of the self-oscillation is assumed and whatever effects caused by the harmonics generated by the system nonlinearity are neglected. This has remained, to this date, one of the most useful approaches in the study of self- and forced oscillations. Indeed in many cases it has proved to be more accurate than it has any right to be from a mathematical point of view. Even when the third harmonic turns out to be not negligible as compared to the fundamental, the describing function often yields useful results. But the fact remains that the approach sometimes does fail.

When the result due to the use of the describing function seems in doubt, a natural course of action is to go one step further and examine whether the system shows any likelihood of sustaining a harmonic (or subharmonic) of the main oscillating frequency. If it does, this fact is then taken into account.

It is therefore natural to attempt to improve on the describing function approach by assuming an input consisting of two harmonic components and seek to balance both components around the loop in the usual manner. This is the rationale for many of the classical approaches using higher order approximations as well as the Dual-Input Describing Function (DIDF) method as proposed by West [W2].

The debit that we incur here is considerable added labor. The fundamental problem that one faces when two harmonic components are assumed is the computation of the intermodulation product as they pass through a nonlinearity. To find these products and then to establish the equilibrium conditions for these components around a closed loop are not trivial tasks even for a simple zero-memory type nonlinearity, as the number of variables now increases to four. Because of the intermodulation effect, moreover, the resulting describing function, even for a zero-memory type nonlinearity, will in general be phase dependent.

On the credit side is the fact that, by keeping track of one more component, some of the phenomena not amenable to analysis by describing-function type approaches can now be attacked. This includes the problems of subharmonic generation and synchronization. As a by-product, it also turns out that self-oscillation in systems with a steady-state dc component can now be quite readily handled within the framework of the DIDF. Indeed, if the frequencies or the amplitudes of the two harmonic components are sufficiently different, we can show that very little error occurs even if we assume the lower frequency to be dc. Using this fact, many problems can be attacked more readily.

In the context of the DIDF, the interesting class of systems known as the oscillating servo can also be readily analyzed.

While DIDF is again inexact, it promises to be considerably more accurate then describing function in predicting the existence and stability of self-oscillation. Thus far there has been no systematic study in determining the conditions under which DIDF fails to predict correctly.

7.1 Introduction to the Dual-Input Describing Function—The Balancing of the dc Component

We can gain an appreciation for the use of the DIDF by first considering the case of a nonsymmetrical zero-memory element.

The astute reader may have observed that in Chap. 6, most of the nonlinearities that have been studied have odd symmetry $f(x) = -f(-x)$. In one of the exceptional cases (Example 6-3), the asymmetric nonlinearity is followed by a plant with a stage of differentiation. Thus any dc component created by the asymmetric nonlinearity does not appear at the output of the plant because of differentiation. The origin therefore remains a system equilibrium state. These examples are not chosen accidently, for if the nonlinearity were not odd symmetric or if a dc component should exist within the system in the steady state, solving for the oscillatory component could become a much more difficult task, (as was illustrated in Example 6-8).

The difficulty arises because any dc component tends to serve as a *bias* on the nonlinearity. The amplitude of the fundamental component of the output of the nonlinearity thus becomes not only a function of the amplitude of the sinusoidal input, but also that of the input dc component. Because of the bias, there will be another dc component in the output of the nonlinearity which will also be a function of both the input dc component and the input sinusoidal component. Thus there are now three unknowns to be solved for: the amplitude and frequency of the oscillating component, and the amplitude of the dc component.

One important fact that we can make use of in asymmetric zero-memory type nonlinearity is that given by Theorem 6-1 in the previous chapter. Even for an asymmetric zero-memory type nonlinearity, there is no phase shift between the input sinusoid and the output fundamental component.

Consider the following example:

◆◆Example 7-1. Discuss the self-oscillating possibilities in the relay control system of Fig. 7-1 for various types of the linear plant $G(p)$. The relay is asymmetric $(A \neq B)$.

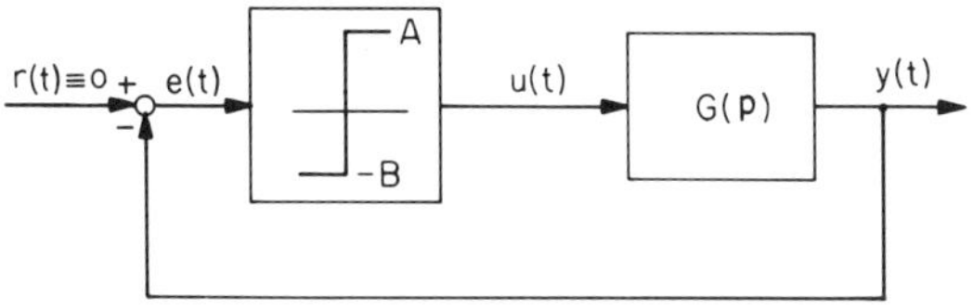

Fig. 7-1. A control system with asymmetrical relay.

First let us consider the case where $G(p)$ contains an integration. In this case, if the input to $G(p)$ contains a dc component, the system output will become unbounded. An operating relay control system then must self-oscillate in such a way that $u(t)$ does not contain any dc component. Thus if there is any oscillation at the fundamental frequency at all, the oscillation must be such that the duty cycles of the positive and negative drives for the relay equal each other over one fundamental period of oscillation. This is shown in Fig. 7-2. Note that the fact that $u(t)$ contains no dc component implies that an assumed input sine wave at the point $e(t)$ must have the shape such as that shown in Fig. 7-2. This indicates that $e(t)$ (and hence $y(t)$) does possess a dc component which is built up during the initial transient prior to steady-state oscillations.

In this particular case where $G(p)$ contains at least one integration, the describing function approach can readily be applied. We simply obtain the fundamental component of the waveform $u(t)$ and then, utilizing the given $G(p)$, solve for the fundamental period T.

More difficult is the case where $G(p)$ contains no integration. Then, in addition to a steady-state oscillation, there can also be a dc component which is sustained in the loop and must be solved for.

Some reflection will indicate that, in this case, the proper form of input at the point $e(t)$ should include a dc as well as a sinusoidal component, namely

$$e(t) = \alpha + \beta \sin \omega t \tag{7-1}$$

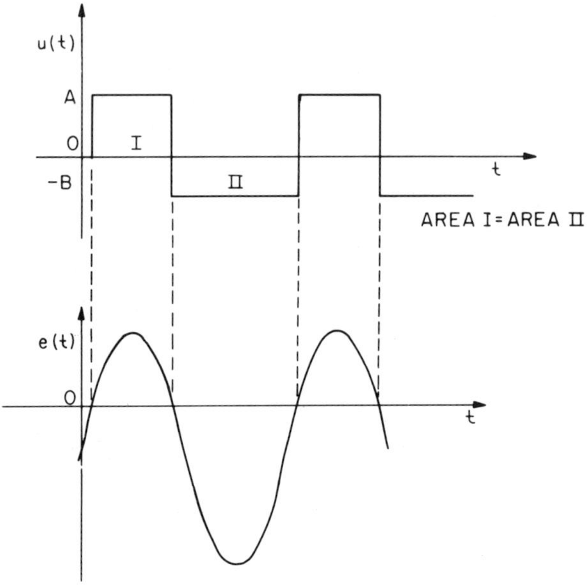

Fig. 7-2. Relay output $u(t)$ and system error $e(t)$ of relay control system of Fig. 7-1.

It should be clear that the magnitude of the dc component significantly affects the output wave shape and hence the amplitude of the fundamental component of the output. This is easily analyzed by using Fourier series.

The input (7-1), when passed through the relay shown in Fig. 7-1, will cause the relay to switch whenever $\alpha + \beta \sin \omega t = 0$; thus we have:

$$u(t) = \begin{cases} +A, & -\sin^{-1} \dfrac{\alpha}{\beta} \le \omega t < \pi + \sin^{-1} \dfrac{\alpha}{\beta} \\ -B, & \pi + \sin^{-1} \dfrac{\alpha}{\beta} \le \omega t < 2\pi - \sin^{-1} \dfrac{\alpha}{\beta} \end{cases} \tag{7-2}$$

By Fourier series analysis, we have the following dc value of the output:

$$\begin{aligned} \frac{1}{2\pi} \int_0^{2\pi} u(t)\, d\omega t &= \frac{A}{2\pi}\left(\pi + 2 \sin^{-1} \frac{\alpha}{\beta}\right) - \frac{B}{2\pi}\left(\pi - 2 \sin^{-1} \frac{\alpha}{\beta}\right) \\ &= \frac{1}{2}(A - B) + \frac{1}{\pi}\left(A \sin^{-1} \frac{\alpha}{\beta} + B \sin^{-1} \frac{\alpha}{\beta}\right) \end{aligned} \tag{7-3}$$

At the same time the quadrature component of output fundamental is:

$$\frac{1}{\pi}\int_0^{2\pi} u(t)\cos\omega t\,d\omega t = -\frac{B}{\pi}\int_0^{-\sin^{-1}(\alpha/\beta)} \cos\omega t\,d\omega t$$

$$+\frac{A}{\pi}\int_{-\sin^{-1}(\alpha/\beta)}^{\pi+\sin^{-1}(\alpha/\beta)} \cos\omega t\,d\omega t \tag{7-4}$$

$$-\frac{B}{\pi}\int_{\pi+\sin^{-1}(\alpha/\beta)}^{2\pi} \cos\omega t\,d\omega t = \frac{1}{\pi}\left[B\frac{\alpha}{\beta} + 0 - B\frac{\alpha}{\beta}\right] = 0$$

and the in-phase component of output fundamental is given by:

$$\frac{1}{\pi}\int_0^{2\pi} u(t)\sin\omega t\,d\omega t = -\frac{B}{\pi}\int_0^{-\sin^{-1}(\alpha/\beta)} \sin\omega t\,d\omega t$$

$$+\frac{A}{\pi}\int_{-\sin^{-1}(\alpha/\beta)}^{\pi+\sin^{-1}(\alpha/\beta)} \sin\omega t\,d\omega t - \frac{B}{\pi}\int_{\pi+\sin^{-1}(\alpha/\beta)}^{2\pi} \sin\omega t\,d\omega t \tag{7-5}$$

$$= \frac{1}{\pi}\left\{2B\sqrt{1-\left(\frac{\alpha}{\beta}\right)^2} + 2A\sqrt{1-\left(\frac{\alpha}{\beta}\right)^2}\right\} = \frac{2}{\pi}(B+A)\sqrt{1-\left(\frac{\alpha}{\beta}\right)^2}$$

As noted above, the quadrature component is 0, which, in this particular case of a dc bias, is a cirect consequence of Theorem 6-1. Thus the sinusoidal describing function for all values of dc bias is real.

Taking into account the intermodulation effect as the composite dc and sinusoidal inputs are passed through the nonlinearity, we now seek the condition in the loop such that simultaneously both the dc component and the fundamental component are balanced.

We can define a dc describing function $N_0(\alpha, \beta)$ through the nonlinearity as the dc component of the output divided by the dc component of the input, or

$$N_0(\alpha, \beta) = \frac{1}{\alpha}\left[\frac{1}{2\pi}\int_0^{2\pi} u(t)\,d\omega t\right]$$

$$= \frac{1}{2\alpha}(A - B) + \frac{1}{\pi\alpha}\left(A\sin^{-1}\frac{\alpha}{\beta} + B\sin^{-1}\frac{\alpha}{\beta}\right) \tag{7-6}$$

Similarly we have the first harmonic describing function $N_1(\alpha, \beta)$ defined in the usual way

$$N_1(\alpha,\beta) = \frac{1}{\beta}\left[\frac{1}{\pi}\int_0^{2\pi} u(t)\sin\omega t\,d\omega t + j\frac{1}{\pi}\int_0^{2\pi} u(t)\cos\omega t\,d\omega t\right]$$

$$= \frac{2}{\pi\beta}(B + A)\sqrt{1 - \left(\frac{\alpha}{\beta}\right)^2} \tag{7-7}$$

Now the balance condition for both the dc component and the fundamental component will be given by the following two simultaneous equations:*

$$N_0(\alpha, \beta)\,G(0) = -1 \tag{7-8a}$$

$$N_1(\alpha, \beta)\,G(j\omega) = -1 \tag{7-8b}$$

When there is no integration, $G(0)$ is a well-defined quantity, in contrast to $G(j\omega)$, which is not determined unless a value of ω is specified. Thus Eqs. (7-8a) and (7-8b) can be readily solved graphically or otherwise. The obvious approach is to solve for the possible value of β for each value of α from (7-8a). This yields a function $\beta(\alpha)$ which when used in (7-8b) will yield the correct value of ω and β (and hence α).

A possible graphical procedure is as illustrated in Fig. 7-3. As a first step, $N_0(\alpha, \beta)$ for various values of α is plotted vs. β (Fig. 7-3a). Next a horizontal line with value $-1/G(0)$ is drawn. The intersection of the curves $N_0(\alpha, \beta)$ with this line will define a function $\beta(\alpha)$ as shown in Fig. 7-3b.** As a final step, it is convenient to use (7-8b) in the form

$$G(j\omega) = -\frac{1}{N_1(\alpha, \beta(\alpha))} \tag{7-9}$$

The describing function $N_1(\alpha, \beta(\alpha))$ is found for each α by using Eq. (7-7). Its negative reciprocal is located along the negative real axis of the Nyquist plane. The Nyquist plot $G(j\omega)$ can then be plotted (Fig. 7-3c). ◆◆

The quantities $N_0(\alpha, \beta)$ and $N_1(\alpha, \beta)$ jointly constitute the two describing functions appropriate for a two-component input consisting of a dc component and a sinusoidal component. These are called the DIDF for these two input components.

*The reader should of course recognize that Eqs. (7-8a) and (7-8b) actually constitute three equations (with (7-8a) a scalar equation and (7-8b) a complex equation). These three equations are used to solve for the three unknowns α, β, and ω.

**Note that with $A > B$, only a negative value of α can bring about balance of the dc component, as may be expected. Further, due to the shape of the curves of $N_0(\alpha, \beta)$ for negative values of α, there is only a finite range of α that yields curves for $N_0(\alpha, \beta)$ which intersect with the $-1/G(0)$ line. (See Exercise 7-8.)

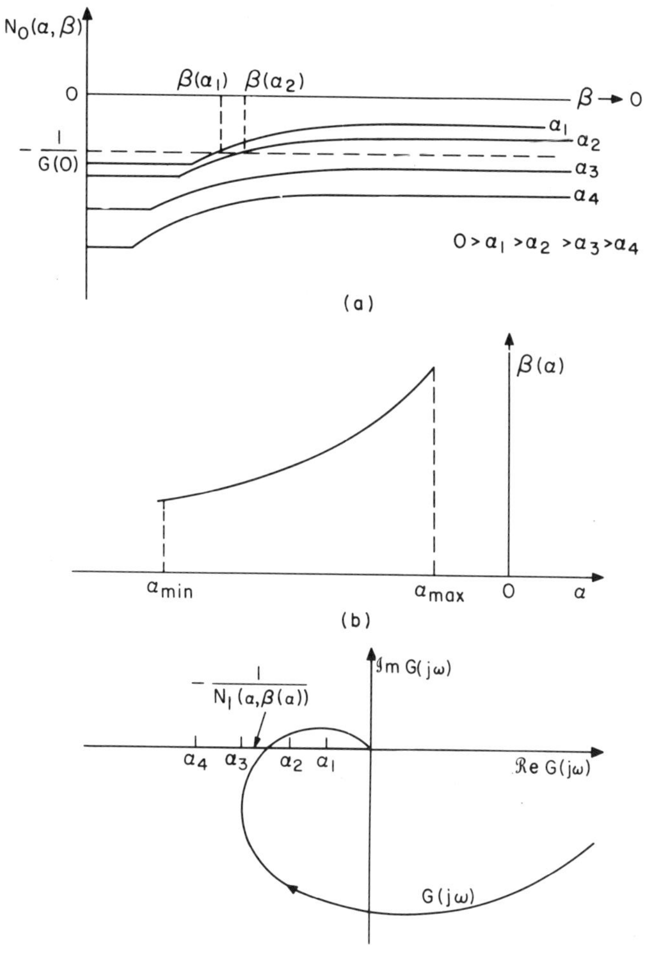

Fig. 7-3. Graphical procedure for obtaining the dc value α and the ac amplitude β in a control system. (a) The dc describing function $N_1(\alpha,\beta)$ is drawn vs. β for various values of α. (b) The functional relation $\beta = \beta(\alpha)$ for a given value of $N_0(\alpha,\beta) = -1/G(0)$, is obtained from (a). (c) The Nyquist plot $G(j\omega)$ whose intersection with the inverse ac describing function locus, $-1/[N_1(\alpha,\beta(\alpha))]$ determines the value of α.

7.2 The Dual-Input Describing Function and the Investigation of Subharmonic Oscillation

In the general case for the DIDF, a two-component trial solution at the input to a nonlinearity $f(x)$ takes the form

$$x = \alpha_1 \sin(\omega t + \phi) + \alpha_h \sin h\omega t \tag{7-10}$$

As before, we then consider the describing function of each component separately, taking into account, however, the intermodulation effects brought about by the nonlinearity.

Whereas the DIDF for a zero-memory type nonlinearity is real when the input is composed of a dc component and an ac component, this is not necessarily so when the input consists of two sine waves of different frequency. In particular, when the ratio of the two frequency components involved becomes a rational number (i.e., of the form m/n where m and n are integers) the DIDF of a zero-memory element can become phase dependent.

We shall illustrate the above points by using DIDF in establishing whether a subharmonic can exist in a system.

It is important to appreciate the fact that *when a system shows a tendency toward a (1/n)th subharmonic oscillation when it is driven by a sinusoidal input of frequency* ω_1, *then it is usually true that the system is at the verge of self-oscillation near the frequency* ω_1/n.

In the present case, the conditions for the $(1/n)$th subharmonic generation is equivalent to the dual requirements of:

1) Balance of the $(1/n)$th subharmonic within the loop, and
2) Balance of the driving frequency component.

To calculate each component, we of course take into consideration the effects of their mutual modulation as they pass through the nonlinearity. This we can do by making use of the appropriate DIDF.

Let us examine this question in terms of an example:

◆◆Example 7-2. The celebrated Duffing equation is of the form

$$\ddot{y} + \omega_0{}^2 y + ay^3 = R \sin(\omega_1 t + \theta)$$

This equation can be cast into the block diagram form of Fig. 7-4a, which is a particular case of a system of the form of Fig.

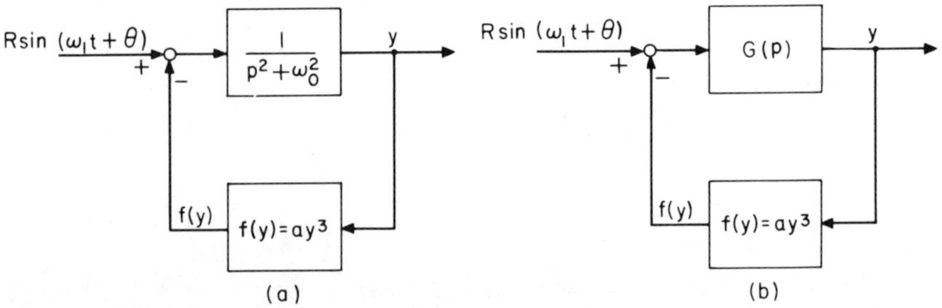

Fig. 7-4. (a) Block diagram representation of the Duffing equation. (b) A more general system with a cubic nonlinearity.

7-4b. This class of systems is characterized by a cubic nonlinearity in the feedback loop.

Let us assume an output $y(t)$ of the form

$$y(t) = \alpha_1 \sin(\omega t + \phi) + \alpha_h \sin h\omega t$$

then the output $f(y)$ of the cubic nonlinearity can be written as

$$\begin{aligned} f(y) &= ay^3(t) \\ &= \frac{3a}{4}\left(\alpha_1^2 + 2\alpha_h^2\right)\alpha_1 \sin(\omega t + \phi) + \frac{3a}{4}\left(2\alpha_1^2 + \alpha_h^2\right)\alpha_h \sin h\omega t \\ &\quad - \frac{a\alpha_1^3}{4}\sin 3(\omega t + \phi) - \frac{a\alpha_h^3}{4}\sin 3h\omega t \\ &\quad - \frac{3}{4}a\alpha_1^2\alpha_h\left\{\sin\left[(h-2)\omega t - 2\phi\right] + \sin\left[(h+2)\omega t + 2\phi\right]\right\} \\ &\quad + \frac{3}{4}a\alpha_1\alpha_h^2\left\{\sin\left[(2h-1)\omega t - \phi\right] - \sin\left[(2h+1)\omega t + \phi\right]\right\} \end{aligned} \tag{7-11}$$

Assume that we wish to investigate the (1/3)rd subharmonic.* In this case $h = 3$. Collecting terms in (7-11), we can establish the DIDF's:

$$N_1(\alpha_1, \alpha_3, \phi)\alpha_1 \sin(\omega t + \phi)$$

$$= \frac{3}{4}a\alpha_1\left[\left(\alpha_1^2 + 2\alpha_3^2\right)\sin(\omega t + \phi) - \alpha_1\alpha_3 \sin(\omega t - 2\phi)\right] \tag{7-12a}$$

$$N_3(\alpha_1, \alpha_3, \phi)\alpha_3 \sin 3\omega t = \frac{3a}{4}\left(2\alpha_1^2 + \alpha_3^2\right)\alpha_3 \sin 3\omega t - \frac{a\alpha_1^3}{4}\sin(3\omega t + 3\phi) \tag{7-12b}$$

The DIDF can be converted to the complex quantities

$$N_1(\alpha_1, \alpha_3, \phi) = \frac{3a}{4}\left[\left(\alpha_1^2 + 2\alpha_3^2 - \alpha_1\alpha_3 \cos 3\phi\right) + j\alpha_1\alpha_3 \sin 3\phi\right] \tag{7-13a}$$

$$N_3(\alpha_1, \alpha_3, \phi) = \frac{3a}{4}\left[\left(2\alpha_1^2 + \alpha_3^2\right) - \frac{\alpha_1^3}{3\alpha_3}\cos 3\phi - j\left(\frac{\alpha_1^3}{3\alpha_3}\sin 3\phi\right)\right] \tag{7-13b}$$

*We see that the investigation of each possible subharmonic represents an entirely separate problem.

We note that in contrast to the case discussed in Sec. 7.1, both DIDF's are complex in the present example.

The conditions for subharmonic generation are then the simultaneous realization of the following:

1) There must exist amplitudes α_1 and α_3, and phase angle ϕ at the output such that the (complex) equation

$$N_1(\alpha_1, \alpha_3, \phi)\, G\left(j\frac{\omega_1}{3}\right) = -1 \tag{7-14a}$$

is realized. In other words the parameters α_1, α_3, and ϕ must first be such as to be able to sustain a stable self-oscillation at the frequency $\omega_1/3$.

2) α_1, α_3, and ϕ must further be such that under the input $R\sin(\omega_1 t + \theta)$. the amplitude of the ω_1 component is sustained at the value α_3 at the output. Under elementary manipulation (show this), the condition for balancing the ω_1 component for the system of Fig. 7-4b can be expressed in the complex equation

$$N_3(\alpha_1, \alpha_3, \phi)\, G(j\omega_1) = \frac{R}{\alpha_3}(\cos\theta + j\sin\theta)\, G(j\omega) - 1 \tag{7-14b}$$

Equations (7-14a) and (7-14b) are represented respectively by Figs. 7-5a and 7-5b.

When R and ω_1 are given, the set (7-14) constitutes four simultaneous transcendental equations in the four unknowns α_1, α_3, ϕ, and θ. If this set of equations somehow can be solved, then the subharmonic oscillation problem is solved in the approximate DIDF sense (i.e., all frequency components other than the driving frequency and the (1/3)rd subharmonic are neglected). However, there is no ready procedure to solve the simultaneous transcendental equations (7-14) in the general case.

In the particular case of the Duffing equation, we note that $G(j\omega)$ is given by $1/(\omega_0^2 - \omega^2)$ and is real for all values of ω. This indicates that the phase angles ϕ and θ must both be 0. Using this fact, Eqs. (7-13) and (7-14) reduce to two simultaneous algebraic equations in two unknowns α_1 and α_3:

$$\frac{3a}{4}\left[\alpha_1^2 + 2\alpha_3^2 - \alpha_1\alpha_3\right] = \frac{\omega_1^2}{9} - \omega_0^2 \tag{7-15a}$$

$$\frac{3a}{4}\left[\left(2\alpha_1^2 + \alpha_3^2\right) - \frac{\alpha_1^3}{2\alpha_3}\right] = \frac{R}{\alpha_3} - \left(\omega_0^2 - \omega_1^2\right) \tag{7-15b}$$

With R, ω_1, and ω_0 given, these equations can be solved by a variety of means.

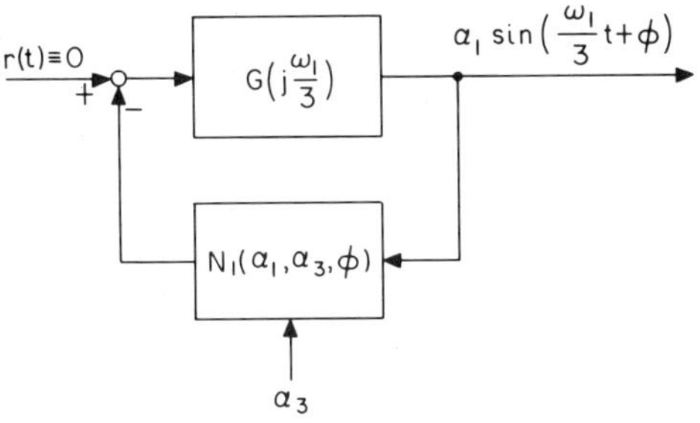

(a)

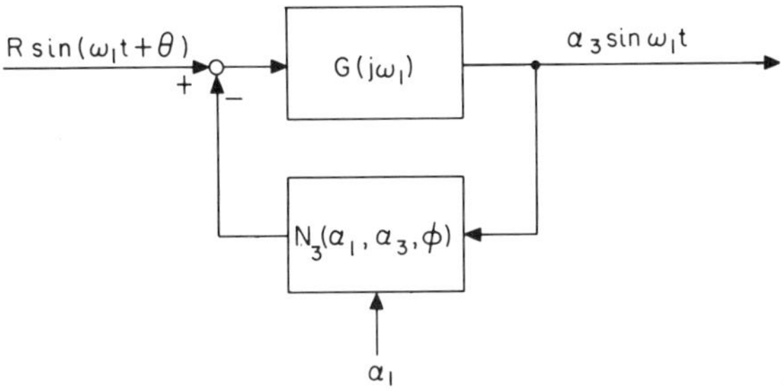

(b)

Fig. 7-5. (a) Block diagram representation of Eq. (7-14a). (b) Block diagram representation of Eq. (7-14b).

It is interesting to note the general trend of behavior of the subharmonic generation ability of the Duffing equation by assuming that the nonlinearity is small.

Equation (7–15a) can be put into the form:

$$\frac{27a}{4}\left[\alpha_1^2 + 2\alpha_3^2 - \alpha_1\alpha_3\right] + 9\omega_0^2 = \omega_1^2 \tag{7–16a}$$

which can be used to eliminate ω_1^2 in (7–15b) to obtain:

$$R + \frac{a}{4}\left[\alpha_1^3 + 21\alpha_1^2\alpha_3 - 27\alpha_1\alpha_3^2 + 51\alpha_3^3\right] = -8\alpha_3\omega_0^2 \tag{7–16b}$$

Let us assume that the gain a of the cubic nonlinearity is small; in that case, we can estimate the approximate amplitude of α_1 and α_3 as well as find the trend of behavior of the subharmonic resonance frequency.

If $a = 0$, then (7–15b) indicates that $\omega_1 = 3\omega_0$ and α_{30}, the value of α_3 when $a = 0$, is

$$\alpha_{30} = -\frac{R}{8\omega_0^2} \tag{7–17}$$

For small but nonzero values of a we would expect that an approximate value of α_3 can be obtained by substituting (7-17) into the lhs of (7-16b); this yields

$$\alpha_3 \simeq \alpha_{30} - \frac{a}{32\omega_0^2}\left(\alpha_1^3 + 21\alpha_1^2 - 27\alpha_1\alpha_{30}^2 + 51\alpha_{30}^3\right) \tag{7-18}$$

Equations (7-16a) and (7-18) allow us to make some qualitative and quantitative observations for the subharmonic oscillation in the Duffing equation when a is small.

Consider the case when $a > 0$; a plot of ω_1 vs. α_1 using (7-16a) yields the curve with the shape of Fig. 7-6. It is seen that there exists a minimum value of ω, ω_{min}, below which a real solution of (7-16a) cannot occur. This, of course, means that there can be no (1/3)rd-order subharmonic resonance for ω_1 below ω_{min}.

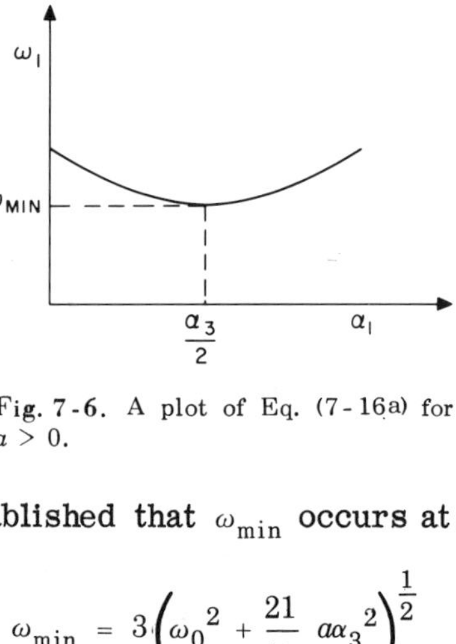

Fig. 7-6. A plot of Eq. (7-16a) for $a > 0$.

It can be established that ω_{min} occurs at $\alpha_1 = \alpha_3/2$ and has the value

$$\omega_{min} = 3\left(\omega_0^2 + \frac{21}{16}\, a\alpha_3^2\right)^{\frac{1}{2}} \tag{7-19}$$

(show this). From Eq. (7-19) we note that the minimum driving frequency to excite the (1/3)rd-mode subharmonic resonance will always have to be greater than $3\omega_0$. In other words the (1/3)rd-subharmonic frequency will always be higher than the resonance frequency ω_0 of the linear plant.

For a given value of R and ω_1, we can thus determine α_1 from Fig. 7-6. On substituting this value of α_1 into Eq. (7-19) we can then obtain an approximate value of α_3.◆◆

The Duffing equation, which has no damping and hence imparts no phase shift, is a special case of a more general system of the form of Fig. 7-4b. Here a complete solution would involve the solving of the four simultaneous transcendental equations as embodied in (7-14), which is not generally a profitable undertaking. We can, however, establish sufficient conditions for no subharmonic oscillation (or, conversely, necessary conditions for the existence of subharmonic oscillation) by considering Eq. (7-14a). This is the illuminating procedure first suggested by J. C. West and his colleagues [W2].

Let (7-14a) be put into the form

$$G\left(j\frac{\omega_1}{3}\right) = -\frac{1}{N_1(\alpha_1, \alpha_3, \phi)}$$

where

$$-\frac{1}{N_1(\alpha_1, \alpha_3, \phi)} = -\frac{4}{3a\left[\left(\alpha_1^{\,2} + 2\alpha_3^{\,2} - \alpha_1\alpha_3 \cos 3\phi\right) + j\alpha_1\alpha_3 \sin 3\phi\right]} \tag{7-20}$$

West has shown that for given values of α_1 and α_3, as ϕ is varied from 0 to 2π, $-1/N_1$ will describe a circle in the complex plane. Moreover, all such circles will lie within the wedge with approximately a 21° half-angle as shown in Fig. 7-7 (Exercise 7-9). Thus we see that within the approximations of the DIDF, a *sufficient* condition for no subharmonic oscillation is that the Nyquist plot of $G(j\omega)$ not enter the 21° wedge. Conversely, a *necessary* condition for subharmonic generation is that the plot for $G(j\omega)$ enter the 21° wedge.

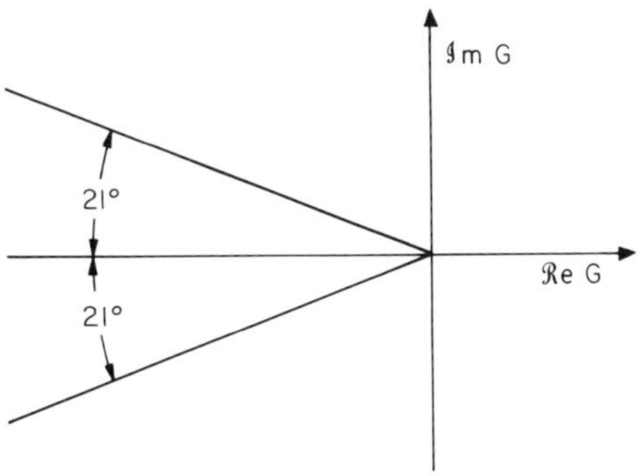

Fig. 7-7. Region in $G(j\omega)$ plane ($-159° < \underline{/G(j\omega)} < 159°$) which is sufficient for the system of Fig. 7-4b to exhibit no subharmonic oscillation.

7.3 Other Applications for the Dual-Input Describing Function

1. The Determination of a Harmonic Component in Self-Oscillation

An obvious area where the DIDF is useful is the estimation of the third-harmonic component in self-oscillation.

For a nonlinear system in the standard form of Fig. 6–5, if a signal of the form

$$e(t) = \alpha_1 \sin(\omega t + \phi) + \alpha_3 \sin 3\omega t \qquad (7\text{–}21)$$

is assumed to exist at the input to the nonlinearity, then the conditions for self-oscillation in the loop are given by:

$$N_1(\alpha_1, \alpha_3, \phi)G(j\omega) = -1, \qquad N_3(\alpha_1, \alpha_3, \phi)G(3j\omega) = -1 \qquad (7\text{–}22)$$

These represent four real equations in the four unknowns α_1, α_3, ϕ, and ω.

The major difficulty associated with the solving of (7–22) is that for most nonlinearities, it is extremely difficult to find the DIDF's N_1 and N_3 and to display them in a useful form. One may suppose for example that (7–22) may be solved graphically by plotting $G(j\omega)$ in turn against $-1/[N_1(\alpha_1, \alpha_3, \phi)]$ and $-1/[N_3(\alpha_1, \alpha_3, \phi)]$. The only problem here is that since both N_1 and N_3 are functions of two amplitudes α_1 and α_3, an entire family of functions $-(1/N_1)$ and $-(1/N_3)$ will have to be plotted. For example, for each given α_1, the $-(1/N_1)$ and $-(1/N_3)$ contours for the various values of α_3 and ϕ can be plotted. This, however, yields two families of plots as α_1 is varied.

For certain nonlinearities, such as one obeying a power law $f(e) = Ke^n$, the DIDF can be expressed by a harmonic series with a finite number of terms, and the third harmonic can be determined by using iteration. For most systems, a starting value of α_1 and ω for iteration can be taken to be that given by the ordinary describing function method. (On rare occasions (see Exercise 7–3), however, there can be situations where the ordinary describing function fails to show the existence of self-oscillation while the DIDF does.)

The ideal relay is another nonlinear characteristic whose DIDF is relatively easy to display. Indeed here the output harmonic component is only dependent on the relative value α_1/α_3 and not on the absolute values of α_1 and α_3. It is thus possible to give the complete description of the DIDF by giving the two plots of $-1/(\alpha_3 N_1)$ and $-1/(\alpha_1 N_3)$.

The normalized negative inverse DIDF's, $-1/(\alpha_3 N_1)$ and $-1/(\alpha_1 N_3)$, of the relay with unity output level have been plotted by Bonenn [B15] and are reproduced in Figs. 7–8a and 7–8b respectively. The normalized negative inverse DIDF's are given because then the resulting plot is only a function of the ratio of the amplitudes k where

$$k = \frac{\alpha_1}{\alpha_3} \qquad (7\text{–}23)$$

Using these plots, one of the possible ways to find the quantities α_1, α_3, ϕ, and ω relative to a relay control system of the form of Fig. 6-5 with a relay as a nonlinearity is the following:

1) Using the regular describing function for the relay, find the approximate amplitude α and frequency ω_1 of the oscillation.
2) Letting the amplitude thus found be the first trial value of α_1, scale the $G(j\omega)$ plot to $G(j\omega)/\alpha_1$ and find the possible values of k and ϕ in the vicinity of $G(j3\omega_1)/\alpha_1$ when the $G(j\omega)/\alpha_1$ plot is superimposed on the $-1/(\alpha_1 N_3)$ plots.
3) From a value of the possible k, obtain α_3 and then scale the $G(j\omega)$ plot to $G(j\omega)/\alpha_3$. Find the values of k and ϕ in the vicinity of $G(j\omega_1)/\alpha_3$.
4) Repeat steps (2) and (3) until the values of k and ϕ from steps (2) and (3) correspond.

With some practice, one can perform the above iterative process in a short period of time.

We can make some general observations concerning Figs. 7-8a and 7-8b. The loci are drawn for the range of $k = \alpha_1/\alpha_3$ from $k = 0.5$ to $\omega = 4$. Now for any plants that are suitably low-pass in character, we can see by carrying out the steps just described that the amplitude of the third harmonic will usually be less than a quarter of the amplitude of the fundamental. Thus it will require a reasonably complex plant (e.g., one with a resonance near the third harmonic of the crossover frequency) to yield an oscillating system with a significant third-harmonic component.

◆◆Example 7-3. Consider a system of the form of Fig. 6-5 with a linear block of the form $G(p) = 160/[p(p+4)(p+10)]$ preceded by a unit limiter.

The $G(p)$ given is definitely of a low-pass type. By inspection the frequency at which the phase is $-180°$ is at $\omega = 6.3$. For zero-memory nonlinearities, the crossover frequency of $G(p)$ is also the self-oscillation frequency. The amplitude of the self-oscillation, using the describing function of the unit limiter, is readily calculated as follows: The gain for $G(p)$ at $\omega = 6.3$ is approximately 0.32. This means that $N = 1/0.32$, where N is the describing function for the nonlinearity. In the present case $N = 4/\pi\hat{e}$ (see Table 6-2); solving for $\hat{e}$, we obtain a value $\hat{e} = 0.405$.

Using $\hat{e}$ as the first guess for α_1, and scaling the $G(j\omega)$ plot to $G(j\omega)/\alpha_1$, it is readily seen (show this) that the point $G(j3\omega_1)/\alpha_1$ will fall well inside the $k = 4$ circle on the DIDF plot of Fig. 7-8b. This means the amplitude of the third harmonic in this case is well below a quarter of that of the fundamental.

Even though the loci for $k > 4$ are not plotted, we can in fact estimate the magnitude of the third harmonic to a high degree of accuracy. This we shall leave as an exercise. (See Exercise 7-1.)◆◆

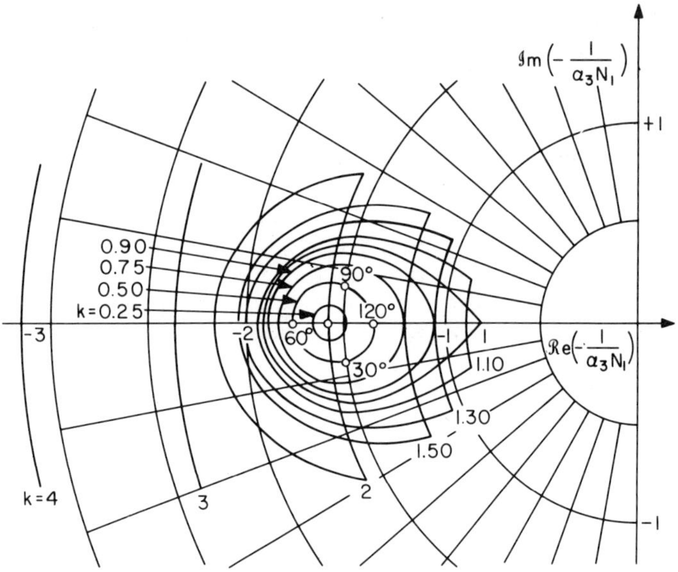

(a)

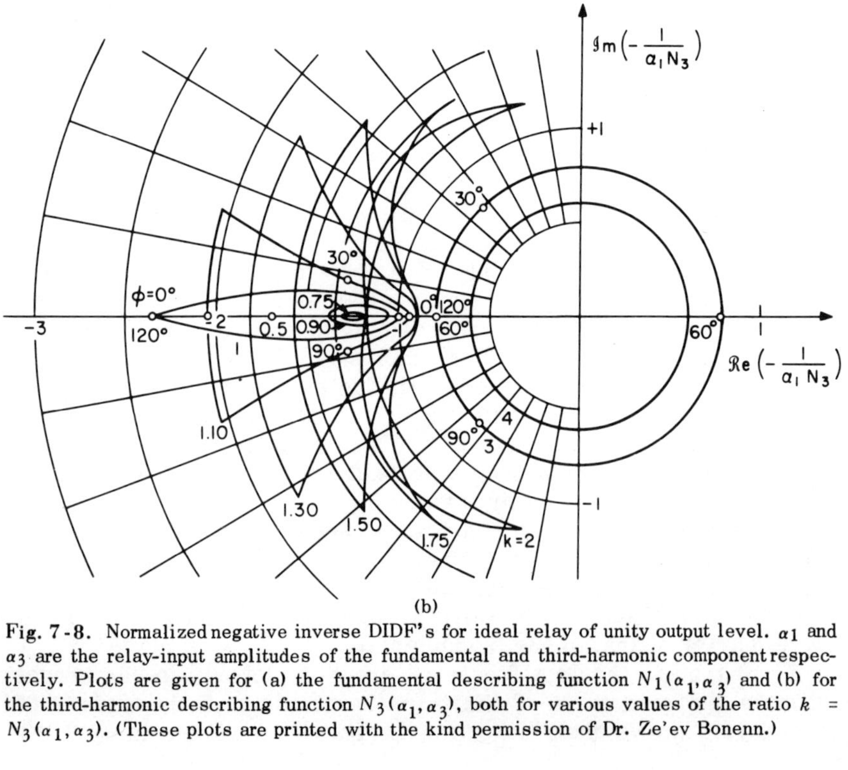

(b)

Fig. 7-8. Normalized negative inverse DIDF's for ideal relay of unity output level. α_1 and α_3 are the relay-input amplitudes of the fundamental and third-harmonic component respectively. Plots are given for (a) the fundamental describing function $N_1(\alpha_1, \alpha_3)$ and (b) for the third-harmonic describing function $N_3(\alpha_1, \alpha_3)$, both for various values of the ratio $k = N_3(\alpha_1, \alpha_3)$. (These plots are printed with the kind permission of Dr. Ze'ev Bonenn.)

Harmonics other than the third can be attacked in a similar fashion provided that the appropriate DIDF is available.

2. The Determination of the Conditions for Synchronization

An interesting phenomenon in nonlinear oscillations is that of synchronization. This occurs when a system originally undergoing self-oscillation at a period T_1 is subjected to a periodic input of period $T_2 \neq T_1$ (generally $T_2 > T_1$). When the input periodic function is of sufficiently small amplitude, the output of the system will quite naturally contain both frequency components, $\omega_1 = 2\pi/T_1$ and $\omega_2 = 2\pi/T_2$, as well as their harmonics. When T_1 and T_2 are not commensurate, the output will not be periodic. As the amplitude of the input signal is raised, however, there may come a point where the output suddenly becomes a periodic function with period T_2. In other words, the output becomes "synchronized" with the input.*

From physical considerations, it is intuitively clear that when synchronization takes place, the system self-oscillation period can no longer be T_1 but instead it must be T_2 or a submultiple thereof. From this we can appreciate the observed fact that synchronization or forced oscillation takes place more readily when T_1 is close to T_2 or a submultiple of T_2.

Typically, for a given system undergoing self-oscillation at a period T_1, if an input $R(\sin(2\pi/T_2)t)$ is applied, then the zones where synchronization can occur are given in the (T_1/T_2) vs. R plane by the shaded regions of Fig. 7-9. We see that when synchronization occurs the self-oscillation period is usually decreased.

With the above knowledge, we can quite readily analyze forced oscillation or synchronization using DIDF.

For a system of the form of Fig. 6-5, we must first of all require that the system be capable of self-oscillation. This means that there is a $\omega_1 = 2\pi/T_1$ such that the equation $N(\hat{e})\,G(j\omega_1) = -1$ is observed, where $N(\hat{e})$ is the ordinary describing function.

Now for an input $R \sin[(2\pi/T_2)\,t + \theta]$, if we wish to investigate the synchronization of the frequency component to $3T_2$, we first require that $T_1 > 3T_2$. Next, by DIDF, assuming an input to the nonlinearity of the form $e(t) = \alpha_1 \sin[(2\pi/3T_2)\,t + \phi] + \alpha_3[\sin(2\pi/T_2)\,t]$ we can immediately write down the two equations

$$N_1(\alpha_1, \alpha_3, \phi)\,G\left(j\,\frac{2\pi}{3T_2}\right) = -1 \qquad \text{(7-24a)}$$

* We may observe that oscilloscope and television sweep circuits capitalize on the nonlinear phenomenon of synchronization.

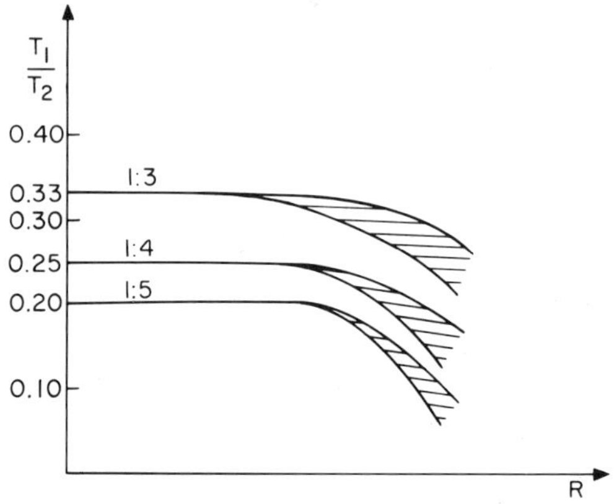

Fig. 7-9. Zones for synchronization in a typical self-oscillatory system for several ratios of T_1:T_2. If unexcited, the period of self-oscillation is T_1. If a sinusoidal input of period T_2 and amplitude R is applied, then the shaded regions represent zones in which synchronization can occur.

and

$$N_3(\alpha_1, \alpha_3, \phi)\, G\left(j\frac{2\pi}{T_2}\right) = \frac{R}{\alpha_3}(\cos\theta + j\sin\theta) - 1 \tag{7-24b}$$

We note that solving (7-22) for the third-harmonic component and (7-24) for the forced-oscillation condition can be arduous. Numerical iteration using a digital computer may have to be resorted to.

Two facts can be used to simplify calculations. Consider the DIDF for an input of the form $e(t) = \alpha_1 \sin(\omega t + \theta) + \alpha_h \sin h\omega t$ with h an integer. If h is sufficiently large, i.e., if the two frequency components are sufficiently far apart, then the role of the phase angle θ becomes minor (why?), and for all intents and purposes the DIDF N_1 and N_h can be treated as being real. In fact for some purposes the lower frequency component can be approximated by dc, this permits the use of the technique given in Sec. 7.1.

Similarly if the ratio of the amplitudes α_1/α_h is sufficiently large, N_1 and N_h can again be considered real and the suitable approximations can be made.

7.4 The Finding of the DIDF by Means of the Integral Representation of Zero-Memory Nonlinear Functions

To find the DIDF means to find the modulation products at the output of a nonlinear device when the input consists of two sinusoidal components. Only the modulation components at each of the input frequencies need to be found; nevertheless, for most nonlinearities, this is a difficult undertaking.

A useful approach for zero-memory elements, when the input frequencies ω_1 and ω_2 are not commensurate with each other* or when the amplitude or frequency of one component is significantly larger than the other, is to cast their input-output relationship in integral representations. Such representations initially have rather formidable appearances, but in many cases they can readily be reduced to well-defined functions such as the hypergeometric functions or the elliptic integrals. This approach has been extensively used by Bennet, Rice, and others.**

To begin with, let us consider the integral

$$f(e) = \int_0^\infty \frac{\sin e\lambda}{\lambda} d\lambda = \begin{cases} \dfrac{\pi}{2}, & e > 0 \\ -\dfrac{\pi}{2}, & e < 0 \end{cases} \tag{7-25}***$$

which is a representation of a relay function with relay level $\pm(\pi/2)$. Using (7-25), we can generate further nonlinear functions:

1) Bang-bang relay

$$f_1(e) = \frac{2U}{\pi}\int_0^\infty \frac{\sin e\lambda}{\lambda} d\lambda = \begin{cases} U, & e > 0 \\ -U, & e < 0 \end{cases} \tag{7-26}$$

*That is when the $\omega_1 \;\; \omega_2$ is not a rational number.

**See [H17]. This reference contains a more detailed discussion of the potentialities of the approach and a list of pertinent references.

***This may be shown as follows: Consider the integral $I(v,e) = \int_0^\infty [\exp(-v\lambda)][(\sin e\lambda)/\lambda]\, d\lambda$; on differentiating under the integral sign we obtain: $\partial I/\partial v = -\int_0^\infty [\exp(-v\lambda)](\sin e\lambda)\, d\lambda = -e/(v^2 + e^2)$. Hence, $I(v,e) = -\int [e/(v^2 + e^2)]\, dv + k = -\tan^{-1}(v/e) = k$. Since $\lim_{v\to\infty} I(v,e) = 0$, one obtains $k = \lim_{v\to\infty} \tan^{-1}\frac{v}{e} = \begin{cases} \frac{\pi}{2}, & e > 0 \\ -\frac{\pi}{2}, & e < 0 \end{cases}$. Thus, $I(v,e) = \int_0^\infty [\exp(-v\lambda)][(\sin e\lambda)/\lambda]d\lambda = \begin{cases} \frac{\pi}{2} - \tan^{-1}\frac{v}{e}, & e > 0 \\ -\frac{\pi}{2} - \tan^{-1}\frac{v}{e}, & e < 0 \end{cases}$ and therefore $I(0,e) = f(e) = \begin{cases} \frac{\pi}{2}, & e>0 \\ -\frac{\pi}{2}, & e<0 \end{cases}$

2) Ideal half-wave rectifier

$$f_2(e) = \frac{e}{2} + \frac{e}{\pi}\int_0^{\infty} \frac{\sin e\lambda}{\lambda} d\lambda = \begin{cases} e, & e > 0 \\ 0, & e < 0 \end{cases} \qquad (7\text{-}27)$$

3) Relay with dead zone

$$f_3(e) = \frac{U}{\pi}\int_0^{\infty} \frac{\sin(e - c)\lambda + \sin(e + c)\lambda}{\lambda} d\lambda$$

$$= \frac{2U}{\pi}\int_0^{\infty} \frac{\sin e\lambda \cos c\lambda}{\lambda} d\lambda = \begin{cases} U, & e > c \\ 0, & -c < e < c \\ -U, & e < -c \end{cases} \qquad (7\text{-}28)$$

4) Limiter

$$f_4(e) = \frac{e + U}{2} + \frac{e + U}{\pi}\int_0^{\infty} \frac{\sin(e + U)\lambda}{\lambda} d\lambda - U$$

$$- \frac{e - U}{2} - \frac{e - U}{\pi}\int_0^{\infty} \frac{\sin(e - U)\lambda}{\lambda} d\lambda$$

$$= \frac{2e}{\pi}\int_0^{\infty} \frac{\cos e\lambda \sin U\lambda}{\lambda} d\lambda + \frac{2U}{\pi}\int_0^{\infty} \frac{\sin e\lambda \cos U\lambda}{\lambda} d\lambda \qquad (7\text{-}29)$$

$$= \frac{2}{\pi}\int_0^{\infty} \frac{\sin e\lambda \sin U\lambda}{\lambda^2} d\lambda = \begin{cases} -U, & e < -U \\ e, & -U < e < U \\ U, & e > U \end{cases}$$

For all the functions above, e is the input to the nonlinearity and $f(e)$ is the output. To find the DIDF corresponding to the inputs x and y, it is necessary to find the amplitude and phase of the output at the corresponding frequencies.

To be specific, consider the bang-bang relay characteristic of (7-26). Let the input e to the nonlinear element be of the form

$$e(x, y) = P(\cos x + k \cos y) \qquad (7\text{-}30)$$

where

$$x = \omega_1 t + \theta_1, \quad y = \omega_2 t + \theta_2$$

Recognizing that the amplitude P does not affect the output in the case of the relay, the output $f(e)$, written as $f(x, y)$, is then

$$f(x, y) = \begin{cases} +U, & \cos x + k \cos y > 0 \\ -U, & \cos x + k \cos y < 0 \end{cases} \qquad (7\text{-}31)$$

It is clear that $f(x, y)$ is a double periodic function of x and y; i.e.,

$$f(x, y) = f(x \pm 2m\pi, y \pm 2n\pi), \qquad n, m = 0, 1, \ldots \qquad (7\text{-}32)$$

Such functions can be expanded in a double Fourier series*

$$f(x, y) = \sum_{n=0}^{\infty} \sum_{m=0}^{\infty} [A_{\pm mn} \cos (mx \pm ny) + B_{\pm mn} \sin (mx \pm ny)] \qquad (7\text{-}33)$$

where

$$A_{\pm mn} = \frac{1}{2\pi^2} \int_{-\pi}^{\pi} \int_{-\pi}^{\pi} f(x, y) \cos (mx \pm ny)\, dy\, dx$$

$$B_{\pm mn} = \frac{1}{2\pi^2} \int_{-\pi}^{\pi} \int_{-\pi}^{\pi} f(x, y) \sin (mx \pm ny)\, dy\, dx$$

$$A_{00} = \frac{1}{\pi^2} \int_{-\pi}^{\pi} \int_{-\pi}^{\pi} f(x, y)\, dy\, dx \qquad (7\text{-}34)$$

$$B_{00} = 0$$

From symmetry considerations, $B_{\pm mn} \equiv 0$ for all m and n in this particular case; moreover, $A_{+mn} = A_{-mn}$. Thus we may drop the $\pm$ sign in the subscript.

Making use now of the relation (7-26) in (7-34) we have:

$$A_{mn} = \frac{U}{\pi^3} \int_{-\pi}^{\pi} \int_{-\pi}^{\pi} \left[\int_0^{\infty} \frac{d\lambda \sin (\cos x + k \cos y)\lambda}{\lambda} \right] \cos (mx + ny)\, dy\, dx \qquad (7\text{-}35)$$

On interchanging the order of integration we have

$$A_{mn} = \frac{U}{\pi^3} \int_0^{\infty} \frac{d\lambda}{\lambda} \int_{-\pi}^{\pi} dx \int_{-\pi}^{\pi} dy \left\{ \sin [(\cos x + k \cos y)\lambda] \cos (mx + my) \right\} \qquad (7\text{-}36)$$

* See, e.g., [H13], pp. 698-719. In Eq. (7-33) the notation $A_{\pm mn} \cos (mx \pm ny)$ is used to indicate the terms $A_{mn} \cos(mx + ny) + A_{mn}\cos(mx - ny)$. The same applies to the notation $B_{\pm mn} \sin (mx \pm ny)$.

which can be integrated to:

$$A_{mn} = \begin{cases} \dfrac{4U}{\pi}(-1)^{(m+n-1)/2} \displaystyle\int_0^{\infty} \frac{J_n(k\lambda)\, J_m(\lambda)}{\lambda}\, d\lambda, & m + n \text{ odd} \\ 0 \quad , & \text{otherwise} \end{cases} \tag{7-37)*}$$

Now it is known that**

$$\int_0^{\infty} \frac{J_n(a\lambda)\, J_m(b\lambda)}{\lambda^r}\, d\lambda = \frac{a^n \Gamma\left(\dfrac{n + m - r + 1}{2}\right)}{2^r b^{n-r+1}\, \Gamma\left(\dfrac{-n + m + r + 1}{2}\right) \Gamma(n + 1)}$$

$$\cdot\, F\left(\frac{n + m - r + 1}{2}, \frac{n - m - r + 1}{2}, n + 1, \left(\frac{a}{b}\right)^2\right)$$

$$\text{for } n + m - r + 1 > 0,\ r > -1, \text{ and } 0 < a < b \tag{7-38a}$$

$$\int_0^{\infty} \frac{J_n(a\lambda)\, J_m(b\lambda)}{\lambda^r}\, d\lambda$$

$$= \frac{\left(\dfrac{a}{2}\right)^{r-1} \Gamma(r)\, \Gamma\left(\dfrac{n + m - r + 1}{2}\right)}{2\Gamma\left(\dfrac{-n + m + r + 1}{2}\right)\Gamma\left(\dfrac{n + m + r + 1}{2}\right)\Gamma\left(\dfrac{n - m + r + 1}{2}\right)}$$

$$\text{for } n + m + 1 > 0,\ r > 0, \text{ and } a = b \tag{7-38b}$$

$$\int_0^{\infty} \frac{J_n(a\lambda)\, J_m(b\lambda)}{\lambda^r}\, d\lambda = \frac{b^m\, \Gamma\left(\dfrac{n + m - r + 1}{2}\right)}{2^r a^{m-r+1}\, \Gamma\left(\dfrac{n - m + r + 1}{2}\right) \Gamma(m + 1)}$$

$$\cdot\, F\left(\frac{n + m - r + 1}{2}, \frac{-n + m - r + 1}{2}, m + 1, \left(\frac{b}{a}\right)^2\right)$$

$$\text{for } n + m - r + 1 > 0,\ r > -1, \text{ and } 0 < b < a \tag{7-38c}$$

*To arrive at (7-37) we make use of the following identities:

$$\frac{2}{\pi}\int_0^{\pi/2} \cos(z \sin\phi) \cos 2n\phi\, d\phi = J_{2n}(z)$$

$$\frac{2}{\pi}\int_0^{\pi/2} \sin(z \sin\phi) \sin(2n + 1)\phi\, d\phi = J_{2n+1}(z)$$

where $J_n(x)$ is the Bessel function of the first kind of order n.

**See, e.g., [M2], p. 35.

where $F(\alpha, \beta, \gamma, x)$ is the hypergeometric function and $\Gamma(x)$ is the gamma function.* Thus,

$$A_{mn} = \frac{2U}{\pi}(-1)^{(n+m-1)/2} \frac{k^n \Gamma\left(\frac{n+m}{2}\right)}{\Gamma\left(\frac{2-n+m}{2}\right)\Gamma(n+1)} \cdot F\left(\frac{n+m}{2}, \frac{n-m}{2}, n+1, k^2\right)$$

for $k < 1$ **(7-39a)**

$$A_{mn} = \frac{2U}{\pi}(-1)^{(n+m-1)/2} \frac{\Gamma\left(\frac{n+m}{2}\right)}{\Gamma\left(\frac{2-n+m}{2}\right)\Gamma\left(\frac{2+n+m}{2}\right)\Gamma\left(\frac{n-m+2}{2}\right)}$$

for $k = 1$ **(7-39b)**

$$A_{mn} = \frac{2U}{\pi}(-1)^{(n+m-1)/2} \frac{\Gamma\left(\frac{n+m}{2}\right)}{k^m \Gamma\left(\frac{n-m+2}{2}\right)\Gamma(m+1)}$$

$$\cdot F\left(\frac{n+m}{2}, \frac{m-n}{2}, m+1, \left(\frac{1}{k}\right)^2\right)$$

for $k > 1$ **(7-39c)**

Suppose the input frequencies ω_1 and ω_2 are incommensurate, i.e., the ratio ω_1/ω_2 is not a rational number, then the DIDF corresponding to the frequencies ω_1 and ω_2 are seen to be A_{10}/P and A_{01}/kP respectively. For the symmetrical relay, we therefore have

$$A_{10} = \frac{4U}{\pi} F\left(\tfrac{1}{2}, -\tfrac{1}{2}, 1, k^2\right), \qquad A_{01} = \frac{2Uk}{\pi} F\left(\tfrac{1}{2}, \tfrac{1}{2}, 2, k^2\right) \tag{7-40}$$

We should warn that the coefficients A_{10} and A_{01} are not the only ones that contribute to the output at the driving frequencies if the driving frequencies are commensurate with each other. For example, if $x = \omega t + \theta$, $y = 3\omega t$, then coefficients A_{10}, A_{21}, A_{41}, A_{72}, ... all constitute frequency components of the output at the frequency ω. Similarly, the coefficients A_{01}, A_{30}, A_{61}, A_{92}, ... all constitute frequency components of the output at the frequency 3ω.

* See, e.g., [W3], pp. 235-264, 281-301.

Moreover, the phase angles associated with these components will also have to be taken into account whenever the two input frequencies have a ratio that is a rational number. However, it is clear that since the coefficient A_{mn} for $k < 1$ essentially varies as k^n, it is seen that if k is sufficiently small, then A_{mn} for $n > 3$ can probably be neglected.

One area where these special DIDF's can be of use is the area of oscillating servos. This is the topic for the next sections.

7.5 The Oscillating Servo*

We have indicated in Sec. 6.6 that often one of the most important measures of a control system's effectiveness is its self-oscillation when the system gain is raised sufficiently for it generally prescribes an upper bound on the system bandwidth and hence on the system response time.

This bandwidth and response time are not attainable since to attain them would mean reaching the threshold of instability. In particular, if a system were completely linear, good design practice would dictate a gain margin of some 10 dB or more and also an appropriate phase margin.

It is interesting to note that in nonlinear systems this amount of margin is sometimes not necessary. Indeed in the case of the oscillating servo, the system is deliberately made to oscillate at its natural frequency. The limiting characteristics of a relay are used to prevent the output from growing to destructive proportions. The net result is the maximum utilization of the system bandwidth as the system equivalent gain is then automatically set to within 6 dB or less of the critical gain.

This is an instance of clever design in which nonlinearities are deliberately used to improve the performance of the system.

The idea of the oscillating servo is attributed to Lozier [M5], [T4]. The exact advantages of the approach can best be studied through the use of the DIDF.

Consider the relay system of Fig. 7-10 with $U = 1$. Let the system be such that, in the absence of the input $r(t)$, it self-oscillates at a frequency ω_0. Now let us determine its behavior when an input $r(t)$ is imposed. To facilitate the arithmetic, let us first assume that $r(t)$ is sufficiently slow-varying relative to the self-oscillating frequency ω_0 so that over several cycles at ω_0, for all intents and purposes, $r(t)$ is a dc input.

Let us moreover assume that the amplitude of $r(t)$ is small. Just how small it needs to be will be indicated presently.

* See [M5], [T4], [L15], and [G2].

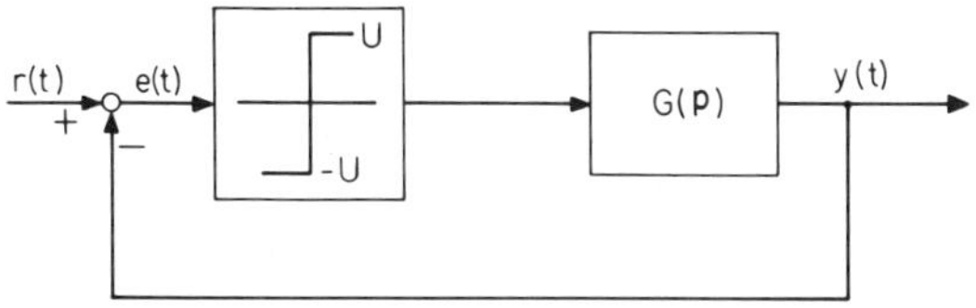

Fig. 7-10. Control system with ideal relay. This arrangement forms the basic configuration of the relay of oscillating servo.

Provided that $G(j\omega)$ observes the usual low-pass properties, the input to the relay $e(t)$ can be approximated by

$$e(t) = \alpha + \beta \sin \omega_0 t \tag{7-41}$$

where α is the average value of the input over several cycles of the self-oscillation of the system in the time interval under consideration.

If $r(t)$ is strictly dc; the result of Sec. 7.1 can be used, where, setting $A = B$ in (7–6), we have:

$$N_{dc}(\alpha, \beta) = \frac{2A}{\pi\alpha} \sin^{-1} \frac{\alpha}{\beta} \tag{7-42a}$$

and

$$N_{\omega_0}(\alpha, \beta) = \frac{4A}{\pi\beta} \sqrt{1 - \left(\frac{\alpha}{\beta}\right)^2} \tag{7-42b}$$

As $\alpha/\beta \to 0$, we note that $N_{dc} \to 2A/\pi\beta$ while $N_{\omega_0} \to 4A/\pi\beta$. In fact, we can show that whenever $\alpha/\beta < 0.8$, we will have

$$1 > \frac{N_{dc}}{N_{\omega_0}} > \frac{1}{2} \tag{7-43}$$

From (7–43) it follows that whenever $\alpha/\beta < 0.8$, the equivalent gain N_{dc} of the signal component is always smaller than that for the oscillatory component, which of course is the critical gain of the system. However, N_{dc} *can be as much as 6 dB below the critical gain. Since a linear system generally requires some 10 dB or more of stability margin, the oscillating servo can come closer to the critical gain.*

Indeed when $r(t)$ is a sinusoidal function $r(t) = R \sin \omega_s t$ and if $\omega_s \ll \omega_0$ or if the two frequencies are incommensurable, then it is clear that as $k = \beta/\alpha > 1$, the output components of the relay can be given by expression (7–39c).

Since the hypergeometric function $F(a, b, c, x)$ has the expansion

$$F(a, b, c, x) = 1 + \frac{ab}{c}x + \frac{a(a+1)\,b(b+1)}{2!\,c(c+1)}x^2 + \frac{a(a+1)(a+2)\,b(b+1)(b+2)}{3!\,c(c+1)(c+2)}x^3 + \ldots \qquad (7\text{-}44)$$

we then have for $\alpha/\beta < 1$

$$N_{\omega_0} = \frac{2U}{\pi\beta}F\left(\frac{1}{2}, \frac{1}{2}, 2, \left(\frac{\alpha}{\beta}\right)^2\right) = \frac{2U}{\pi\beta}\left[1 + \frac{1}{8}\left(\frac{\alpha}{\beta}\right)^2 + \frac{3}{64}\left(\frac{\alpha}{\beta}\right)^4 + \ldots\right] \qquad (7\text{-}45a)$$

$$N_{\omega_s} = \frac{4U}{\pi\beta}F\left(\frac{1}{2}, -\frac{1}{2}, 1, \left(\frac{\alpha}{\beta}\right)^2\right) = \frac{4U}{\pi\beta}\left[1 - \frac{1}{4}\left(\frac{\alpha}{\beta}\right)^2 - \frac{3}{64}\left(\frac{\alpha}{\beta}\right)^4 - \ldots\right] \qquad (7\text{-}45b)$$

Again we see that $N_{\omega_s}/N_{\omega_0} \to \frac{1}{2}$ as $\alpha/\beta \to 0$; hence, N_{ω_s} can also be as much as 6 dB below the critical gain.

There are some other characteristics of the oscillating servo which make it very desirable in practical applications.

First, this class of system has certain "adaptive" manifestations, since for typical high-order plants, the system can generally maintain its oscillation over a large range of parameter variations. (Self-oscillation is, of course, necessary for the oscillating servo.) In particular, if the linear portion $G(j\omega)$ is shaped such that its Nyquist plot crosses the negative imaginary axis almost at right angles, then the system self-oscillation frequency will be relatively independent of system parameter variations and the overall system behavior can remain unimpaired.

Second, because of the high-frequency self-oscillation, we expect the system transient response time to be fast. These points can be made clear by the following specific example:

♦♦Example 7-4. Consider a system with the configuration of Fig. 7-10. With $G(p) = B[1 - (p/b)]/[p(p + a)]$, it is not difficult to show (exercise for the reader) that for this system, in the absence of input, there will be a stable oscillation at the output of amplitude $\hat{y} = 4BU/\pi ab$ and frequency $\omega_0 = \sqrt{ab}$. Let us now ask the following questions:

1) For a given constant input R, what is the average value of the output $y(t)$ of the system in the steady state?
2) How fast will the system follow a changing input, say a unit-step change in $r(t)$? Consider the special case where $U = 2$, $B = 10\ \text{sec}^{-2}$, $b = 25\ \text{sec}^{-1}$, and $a = 1\ \text{sec}^{-1}$.
3) What are the advantages and disadvantages of this type of self-oscillating servo, as compared to a conventional servo,

where the relay is replaced by a linear gain K, saturated at $u = \pm U$? Let this gain K have a value such that the closed-loop system is stable with a damping-constant of say $\xi = 0.48$.

Solutions:

1) Because of the presence of the integrator in the linear element, it is clear that, for any steady-state self-oscillation to exist, the input to the linear element must have 0 average value. Therefore, e must have 0 average value. This means that in the steady state, the average value of $y(t)$ will be R.

2) Consider Fig. 7-10, let:

$$r(t) = R_0, \ t < t_0, \qquad r(t) = R_0 + R_1, \ t > t_0 \tag{7-46}$$

Assume that at $t = t_0$, the system has reached steady state, thus the output signal y has an average value $\bar{y} = R_0$ before $t = t_0$. The input to the relay has 0 average value before $t = t_0$.

Now at time $t = t_0$, the input is changed by a step R_1. Letting $\hat{e}_0$ be the self-oscillating amplitude at the output, consider first the case of small step change of input $|R_1| < \hat{e}_0$. We can see from Fig. 7-11 that the transient operation from the old equilibrium (average value $y = R_0$ for $t < t_0$) to the new equilibrium (average value $y = R_0 + R_1$) will be associated with uninterrupted periodic switching of the relay. It is to be expected that the transient time would be of the order of magnitude of the period of self-oscillation.

Consider now the case $|R_1| > \hat{e}_0$, we can see from Fig. 7-10 that, if $R_1 > 0$, $e(t)$ will remain greater than 0 until y has grown enough to reduce e to 0, at which time oscillatory operation commences again. Let $R_1 >> \hat{e}_0$, then, the response time of the output $y(t)$ to the step change will be approximately equal to the time it takes to bring the linear plant from output-value R_0 to output-value $R_0 + R_1$ when the input to the linear plant is U. The approximate transient relation thus becomes

$$y(t - t_0) \simeq R_0 + \frac{UB\left(1 + \dfrac{a}{b}\right)}{a^2}\left[e^{-a(t-t_0)} - 1\right] + \frac{UB}{a}(t - t_0), \qquad t_0 \le t \le t_0 + t_1$$

$$y(t_1) = R_0 + R_1, \qquad R_1 >> \hat{e}_0 \tag{7-47}$$

where t_1 is the approximate response time.

For the numerical values given in the statement of this problem, Eqs. (7-47) become

$$y(t - t_0) \simeq R_0 + 20.8\,[e^{-(t - t_0)} - 1] + 20(t - t_0), \quad t_0 \le t \le t_0 + t_1$$

$$y(t_1) \simeq R_0 + R_1, \tag{7–48}$$

The amplitude of self-oscillation can approximately be calculated as $\hat{e}_0 \approx 1.0$. (Show this.)

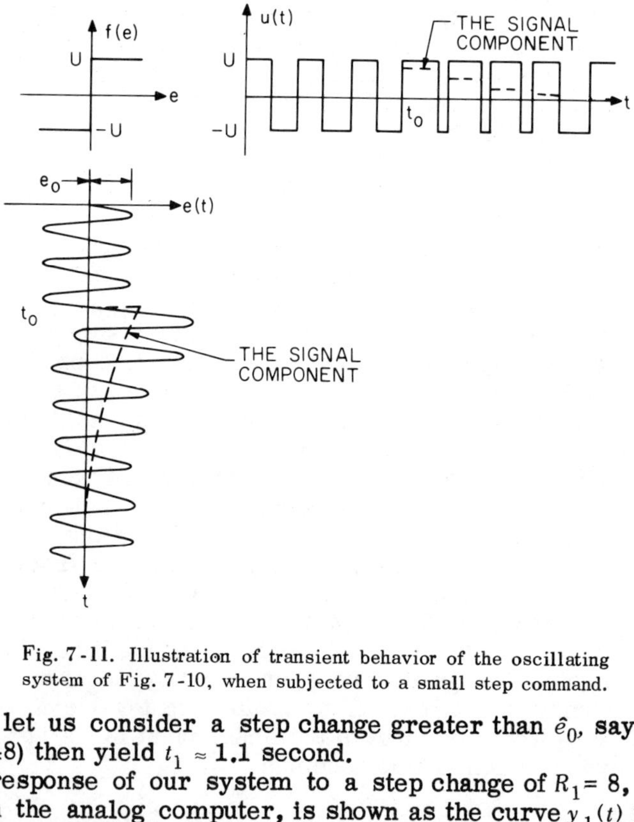

Fig. 7-11. Illustration of transient behavior of the oscillating system of Fig. 7-10, when subjected to a small step command.

Now, let us consider a step change greater than $\hat{e}_0$, say $R_1 = 8$, Eqs. (7–48) then yield $t_1 \approx 1.1$ second.

The response of our system to a step change of $R_1 = 8$, as obtained on the analog computer, is shown as the curve $y_1(t)$ in Fig. 7–12a. Before the step was applied, the system was operating in self-oscillatory steady state. From Fig. 7–12a we can determine the various quantities tabulated in Table 7–1.

Table 7-1. Comparison of Measured and Calculated Values for Example 7-4

	Measured	Calculated
Amplitude $\hat{e}_0$:	1.2	1.0
ω_0:	4.3 sec^{-1}	5.0 sec^{-1}
Response time to Step-change $R_1 = 8$,* t_1:	1.3 sec	1.1 sec

*Here, the response time has been taken to be the time at which the output-signal x first reaches the value $R_0 + R_1$.

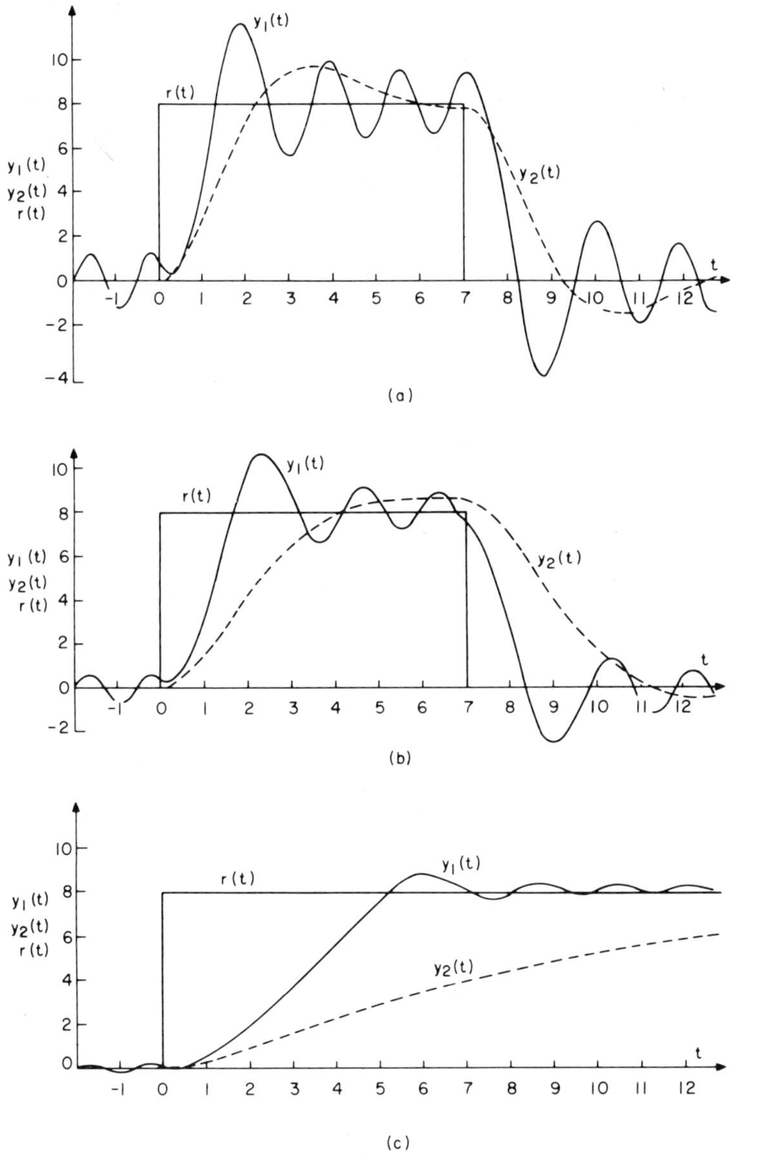

Fig. 7-12. (a) Response of oscillating system of Fig. 7–10 to a large step with the linear plant of Example 7-4 (solid curve $y_1(t)$) as compared to the response of a linear servo with a damping ratio of 0.48, whose control signal is saturated at the same level as the relay output level (dotted curve $y_2(t)$). In both cases, the plant gain has the value $B = 10\ \text{sec}^{-2}$. (b) Same as in (a) except that $B = 5\ \text{sec}^{-2}$. (c) Same as in (a) except that $B = 1\ \text{sec}^{-2}$

3) Our ability to control a plant is always limited by the available control power. Therefore, when comparing the performance of different types of servos for a given plant, it is important that the limit of the control variable be kept the same. Here our control variable u is limited to $\pm U$.

For a linear servo with saturation $\pm U$ the gain K can be chosen such that the unsaturated system operation is stable and suitably damped. The characteristic equation for unsaturated operation is $p^2 + [a - (KB/b)]p + KB = 0$, or

$$p^2 + 2\xi\omega_n p + \omega_n^2 = 0 \tag{7-49}$$

where

$$\omega_n = \sqrt{KB}, \qquad \xi = \frac{a - \dfrac{\omega_n^2}{b}}{2\omega_n} = \frac{a - \dfrac{KB}{b}}{2\sqrt{KB}} \tag{7-50}$$

Let $K = 0.1$, $B = 10\ \text{sec}^{-2}$; then, $\omega_n = 1\ \text{sec}^{-1}$, $\xi = 0.48$.

This system has also been simulated on the analog computer. The response to a step change of $R_1 = 8$ is plotted as the curve $y_2(t)$ in Fig. 7-12a.

Comparing the response of the oscillating servo $y_1(t)$ with $y_2(t)$ in Fig. 7-12a, we note that the response of the linear system is somewhat slower than that of the self-oscillating servo. The reason for this is that the oscillating servo makes full use of its available control power. The linear saturated-type servo, on the other hand, does not utilize its full available power.

Consider now the "adaptive" feature of the oscillating servo. In a practical plant, the parameters may alter their values with time or they may not even be known within reasonable accuracy. A typical example for this is the flight of a missile through a drastically changing environment. The designer of a linear-type controller with saturation must first determine the expected ranges of his plant parameters and then determine his controller gain safely below a certain margin in order to keep the linear operation stable.

Figures 7-12b and 7-12c show comparisons of the step responses of both types of systems for plant gains of $B = 5\ \text{sec}^{-2}$ and $B = 1\ \text{sec}^{-2}$ respectively. In each case the self-oscillating servo responds considerably faster to a step input than the linear servo.

Regardless of the value of the plant parameters, the equivalent gain of the relay will adjust itself to the value of the critical gain. This means that the steady-state amplitude of oscillation $\hat{e}_0$ will be a function of the plant parameters, as can be seen in Fig. 7-12b and 7-12c.

It is constructive to look at the oscillating servo of this example from another point of view. Suppose that over several cycles of the oscillating frequency, the input $r(t)$ changes but slightly. In this case good approximation can be obtained if we assume $r(t)$ is a constant relative to the oscillating component.

If $r(t)$ were held at a constant value R, we have shown that $\bar{y}(t) = R$; thus if $r(t)$ changes sufficiently slowly, the input to the relay can be approximated by the form $e_s + \hat{e}_0 \sin \omega_0 t$ with $e_s/\hat{e}_0$ small. In this case, the set (7–42) will hold. Since e_s is now a measure of the signal component of the input, then by (7–42a) $N_s(e_s, \hat{e}_0) \approx (2U/\pi e_s) \sin^{-1}(e_s/\hat{e}_0)$ is the equivalent gain of the signal component. This means that the signal components of the input e_s and the signal component of the output u_s are approximately related as shown in Fig. 7–13. Interestingly enough, the figure shows that, with the modulation of the oscillation component, the relay has been rendered "more linear."

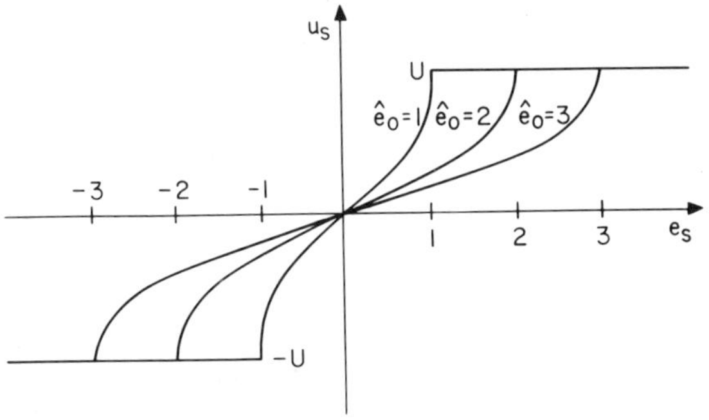

Fig. 7-13. The relationship between dc output and dc input components of an ideal relay for various amplitudes $\hat{e}_0$ of the oscillating component.

Denoting the DIDF for the signal component as N_s and the DIDF for the oscillating component as N_{ω_0} as before, and letting e_s and $\hat{e}_0$ be the amplitude signal and oscillating components of $e(t)$ respectively, we have (show this)

$$\frac{2U}{\pi\hat{e}_0} < N_s < \frac{U}{\hat{e}_0}\ , \qquad |e_s| < \hat{e}_0 \tag{7–51a}$$

and as before

$$\frac{1}{2} < \frac{N_s}{N_{\omega_0}} < 1\ , \qquad |e_s| < 0.8\ \hat{e}_0 \tag{7–51b}$$

The two equivalent systems, one for the oscillating component, and the other for the signal component, are shown respectively in Figs. 7-14a and 7–14b. In the figures, R denotes the constant

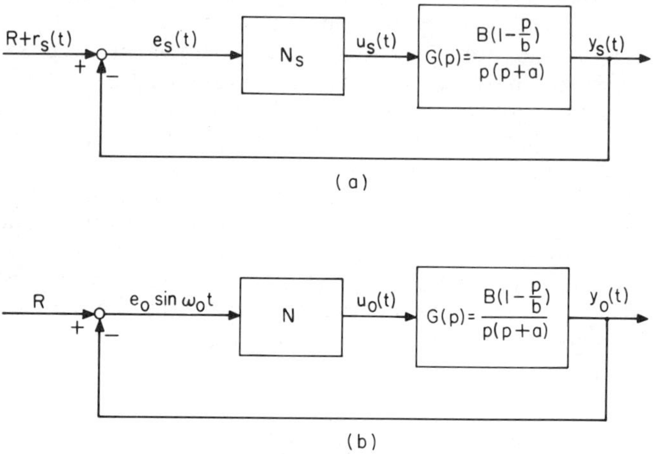

Fig. 7-14. (a) Equivalent block diagrams of system of Example 7-4 for the low-frequency signal component; (b) Equivalent block diagram of the system of Example 7-4 for the higher frequency oscillating component.

component of the input and $r_s(t)$ is the slowly varying component of the input. ♦♦

Inequality (7-51b) indicates once more that for a reasonable range of $|e_s|/\hat{e}_0$ ratio the equivalent signal gain is always slightly smaller than that for the oscillatory component, which, of course, is the critical gain of the system. The equivalent gain for the signal, however, is never smaller than 6 dB below critical gain. Thus we conclude that two of the advantages of an oscillating servo are:

1) The equivalent system for the signal will always be stable. Moreover, it will always operate slightly below its stability limit.
2) The transient times are likely to be of the same order of magnitude as the period of self-oscillation for small step changes at the input.

The presence of self-oscillation sometimes represents a disadvantage of the oscillating servo. However, the amplitude of self-oscillation can often be held small enough with respect to the signal levels. It may also happen that the oscillating servo represents a subsystem of a larger system and that the oscillatory components of the output signal of the oscillating servo will be filtered out in the elements of the larger system.

Finally, in many instances, a small oscillatory component may improve the system performance because it reduces the undesirable effects of certain nonlinearities such as backlash and Coulomb friction.

The previous example was intended to shed some light on the basic idea of the oscillating servo. In the general case, the oscillating component is sometimes supplied to the system from an external source. A high-frequency signal added to a relay input has a linearizing effect on the relay. More importantly, the effective low-frequency signal gain of the relay is controlled by the amplitude of the high-frequency oscillatory control signal. Thus, we have a simple way of achieving gain control.

7.6 Summary

The Dual-Input Describing Function (DIDF) is a logical extension to the describing function. DIDF is a set of two equivalent gains for two different frequency components as they pass through a given nonlinearity. The fact that two frequency components are used rather than one makes the DIDF more accurate than the describing function. In calculating the DIDF, only the input and the output amplitudes and phases of the two given frequency components are taken into account. All other frequency components are neglected.

Generally speaking, the calculation of DIDF for even a simple zero-memory nonlinearity is very laborious. Only the simple power-law nonlinearities and the ideal relay possess DIDF's that can be handled in a straightforward manner. However, the DIDF for other nonlinearities can be solved for on the digital computers, and numerical iterative schemes using the computer can be devised.

DIDF can be used to investigate subharmonic generation (Sec. 7.2), to find the third-harmonic component in self-oscillation (Sec. 7.3), and to analyze conditions for synchronization (Sec. 7.3).

If one of the frequency components to be analyzed is dc, analysis using DIDF promises to be much simpler. This is shown in Sec. 7.1. Fortunately, when the frequency of one component is significantly higher than the other, treating the fundamental component as dc frequently yields acceptable results. Using this fact, the workings of the class of systems known as oscillating servos can be analyzed (Sec. 7.5). This class of systems display "adaptive" properties in that its functions are relatively insensitive to parameter variations.

When the two input frequency components are incommensurate, or when the amplitudes or the frequencies or the components are significantly different, the DIDF for some standard nonlinearities can be found through representing the nonlinearity in an integral form (Sec. 7.4). For nonlinearities not amenable to this treatment, computers will have to be used.

7.7 Exercises

7-1 Explain why the DIDF $-1/(\alpha_1 N_3)$ for the ideal relay as plotted in Fig. 7-8b becomes circles for $k \geq 3$. On the basis of your explanation, find the amplitude of the third-harmonic component of Example 7-3.

7-2 Discuss the behavior of the Duffing equation (see Example 7-2) when $a < 0$. Do this with respect to
a) Subharmonic generation
b) Synchronization.

7-3 (Fitts) Consider an autonomous system of the form of Fig. 6-5 consisting of a linear plant

$$G(p) = \frac{p^2}{[(p + 0.01)^2 + (0.9)^2][(p + 0.01)^2 + (1.1)^2]}$$

preceded by a nonlinearity $f(e) = 10e^3$. Show that
a) The condition for the Kalman conjecture is obeyed by the system. Prove that this implies that the use of the describing function for this system will show that there is no oscillation.
b) Using DIDF, show that it is possible for a signal of the form $e = \alpha \sin(\omega t + \phi) + \beta \sin 3\omega t$ to be sustained. Find the values α, β, ω, and ϕ that are necessary to sustain the self-oscillation.

7-4 Develop the DIDF for the nonlinearity $f(e) = e|e|$ if we assume a general input of the form

$$e(t) = \alpha_1 \sin(\omega t + \phi) + \alpha_h \sin h\omega t$$

Find $N_1(\alpha_1, \alpha_h, \phi)$ and $N_h(\alpha_1, \alpha_h, \phi)$ for $h = 2$, 3, and 4.

7-5 Discuss under what condition a system of the form of Fig. 6-5 would indicate the existence of a limit cycle under the DIDF analysis but not under the ordinary describing function analysis.

7-6 As an example of the difficulty of analysis using the DIDF for a general nonlinear system try to establish the amplitude of the third harmonic in the limit cycle of the Van der Pol's equation $\ddot{x} + 10(x^2 - 1)\dot{x} + x = 0$.

7-7 For the system of Fig. 7-15, find the dc component, oscillating frequency, and oscillating amplitude for $R = 0$ and $R = 8$. Give an estimate of the third-harmonic component in each case.

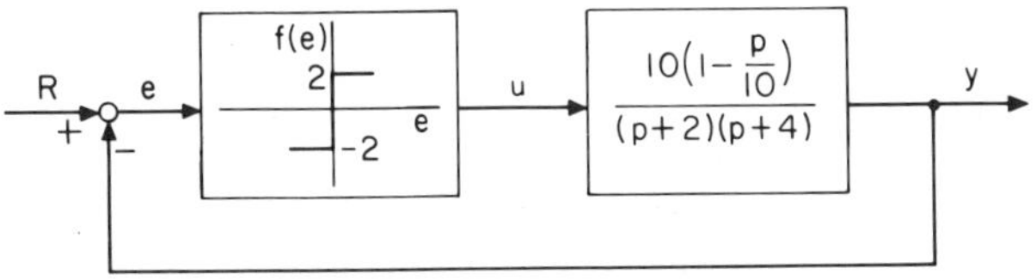

Fig. 7-15. Self-oscillating servo of Exercise 7-7.

7-8 Plot to scale the corresponding Figs. 7-3a, 7-3b, and 7-3c if in the system of Example 7-1, we have $A = 2$, and $B = 1$, and $G(p) = 60/[(p + 1)(p + 2)(p + 3)]$.

7-9 Prove independently some of the assertions made in the last paragraph of Sec. 7.2:

a) "... for given values of α_1 and α_3, as ϕ is varied from 0 to 2π, $-(1/N_1)$ will describe a circle in the complex plane."

b) "... all such circles (as described in (a) above) will lie within the wedge with approximately a 21° half angle as shown in Fig. 7-7.

7-10 Generate a digital computer program (a detailed flow chart will suffice) to calculate and plot the $-(1/N_1)$ and $-(1/N_3)$ DIDF's for the unit limiter. Consider the need for normalizing the curves. Discuss the problems involved in producing a set of curves of $-(1/N_3)$ and $-(1/N_1)$ for design purposes.

7-11 Suppose that the input to a symmetrical ideal relay is $r_s(t) + \Delta(t)$, where $r_s(t)$ is a slowly varying signal component and $\Delta(t)$ is a symmetrical periodic wave with the triangular waveform (see Fig. 7-16). Show that in the sense of DIDF, whenever the amplitude of $r_s(t)$ is less than that of $\Delta(t)$, $\Delta(t)$ causes the equivalent gain of the relay relative to the signal component $r_s(t)$ to be linear. What is the significance of this exercise?

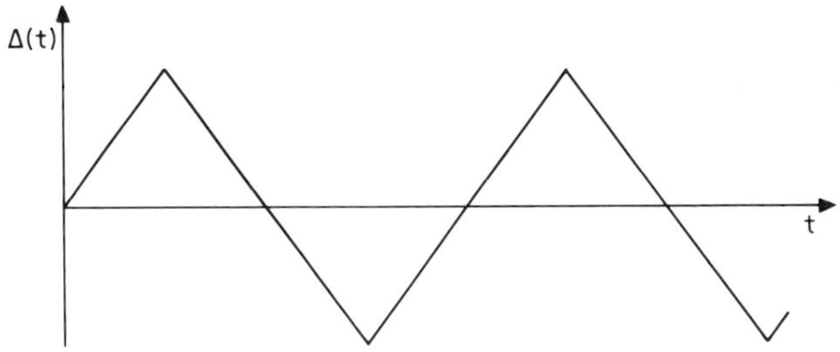

Fig. 7-16. Triangular carrier signal to be used in Exercise 7-11. Waveshape assumed to have odd symmetry.

7.8 References

J. C. West and his associates coined the term dual-input describing function and did much of the pioneering work which is summarized in Chaps. 10 and 11 of [W2].

An important though apparently little recognized paper on DIDF is [B15].

The idea of the oscillating servo is discussed in [M5] (pp. 73–87) and [T4] (pp. 70–82). The latter reference, incidentally, gives an eclectic and concise review of the science of control. Though written in 1954, it should not be missed by serious students in control engineering.

J. C. Lozier, who conceived the idea of oscillating servo, did not completely document his ideas in the open literature. Some insight, however, can be gained through [L15].

The idea of the oscillating servo inspired a Ph.D. dissertation by Gelb at M.I.T. The gist of his results is given in [G2]. The adaptive feature of the oscillating servo is used in certain flight control systems. As an example, see [S8].

8

Exact Methods for the Analysis of Relay Control Systems

Because the describing function and the dual-input describing function (DIDF) are not exact, there is always the nagging doubt of their validity in certain situations and of the closeness of approximations they can give.

We must, of course, be aware that the question of exactness can sometimes be highly illusory. For example, seldom can a control system be found that is separable into an *exact* linear part and a readily characterized nonlinear part. In every case, much judgment must be exercised in deriving an approximate mathematical model for subsequent analysis. Therefore, when we speak of exact methods, we only mean methods which permit us to obtain exact solutions of certain mathematical models. The models themselves, however, may constitute inexact representations of the physical system under consideration. Only when the degree of approximation in the mathematical model is not excessive does the exact method become meaningful.

In this and almost all of the chapters to follow, we shall discuss exact approaches. By and large, the exact approaches can be divided into two classes: those which provide quantitative answers and those which provide qualitative answers. In the chapters on the Lyapunov second method and the method of Popov, exact methods that provide qualitative answers will be discussed. In those cases, we are interested in a particular type of stability, and the methods to be described can provide us with *sufficient conditions* for that stability. In part III of this book, exact (generally necessary) conditions on the optimality of control can be obtained using various approaches related to the calculus of variations. These conditions can in many cases permit us to obtain quantitative answers, e.g., the exact optimum control function.

In the present chapter, we discuss some exact approaches that can be applied to a class of relay control systems. These approaches are quantitative in nature, since aside from yielding answers on the existence (and stability) of limit cycles or subharmonic resonance, the period and amplitude of these oscillations can also be ascertained.

Relay systems are of widespread usefulness. The relay as a power element, for example, is simple and rugged and is capable of applying full power to a plant in a short time. For this reason, a well-designed relay system often possesses optimum manifestations in achieving fast response time.

A disadvantage of the relay system is that when the goal of control is nearly reached (e.g., when the output and the input nearly correspond in a follow-up system) the relay tends to chatter. This may not be objectionable in cleverly designed systems such as the oscillating servo treated in Chap. 7. Otherwise, we may resort to the so-called dual-mode design where a linear system is switched in when the error becomes sufficiently small.

We will be dealing with relay systems of the form of Fig. 8-1.

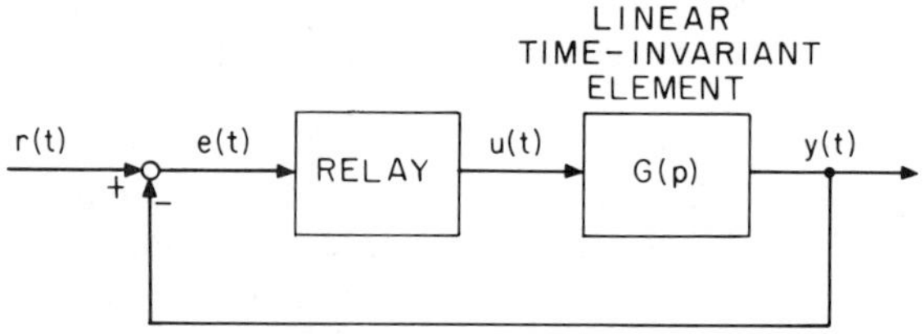

Fig. 8-1. A relay system.

The relay characteristics can be fairly general and can have a dead zone, hysteresis, or both, so that any of the relay characteristics of Fig. 8-2 can be analyzed.

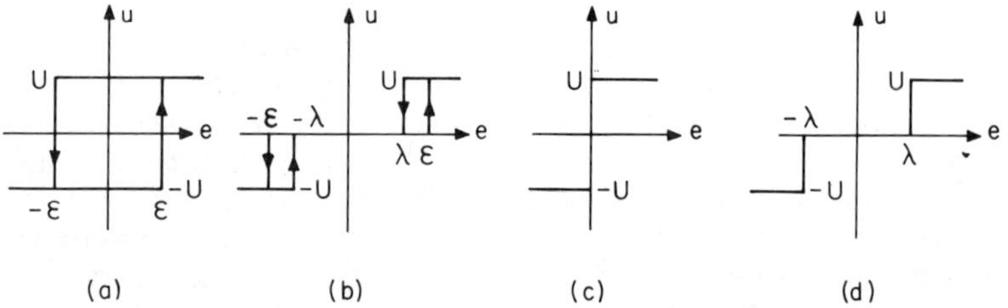

Fig. 8-2. Several types of relays: (a) a relay with hysteresis, (b) a relay with dead zone and hysteresis, (c) an ideal relay, (d) a relay with dead zone.

The basic approach underlying all the material discussed in this chapter is similar to that for the describing function. The form of the solution is assumed, we then investigate whether such a solution can exist. For a general system, it is difficult to know *a priori* what form of a solution to assume. A relay characteristic, however, restricts its output signal to a certain form as shown in Fig. 8-3. With this restrictive property, the existence of periodic operation can be established by investigating whether parameters of the relay-output signal can be found that will satisfy the system equations.

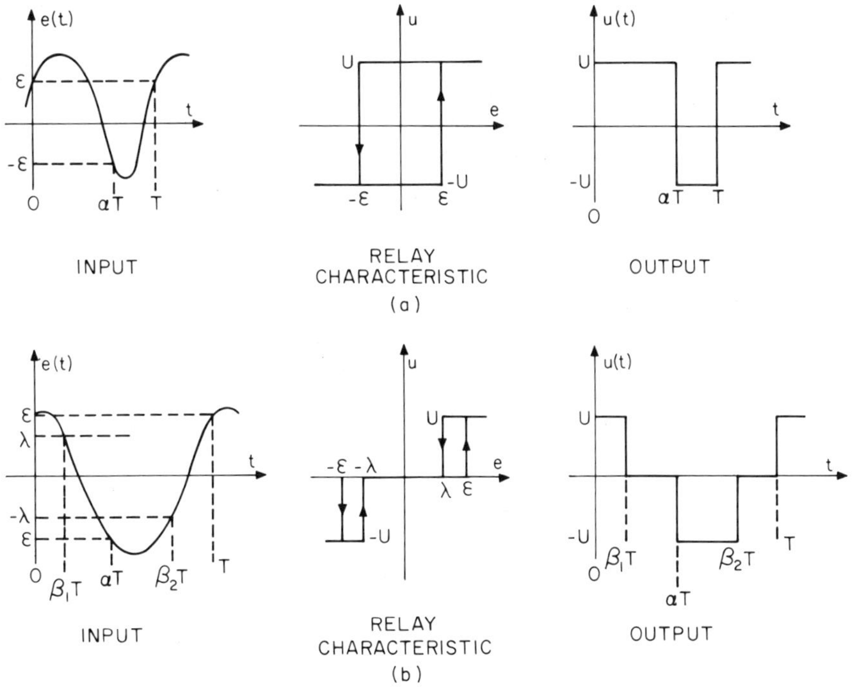

Fig. 8-3. (a) The input-output relationship of a relay with hysteresis; (b) The input-output relationship of a relay with dead zone and hysteresis.

In the light of the above, for a relay system, it is helpful to isolate certain *signal parameters* related to the waveform or the signal within the system. These include the period of oscillation, the duty cycle of the oscillation, etc. They are treated as distinct from the *system parameters* such as gain, poles, and zeros. This point of view is particularly useful for oscillatory motion and can lead to the following analysis and synthesis procedures for relay systems.

1) Analysis—The system parameters are fixed. A suspected shape of the relay output for oscillatory motion is assumed,

up to certain signal parameters. The task is to find the values of these signal parameters which will allow the assumed mode of oscillation to be sustained.

2) Synthesis—Again we assume a suspected relay output waveform for oscillatory motion, except here the signal parameters are fixed while certain plant parameters are to be determined to permit the assumed mode of oscillation to be sustained.

It turns out that some of the techniques that have been advanced for the analysis of sampled-data systems can also be used to advantage for relay systems. In this chapter, we will make important use of the z-transform and the so-called advanced z-transform methods. For those unfamiliar with these techniques, Appendix B is devoted to a capsule discussion of their basis, definition, and utility.

8.1 The Transient Response for a Relay System under Arbitrary Input

Before delving into the analysis of periodic motion of relay control systems, let us establish the equations of motion in general. We should note that if the input and initial conditions are known, then, in principle at least, we can always find the response of a relay system. To see this, consider the system of Fig. 8-1 with the relay characteristic of Fig. 8-2a.* The relay output then must be of the form (see Fig. 8-3a)

$$u(t) = U\kappa\left[\mu_{-1}(t) + 2\sum_{k=1}^{\infty}(-1)^k\mu_{-1}(t - t_k)\right] \tag{8-1}$$

where $\kappa = \pm 1$ is the polarity of the relay output at $t = 0$, $\mu_{-1}(t)$ is the unit-step function,** and t_k $(k = 1, 2, \ldots)$ are the switching instants of the relay. The response of the linear element to this signal can be written as

$$y(t) = y_0(t) + U\kappa\left[h(t) + 2\sum_{k=1}^{\infty}(-1)^k h(t - t_k)\right] \tag{8-2}$$

*The analysis for the other relay characteristics must be suitably modified according to the different (relay) switching conditions; but this modification is straightforward.

**$\mu_{-1}(t) = 0$ for $t < 0$ and $= 1$ for $t \geq 0$.

where

$$h(t) \triangleq \mathcal{L}^{-1}\left[\frac{G(s)}{s}\right] = \begin{cases} \int_0^t g(\tau)\,d\tau\,, & t \geq 0 \\ 0\,, & t < 0 \end{cases} \tag{8-3}$$

is the unit-step response of the linear element (of unit-impulse response $g(t)$) and $y_0(t)$ is its initial-condition response for a given set of initial conditions. The relay input from Fig. 8-1 is

$$e(t) = r(t) - y(t) \tag{8-4}$$

If the switching instants t_k are known, then the response $y(t)$ follows directly from (8-2). Thus the problem lies in the finding of these switching instants. For the relay characteristic of Fig. 8-2a, the switching instants will be defined by

$$e(t_k) = \epsilon\kappa(-1)^k\,, \quad \dot{e}(t_k)\kappa(-1)^k > 0 \tag{8-5}$$

as is evident from inspecting Fig. 8-3a.

For a given input $r(t)$ and an initial-condition response $y_0(t)$, we can use Eqs. (8-2), (8-4), and (8-5) to successively obtain each switching time and the response $y(t)$ until the next switching time. For convenience, let

$$y_{n+1}(t) \triangleq y_0(t) + U\kappa\left[h(t) + 2\sum_{k=1}^{n}(-1)^k h(t - t_k)\right] \tag{8-6}$$

and note by comparison of Eqs. (8-2) and (8-6) that

$$y_{n+1}(t) = y(t)\,, \quad 0 \leq t \leq t_{n+1} \tag{8-7}$$

We may write Eq. (8-6) also in terms of the following recursion formula

$$y_{n+1}(t) = y_n(t) + 2U\kappa(-1)^n h(t - t_n)\,, \quad n = 0, 1, 2, \ldots \tag{8-8}$$

From Eqs. (8-4) and (8-5), the relation defining the switching times t_{n+1} is

$$y_{n+1}(t_{n+1}) = r(t_{n+1}) - \kappa(-1)^{n+1}\epsilon\,, \quad n = 0, 1, 2, \ldots \tag{8-9}$$

It follows from Eqs. (8-2) and (8-4) that

$$\kappa = \operatorname{sgn}[r(0) - y_0(0)] \tag{8-10}$$

Equations (8-7) to (8-10) completely specify the output behavior of the system. They can be used graphically, numerically, or analytically, depending on the complexity of the system. A graphical procedure is illustrated in Fig. 8-4.

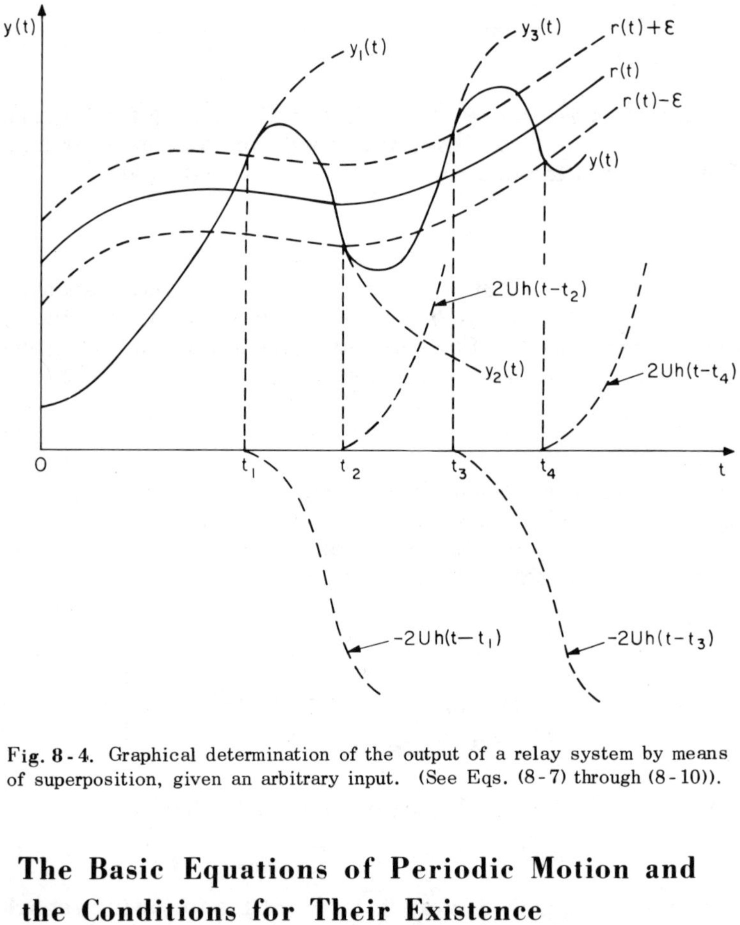

Fig. 8-4. Graphical determination of the output of a relay system by means of superposition, given an arbitrary input. (See Eqs. (8-7) through (8-10)).

8.2 The Basic Equations of Periodic Motion and the Conditions for Their Existence

Typical relay inputs and outputs during periodic motion were shown in Fig. 8-3. For the relay without dead zone, the output can be written as

$$u_p(t) = U \sum_{k=0}^{\infty} \left[\mu_{-1}(t - kT) - 2\mu_{-1}\big(t - (k + \alpha)T\big) + \mu_{-1}\big(t - (k + 1)T\big)\right] \tag{8-11a}$$

and for the relay with dead zone, the output is

$$u_p(t) =$$

$$U \sum_{k=0}^{\infty} \left[\mu_{-1}(t-kT) - \mu_{-1}\big(t-(k+\beta_1)T\big) - \mu_{-1}\big(t-(k+\alpha)T\big) + \mu_{-1}\big(t-(k+\beta_2)T\big)\right] \tag{8-11b}$$

Here, $T, \alpha, \beta_1, \beta_2$ are the signal parameters to be evaluated so that the system equations are satisfied. If such signal parameters can be found, then periodic motion of this form exists and its shape can be identified.

Note that if we establish by analysis that an oscillation of form (8-11) exists, it does not mean that other oscillatory modes are not possible. Thus, in theory, one must examine each possible oscillatory mode. Fortunately, however, the fundamental mode of oscillation, defined by (8-11), is the most likely one to occur in practice. We shall restrict this chapter to the discussion of this fundamental mode, which we may call the *basic oscillation*.*

The basic oscillation, as defined in (8-11), is represented in an unsymmetrical form. A special case that occurs frequently is that of symmetrical oscillation for which we have $\alpha = 1/2$ and $\beta_2 = (1/2) + \beta_1$. For example, consider a system consisting of a relay characteristic of Fig. 8-3a and a linear plant $G(p)$ that has a pole at $p = 0$. Because of the integration in the linear element, no steady state can exist unless its input signal $u(t)$ has 0 average value. But in view of Fig. 8-3a, we can see that this implies that $\alpha = 1/2$. Similarly, if the feedback system with any $G(p)$ is unforced, then we also expect symmetrical oscillation.

Symmetrical oscillation reduces the amount of analytical work necessary since in the case of the relay without dead zone, we have only one signal parameter, the period T, to evaluate. In case of a relay with dead zone, we have only one additional parameter, β_1, to evaluate. In most of this chapter we will assume symmetry, i.e.

$$\alpha = \frac{1}{2}, \qquad \beta_2 = \frac{1}{2} + \beta_1 \tag{8-12}$$

Now for the assumed periodic relay output of (8-11) we must establish the periodic steady-state response of the linear element $y(t)$, and then check by comparison of $y(t)$ with the system input, $r(t)$, whether the switching conditions of the relay are satisfied. Let $e_p(t)$

*Extensions of the results of this chapter to more complicated modes of oscillation are conceptually straightforward but will lead to rather involved calculations.

be the periodic input to a relay with period T. It follows from Fig. 8-3 that for a relay without dead zone, the conditions for periodic switchings of the relay are:

$$\begin{aligned} e_p(0) &= \epsilon, & \dot{e}_p(0) &> 0 \\ e_p(\alpha T) &= -\epsilon, & \dot{e}_p(\alpha T) &< 0 \end{aligned} \tag{8-13a}$$

For a relay with dead zone, the conditions are:

$$\begin{aligned} e_p(0) &= \epsilon, \quad \dot{e}_p(0) > 0; & e_p(\beta_1 T) &= \lambda, & \dot{e}_p(\beta_1 T) &< 0 \\ e_p(\alpha T) &= -\epsilon, \; \dot{e}_p(\alpha T) < 0; & e_p(\beta_2 T) &= -\lambda, & \dot{e}_p(\beta_2 T) &> 0 \end{aligned} \tag{8-13b}$$

These we call the *switching conditions*. For symmetrical oscillation, we will find that some of these conditions are redundant.

Conditions (8-13) represent *necessary conditions* for oscillation. In addition to these, we must also establish that $e_p(t)$ is not of a form that will cause the relay to switch at instants other than those assumed. This implies that for a relay without dead zone

$$\begin{aligned} e_p(t) &> -\epsilon, & 0 \le t &< aT \\ e_p(t) &< \epsilon, & aT \le t &< T \end{aligned} \tag{8-14a}$$

and for a relay with dead zone

$$\begin{aligned} e_p(t) &> \lambda, & 0 \le t &< \beta_1 T; & -\epsilon < e_p(t) &< \lambda, & \beta_1 T < t &< aT \\ e_p(t) &< -\lambda, & aT \le t &< \beta_2 T; & -\lambda < e_p(t) &< \epsilon, & \beta_2 T < t &< T \end{aligned} \tag{8-14b}$$

We shall call (8-14) the *continuity conditions*. Again, we will find that for symmetrical oscillation, some of the conditions in (8-14) are redundant. Together, conditions (8-13) and (8-14) represent the necessary and sufficient conditions for the existence of self-oscillation. In practice, it suffices to check only for the necessary switching conditions (8-13). From these, we obtain the signal parameters for periodic operation and calculate the periodic response $e_p(t) = r_p(t) - y_p(t)$ which must satisfy conditions (8-14).

8.3 The Advanced Z-Transform Method

Jury [J5] has demonstrated how the modified z-transform* can be used to obtain the periodic steady-state response for certain

*The modified z-transform and the advanced z-transform are essentially the same. The former is related to the latter by a multiplying factor z. We shall use the advanced z-transform, For a brief review of z-transform and advanced z-transform, see Appendix B.

stable linear networks excited by a periodic signal. We can extend this method to a more general class of linear time-invariant elements $G(p)$ that may also contain poles at $p = 0$ or even in the right-half plane [M11]. In the latter case, proper initial conditions must be present in order for a periodic steady state to exist.

Consider the basic oscillation defined in Eq. (8-11). The Laplace transforms of these expressions are:*

1) for the relay without dead zone

$$U_p(s) = \frac{U}{s}\left(1 - 2e^{-\alpha Ts} + e^{-Ts}\right)\sum_{k=0}^{\infty} e^{-sTk} = \frac{U(1 - 2e^{-\alpha Ts} + e^{-Ts})}{s(1 - e^{-Ts})}$$

$$\Re e\, s > 0 \qquad (8\text{-}15a)$$

2) for the relay with dead zone

$$U_p(s) = \frac{U}{s}\left(1 - e^{-\beta_1 Ts} - e^{-\alpha Ts} + e^{-\beta_2 Ts}\right)\sum_{k=0}^{\infty} e^{-sTk} = \frac{U\left(1 - e^{-\beta_1 Ts} - e^{-\alpha Ts} + e^{-\beta_2 Ts}\right)}{s(1 - e^{-sT})}$$

$$\Re e\, s > 0 \qquad (8\text{-}15b)$$

The Laplace transform of the output of the linear element is

$$Y(s) = Y_0(s) + U_p(s)G(s) \qquad (8\text{-}16)$$

where $Y_0(s)$ is the Laplace transform of the initial-condition response $y_0(t)$, i.e., the response of the linear element to the set of initial conditions corresponding to the state at the system at $t = 0$. Equation (8-16) can be written as

$$Y(s) = Y_0(s) + \frac{U_1(s)G(s)}{1 - e^{-sT}} \qquad (8\text{-}17)$$

where

$$U_1(s) = U_p(s)(1 - e^{-sT}) \qquad (8\text{-}18)$$

By (8-15), for a relay without dead zone we have

$$U_1(s) = \frac{U}{s}(1 - 2e^{-\alpha Ts} + e^{-Ts}) \qquad (8\text{-}19a)$$

*Here we are using the relation

$$\sum_{k=0}^{\infty} e^{-sTk} = \frac{1}{1 - e^{-sTk}}$$

which is valid for $\Re e\, s > 0$.

and for a relay with dead zone we have

$$U_1(s) = \frac{U}{s}(1 - e^{-\beta_1 Ts} - e^{-\alpha Ts} + e^{-\beta_2 Ts}) \tag{8-19b}$$

Let us now define a function $Y_1(s)$ such that

$$Y(s) \triangleq \frac{Y_1(s)}{1 - e^{-sT}} = Y_1(s) \sum_{k=0}^{\infty} e^{-sTk} \tag{8-20}$$

By comparison of (8-17) and (8-20), we have:

$$Y_1(s) = (1 - e^{-sT}) Y_0(s) + U_1(s) G(s) \tag{8-21}$$

We can now state the main result of this section.

♦♦Theorem 8-1. If $Y_1(s)$ is analytic* in $\Re e\, s \geq 0$ then an output periodic steady-state solution $y_p(t)$ exists and is given by

$$y_p(t) = \sum_{k=0}^{\infty} y_1(t + kT), \quad 0 \leq t < T \tag{8-22}$$ ♦♦

To show the above we note that since the inverse Laplace transform of Eq. (8-20) is

$$y(t) = \sum_{k=0}^{\infty} y_1(t - kT) \tag{8-23}$$

it follows from the definition of the Laplace transform, that the analyticity of $Y_1(s)$ in $\Re e\, s \geq 0$ implies that $|y_1(t)| = |\mathcal{L}^{-1} Y_1(s)| < \gamma e^{-\delta t}$ for some $\gamma, \delta > 0$. This means the series in (8-23) converges to a steady-state periodic solution of period T as $t \to \infty$. This means

$$y_p(t) = \lim_{N\to\infty} y(t + NT) = \lim_{N\to\infty} \sum_{k=0}^{\infty} y_1(t + (N+k)T), \quad 0 \leq t < T$$

which leads to Eq. (8-22).

We can write (8-23) also as

$$y_p(mT) = \lim_{z\to 1} \mathcal{Y}_1(z, m), \quad 0 \leq m < 1 \tag{8-24}$$

*We recall that a function $Y(s)$ of a complex variable s is analytic in a region of the complex plane if it is defined and differentiable throughout the region.

where $\mathcal{Y}_1(z, m)$ is the advanced z-transform of $y_1(t)$ and is defined by

$$\mathcal{Y}_1(z,m) \triangleq \sum_{k=0}^{\infty} y_1\big((k+m)T^+\big)z^{-k}, \quad 0 \leq m < 1 \tag{8-25}*$$

Equation (8-24) allows us to make use of available tables of advanced z-transforms or of modified z-transforms.** The limit $z \to 1$ exists if $\mathcal{Y}_1(z,m)$ is analytic in $|z| \geq 1$ (see Eq. (B-16), Appendix B). The problem thus is to make $\mathcal{Y}_1(z,m)$ analytic in $|z| \geq 1$. This will automatically be satisfied if the linear element is stable, i.e., if all the singularities of $G(s)$ and of $Y_0(s)$ lie in $\mathcal{R}e\ s < 0$. Otherwise, it will be necessary to choose initial conditions such that the terms of $\mathcal{Y}_1(z,m)$ with singularities in $|z| \geq 1$ will cancel out. This procedure is best illustrated by examples:

◆◆Example 8-1. Examine the basic oscillation of a relay control system (Fig. 8-1) with a relay without dead zone shown in Fig. 8-2a, with

$$r(t) = R, \quad G(s) = \frac{a^3}{s^2(s+a)}, \quad Y_0(s) = \frac{x_{10}}{s} + \frac{x_{20}}{s^2} + \frac{x_{30}}{s+a}, \quad a > 0 \tag{8-26}$$

where R is a constant and x_{10}, x_{20}, x_{30} are the initial conditions at $t = 0$. For the basic oscillation of this system, we obtain from (8-19a) and (8-21)

$$Y_1(s) = (1 - e^{-sT})\left(\frac{x_{10}}{s} + \frac{x_{20}}{s^2} + \frac{x_{30}}{s+a}\right) + U(1 - 2e^{-\alpha Ts} + e^{-Ts})\frac{a^3}{s^3(s+a)} \tag{8-27}$$

We note that because of the pole of $G(s)$ at $s = 0$, the input to the linear element must have zero average value which implies

$$\alpha = \frac{1}{2} \tag{8-28}$$

Taking the advanced z-transform*** of (8-27), and using (8-28), gives:

*See Appendix B.

**It is important to note that (8-24) is equally valid if $\mathcal{Y}_1(z,m)$ is the modified z-transform. This is so because in the limit $z \to 1$, both advanced and modified z-transforms are identical. Thus, tables for either can be used. The available literature is about equally divided in the use of the two notations.

For tables of advanced or modified z-transforms, see [T5], [J6].

***In taking advanced z-transforms of delayed functions, we may make use of the shift-in properties (B-12) and (B-13), Appendix B.

$$\mathcal{Y}_1(z,m) = \frac{T\left(\dfrac{UTa^2}{4} + x_{20}\right)}{(z-1)} + U\left(\frac{T^2a^2}{2} m^2 - aTm + 1\right) + x_{20}Tm + x_{10}$$

$$- \frac{2U\, e^{-aTm}}{z - e^{-aT}} (z - e^{-(1/2)aT}) + (z-1)(U + x_{30}) \frac{e^{-aTm}}{z - e^{-aT}}$$

$$\text{for } 0 \le m < \tfrac{1}{2} \qquad \text{(8-29a)}$$

and

$$\mathcal{Y}_1(z,m) = \frac{T\left(\dfrac{Ta^2U}{4} + x_{20}\right)}{z-1} - \frac{U}{2}\left\{[Ta(1-m)+1]^2 + 1 - \frac{T^2a^2}{2}\right\}$$

$$+ Tmx_{20} + x_{10} + 2U\, e^{-aTm}(e^{-(1/2)aT} - 1)\frac{z}{z - e^{-aT}}$$

$$+ (U + x_{30})\, e^{-aTm} \frac{z-1}{z - e^{-aT}}, \qquad \text{for } \tfrac{1}{2} \le m < 1$$

$$\text{(8-29b)}$$

In order to make $\mathcal{Y}_1(z,m)$ analytic in $|z| \ge 1$, we must set the terms in $1/(z-1)$ to 0. This yields

$$x_{20} = -\frac{Ta^2U}{4} \qquad \text{(8-30)}$$

With Eq. (8-30), the limit $z \to 1$ exists in (8-29a) and (8-29b). By (8-24), we then have

$$y_p(mT) = x_{10} + U\left[1 - aTm - \frac{T^2a^2}{4} m(1-2m)\right] - 2U\, e^{-aTm}\frac{(1 - e^{-(1/2)aT})}{(1 - e^{-aT})},$$

$$0 \le m < \tfrac{1}{2}$$

$$y_p(mT) = x_{10} + \frac{U}{2}\left[\frac{T^2a^2}{2}(1-m) - (Ta(1-m)+1)^2 - 1\right]$$

$$+ 2U\, e^{-aTm}\frac{(e^{-(1/2)aT} - 1)}{(1 - e^{-aT})}, \qquad \tfrac{1}{2} \le m < 1 \qquad \text{(8-31)}$$

With $r(t) = R$, then by (8-31) and (8-13a) the switching conditions are

$$y_p(0) = R - \epsilon = x_{10} - U\zeta(aT), \quad y_p\left(\frac{T}{2}\right) = R + \epsilon = x_{10} - \frac{Ta}{2}U + U\zeta(aT) \tag{8-32}$$

where

$$\zeta(aT) \triangleq \frac{\left(1 - e^{-(1/2)aT}\right)^2}{1 - e^{-aT}} = \frac{\sinh^2\left(\frac{aT}{4}\right)}{\sinh\left(\frac{aT}{2}\right)} \tag{8-33}$$

From (8-32) and (8-33), we obtain

$$x_{10} = R + \frac{aT}{4}U \tag{8-34}$$

and

$$\zeta(aT) = \frac{\epsilon}{U} + \frac{aT}{4} \tag{8-35}$$

Note that we can always find a value for x_{10} that satisfies Eq. (8-34). However, from the graph of $\zeta(aT)$ shown in Fig. 8-5 we have

$$\frac{4\zeta(aT)}{aT}\begin{cases} < 1, & aT \neq 0 \\ = 1, & aT = 0 \end{cases} \tag{8-36}$$

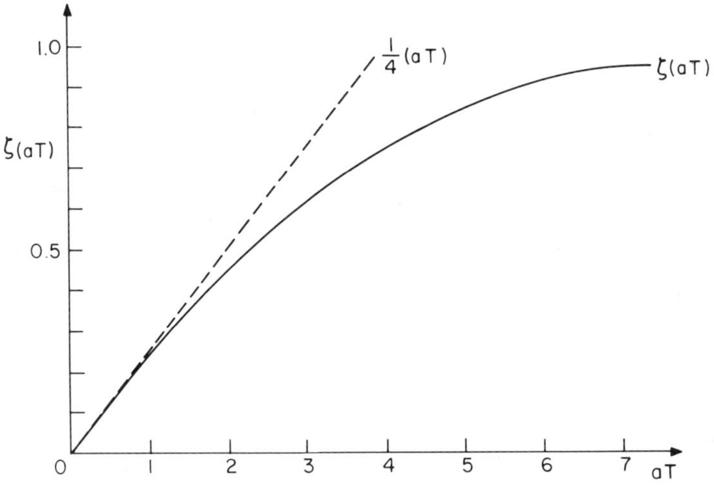

Fig. 8-5. A plot of the function $\zeta(aT)$ of Eq. (8-33).

It follows immediately that for positive ϵ, U, and a, a positive T cannot be found to satisfy Eq. (8–35). Thus our assumptions cannot be satisfied. Therefore, for this system, a basic oscillation cannot exist. ♦♦

♦♦Example 8-2. Consider the same system of Example 8–1 except that there is positive instead of negative feedback. We can see from Figs. 8–1 and 8–2a that this corresponds to reversing the sign of the relay level U. Thus, we substitute $U = -V;\ V > 0$. Then Eq. (8–35) becomes

$$\zeta(aT) = -\frac{\epsilon}{V} + \frac{aT}{4}$$

This can be satisfied. Hence, for positive feedback, a basic oscillation may exist. However, here we must have $\epsilon > 0$, i.e., there must be hysteresis (show this). ♦♦

♦♦Example 8-3. Consider the negative feedback system of Example 8–1, except that $a < 0$. It follows from (8–27) that we now have an unstable plant because of the pole at $s = -a > 0$. This, in turn, will produce a pole of $|z| = |e^{-aT}| > 1$ of the function $\mathcal{Y}_1(z, m)$ in (8–29). Thus, in order to make $\mathcal{Y}_1(z, m)$ analytic in $|z| \geq 1$, we must not only cancel out all terms of $\mathcal{Y}_1(z, m)$ in $(1/z)$ as was done in Example 8–1, but we must also cancel out all terms in $1/(z - e^{-aT})$. Doing this in either (8–29a) or (8–29b) yields (Exercise 8–4)

$$x_{30} = -U\zeta(aT) \tag{8–37}$$

where $\zeta(aT)$ is the function defined in (8–33). Condition (8–37) can be satisfied.

With (8–37) and, as previously with (8–30), $\mathcal{Y}_1(z, m)$ will be analytic in $|z| \geq 1$ and we can take the limit $z \to 1$ in (8–29). Interestingly enough, this also yields (8–31) as in Example 8–1 (exercise for the reader). Hence, the switching conditions (8–34) and (8–35) are also valid for the case $a < 0$. We already noted that (8–34) can always be satisfied.

Note that $\zeta(-aT) = -\zeta(aT)$; thus, if $\epsilon > 0$ and $U > 0$, we can see from (8–35) that a value $T > 0$ can be found if $a < 0$. Therefore, for the system of this example, a basic oscillation may exist. However, again we must have $\epsilon > 0$, or there must be hysteresis, as in the previous example. ♦♦

For both Examples 8–2 and 8–3, the necessary switching conditions (8–13a) are satisfied. However, to be certain, the continuity conditions (8–14a) should also be satisfied. This can be done for particular numerical values, using (8–31) (see Exercises 8–2 and 8–5).

We note that, in the examples of this section, the basic oscillation is independent of the constant input R. This is because of the pole at $s = 0$ of the transfer function $G(s)$. With an integrating stage we have found that the oscillation must be symmetrical (i.e., $\alpha = 1/2$); thus $u(t)$ and $e(t)$ in steady state must have zero average values. This means that the steady-state average value of the output $\overline{y(t)}$ must be equal to the constant value of the input R, i.e., in steady state,

$$\overline{y(t)} = R \tag{8-38}$$

We have already made use of this property in Chap. 7, when we discussed the oscillating servo which contained a relay.

Let us now establish a useful relationship between the closed-form expression of $y_p(mT)$ as obtained from (8-24) and the Fourier series representation of this signal. We shall need this expression in the next section where we will discuss the method of Tsypkin.

Let us make the following reasonable assumptions on the transfer function $G(s)$ and the initial-condition response $Y_0(s)$:

1) $h(t) \triangleq \int_0^t g(\tau)\,d\tau$ is continuous for $0 \leq t \leq \infty$
2) $y_0(t)$ is continuous for $0 \leq t \leq \infty$
3) $G(s)$ and $Y_0(s)$ have no singularity at $s = \pm j2n\pi/T, n = 1, 2, 3, \ldots$, ($G(s)$ and $Y_0(s)$ may have poles at $s = 0$.)

From Eq. (8-24) and Eq. (B-28a) of Appendix B, we obtain

$$y_p(mT) = \frac{\omega_0}{2\pi} \sum_{n=-\infty}^{\infty} Y_1(j\omega_0 n)\, e^{j2\pi mn} \tag{8-39*}$$

where $\omega_0 \triangleq 2\pi/T$.

With (8-21) in (8-39) and in view of assumption (3) above, we have

$$y_p(mT) = Y_0 + \frac{\omega_0}{2\pi} \sum_{\substack{n=-\infty \\ n\neq 0}}^{\infty} U_1(j\omega_0 n) G(j\omega_0 n)\, e^{j2\pi mn} \tag{8-40}$$

where Y_0 is the average value of $y_p(mT)$, given by

$$Y_0 = \overline{y(mT)} = \lim_{s\to 0}\,[TsY_0(s) + U_1(s)G(s)] \tag{8-41}$$

*Because of (8-19a), (8-21), and the assumptions on $G(s)$ and $Y_0(s)$, the function $y_1(t) = \mathcal{L}^{-1}[Y_1(s)]$ (see (8-20)) is continuous in $0 < t \leq \infty$. Therefore the term $(1/2)[y_1(mT^+) - y_1(mT^-)]$ vanishes for $m > 0$. Thus, from (B-28a) of Appendix B, (8-39) is valid for $0 < m < 1$. However, it also follows from (8-22) that the periodic function $y_p(t)$ is continuous, hence (8-39) is valid for all values of m.

If $G(s)$ and $Y_0(s)$ each have a pole at $s = 0$, then we already know that the oscillation must be symmetrical, the average values of the relay output $u(t)$ and, also, of the relay input $e(t)$ must be 0. Thus (see Fig. 8-1), the average value of the system output $y(t)$ must be equal to that of the input $r(t)$ or

$$Y_0 = \overline{r(t)} \qquad \text{(if } G(s) \text{ has a pole at } s = 0) \tag{8-42a)*}$$

If $G(s)$ and $Y_0(s)$ have no singularity at $s = 0$, then $\lim_{s\to 0} sY_0(s) = 0$. In this case, we see from (8-41) that

$$Y_0 = \lim_{s\to 0} U_1(s)\, G(s) \qquad \text{(if } G(s) \text{ has no singularity at } s = 0) \tag{8-42b}$$

As in the previous case, we would also expect that the average value Y_0 of the output $y(t)$ is in some way related to that of the input $r(t)$. In fact, the relation between average input and average output can be given in terms of duty cycle of oscillation which, by (8-19), is defined by the signal parameters α for relays without dead zone and α, β_1, β_2 for relays with dead zone. For $r(t) = 0$, we expect zero average output or $Y_0 = 0$ which, by (8-19), will result from a symmetrical oscillation corresponding to $\alpha = 1/2$ and $\beta_2 = (1/2) + \beta_1$.

Before leaving this section we may mention that if $Y_1(s)$ can be made an *entire function*** which can, for example, be accomplished by proper choice of the set of initial conditions so as to cancel out all terms containing singularities, then it can be shown [K1] that

$$y_1(t) = \begin{cases} y_p(t) & 0 \le t < T \\ 0 & \text{elsewhere} \end{cases}$$

This *entire function method* then gives an alternate way to establish periodic motion in a relay system. The method has the advantage that the advanced z-transform need not be resorted to. On the other hand, attention must be paid to all initial conditions of the linear element under the entire-function approach, whereas for the advanced z-transform method, only those initial conditions that correspond to singularities of $G(s)$ in $\mathcal{R}e\, s \geq 0$ need to be considered.

* If $G(s)$ has a pole at $s = 0$, then $Y_0(s)$ has one also.

** An entire function is a function of a complex variable which is analytic in the entire finite part of the s-plane.

8.4 Tsypkin's Method for Investigation of Self-Oscillation

Among the methods that can be used for the investigation of periodic oscillation in relay control systems, the most prominent ones are probably the closely related methods of Tsypkin [T6] and Hamel [G4]. We shall concentrate here on the method of Tsypkin which also permits a ready evaluation of the degree of approximation of the describing function approach. For a lucid account in English of the method of Hamel and its relation with Tsypkin's method, the reader is referred to the text by Gille, Pélegrin, and Decaulne [G4].

Tsypkin's method only makes use of the switching conditions (8-13) which are necessary for the existence of periodic operation. The switching conditions yield the signal parameters (with period T and duty-cycle parameters α, β_1, and β_2) necessary for periodic system operation. Generally speaking, if the switching conditions (8-13) are satisfied, then the continuity conditions (8-14) are usually also satisfied. When in doubt, it is a matter of straightforward linear analysis to calculate the response $y_p(t)$ in order to check the continuity conditions.

We shall limit the discussion of Tsypkin's method to the basic oscillation. Moreover, we shall only consider symmetrical oscillation, i.e., $\alpha = 1/2$ and $\beta = (1/2) + \beta_1$. By the end of the previous section, we had already established that this will be the case if the transfer function $G(s)$ has a pole at $s = 0$ or if the input $r(t)$ is 0. We shall assume here that the latter condition is satisfied. This does not entail any loss of generality since if $G(s)$ has a pole at $s = 0$ and $r(t) = R$, a constant, then we know from the last section that the periodic output, $y_p(t)$, will contain a constant term Y_0 which is equal to R. Thus, the switching conditions (8-13) will be independent of the value of R.

For symmetrical basic oscillation, with $\alpha = 1/2$, $\beta = (1/2) + \beta_1$, and $y(t) = -e(t)$, the switching conditions (8-13) for relay without dead zone become

$$y_p\left(\frac{\pi}{\omega_0}\right) = \epsilon, \quad \dot{y}_p\left(\frac{\pi}{\omega_0}\right) > 0 \tag{8-43a}$$

and for relay with dead zone

$$\begin{aligned} y_p\left(\frac{\pi}{\omega_0}\right) &= \epsilon, \quad y_p\left(\gamma\frac{\pi}{\omega_0}\right) = -\lambda \\ \dot{y}_p\left(\frac{\pi}{\omega_0}\right) &> 0, \quad \dot{y}_p\left(\gamma\frac{\pi}{\omega_0}\right) > 0, \end{aligned} \tag{8-43b}$$

where $\gamma = 2\beta_1$ and where $\omega_0 = 2\pi/T$ is the angular frequency of self-oscillation. Because of the symmetry of the oscillation, the other switching conditions in (8-13) are superfluous.

Tsypkin's main achievement consists in restating the switching conditions (8-43) in a form involving the frequency response of the linear plant $G(j\omega)$. This restatement involves the construction of a complex characteristic function which can be graphically represented in the form of a Tsypkin locus. For a particular system, once this locus is constructed, the existence of the basic periodic solution can be quickly determined, inasmuch as the transformation of conditions (8-43) into graphical form involving the Tsypkin locus is simple and straightforward.

Let us first consider the system with a relay without dead zone. For this case, Tsypkin defined the following complex function:

$$J(\omega) \triangleq -\frac{1}{\omega}\,\dot{y}_p\left(\frac{\pi}{\omega}\right) - jy_p\left(\frac{\pi}{\omega}\right) \tag{8-44}$$

This function, which we may call the *Tsypkin function*, is defined for all frequencies ω. Its locus in the complex plane is called the *Tsypkin locus*.

If ω_0 is the frequency of self-oscillation for the system, then the switching conditions (8-43) rewritten in terms of the function $J(\omega)$ are

$$\Re e\ J(\omega_0) < 0, \quad \Im m\ J(\omega_0) = -\epsilon \tag{8-45}$$

These follow directly from (8-43a). The above suggests that if we can plot $J(\omega)$ as a function of ω on a complex plane, then the frequency of oscillation can be established from a simple geometrical construction. This is illustrated in Fig. 8-6.

The frequency of oscillation, ω_0, is the only unknown to be found. We shall construct $J(\omega)$ as a function of $\omega = 2\pi/T$. First, we must establish $y_p(t)$ as a function of ω. For the symmetrical basic oscillation assumed here, i.e., with $r(t) = 0$, $Y_0 = 0$, and $\alpha = 1/2$, it follows from (8-19a) and (8-40) that

$$y_p(t) = \frac{\omega}{2\pi} U \sum_{\substack{n=-\infty \\ n\neq 0}}^{\infty} \frac{G(j\omega n)}{j\omega n}(1 - e^{-j\pi n})^2 e^{j\omega n t}$$

But

$$(1 - e^{-j\pi n})^2 = \begin{cases} 4; & \pm n = 1, 3, 5, \ldots \\ 0; & \pm n = 0, 2, 4, \ldots \end{cases}$$

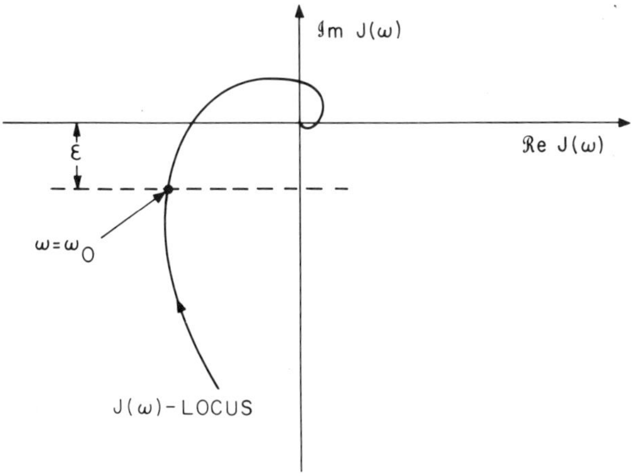

Fig. 8-6. A typical Tsypkin locus (Eq. (8-44)). For a relay with hysteresis of Fig. 8-2a, the construction to find the fundamental self-oscillation frequency ω_0 is shown.

Therefore

$$y_p(t) = \frac{2\omega}{\pi}U\sum_{n=1}^{\infty}\left[\frac{G\big(j\omega(2n-1)\big)}{j\omega(2n-1)}\,e^{j\omega(2n-1)t} - \frac{G\big(-j\omega(2n-1)\big)}{j\omega(2n-1)}\,e^{-j\omega(2n-1)t}\right]$$

and

$$\dot{y}_p(t) = \frac{2\omega}{\pi}U\sum_{n=1}^{\infty}\left[G\big(j\omega(2n-1)\big)\,e^{j\omega(2n-1)t} + G\big(-j\omega(2n-1)\big)\,e^{-j\omega(2n-1)t}\right]$$

Now, for an analytic function of a complex variable, the function of the conjugate of the complex variable is equal to the conjugate of the function.* Using this fact in the above two equations yields

$$y_p(t) = \frac{4U}{\pi}\sum_{n=1}^{\infty}\mathcal{I}m\left[\frac{G\big(j\omega(2n-1)\big)}{2n-1}\,e^{j\omega(2n-1)t}\right]$$

$$\dot{y}_p(t) = \frac{4U}{\pi}\,\omega\sum_{n=1}^{\infty}\mathcal{R}e\left[G\big(j\omega(2n-1)\big)e^{j\omega(2n-1)t}\right] \tag{8-46}$$

*Provided that the analytic function takes on real values for real arguments. This condition is met by the functions at the *rhs* of the equations for $y_p(t)$ and $\dot{y}_p(t)$ above.

In particular,

$$y_p\left(\frac{\pi}{\omega}\right) = -\frac{4U}{\pi}\sum_{n=1}^{\infty} \mathfrak{Im}\, \frac{G(j\omega(2n-1))}{2n-1}$$
$$\dot{y}_p\left(\frac{\pi}{\omega}\right) = -\frac{4U}{\pi}\omega \sum_{n=1}^{\infty} \mathfrak{Re}\, G(j\omega(2n-1)) \tag{8-47}$$

Thus, the Tsypkin function $J(\omega)$, defined in (8-44), becomes

$$J(\omega) = \frac{4U}{\pi}\sum_{n=1}^{\infty}\left[\mathfrak{Re}\, G(j(2n-1)\omega) + j\frac{\mathfrak{Im}\, G(j(2n-1)\omega)}{2n-1}\right] \tag{8-48}$$

Equation (8-48) suggests that for a given frequency ω, $J(\omega)$ can be constructed from the Nyquist plot of $G(j\omega)$ by taking the phasor $G(j\omega)$ and add successively the phasors $\mathfrak{Re}\, G(j3\omega) + j(1/3)\,\mathfrak{Im}\, G(j3\omega)$, $\mathfrak{Re}\, G(j5\omega) + j(1/5)\,\mathfrak{Im}\, G(j5\omega)$, ... etc. This construction is shown in Fig. 8-7. For any practical system, the real and imaginary values of $G(j(2n-1)\omega)$ will become vanishingly small after a few terms.

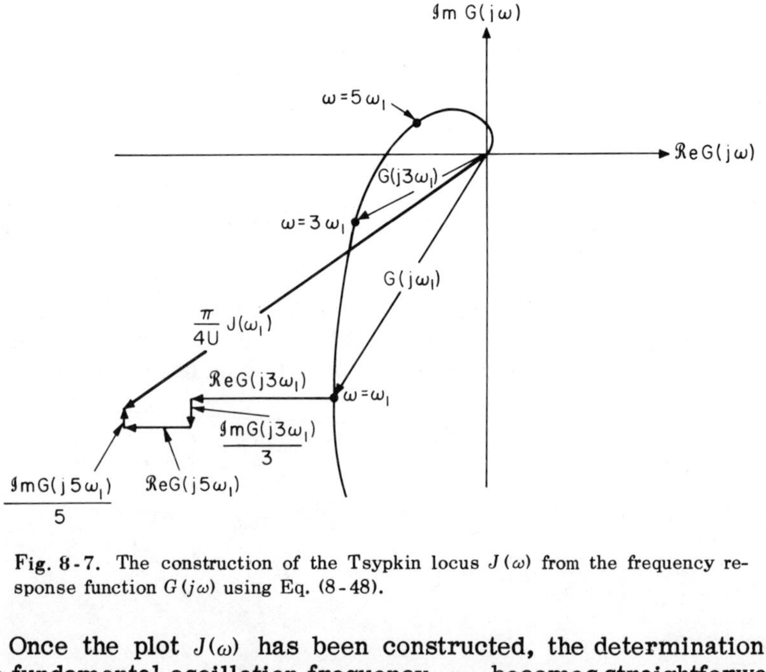

Fig. 8-7. The construction of the Tsypkin locus $J(\omega)$ from the frequency response function $G(j\omega)$ using Eq. (8-48).

Once the plot $J(\omega)$ has been constructed, the determination of the fundamental oscillation frequency, ω_0, becomes straightforward by Eq. (8-45), as is suggested by Fig. 8-6.

If we use only the first term in the series expression for $J(\omega)$ (8-48), then conditions (8-45) reduce to those necessary for the describing function. This can be shown as follows: Let

$$\frac{\pi}{4U} J(\omega) \simeq G(j\omega) \tag{8-49}$$

which, for example, can be quite valid for practical systems at large values of ω. Expression (8-49) is equivalent to approximating $y_p(t)$ by

$$y_p(t) \simeq \frac{4U}{\pi} |G(j\omega)| \sin\big(\omega t + \theta(\omega)\big) \tag{8-50}$$

where

$$\theta(\omega) = \underline{/G(j\omega)} \tag{8-51}$$

From the switching condition (8-45) we have, at the oscillating frequency ω_0,

$$|G(j\omega_0)| \sin\big(\theta(\omega_0)\big) = -\frac{\pi}{4U}\epsilon, \text{ or } \sin\big(\theta(\omega_0)\big) = -\frac{\pi\epsilon}{4U|G(j\omega_0)|}$$

Let $\hat{y}_0 \triangleq (4U/\pi)|G(j\omega_0)|$, which is the amplitude of the first harmonic of the periodic output $y_p(t)$. Then, $\sin\big(\theta(\omega_0)\big) = -\epsilon/\hat{y}_0$; or $\theta(\omega_0) = \pi + \sin^{-1}(\epsilon/\hat{y}_0)$. Therefore,

$$G(j\omega_0) = |G(j\omega_0)| \exp\big(j\theta(\omega_0)\big) = -\frac{\pi\hat{y}_0}{4U} \exp\Big[j \sin^{-1}(\epsilon/\hat{y}_0)\Big] \tag{8-52}$$

The necessary condition (8-52), under the approximation (8-49), however, is simply the necessary condition arrived at from describing function consideration:

$$G(j\omega_0) = -\frac{1}{N(\hat{y}_0)} \tag{8-53}$$

where $N(\hat{y}_0) = (4U/\pi\hat{y})\exp\big(-j\sin^{-1}(\epsilon/\hat{y}_0)\big)$ is simply the describing function of a relay with hysteresis, as has been shown in Sec. 6.3.

Let us now consider the system with a relay with hysteresis and dead zone. For this case, the approach of Tsypkin is still valid, although the relevant conditions to be satisfied become somewhat more complicated. Here, we need two Tsypkin functions which are defined as

$$\begin{aligned} J_1(\omega) &\triangleq -\frac{1}{\omega}\dot{y}_p\left(\frac{\pi}{\omega}\right) - jy_p\left(\frac{\pi}{\omega}\right) \\ J_2(\omega) &\triangleq -\frac{1}{\omega}\dot{y}_p\left(\gamma\frac{\pi}{\omega}\right) - jy_p\left(\gamma\frac{\pi}{\omega}\right) \end{aligned} \tag{8-54}$$

If ω_0 is the frequency of self-oscillation, then the switching conditions on the functions $J_1(\omega)$ and $J_2(\omega)$ follow from (8-43b) and (8-54):

$$\begin{aligned} \mathcal{I}m\ J_1(\omega_0) &= -\epsilon, & \mathcal{I}m\ J_2(\omega_0) &= \lambda \\ \mathcal{R}e\ J_1(\omega_0) &< 0, & \mathcal{R}e\ J_2(\omega_0) &< 0 \end{aligned} \tag{8-55}$$

Note from (8-55) that the switching conditions on $J_1(\omega)$ are the same ones as those for $J(\omega)$ for the case of a relay without dead zone. However, because of the different waveforms for the two cases, the functions $J(\omega)$ and $J_1(\omega)$ are not the same. To obtain expressions for $J_1(\omega)$ and $J_2(\omega)$ we proceed as for $J(\omega)$. We must establish $y_p(t)$ as a function of ω. For the symmetrical basic oscillation (i.e., with $r(t) = 0$, $Y_0 = 0$, $\alpha = 1/2$, $\gamma = 2\beta_1$, and $\beta_2 = (1/2)(1+\gamma)$), it follows from (8-19b) and (8-40) that

$$y_p(t) = \frac{\omega}{2\pi} U \sum_{\substack{n=-\infty \\ n\neq 0}}^{\infty} \frac{G(j\omega n)}{j\omega n} (1 - e^{-j\pi\gamma n})(1 - e^{-j\pi n})\, e^{j\omega n t}$$

Taking the steps analogous to those leading to (8-46), we have

$$\begin{aligned} y_p(t) &= \frac{2U}{\pi} \sum_{n=1}^{\infty} \mathcal{I}m \left\{ \frac{G\big(j(2n-1)\omega\big)}{2n-1} \left[1 - e^{-j\pi(2n-1)\gamma}\right] e^{j(2n-1)\omega t} \right\} \\ \dot{y}_p(t) &= \frac{2U}{\pi} \omega \sum_{n=1}^{\infty} \mathcal{R}e \left\{ G\big(j(2n-1)\omega\big)\left[1 - e^{-j\pi(2n-1)\gamma}\right] e^{j(2n-1)\omega t} \right\} \end{aligned} \tag{8-56}$$

Note that for the special case where $\gamma = 2\beta_1 = 1$, Eqs. (8-55) reduce to (8-46). This, of course, we would expect since this corresponds to making the dead zone 0. For $t = \pi/\omega$ and $t = \gamma\pi/\omega$, we obtain from (8-56)

$$\begin{aligned} y_p\left(\frac{\pi}{\omega}\right) &= -\frac{2U}{\pi} \sum_{n=1}^{\infty} \mathcal{I}m \left\{ \frac{G\big(j(2n-1)\omega\big)}{2n-1} \left[1 - e^{-j\pi(2n-1)\gamma}\right] \right\} \\ \dot{y}_p\left(\frac{\pi}{\omega}\right) &= -\frac{2U}{\pi} \omega \sum_{n=1}^{\infty} \mathcal{R}e \left\{ G\big(j(2n-1)\omega\big)\left[1 - e^{-j\pi(2n-1)\gamma}\right] \right\} \\ y_p\left(\gamma\frac{\pi}{\omega}\right) &= -\frac{2U}{\pi} \sum_{n=1}^{\infty} \mathcal{I}m \left\{ \frac{G\big(j(2n-1)\omega\big)}{2n-1} \left[1 - e^{j\pi(2n-1)\gamma}\right] \right\} \\ \dot{y}_p\left(\gamma\frac{\pi}{\omega}\right) &= -\frac{2U}{\pi} \omega \sum_{n=1}^{\infty} \mathcal{R}e \left\{ G\big(j(2n-1)\omega\big)\left[1 - e^{j\pi(2n-1)\gamma}\right] \right\} \end{aligned} \tag{8-57}$$

Comparing (8-57) with (8-54), we have

$$\mathfrak{Im}\ J_1(\omega) = \frac{2U}{\pi}\sum_{n=1}^{\infty}\left[\frac{\sin\big((2n-1)\gamma\pi\big)}{2n-1}\,\mathfrak{Re}\ G\big(j(2n-1)\omega\big) + \frac{1-\cos(2n-1)\gamma\pi}{2n-1}\,\mathfrak{Im}\ G\big(j(2n-1)\omega\big)\right]$$

$$\mathfrak{Re}\ J_1(\omega) = \frac{2U}{\pi}\sum_{n=1}^{\infty}\Big[\big(1-\cos(2n-1)\gamma\pi\big)\,\mathfrak{Re}\ G\big(j(2n-1)\omega\big) - \sin\big((2n-1)\gamma\pi\big)\,\mathfrak{Im}\ G\big(j(2n-1)\omega\big)\Big]$$

$$\mathfrak{Im}\ J_2(\omega) = -\frac{2U}{\pi}\sum_{n=1}^{\infty}\left[\frac{\sin\big((2n-1)\gamma\pi\big)}{2n-1}\,\mathfrak{Re}\ G\big(j(2n-1)\omega\big) - \frac{1-\cos\big((2n-1)\gamma\pi\big)}{2n-1}\,\mathfrak{Im}\ G\big(j(2n-1)\omega\big)\right]$$

$$\mathfrak{Re}\ J_2(\omega) = \frac{2U}{\pi}\sum_{n=1}^{\infty}\Big[\big(1-\cos(2n-1)\gamma\pi\big)\,\mathfrak{Re}\ G\big(j(2n-1)\omega\big) + \sin\big((2n-1)\gamma\pi\big)\,\mathfrak{Im}\big(G\ j(2n-1)\omega\big)\Big] \tag{8-58}$$

We note that both $J_1(\omega)$ and $J_2(\omega)$ depend on $G(j\omega)$ and on the parameter γ. Moreover, from (8-58), we see that the construction of $J_1(\omega)$ and $J_2(\omega)$, even for given values of γ, will be more laborious than the construction of $J(\omega)$ for relays without dead zone. To find the two signal parameters, ω_0 (frequency of self-oscillation) and γ, we must use (8-55).

The idea of finding ω_0 and γ by using the plots of $J_1(\omega)$ and $J_2(\omega)$ is quite straightforward (and is akin to the application of DIDF to systems with unsymmetrical zero-memory nonlinearities as expounded in the previous chapter). Basically we can plot a family of $J_1(\omega)$ as a function ω with γ as parameters. Each of the points where one of these curves crosses the $\mathfrak{Im}\ J_1(\omega) = -\epsilon$ line yield a possible solution in the pair of values ω_0 and γ. This then yields a curve $\omega_a(\gamma)$ which may be plotted.

Similarly, we can obtain another curve $\omega_b(\gamma)$ by considering the points at which the family of $J_2(\omega)$ curves (with γ as a parameter) crosses the $\mathfrak{Im}\ J_2(\omega) = \lambda$ line. The intersection of $\omega_a(\gamma)$ with $\omega_b(\gamma)$ then yields the correct values of ω_0 and γ_1 at which the system can sustain an oscillation at the basic mode.

♦♦**Example 8-4.** Consider a system of the form of Fig. 8-1 with $r = 0$. The relay is one of the form of Fig. 8-2b with $U = 1$, $\epsilon = 0.2$, $\lambda = 0.1$. The linear plant is given by $G(p) = 10/[p(p+1)]$. Find the frequency of oscillation and the associated value of the parameter γ_1. Compare these values with those obtained by the describing function analysis.

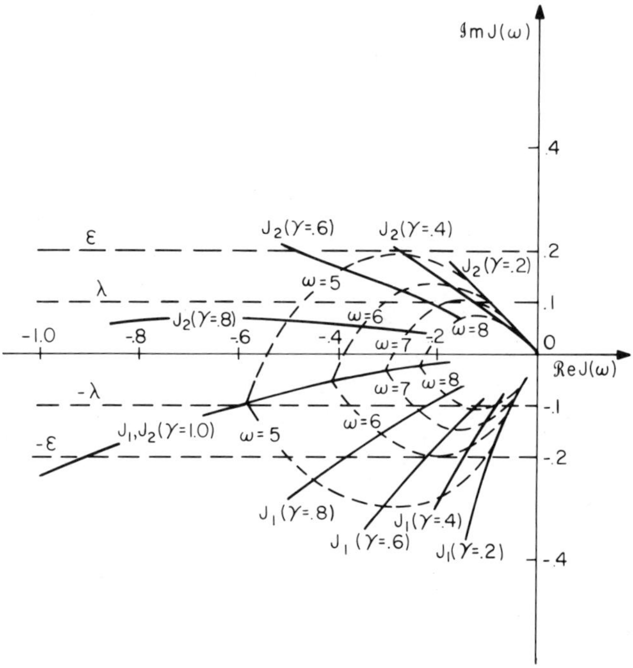

Fig. 8-8. The Tsypkin loci of the system of Example 8-4 for a relay with dead zone and hysteresis. Here two families of loci $J_1(\omega)$ and $J_2(\omega)$ for various values of γ (where $\gamma = 2\beta_1$, see Fig. 8-3b) need to be plotted. The switching conditions are determined from Eq. (8-55).

The Tsypkin loci for the system are as shown in Fig. 8-8.* From the intersections of the loci $J_1(\omega)$ with the $-\epsilon$ line and those of the loci $J_2(\omega)$ with the $+\lambda$ line, we obtain the plots $\omega_a(\gamma)$ and $\omega_b(\gamma)$ respectively as shown in Fig. 8-9a. From these we determine that $\omega_0 = 5.5$ and $\gamma_1 = 0.1$.

The describing function analysis is displayed graphically in Fig. 8-9b where the Nyquist plot of the system is exhibited

*Note that since only the values of $J_1(\omega)$ near the $-\epsilon$ line and the values of $J_2(\omega)$ near the $+\lambda$ line need to be computed, much labor can be saved if the computation is well planned. Thus a desk calculator can readily be used to sum Eq. (8-58).

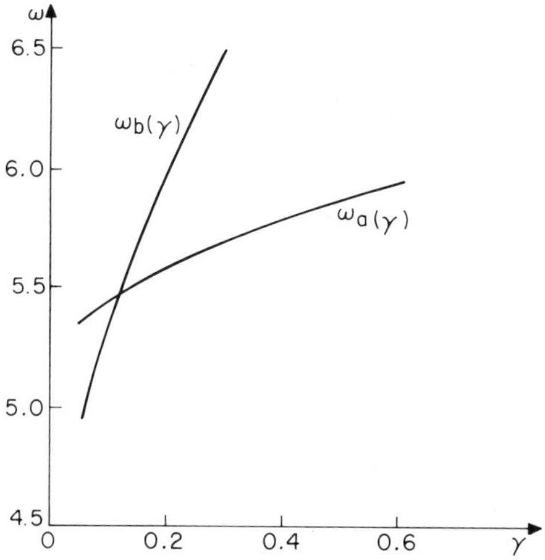

(a)

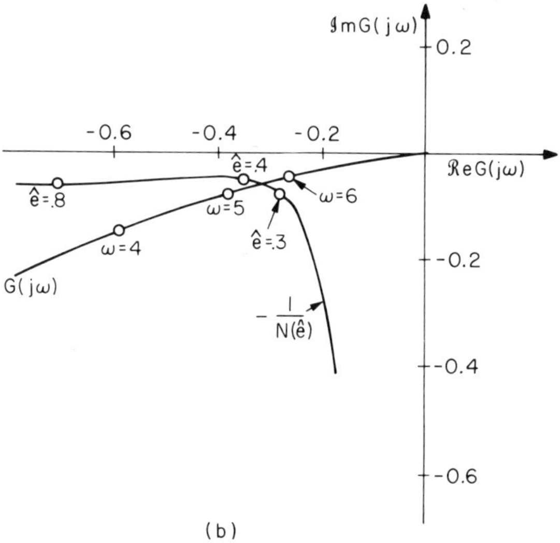

(b)

Fig. 8-9. (a) The curve $\omega_a(\gamma)$ representing the intersection of the locus $J_1(\omega)$ with the $-\epsilon$ line of Fig. 8-8 is plotted with the line $\omega_b(\gamma)$ determined by the intersection of the locus $J_2(\omega)$ with the $+\lambda$ line of Fig. 8-8. The intersection of $\omega_a(\gamma)$ and $\omega_b(\gamma)$ determines ω_0 in accordance with Eq. (8-55). (b) The determination of ω_0 and $\hat{e}$ by the describing function method.

against $-[1/N(\hat{e})]$, the negative inverse of the describing function. Since there is hysteresis in the nonlinear characteristics, we expect the $-[1/N(\hat{e})]$ to show a phase angle which varies with the input amplitude $\hat{e}$. In fact it is readily shown that the real and imaginary parts of $N(\hat{e})$ are given by

$$\mathcal{R}e\ N(\hat{e}) = \frac{2U}{\pi}\left[\sqrt{1-\frac{\epsilon}{\hat{e}}}+\sqrt{1-\frac{\lambda}{\hat{e}}}\right]$$

$$\mathcal{I}m\ N(\hat{e}) = \frac{-2U}{\pi\hat{e}^2}[\epsilon-\lambda]$$

From Fig. 8-9b, we obtain $\omega_0 \simeq 5.5$ rad/sec, and $\hat{e}_0 \simeq 0.36$. It is interesting to note that the frequency of oscillation is predicted remarkably closely by the describing function approach. However, the value of $\hat{e}_0$ above is unreasonable. (It would predict a γ_0 of 0.6!) Using the value of γ_0 obtained by Tsypkin locus, however, we discover (by using Eq. (8-56)) that the true value of the fundamental component of $e_p(t) = -y_p(t)$ is equal to 0.2. ♦♦

The above is a graphic demonstration that the result of describing function analysis may be quite unreliable in predicting waveforms but can be almost uncanny in predicting the existence and even the period of limit cycles in many systems.

8.5 An Alternate Approach for the Construction of the Tsypkin Locus

In this section, we shall show a simple relation between $J(\omega)$ and z-transform expressions involving the linear element. This will eliminate the need to sum infinite series.

We shall limit this discussion to the case of a relay without dead zone. For the case with dead zone, the derivation follows the same ideas.

Until now in this chapter, we did not require the linear element to be stable. However, in this section, we shall require that both the transfer function $G(s)$ and the initial condition response be analytic in $\mathcal{R}e\ s \geq 0$ except possibly for a simple pole at $s = 0$. Also, we consider symmetrical oscillation only.

As before, we let $g(t) = \mathcal{L}^{-1}[G(s)]$ be the impulse response of the plant, and let $h(t) = \mathcal{L}^{-1}[G(s)/s]$ be its unit-step response. For the basic symmetrical oscillation, starting at $t = -NT$, we can write (8-11a) with $\alpha = 1/2$ and $T = 2\pi/\omega$, as

$$u_p(t) = \lim_{N\to\infty} U \sum_{k=-N}^{\infty} (-1)^k\left[\mu_{-1}\left(t - k\frac{\pi}{\omega}\right) - \mu_{-1}\left(t-(k+1)\frac{\pi}{\omega}\right)\right] \qquad (8\text{-}59)$$

The response of the linear element and derivative of the response, evaluated at $t = \pi/\omega$ will then be:

$$y\left(\frac{\pi}{\omega}\right) = \lim_{N\to\infty}\left\{y_0\left(t + N\frac{\pi}{\omega}\right) + \sum_{k=-N}^{0}(-1)^k\left[h\left((1-k)\left(\frac{\pi}{\omega}\right)^+\right) - h\left((2-k)\left(\frac{\pi}{\omega}\right)^+\right)\right]\right\} + Uh\left(\frac{\pi^+}{\omega}\right) = y_0(\infty) - 2U\sum_{k=0}^{\infty}(-1)^k\, h\left(k\frac{\pi^+}{\omega}\right) + 2Uh(0^+) \tag{8-60a}$$

$$\dot{y}\left(\frac{\pi}{\omega}\right) = \dot{y}_0(\infty) - 2U\sum_{k=0}^{\infty}(-1)^k\, g\left(k\frac{\pi^+}{\omega}\right) + 2Ug(0^+) \tag{8-60b}$$

Since we assume that $Y_0(s)$ and $G(s)$ are both analytic in $\mathcal{R}e\ s \geq 0$ except possibly for a simple pole at $s = 0$, the limit $y_0(\infty)$ exists and $\dot{y}_0(\infty) = 0$. Moreover, because of (8–3), $h(0^+) = 0$. The convergence of the infinite series in (8–60) can be demonstrated if (8–60) is rewritten with $\dot{y}_0(\infty) = 0$ and $h(0^+) = 0$, as follows:

$$y\left(\frac{\pi}{\omega}\right) = y_0(\infty) - 2U\lim_{z\to-1}\mathcal{H}'(z), \qquad \dot{y}\left(\frac{\pi}{\omega}\right) = 2U\left[g(0^+) - \lim_{z\to-1}\mathcal{G}'(z)\right] \tag{8-61}$$

where $\mathcal{H}'(z)$ and $\mathcal{G}'(z)$ are the z–transforms of $h(t)$ and $g(t)$ respectively, but with a sampling interval of $T/2$ or π/ω. Thus

$$\mathcal{H}'(z) \triangleq \sum_{k=0}^{\infty} h\left(k\frac{\pi}{\omega}\right)z^{-k}, \qquad \mathcal{G}'(z) \triangleq \sum_{k=0}^{\infty} g\left(k\frac{\pi}{\omega}\right)z^{-k} \tag{8-62}$$

Since $H(s)$ and $G(s)$ are both analytic in $\mathcal{R}e\ s \geq 0$ except possibly for poles at $s = 0$, we can show that their z–transforms are analytic in $|z| \geq 1$, except possibly at $z = +1$. Thus the limits of $\mathcal{H}'(z)$ and $\mathcal{G}'(z)$ in (8–61), $z \to -1$, exist and yield the converging series in (8–59).

With (8–61), the Tsypkin function $J(\omega)$, defined in (8–44), becomes

$$J(\omega) = \frac{2U}{\omega}\left[\mathcal{G}'(-1) - g(0)\right] + j\left[2U\mathcal{H}'(-1) - y_0(\infty)\right] \tag{8-63}$$

Since $\mathcal{G}'(z)$ and $\mathcal{H}'(z)$ were determined on the basis of a period π/ω, they depend on ω and so do the expressions $\mathcal{G}'(-1)$ and $\mathcal{H}'(-1)$. To emphasize their dependence on ω, it may be more suitable to express (8–63) in terms of the so-called pulse-transfer functions

$G'^*(s)$ and $H'^*(s)$ which here, with a period of π/ω, are defined as

$$G'^*(s) \triangleq \mathcal{G}(\exp(s\pi/\omega)), \qquad H'^*(s) \triangleq \mathcal{H}(\exp(s\pi/\omega)) \tag{8-64}$$

From (8-64) it follows that $G'^*(j\omega) = \mathcal{G}'(e^{j\pi}) = \mathcal{G}'(-1)$ and $H'^*(j\omega) = \mathcal{H}'(-1)$; therefore, (8-63) can be written as

$$J(\omega) = \frac{2U}{\omega}[G'^*(j\omega) - g(0)] + j[2UH'^*(j\omega) - y_0(\infty)] \tag{8-65}$$

which is the expression sought for. The switching conditions (8-45) can thus be written as

$$\frac{2U}{\omega}[G'^*(j\omega) - g(0^+)] < 0, \qquad 2UH'^*(j\omega) - y_0(\infty) = -\epsilon \tag{8-66}$$

8.6 Forced Oscillations in Relay Systems

Tsypkin's method can also be extended to the case of forced oscillations in relay systems.

We recall that the existence or nonexistence of forced oscillation does not necessarily preclude other modes of oscillation, such as self-oscillation or oscillation at a harmonic or subharmonic. They must be separately investigated.

Consider now the system of Fig. 8-1. This time, let $r(t)$ be of the form

$$r(t) = r_p(\omega_0 t - \phi) \tag{8-67}$$

where $r_p(\omega_0 t - \phi)$ is a periodic function of period $2\pi/\omega_0$ with absolute value less than or equal to a constant A.

We then have

$$e(t) = r_p(\omega_0 t - \phi) - y(t) \tag{8-68}$$

If the relay does not have a dead zone, then it is clear that in order for $u(t)$ to have the basic period $2\pi/\omega_0$, the switching conditions on the periodic function $e_p(t)$ must still obey (8-13a). Thus we have

$$e_p\left(\frac{\pi}{\omega_0}\right) = r_p(\pi - \phi) - y_p\left(\frac{\pi}{\omega_0}\right) = -\epsilon \tag{8-69a}$$

$$\frac{1}{\omega_0}\dot{e}_p\left(\frac{\pi}{\omega_0}\right) = \dot{r}_p(\pi - \phi) - \frac{1}{\omega_0}\dot{y}_p\left(\frac{\pi}{\omega_0}\right) < 0 \tag{8-69b}$$

To adapt to the Tsypkin characteristic function formulation let

$$R(\pi - \phi) \triangleq \dot{r}_p(\pi - \phi) + jr_p(\pi - \phi) \tag{8-70}$$

along with the usual

$$J(\omega) = -\frac{1}{\omega_0}\dot{y}_p\left(\frac{\pi}{\omega}\right) - jy_p\left(\frac{\pi}{\omega}\right) \tag{8-71}$$

Combining (8-70) and (8-71) we obtain the new switching conditions

$$\mathcal{I}m\ [R(\pi - \phi) + J(\omega_0)] = -\epsilon, \quad \mathcal{R}e\ [R(\pi - \phi) + J(\omega_0)] < 0 \tag{8-72}$$

The conditions given in (8-72) suggest the following graphical construction: Construct the locus $J(\omega)$ as before, and at the point $J(\omega_0)$ construct the locus $R(\pi - \phi)$ as a function of ϕ. If the $R(\pi - \phi)$ locus constructed about the point $J(\omega_0)$ intersects the $-\epsilon$ line to the left of the $\mathcal{I}m\ J(\omega)$ axis, then there will be forced oscillation. This procedure is shown in Fig. 8-10.

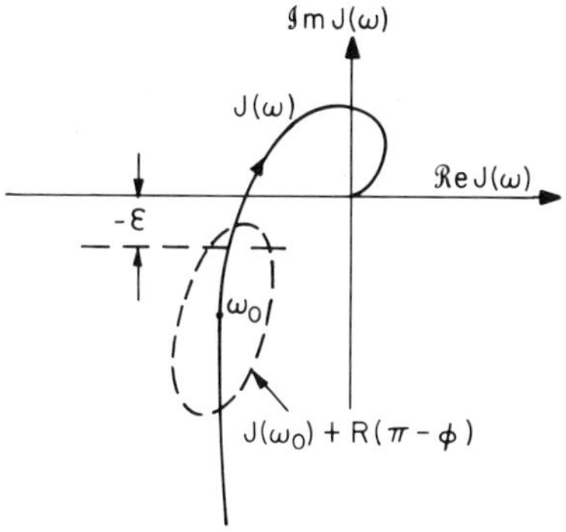

Fig. 8-10. The determination of forced oscillation using the Tsypkin locus for a relay without dead zone. The locus $R(\pi - \phi)$ is determined from the periodic input function $r(t) = r_p(\pi - \phi)$ via Eq. (8-70).

The locus $R(\pi - \phi)$ is easily plotted from its definition (8-70) and is seen to be a Lissajous figure for the input $r_p(t)$. A typical $R(\pi - \phi)$ locus for the triangular waveform of Fig. 8-11a is shown in Fig. 8-11c. In the special case of a sinusoidal $r_p(t)$, the $R(\pi - \phi)$ locus is an ellipse. For more general periodic waves $r_p(t)$, it is not uncommon for the $R(\pi - \phi)$ locus to cross itself.

In determining the possibility of forced oscillation, we should differentiate among several possibilities. These can be shown geometrically in Figs. 8-12a through 8-12e. Case 8-12a indicates that there is no forced oscillation, however, there may be other modes of oscillation in the system. Case 8-12b indicates that two

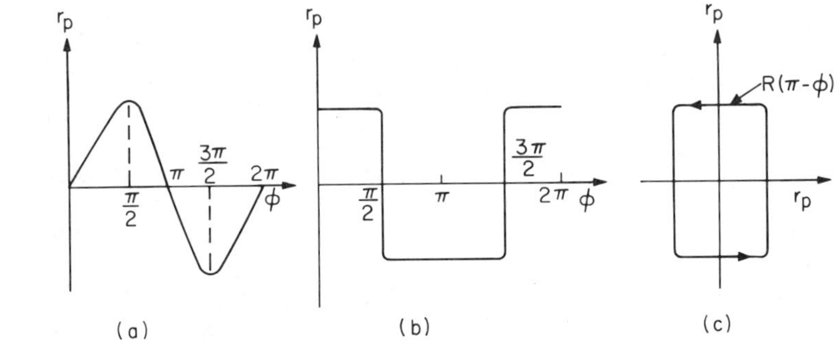

Fig. 8-11. The construction of a typical $R(\pi - \phi)$ locus.

modes of self-oscillation are possible as given by two different values of the input phase angle ϕ as related to the output. In general, however, only one of these modes will be stable (see the next section). Case 8-12c shows that the $R(\pi - \phi)$ locus is tangent to the $-\epsilon$ line; it essentially establishes the minimum amplitude of the input at which oscillation is possible. Case 8-12d indicates another threshold case where $R(\pi - \phi)$ is more than large enough to cross the $-\epsilon$ line but, however, is barely large enough to reach the imaginary axis. Case 8-12e represents a case where the driving amplitude is large; however, for this particular case there is only one unique mode of oscillation.

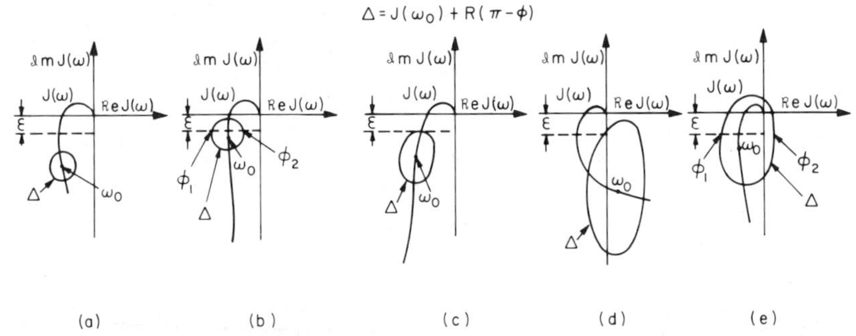

Fig. 8-12. Several possible cases of forced oscillation in a relay system for a relay without dead zone: (a) no forced oscillation. (b) two possible modes of forced oscillation. (c) and (d) incipient forced oscillation. (e) a single possible mode of forced oscillation.

The foregoing approach can readily be extended to the case of a relay with dead zone. Here, the switching conditions become:

$$\begin{aligned} &\mathcal{I}m\left[R(\pi - \phi) + J_1(\omega_0)\right] = -\epsilon, \quad \mathcal{R}e\left[R(\pi - \phi) + J_1(\omega_0)\right] < 0, \\ &\mathcal{I}m\left[R(\gamma\pi - \phi) + J_2(\omega_0)\right] = \lambda, \quad \mathcal{R}e\left[R(\gamma\pi - \phi) + J_2(\omega_0)\right] < 0 \end{aligned} \tag{8-73}$$

The basic graphical approach is then to construct the $R(\pi - \phi)$ locus at the frequency ω_0 on the $J_1(\omega)$ locus for each γ and inspect whether the $R(\pi - \phi)$ locus satisfies the first two conditions of (8-73). Similarly, we construct the $R(\gamma\pi - \phi)$ locus at the frequency ω_0 on the $J_2(\omega)$ locus for each γ and inspect whether the $R(\gamma\pi - \phi)$ locus satisfies the second two conditions of (8-73). If there is a set of values of γ which simultaneously satisfies all four of the conditions (8-73), then forced oscillation will be possible.

8.7 The Stability of Oscillations in Relay Systems

The stability of oscillations, both self and forced, can be analyzed by the approach of small signal perturbations about a known periodic motion. The interesting aspects of applying this approach, however, are that the resulting system in terms of the perturbed signals is a linear sampled-data system whose stability can then be readily analyzed by well-developed theories concerning such systems. This interesting and important result is due again to Tsypkin [T6].

It is perhaps not entirely surprising that a sampled-data system should result when we apply small signal perturbations. This is so because small perturbations about the basic relay waveform such as that given by Eq. (8-59) would naturally result in positive and negative pulses which in the limit can be approximated by impulses.

To develop the approach for a relay without dead zone, let us assume that $g(0) = 0$ and $h(0) = 0$, and that $g(t)$ and $h(t)$ are both continuous everywhere.*

Suppose that a basic periodic oscillation has already been found to exist in the system with the steady-state oscillation given by $r_p(t)$, $e_p(t)$, $u_p(t)$, and $y_p(t)$. Consider now small perturbations $\delta r(t)$, $\delta e(t)$, $\delta u(t)$, and $\delta y(t)$ on the respective periodic functions.

Consider a perturbation on $e_p(t)$ as shown in Fig. 8-13a. The resultant perturbed function $u(t)$ is shown in Fig. 8-13b. The difference between the unperturbed oscillation $u_p(t)$ and the perturbed function $u(t)$ is then shown in Fig. 8-13c. It is seen to consist of pulses near the points $t = n\pi/\omega$ $(n = 0, 1, \ldots)$ at which $e(t)$ reaches the value of 0.

In the limit as $\delta e(t) \to 0$, these pulses in $\delta u(t)$ can be represented in terms of impulses at the instants $t = n\pi/\omega$.

In order to relate $\delta u(n\pi/\omega)$ to $\delta e(n\pi/\omega)$ let us note that a switch of the relay from $-$ to $+$ can only occur when the situation of

*If $G(p)$ is a rational function then this means that it must have at least two more poles than zeros.

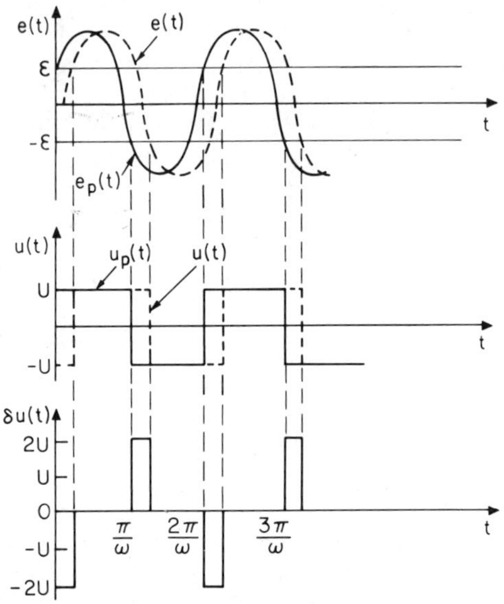

Fig. 8-13. Illustration of the fact that small perturbations on the signal $e(t)$ cause changes in the relay output $u(t)$ that are given by small pulses.

Fig. 8-14a pertains, while a switch in the reverse direction can only occur if the situation of Fig. 8-14b holds. The width of the pulse in $\delta u(n\pi/\omega)$, denoted by $\delta\tau\,(n\pi/\omega)$, is approximately given by:

$$\delta\tau\left(\frac{n\pi}{\omega}\right) \simeq -\frac{\delta e\left(\frac{n\pi}{\omega}\right)}{\dot{e}_p\left(\frac{n\pi}{\omega}\right)} = -\frac{\delta e\left(\frac{n\pi}{\omega}\right)}{\left|\dot{e}_p\left(\frac{\pi}{\omega}\right)\right|}(-1)^n \tag{8-74}$$

where we made use of the fact that $|\dot{e}_p(n\pi/\omega)| = |\dot{e}_p(\pi/\omega)|$ for all n. In the limit, we can then write

$$\delta u(t) = \frac{2U}{\left|\dot{e}_p\left(\frac{\pi}{\omega}\right)\right|}\sum_{k=0}^{\infty} \delta e\left(\frac{k\pi}{\omega}\right)\mu_0\left(t - \frac{k\pi}{\omega}\right) \tag{8-75}$$

where $\mu_0(t)$ represents a unit impulse at $t = 0$. Equation (8-75), along with the relationships among the variables $\delta u(t)$, $\delta y(t)$, and $\delta r(t)$, suggests the sampled-data system of Fig. 8-15, which completely represents the relationship among the perturbed variables. We then can make the following statement:

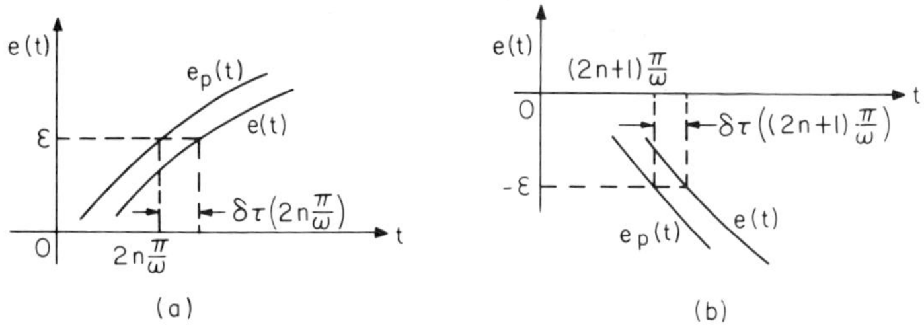

Fig. 8-14. The relationship between $\delta e(n\pi/\omega)$ and the width of the pulses $\delta\tau(n\pi/\omega)$.

♦♦Theorem 8-2. Consider a system of Fig. 8-1, in which the relay has no dead zone. The stability in the small of the basic self-oscillating motion $(r(t) \equiv 0)$, or forced oscillatory motion $e_p(t)$ under a periodic input $r_p(t)$ is the same as the stability of the linear sampled data system of Fig. 8-15.♦♦

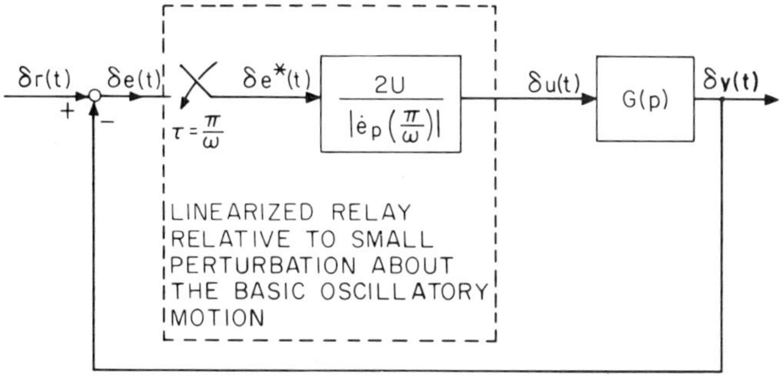

Fig. 8-15. For a system of the form of Fig. 8-1, the stability in the small of an assumed self-oscillation motion or forced oscillation motion is equivalent to the stability of the linear sampled data system shown.

Note that the sampling period of the sampled data system of Fig. 8-15 is $\tau = T/2 = \pi/\omega$. Let us therefore define the following advanced z-transform

$$\mathcal{G}'(z, m) \triangleq \sum_{k=0}^{\infty} g\left((m + k)\frac{\pi}{\omega}\right)z^{-k} \tag{8-76}$$

For $m = 0$, $\mathcal{G}'(z, 0)$ reduces to the quantity $\mathcal{G}'(z)$ defined in (8-62).

From Theorem 8-2 and Theorem B-4 of Appendix B, we have:

♦♦Theorem 8-3. For a system of Fig. 8-1, in which the relay has no dead zone, if

1) the linear element is governed by a time-invariant ordinary differential equation whose states are completely controllable and completely observable,
2) for every m, $\mathcal{G}'(z, m)$ has the same set of poles as $\mathcal{G}'(z, 0) = \mathcal{G}'(z)$, and
3) all the zeros of

$$1 + \frac{2U}{\left|\dot{e}_p\left(\frac{\pi}{\omega}\right)\right|}\mathcal{G}'(z) = 0 \tag{8-77}$$

lie in $|z| < 1$ ($|z| > 1$),

then a given self-oscillatory motion or forced-oscillatory motion is asymptotically stable (unstable).♦♦

Note that conditions (1) and (2) in the statement of Theorem 8-3 are satisfied in most practical cases.

If all the roots of (8-77) lie in $|z| < 1$ except for one or more roots at $|z| = 1$, then by consideration analogous to that which led to Lyapunov's first method, we can reach the conclusion that further investigations will be necessary.

Since $g(0)$ is assumed to be 0, we can also make use of the stability criterion above in terms of the Tsypkin function $J(\omega)$. By Eq. (8-65) we have

$$G'^*(j\omega) = \frac{\omega}{2U}\,\mathcal{R}e\, J(\omega) \tag{8-78}$$

Consider now the case where all poles of $G(s)$ lie in $\mathcal{R}e\, s < 0$ except possibly for a simple pole at $s = 0$. For the sampled-data system of Fig. 8-15, the Nyquist criterion yields the requirement (show this)

$$\frac{2U}{\left|\dot{e}_p\left(\frac{\pi}{\omega}\right)\right|}\, G'^*(j\omega) > -1 \tag{8-79}$$

This means that $(\omega/|\dot{e}_p(\pi/\omega)|)\,\mathcal{R}e\ J(\omega) > -1$, or

$$\mathcal{R}e\, J(\omega) > -\frac{\left|\dot{e}_p\left(\frac{\pi}{\omega}\right)\right|}{\omega} \tag{8-80}$$

Condition (8-80) can be used to resolve the question of stability of forced oscillations when there exist two possible modes of oscillation as predicted by the method of Tsypkin. This occurs for example in a situation as depicted in Fig. 8-12b. For this case, since

$$\frac{\dot{e}_p\left(\frac{\pi}{\omega}\right)}{\omega} = \dot{r}_p\left(\frac{\pi}{\omega}\right) - \frac{\dot{y}_p\left(\frac{\pi}{\omega}\right)}{\omega} = \Re\mathrm{e}\Big(R(\pi - \phi) + J(\omega)\Big) \tag{8-81}$$

the condition (8-80) becomes $\Re\mathrm{e}\, J(\omega_0) > -\left|\Re\mathrm{e}\Big(R(\pi - \phi) + J(\omega_0)\Big)\right|$ and the stability condition is satisfied only if

$$\Re\mathrm{e}\Big(R(\pi - \phi) + J(\omega_0)\Big) < \Re\mathrm{e}\; J(\omega_0) \tag{8-82}$$

Thus in the case illustrated in Fig. 8-12b, the forced oscillation given by ϕ_1 is stable and that of ϕ_2 is unstable. In general, an oscillation indicated by an intersection of the $R(\pi - \phi)$ locus with the $-\epsilon$ line that lies to the left of the $J(\omega_0)$ point will always be stable. If this intersecting point lies to the right of the $J(\omega_0)$ point, the corresponding oscillation will be unstable.

To summarize the case of *forced oscillation* using the method of Tsypkin for a relay without dead zone, we have:

1) Existence condition

$$\Re\mathrm{e}\Big(R(\pi - \phi) + J(\omega_0)\Big) < 0$$
$$\Im\mathrm{m}\Big(R(\pi - \phi) + J(\omega_0)\Big) = -\epsilon$$

2) Condition for stability

$$\Re\mathrm{e}\Big(R(\pi - \phi) + J(\omega_0)\Big) < \Re\mathrm{e}\; J(\omega_0)$$

3) Condition for instability

$$\Im\mathrm{m}\Big(R(\pi - \phi) + J(\omega_0)\Big) > \Re\mathrm{e}\; J(\omega_0).$$

Unfortunately the above approach does not yield information concerning the stability of self-oscillation when there exists more than one such mode, in which case $R(\pi - \phi) = 0$ and the condition (8-82) reduces to $\Re\mathrm{e}\; J(\omega_0) > \Re\mathrm{e}\; J(\omega_0)$, an impossibility. Thus the self-oscillation case requires further analysis; in particular, we need to pay attention to the neighborhood of the point $z = -1$ on the unit circle for the characteristic equation (8-77). Indeed we have

◆◆Theorem 8-4. Consider the relay system of Fig. 8-1 with $r(t) \equiv 0$, a relay without dead zone, and a completely controllable and observable linear element of transfer function $G(s)$ whose poles lie in $\Re\mathrm{e}\; s < 0$ except possibly for a simple pole at $s = 0$. If $[\partial \Im\mathrm{m}\, J(\omega)/\partial\omega] > 0$ at the point where $J(\omega)$ crosses the $\Im\mathrm{m}\, J(\omega) = -\epsilon$ line, then the self-oscillation is stable and orbitally asymptotically stable.◆◆

A guide to the proof of this theorem will be given in Chap. 11.

For the case shown in Fig. 8-16, we can see that the self-oscillations at ω_1 and ω_3 are stable and that the one at ω_2 may not be stable. This, perhaps, reinforces our physical intuition concerning the system.

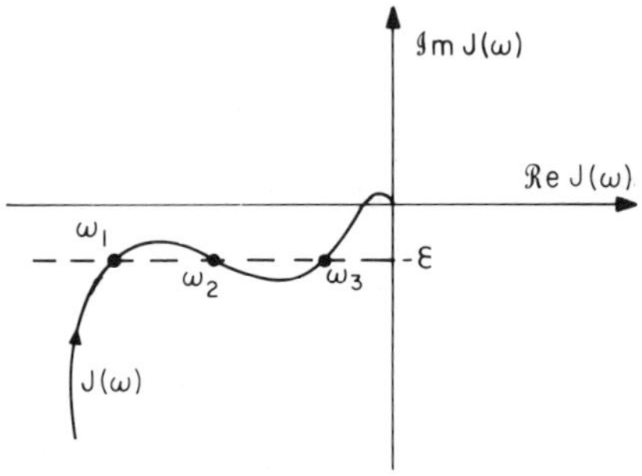

Fig. 8-16. By Theorem 8-4, the self-oscillations with fundamental frequency ω_1 and ω_3 are stable, that with ω_2 may not be stable.

The method of Tsypkin can also be extended to produce a necessary condition for the existence of subharmonic oscillations. The extension is relatively straightforward once the basis of the approach is understood.*

8.8 Summary

Exact methods for the mathematical treatment of relay control systems of the form of Fig. 8-1 with characteristics shown in Fig. 8-2 are discussed in this chapter.

In Sec. 8.1, it is shown how the transient response can be obtained in terms of the initial condition and unit-step responses of the linear element and the relay characteristic. The method can be utilized either graphically or numerically. The other sections in this chapter deal with the investigation of periodic motion in relay systems. The basic philosophy of all methods discussed consists of assuming a form of the solution, involving a set of signal parameters, and then investigating under what conditions such a solution can exist.

Two sets of conditions for existence of periodic oscillation are presented in Sec. 8.2, the necessary switching conditions (8-13) and the continuity conditions (8-14). The material of this chapter is limited to the most important mode of oscillation, the basic oscillation, as illustrated in Fig. 8-3.

Two methods are presented for the investigation of existence of periodic motion. The first one, the advanced z-transform method (Sec. 8.3), is based on the idea that the periodic steady-state response of the linear element, excited by the relay output of assumed periodic form, can be obtained as the limiting value of a

*The interested reader is referred to the exercises as well as to [S1] and [G5].

suitably chosen advanced (or modified) z-transform expression (8-24) and (8-25). The expression is given in terms of the signal parameters and the transfer function of the linear element. Standard tables of the advanced z-transform can then be used. Theorem 8-1 is basic to the development.

The method of Tsypkin, introduced in Sec. 8.4, consists of representing the switching conditions in terms of a locus in the complex plane, the Tsypkin locus. This locus is defined by (8-44) and (8-54) for relays without and with dead zone respectively. The Tsypkin locus is based on the Fourier series expansion of the relay output during periodic operation. It can be obtained not only from the frequency locus $G(j\omega)$ of the linear element (Sec. 8.5) but also in terms of z-transform expressions obtained from $G(p)$ (Sec. 8.6; particularly see Eqs. (8-63) and (8-65)).

The advanced z-transform method will not only facilitate the examination of the switching conditions but will also yield closed-form expressions for the periodic system output (Eq. (8-24)) that can be used to examine the continuity conditions (8-14). Tsypkin's method is limited to the examination of the switching conditions. However, once values for the signal parameters have been found that satisfy the switching conditions, then the task of examining the continuity conditions, though sometimes laborious, becomes straightforward. Fortunately, in almost all practical systems, the continuity conditions are satisfied if the switching conditions hold.

In the advanced z-transform method, those initial conditions that correspond to singularities of the transfer function $G(s)$ in $\mathcal{R}e\,(s) \geq 0$ need to be considered. Tsypkin's method requires no such consideration. However, certain symmetry conditions of the basic oscillation must be ascertained before Tsypkin's method can be used without major modification.

Though the advanced z-transform method can be readily used for the investigation of forced oscillation, Tsypkin's method as extended to forced oscillations (Sec. 8.6) appears to be more elegant. Here an input locus for a periodic input of a given form (Eq. (8-70)) is constructed. The switching conditions for this case are given by Eqs. (8-72) and (8-73) and illustrated in Fig. 8-12.

In Sec. 8.7, the stability of periodic motion, both with and without input, is discussed. It is shown that the stability in the small of periodic motion is equivalent to that of a linear sampled-data system such as the one shown in Fig. 8-15. The stability conditions derived from this sampled-data system can also be expressed in terms of the Tsypkin locus to reveal both the existence and the stability of a periodic motion. This is shown for both forced oscillation (conditions (8-82)) and self-oscillation (Theorem 8-4).

The extensions of the methods to modes of oscillation other than the basic oscillation, and to relay characteristics different from those considered here, are conceptually straightforward, though they may lead to rather involved calculations.

8.9 Exercises

8-1 For the system of Example 8-4, with an initial condition response of the linear element of

$$y_0(t) = -0.407 + 0.207e^{-t}$$

obtain the transient response $y(t)$ by the method described in Sec. 8.1.

8-2 For the system of Example 8-1, investigate whether the continuity conditions given in (8-14a) are satisfied.

8-3 In Example 8-1, show that by leaving the duty-cycle α unspecified, condition (8-28) will automatically be assured from the requirement that $\mathcal{Y}_1(z, m)$ must be analytic in $|z| \geq 1$.

8-4 Verify Eq. (8-37). Moreover, show that Eq. (8-31) is valid not only for $a > 0$ but also for $a < 0$.

8-5 Examine the continuity conditions (Eq. (8-14a)) for the system of Example 8-2, with $a = 2$, $U = 10$, $\epsilon = 1/2$. Repeat for $a = -2$.

8-6 Examine the basic oscillation of a relay system (Fig. 8-1) with a relay of Fig. 8-2a. Let $G(s) = a^2/[s(s + a)]$, $a > 0$, $Y_0(s) = (x_{10}/s) + x_{20}/(s + a)$, and $r(t) = R$. What necessary conditions must be satisfied in order for self-oscillation to exist?

8-7 For the system of Exercise 8-6, let $U = 1$, $\epsilon = 1/2$, $a = 1$, and $R = 6.5$; obtain the period of self-oscillation and a closed-form expression for $y_p(t)$. Check whether the continuity conditions are satisfied.

8-8 Investigate the stability of the self-oscillations established for the system of Examples 8-1, 8-2, and 8-3. Use Theorems 8-2 and 8-3 for this purpose.

8-9 Investigate both the existence and stability of self-oscillation of the systems of Examples 8-2 and 8-3 by the use of the Tsypkin locus.

8-10 Consider the relay system of Fig. 8-1 with $r(t) \equiv 0$. For each of the two relay characteristics of Fig. 8-17,

a) Write the switching conditions for basic periodic operation.
b) If $G(p)$ has a pole at $p = 0$, what is the average value $\overline{y(t)}$ of the system output?
c) Comment on the applicability of each of the methods for investigating periodic self-oscillation discussed in this

chapter, and indicate any modification of the method(s) if necessary and feasible.

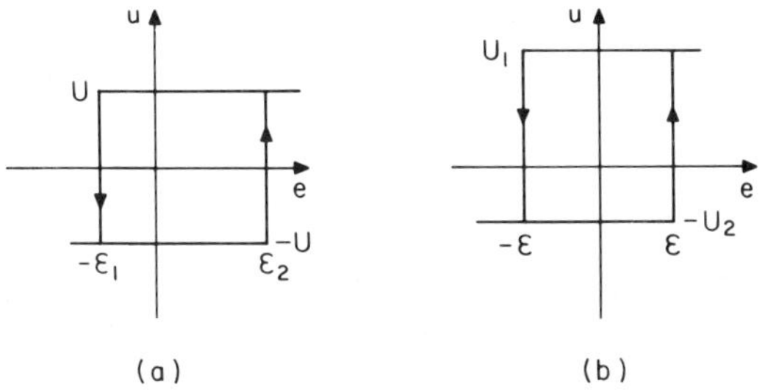

Fig. 8-17. The relay characteristics for the system of Exercise 8-10.

8-11 Consider a system of the form of Fig. 8-1, where the relay is the ideal type (Fig. 8-2c). What type of linear time-invariant element will indicate the absence of self-oscillation under the describing function analysis but which will indicate self-oscillation under the Tsypkin locus approach? Cite an example for such a linear plant. Repeat for a system with the relay characteristics of Fig. 8-1a.

8-12 Derive Eq. (8-46) without using the advanced z-transform.

8-13 Construct the Tsypkin locus for plants with the following transfer functions

a) $\dfrac{1}{(s+2)(s+4)}$

b) $\dfrac{s+2}{s^2(s+4)}$

c) $\dfrac{1}{s(s^2+s+2)}$

Obtain the loci approximately on the complex plane by first sketching the Nyquist plot of the transfer functions and then using Eq. (8-48).

8.10 References

The most comprehensive book on relay control systems is [T6]. This book forms the basis for Secs. 8.4 through 8.7 of this chapter. Unfortunately there does not yet seem to be an English version of the book.

A method very closely related to that of Tsypkin is one due to Hamel. For a lucid account in English of the method of Hamel and its relation to Tsypkin's method, the reader is referred to [G4].

Good tables of advanced or modified z-transforms can be found in [J6] and [T5].

A method for examining periodic motion that is not discussed in this chapter consists of expressing the switching conditions of a relay system in terms of certain matrix equations involving the transition matrix of the linear element. The basic ideas of the *state transition method* are discussed in [M13]. A procedure particularly suited for relay control systems (though also applicable for certain other systems) is presented in [K21].

9

Stability in the Large and the Second Method of Lyapunov

The concepts of asymptotic stability in the large and global asymptotic stability have been introduced at the end of Chap. 5. At that point, we indicated that for these in-the-large stabilities, there is no general rule similar to Lyapunov's first method which, in the case of in-the-small stability, permitted us to separate the unstable cases from the stable ones through linearization. Such rules do not exist even for a simple system composed of a time-invariant linear plant preceded by a zero-memory nonlinearity, as Aizerman and Kalman's conjectures have both been shown to be false.

We can, of course, relax our requirements and settle for methods that yield more restrictive conditions which are however sufficient to ensure stability in the large. The basic (exact) methods in this regard are the second method of Lyapunov, the method of Popov, and certain approaches in functional analysis such as that provided by the contraction-mapping fixed-point theorems. These constitute the topics to be discussed in this and the following two chapters.

Lyapunov's second method was originally advanced by A. M. Lyapunov [L18] to investigate stability in the small. Specifically, the method was introduced to determine whether an equilibrium state of a system is stable (in the sense of Lyapunov) or asymptotically stable. An important advantage of the method is that stability of systems can be determined without having to explicitly study the system solutions. Furthermore, it was soon discovered that the method can readily be used to determine stability in the large or even global asymptotic stability as well. This brought about intensive efforts in Russia, and subsequently in the U.S. and other nations, to extend the original approaches and to enlarge the scope of their applicability. Only recently is this interest waning as certain fundamental limitations in the approach become apparent.

In this chapter, we will first study the application of the approach to stability in the small. Next, we will consider its extension to the analysis of stability in the large. We shall survey the important accomplishments achieved thus far using the method, and we shall point out the main limitations of the method as we see it today.

9.1 The Lyapunov Function

The basis of Lyapunov's second method is relatively simple and has a good deal of intuitive appeal. Consider any autonomous physical system. If the total energy of the system decreases monotonically, then it follows that the system state will tend toward some equilibrium. This holds because energy is a *nonnegative functions of the system state* which reaches a minimum only if the system motion stops, implying the attainment of a stable equilibrium state.

But there is nothing sacred or unique about the total energy of the system which allows us to determine system stability in the way described above. Other nonnegative functions of the system state should also qualify provided that our viewpoint is suitably taken.

Let us consider a second-order autonomous system:

$$\dot{x}_1 = f_1(x_1, x_2), \qquad \dot{x}_2 = f_2(x_1, x_2)$$

To lend uniformity to our discussion, assume that the system coordinates have been translated in such a way that the origin becomes the equilibrium state whose stability we wish to investigate, i.e.,

$$f_1(0, 0) = f_2(0, 0) = 0$$

Assume that associated with the system, a function of the states $V(x_1, x_2)$ is found such that it is always positive except at the origin, where it is 0. Such a function, if constructed along an axis $x_3 = V(x_1, x_2)$ perpendicular to the x_1—x_2 plane, will take on the general aspect of a cup in the vicinity of the origin as shown in Fig. 9-1.

Now if in the vicinity of the origin it can be established that the system state always progresses in the direction of decreasing V, irrespective of the initial point (x_{10}, x_{20}), then clearly there is no place else for the system state to go except to the origin. The origin then will be asymptotically stable.

On the other hand, if the movement of the system state is such that V never increases (i.e., V either decreases or stays constant), then there is a possibility that the system state may stay at a certain set of points, namely, points at which the function V stays constant. Unless we can rule out such possibilities, we cannot, in general, conclude asymptotic stability of the system relative to the origin, although it is reasonable to expect that the origin will at least be stable.

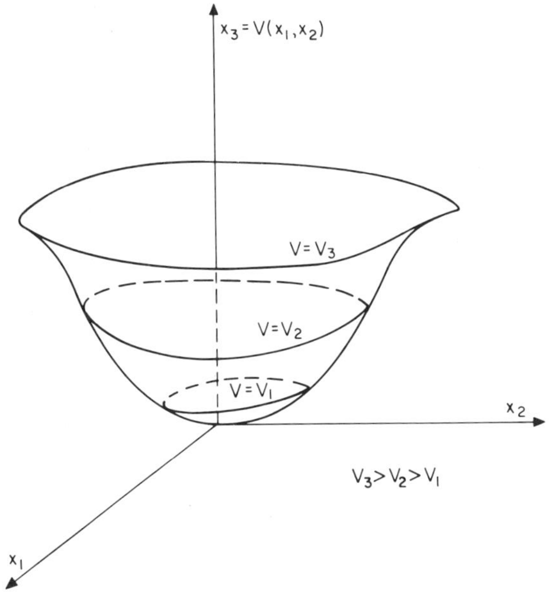

Fig. 9-1. A function $V(x_1, x_2)$ that is always positive except at $x_1 = x_2 = 0$.

To relate the change of V to system parameters, we note that

$$\frac{dV}{dt} = \sum_{i=1}^{2} \frac{\partial V}{\partial x_i} \frac{dx_i}{dt} = \sum_{i=1}^{2} \frac{\partial V}{\partial x_i} f_i(x_1, x_2)$$

Since both V and $\mathbf{f}$ are known, it is not necessary to explicitly solve for any system time response. The stability information can in the above cases be obtained from inspection.

The above ideas, extended to n dimensions, form the basis of Lyapunov's second method. Here to each nth order system we wish to associate a function $V(\mathbf{x})$ which satisfies the following conditions:

1) $V(\mathbf{x})$ is continuous and has continuous first partial derivatives in some (open) region $\mathcal{R}$ about the origin, defined by $\|\mathbf{x}\| < a$, where a is a positive constant. (In this region $\mathcal{R}$, the system under consideration should of course be such

that a unique solution of the system exists through each point of $\mathcal{R}$.)

2) $V(\mathbf{x})$ is positive definite (p.d.)* in the region $\mathcal{R}$.
3) Relative to a system $\dot{\mathbf{x}} = \mathbf{f}(\mathbf{x})$, the time derivative $\dot{V}(\mathbf{x})$ along the trajectories of the system is negative semidefinite in the region $\mathcal{R}$. Where, as per the discussion in the previous section:

$$\dot{V}(\mathbf{x}) = \sum_{i=1}^{n} \frac{\partial V}{\partial x_i} \frac{dx_i}{dt} = (\text{grad } V)^T \dot{\mathbf{x}} = (\nabla V)^T \mathbf{f}(\mathbf{x}) \tag{9-1}$$

(grad $V \equiv \nabla V$ is an n-dimensional vector whose ith component is given by $\partial V / \partial x_i$).

If a function $V(\mathbf{x})$ satisfies all three of the properties above, it is then called a Lyapunov function.

When $n = 2$, the Lyapunov function lends itself to the geometric interpretation as discussed at the beginning of this section.

It is an unfortunate fact that *for a given scalar function* $V(\mathbf{x})$, *there is no general method which will easily allow us to ascertain whether it is positive definite or positive semidefinite*. This fact greatly restricts the potentialities of the powerful theorems that we will be presenting below. Moreover, this fact also prevents many methods of constructing Lyapunov functions from being completely useful. As the reader considers the presentation in the sequel, he should keep this fact in mind.

Let us list the following two principal results which permit the sign (positive or negative) definiteness of functions $V(\mathbf{x})$ of a particular form to be determined.

1) If $V(\mathbf{x})$ is in a quadratic form in the x_i's, i.e., $V(\mathbf{x})$ is in the form (see Appendix A)

$$V(\mathbf{x}) = \sum_{i=1}^{n} \sum_{j=1}^{n} k_{ij} x_i x_j, \quad k_{ij} \text{ real constants} \tag{9-2}$$

*A function $V(\mathbf{x})$ is positive (negative) definite if (i) $V(\mathbf{0}) = 0$, and (ii) $V(\mathbf{x}) > 0\ (<0)$ for $\mathbf{x} = 0$. A function $V(\mathbf{x})$ is positive (negative) semidefinite if $V(\mathbf{x}) \geq 0$ (≤ 0) and it equals 0 at the origin as well as at least one other point. If a function $V(\mathbf{x})$ is positive definite (positive semidefinite), then $-V(\mathbf{x})$ is negative definite (negative semidefinite). A function that is not definite or semidefinite in either sense is defined to be indefinite. Thus for a third-order system the functions $V_1(\mathbf{x}) = x_1^2 + 2x_2^2 + 2x_1x_2 + x_3^2 = (x_1 + x_2)^2 + x_2^2 + x_3^2$ and $V_2(\mathbf{x}) = x_1^4 + x_2^4 + x_3^2$ are both positive definite. The function $V_3(\mathbf{x}) = x_1^2 + x_2^2 + 3x_3^2 - x_3^4$ is positive definite in a region $\mathcal{R}$ defined by $|x_3| < \sqrt{3}$. The function $V_4(\mathbf{x}) = (x_1 + x_2)^2 + x_3^2$ is positive semidefinite since it equals 0 for $x_1 = -x_2$, $x_3 = 0$. The function $V_5(\mathbf{x}) = x_1 + x_2 + x_3^2$ is indefinite.

by Sec. A-7 of Appendix A, we can write

$$V(\mathbf{x}) = \mathbf{x}^T \mathbf{Q} \mathbf{x}$$

where

$$\begin{aligned} q_{ij} &= k_{ij} \quad \text{for} \quad i = j \\ q_{ij} &= \tfrac{1}{2}(k_{ij} + k_{ji}) = q_{ji} \quad \text{for} \quad i \neq j \end{aligned} \tag{9-3}$$

We can then make use of Theorem A-2 of Appendix A: *A quadratic form (9-2) is positive definite if and only if all the determinants* $|\mathbf{Q}_1|, \ldots, |\mathbf{Q}_n|$ *of the matrix* $\mathbf{Q}$ *are positive.**

2) If $V(\mathbf{x})$ is *homogeneous of degree k, i.e.*,

$$V(\alpha x_1, \ldots, \alpha x_n) = \alpha^k V(x_1, \ldots, x_n)$$

then $V(\mathbf{x})$ is indefinite if k is odd.

◆◆Example 9-1. Consider

$$V(\mathbf{x}) = 2x_1^2 + 4x_1x_3 + 3x_2^2 + 6x_2x_3 + x_3^2$$

$$= [x_1 \; x_2 \; x_3] \begin{bmatrix} 2 & 0 & 2 \\ 0 & 3 & 3 \\ 2 & 3 & 1 \end{bmatrix} \begin{bmatrix} x_1 \\ x_2 \\ x_3 \end{bmatrix}$$

The determinants $|\mathbf{Q}_1| \ldots |\mathbf{Q}_3|$ are:

$$|\mathbf{Q}_1| = |2| > 0; \qquad |\mathbf{Q}_2| = \begin{vmatrix} 2 & 0 \\ 0 & 3 \end{vmatrix} = 6 > 0;$$

$$|\mathbf{Q}_3| = \begin{vmatrix} 2 & 0 & 2 \\ 0 & 3 & 3 \\ 2 & 3 & 1 \end{vmatrix} = -24 < 0$$

Since $|\mathbf{Q}_3|$ is negative, $V(\mathbf{x})$ is not p.d.◆◆

*It is important to realize that the converse of the theorem is not true, i.e., a quadratic form (9-2) need not be negative definite even though $|\mathbf{Q}_1|, \ldots, |\mathbf{Q}_n|$ are all negative. However, we can say that *a quadratic form (9-2) is negative definite if and only if all the determinants* $|\mathbf{Q}_1|, \ldots, |\mathbf{Q}_n|$ *of the matrix* $-\mathbf{Q}$ *are positive.*

♦♦Exanple 9-2. Consider

$$V(\mathbf{x}) = 3x_1x_2x_3 + 18x_1^2x_3 + 7x_2x_3^2$$

Here $V(\mathbf{x})$ is homogeneous of degree 3, thus it is indefinite.♦♦

9.2 Theorems Governing Stability in the Small for Autonomous Systems

The theorems of Lyapunov for autonomous systems are given as the first four theorems below. In addition, we also give the theorem of Chetaev on instability, which can be more useful in some cases than the Lyapunov instability theorems. The proofs for the theorems are also provided, although if the Lyapunov function is well understood the proofs are obvious. A number of examples are also given to illustrate the theorems. In the following, let us again assume that a coordinate translation has been made so that the equilibrium state being studied is translated to the origin. Thus we deal with a system

$$\dot{\mathbf{x}} = \mathbf{f}(\mathbf{x}), \quad \mathbf{f}(0) = 0 \tag{9-4}$$

♦♦Theorem 9-1 (Lyapunov's First Stability Theorem). If for the system (9-4) a Lyapunov function can be found in some neighborhood $\mathcal{R}$ about the origin, then the original is stable.♦♦

Proof. The theorem is obvious when we restate it to read: The origin of a system is stable if its trajectory is always proceeding in a direction such that the associated V function never increases. Since the V function is by definition p.d., the above implies that the system trajectory must remain within a bounded region about the origin. To be more precise, let the region $\mathcal{R}$ be given by $||\mathbf{x}|| < h$, and let $V(\mathbf{x})$ be the Lyapunov function found. Suppose we are challenged by an $\epsilon < h$; let us consider the points on the surface of a sphere of radius ϵ centered at the origin. Let l be the lower bound for the value of $V(\mathbf{x})$ over these points, i.e., $V(x_1, \ldots, x_n) \geq l$ over the surface of the sphere $||\mathbf{x}|| = \epsilon$. Since V is continuous, this lower bound must exist; moreover, $l > 0$ since V is p.d.

Now we simply choose a value of $\delta \leq \epsilon$ (see Definition 5-1) such that $V(\mathbf{x}) < l$ in the entire neighborhood $||\mathbf{x}|| < \delta$. Again this can always be done since V is continuous and vanishes only at the origin.

Since $(dV/dt) \leq 0$ by assumption, then it follows that $V(\mathbf{x}(t)) \leq V(\mathbf{x}(t_0)) < l$ for all $t > t_0$. Thus $||\mathbf{x}(t)|| < \epsilon$ for all $t > t_0$. This proves the theorem.

♦♦Theorem 9-2 (Lyapunov's Second Stability Theorem). For the system (9-4), if in a neighborhood $\mathcal{R}$ about the origin a Lyapunov function $V(\mathbf{x})$ can be found such that $\dot{V}$ is negative definite (n.d.), then the origin is asymptotically stable.◆◆

Proof. Again the theorem is obvious since if all trajectories are such that the associated V function always decreases, then with V p.d., all trajectories must end at the origin, which is the only absolute minimum point for V. Mathematically, we first note that clearly the origin is stable for $\|\mathbf{x}(t)\| < \epsilon$ for $t > t_0$. It needs to be shown that $\lim_{t\to\infty} \mathbf{x}(t) \to 0$. Now $V(\mathbf{x})$ is monotonically decreasing in $\mathcal{R}$; therefore, it must tend to some positive limit A. The proof will be complete if we can show that $A = 0$.

Suppose that $A \neq 0$, this implies that $\|\mathbf{x}(t)\|$ cannot go to 0. There is thus a positive constant B such that $\|\mathbf{x}(t)\| > B > 0$. In this case, we will further have a third positive constant C such that $(dV/dt) \leq -C$ since (dV/dt) is n.d. Then we can write

$$V(\mathbf{x}(t)) = V(\mathbf{x}(t_0)) + \int_{t_0}^{t} \frac{dV}{dt}\, dt \leq V(\mathbf{x}(t_0)) - (t - t_0)C$$

Since the rhs will eventually become negative, the above inequality will violate the assumption of the problem. Thus we prove that $A = 0$ by contradiction; this shows that $\lim_{t\to\infty} \mathbf{x}(t) \to 0$.

An important point to remember is that Theorems 9-1 and 9-2 (and most of the other theorems on Lyapunov's second method) merely provide sufficient conditions; thus *for a given system, if a Lyapunov function of the required type cannot be found, it does not mean that the system is unstable. It merely means that our attempt in trying to establish the stability of the system has failed.* However, we do have the following three theorems on instability. These are frequently quite useful in a destructive sense.

◆◆Theorem 9-3 (Lyapunov's First Instability Theorem). For the system (9-4), if a continuous function $V_1(\mathbf{x})$ with continuous first partial derivatives can be found in a neighborhood $\mathcal{R}$ of the origin such that $V_1(0) = 0$, and $\dot{V}_1$ following the motion is positive definite, but V_1 itself is not negative definite or negative semidefinite arbitrarily near the origin, then the origin is unstable.◆◆

Proof. The physical picture is again clear, mathematically. Take the region $\mathcal{R}$ to be $\|\mathbf{x}\| < \epsilon$. We are to show that if $\|\mathbf{x}_0\| < \delta$, then however small the value of δ is, there will be an $\mathbf{x}_0$ and a time t_1 such that $\|\mathbf{x}(t_1)\| \geq \epsilon$ or $\|\mathbf{x}(t_1)\|$ escapes the region $\mathcal{R}$.

Choose $\mathbf{x}_0$ such that $V(\mathbf{x}_0) > 0$. Since $\dot{V} > 0$, we will have $V(\mathbf{x}(t)) > V(\mathbf{x}_0)$. Thus there will be a positive number A such that $\|\mathbf{x}(t)\| > A$. Also, since the trajectory cannot tend to the origin (characterized by $V = 0$), there will also be a positive number B such that $\dot{V}(\mathbf{x}(t)) \geq B$. Thus we have the following:

$$V(\mathbf{x}(t)) = V(\mathbf{x}_0) + \int_{t_0}^{t} \frac{dV}{dt}\, dt \geq V(\mathbf{x}_0) + (t - t_0) B$$

which indicates that $V(\mathbf{x}(t))$ increases without bound. But if $\|\mathbf{x}(t)\|$ remains forever in $\mathcal{R}$, V will be bounded; thus there must be a time t_1 at which $\|\mathbf{x}(t)\|$ escapes the region $\mathcal{R}$. This proves the theorem.

♦♦Theorem 9-4 (Lyapunov's Second Instability Theorem). For the system (9-4), if in a neighborhood $\mathcal{R}$ of the origin, a function $V_1(\mathbf{x})$ exists such that $V_1(0) = 0$ and $\dot{V}_1$ following the motion of the system is of the form

$$\dot{V}_1 = \lambda V_1 + W(\mathbf{x}) \qquad \lambda > 0$$

with $W(\mathbf{x}) \geq 0$ in $\mathcal{R}$, and if $V_1(\mathbf{x})$ is not negative definite or negative semidefinite arbitrarily near the origin, then the origin is unstable.♦♦

Proof. As before, choose $\|\mathbf{x}_0\| < \delta$ such that $V_1(\mathbf{x}_0) > 0$. Assume that $W(\mathbf{x})$ is positive semidefinite; then we will have $\dot{V}_1(\mathbf{x}(t)) \geq \lambda V_1(\mathbf{x}(t))$ for all t. Thus $\dot{V}_1$ for this particular motion will be always positive and moreover $\dot{V}_1(\mathbf{x}(t)) \geq \lambda V_1(\mathbf{x}(t)) \geq \lambda V_1(\mathbf{x}_0)$. Thus we have the inequality $V_1(\mathbf{x}(t)) \geq (\lambda + 1) V_1(\mathbf{x}_0)(t - t_0)$. Therefore, V_1 increases without bound and the motion is unstable.

A more powerful instability theorem than those of Lyapunov is that of Chetaev [L6]. The idea of Chetaev's instability theorem is the following: For the unstable systems, generally a function $V_1(\mathbf{x})$ can be found so that the origin is on the boundary of two regions. In one region we have V_1 and $\dot{V}_1$ both p.d., and in the other we have V_1 p.d. and $\dot{V}_1$ n.d. If we can ascertain that the trajectory from the first region does not enter the second region, then instability will surely follow. This leads to

♦♦Theorem 9-5 (The Instability Theorem of Chetaev). Let $\mathcal{R}$ be a neighborhood of the origin and let $\mathcal{R}_1$ be a region contained in $\mathcal{R}$. Let a function $V(\mathbf{x})$ be found such that (*i*) it has continuous first partial derivatives in $\mathcal{R}_1$, (*ii*) $V(\mathbf{x})$ and $\dot{V}(\mathbf{x})$ are *both* p.d. in $\mathcal{R}_1$, (*iii*) at those boundary points of $\mathcal{R}_1$ inside $\mathcal{R}$, $V(\mathbf{x}) = 0$, and (*iv*) the origin is on the boundary of $\mathcal{R}_1$; then the origin 0 is unstable.♦♦

Proof. (See Fig. 9-2.) The conditions clearly indicate that starting in $\mathcal{R}_1$, it is impossible for the system trajectory to cross the boundary line Ω of $\mathcal{R}_1$ inside $\mathcal{R}$. This is because the value of V, already positive in $\mathcal{R}_1$, can only increase monotonically along any system trajectory in $\mathcal{R}_1$. Thus no trajectory starting in $\mathcal{R}_1$ can reach the boundary between $\mathcal{R}$ and $\mathcal{R}_1$ where by assumption $V = 0$. V increases monotonically in $\mathcal{R}_1$. However, the condition also implies that the trajectory must leave $\mathcal{R}_1$; hence, it must leave that part of $\mathcal{R}_1$ not bounded by Ω. (Observe that the conditions of the statement imply that there must be a "frontier" type of boundary Ω and a "shared" type of bounday Ω_1.)

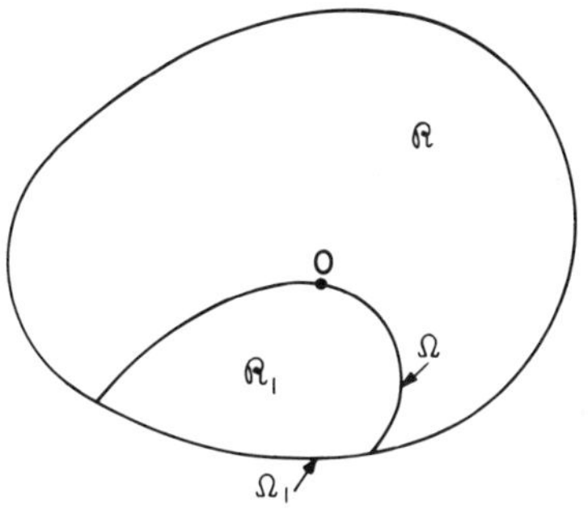

Fig. 9-2. The geometric requirements of Chetaev's instability theorem. $\mathcal{R}_1$ is contained in $\mathcal{R}$ in such a way that they lie on opposite sides of the boundary Ω and on the same side of the boundary Ω_1.

♦♦Example 9-3. The equation of motion of a simple pendulum of unit mass is

$$\ddot{\theta} + \frac{g}{L} \sin \theta = 0 \tag{9-5}$$

where g is the gravitational acceleration and L is the length of the pendulum.

To find the stability of the origin of the simple pendulum we try a function V of the following form.

$$V(\theta, \dot{\theta}) = \frac{g}{L}(1 - \cos \theta) + \frac{1}{2}\dot{\theta}^2 \tag{9-6}$$

We see that $V(\theta, \dot{\theta})$ is p.d. for $|\theta| < 2\pi$ and

$$\frac{dV(\theta, \dot{\theta})}{dt} = \frac{g}{L}(\sin \theta)\dot{\theta} + \dot{\theta}\left(-\frac{g}{L} \sin \theta\right) \equiv 0$$

Thus V qualifies to be a Lyapunov function and the origin of a simple pendulum is stable by Theorem 9-1.♦♦

The astute reader will recognize that the function $V(\theta, \dot{\theta})$ of Eq. (9-6) is proportional to the total energy of the system which is, by definition, p.d. Moreover, since the system (9-5) is a conservative system (see Chap. 4), it is expected that the total energy will be conserved. Thus $\dot{V}$ should vanish identically. This example shows that all conservative systems are stable since the total energy is a Lyapunov function.

◆◆Example 9-4. Consider now a simple pendulum with a linear damping term, so that the equation of motion is now

$$\ddot{\theta} + k\dot{\theta} + \frac{g}{L}\sin\theta = 0 \qquad k > 0 \tag{9-7}$$

Again taking the $V(\theta, \dot{\theta})$ of Eq. (9-6) we quickly find that

$$\dot{V} \equiv -k\dot{\theta}^2 \tag{9-8}$$

which is negative semidefinite, as $\dot{V}$ is negative everywhere except on the line $\dot{\theta} \equiv 0$ where $\dot{V} = 0$. Thus (9-7) is clearly stable. But observe that unless $\theta = 0$, it is impossible for the system to maintain the $\dot{\theta} \equiv 0$ condition. Thus we conclude that the system (9-7) is asymptotically stable as well.◆◆

Indeed we have formally shown the following.

◆◆Corollary 9-1. If, in the region $\mathcal{R}$ about the origin, a Lyapunov function is found whose time derivative following the motion is negative semidefinite, and it can be established that no system trajectory can stay forever at the points at which $\dot{V} = 0$ other than at the origin, then the origin is asymptotically stable.◆◆

◆◆Example 9-5. Lyapunov's first method has been given in Chap. 5 (see Theorem 5-1); we are now in a position to prove it.

Take a system of the form

$$\dot{\mathbf{x}} = \mathbf{A}\,\mathbf{x} + \mathbf{h}(\mathbf{x}) \tag{9-9}$$

where $\lim_{\|\mathbf{x}\| \to 0} (\|\mathbf{h}(\mathbf{x})\| / \|\mathbf{x}\|) \to 0$ or $\|\mathbf{h}(\mathbf{x})\|$ goes to 0 faster than $\|\mathbf{x}\|$. Consider now:

Case 1. The eigenvalues of the linear approximation of system (9-9), $\dot{\mathbf{x}} = \mathbf{A}\,\mathbf{x}$, are all real, distinct, and negative; thus the linearized system is asymptotically stable, and we must show that the exact system (9-9) is also asymptotically stable.

First, in accordance with the procedure of Chap. 3, we find the transformation $\mathbf{y} = \mathbf{P}\,\mathbf{x}$ so as to transform (9-9) to the form

$$\dot{\mathbf{y}} = \mathbf{\Lambda}\,\mathbf{y} + \mathbf{h}'(\mathbf{y}) \tag{9-10}$$

where as before $\mathbf{\Lambda}$ is the diagonal matrix of the eigenvalues.

Let

$$V(\mathbf{y}) = \sum_{i=1}^{n} y_i^2$$

then

$$\dot{V}(\mathrm{y}) = 2\sum_{i=1}^{n} y_i\dot{y}_i = 2\sum_{i=1}^{n}\left\{y_i\left[\lambda_i y_i + h_i'(\mathrm{y}, t)\right]\right\} = 2\sum_{i=1}^{n}\lambda_i y_i^2 + g(\mathrm{y}, t) \tag{9-11}$$

where

$$g(\mathrm{y}, t) = \sum_{i=1}^{n} y_i h_i'(\mathrm{y}, t)$$

It is seen that $|g(\mathrm{y}, t)| \to 0$ faster than $\|\mathrm{y}\|^2$ for each i. Thus in a sufficiently small region about the origin, the first term of the rhs of (9-11) will be dominating and $\dot{V}(\mathrm{y})$ will be n.d. The origin is therefore asymptotically stable by Theorem 9-2.

Case 2. Some of the roots, say $\lambda_1, \ldots, \lambda_l$ $(l < n)$, are positive and distinct; the remaining ones are negative and distinct.

Here the linearized system is unstable. To show that the nonlinear system is unstable also, take

$$V = y_1^2 + \cdots + y_l^2 - y_{l+1}^2 - \cdots - y_n^2$$

then

$$\dot{V} = 2\left(\lambda_1 y_1^2 + \cdots + \lambda_l y_l^2 - \lambda_{l+1} y_{l+1}^2 - \cdots - \lambda_n y_n^2\right) + g(\mathrm{y}, t)$$

At some points that are sufficiently near the origin, namely those where $y_{l+1} = y_{l+2} = \cdots = y_n = 0$, V is greater than 0; however, $\dot{V}$ at points very close to the origin is p.d.; thus the origin is unstable by Theorem 9-3.

The case for the complex roots is left to the exercises. (See Exercise 9-3.) ◆◆

◆◆Example 9-6. Consider the system:

$$\dot{x}_1 = ax_1^2 + bx_2^3, \qquad \dot{x}_2 = -cx_2 + dx_1^3$$

where $a, b, c, d > 0$. Linearizing yields a system with poles at 0 and $-c$. This represents a critical case, and Lyapunov's first method cannot be applied.

Now take $V = x_1 - (1/2)x_2^2$, then

$$\dot{V} = \dot{x}_1 - x_2\dot{x}_2 = \left(ax_1^2 + bx_2^3\right) - x_2\left(-cx_2 + dx_1^3\right)$$

Here $V > 0$ in the unshaded area of Fig. 9-3, bounded by the curve $x_1 = (1/2)x_2^2$, which is the curve $V = 0$. However, inside the unshaded area and sufficiently close to the origin, $\dot{V}$ will take on the sign of the quantity $ax_1^2 + cx_2^2$; and thus, it is also p.d., the conditions for the Chetaev instability theorem are met, and the origin is unstable by Theorem 9-5.◆◆

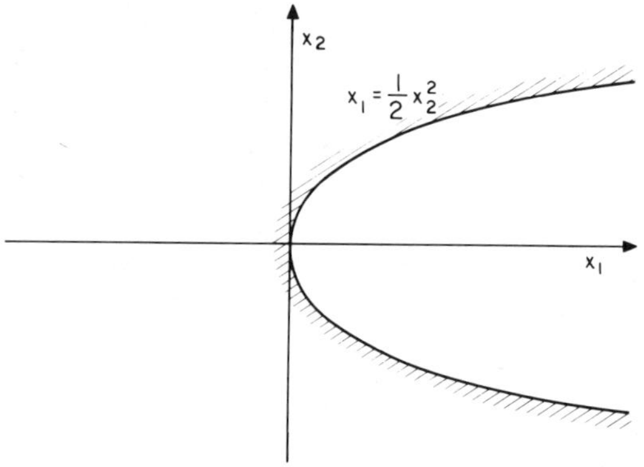

Fig. 9-3. The Lyapunov function of Example 9-6 is positive in the unshaded region bounded by the curve $x_1 = (1/2)x_2^2$. $\dot{V}$ however can also be positive in the region.

◆◆Example 9-7. Consider the system

$$\dot{x}_1 = x_2 + x_1\left(x_1^2 + x_2^4\right), \qquad \dot{x}_2 = -x_1 + x_2\left(x_1^2 + x_2^4\right)$$

Linearizing yields $\dot{x}_1 = x_2$, and $\dot{x}_2 = -x_1$. The roots of the characteristic equations are $\lambda = \pm j$. The case is critical and Lyapunov's first method again cannot be applied. However, take

$$V = \frac{1}{2}\left(x_1^2 + x_2^2\right), \qquad \dot{V} = \left(x_1^2 + x_2^2\right)\left(x_1^2 + x_2^4\right)$$

We see that both V and $\dot{V}$ are p.d. The conditions of Theorem 9-3 are satisfied; thus the origin is unstable.◆◆

9.3 Theorems Governing Stability in the Large and Global Asymptotic Stability

A great advantage of Lyapunov's second method is that the approach can readily be extended to consider asymptotic stability in the large and global asymptotic stability [L6].

In systems analysis and synthesis, if asymptotic stability in the large or even global asymptotic stability can be established, the designer's faith in the system that he has created can greatly increase. However, we must realize that a given mathematical model for a system seldom applies throughout the state space; thus, establishment of asymptotic stability in the large or global asymptotic stability may give the designer a false sense of security. Therefore, in-the-large stability is completely meaningful only if a given model applies throughout the region under question.

If we translate the system equilibrium state under study to the origin, then the basic theorem concerning asymptotic stability in the large is

♦♦Theorem 9-6. For the system (9-4) let $\mathcal{R}_k$ be the bounded region about the origin in which a function $V(\mathbf{x})$ of the system states is everywhere less than a constant k. In $\mathcal{R}_k$, if $V(\mathbf{x})$ is a Lyapunov function with $\dot{V}(\mathbf{x})$ negative definite, then the origin is asymptotically stable in the large with respect to $\mathcal{R}_k$.♦♦

The proof for the above theorem follows almost immediately from that for Theorem 9-2. (Exercise for the reader.)

We also have

♦♦Corollary 9-2. In Theorem 9-6, if $\dot{V}(\mathbf{x})$ is negative semidefinite in $\mathcal{R}_k$ but it can be established that no system trajectory can stay forever at the points at which $\dot{V} = 0$ other than at the origin, then the origin is asymptotically stable in-the-large with respect to $\mathcal{R}_k$.♦♦

When $\mathcal{R}_k$ is the entire state space, we have global asymptotic stability, for which we have:

♦♦Theorem 9-7 (Barbashin and Krasovskii). For the system (9-4), if a Lyapunov function $V(\mathbf{x})$ defined in the entire state space can be found with $\dot{V}(\mathbf{x})$ negative definite, and $V(\mathbf{x}) \to \infty$ as $\|\mathbf{x}\| \to \infty$, then the origin is globally asymptotically stable.♦♦

♦♦Corollary 9-3. In Theorem 9-7, if $\dot{V}(\mathbf{x})$ is negative semidefinite, but it can be established that no system trajectory can stay forever at the points at which $\dot{V} = 0$ other than the origin, then the origin is globally asymptotically stable.♦♦

The proof of Theorem 9-7 is again straightforward. The important additional requirement for this case as compared to the previous theorems is that $V(\mathbf{x})$ must approach ∞ as the distance from the point $\mathbf{x}$ to the origin approaches ∞ irrespective of direction. Essentially, this requirement is to assure that points of constant values of $V(\mathbf{x})$ form closed surfaces in the state space. If $V(\mathbf{x})$ does not form closed surfaces then it is possible for system trajectories to go toward ∞ even if $V(\mathbf{x})$ were p.d. and $\dot{V}(\mathbf{x})$ were n.d., as we can see below.

♦♦Example 9-8. Suppose the contour lines were not closed at a sufficiently large distance from the origin (the contour lines must be closed near the origin if $V(\mathbf{x})$ is p.d. and $\dot{V}(\mathbf{x})$ is n.d. (why?))

such as shown in Fig. 9-4 for a second-order system, then it is possible for a system trajectory to go to ∞ by following close to (but not exactly following) an open contour line as shown.

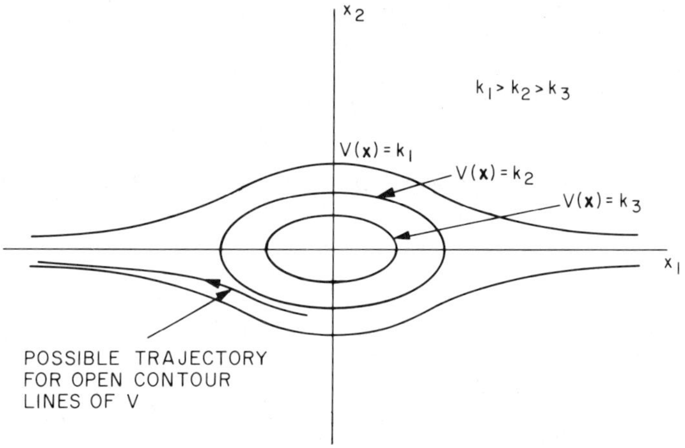

Fig. 9-4. If there are open contour lines of $V(\mathbf{x})$, then even if $V(\mathbf{x})$ is p.d. and $\dot{V}(\mathbf{x})$ is n.d., it is still possible for the system trajectory to go to infinity. If $V(\mathbf{x}) \to \infty$ as $\|\mathbf{x}\| \to \infty$, then the above situation cannot occur.

For a $V(\mathbf{x})$ of the form

$$V(\mathbf{x}) = \sum_{i=1}^{n} V_i(x_i)$$

if one or more, but not all, of the V_i's approach a finite limit as the corresponding $x_i \to \infty$ [e.g., $V_i(x_i) = x_i^2/(1 + x_i^2)$], then it is seen that open contour surfaces would result. (Show this.)♦♦

♦♦Example 9-9. Consider again the case of the simple pendulum (Example 9-3). Since the Lyapunov function chosen

$$V(\theta, \dot{\theta}) = \frac{g}{L}(1 - \cos\theta) + \frac{1}{2}\dot{\theta}^2$$

happens to be the total energy of the system, it is clear that there is a largest region in which no maxima in V occurs.* This region is enclosed by the separatrix of the problem, i.e., the trajectories that are approached by starting the pendulum arbitrarily close to the point $\theta_0 = \pm\pi$, $\dot{\theta}_0 = 0$. In this region V is clearly bounded by the

*This is implied by the condition of Theorem 9-6 (see Exercise 9-12).

value $2(g/L)$, which is equal to the value of potential energy at the point $\theta_0 = \pm\pi$, $\dot{\theta}_0 = 0$. The conditions of Corollary 9-2 are satisfied in this region and hence we conclude that the origin for the simple damped pendulum is asymptotically stable in the large with respect to this region.◆◆

In this particular case, we are able to obtain a region $\mathcal{R}$ for asymptotic stability in the large which corresponds to the largest possible one because of the special nature of the problem. Usually we are not so fortunate.

◆◆Example 9-10. Pitch-Axis Attitude Control Schemes for a Gravitationally Stabilized Satellite.* A dumbbell-shaped satellite in a circular orbit tends to execute slow rotational oscillation about its center as it traverses its orbit. This oscillation is due to the fact that there is a small difference in the gravitational force acting on the upper and lower masses of the dumbbell. Since the restoring moment thus introduced by the gravitational gradient provides a reference line toward the earth, a number of schemes have been advanced to make use of a gravitationally stabilized satellite. This example shows a method to actively damp out the oscillation introduced by the gravitational gradient.

The linearized approximation of the attitude motion of a gravitationally stabilized satellite in its pitch plane can be shown to be of the form

$$I_1\ddot{\theta} + 3\Omega^2(I_2 - I_3)\theta = u(t) \tag{9-12}$$

where I_1, I_2, and I_3 are the moments of inertia of the satellite about the pitch, roll, and yaw axes, respectively; Ω is the satellite orbiting angular rate; and θ is the pitch plane angular deviation from the local gravitational vertical. Our task is to devise feedback control (i.e., to make u a function of θ and $\dot{\theta}$) so that the pitch oscillatory motion will be damped out.

If u is a linear function of θ and $\dot{\theta}$, the problem will be trivial, since a linear system will result. Let us thus consider the feedback to be of the form $u = -f(\alpha\theta + \beta\dot{\theta})$, where the only restriction on the function f is that:

$$f(0) = 0, \quad xf(x) > 0 \quad \text{for} \quad x \neq 0 \tag{9-13}$$

i.e., $f(x)$ is a function which lies strictly in the first and third quadrant of the $f(x)$ vs. x plot and passes through the origin.

Try a function $V(\theta, \dot{\theta})$ of the form

$$V(\theta, \dot{\theta}) = \frac{1}{2}(\theta^2 + a\dot{\theta}^2) + b\int_0^{\alpha\theta+\beta\dot{\theta}} f(\xi)\,d\xi, \quad a > 0,\ b > 0$$

*This problem is discussed to some extent in [H18].

Then

$$\dot{V}(\theta, \dot{\theta}) = \theta\dot{\theta} + a\dot{\theta}\ddot{\theta} + b(\alpha\dot{\theta} + \beta\ddot{\theta})f(\alpha\theta + \beta\dot{\theta})$$

$$= (1 - Ka)\,\theta\dot{\theta} - \left[\left(\frac{a}{I_1} - b\alpha\right)\dot{\theta} + b\beta K\theta\right] f - \frac{b\beta}{I_1} f^2$$

where $K = 3\Omega^2(I_2 - I_3)/I_1$.

If we choose $a = 1/K$ and $b = \alpha/[I_1K(\alpha^2 + K\beta^2)]$, then the expression for $\dot{V}$ simplifies to

$$\dot{V} = -\frac{\beta}{I_1(\alpha^2 + K\beta^2)}\left[(\alpha\theta + \beta\dot{\theta})f(\alpha\theta + \beta\dot{\theta}) + \frac{\alpha}{I_1K} f^2(\alpha\theta + \beta\dot{\theta})\right]$$

Since by definition the nonlinear function is of the form of Eq. (9-13), we see that if $\alpha > 0$ and $\beta > 0$, $\dot{V}$ will be n.d. and the origin ($\theta = 0$, $\dot{\theta} = 0$) will be asymptotically stable.

If $\alpha = 0$, $\dot{V}$ will be negative semidefinite. However, here it is again not possible for the system state to dwell forever at the points where $\dot{V} = 0$ (namely those where $\dot{\theta} = 0$) except at the origin. (Why?) Thus we conclude that the origin of the system (9-12) is also asymptotically stable with the feedback control $u = -f(\beta\dot{\theta})$. The function f is defined by (9-13).

Finally, let us observe that if the function $f(x)$ is of the form

$$\lim_{x \to \infty} \int_0^x f(x)\,dx = \infty$$

(which is satisfied, e.g., by a limiter type nonlinearity), then $V(\theta, \dot{\theta}) \to \infty$ as $(\theta^2 + \dot{\theta}^2) \to \infty$, and we conclude that the origin is globally asymptotically stable. But since our mathematical model is only derived through linearization, the model itself is valid only in the small. Thus, practically speaking, global asymptotic stability is not meaningful relative to the model employed.♦♦

9.4 Lyapunov Function for Linear Autonomous Systems

For linear autonomous systems, the existence of a Lyapunov function that is a quadratic form in the system state variables turns out to be both necessary and sufficient for global (uniform) asymptotic stability [L18], [K8], [L6].

Consider the linear time-invariant system

$$\dot{x} = A\,x \tag{9-14}$$

Suppose we can find a Lyapunov function which is a quadratic form $V(x) = x^T Q x$, where the matrix Q is symmetric and p.d.* Then

$$\dot{V}(x) = \dot{x}^T Q\,x + x^T Q\,\dot{x} = x^T A^T Q\,x + x^T Q\,A\,x = x^T(A^T Q + Q\,A)\,x \tag{9-15}$$

Let

$$A^T Q + Q\,A = -C \tag{9-16}$$

then if C is p.d., the system is clearly globally asymptotically stable; further because

$$C^T = -(A^T Q + Q\,A)^T = -(Q^T A + A^T Q^T) = -(Q\,A + A^T Q) = C$$

C is also symmetric.

Often, however, it is more useful to consider the inverse situation. Suppose we begin with a C matrix which is p.d. and conveniently chosen, say C = I, then we can theoretically solve for Q by means of Eq. (9-16). In that case if the resultant Q is indefinite, then the origin is unstable by the first theorem of instability. On the other hand if Q is p.d., then since the system is linear and time-invariant, the origin is globally asymptotically stable. The key to this inverse approach hinges on whether or not Q is uniquely determined by Eq. (9-16), given a C that is symmetric and p.d.

It can be shown that the following propositions are true:

1) Consider the n eigenvalues $\lambda_1, \ldots, \lambda_n$ of the matrix A, if every sum $\lambda_i + \lambda_j \neq 0$ $(i, j = 1, \ldots, n)$. Then Q is uniquely determined by C through Eq. (9-16). (See Exercise 9-13.) Note here that if A is stable, the above condition is satisfied.
2) If A is stable and if C is p.d., then Q is also p.d. (See Exercise 9-14.)

Note that if C is p.d., then the condition that Q is also p.d. is a *sufficient* condition for the stability of A, inasmuch as $V = x^T Q\,x$ is a Lyapunov function of the system. However, proposition (2) also indicates that a positive definite Q is a *necessary* condition for a stable A, provided that C is a p.d. Thus, we can state the following theorem, first proved by Lyapunov himself:

*See Appendix A.

♦♦Theorem 9-8 (Lyapunov). The necessary and sufficient condition for the origin 0 of an autonomous linear system $\dot{x} = A x$ to be globally (uniformly) asymptotically stable is that given any symmetric, positive-definite matrix C, there exists a symmetric, positive-definite matrix Q which satisfies the set of $n(n + 1)/2$ equations* $A^T Q + Q A = -C$.♦♦

The converse of this is also useful:

♦♦Corollary 9-4. If the origin 0 of a linear autonomous system $\dot{x} = A x$ is stable, then there exists a unique Lyapunov function for the system of the form $V(x) = x^T Q x$, where $A^T Q + Q A = -C$, and C is any symmetric, positive-definite matrix.♦♦

It turns out that using this theorem and corollary, the Routh-Hurwitz criteria for the stability of a linear autonomous system can be rather conveniently derived using Lyapunov's second method [P1]. The traditional proofs are rather long and complicated [R4].

9.5 The Problem of Lur'e**

The Aizerman conjecture (see Chap. 5) has been demonstrated not to hold in general. We must thus look for other, and perhaps more restrictive, conditions for global asymptotic stability. In an approach advanced by Lur'e around 1950, the question is asked: For a system of (essentially) the Aizerman form, what combination of system parameters and system nonlinearities can cause a particular V function to become a Lyapunov function for the system? The V function used by Lur'e is a quadratic form in the system states plus an integral of the nonlinearity.

The development of this so-called problem of Lur'e follows an interesting history, and it takes on a rather international character. The initial work, pioneered by Lur'e and continued largely by Letov, makes use of a *particular* V function in the already special form mentioned above. What results from applying the V function is a set of n simultaneous quadratic algebraic equations in certain parameters. The finding of a set of parameters to satisfy these equations will guarantee the global asymptotic stability of the system being investigated. (See Exercises 9-7 and 9-8.)

For high-order systems, the solution of many simultaneous quadratic algebraic equations does not promise to be an easy task. In 1961, LaSalle and Lefschetz showed that, for a more general V function that is of the form of a quadratic in x and an integral of the nonlinearity, the necessary and sufficient condition that this chosen V function be a Lyapunov function of the system

*Only $n(n + 1)/2$ equations need to be solved for in $A^T Q + Q A = -C$ since C is a symmetric matrix.

**See [L17], [L6], [H2], [L8], [G3], [L10], [L13].

in the so-called indirect configuration (see below) is that a *scalar inequality* relating the system parameters be satisfied. This finding puts the Lur'e problem on a much more practical footing.

As it happened, however, while these new results were being developed in Russia and the U.S., the Rumanian mathematician V. M. Popov was developing a more encompassing criterion. His results however were published in the Rumanian journals and his accomplishments were not known to the West until a paper appeared in *Avtomatika i Telemekhanika* in 1961. The interesting aspect of the Popov criterion is that it is a *frequency domain* criterion. Moreover, it is of such generality that it implies the Lefschetz criterion on the Lur'e problem.

Since the results of Popov (and their subsequent extensions) represent the most general ones to date, we will devote the entire next chapter to it. The result of Lefschetz, however, is probably still the easiest to apply in some cases. It will be considered in this section.

The types of systems for the Lur'e problem fall essentially into two categories. They are (1) the "direct" control system, shown in Fig. 9-5 and similar to the type of systems we have considered hitherto, and (2) the "indirect" control system, Fig. 9-6a, in which $f(e)$ is shown as part of an actuator loop which precedes the linear part $G(p)$.

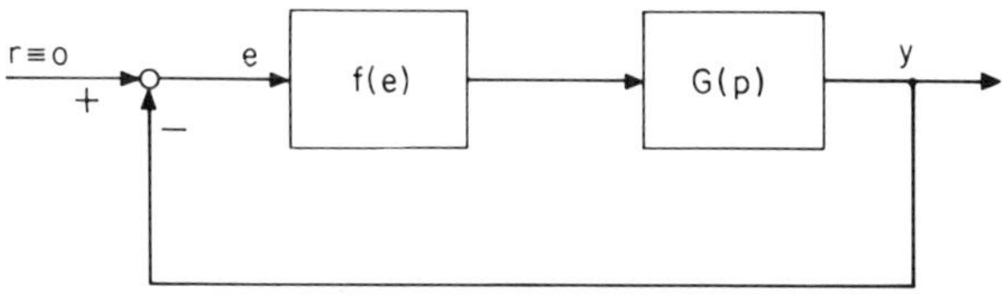

Fig. 9-5. A "direct" control system.

The indirect control system configuration is of advantage for systems such as aircraft or missile autopilot in which a hydraulic actuator controls the elevon and hence the motion of the vehicle. It is clear that the indirect control system can be arranged in the form of the direct control system and vice versa; but frequently, in the process, some pertinent parameters will be masked.

Traditionally, the nonlinearity $f(e)$ that is considered has the following characteristics:

$$\begin{aligned} f(e) &= 0, & e &= 0 \\ \int_0^e f(z)\,dz &> 0, & e &\neq 0 \end{aligned} \tag{9-17}$$

where $f(e)$ is continuous except possibly at $e = 0$.

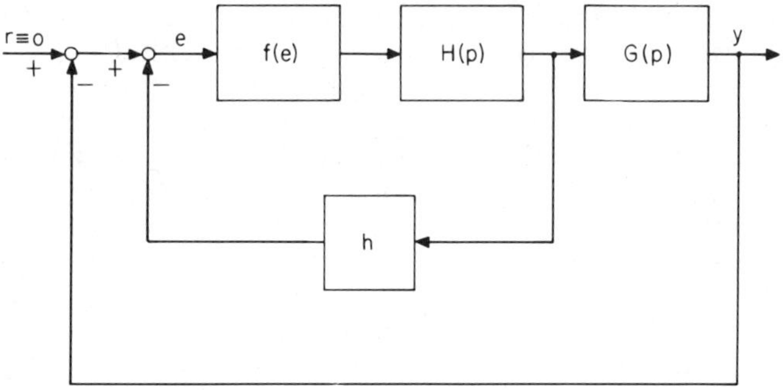

Fig. 9-6a. An "indirect" control system, the inner loop is usually an actuator loop. $H(p)$ is typically the integrator $(1/p)$.

It is clear that the characteristics (9-17) includes the class of nonlinearities that are considered in the Aizerman conjecture.

Lur'e attempted to establish the conditions on a direct or indirect system so that they are globally asymptotically stable for all nonlinearities of the class (9-17). This leads to the following definition.

◆◆Definition 9-1. An autonomous system of the form of Fig. 9-5 or Fig. 9-6a is absolutely stable if its origin is globally asymptotically stable for all nonlinearities $f(e)$ of the class (9-17).◆◆

Consider the more general case of indirect control. In Fig. 9-6a, let the linear plant $G(p)$ be such that all the poles are distinct and have negative real parts. Consider the case where $H(p) = (1/p)$; by means of manipulation of the linear portion of the system, making use of the fact that the system is autonomous, it is readily shown that an equivalent representation of the system is that of Fig. 9-6b as far as stability is concerned, provided that $h + \mathbf{c}^T\mathbf{A}^{-1}\mathbf{b} \neq 0$ (see Exercise 9-16). We note, however that the new output y_1 is no longer the same as the original output y.

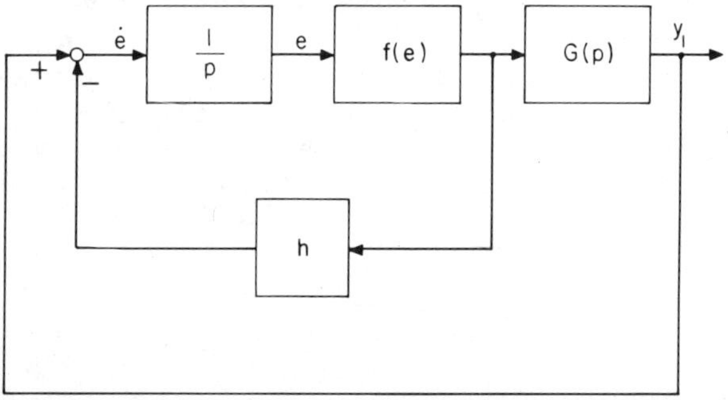

Fig. 9-6b. The system of Fig. 9-6a can be transformed into a form that is more amenable to treatment using the Lur'e approach. As shown here is the transformed configuration with $H(p) = (1/p)$.

The system of Fig. 9-6b can, by inspection, be represented by*

$$\dot{\mathbf{x}} = \mathbf{A}\mathbf{x} + \mathbf{b}f(e), \qquad \dot{e} = \mathbf{c}^T\mathbf{x} - hf(e), \qquad y_1 = \mathbf{c}^T\mathbf{x} \tag{9-18}$$

Try now a V function

$$V(\mathbf{x}, e) = \mathbf{x}^T\mathbf{Q}\,\mathbf{x} + \int_0^e f(z)\,dz \tag{9-19}$$

where $\mathbf{Q}$ is a yet unspecified, symmetric p.d. matrix. Then

$$\begin{aligned} \dot{V}(\mathbf{x}, e) &= \mathbf{x}^T\mathbf{Q}\,\dot{\mathbf{x}} + \dot{\mathbf{x}}^T\mathbf{Q}\mathbf{x} + f(e)\dot{e} \\ &= \mathbf{x}^T(\mathbf{A}^T\mathbf{Q} + \mathbf{Q}\,\mathbf{A})\mathbf{x} + f(e)\left[\mathbf{b}^T\mathbf{Q}\,\mathbf{x} + \mathbf{x}^T\mathbf{Q}\,\mathbf{b} + \mathbf{c}^T\mathbf{x}\right] - hf^2(e) \end{aligned} \tag{9-20}$$

Since the linear plant is stable, by Corollary 9-4, we see that if we solve for $\mathbf{Q}$ from

$$\mathbf{A}^T\mathbf{Q} + \mathbf{Q}\mathbf{A} = -\mathbf{C} \tag{9-21}$$

for any arbitrary choice of a symmetric p.d. matrix $\mathbf{C}$, then $\mathbf{Q}$ is guaranteed to be symmetric and p.d.

We can now write (9-20) as

$$\begin{aligned} \dot{V}(\mathbf{x}, e) &= -\mathbf{x}^T\mathbf{C}\,\mathbf{x} + f(e)(\mathbf{g}^T\mathbf{x} + \mathbf{x}^T\mathbf{g}) - hf^2(e) \\ &= -\mathbf{x}^T\mathbf{C}\,\mathbf{x} + 2f(e)\,\mathbf{g}^T\mathbf{x} - hf^2(e) \end{aligned} \tag{9-22}$$

where we have defined

$$\mathbf{g} = \mathbf{Q}\,\mathbf{b} + \frac{\mathbf{c}}{2} \tag{9-23}$$

Equation (9-22) can be written in a partitioned matrix form

$$\dot{V}(\mathbf{x}, e) = -\begin{bmatrix} \mathbf{x} \\ f(e) \end{bmatrix}^T \begin{bmatrix} \mathbf{C} & -\mathbf{g} \\ -\mathbf{g}^T & h \end{bmatrix} \begin{bmatrix} \mathbf{x} \\ f(e) \end{bmatrix} \tag{9-24}$$

*We are following the development of Lefschetz [L6], [L10].

For $\dot{V}$ to be n.d., the matrix

$$\mathrm{P} = \begin{bmatrix} \mathrm{C} & -\mathrm{g} \\ -\mathrm{g}^T & h \end{bmatrix}$$

must be p.d. However, by a theorem in Appendix A, since C is already p.d., we only require that the determinant of P be positive. Now the determinant of the matrix

$$\mathrm{R} = \begin{bmatrix} \mathrm{C}^{-1} & 0 \\ 0^T & 1 \end{bmatrix}$$

is positive (where 0 is a n vector of zeros). This implies that the determinant of the product R P is also positive, which leads to

$$|\mathrm{R}\ \mathrm{P}| = \begin{vmatrix} \mathrm{I} & -\mathrm{C}^{-1}\mathrm{g} \\ -\mathrm{g}^T & h \end{vmatrix} > 0$$

or

$$h > \mathrm{g}^T\mathrm{C}^{-1}\mathrm{g} \tag{9-25}$$

Equation (9-25) is the inequality relationship of Lefschetz [L6]. It, along with the assumed condition that C is p.d., ensures that the V function of (9-19) is a Lyapunov function of the system. If the condition

$$\lim_{e \to \infty} \int_0^e f(z)\,dz = \infty \tag{9-26}$$

is further appended, then $V \to \infty$ as $||\mathrm{x}|| + |e| \to \infty$ and by Theorem 9-7 the system (9-18) is absolutely stable.*

♦♦Example 9-11. Consider a system of the form of Fig. 9-6b. Let $G(p) = (p+6)/[(p+2)(p+3)]$. Using the approach of Lefschetz, find the smallest value of h which guarantees the absolute stability of the system if we use a diagonal C matrix.

*It has been shown by LaSalle that condition (9-26) is not needed for absolute stability of the system. His result is contained in [L4].

The system equation in the canonical representation for $G(p)$ is

$$\dot{\mathbf{x}} = \begin{bmatrix} -2 & 0 \\ 0 & -3 \end{bmatrix} \begin{bmatrix} x_1 \\ x_2 \end{bmatrix} + \begin{bmatrix} 1 \\ 1 \end{bmatrix} f(e), \qquad \dot{e} = 4x_1 - 3x_2 - hf(e)$$

Let

$$\mathbf{C} = \begin{bmatrix} \alpha & 0 \\ 0 & \beta \end{bmatrix}, \qquad \alpha, \beta > 0$$

Let $\mathbf{Q} = [q_{ij}]$, $i, j = 1, 2$; from $\mathbf{A}^T\mathbf{Q} + \mathbf{Q}\,\mathbf{A} = -\mathbf{C}$ we readily obtain

$$\begin{bmatrix} -4q_{11} & -5q_{12} \\ -5q_{21} & -6q_{22} \end{bmatrix} = \begin{bmatrix} -\alpha & 0 \\ 0 & -\beta \end{bmatrix}, \text{ hence } \mathbf{Q} = \begin{bmatrix} \frac{\alpha}{4} & 0 \\ 0 & \frac{\beta}{6} \end{bmatrix}$$

Since,

$$\mathbf{b} = \begin{bmatrix} 1 \\ 1 \end{bmatrix} \text{ and } \mathbf{c} = \begin{bmatrix} 4 \\ -3 \end{bmatrix}$$

$$\mathbf{g} = \mathbf{Q}\,\mathbf{b} + \frac{\mathbf{c}}{2} = \begin{bmatrix} 2 + \frac{\alpha}{4} \\ \frac{\beta}{6} - \frac{3}{2} \end{bmatrix}$$

we have

$$h > \frac{\left(2 + \frac{\alpha}{4}\right)^2}{\alpha} + \frac{\left(\frac{\beta}{6} - \frac{3}{2}\right)^2}{\beta}$$

We wish now to choose α and β so as to minimize the rhs of the above inequality, subject to the constraint $\alpha > 0$, $\beta > 0$. By simple calculus (see also Chap. 13) we find that the minimizing values are $\alpha = 8$, $\beta = 9$, which thereby gives $h > 2$.◆◆

9.6 The Application of the Second Method of Lyapunov to Time-Varying Systems*

For time-varying systems, if a Lyapunov function V that is independent of time is used, the time derivative $\dot{V}$ of the Lyapunov function following the system trajectory will be explicitly a function of time. Of course a time-varying Lyapunov function will also, in general, give rise to a $\dot{V}$ that is time-varying. Occasionally a time-varying Lyapunov function may prove to be more useful because it yields simpler, or perhaps more comprehensive, stability conditions.

Because of the appearance of time in the expression for $\dot{V}$, and possibly for V, some modifications to the statements of the theorems have to be made; these involve the introduction of requirements to suitably bound $V(\mathbf{x}, t)$ and $\dot{V}(\mathbf{x}, t)$ by scalar functions that are independent of time.

For a time-varying scalar function to be p.d., we require the following:

♦♦Definition 9-2. A time-varying scalar function $V(\mathbf{x}, t)$ is positive definite in a region $\mathcal{R}$ containing the origin if $V(0, t) = 0$ and if a continuous and strictly increasing function** $\phi(z)$ exists such that $\phi(0) = 0$ and

$$V(\mathbf{x}, t) \geq \phi(\|\mathbf{x}\|) \tag{9-27}$$

in $\mathcal{R}$.♦♦

Let us study a free system of the form

$$\dot{\mathbf{x}} = \mathbf{f}(\mathbf{x}, t) \tag{9-28a}$$

with

$$\mathbf{f}(0, t) = 0 \quad \text{for all } t \tag{9-28b}$$

The time derivative of a scalar function $V(\mathbf{x}, t)$ along the trajectory of the system (9-28) is then

$$\frac{dV(\mathbf{x}, t)}{dt} = \sum_{i=1}^{n} \frac{\partial V}{\partial x_1} f_i(\mathbf{x}, t) + \frac{\partial V}{\partial t} = (\text{grad } V)^T \mathbf{f} + \frac{\partial V}{\partial t} \tag{9-29}$$

We have the following theorems:

♦♦Theorem 9-9. Relative to the system of (9-28), if (i) a positive definite scalar function $V(\mathbf{x}, t)$ possessing continuous first partial

*See [L18], [K8], and [L10].

**A strictly increasing function $\phi(z)$ obeys the property that if $z_2 > z_1$, $\phi(z_2) > \phi(z_1)$ for any z_1, z_2.

derivatives with respect to x and t can be found in the neighborhood $\mathcal{R}$ of the origin such that (ii) $\dot{V}(\mathbf{x}, t) < 0$ in $\mathcal{R}$, then the origin of (9-28) is stable.♦♦

♦♦Theorem 9-10. If there exists a positive (but not necessarily strictly increasing) scalar function of one variable $\theta(z)$ such that in addition to condition (i) of Theorem 9-9, we also have (iii)

$$\dot{V}(\mathbf{x}, t) \leq -\theta(\|\mathbf{x}\|) \tag{9-30}$$

in $\mathcal{R}$, then the origin of (9-28) is equiasymptotically stable.♦♦

♦♦Theorem 9-11. If there exists a continuous, strictly increasing scalar function of one variable $\rho(z)$ with $\rho(0) = 0$ such that, in addition to the conditions (i) and (iii) of Theorems 9-9 and 9-10 we also have (iv)

$$V(\mathbf{x}, t) \leq \rho(\|\mathbf{x}\|) \tag{9-31}$$

in $\mathcal{R}$ for all t, then the origin of (9-28) is uniformly asymptotically stable.♦♦

♦♦Theorem 9-12. If the conditions (i), (iii) and (iv) in the above theorems are satisfied, with $\mathcal{R}$ the entire state space of (9-28), and if (v) the function $\phi(\|\mathbf{x}\|)$ dominated by $V(\mathbf{x}, t)$ in (9-27) is such that $\phi(\|\mathbf{x}\|) \to \infty$ as $\|\mathbf{x}\| \to \infty$, then the origin of (9-28) is globally equiasymptotically stable.♦♦

♦♦Theorem 9-13. If the conditions (i), (iii), (iv) and (v) in the above theorems are satisfied with $\mathcal{R}$ the entire state space of (9-28) and if (vi) the function $\rho\|\mathbf{x}\|$ dominating $V(\mathbf{x}, t)$ in (9-31) is such that $\rho(\|\mathbf{x}\|) \to \infty$ as $\|\mathbf{x}\| \to \infty$, then the origin of (9-28) is globally uniformly asymptotically stable.* ♦♦

We may briefly sketch the ideas behind the proofs to these theorems. Let us note first that, with V a time-varying function, merely requiring that $V > 0$ for all $\mathbf{x} \neq 0$ and all t is insufficient to guarantee asymptotic stability even if $\dot{V} < 0$ (for all $\mathbf{x} \neq 0$ and all t). For when V is time varying, as long as $\partial V/\partial t$ in Eq. (9-29) is negative and less than $(\text{grad } V)^T\mathbf{f}$, dV/dt will be negative. Since it is the $(\text{grad } V)^T\mathbf{f}$ term that governs the motion of the system state, it is possible for $\dot{V}$ to be < 0 while the trajectory moves outside of any bounding region $\mathcal{R}$.

With $V(\mathbf{x}, t)$ dominating a scalar function of $\|\mathbf{x}\|$ as in (9-27), the above can no longer occur. If challenged with an ϵ, for example,

* We recall from Sec. 5.6 that global uniform asymptotic stability includes the following features: (*i*) Lyapunov stability that is uniform in $\mathbf{x}_0$ and t_0 (uniform stability). (*ii*) Uniform boundedness; i.e., given any $r > 0$, there exists a value B depending only on r such that $\|\mathbf{x}_0 - \mathbf{x}_e\| \leq r$ implies $\|\mathbf{x}(t) - \mathbf{x}_e\| \leq B$ for all $t \geq t_0$. (*iii*) Every trajectory in the state space tends to $\mathbf{x}_e$ as $t \to \infty$ uniformly both in $\mathbf{x}_0$ and t_0.

we can always find a $\delta < \epsilon$ (depending on ϵ and t_0) such that $V(x_0, t_0) < \phi(\epsilon)$. From this, stability and asymptotic stability follow, since with $\dot{V} < 0$, the trajectory cannot be such that V increases beyond $\phi(\epsilon)$. Moreover, the aysmptotic stability is uniform in x_0, hence the origin is really equiasymptotically stable.

For uniform stability, it is further necessary to let $V(x, t)$ be dominated by a function $\rho(||x||)$ as in (9-31). Here, given any $\epsilon > 0$, we can now take a δ such that $\rho(\delta) < \phi(\epsilon)$. This leads to $\phi(\epsilon) > \rho(\delta) \geq V(x_0, t_0) \geq V(x(t), t) \geq \phi(||x(t)||)$ for all $t > t_0$. Uniform stability then follows since the δ chosen this way is clearly independent of t_0.

It is more involved to show that, if the conditions of Theorem 9-11 are satisfied, the origin is approached by $x(t)$ uniformly in x_0 and t_0. This proof, due to Massera [M4], is outlined here.*

In region $\mathcal{R}$, take a number c such that there is a number δ_a obeying $\rho(\delta_a) < \phi(c)$. With $||x_0|| \leq \delta_a$, it then follows that $\delta(c)$ constitutes a uniform bound on $||x(t)||$. Suppose now a value of $\mu \leq ||x_0||$ is given; then we can find a number $\mu' > 0$ such that $\rho(\mu') < \phi(\mu)$. Since $\mu' \leq \mu \leq c$, the continuous function $\theta(z)$ of Theorem 9-10 has a minimum over the interval $\mu' \leq z \leq c$. We designate the value of this minimum as c'. We now show that the value of T in the definition of uniform asymptotic stability can be given by $T = [\rho(\delta_a)/c']$.

First we show that between t_0 and $t_1 = t_0 + T$, there will be a time t' at which $||x(t')|| = \mu'$. By definition, $||x_0|| > \mu'$. If $||x(t)|| > \mu'$ throughout the interval $t_0 \leq t \leq t_1$, then we have

$$\phi(\mu') \leq \big(V\ x(t_1), t_1\big) \leq V(x_0, t_0) - (t_1 - t_9)c'$$

Since $\rho(\delta_a) \geq V(x_0, t_0)$ and with $T = [\rho(\delta_a)/c']$ we have

$$0 < \phi(\mu') \leq \rho(\delta_a) - Tc' = 0$$

which is a contradiction. Thus $||x(t')|| \triangleq ||x'|| = \mu'$. Consider now the above trajectory starting at the time t'. We have

$$\phi\big(||x(x', t'; t)||\big) \leq V\big(x(x', t'; t), t\big) \leq V(x', t') \leq \rho(\mu') < \phi(\mu)$$

which implies that $||x(x_0, t_0; t)|| < \mu$ for all $t \geq t_0 + T$. Uniform asymptotic stability is thus proven.

It is a relatively simple matter to prove that the stability properties are global when $\phi(||x||) \to \infty$ as $||x|| \to \infty$.

We may emphasize again that for time-varying systems, it is perfectly legitimate to choose a V function which is independent of time; in that case, it is reasonably clear that $V(x)$ need only be p.d. in the time-invariant sense (i.e., $V(x) > 0$, $x \neq 0$, $V(0) = 0$) for uniform

*See also [H2], p. 65.

asymptotic stability provided that $\dot{V}$, which is time varying, satisfies the condition of (9-30).

◆◆Example 9-12 (Lim and Kazda).* Consider the time-varying differential equation of the following general form

$$\ddot{x} + p(t)\dot{x} + q(t)x = 0$$

or

$$\dot{x}_1 = x_2 \qquad \dot{x}_2 = -q(t)x_1 - p(t)x_2 \tag{9-32}$$

Assume that $p(t)$ and $q(t)$ are continuous and $q(t) \geq q_1 > 0$. It is desired to find bounds on $p(t)$ and $q(t)$ so as to guarantee the asymptotic stability of the origin. We shall produce two such bounds by using two Lyapunov functions, one of these being time-invariant and the other time-varying.

Case 1. Take the function

$$V = \frac{1}{2} a_1 x_1^2 + x_1 x_2 + \frac{1}{2} a_2 x_2^2 \tag{9-33}$$

if $a_1 > 0$, $a_1 a_2 > 1$, then V is positive definite. Moreover,

$$\frac{dV}{dt} = -\left\{q(t)x_1^2 + [a_2 q(t) + p(t) - a_1]\, x_1 x_2 + [a_2 p(t) - 1]\, x_2^2\right\}$$

$$= -\left\{q(t)\left[x_1 + \frac{a_2 q(t) + p(t) - a_1}{2q(t)}\, x_2\right]^2 + \left[a_2 p(t) - 1 - \frac{\left(p(t) + a_2 q(t) - a_1\right)^2}{4q(t)}\right] x_2^2\right\} \tag{9-34}$$

As $q(t) \geq q_1 > 0$, then if the coefficient of the x_2^2 term above is greater than 0, $\dot{V}$ will be negative definite. We can thus impose the condition that

$$\left\{a_2 p(t) - 1 - \frac{\left[p(t) + a_2 q(t) - a_1\right]^2}{4q(t)}\right\} \geq \epsilon \tag{9-35a}$$

* See [L14].

where ϵ is a positive constant. After some manipulations, Eq. (9-35a) can be rewritten as

$$[p(t) - a_2 q(t) - a_1]^2 - 4(a_1 a_2 - 1 - \epsilon)\, q(t) \leq 0 \qquad \text{(9-35b)}$$

moreover, (9-35a) implies that

$$p(t) \geq \frac{1}{a_2}\left\{1 + \epsilon + \frac{[p(t) + a_2 q(t) - a_1]^2}{4q(t)}\right\} > 0 \qquad \text{(9-36)}$$

Equations (9-35) and (9-36), along with the condition $q(t) \geq q_1 > 0$, give the shaded region in the first quadrant of the q—p plane of Fig. 9-7. Within this region the excursions in p and q must take place in order to guarantee asymptotic stability. This shaded region consists of all points inside the parabola

$$(p - a_2 q - a_1)^2 - 4(a_1 a_2 - 1 - \epsilon)q = 0 \qquad \text{(9-37)}$$

and lying to the right of the line $q = q_1$.

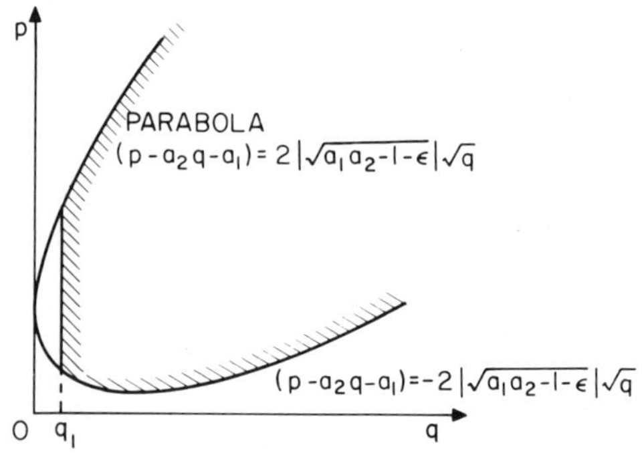

Fig. 9-7. Shaded region is the region in the q–p plane inside the parabola of Eq. (9-37) ana lying to the right of the line $q = q_1$.

If we require that

$$0 < p_1 \leq p(t) \leq p_2 \quad \text{and} \quad 0 < q_1 \leq q(t) \leq q_2 \qquad \text{(9-38)}$$

with p_1, p_2, q_1, and q_2 constants; then, given any two of these four constants, the stability zone will be completely determined in the q—p plane in terms of the constants a_1 and a_2. Since a_1 and a_2 play no role other than that of assuring that V is p.d., we can in principle eliminate a_1 and a_2 by finding the maximum possible zone in the q—p plane consistent with the requirements imposed by the Lyapunov function.

Consider a parabola which passes through the point (q_1, p_1) given by the lower bound values. Now let it pass through another point (q_2', p_1) with the same ordinate value p_1. (See Fig. 9-8.) Assume $q_2' \geq q_1$; then by substituting these points respectively into (9-37) we can first eliminate a_1 and obtain an expression for a_2; then we can express a_1 in terms of a_2. It is clear that two pairs of values (a_{1+}, a_{2+}) and (a_{1-}, a_{2-}) are possible, i.e., two parabolas can pass through the same points; they are

$$a_{2\pm} = \frac{2}{\left(\sqrt{q_2'} - \sqrt{q_1}\right)^2}\left[p_1 \pm \sqrt{p_1^{\,2} - \left(\sqrt{q_2'} - \sqrt{q_1}\right)^2 (1 + \epsilon)}\right] \tag{9-39a}$$

$$a_{1\pm} = \frac{\left(\sqrt{q_2'} + \sqrt{q_1}\right)^2}{4} a_{2\pm} + \frac{1 + \epsilon}{a_{2\pm}} \tag{9-39b}$$

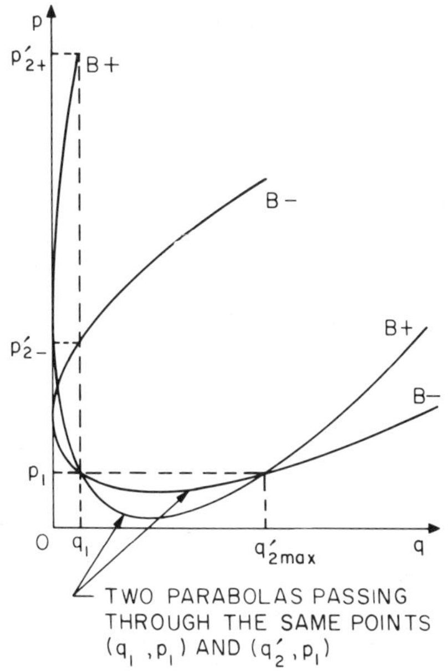

Fig. 9-8. Geometric considerations to find the maximum possible zone in the q–p plane consistent with the requirements imposed by the Lyapunov function.

From (9-39a) for $a_{2\pm}$ to be real, the condition

$$p_1^2 \geq \left(\sqrt{q_2'} - \sqrt{q_1}\right)^2 (1 + \epsilon) \tag{9-40}$$

must be observed.

Now consider at what value p_2' these parabolas (which pass through the points (q_1, p_1) and (q_2', p_1)) must pass through the value of abscissa q_1 (see Fig. (9-8)). The values of p_2', depending on the choice of q_1, p_1, q_2' and ϵ, turn out to be (from 9-37)

$$p_2'(q_1, p_1, q_2', \epsilon)_{\pm} = p_1 + 4\sqrt{a_1 a_2 - 1 - \epsilon}\sqrt{q_1}$$

$$= p_1 + \frac{4\left(\sqrt{q_2'} + \sqrt{q_1}\right)}{\left(\sqrt{q_2'} - \sqrt{q_1}\right)^2}\left(p_1 \pm \sqrt{p_1^2 - \left(\sqrt{q_2'} - \sqrt{q_1}\right)^2 (1 + \epsilon)}\right) \tag{9-41}$$

It can be seen that $p_2'(q_1, p_1, q_2', \epsilon)_+ > p_2'(q_1, p_1, q_2', \epsilon)_-$. Since $p_2'(q_1, p_1, q_2', \epsilon)_+$ varies inversely as q_2', it takes on the maximum value at the lower bound for q_2', namely q_2. Thus, we see that $p_2 \leq p_2'(p_1, q_1, q_2, \epsilon)_+$. A similar reasoning using (9-40) leads to

$$p_1 \geq \left(\sqrt{q_2} - \sqrt{q_1}\right)\sqrt{1 + \epsilon} \tag{9-42}$$

From (9-41), we see that $p_2'(p_1, q_1, q_2, 0) > p_2'(p_1, q_1, q_2, \epsilon)_+ > p_2$. Thus we have, from (9-41)

$$\lim_{\epsilon \to 0} p_2'(q_1, p_1, q_2, \epsilon)_+ = p_2'(q_1, p_1, q_2, 0)_+$$

$$= \frac{p_1\left(5q_1 + q_2 + 2\sqrt{q_1 q_2}\right) + 4\left(q_1 + \sqrt{q_1 q_2}\right)\sqrt{p_1^2 - \left(\sqrt{q_2} - \sqrt{q_1}\right)^2}}{\left(\sqrt{q_2} - \sqrt{q_1}\right)^2} \tag{9-43}$$

From (9-42) and (9-43), we have, in terms of q_1, q_2

$$p_1 > \sqrt{q_2} - \sqrt{q_1} \tag{9-44a}$$

$$p_2 < \frac{p_1\left(5q_1 + q_2 + 2\sqrt{q_1 q_2}\right) + 4\left(q_1 + \sqrt{q_1 q_2}\right)\sqrt{p_1^2 - \left(\sqrt{q_2} - \sqrt{q_1}\right)^2}}{\left(\sqrt{q_2} - \sqrt{q_1}\right)^2} \tag{9-44b}$$

which constitute the bounds sought.

Case 2. Take the function

$$V = x_1^2 + \frac{1}{q(t)} x_2^2, \quad 0 < q_1 \leq q(t) \leq q_2 \tag{9-45}$$

which dominates the function $x_1^2 + (1/q_2) x_2^2$; hence V satisfies (9-27). (Why?) Then,

$$\dot{V} = 2x_1\dot{x}_1 + \frac{1}{q(t)} 2x_2\dot{x}_2 - \frac{x_2^2\dot{q}(t)}{q^2(t)} = -\frac{\dot{q}(t) + 2p(t)q(t)}{q^2(t)} x_2^2 \tag{9-46}$$

If

$$\frac{\dot{q} + 2pq}{q^2} \geq \epsilon > 0 \qquad \text{or} \qquad p \geq \frac{\epsilon q}{2} - \frac{\dot{q}}{2q} \tag{9-47}$$

$\dot{V}$ is seen to be negative semi-definite and the origin is stable by Theorem 9-9. However, Lim [L14] manages to show that as $t \to \infty$, $V \to 0$ provided that $p(t)$ is bounded from above. Thus the origin is asymptotically stable if condition (9-47) is observed. Compared to (9-44), we see that condition (9-47) requires that $\dot{q}(t)$ exist.♦♦

9.7 Some Further Applications of Lyapunov's Second Method

1. The Estimation of the Transient Performance of a System

Frequently Lyapunov functions can be used in the estimation of the transient behavior of a system. The idea here is basically a simple and obvious one. Consider a Lyapunov function that is time-invariant; for a given initial condition, the value of $V(t_0)$ is immediately known. Using the expression of $\dot{V}$, the rate of decrease of V can be estimated. Since, in most cases, constant V contours are closed curves around the origin, we have a way of estimating the distance from the origin of the system state as a function of time.

However, for the method to be useful, $\dot{V}$ must first be found as a function of time without having to integrate the system equations. Second, the resulting expressions should be simple. These two requirements thus far seem to have been sufficient to stymie systematic development in this area. On occasion, however, interesting isolated results can be obtained. In this section, we will examine the question of transient estimation by using Lyapunov functions and show some examples.

First, let us note that

$$\dot{V}(\mathrm{x}, t) = \left(\frac{\dot{V}(\mathrm{x}, t)}{V(\mathrm{x}, t)}\right) V(\mathrm{x}, t) \tag{9-48}$$

Thus, in a region about the origin if it can be established that the quantity $\dot{V}/V$ is never larger than a constant $-k$, we have

$$\dot{V} \leq -kV \qquad \text{and} \qquad V(\mathrm{x}(t), t) \leq V(\mathrm{x}_0, t_0)\, e^{-k(t-t_0)}$$

Suppose that the V function chosen for a system satisfies the conditions of Theorem 9-13, so that the origin of the system in question is globally uniformly asymptotically stable, then $V(\mathrm{x}, t) \leq \rho(\|\mathrm{x}\|)$ and $\dot{V}(\mathrm{x}, t) \leq -\theta(\|\mathrm{x}\|)$. In this case the constant k is simply the smallest value that the ratio $\theta(\|\mathrm{x}\|)/\rho(\|\mathrm{x}\|)$ takes on in the region of interest.

Indeed we may increase the accuracy of the estimation for the convergence time by using a different value of k between adjacent contours of equal V's so that the estimate of the transient time is given by a piece-wise exponential curve. Since there is a one-to-one correspondence between constant V contours and maximum distance to the origin, we then obtain an estimate of the rate at which the system state is approaching the origin.

Occasionally, for a nonlinear system, we may be able to improve on the accuracy of the estimate of the speed of transient response by not using an exponential bound since using such a bound is equivalent to matching the nonlinear system with a linear system. A linear system takes infinite time to reach the origin whereas for a nonlinear system this need not be the case. The example below can perhaps indicate a new area of investigation.

♦♦Example 9-13.* The tumbling motion of an orbiting satellite whose tumbling rate far exceed the orbiting rate can be given by the Euler dynamical equations

$$I_1\dot{\omega}_1 - (I_2 - I_3)\,\omega_2\omega_3 = u_1\,, \qquad I_2\dot{\omega}_2 - (I_3 - I_1)\,\omega_3\omega_1 = u_2$$

$$I_3\dot{\omega}_3 - (I_1 - I_2)\,\omega_1\omega_2 = u_3 \tag{9-49}$$

where the symbols have the same meaning as given in Example 5-10. We assume that $I_1 \neq I_2 \neq I_3$.

The square of the magnitude of the angular momentum of the satellite is

$$L^2 = (I_1\omega_1)^2 + (I_2\omega_2)^2 + (I_3\omega_3)^2 \tag{9-50}$$

*This example is discussed (without proof) in [H18].

The quantity L^2 is p.d. and approaches ∞ as $||\omega|| \to \infty$ and, hence, is a suitable candidate for a Lyapunov function.

By (9-50) and (9-49) we have

$$\frac{dL^2}{dt} = 2\Big[(I_1\omega_1)u_1 + (I_2\omega_2)u_2 + (I_3\omega_3)u_3\Big] \tag{9-51}$$

This quantity will be globally n.d. if the u_i's observe the feedback relationship $u_i = -f_i(\omega_i)$ with $f_i(\omega_i)$ such that

$$\left.\begin{aligned} &\omega_i f_i(\omega_i) > 0 \quad \text{for} \quad \omega_i \neq 0 \\ &-\infty < f_i(0) < \infty \\ &\lim_{\omega_i \to \infty} \int_0^{\omega_i} f_i(z)\,dz = \infty \end{aligned}\right\} i = 1, 2, 3 \tag{9-52}$$

Thus the origin will be globally asymptotically stable under the feedback control $u_i = -f_i(\omega_i)$ provided that $f_i(\omega_i)$ satisfies (9-52).

Consider now the particular case of "bang-bang" control

$$-u_i = f_i(\omega_i) = U_i \operatorname{sgn} \omega_i = \begin{cases} U_i, & \omega_i > 0 \\ -U_i, & \omega_i < 0 \end{cases}$$

$$U_i > 0, \quad i = 1, 2, 3 \tag{9-53}$$

which satisfies condition (9-52). Let us try to find a bound for the maximum time that is required to reach the origin from an arbitrary initial state.

Let U be the smallest of the three values U_1, U_2, and U_3; it is readily seen that

$$|f_i(\omega_i)| \geq \frac{U}{||\mathbf{L}||} I_i |\omega_i| \quad \text{for} \quad |\omega_i| \leq \frac{||\mathbf{L}||}{I_i} \tag{9-54}$$

However, from (9-50) we see that $|\omega_i|$ is always less than or equal to $||\mathbf{L}||/I_i$. Thus (9-54) is always valid. Since $\omega_i f_i(\omega_i) > 0$ for $\omega_i \neq 0$, we have:

$$I_i\omega_i f_i(\omega_i) \geq \frac{U}{||\mathbf{L}||} I_i^2 \omega_i^2 \tag{9-55}$$

Substituting (9-54) into (9-51) we obtain

$$-\frac{dL^2}{dt} = 2\|\mathbf{L}\| \frac{d\|\mathbf{L}\|}{dt} = 2\left[\sum_{i=1}^{3} I_i\omega_i f_i(\omega_i)\right] \geq 2 \frac{U}{\|\mathbf{L}\|} L^2 = 2U\|\mathbf{L}\| \quad \text{(9-56)}$$

Thus

$$\frac{d\|\mathbf{L}\|}{dt} \leq -U \qquad \text{and}$$

$$\|\mathbf{L}(t)\| \leq \|\mathbf{L}(t)\| - U(t - t_0), \qquad t_0 \leq t \leq t_0 + \frac{\|\mathbf{L}(t_0)\|}{U} \quad \text{(9-57)}$$

This means that the angular momentum is brought from an initial value $\|\mathbf{L}(t_0)\|$ to 0 in a finite time T, where

$$T \leq \frac{\|\mathbf{L}(t_0)\|}{U} \quad \text{(9-58)}$$

A corresponding statement can obviously be made concerning the system state.◆◆

2. The Synthesis of a Class of "Adaptive" Systems

Sometimes the parameters of a plant are known to vary in an unprescribed manner. In spite of such variations, it is desired to make the plant respond in a specific way to given inputs (e.g., to make the system response time to a step input fall within certain bounds). This has led to research efforts in the "model-reference" class of adaptive systems.

The basic form of a model-reference adaptive system is as shown in Fig. 9-9. A model block (either actually in existence or implicitly programmed in the controller) is used to arrive at the desired response $\mathbf{x}_d$ to an input $r(t)$. Meanwhile the plant is subjected to a control function $\mathbf{u}(t)$. The output of the plant $\mathbf{x}(t)$,

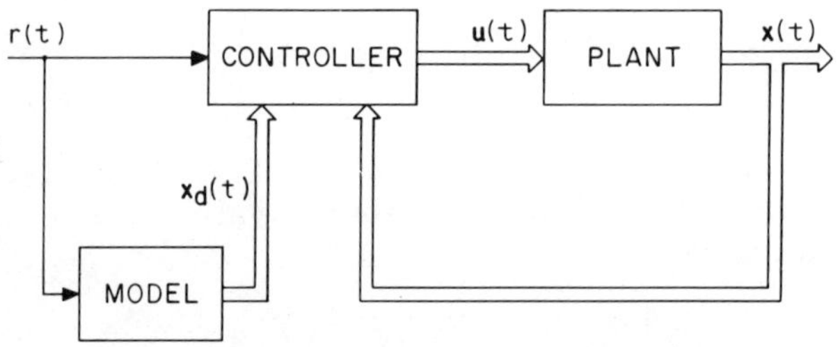

Fig. 9-9. A form of a model-reference adaptive system.

the output of the model $x_d(t)$, and the input $r(t)$ are fed into the controller. The task of the controller is to generate a control function $u(t)$ to force the plant response $x(t)$ to follow $x_d(t)$ as closely as possible.

For this class of systems, it is meaningful to consider the error between the desired output and the actual output; let $e(t) = x_d(t) - x(t)$. In a state space with the components of $e(t)$ as the coordinates, if it can be established that the workings of the system are such that the origin is globally asymptotically stable, then it is clear that, as time goes on, the plant will behave more and more like the model.

If the model is a time-invariant linear differential system and the plant is a time-varying linear differential system, a possible solution to the above problem is given as follows:

♦♦Example 9-14 (Grayson*). Let the plant be given by $\dot{x} = A_1(t)x + B_1(t)u$ and let the model be given by $\dot{z} = A_2 z + B_2 r$, where A_2, B_2 are constant matrices. Assume that with $r \equiv 0$, the model is asymptotically stable. This, by Corollary 9-4 (page 336), implies that there exists a p.d. matrix Q such that with

$$V_1(z) = z^T Q\, z \tag{9-59}$$

we will have

$$\dot{V}_1(z) = z^T(A_2^T Q + Q\, A_2)z = -z^T C\, z \tag{9-60}$$

As $C = (A_2^T Q + Q\, A_2)$ is a p.d. matrix, the function $\dot{V}_1(z)$ is n.d. following the trajectories of the system $\dot{z} = A_2 z$.

Let $e \triangleq z - x$, $\Delta A \triangleq A_1(t) - A_2$, and $\Delta B \triangleq B_1(t) - B_2$; then

$$\dot{e} = A_2 e - \Delta A\, x - B_1(t)u + B_2 r \tag{9-61}$$

If we choose a function $V(e) = e^T Q\, e$, where Q is as defined in (9-59), then

$$\dot{V}(e, t) = e^T C\, e - 2e^T Q[\Delta A\, x + \Delta B\, r + B_1(u - r)] \tag{9-62}$$

Since C is p.d., all that is necessary to bring about convergence of the model-reference adaptive system of this example is to choose $u(t)$ such that

$$e^T(t)\,Q\left[\Delta A(t)x(t) + \Delta B(t)r(t) + B_1(t)\Big(u(t) - r(t)\Big)\right]\begin{cases} = 0 & \Delta A = \Delta B = 0 \\ \geq 0 & \text{otherwise} \end{cases} \tag{9-63}$$

*See [G9]. The reference also features excellent tutorial accounts of other synthesis techniques using Lyapunov's second method.

This is because when (9-63) is satisfied $\dot{V}(\mathbf{e}, t)$ in (9-62) will always be less than or equal to $-\mathbf{e}^T\mathbf{C}\,\mathbf{e}$ and the origin in the error state space will be globally asymptotically stable.♦♦

9.8 Summary

The second method of Lyapunov gives a sufficient condition for stability or asymptotic stability. In-the-large stabilities can also be determined through the application of the method.

The advantage of the method lies in the fact that stability information is deduced from the sign definiteness of the time rate of change of an arbitrarily chosen definite function of the system states as the system pursues free motion. The system trajectories need not be explicitly solved for. Thus, when the method is successfully used, the stability results are obtained rather painlessly. The drawbacks of the method are: (1) Only a sufficient condition test for stability is given. If the test should fail, nothing can be said concerning the stability of the system, and another attempt must be made with another sign-definite function of the system states. If the test is successful on the other hand, the resultant region of stability need not be the largest possible. (2) There is no systematic procedure in determining the sign definiteness of an arbitrary function of several variables. This greatly restricts our ability to select test functions. Because of this fact, the only test functions that are frequently used are quadratic forms. Finally, the very idea of deriving stability information painlessly is contrary to sound engineering procedure. What is sacrificed is insight into the various possible modes of system behavior, insight which can only be obtained through thorough system analysis. The second method thus appears to be a useful supplementary tool for determining system stability where other methods can also be used.

The basic idea of the second method of Lyapunov is given in Sec. 9.1. Five principal theorems governing the use of the method in determining stability in the small appear in Sec. 9.2. The extension of the results to stability in the large is given in Sec. 9.3.

For linear autonomous systems, there is a theorem (Theorem 9-8) that yields a necessary and sufficient condition for the origin of the system to be stable. This fact is used in the so-called problem of Lur'e to construct test functions for a specific class of systems (namely, those that take the form of Fig. 9-5 or 9-6).

For time-varying systems, some refinement of the basic theorems will have to be made. These usually involve the bounding of the (time-varying) test functions by time-invariant functions of the norm $||\mathbf{x}||$. (See Theorems 9-9 through 9-13.) Time-varying systems are usually much more difficult to test. A nontrivial example is given (Example 9-12).

Lyapunov's second method can, in principle, be used to estimate the transient performance of a system. Known results in this direction, however, are relatively scarce. Example 9-13 provides an interesting illustration. The second method has also been used to ensure convergence in a class of model-reference adaptive systems. Example 9-14 gives one such realization.

9.9 Exercises

9-1 Determine the sign definiteness of the following functions:

a) $V(x_1, x_2, x_3) = x_1^2 + 4x_1x_2 + x_2^2 + x_2x_3 + 3x_3^2$

b) $V(x_1, x_2) = |x_1| \cos x_2 + x_2^2$

c) $V(x_1, x_2) = \sin^2 x_1 + \sin^2 x_2$

d) $V(x_1, x_2, x_3) = x_1^4 + x_1^2 x_2^2$

e) $V(x_1, x_2) = e^{x_1^2} + e^{x_2^2}$

If the functions are definite or semidefinite only in a given region about the origin, give the region.

9-2 By the use of the approach of Sec. 9.4, find the range of K for the system given in Fig. 9-10 such that the origin is asymptotically stable.

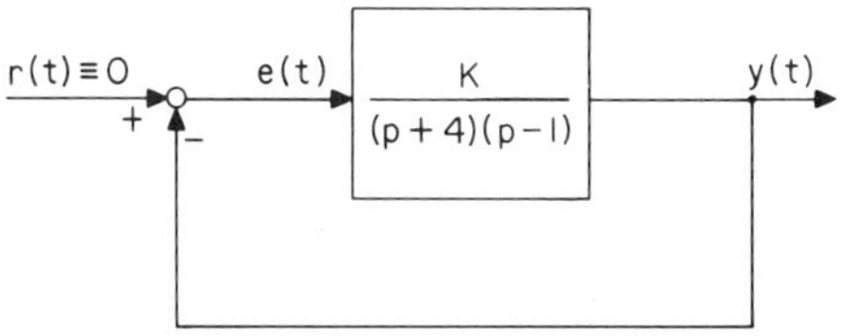

Fig. 9-10. The system of Exercise 9-2.

9-3 Consider systems whose linearized equations have distinct eigenvalues which are not all real. If all the eigenvalues which lie in the left half-plane (i.e., $\Re e\, \lambda_i < 0$ for all i) find a suitable Lyapunov function and prove that the origin is asymptotically stable. (Hint: Use the canonical representation for the system.)

9-4 A mass, dash-pot and spring system with a soft-spring can be given by the equation

$$m\ddot{x} + d\dot{x} + k\left(x - \frac{x^3}{6}\right) = 0$$

a) Use as the Lyapunov function the total energy of the system and show that the origin is *asymptotically* stable.
b) Find the largest region $\mathcal{R}$ about the origin such that the Lyapunov function used will still indicate asymptotic stability.

9-5 A phase-locked loop for communications application is given by $\ddot{x} + (a + b \cos x)\dot{x} + c \sin x = 0$. Assume that $a > b > 0$ and $c > 0$. By the use of the function $V(x, \dot{x}) = c(1 - \cos x) + \dot{x}^2/2$, find the largest region in state space in which the system is guaranteed to be asymptotically stable. Compare this with the result obtained in Exercise 5-16.

9-6 (Popov) Consider the system

$$\dot{x}_1 = -x_1 + f(x_3)$$

$$\dot{x}_2 = -f(x_3)$$

$$\dot{x}_3 = (\gamma - 1)x_1 + \gamma x_2 - hf(x_3)$$

where $f(x_3)$ is a function such that

$$f(x_3) = \begin{cases} +c, & x_3 \geq a_2 \\ 0, & |x_3| \leq a_1 \\ -c, & x_3 \leq -a_2 \end{cases}$$

and $f(x_3)$ varies smoothly in the ranges $a_1 < x_3 < a_2$ and $-a_2 < x_3 < -a_1$.

a) Find the equilibrium state(s) of the system.
b) If $\gamma > 0$, establish the stability of the system relative to the equilibrium state(s) by means of a Lyapunov function

$$V(\mathbf{x}) = \frac{\gamma - 1}{2}x_1^2 + \frac{\gamma}{2}x_2^2 + \int_0^{x_3} f(x_3)\,dx_3$$

c) Draw the system diagram in a form such that describing functions can be applied. What can be concluded on applying the method?

9-7 (The Lur'e Resolvant Equations for "Direct" Control Systems). Consider a system of the form of Fig. 9-5. Assume that $G(p)$ possesses only real, distinct, and negative eigenvalues and that $f(e)$ is of the form of Eq. (9-17).

a) Show that the system equation can be written in the form

$$\dot{\mathbf{x}} = \mathbf{\Lambda}\,\mathbf{x} + \mathbf{b}\,f(e), \qquad e = \mathbf{c}^T\mathbf{x}, \qquad \frac{de}{dt} = \mathbf{d}^T\mathbf{x}$$

where Λ is the diagonal matrix of the eigenvalues, b is a column vector with unity at every position, c is some constant column vector, and $\mathbf{d} = \mathbf{\Lambda}\ \mathbf{c}$.

b) Show that, for the arbitrary real constants $k_1, \ldots, k_n$, the matrix G with the i, jth element given by $G_{ij} = -k_ik_j\,(\lambda_i + \lambda_j)$ is p.d. if $\lambda_j < 0$ for all j. Hint: Show that $\mathbf{x}^T G\mathbf{x}$ for any vector x can be written as

$$\int_0^{\infty} \left(\mathbf{x}^T\mathbf{w}(t)\right)^2 dt$$

where $\mathbf{w}(t)$ is the n-dimensional column vector whose ith component is $k_i\,\exp(\lambda_1 t)$.

c) In view of (b), consider a Lyapunov function of the form

$$V = \left(\frac{1}{2}\right)\mathbf{x}^T\mathbf{M}\mathbf{x} + \mathbf{x}^T\mathbf{G}\mathbf{x} + \int_0^e f(z)\,dz$$

where $\mathbf{M} = \text{diag}(m_1 \ldots m_n)$ with $m_i > 0$ for all i. Show that a sufficient condition for absolute stability of the origin is that there exist constants k_i, m_i such that the Lur'e resolvant equations

$$\sum_{j=1}^{n} \frac{2k_ik_j}{\lambda_i + \lambda_j} = d_i + m_i$$

are satisfied for all i.

d) Discuss the consequence of setting $m_i = 0$, $i = 1, \ldots, n$.

e) Apply the above to a system of the form of Fig. 9-5 where $G(p) = (p +)/[(p+2)(p+3)(p+5)]$ and find the Lur'e resolvant equations. Comment on the ease of solution.

9-8 (The Lur'e resolvant equations for "Indirect" control systems). For an "indirect" control system of Fig. 9-6b, assume that $G(p)$ possesses only real, distinct, and negative eigenvalues and $f(e)$ is of the form of Eq. (9-17).

a) Show that the system equations can be written in the form:

$$\dot{\mathbf{x}} = \mathbf{\Lambda}\mathbf{x} + \mathbf{b}\,f(e), \qquad e = \mathbf{c}^T\mathbf{x}, \qquad \frac{de}{dt} = \mathbf{d}^T\mathbf{x} - hf(e)$$

(The symbols have the same meaning as in Exercise 9-7.)

b) Again use a Lyapunov function

$$V = \frac{1}{2}\mathbf{x}^T\mathbf{M}\mathbf{x} + \mathbf{x}^T\mathbf{G}\mathbf{x} + \int_0^e f(z)\,dz$$

to show that the Lur'e resolvant equations now become

$$\sum_{j=1}^{n} \frac{2k_i k_j}{\lambda_i + \lambda_j} - 2k_i,\ h = d_i + m_i\ (i = 1, \ldots, n).$$

c) Discuss the consequence of setting $m_i = 0$, $i = 1, \ldots, n$.
d) Find the resolvant equations for the system treated in Example 9-11.

9-9 Determine whether each of the following time-varying scalar functions is p.d. Use $n = 2$ for all of the examples. For those which are p.d., determine which one(s) can be dominated by a scalar function $\rho\|\mathbf{x}\|$ in accordance with Eq. (9-31). Find that function.

a) $V(\mathbf{x}, t) = x_1^2 + \dfrac{x_2^2}{t}$

b) $V(\mathbf{x}, t) = x_1^2 + tx_2^2$

c) $V(\mathbf{x}, t) = x_1^2 + (1 + \cos^2 t)\, x_2^2$

9-10 Some systems with parametric excitation can be approximated by a Mathieu equation with a damping term: $\ddot{x} + 2\dot{x} + (a - b\cos\omega t)x = 0$. Suppose $a > b > 0$; by means of a V function of the form of (9-45) find a relationship among a, b, and ω so as to guarantee asymptotic stability.

9-11 The small angle roll—yaw motion of a gravitationally stabilized satellite that is symmetrical about the yaw axis can be expressed as (see Exercise 2-12)

$$\ddot{\theta}_1 + k_1\theta_1 + k_2\dot{\theta}_3 = u_1$$

$$\ddot{\theta}_2 - k_3\dot{\theta}_1 = u_2$$

where θ_1 and θ_2 are the roll and yaw angles of the satellite, respectively; k_1, k_2 and k_3 are the parameters of the system; and u_1 and u_2 are the normalized control torques about the roll and yaw axis respectively.

a) For some missions, the roll motion alone is to be controlled. Using a suitable Lyapunov function, obtain a class of nonlinear feedback controls $u_1(\theta_1, \theta_2)$ and $u_2(\theta_1, \theta_2)$ that will cause $\theta_1(t)$ to go to 0.

b) Can one of the control torques T_1 or T_2 be eliminated without affecting the goal of control?

9-12 Show that Theorem 9-6 implies that inside $\mathcal{R}_k$, the function $V(\mathbf{x})$ does not have a maximum point.

9-13 Prove proposition (1) of Sec. 9.4 (page 335). (Hint: consider an $\mathbf{A}$ matrix in the Jordan canonical form.)

9-14 Prove proposition (2) of Sec. 9.4 (page 335). (Hint: try

$$\mathbf{Q} = \int_{-\infty}^{0} \mathbf{\Psi}^T(t)\,\mathbf{C}\,\mathbf{\Psi}(t)\,dt$$

where the matrix $\mathbf{\Psi}(t)$ satisfies $\dot{\mathbf{\Psi}} = -\mathbf{\Psi}\,\mathbf{A}$, $\mathbf{\Psi}(0) = \mathbf{I}$. Show that $\mathbf{Q}$ is symmetric if $\mathbf{C}$ is symmetric and, moreover, that $\mathbf{Q}$ satisfies Eq. (9-16).)

9-15 Show physically and mathematically that the following is untrue: "For the system (9-4), if a continuous function $V_1(\mathbf{x})$ with continuous first partial derivatives can be found in a neighborhood $\mathcal{R}$ of the origin such that $V_1(\mathbf{x})$ is p.d. and $\dot{V}_1$ is not n.d. or negative semidefinite arbitrarily near the origin, then the origin is unstable."

9-16 Show that the system shown in Fig. 9-6a is equivalent to that shown in Fig. 9-6b as far as stability is concerned provided that $h + \mathbf{c}^T\mathbf{A}^{-1}\mathbf{b} \neq 0$.

9.10 References

Lyapunov's second method was given in his 1892 treatise [L18]. A clear and highly readable exposition of the method is found in [L6], which is particularly commendable for pinpointing the basic ideas without relying on overbearing methematical symbolism and jargon.

Well-written surveys of the scope of applicability of the method are found in [H2] and [K8]. The latter in particular is addressed to the control engineer, as is the more recent work [L8], which has a large number of examples.

The problem of Lur'e (as well as the more recent problem of Popov, to be discussed in Chap. 10) is considered in [L6] and [H2], as well as in [A1] and [L10]. The problem of Lur'e, except for a few misprints, is also well treated in the textbook [G3].

A relatively significant area that is not covered in this chapter is that of generation of Lyapunov functions. This area is left out because, first, for large systems all the techniques are laborious and, second, they are limited by our inability to determine the sign definiteness of complex functions. These techniques are, however, useful for low-order, highly nonlinear systems. An excellent survey paper, including many examples, can be found in [S9].

10

Exact Frequency Domain Stability Criteria—Popov's Method and Its Extensions

We now return to consider systems in the standard form of Fig. 10-1 (or Fig. 6-5). This class of systems could be treated by the approximate methods of describing function and dual-input describing function. In Chap. 9 we have further shown that exact stability information could sometimes be obtained with this class of systems through the approach of Lur'e. The latter approach, however, becomes rather difficult, especially for high-order plants. It ceases to be useful when the plant is one with distributed parameters and delays.

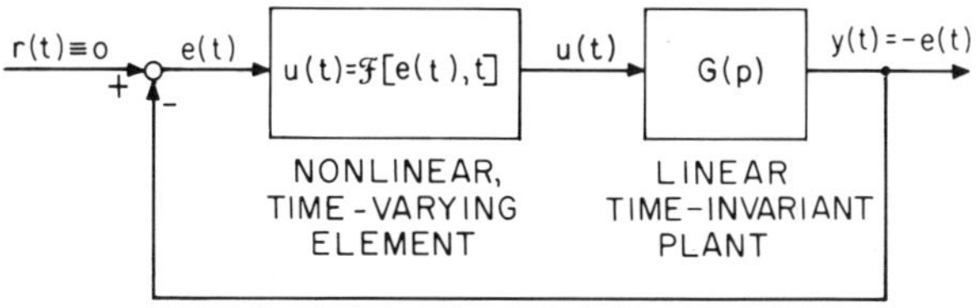

Fig. 10-1. The basic feedback control system to be considered in Chap. 10.

A departure from the use of Lyapunov's second method was introduced in 1959 by V. M. Popov, who obtained a *frequency domain criterion* as a sufficient condition for asymptotic stability of a single-loop control system in the standard form with a time-invariant linear plant and a single-valued nonlinearity. Popov's stability criterion is presented in terms of inequality constraints on the nonlinear element and the gain-phase locus (Nyquist plot) of the linear element.

Being an exact frequency domain approach, Popov's criterion is readily applied to systems of high order as well as those featuring plants with distributed parameters or delays. Once the frequency response of the linear element is known, then little calculation is required to determine the absolute stability* of the system for a certain class of nonlinear elements.

The original results of Popov have since been extended to more general types of systems, including those with nonlinear elements that contain certain types of hysteresis as well as time-varying nonlinearities.

In this chapter, we shall present a unified theory that will allow us to derive most of the presently available frequency-response criteria of the Popov type. The requirements on the system parameters will be made as unrestricted as possible in order to make the theory applicable to the widest possible class of applications. Emphasis will be placed on the relationship between the various criteria and their common origin.

The trade-off between the restrictions on the class of nonlinear functions and those on the linear element will be stressed. We will find that the method of Popov provides an easy vehicle to obtain this trade-off, which is of obvious importance to system design.

Furthermore, in our approach to the problem, the least restrictive practical stability definition is used. All that is essentially required is that the control signal or the output signal ultimately go to zero. This gives rise to the stability concepts of "control asymptoticity" and "output asymptoticity," which are introduced in Sec. 10.2. From these properties, an engineer knowing the physical structure of his system can, if needed, easily deduce other stability properties of his system. In addition we will present a theorem by which we can deduce absolute stability from control asymptoticity of a system, provided that certain conditions are satisfied.

The main results of this chapter can be given in terms of a single fundamental theorem which, in turn, will be used in the derivation of all other stability criteria. These criteria can be applied to lumped-parameter systems with or without transportation lag and to certain distributed-parameter systems. We will show that the methods can be readily used not only for stability investigation but also for establishing the degree of stability, or damping, of a system. Finally, we will present some practical ways to make use of the stability and damping criteria, including the use of logarithmic gain/phase charts.

*See Definition 9-1.

The results of this chapter will be basic to certain topics to be discussed in the next chapter, where the present methods are extended to the determination of stability and uniqueness of forced solutions.

For the proof of the several theorems in this chapter, some basic tools from mathematical analysis are used, including the Parseval theorem and the inequalities due to Schwarz and Minkowski. In addition, by casting the basic system equations in an integral equation form, disciplines from functional analysis are applied. In this chapter we relegate the mathematics to the background (and to Appendix C) in order to emphasize the results. In the next chapter the underlying mathematical ideas receive more stress.

10.1 The Basic Feedback System and Its Assumed Properties

The basic feedback system considered is the same as that in Fig. 10-1. It consists of a nonlinear element and a linear, time-invariant plant. Many systems with a single nonlinearity can be reduced to this basic form. The stability study of this system gives rise to the generalized Lur'e problem;* generalized in the sense that the nonlinear element may also be time-varying and/or contain hysteresis of a certain type. Moreover, the linear element may contain transportation lag or may be of the distributed parameter type. Due to the generality involved, the system equations are best given in the integral form (see Sec. 3.9)

$$e(t) = e_0(t) - \int_0^t g(t - \tau)\, u(\tau)\, d\tau \tag{10-1a}$$

$$u(t) = \mathcal{F}[e(t), t] \tag{10-1b}$$

where $g(t) = \mathcal{L}^{-1}[G(s)]$ and $-e_0(t)$ are the unit-impulse response and the initial-condition response respectively of the linear element (see below), and $-e(t)$ represents the output of the system.

The restrictions on the nonlinear element and the linear plant will now be discussed.

1. The Nonlinear Element

The functional relationship between input and output of the nonlinear element is represented by (10-1b). Special cases are listed in Table 10-1. The only condition on the nonlinear element that

*See Sec. 9.5.

shall hold throughout this chapter is that the output vs. input characteristic is restricted to lie within a sector bounded by two straight lines that pass through the origin (see figure below Table 10-1). In other words we shall require that

$$a \leq \frac{u(t)}{e(t)} \leq b \tag{10-2a}$$

for all t, where $a < b \leq \infty$.* Other possible conditions that might be required are

$$a < \frac{u(t)}{e(t)} < b \tag{10-2b}$$

$$a \leq \frac{u(t)}{e(t)} < b \tag{10-2c}$$

$$a < \frac{u(t)}{e(t)} \leq b \tag{10-2d}$$

♦♦Definition 10-1. If condition (10-2a) holds, then we say $(u/e) \in [a, b]$. If condition (10-2b), (10-2c), or (10-2d) holds, then we say $(u/e) \in (a, b)$, $(u/e) \in [a, b)$, and $(u/e) \in (a, b]$ respectively.**♦♦

If b is finite, then by (10-2) $|u(t)|$ is bounded for every finite $|e(t)|$. To ensure that this also holds for $(u/e) \in [a, \infty]$, we impose the further requirement that for all t and for every value e_m, there is a finite value u_m such that

$$|u(t)| \leq u_m < \infty \quad \text{if} \quad |e(t)| \leq e_m \tag{10-3}$$

Condition (10-3) holds for virtually all practical nonlinear functions $u(t) = \mathfrak{F}(e, t)$ with $(u/e) \in [a, \infty]$. For example, for the ideal relay $u = \operatorname{sgn} e$, we have $(u/e) \in [0, \infty]$ and $u_m = 1$ for any value e_m. For the cubic nonlinearity $u = e^3$, we have $(u/e) \in [0, \infty]$ and $u_m = {e_m}^3$.

As in Chap. 6, we will again classify the time-invariant hysteresis characteristics into active and passive types. To be precise, we shall define them as follows:

♦♦Definition 10-2. A time-invariant hysteresis characteristic $u = \mathfrak{F}[e(t)]$ can be defined in terms of line integrals. The nonlinearity is said to contain *passive hysteresis*, if

*We recall that (10-2a) represents the same type of restrictions needed for the Aizerman conjecture.

**The symbol ϵ means "belongs to," viz., $c \in C$ means c belongs to the set C. The symbol $[a, b]$ means "the *closed* interval between a and b," i.e., the interval $a \leq (u/e) \leq b$. We also use the symbol (a, b) to mean "the *open* interval between a and b" or $a < (u/e) < b$. In like manner, we define $(a, b]$ and $[a, b)$ as "*semi-open* intervals" to represent the intervals $a < (u/e) \leq b$ and $a \leq (u/e) < b$ respectively.

Table 10-1

The Nonlinear Element

General case: $u(t) = \mathfrak{F}[e(t), t]$

Special cases:

$u(t) = f(e(t))$	(single-valued, time-invariant)
$u(t) = f(e(t), t)$	(single-valued, time-varying)
$u(t) = \mathfrak{F}[e(t)]$	(hysteresis, time-invariant)
$u(t) = k(t)e(t)$	(linear, time-varying)
$u(t) = he(t)$	(linear, time-invariant)

Conditions imposed are given by Eqs. (10-2) and (10-3) and are shown in the figure below.

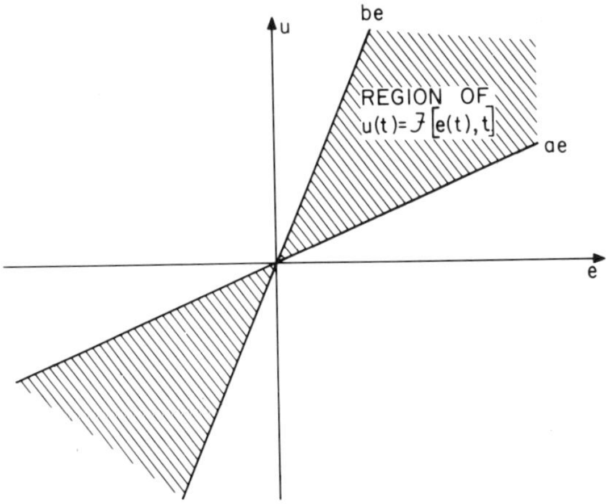

$$-\int_{\Gamma\,e_1}^{e_2} ude \geq -\int_{\Gamma_{12}\,e_1}^{e_2} ude = \int_{\Gamma_1\,0}^{e_1} ude - \int_{\Gamma_1+\Gamma_{12}\,0}^{e_2} ude \qquad (10\text{–}4a)$$

holds for every pair of numbers e_1, e_2, where Γ represents the path in the (u, e) characteristic due to any possible history $e(t)$ and where Γ_1 and Γ_{12} represent any given *single* path (not a closed path) on the characteristic between 0 and e_1 and between e_1 and e_2 respectively. A nonlinearity is said to contain *active hysteresis* if

$$-\int_{e_1\,\Gamma}^{e_2} u\,de \le -\int_{e_1\,\Gamma_{12}}^{e_2} u\,de = \int_{0\,\Gamma_1}^{e_1} u\,de - \int_{0\,\Gamma_1+\Gamma_{12}}^{e_2} u\,de \qquad \text{(10-4b)}$$

holds for every pair of numbers e_1, e_2.◆◆

Examples for these two types of hysteresis characteristics are illustrated in Fig. 10-2. The passive type is, of course, the one that is usually of practical importance. However, a system containing passive hysteresis can be transformed into another one containing active hysteresis. One such example is illustrated in Fig. 10-2b which was obtained from Fig. 10-2a by the transformation $u' = ke - u$. (Show this.) We will be making use of such a transformation in the proof of the stability theorems to be presented in the sequel.

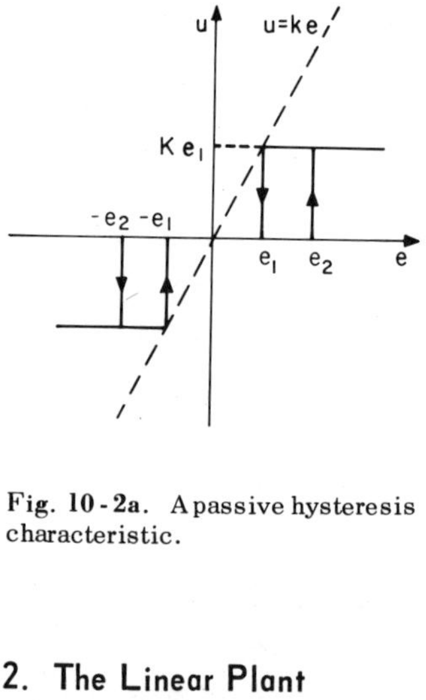

Fig. 10-2a. A passive hysteresis characteristic.

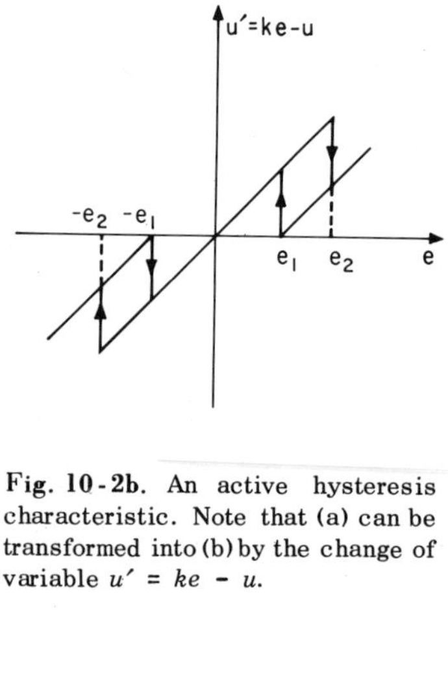

Fig. 10-2b. An active hysteresis characteristic. Note that (a) can be transformed into (b) by the change of variable $u' = ke - u$.

2. The Linear Plant

The time-invariant linear plant will be described in terms of its input-output relation which is presented in (10-1a) and is defined in terms of its unit-impulse response, $g(t) = \mathcal{L}^{-1}[G(s)]$, and its initial-condition response for a given set of initial conditions, $-e_0(t)$.

◆◆Example 10-1. Consider the special case of a time-invariant linear differential system,

$$\dot{\mathbf{x}}(t) = \mathbf{A}\mathbf{x}(t) + \mathbf{b}u(t), \qquad -e(t) = \mathbf{c}^T\mathbf{x}(t) \qquad \text{(10-5)}$$

If as in Chap. 3, we define

$$\Phi(t) = \mathcal{L}^{-1}[(Is - A)^{-1}] = \Phi(t, 0) \tag{10-6}$$

as the transition matrix. The output of the linear element, according to (10-5), is $-e(t) = c^T x(t)$; thus we have

$$e(t) = -c^T\Phi(t)x(0) - \int_0^t c^T\Phi(t-\tau)bu(\tau)\,d\tau \tag{10-7}$$

Comparing (10-1a) with (10-7), we see that

$$-e_0(t) = c^T\Phi(t)x(0) = \mathcal{L}^{-1}[c^T(Is - A)^{-1}x(0)] \tag{10-8a}$$

$$g(t) = c^T\Phi(t)b = \mathcal{L}^{-1}[c^T(Is - A)^{-1}b] \tag{10-8b}$$ ♦♦

Equations (10-8) indicate an important property of a time-invariant linear element; namely, the initial condition response $-e_0(t)$ for any given set of initial conditions has the same form as the unit-impulse response $g(t)$.

The only condition that we shall impose on the linear element in this chapter is that it be output stable of degree α for some value α. Basically, this means that for $\alpha > 0$ the system *output*, in response to either an impulse or to an initial condition, will be in such a form that it eventually tends to 0 faster than the function $e^{-\alpha t}$. For $\alpha < 0$, the term output stable of degree α means that the output in response to an impulse or an initial condition may diverge, but the output multiplied by $e^{\alpha t}$ ultimately tends to 0.* The specific mode of tending to 0 is in the absolute integrable and square integrable sense as defined below:

♦♦Definition 10-3. The linear element is *output stable of degree* α if there exists a real number α such that *for every set of initial conditions* the unit-impulse response $g(t)$ and the initial condition response $-e_0(t)$ satisfy the relations:

$$\int_0^\infty [e^{\alpha t}g(t)]^2\,dt < \infty, \qquad \int_0^\infty e^{\alpha t}|g(t)|\,dt < \infty$$

$$\int_0^\infty [e^{\alpha t}e_0(t)]^2\,dt < \infty, \qquad \int_0^\infty [e^{\alpha t}\dot{e}_0(t)]^2\,dt < \infty \tag{10-9}$$ **

$$|e^{\alpha t}e_0(t)| < \infty, \qquad 0 \le t \le \infty$$

*See, however, Example 10-2 below.

**Conditions (10-9) imply that tne functions $e^{\alpha t}g(t)$, $e^{\alpha t}e_0(t)$, and $e^{\alpha t}\dot{e}_0(t)$ belong to the class of all square-integrable functions commonly denoted by the class $\mathcal{L}_2$. Thus, we can write $e^{\alpha t}g(t) \in \mathcal{L}_2$, $e^{\alpha t}e_0(t) \in \mathcal{L}_2$, and $e^{\alpha t}\dot{e}_0(t) \in \mathcal{L}_2$ for every set of initial conditions. Furthermore, $e^{\alpha t}g(t)$ also belongs to the class of all absolutely integrable functions, denoted by $\mathcal{L}_1$. (See Appendix C.)

Furthermore, if $\alpha = 0$, then we say that the linear element is *output stable*. ♦♦

We remark that a linear element will be output stable of degree α if its transfer function $G(s)$ and initial-condition response function $E_0(s)$ are rational functions of s, the poles of which all lie in $\Re e\, s < -\alpha$. Thus, α represents the degree of damping of the linear element.

10.2 The Concepts of Control Asymptoticity and Output Asymptoticity

The usual stability definitions, such as those used in Chap. 9, are given in terms of the asymptotic behavior of all the state variables. Global asymptotic Lyapunov stability of Chaps. 5 and 9 not only requires that all state variables approach 0 asymptotically, but also places certain boundedness requirements on their dynamic behavior. These requirements frequently are too restrictive in a practical sense. In engineering practice, we are not necessarily interested in the dynamic behavior of all the state variables except for the effect of their initial conditions on the behavior of the output. (Indeed, if required, the behavior of the other state variables can be ascertained from the structure of the system and the asymptotic behavior of the control or the output signal.)

For this chapter we shall concern ourselves mainly with the asymptotic behaviors of the control and output variables of the linear element. With this in mind, we shall introduce the following stability definition for the basic feedback system of Fig. 10-1 or Eqs. (10-1):

♦♦Definition 10-4. (Control Asymptoticity and Output Asymptoticity).* The basic feedback system of Eq. (10-1) will be called:

(i) *Control asymptotic of degree* α if there exists a real α such that for every set of initial conditions

$$\int_0^\infty [e^{\alpha t}u(t)]^2 dt < \infty \tag{10-10}$$

(ii) *Output asymptotic of degree* α if there exists a real α such that for every set of initial conditions

$$\int_0^\infty [e^{\alpha t}e(t)]^2 dt < \infty \tag{10-11}$$

*The concepts of control and output asymptoticity are similar to the concept of $\mathcal{L}_2$ stability. See [S2].

(iii) *Absolutely control asymptotic of degree* α *for* $(u/e) \in [a, b]$ *(absolutely output asymptotic of degree* α *for* $(u/e) \in [a, b]$*)* if condition (10–10) (condition 10–11) holds for every nonlinear element satisfying (10–2a). We may also use the open or semi-open intervals $(u/e) \in (a, b)$, $(u/e) \in (a, b]$, or $(u/e) \in [a, b)$ as defined in Definition 10–1.

(iv) *Control asymptotic, output asymptotic, or absolutely control asymptotic for* $(u/e) \in [a, b]$ *(absolute output asymptotic for* $(u/e) \in [a, b]$*)* if $\alpha = 0$ in (i), (ii), and (iii) above, respectively.♦♦

The physical meaning of the above definitions will become clear from the following lemma:

♦♦Lemma 10-1. For the basic feedback system (10–1), if the linear element is output stable of degree α and the nonlinear element satisfies condition (10–3), then, if the system is control asymptotic of degree α, it is implied that

$$\lim_{t \to \infty} e^{\alpha t} e(t) = 0 \tag{10–12}$$♦♦

Thus if Lemma 10–1 is satisfied, $e(t)$ ultimately tends to 0 faster than $e^{-\alpha t}$ if $\alpha > 0$. Although Lemma 10–1 appears almost obvious, its formal proof, given in Appendix C, contains certain subtleties. The subleties arise if $e^{\alpha t}e(t)$, for example, should become nonzero during a countably infinite number of intervals of diminishing size. In this case $e^{\alpha t}e(t)$ can be square integrable without satisfying the requirement $\lim_{t \to \infty} e^{\alpha t}e(t) \to 0$.

♦♦Example 10-2. If

$$e^{\alpha t}e(t) = \begin{cases} a, & t_k \le t \le t_k + \left(\dfrac{1}{2}\right)^k, \quad k = 0, 1, 2, \ldots \\ 0, & \text{elsewhere} \end{cases}$$

then

$$\int_0^\infty [e^{\alpha t}e(t)]^2 dt = a^2 \sum_{k=0}^{\infty} \left(\frac{1}{2}\right)^k = 2a^2 < \infty$$

but it cannot be said that $e^{\alpha t}e(t)$ converges to 0.♦♦

The above situation is however rather pathological and Lemma 10–1 holds that we will not encounter it in a system of the form of (10–1).

The properties of control asymptoticity and output asymptoticity can be related to each other by the properties of the linear element. The following lemma holds:

♦♦Lemma 10-2. Let the linear element be output stable of degree α. If the basic feedback system (10–1) is control asymptotic of degree

α, then it is also output asymptotic of degree α. Moreover, if for each set of initial conditions there exists a number M_0 such that $|e_0(t)| \leq M_0 e^{-\alpha t}$, then there exists a number M depending on M_0 such that $|e(t)| \leq Me^{-\alpha t}$ for all t.*◆◆

This lemma seems reasonable, since a (decaying) control signal $u(t)$ satisfying (10-10), when fed into a linear element whose unit-impulse response is decaying in the same manner as $u(t)$, will result in an output $-e(t)$ that will decay likewise. Before proceeding with the proof, let us note that, in general, a feedback system that is control asymptotic is not necessarily output asymptotic.

◆◆Example 10-3. Consider a basic feedback system (10-1) with

$$g(t) = 1 - e^{-t} = \mathfrak{L}^{-1}[1/s(s+1)], \qquad e_0(t) = x_{10} + x_{20}e^{-t}$$

where (x_{10}, x_{20}) represents the set of initial conditions and $f(e)$ is the relay with dead zone:

$$u = f(e) = \begin{cases} 1, & e > 2 \\ 0, & |e| \leq 2 \\ -1, & e < -2 \end{cases} \tag{10-13}$$

It can be shown that this system is control asymptotic and that $u(t) \to 0$ for $t \to \infty$.** The linear element is output stable of degree $\alpha < 0$. Therefore, the conditions of Lemma 10-2 are not fulfilled. Indeed, this system is not output asymptotic. This is so, because, due to the dead zone in the nonlinear element and the integrator in the linear element, the output signal $-e(t)$ can have any steady-state value lying in the equilibrium zone $-2 \leq e(\infty) \leq 2$, depending on the set of initial conditions.◆◆

Proof of Lemma 10-2. First we shall consider the case $\alpha = 0$. From (10-1a), we can write

$$|e(t)| \leq |e_0(t)| + \left| \int_0^t g(t-\tau)\,u(\tau)\,d\tau \right| \tag{10-14}$$

Because of (10-9) and (10-10) for $\alpha = 0$, we can use Parseval's relation*** on the convolution integral in (10-14)

*The property $|e_0(t)| \leq M_0 e^{-\alpha t}$ is satisfied, for example, in all linear elements governed by ordinary differential equations whose eigenvalues all have negative real parts. See Exercise 10-7.

**The asymptotic behavior of this system could of course be investigated by the state-plane methods of Chap. 4. See Exercise 4-17.

***See Appendix C.

$$\int_0^\infty \left(\int_0^t g(t-\tau)\,u(\tau)\,d\tau\right)^2 dt = \frac{1}{2\pi}\int_{-\infty}^{\infty} |G(j\omega)|^2\,|U(j\omega)|^2\,d\omega \quad (10\text{-}15)$$

But because of (10-9), we also have

$$|G(j\omega)| \le \int_0^\infty |g(t)|\,dt < \infty \quad (10\text{-}16)$$

Making use of (10-15), (10-16), and Minkowski's inequality,* we obtain from (10-14)

$$\left(\int_0^\infty e^2(t)\,dt\right)^{\frac{1}{2}} \le \left(\int_0^\infty e_0^2(t)\,dt\right)^{\frac{1}{2}} + \left(\frac{1}{2\pi}\int_{-\infty}^{\infty} |G(j\omega)|^2|U(j\omega)|^2\,d\omega\right)^{\frac{1}{2}}$$

$$\le \left(\int_0^\infty e_0^2(t)\,dt\right)^{\frac{1}{2}} + \left(\int_0^\infty |g(t)|\,dt\right)\left(\int_0^\infty u^2(t)\,dt\right)^{\frac{1}{2}} < \infty \quad (10\text{-}17)$$

By (10-9) and (10-10), all expressions on the rhs of (10-17) are finite; thus (10-11) is satisfied for $\alpha = 0$ and the lemma is proved for $\alpha = 0$. To show that the lemma is satisfied for any α, we can simply set

$$\begin{aligned} g_\alpha(t) &\triangleq e^{\alpha t}g(t), & e_{0\alpha}(t) &\triangleq e^{\alpha t}e_0(t) \\ u_\alpha(t) &\triangleq e^{\alpha t}u(t), & e_\alpha(t) &\triangleq e^{\alpha t}e(t) \end{aligned} \quad (10\text{-}18)$$

Using these expressions in (10-14) yields

$$|e_\alpha(t)| \le |e_{0\alpha}(t)| + \left|\int_0^t g_\alpha(t-\tau)\,u_\alpha(\tau)\,d\tau\right|$$

Since all expressions in the above inequality satisfy (10-9) and (10-10) for $\alpha = 0$, we merely need to repeat the steps of (10-15) through (10-17) to obtain the necessary proof.

If in addition to output stability of degree α, the linear element satisfies $|e_0(t)| \le M_0 \exp(-\alpha t)$, where M_0 depends on the set of initial conditions, then we can write (10-14) as

$$|e(t)| \le M_0 e^{-\alpha t} + e^{-\alpha t}\left|\int_0^t e^{\alpha(t-\tau)}\,g(t-\tau)\,e^{\alpha\tau}u(\tau)\,d\tau\right|$$

*See Appendix C.

In the above expression, the integrand was multiplied and divided by $\exp(-\alpha(t - \tau))$. Upon using Schwarz' inequality (see Appendix C) we obtain

$$|e(t)| \leq \left[M_0 + \left(\int_0^t e^{2\alpha\tau} g^2(\tau)\, d\tau \right)^{\frac{1}{2}} \left(\int_0^t e^{2\alpha\tau} u^2(\tau)\, d\tau \right)^{\frac{1}{2}} \right] e^{-\alpha t} \leq Me^{-\alpha t}$$

where

$$M = M_0 + \left(\int_0^\infty e^{2\alpha t} g^2(t)\, dt \right)^{\frac{1}{2}} \left(\int_0^\infty e^{2\alpha t} u^2(t)\, dt \right)^{\frac{1}{2}} < \infty$$

M is finite, and therefore $e(t)$ is finite because of the conditions of the lemma.

10.3 The Fundamental Theorem and Some Direct Applications

We now state the central theorem of this chapter:

♦♦Theorem 10-1 (The Generalized Theorem of Popov). Consider the basic feedback system of Eq. (10-1) (or Fig. 10-1). Let the linear element be output stable. In order for the system to be both absolutely control and output asymptotic for $(u/e) \in [0, K]$, it is sufficient that a real number q exists such that for all real $\omega \geq 0$ and an arbitrarily small $\delta > 0$, the following condition is observed:

$$\Re\text{e}\, [(1 + j\omega q)\, G(j\omega)] + \frac{1}{K} \geq \delta > 0 \tag{10-19}$$

The restrictions on q and K, depending on the nature of the nonlinear element, are:

1) for $u = f(e)$, *a single-valued, time-invariant element*:

$$\text{if} \quad 0 < K < \infty, \quad \text{then} \quad -\infty < q < \infty$$

$$\text{if} \quad K = \infty, \quad \text{then} \quad 0 \leq q < \infty$$

2) for $u = \mathcal{F}[e(t)]$, *a nonlinearity with passive hysteresis*:

$$0 < K < \infty \quad \text{and} \quad -\infty < q \leq 0$$

3) for $u = \mathcal{F}[e(t)]$, *a nonlinearity with active hysteresis*:

$$0 < K \leq \infty \quad \text{and} \quad 0 \leq q < \infty$$

4) for $u = \mathfrak{F}[e(t), t]$, *a general nonlinearity* (time varying, and possibly with hysteresis):

$$0 < K \leq \infty \quad \text{and} \quad q = 0$$

If in cases (1), (2), or (4) above, $K = \infty$, then (10–3) must be satisfied.* ◆◆

The proof of Theorem 10–1 is given in Appendix C. This theorem is fundamental. In fact, we will show that all other stability problems to be discussed in this chapter can be transformed into a form for which the above theorem applies. The condition (10–19) of this theorem will be called the *Popov condition*.

Note that the theorem offers a trade-off between the requirements on the linear element and those on the nonlinear element. For example, for the most general type of nonlinear element, which may be time varying and/or contain hysteresis, we must take $q = 0$ in condition (10–19). This places certain restrictions on $G(j\omega)$. On the other hand, if the nonlinear element is single-valued and time invariant, then we are allowed to extend the range of $G(j\omega)$ by a suitable choice of a real q in condition (10–19). More examples of such trade-offs will be given below.

Let us now discuss the geometrical interpretation of the theorem in terms of the Nyquist plot of $G(j\omega)$. The simplest case is that for which $q = 0$. Here we have

$$\mathfrak{Re}\, G(j\omega) > -\frac{1}{K} \quad \text{for} \quad q = 0$$

This means that the system is absolutely control asymptotic for $(u/e) \in [0, K_1]$ if the locus $G(j\omega)$ lies to the right of a vertical line passing through the point $-(1/K_1)$ as is illustrated in Fig. 10–3a. According to Theorem 10–1, the case $q = 0$ applies to a nonlinear

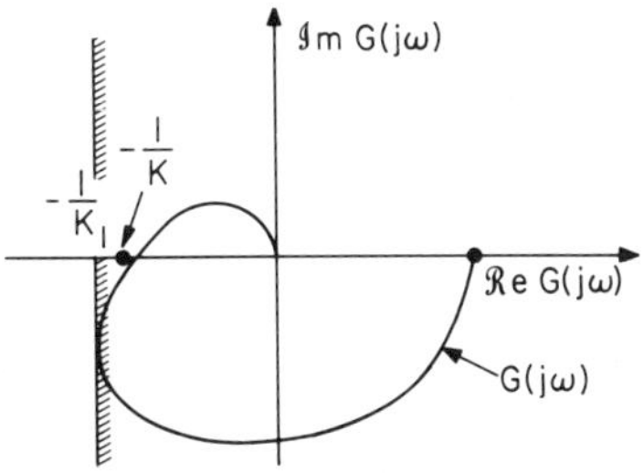

Fig. 10-3a. Illustration of condition (10-19) for $q = 0$. If the locus $G(j\omega)$ lies to the right of the vertical line shown and all other conditions of Theorem 10-1 are satisfied, then the basic feedback system is absolutely control and output asymptotic for $(u/e) \in [0, K_1]$.

*The inclusion of $\delta > 0$ in (10-19) is needed for the proof of Theorem 10-1. For practical purposes, (10-19) can be written as $\mathfrak{Re}[(1 + j\omega q)\, G(j\omega)] + (1/K) > 0$.

element having the least restriction. For this, the greatest restriction must be imposed on the linear element.

In the other extreme, consider a linear time-invariant gain in place of the nonlinear element. Here, from Nyquist's criterion,* the largest permissible gain for feedback system stability must be less than that corresponding to the point where $G(j\omega)$ crosses the negative real axis. This point is indicated by $-(1/K)$ in Fig. 10-3a. Thus, the largest permissible gain must be less than K. This is illustrated in Fig. 10-3b. The permissible sector in the u vs. e plane for a nonlinear relation $u = \mathfrak{F}[e(t), t]$ is called the *Popov sector*, the permissible sector for a linear time-invariant relation $u = he$ is called the *Hurwitz sector*. Since the linear time-invariant gains $u = he$ are members of the class $(u/e) \in [0\ ;K]$ for $0 \le h \le K$ and since for linear time-invariant gains the Hurwitz sector is the largest possible sector to guarantee stability, it is clear that the Hurwitz sector will always be equal or greater than the Popov sector.

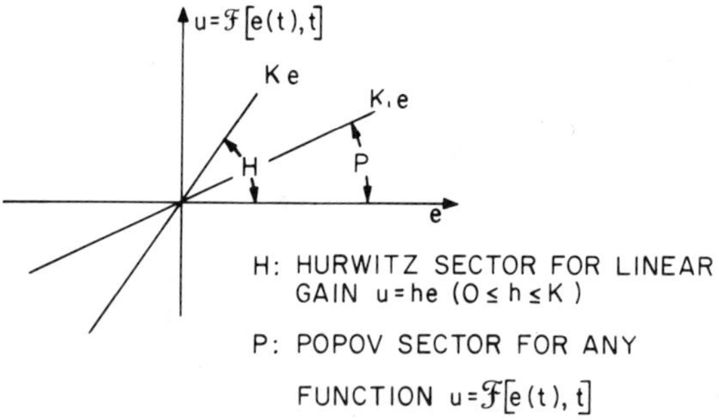

Fig. 10-3b. Permissible (Popov) sector of nonlinear function $u(t) = \mathfrak{F}[e(t), t]$ guaranteeing control and output asymptoticity of the basic feedback system. It is always smaller than or equal to the Hurwitz sector for a linear time-invariant gain $0 \le h = (u/e) \le K$.

This leads us to the more general case of $q \neq 0$. By choosing a suitable value of q, we may be able to extend the permissible stability sector of the nonlinear element to the value of the largest permissible linear gain. However, we pay for this choice of q by having to place other restrictions on the nonlinear element. For example, by the statement of Theorem 10-1, if q is permitted to have any real value, either positive or negative, then the nonlinear function must be single valued and time invariant.

*For the linear element satisfying the conditions of this discussion, its transfer function $G(s)$ will have no singularity in $\Re e\ s \ge 0$; hence, the above interpretation of Nyquist's criterion applies.

Condition (10-19) may also be written as

$$\mathcal{R}e\ G(j\omega) > -\frac{1}{K} + \omega q\ \mathcal{I}m\ G(j\omega) \qquad (10\text{-}20)$$

which means that for each frequency ω, the Nyquist plot of $G(j\omega)$ must lie to the right of a straight line defined by

$$\mathcal{R}e\ G(j\omega) = -\frac{1}{K} + \omega q\ \mathcal{I}m\ G(j\omega)$$

This line is known as the *Popov line* and is illustrated in Fig. 10-4a. The slope of this line depends on the product ωq as shown. Its evolution with increasing frequency is illustrated in Fig. 10-4b. The value of q must be chosen such that for each frequency ω, the phasor $G(j\omega)$ lies to the right of the Popov line at that particular frequency. To facilitate the finding of this q, the following simple transformation may be used [A1]: Let us define the *modified frequency response function* of the linear element with transfer function $G(s)$ as:

$$G^{\star}(j\omega) \triangleq \mathcal{R}e\ G(j\omega) + j\omega\ \mathcal{I}m\ G(j\omega) \qquad (10\text{-}21)$$

In other words,

$$\mathcal{R}e\ G^{\star}(j\omega) \triangleq \mathcal{R}e\ G(j\omega), \qquad \mathcal{I}m\ G^{\star}(j\omega) \triangleq \omega\ \mathcal{I}m\ G(j\omega)$$

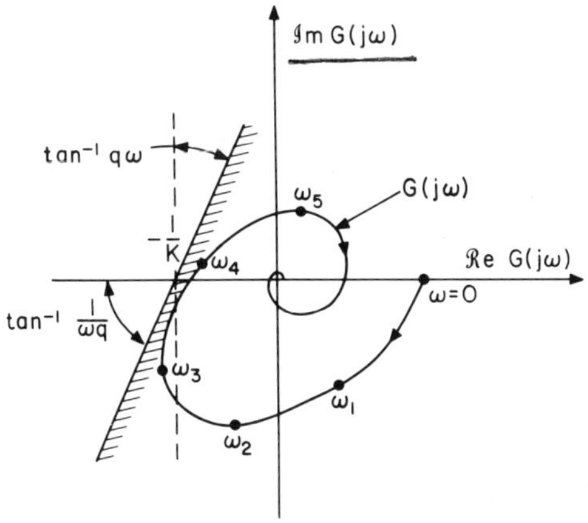

Fig. 10-4a. Illustration of stability condition (10-19) or (10-20). For each frequency ω, the phasor $G(j\omega)$ must lie to the right of a line whose slope depends on the product $q\omega$ as shown. This figure is drawn for $q > 0$.

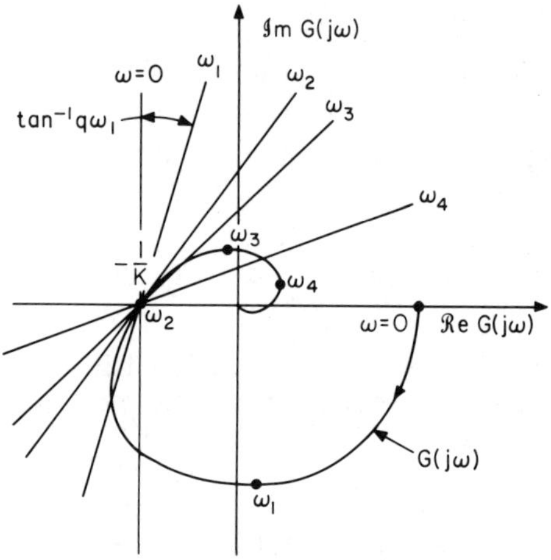

Fig. 10-4b. Evolution of the Popov lines in the $G(j\omega)$ plane for the case $q > 0$.

The locus of $G^\star(j\omega)$ can be obtained simply by multiplying the imaginary part of $G(j\omega)$ by ω for every ω. With (10-21), condition (10-20) becomes

$$\mathscr{R}\text{e } G^\star(j\omega) > -\frac{1}{K} + q\,\mathscr{I}\text{m } G^\star(j\omega) \tag{10-22}$$

which implies that the Popov line in the $G^\star(j\omega)$ plane, defined by

$$\mathscr{R}\text{e } G^\star(j\omega) = -\frac{1}{K} + q\,\mathscr{I}\text{m } G^\star(j\omega)$$

is frequency independent. This is illustrated in Figs. 10-5a and 10-5b.

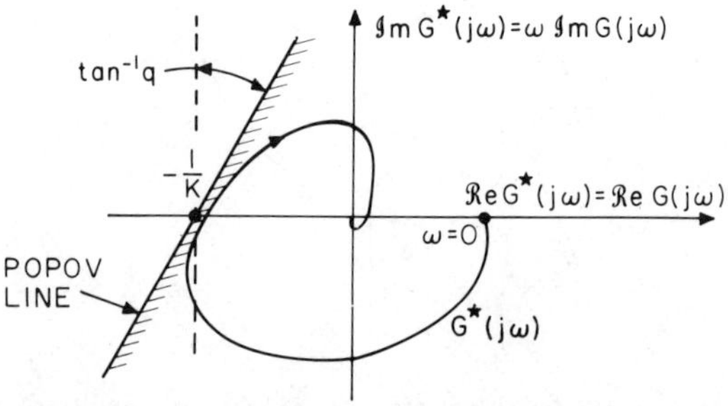

Fig. 10-5a. The Popov line in the $G^\star(j\omega)$ plane, for $q > 0$, applicable to systems with a single-valued nonlinear function or nonlinear functions with active hysteresis.

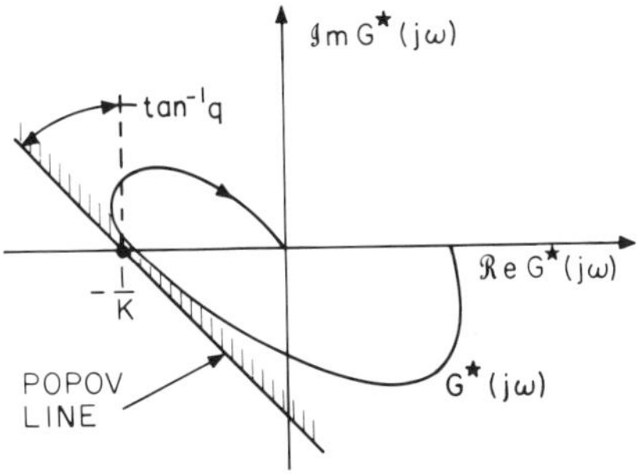

Fig. 10-5b. The Popov line for $q < 0$, applicable to systems with a single-valued nonlinear function or nonlinear functions with passive hysteresis.

From Figs. 10-5 we can make an interesting observation. Suppose that it is possible to draw a tangent line through the point where $G^{\star}(j\omega)$ passes through the negative real axis such that the $G^{\star}(j\omega)$ locus falls completely to the right of it. Let this point be $-(1/K)$. Then, K is not only the maximum permissible gain for a linear function* $f(e) = he$ but also represents the largest possible ratio $f(e)/e$. For such a system the Aizerman conjecture** will hold relative to absolute control and output asymptoticity; that is, if the system (10-1) with linear time-invariant gain $u(t) = he(t)$ is control and output asymptotic for $0 \le h \le K$, then the system with any nonlinear single-valued time-invariant function $u(t) = f(e(t))$ will also be control and output asymptotic as long as $f(0) = 0$ and $0 \le f(e)/e \le K$. We note that *Aizerman's conjecture relative to absolute control and output asymptoticity implies that the Popov sector coincides with the Hurwitz sector.*

In most practical cases, it will indeed be possible to draw the tangent line described above. Thus, though not generally true, Aizerman's conjecture does hold for most practical cases, which is in agreement with our observations in Chap. 5.

Figure 10-6 shows a situation where Aizerman's conjecture may not necessarily hold. Here, $K_1 > K$; that is, the Hurwitz sector is greater than the Popov sector. We note that the Popov sector defines a region that is sufficient, but not necessary, for absolute control and output asymptoticity. Therefore, if $K < f(e)/e < K_1$ for some range of e, then the nonlinear system may still be control and output asymptotic. Thus, whenever $f(e)$ lies outside the Popov

*This follows from Nyquist's criterion.

**See Chap. 5, where Aizerman's conjecture was presented in terms of global asymptotic stability.

sector, no statement about the asymptotic behavior of the system can be made.

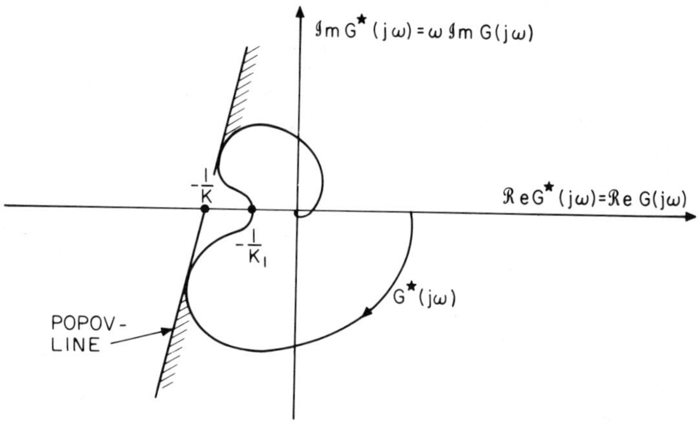

Fig. 10-6. An example where the maximum permissible value for linear time-invariant gain, K_1, is greater than the maximum value K for the ratio $f(e)/e$ satisfying Theorem 10-1. Here, the Popov sector is smaller than the Hurwitz sector. In such a case Aizerman's conjecture may not hold.

♦♦Example 10-4. For the second-order system with transportation lag shown in Fig. 10-7, obtain the largest value of K that guarantees absolute output asymptoticity for $(u/e) \in [0, K]$.

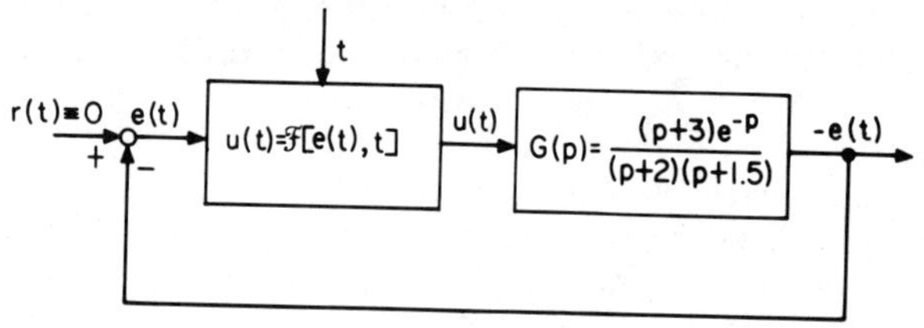

Fig. 10-7. Nonlinear control system with transportation lag considered in Example 10-4.

For the linear element, let the initial-condition response $e_0(t)$ and the unit-impulse response $g(t)$ be given by

$$
\begin{aligned}
e_0(t) &= e_{10}e^{-2t} + e_{20}e^{-1.5t} \\
g(t) &= [3e^{-1.5(t-1)} - 2e^{-2(t-1)}]\mu_{-1}(t-1)
\end{aligned}
\tag{10-23}
$$

where e_{10} and e_{20} represent a set of initial conditions and $\mu_{-1}(t)$ is the unit step function. The linear element is seen to be output stable.

The $G^\star(j\omega)$ locus is shown in Fig. 10-8. From it we can find that

1) For a general nonlinear element $u(t) = \mathcal{F}[e(t), t]$, the Popov condition (with $q = 0$) is satisfied for $0 < K \leq 1.85$.
2) For a single-valued nonlinear element $u = f(e)$ the Popov condition is satisfied (with $q = 0.15$) for $0 < K \leq 1.98$.

Thus the system with a general nonlinear element or a single-valued nonlinear element is absolutely control and output asymptotic for $(u/e) \in [0, 1.85]$ or $(u/e) \in [0, 1.98]$ respectively. This, by Lemma 10-1, implies that $\lim_{t \to \infty} e(t) = 0$ for every set of initial conditions.◆◆

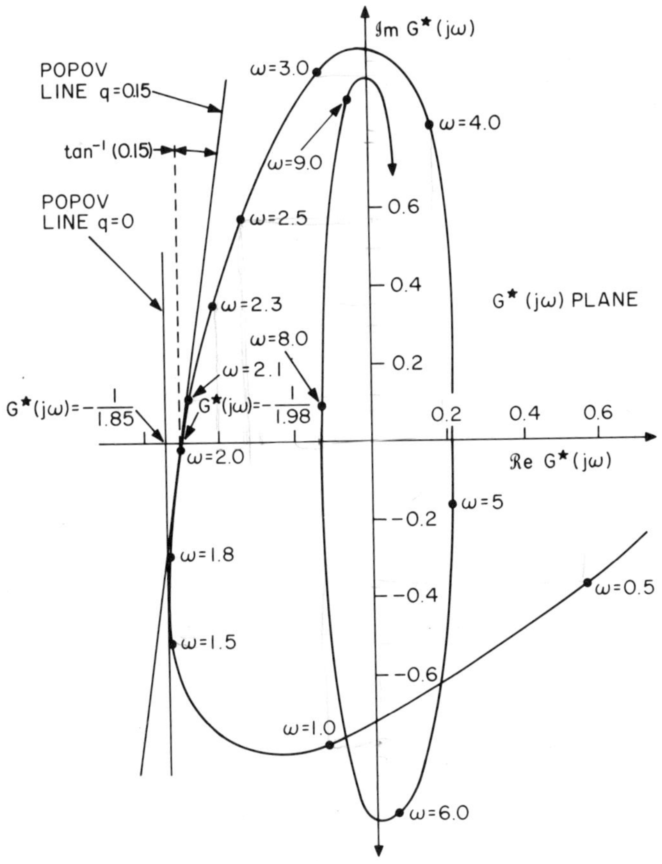

Fig. 10-8. Phasor diagram of $G^\star(j\omega) = \Re e\, G(j\omega) + j\omega\, \Im m\, G(j\omega)$ for the linear element of the system in Fig. 10-7.

10.4 Conditions for Global Asymptotic Stability

Global asymptotic stability in the sense of Lyapunov as given in Chap. 9 deals with the asymptotic behavior of all the state variables of a system and also places certain boundedness requirements on them. It is a relatively restrictive definition. In many cases of practical importance, however, control or output asymptoticity leads directly to global asymptotic stability.

Consider a linear element described by the vector-differential equation (10–5).

$$\begin{aligned} \dot{\mathbf{x}}(t) &= \mathbf{A}\mathbf{x}(t) + \mathbf{b}u(t) \\ e(t) &= -\mathbf{c}^T\mathbf{x}(t), \qquad u(t) = \mathcal{F}[e(t), t] \end{aligned} \tag{10–24}$$

For this system, the following theorem holds:

♦♦Theorem 10-2. For a system (10–24) of order n, let

1) all eigenvalues λ_i $(i = 1, \ldots, n)$ of the system matrix $\mathbf{A}$ have negative real parts,
2) $(u/e) \in [0, K]$ with $0 < K < \infty$, and
3) all requirements of Theorem 10–1 be satisfied and the Popov condition (10–19) be met for $0 \le q < \infty$; then the origin $\mathbf{x} = 0$ will be globally asymptotically stable for every $(u/e) \in [0, K]$.♦♦

The proof of this theorem is presented in Appendix C.

Note that Theorem 10–2 is restricted to the cases where the Popov condition (10–19) is satisfied for $0 \le q < \infty$, which however represents the most important case practically. Theorem 10–2 does not include the cases $-\infty < q < 0$, for which additional requirements must be imposed.

♦♦Example 10-5. Consider a linear element given by

$$\begin{bmatrix} \dot{x}_1 \\ \dot{x}_2 \\ \dot{x}_3 \end{bmatrix} = \begin{bmatrix} 0 & 0 & 0 \\ 1 & -1 & 0 \\ 0 & -2 & -2 \end{bmatrix} \begin{bmatrix} x_1 \\ x_2 \\ x_3 \end{bmatrix} + \begin{bmatrix} 1 \\ 0 \\ 0 \end{bmatrix} u, \qquad e = -[0 \quad 1 \quad 1] \begin{bmatrix} x_1 \\ x_2 \\ x_3 \end{bmatrix}$$

which can be written in the form (10–7), with

$$\mathbf{\Phi}(t) = \begin{bmatrix} 1 & 0 & 0 \\ (1 - e^{-t}) & e^{-t} & 0 \\ (-1 + 2e^{-t} - e^{-2t}) & 2(e^{-2t} - e^{-t}) & e^{-2t} \end{bmatrix}$$

$$b = \begin{bmatrix} 1 \\ 0 \\ 0 \end{bmatrix}, \qquad c^T = [0 \quad 1 \quad 1]$$

The unit-impulse response $g(t)$ and initial-condition response follow also from (10-24) and the above as

$$g(t) = c^T \Phi(t) b = e^{-t} - e^{-2t}$$

$$\begin{aligned} e_0(t) &= -c^T \Phi(t) x(0) \\ &= (e^{-t} - e^{-2t}) x_1(0) + (2e^{-2t} - e^{-t}) x_2(0) + e^{-2t} x_3(0) \end{aligned}$$

Clearly, this element is output stable, since (10-9) can be satisfied. However, one of the eigenvalues of the system matrix is 0; hence the requirements of Theorem 10-2 cannot be satisfied. Therefore, if this element belongs to a feedback system for which we have established control asymptoticity and output asymptoticity, we may not be able to establish global asymptotic stability for this system. In fact, this particular system cannot be globally asymptotically stable because it contains integration followed by differentiation (as the reader may verify). But in many cases, from an application viewpoint, it is the asymptotic behavior of the output rather than global asymptotic stability which is the practical issue. This, of course, depends on each individual problem. ♦♦

10.5 System Damping or Rate of Convergence

A subject of perhaps even greater importance than system stability is the degree of stability or rate of convergence of the system to its equilibrium state after a disturbance. Physically speaking, the rate of convergence constitutes a measure of system damping. We have already presented a definition for the rate of convergence in Definition 10-4, in terms of the degree α of control or output asymptoticity. It turns out that, in the framework of the generalized Popov theorem (Theorem 10-1), system rate of convergence can be handled readily. Indeed, we have already demonstrated this in the proof for Lemma 10-2.

Let us again make the transformations given by (10-18). With this transformation, the original system equations (10-1) become

$$\begin{aligned} e_\alpha(t) &= e_{0\alpha}(t) - \int_0^t g_\alpha(t-\tau) u_\alpha(\tau)\, d\tau \\ u_\alpha(t) &= \mathcal{F}_\alpha[e_\alpha(t), t] \end{aligned} \tag{10-25}$$

where $\qquad \mathcal{F}_\alpha[e_\alpha(t), t] = e^{\alpha t} \mathcal{F}[e^{-\alpha t} e_\alpha(t), t]$

Note further that

$$\frac{u_\alpha(t)}{e_\alpha(t)} = \frac{u(t)}{e(t)} \tag{10-26}$$

Therefore, if $(u/e) \in [a, b]$ then $(u_\alpha/e_\alpha) \in [a, b]$. Thus, we have transformed the original system (10-1) into a new system (10-25) such that:

1) Output stability of degree α of the original linear element of (10-1) implies output stability of the transformed linear element of (10-25) and vice versa.
2) Control (or output) asymptoticity of degree α of the original system (10-1) implies control (or output) asymptoticity of the transformed system (10-25) and vice versa.

The Fourier transform of $g_\alpha(t)$ [see Eq. (10-18)], denoted as $G_\alpha(j\omega)$, can be expressed in terms of $G(j\omega)$, the Fourier transform of $g(t)$, by the following well-known relation

$$G_\alpha(j\omega) = G(j\omega - \alpha) \tag{10-27}$$

Thus, we can state the following theorem:

◆◆Theorem 10-3. All the criteria for control (output) asymptoticity of degree α are identical to those for control (output) asymptoticity except that

1) the requirement of output stability of the linear element must be substituted by that of output stability of degree α, and
2) $G(j\omega)$ must be substituted by $G(j\omega - \alpha)$. ◆◆

For example, the Popov condition (10-19) of Theorem 10-1 for control and output asymptoticity of degree α will be

$$\mathcal{R}\text{e}\ [(1 + j\omega q)\, G(j\omega - \alpha)] + \frac{1}{K} \geq \delta > 0 \tag{10-28}$$

Specific examples will be presented in the sequel.

10.6 The Pole-Shifting Transformation and the Circle Criterion

We will now show how the basic Theorem 10-1 can be used to investigate asymptotic behavior of a much wider class of systems than that for which the theorem was stated. Moreover, we will see how, by the use of simple transformation techniques, we will be able to achieve a "trade-off" between the requirements on the linear element and those on the nonlinear element. Theorem 10-1 already allowed for some amount of such trade-off by virtue of the choice of q, depending on the type of nonlinearity. Considerably more flexibility can be achieved by means of the pole-shifting technique, the zero-shifting technique, or a suitable combination of both. In this section, we consider the pole-shifting technique, which permits certain systems that cannot be treated by a direct application of Theorem 10-1 to be transformed so that they can be. Alternately, without affecting the system, we can adjust the theorem. This leads to the celebrated "circle criterion," given in a generalized form as Theorem 10-4 below (page 385).

1. Pole Shifting

The pole-shifting technique consists of the transformation

$$u_a(t) = u(t) - ae(t) \tag{10-29}$$

By this relation, the sector $(u/e) \in [a_1, b_1]$ of the original element $\mathcal{F}[e(t), t]$ is transformed into the sector $(u_a/e) \in [a_1 - a, b_1 - a]$ of the transformed element $\mathcal{F}_a[e(t), t]$. This is illustrated in Fig. 10-9a.

With (10-29), a system of Fig. 10-9b is transformed into an equivalent one of Fig. 10-9c in which the linear plant is given by

$$G_a(p) = \frac{G(p)}{1 + aG(p)} \tag{10-30}$$

Further, an input $r(t)$ and the initial-condition response of the (open-loop) linear element of the original system will be transformed by (10-29) into an input $r_a(t)$ and an (open-loop) initial-condition response $e_{a0}(t)$, given by their Laplace transforms

$$\mathcal{L}[r_a(t) + e_{a0}(t)] = \frac{1}{1 + aG(s)}\mathcal{L}[r(t) + e_0(t)] \tag{10-31}$$

The derivations of Eqs. (10-30) and (10-31) from the original system are left as an exercise for the reader (Exercise 10-2). We see from (10-30) and (10-31) that transformation (10-29) results in a shift of characteristic roots of the transformed system, hence the name "pole-shifting technique."

This technique can be used to treat systems with linear elements that are unstable or neutrally stable. It is also invoked to prove the basic Theorem 10-1 for the case $-\infty < q \leq 0$. (See Appendix C.)

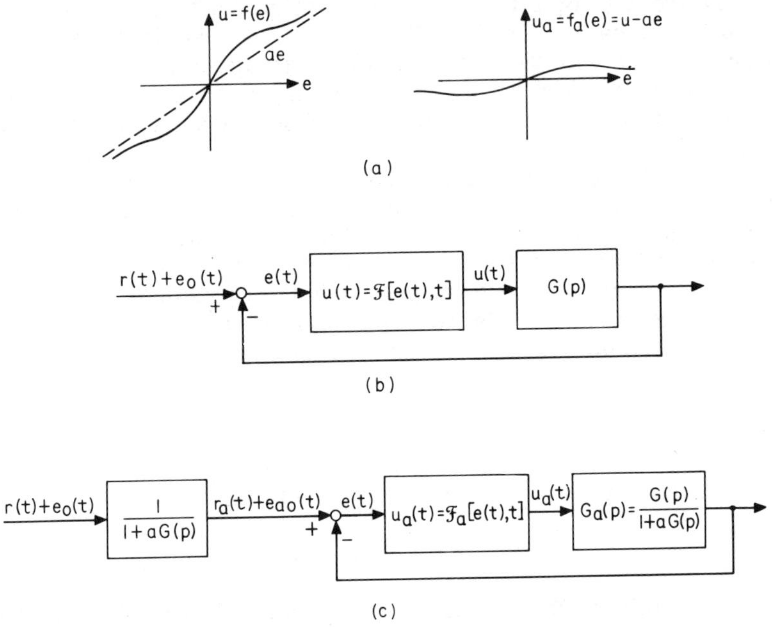

Fig. 10-9. Illustration of the pole-shifting technique: (a) Example of the effect of the pole-shifting transformation on the nonlinear element. (b) Original system, $e_0(t)$ represents the initial-condition response of the linear element and $r(t)$ represents an input. (c) System (b) transformed by the (pole-shifting) transformation $u_a(t) = u(t) - ae(t)$. Note that in the pole-shifting transformation, the error function $e(t)$ is preserved whereas the control function $u(t)$ is not.

♦♦Example 10-6. Consider a linear element whose transfer function and initial-condition response are given by

$$G(p) = \frac{1}{(p-1)(p+3)(p+4)}, \qquad e_0(t) = x_{10}e^{t} + x_{20}e^{-3t} + x_{30}e^{-4t} \tag{10-32}$$

where (x_{10}, x_{20}, x_{30}) represents the set of initial conditions of a particular set of state variables chosen. Clearly, this element is unstable. However, it can be stabilized by a linear negative feedback of gain a. For the transformed linear element, we have, from (10-30) and (10-31):

$$\mathcal{L}[g_a(t)] = G_a(s) = \frac{1}{s(s^2+6s+5)+a-12}$$

$$\mathcal{L}[e_{a0}(t)] = E_{a0}(s) = \frac{(s+3)(s+4)x_{10} + (s-1)(s+4)x_{20} + (s-1)(s+3)x_{30}}{s(s^2+6s+5)+a-12} \tag{10-33}$$

We can show by root locus or any other linear technique that the transformed linear element defined by (10-33) is stable for

$$12 < a < 42 \tag{10-34}$$

In fact, for this range of a, defined in (10-34), it follows from (10-33) that both $g_a(t)$ and $e_{a0}(t)$ will be bounded by a decreasing exponential; i.e., there exist constants $K_1, K_2, \epsilon_1 > 0$ such that $|g_a(t)| < K_1 \exp(-\epsilon_1 t)$ and $|e_{a0}(t)| < K_2 \exp(-\epsilon_1 t)$. Thus, the transformed linear element satisfies condition (10-9) for $\alpha = 0$, and it follows from Definition 10-3 that it is output stable. (Show this.) We can select $a = 12 + \epsilon$ for some sufficiently small $\epsilon > 0$, and then use Theorem 10-1 for the transformed system whose transfer function, from (10-33), becomes

$$G_a(s) = \frac{1}{s(s^2 + 6s + 5) + \epsilon} \qquad \text{for} \quad a = 12 + \epsilon \tag{10-35}$$

From the above analysis we will obtain a Popov sector for the nonlinear element. Let this Popov sector for the transformed system be defined by $(u_a/e) \in [0, K_a]$; then it follows from (10-29) that the Popov sector for the original system will be $(u/e) \in [a, K_a + a]$. In particular, for this example, it will turn out that, if the nonlinear element is time invariant and either single valued or of the active hysteresis type, then we can find a $q > 0$ that will satisfy (10-19), if $(u_a/e) \in [0, 30 - 2\epsilon]$ and $15 \geq \epsilon > 0$ (see Exercise 10-4). Thus, since $a = 12 + \epsilon$, then it follows from (10-29) that the Popov sector of the original system, guaranteeing output asymptoticity, will be given by $(u/e) \in [12 + \epsilon, 42 - \epsilon]$, with $15 \geq \epsilon > 0$. Comparing this with (10-34), we note that in this example the Popov sector coincides with the Hurwitz sector. This means Aizerman's conjecture holds here. ◆◆

2. The Generalized Circle Criterion*

An alternate step to modifying the transfer function is to modify the basic theorem in such a way that the Popov condition (10-19) can be directly applied to the original transfer function. Such a step results in the highly useful circle criterion. This we now state in the form of a theorem.

◆◆Theorem 10-4. Consider the basic feedback system (10-1). Let the linear element obtained by applying negative feedback through a constant feedback gain a to the original linear element

*The circle criterion was originally presented only for the case $q = 0$ (see [B16], [S2], [Z3]). The generalized circle criterion given in Theorem 10-4 represents an extension, valid for $q \neq 0$.

be output stable. In order for the (original) feedback system to be absolutely control and output asymptotic for $(u/e) \in [a, b]$, with $a < b$, it is sufficient that there exists a real number q such that for all real $\omega \geq 0$, the condition

$$\left|G(j\omega) + \frac{(b+a) - j\omega q(b-a)}{2ab}\right|^2 - \left(\frac{b-a}{2ab}\right)^2 (1 + q^2\omega^2) \geq \delta > 0 \quad \text{if} \quad \frac{1}{a} > \frac{1}{b}$$

$$\left|G(j\omega) + \frac{(b+a) - j\omega q(b-a)}{2ab}\right|^2 - \left(\frac{b-a}{2ab}\right)^2 (1 + q^2\omega^2) \leq -\delta < 0 \quad \text{if} \quad \frac{1}{a} < \frac{1}{b} \tag{10-36}$$

is satisfied for an arbitrarily small δ.* The restrictions on the range of q and $(b - a)$, depending on the nature of the nonlinear element, are the same as those given for q and K respectively in Theorem 10-1.♦♦

The geometrical interpretation of condition (10-36) is that if $(1/a) > (1/b)$ $[(1/a) < (1/b)]$, then for each $\omega \geq 0$, the Nyquist plot of $G(j\omega)$ must lie outside (inside) the circle centered at

$$-\frac{1}{2}\left(\frac{1}{a} + \frac{1}{b}\right) + \frac{1}{2}\, jq\omega \left(\frac{1}{a} - \frac{1}{b}\right)$$

and crossing the real axis at the points $(-1/a)$ and $-(1/b)$. This is shown in Fig. 10-10 for the usual case $(1/a) > (1/b)$. An example of the case $(1/b) > (1/a)$ will be given in Sec. 10.8.

We can make the following observations concerning Theorem 10-4:

1) Theorem 10-4 represents a generalization of the basic Theorem 10-1. This can be seen by letting $a \to 0$ and $b \to k$; then, condition (10-36) reduces to condition (10-20) (show this)** which corresponds to condition (10-19) in Theorem 10-1.
2) For absolute control and output asymptoticity of degree α, we require that (i) the linear element obtained by negative feedback gain $a \geq 0$ to the original linear element be output stable of degree α, and (ii) that the frequency response function $G(j\omega)$ in condition (10-36) be substituted by $G(j\omega - \alpha)$. This follows directly from Theorem 10-3.
3) Figure 10-10 illustrates the trade-off between the requirements on the linear and the nonlinear elements. By narrowing

*a and b can have negative values; hence, we can have $(1/a) \geq (1/b)$ or $(1/a) < (1/b)$.

**A graphical appreciation of the fact that (10-36) reduces to (10-20) when $a = 0$ and $b = K$ can be gained from inspecting Fig. 10-10.

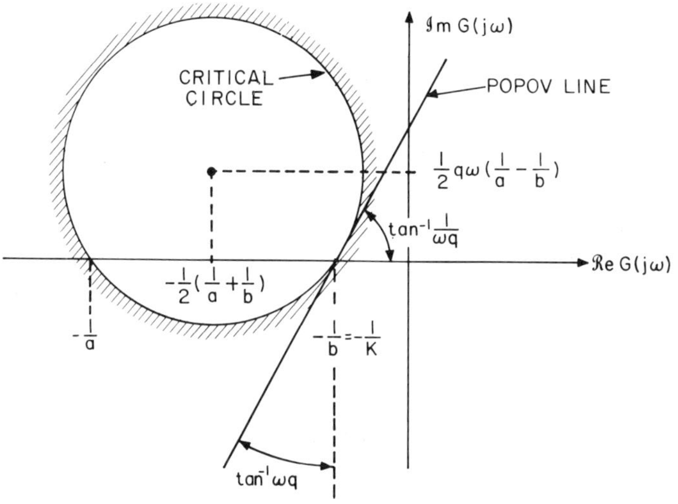

Fig. 10-10. Graphical interpretation of Theorem 10-4, illustrated for the case $(1/a) \geq (1/b)$. Assuming that the other conditions in that theorem hold, the basic feedback system will be absolutely control and output asymptotic for $(u/e) \in [a, b]$ if, for each $\omega \geq 0$, $G(j\omega)$ lies outside the circle shown.

This figure also forms the basis of the proof of Theorem 10-5. Note that the tangent on the critical circle at the point $-1/b$ has the slope $1/(\omega q)$. In fact, if $b = K$, i.e., if $(u/e) \in [a, K]$, then this tangent line is identical to the Popov line of Fig. 10-4a.

down the sector $(u/e) \in [a, b]$, we will reduce the critical circles and therefore increase the permissible range of $G(j\omega)$.

4) If we let $a \to h$ and $b \to h$, we have a linear time-invariant system of gain h. In this case, the critical circle reduces to a point at $-(1/h)$ in the $G(j\omega)$ plane. This is the critical point of Nyquist's criterion for this system.
5) The critical circle defined by condition (10-36) and illustrated in Fig. 10-10 is a function of frequency, or, more properly, of the product $q\omega$. Even though all circles pass through the points $-(1/a)$ and $-(1/b)$, their centers will move upward with increasing values of the product $q\omega$. Only for the case $q = 0$ will the circles remain the same. In that special case, the critical circle will be symmetrically located with respect to the real axis and will also pass through the points $-(1/a)$ and $-(1/b)$. We will make important use of this case in both this and in the next chapter.
6) The requirement in Theorem 10-4 that the linear element obtained by applying a constant negative feedback gain a to the original linear element be output stable may be investigated

by Nyquist's criterion: If $G(s)$ is a rational function of s, and r denotes the number of poles in $\Re e\ s \geq 0$, then the above requirement is satisfied if the $G(j\omega)$ locus over $-\infty \leq \omega \leq \infty$ (where each pole on $\Re e\ s = 0$ is "bypassed" by an infinitesimal semicircle to the left of the pole) encloses the point $-(1/a)$ exactly r times in the counterclockwise direction as ω passes from $-\infty$ to $+\infty$.* For the important special case $q = 0$, the above condition can be combined with condition (10-36). This results, as the reader may show (see Exercise 10-18), in the following:

◆◆Corollary 10-1. Let $G(s)$ be a rational function of s with a greater number of poles than zeros and let r denote the number of poles of $G(s)$ in $\Re e\ s \geq 0$. Let $u(t) = \mathfrak{F}[e(t), t]$ (general time-varying nonlinear element). In order for the basic feedback system (10-1) to be absolutely control and output asymptotic for $(u/e) \in [a, b]$ with $a < b$ and $(1/a) > (1/b)$, it is sufficient that the $G(j\omega)$ locus over $-\infty \leq \omega \leq \infty$ (where each pole on $\Re e\ s = 0$ is "bypassed" by an infinitesimal semicircle to the left of the pole) lies outside the circle passing through the points $-(1/a)$ and $-(1/b)$, centered at $-[(1/a) + (1/b)]/2$, and encloses this circle exactly r times in a counterclockwise direction as ω passes from $-\infty$ to $+\infty$.◆◆

In order to prove Theorem 10-4, consider the (pole-shifting) transformation (10-29). It follows that if $(u/e) \in [a, b]$, then $(u_a/e) \in [0, b - a]$. Furthermore, by the requirements of the theorem, the linear element of the transformed system, given by (10-30) and (10-31), will be assumed to be output stable.** Therefore, Theorem 10-1 applies to the transformed system and the Popov condition (10-19) becomes

$$\Re e\ [(1 + j\omega q)G_a(j\omega)] + \frac{1}{b - a} \geq \delta_a > 0$$

where $G_a(j\omega)$ is as defined in (10-30) and δ_a is an arbitrarily small constant (what is it?).

We note from (10-30) that the pole-shifting transformation of (10-29) corresponds to a bilinear transformation between the $G(j\omega)$ plane and the $G_a(j\omega)$ plane. Such a bilinear transformation maps circles or straight lines into other circles or straight lines. In particular, it transfers the Popov line (Fig. 10-4a) into the circle shown in Fig. 10-10. Moreover, if $(1/a) > (1/b)$, the region to the right of the Popov line transforms to the region outside the critical

*The reader may verify that, because of the generalized circle condition (10-36), encirclement of the point $-(1/a)$ implies encirclement in the same manner of the entire strip $[-(1/a), -(1/b)]$ if $(1/a) > (1/b)$ or of the strips $[-\infty, -(1/b)]$ and $[-(1/a), \infty]$ if $(1/a) < (1/b)$.

**A relaxation of this requirement will be presented in Theorem 10-6.

circle in the $G(j\omega)$ plane as shown in Fig. 10-10.* This region is specified by condition (10-36). Thus, when (10-36) is satisfied, the transformed system is both control and output asymptotic, i.e., we have

$$\int_0^\infty u_a^2(t)\,dt < \infty, \quad \int_0^\infty e^2(t)\,dt < \infty$$

for every set of initial conditions. Therefore, from (10-29), we obtain for the original system**

$$\int_0^\infty u^2(t)\,dt < \infty$$

for every set of initial conditions. Thus, the original system is also both control and output asymptotic. This concludes the proof.

Unlike the case for the Popov line (see Sec. 10.3), it is not helpful to transform the critical circles from the $G(j\omega)$ plane into the $G^\star(j\omega)$ plane because this will only result in a family of curves (not circles) whose shapes depend on both q and ω (see however Exercise 10-17). However, from Theorem 10-4, we can deduce an interesting property. If we draw a tangent on the critical circle, defined by the theorem, at the point $-(1/b)$, then we can easily show that its slope*** is $1/\omega q$. This is illustrated in Fig. 10-10. Comparing Fig. 10-10 with Fig. 10-4a, we note that the tangent line on the critical circle has the same slope as the Popov line, valid for the case $a = 0$. In fact, if we let $b = K$ and $0 \le a < b$, then the tangent line on the critical circle becomes identical to the Popov line shown in Fig. 10-4a. In Sec. 10.3 we indicated that this line can be transformed into a frequency-independent line in the $G^\star(j\omega)$ plane, as was shown in Figs. 10-5. Thus, if $G^\star(j\omega)$ lies to the right of the Popov line of Figs. 10-5, it implies that $G(j\omega)$ lies outside the critical circle shown in Fig. 10-10 for every ω. The only other requirement in Theorem 10-4 that must be satisfied is that the linear

*If $(1/a) < (1/b)$, the region to the right of the Popov line transforms to the region inside the critical circle. This we see by observing the change in the critical circle of Fig. 10-10 when a is changed slowly from a positive to a negative value.

**From (10-29) and Minkowski's inequality (see Appendix C), we have

$$\int_0^\infty u^2(t)dt = \int_0^\infty \left[u_a(t) + ae(t)\right]^2 dt \le \left[\left(\int_0^\infty u_a^2(t)dt\right)^{1/2} + \left(\int_0^\infty a^2 e^2(t)dt\right)^{1/2}\right]^2 < \infty$$

***Or, the angle between this tangent line and a vertical line is $\tan^{-1} \omega q$.

element obtained by applying constant feedback gain a to the original linear element must be output stable. We can formalize this conclusion in terms of the following theorem:

♦♦Theorem 10-5. Consider the basic feedback system (10–1). Let the linear element obtained by applying negative feedback through a constant gain, $a > 0$, to the original linear element be output stable. In order for the (original) feedback system to be absolutely control and output asymptotic for $(u/e) \in [a, K]$, it is sufficient that there exists a real number q such that for all real $\omega \geq 0$ the Popov condition (10–19) is satisfied where the restrictions on q and K are the same as in Theorem 10–1.♦♦

Note that Theorem 10–5 permits graphical evaluation in the $G^\star(j\omega)$ plane by means of (10–22) and is especially useful where the linear element is unstable or neutrally stable. It tells us that we can use the Popov condition on the original linear element without having to go through any transformation such as that of Example 10–6, as long as the linear element obtained by constant feedback gain a on the original linear element is output stable.

Consider now Fig. 10–10, remembering that Theorems 10–4 and 10–5 refer to the critical circle and to the Popov line respectively, we note that Theorem 10–5, though easier to apply, is more conservative than Theorem 10–4. However, if we consider the important case where the linear element contains integration or is purely oscillatory (for which $a > 0$ is "small")* then we can see that the Popov line will lie only slightly to the right of the critical circle for each frequency. Thus, there is virtually no loss in range of permissible $G(j\omega)$ due to the more conservative nature of Theorem 10–5 in this case.

By the use of Theorem 10–3, Theorem 10–5 can also be extended to control and output asymptoticity of degree $\alpha \neq 0$.

♦♦Example 10-7. Consider the same system analyzed in Example 10–6. We had previously established that the linear element obtained by applying continuous feedback gain a over the range $12 < a < 42$ is output stable. Thus, Theorem 10–5 applies to a nonlinear element with $(u/e) \in [a, K]$.

For the $G(p)$ of (10–32), the modified frequency characteristic $G^\star(j\omega) = \mathcal{R}e\, G(j\omega) + j\omega\, \mathcal{I}m\, G(j\omega)$ is plotted in Fig. 10–11. From this, we note that we can draw a Popov line which lies slightly to the left of $\mathcal{R}e\, G^\star(j\omega) = -1/12$. In fact, we may choose this line to be vertical, that is, we may take $q = 0$ which corresponds to the most general case of a nonlinear element. We have $K = 12 - \epsilon$ where $0 < \epsilon$. Thus, the Popov sector becomes $(u/e) \in [a, 12 - \epsilon]$ where $12 < a < 42$. But, as $a > 12$, this sector cannot exist. Therefore, for this particular example, Theorem 10–5 does not yield useful information.♦♦

*The property that the linear element can be stabilized by an arbitrarily small negative feedback gain has been referred to as "stability in the limit"; see [A1].

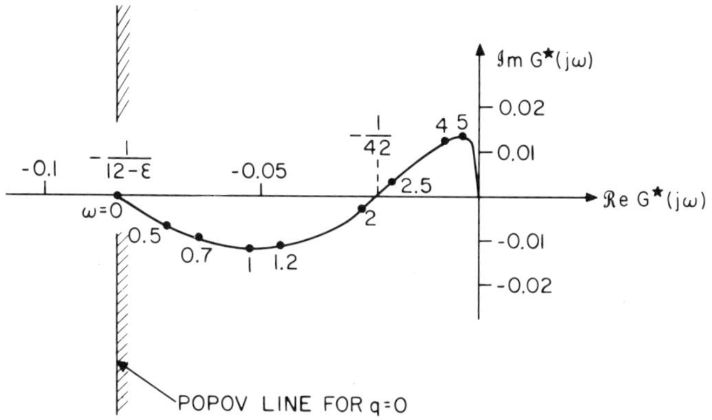

Fig. 10-11. Modified frequency locus for transfer function $G(p) = 1/[(p-1)(p+3)(p+4)]$ of Example 10-7. Note that a Popov line can be found for $q = 0$.

♦♦Example 10-8. Consider the same system as in Examples 10-6 and 10-7 but in the transformed form (10-33) with $a = 12$. We then have*

$$G_a(p) = \frac{1}{p(p^2+6p+5)} = \frac{1}{p(p+1)(p+5)}$$

$$e_{a0}(t) = \frac{1}{5}(12x_{10} - 4x_{20} - 3x_{30}) + \frac{1}{20}(6x_{10} - 6x_{20} - 4x_{30})e^{-t}$$

$$+ \frac{1}{4}(2x_{10} + 6x_{20} + 12x_{30})e^{-5t} \tag{10-37}$$

We had already shown in Example 10-6 that the linear element obtained from (10-37) by linear feedback gain h with $0 < h < 30$ is output stable. However, the element itself is stable. Thus, Theorem 10-5 applies for a nonlinear element with the semi-open sector $(u/e) \in [0,K]$ and a Popov condition

$$\Re e\ G_a^{\star}(j\omega) > -\frac{1}{K} + q\mathscr{I}m\ G_a^{\star}(j\omega)$$

The modified frequency characteristic $G_a^{\star}(j\omega)$ for $a = 12$ is plotted in Fig. 10-12. We can find a Popov line passing through $G_a^{\star}(j\omega) = -1/30$ and having a slope 1/1.2. Thus, Theorem 10-5 is satisfied with $q = 1.2$, and a time-invariant single-valued nonlinearity $u_a = f_a(e)$ having a Popov sector of $(u_a/e) \in (0,30)$.**

*This is the same as (10-35) with $\epsilon = 0$.

**This also holds for the case of active hysteresis.

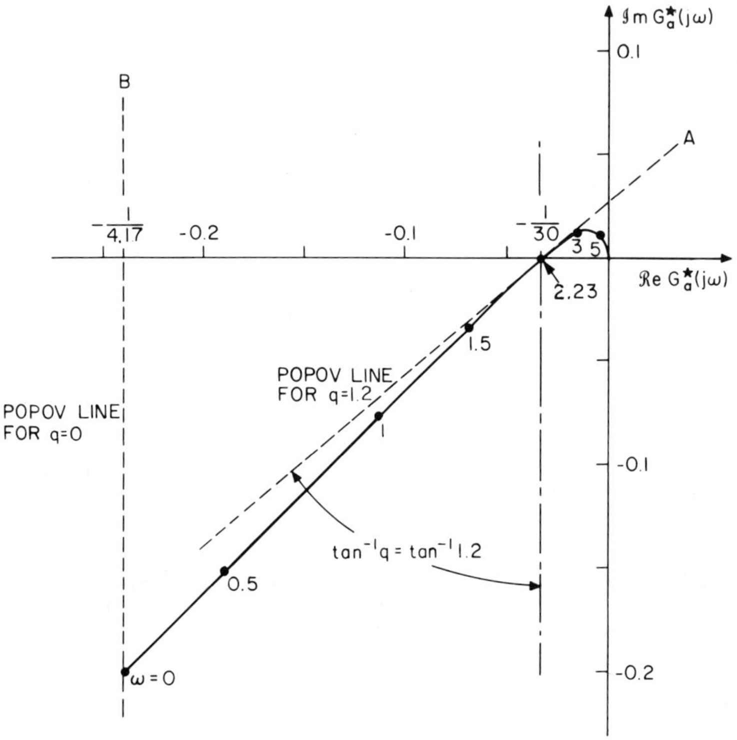

Fig. 10-12. Modified frequency locus for the transfer function $G_a(p) = 1/[p(p+1)(p+5)]$ of Example 10-8. Here, a Popov line (with $q = 1.2$) can be found such that the Popov sector for $u_a = f_a(e)$ becomes $(u_a/e) \in (0,30)$. For the general nonlinearity $u_a = \mathscr{F}_a[e(t), t]$, where q must be zero, the Popov sector will be $(u_a/e) \in (0,4.17)$.

For the more general case of a time-varying nonlinearity or one with passive hysteresis, we must choose a Popov line with $q = 0$, or a vertical line. This gives a Popov sector of $(u_a/e) \in (0, 4.17)$ which is considerably smaller than the sector $(u_a/e) \in (0, 30)$ for a time-invariant, single-valued nonlinearity. ♦♦

The system of this example was obtained from the system (10-32) by the pole-shifting transformation (10-29). We can therefore retransform the result of the present example back into the domain of the original system. Thus, by (10-29), for $a = 12$, we obtain Popov sectors $(u/e) \in (12, 42)$ for single-valued (or active hysteresis type) time-invariant nonlinearities, and $(u/e) \in (12, 16.17)$ for more general types of nonlinearities.

In Example 10-7 we had tried to use Theorem 10-5 on the original (untransformed) system; however, we were unable to produce a Popov sector for any type of nonlinearity. This was due to the conservative character of Theorem 10-5, which, as we recall, represents a restricted case of Theorem 10–4. If we wish to obtain a frequency criterion in terms of the original system rather than having to go through a pole-shifting transformation, the more general Theorem 10–4 can be used.

◆◆Example 10-9. For the system of Examples 10–6 and 10–7, establish the Popov sector for a time-invariant, single-valued nonlinearity $u = f(e)$, using Theorem 10–4.

First of all, we have established in Example 10–6 that the linear element obtained by feedback gain a is output stable, with $12 < a < 42$. Using Theorem 10–4 we can find a q, namely $q = 1.2$, which enables us to draw critical circles, which pass through the points $-1/12$ and $-1/42$, such that for each value of ω the $G(j\omega)$ locus lies on or outside the respective critical circle. This is shown in Fig. 10–13. In this case, the Popov sector will be $(u/e) \in (12, 42)$.

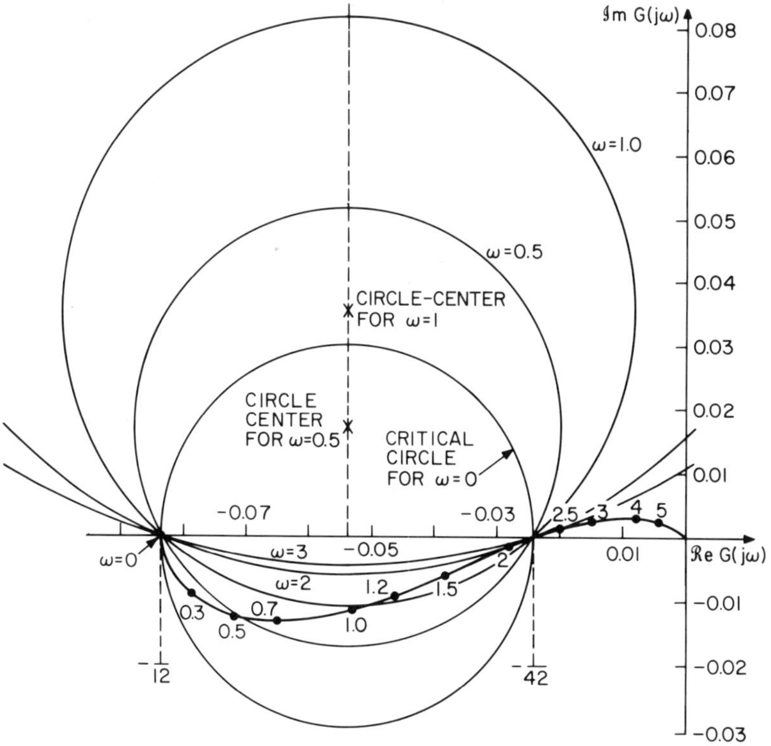

Fig. 10-13. $G(j\omega)$ locus for transfer function $G(p) = 1/[(p - 1)(p + 3)(p + 4)]$ of Examples 10-6, 10-7 and 10-9. For $q = 1.2$, we can draw critical circles such that Theorem 10-4 (see also the graphical illustration of Theorem 10-4 in Fig. 10-10) yields a Popov sector $(u/e) \in (12, 42)$. Since $q = 1.2 > 0$, this figure applies to any nonlinear function that is time invariant and single valued or of the active hysteresis type.

We can see that this procedure is not very simple. The biggest problem is to find the proper value of q for which this circle criterion holds. This may be done by trial and error. In this example, we would suspect from previous considerations that $q = 1.2$ should be satisfactory. Figure 10-13 verifies this. Generally, however, the finding of a suitable value of q by trial and error may be a rather tedious task. Comparing this example with the previous one, we can see that it would be better to transform the original system into one with a Popov sector $(u_a/e) \in [0, b-a]$ and then proceed as in Example 10-8.♦♦

We happened to have obtained the same result by the two approaches above. This need not always be so when we consider the more general types of nonlinearity in this example. Here the direct method (without pole-shifting transformation on the original system), using Theorem 10-4, will actually give us a more general result than the indirect method of Example 10-8. This we will show next.

♦♦Example 10-10. For the original system (10-32) establish the Popov sector for the general nonlinearity $u = \mathcal{F}[e(t), t]$ using Theorem 10-4.

For the general nonlinearity we must choose $q = 0$. Theorem 10-4 yields Popov sectors $(u/e) \in (a,b)$ such that for each Popov sector $(u/e) \in (a,b)$, the $G(j\omega)$ locus lies on* or outside a circle symmetrical about the real axis and passing through the points $-(1/a)$ and $-(1/b)$. In this particular example, we can determine, as shown in Fig. 10-14, that $(u/e) \in (12, 16.71)$, $(u/e) \in (14, 20)$, and $(u/e) \in (23, 31)$ are among the possible Popov sectors. In fact we note from Fig. 10-14 that the "size" of the Popov sector, or the difference between upper bound b and lower bound a, depends on the size of the critical circle, which, in turn, depends on the lower bound a. This relationship, obtained from Fig. 10-14, is presented in Fig. 10-15.

The indirect method of Example 10-8 yielded only one Popov sector $(u/e) \in (12, 16.71)$. Here, by applying the circle criterion of Theorem 10-4 we obtain a continuous range of Popov sectors of which the result of Example 10-8 is only a special case. We note from Fig. 10-15 that for a lower bound $a = 20$, we have the largest possible Popov sector, namely $(u/e) \in (20, 28.5)$. We also note, as we would expect, that each Popov sector lies within the Hurwitz sector, i.e., the sector for which the linear time-invariant feedback system with $u = he$ is stable.♦♦

Examples 10-6 through 10-10 have illustrated that there is no standard way in which to attack a given problem. Sometimes it is better to use the original Theorem 10-1 on a (pole-shifting) transformed system. In other cases it might be better to use

*By considering an open Popov sector $(u/e) \in (a,b)$, we can permit the critical circles to touch the $G(j\omega)$ locus.

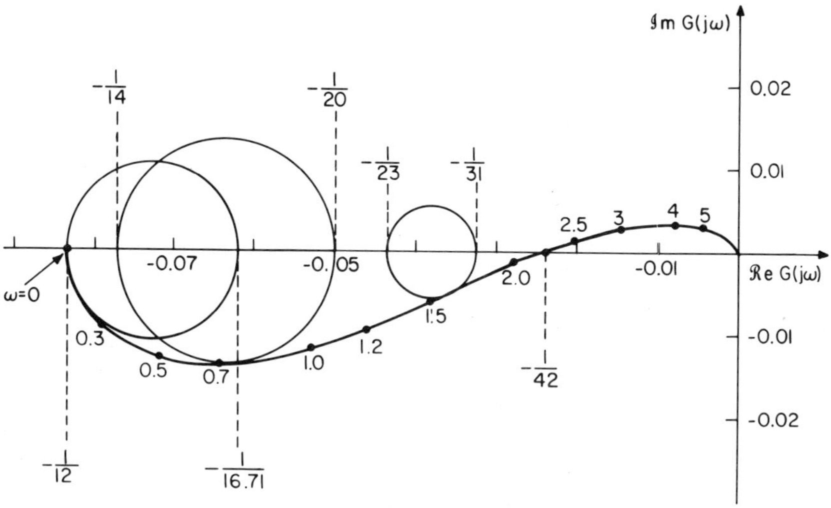

Fig. 10-14. Frequency locus for original transfer function $G(p) = 1/[(p+1)(p+3)(p+4)]$ of Examples 10-6 to 10-10. For $q = 0$, the circle criterion of Theorem 10-4 yields a family of Popov sectors $(u/e) \in (a,b)$ for each of which the $G(j\omega)$ locus lies on or outside a circle that is symmetrical about the real axis and passes through the points $-(1/a)$ and $-(1/b)$. For example, $(u/e) \in (12, 16.71)$, $(u/e) \in (14, 20)$, and $(u/e) \in (23, 31)$ are among the possible Popov sectors.

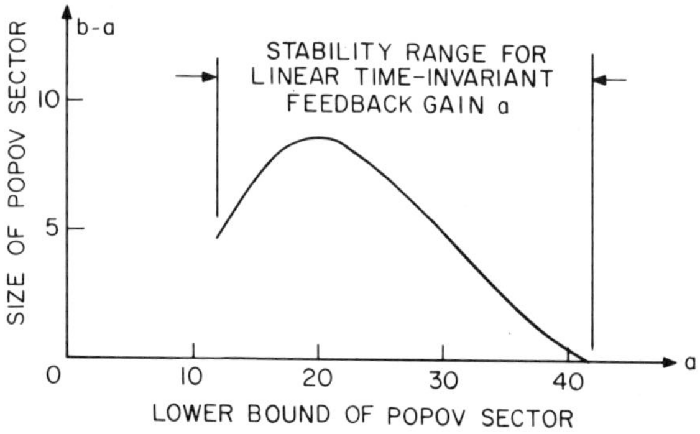

Fig. 10-15. Size of the Popov sector, $b - a$, vs. its lower bound, a, for the system of Example 10-10. Each of the Popov sectors $(u/e) \in (a,b)$, valid for the general type of nonlinearity $u(t) = \mathcal{F}[e(t), t]$, was obtained graphically from Fig. 10-14 by considering all the possible critical circles.

Theorems 10-4 or 10-5 on the original system. Judgment will always be needed for each case.

We can see from the previous examples that the circle criterion of Theorem 10-4 will be most useful for the case $q = 0$ for the more general types of nonlinearities. This we will discuss in greater detail later in the chapter.

10.7 The Zero-Shifting Transformation

We recall that the major purpose of the pole-shifting technique was to make the transformed system output stable so that Theorem 10-1 could be applied. The major purpose of the zero-shifting technique, to be discussed in this section is to manipulate the sector $(u/e) \in [a,b]$ of the nonlinear element without changing the stability properties of the linear element.

The zero-shifting transformation is defined by

$$e_c(t) = e(t) + c\,u(t) \tag{10-38a}$$

From this transformation it follows (show this) that the new transfer function and initial condition response will be given by

$$G_c(p) = G(p) - c \tag{10-38b}$$

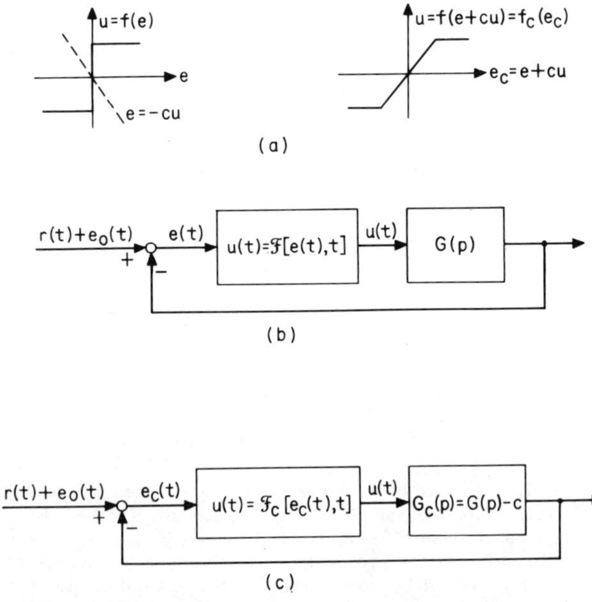

Fig. 10-16. Illustration of the zero-shifting technique: (a) Example of the effect of the zero-shifting transformation on the nonlinear element. (b) The original system. $e_0(t)$ represents the initial-condition response of the linear element and $r(t)$ represents an input. (c) System (b) transformed by the (zero-shifting) transformation $e_c(t) = e(t) + cu(t)$.

and

$$e_{co}(t) = e_0(t) \tag{10-38c}$$

An example of the zero-shifting transformation is illustrated in Fig. 10-16a. The effective system block diagram, on carrying out the transformation (10-38a) on the original system of Fig. 10-16b, becomes that shown in Figs. 10-16c.

Thus, the initial condition response of the transformed system is identical to that of the original system. The transfer function of the transformed system is equal to that of the original one minus a constant c. If $G(p)$ is a rational function of p then $G_c(p)$ will have the same poles as $G(p)$ but different zeros; hence the name "zero-shifting transformation." Note that under the zero-shifting transformation, $u(t)$ is preserved, whereas $e(t)$ is not.

The reader can show that (10-38a) transforms a sector $(u/e) \in [a,b]$ into a sector

$$\frac{u}{e_c} \in \left[\frac{1}{\frac{1}{a}+c}, \frac{1}{\frac{1}{b}+c}\right] = \left[\frac{a}{1+ac}, \frac{b}{1+bc}\right]$$

We can see from (10-38b) that, even if the original element is output stable the transformed element is not;* however, the following theorem holds:

♦♦Theorem 10-6. The requirement in the basic Theorem 10-1 and all the theorems derived from it that the linear element be output stable can be waived if the linear element can be obtained by the zero-shifting transformation (10-38a) from one that is output stable.**♦♦

To prove this theorem, we have to replace $G(p)$ by $G(p) - c$ in the proof of Theorem 10-1, presented in Appendix C. When $G(p)$ is replaced by $G(p) - c$ in (C-18) and (C-19) of Appendix C, we will find that c will be canceled out in the development, so that, from (C-20) on, the proof of the basic theorem is unaltered.

Intuitively, Theorem 10-6 is not surprising. In view of Eq. (10-21), replacing $1/K$ by $(1/K) - c$ corresponds to a horizontal shift of the $G^\star(j\omega)$ locus by c units on a plot such as Fig. 10-5.

♦♦Example 10-11. Find the Popov sector for the basic feedback system of Fig. 10-1 with $G(p) = (p-4)/(p+2)$ and $e_0(t) = e_0 e^{-2t}$.

*The transfer function of the transformed element $G(p) + c$, has the same singularities as that of the original element $G(p)$; thus, the basic stability properties of the linear element are preserved under transformation (10-38a). However, because of the constant c, conditions (10-9) cannot all be satisfied (show this); thus, the transformed element is not output stable. (See Definition 10-3.)

**In the case of Theorems 10-4 and 10-5, this refers to the linear element obtained by negative feedback gain a.

We can write $G(p) = 1 - [6/(p + 2)] = G_1(p) + 1$. Thus, the linear element can be expressed in terms of another linear element of transfer function $G_1(p) = -6/(p + 2)$ and the same initial condition response $e_0(t) = e_{10}(t) = e_0 e^{-2t}$, obtained by the zero-shifting transformation (10-38a).* The element defined by $G_1(p)$ and $e_{10}(t)$ is output stable. Hence, Theorem 10-6 applies, i.e., the basic Theorem 10-1 can be applied to the original system. The Popov condition (10-19) then becomes

$$\Re e \left[(1 + j\omega q) \frac{j\omega - 4}{j\omega + 2} \right] + \frac{1}{K} > 0$$

The reader can verify that this is satisfied if $0 < K < 1/2$ and $-\infty < q < \infty$, including $q = 0$. Thus, the nonlinear element may be of the general type $u(t) = \mathcal{F}[e(t), t]$ with a (semi-open) Popov sector of $(u/e) \in [0, 1/2)$.♦♦

So far, we have discussed the zero-shifting technique as applied to the entire linear element. This technique becomes sometimes even more useful when applied to a portion of the linear element. The following example will illustrate how it may be possible to transform a system with more than one loop into a single-loop system of the basic form so that the original theorem can be applied.

♦♦Example 10-12. Determine the critical feedback gain $h = h_c$ of the actuator control system shown in Fig. 10-17a such that for feedback gains $h > h_c$, the output signal $y(t)$ will asymptotically approach a steady-state value y_e that depends on the constant input value R.

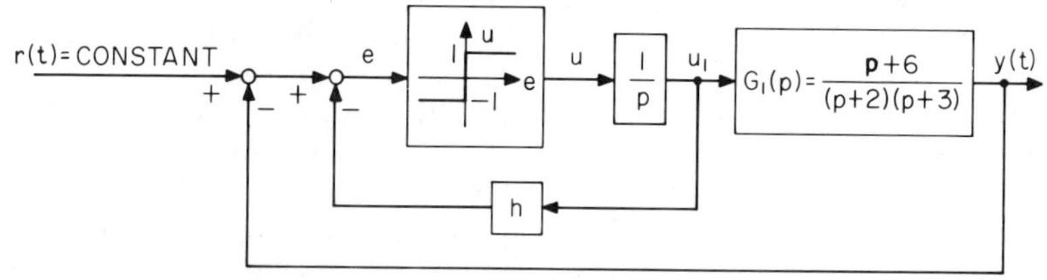

Fig. 10-17a. An actuator-controlled feedback system.

This system is of the type of the so-called "indirect control problem" of Fig. 9-6. In order to bring this problem into a form suitable for the method described here, we obtain the modified block diagram shown in Fig. 10-17b. Here, we have

*$G_c(p)$ and $G(p)$ of (10-38b) correspond to $G(p)$ and $G_1(p)$ respectively of Example 10-11. Moreover, $c = -1$.

$$\frac{u}{e} \in (0, \infty)^*, \quad G(p) = \frac{1}{p}\left[\frac{p+6}{(p+2)(p+3)} + h\right]$$

$$e_0(t) = e_{10} + e_{20}e^{-2t} + e_{30}e^{-3t} + R$$

The constant initial-condition response term, e_{10}, can, without loss of generality, be combined with the constant input value R. Thus, the zero-input feedback system of Fig. 10-17b represents the original system of Fig. 10-17a.

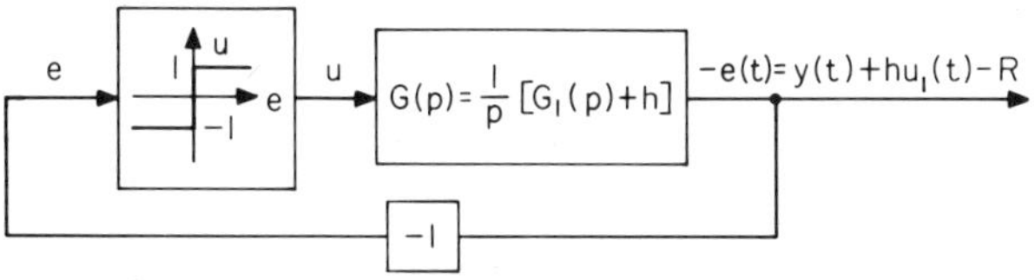

Fig. 10-17b. The modified block diagram of system (a). Note that, because of the integrator, the initial-condition response of the linear element will have a constant term that, without loss in generality, can absorb the constant input value R.

Using (10-21), we obtain

$$G^\star(j\omega) = G_2^\star(j\omega) - jh$$

where

$$G_2^\star(j\omega) \triangleq -\frac{24+\omega^2}{36+13\omega^2+\omega^4} - j\frac{36-\omega^2}{36+13\omega^2+\omega^4}$$

The Popov condition (10-22) then becomes

$$\mathcal{R}\mathrm{e}\, G^\star(j\omega) - q\,\mathcal{I}\mathrm{m}\, G^\star(j\omega) = \mathcal{R}\mathrm{e}\, G_2^\star(j\omega) - q\left(\mathcal{I}\mathrm{m}\, G_2^\star(j\omega) - h\right) > 0$$

By plotting $G_2^\star(j\omega)$ (see Fig. 10-18) it is seen that $\mathcal{I}\mathrm{m}\, G_2^\star(j\omega)$ has a maximum value of about 0.059. Therefore, the Popov condition can be satisfied (with some $q > 0$) if $h > 0.059$.

The above system was investigated by Lyapunov's direct method in Example 9-11** where we had obtained a range $h > 2$ for

*Strictly speaking, we have $(u/e) \in [0,\infty]$. However, for every $A > 0$ there exists a $\delta > 0$ such that, for this relay characteristic $(u/e) \in [\delta,\infty]$ when $|e| \leq A$. (In fact, since $u = \mathrm{sgn}\, e$, we have $\delta = 1/A$.) Hence, we are justified in writing $(u/e) \in (0,\infty]$.

**In Example 9-11, we treated the sector $(u/e) \in (0,\infty]$, which applies to the relay of Fig. 10-17b).

stability. Thus, the frequency response method here yielded a significantly greater range.

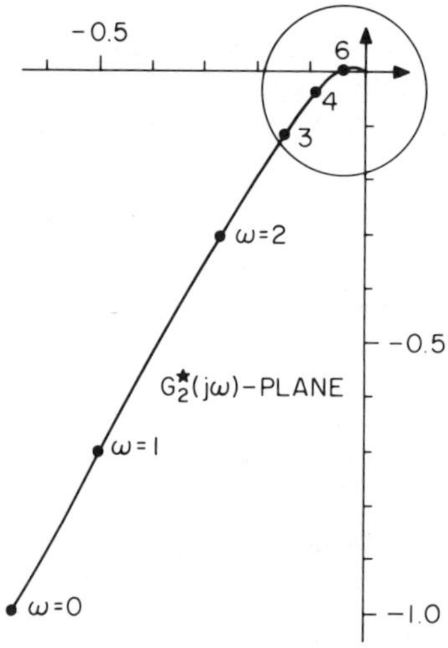

Fig. 10-18a. Locus of $G_2^\star(j\omega)$ for system of Example 10-12.

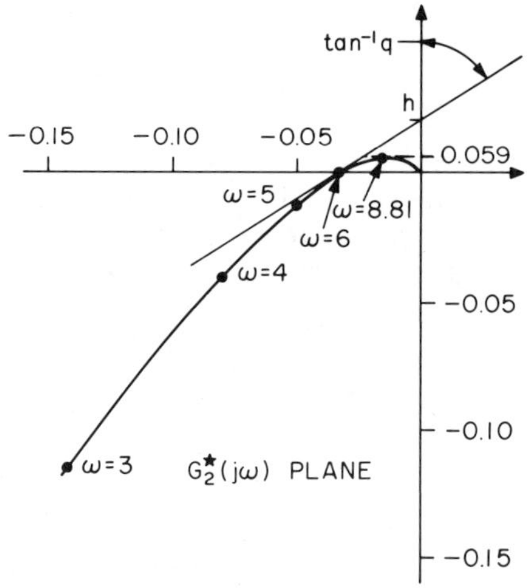

Fig. 10-18b. Enlarged version of (a). Since the modified frequency characteristic for this system (of Fig. 10-17b) is $G^\star(j\omega) = G_2^\star(j\omega) - jh$, the Popov condition (10-22) with $K = \infty$, $\Re e\, G^\star(j\omega) > q\, \Im m\, G^\star(j\omega)$, becomes $\Re e\, G_2^\star(j\omega) > q[\Im m\, G_2^\star(j\omega) - h]$. This can be satisfied for some $q > 0$ if $h > 0.059$.

If $h > 0.059$, then the system of Fig. 10-17b is control and output asymptotic. This implies that $e(\infty) = 0$ and therefore, for the original system of Fig. 10-17a, we have

$$y(\infty) = \frac{G_1(0)}{h + G_1(0)} R = \frac{1}{h+1} R \quad ◆◆$$

10.8 The Popov Criterion and the Nichols Chart

The Nichols chart is a useful tool for linear systems design. We now show how the chart can also be employed to apply the Popov criterion.*

A major advantage of a logarithmic gain-phase plot such as the Nichols plot over the (nonlogarithmic) Nyquist plot lies in its usefulness in the design of compensating networks. Such design, however, cannot easily be carried out using the logarithmic $G^\star(j\omega)$ characteristic because of the fact that

*See [M12].

$$[G_1(j\omega)\,G_2(j\omega)]^\star \neq G_1^\star(j\omega)\,G_2^\star(j\omega) \tag{10-39}$$

It is thus more advantageous to use logarithmic plots of the original frequency response function $G(j\omega)$.*

1. The Case q = 0

Let the original system of the form shown in Fig. 10-19a have a linear plant $G(p)$ and a nonlinear sector $(u/e) \in [a, b]$. Let us consider the following pole-shifting transformation:

$$u_k(t) = u(t) - \frac{a+b}{2}\,e(t), \qquad b > a \tag{10-40}$$

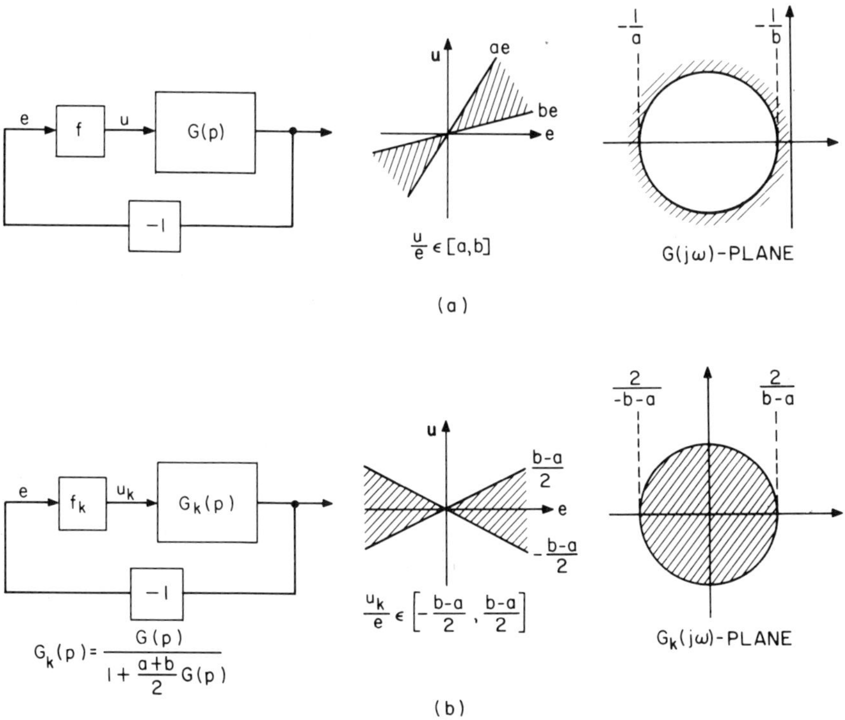

Fig. 10-19. The effect of the pole-shifting transformation (10-40) on the Popov sector of the nonlinear element and the permissible region for $G(j\omega)$ (shaded regions) for $q = 0$: (a) System with transfer function $G(p)$ and nonlinear sector $(u/e) \in [a,b]$ $(0 < a < b < \infty)$. (b) System obtained from (a) by transformation (10-40).

*However, the method for $q \neq 0$ to be introduced in this section will be equally applicable to the logarithmic $G^\star(j\omega)$ characteristic.

This will result in a transfer function

$$G_k(p) = \frac{G(p)}{1 + \frac{a+b}{2} G(p)} \tag{10-41}$$

and initial-condition response

$$e_{k0}(t) = \mathcal{L}^{-1}\left[\frac{1}{1 + \frac{a+b}{2} G(s)} \mathcal{L}[e_0(t)]\right] \tag{10-42}$$

The sector of the transformed element will be

$$\frac{u_k}{e} \in \left[-\frac{b-a}{2}, \frac{b-a}{2}\right] \tag{10-43}$$

Here by Theorem 10-4, the region in the $G(j\omega)$ plane of the original linear element for which the Popov criterion is satisfied (for $q = 0$) lies outside the critical circle shown in Fig. 10-19a. We shall call this region the Popov region.

Now transformation (10-41) maps this Popov region into the *inside* of a circle in the $G_k(j\omega)$ plane, centered at the origin and of radius $2/(b-a)$.* This is illustrated in Fig. 10-19b. Transformation (10-41) therefore maps constant $|G_k(j\omega)|$ circles into appropriate circles in the original $G(j\omega)$ plane. Such a mapping is analogous to that used in the relation between open- and closed-loop transfer functions of linear time-invariant systems and can be expressed in the logarithmic gain vs. phase plane. Specifically, this mapping can be represented in the form of a Nichols chart.

For a complex variable z, we recall that the Nichols chart is a plot of $20 \log |z|$ (in dB) vs. $\angle z$ into which are drawn loci of constant magnitudes $\left|\frac{z}{1+z}\right|$ and phases $\angle \frac{z}{1+z}$. For our case, we

*This result leads to the following theorem (see Exercise 10-5):

The basic feedback system of Fig. 10-1, with time-varying linear gain $u = k(t)e$ and output-stable linear element, is absolutely control and output asymptotic for any $|k(t)| < K$ (i.e., for $(u/e) \in [-K, K]$) if $K|G(j\omega)| < 1$.

This theorem is close to one presented independently of Popov's method by Bongiorno [B16].

are interested only in the loci of constant magnitudes $\left|\dfrac{z}{1+z}\right|$.

The objective here is to map the contours of constant $|G_k(j\omega)| = 2/(b-a)$ into the logarithmic $G(j\omega)$ plane. Thus, from (10-41), we want to obtain the contours

$$\left|\frac{G(j\omega)}{1+\dfrac{a+b}{2}G(j\omega)}\right| = \frac{2}{b-a}$$

or

$$\left|\frac{\dfrac{a+b}{2}G(j\omega)}{1+\dfrac{a+b}{2}G(j\omega)}\right| = \left|\frac{b+a}{b-a}\right| \tag{10-44}$$

Equation (10-44) represents the critical circle or the boundary of the Popov region. Using a Nichols chart, we can readily obtain contours for constant values of $\left|\dfrac{b+a}{b-a}\right|$ in the $[(a+b)/2]G(j\omega)$ plane. This is illustrated in Fig. 10-20. The contours for constant values of $\left|\dfrac{b+a}{b-a}\right|$, expressed in decibels, correspond to the loci for constant closed-loop gain in the Nichols chart.

For given values of a and b, in order to satisfy the circle criterion of Theorem 10-4 for $q = 0$, the $[(a+b)/2]G(j\omega)$ locus should lie outside of the $20 \log \left|\dfrac{b+a}{b-a}\right|$ contour in the Nichols chart. Conversely, the values of a and b corresponding to the largest $20 \log \left|\dfrac{b+a}{b-a}\right|$ contour that is touched by the $[(a+b)/2]G(j\omega)$ locus corresponds to the limits of a possible Popov sector $(u/e) \in [a, b]$ for the given problem. This last idea provides the basis of a method for determining possible Popov sectors. We shall show this by an example.

♦♦Example 10-13. Examine the asymptotic behavior of the linear time-varying equation

$$\ddot{e}(t) + 2\dot{e}(t) + [c - 3 - d\cos\omega_0 t]e(t) = 0 \tag{10-45}$$

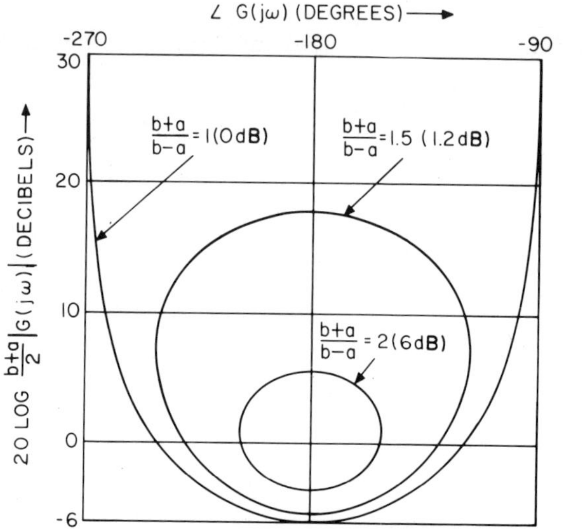

Fig. 10-20. Logarithmic gain-phase curve for $[(b + a)/2]G(j\omega)$. The contours for constant 20 log $[(b + a)/(b - a)]$ are identical to the contours for constant closed-loop gain 20 log$|KG(j\omega)/(1 + KG(j\omega))|$ in the Nichols chart. For given values a and b, the circle criterion of Theorem 10-4 for $q = 0$, will be satisfied if the $[(b + a)/2]$ $G(j\omega)$ locus lies outside the appropriate $|(b + a)/(b - a)|$ contour.

This equation is of the type of the damped Mathieu equation.* In order to investigate this equation by the methods of this chapter, we present (10-45) in the form shown in Fig. 10-21, which represents a system in our standard form, with

$$\frac{u}{e} \in [a, b] = [c - d, c + d], \quad G(p) = \frac{1}{(p - 1)(p + 3)}$$

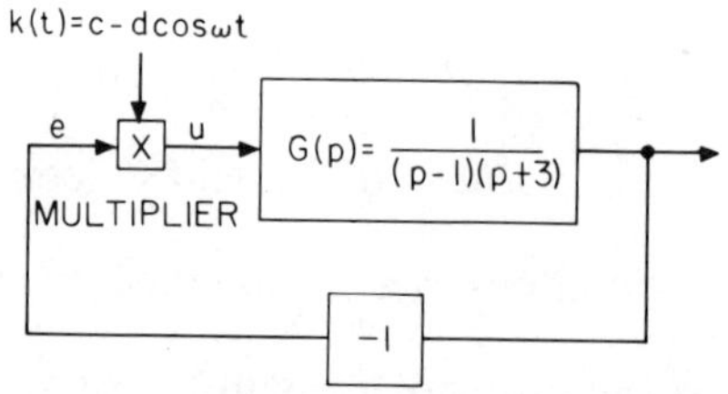

Fig. 10-21. The linear time-varying system representing Eq. (10-45) which is of the form of a damped Mathieu equation.

*See [M7].

The linear element is output stable only for a linear negative-feedback gain of $h > 3$. Thus, in order for the circle criterion (Theorem 10-4) to apply, we must have Popov sectors $(u/e) \in [a,b]$ with $a = c - d > 3$ (9.5 dB).

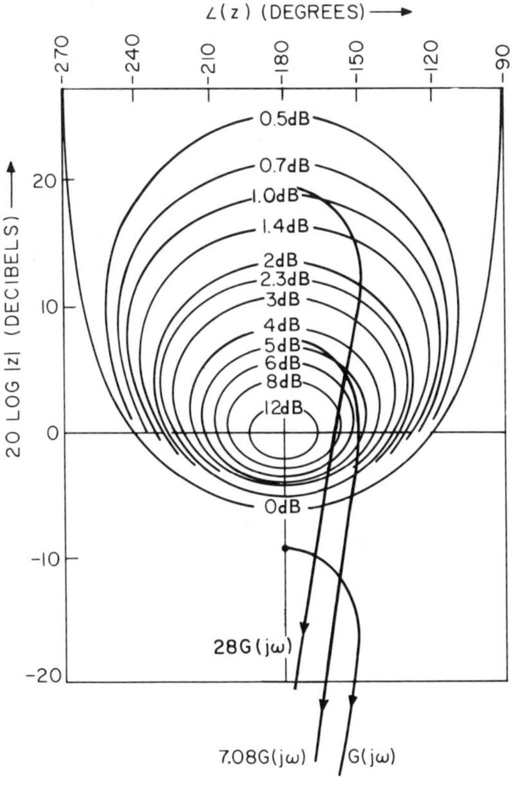

Fig. 10-22. Portion of the Nichols chart, 20 log $|z|$ vs. $\angle z$, showing contours for constant 20 log $|z/(1 + z)|$. To satisfy the circle criterion of Theorem 10-4 for $q = 0$, we take $z = [(a + b)/2]\, G(j\omega)$ and interpret the contours as in Fig. 10-20. Drawn into this chart is the frequency locus $G(j\omega)$ of the system of Example 10-13 and loci of $[(a + b)/2]G(j\omega)$ for $(a + b)/2 = 7.08$ (17 dB) and $(a + b)/2 = 28$ (29 dB). For the latter two loci, we obtain the critical boundaries 5.9 dB, or $|(b + a)/(b + a)| = 1.97$, and 9 dB or $|(b + a)/(b - a)| = 2.82$, respectively.

Figure 10-22 presents the Nichols chart showing only the gain contours for constant values of 20 log $\left|\dfrac{z}{1+z}\right|$. Also drawn in this figure are the $G(j\omega)$ locus for this system and loci for $[(a + b)/2]G(j\omega)$

with the typical values of $(a + b)/2 = 7.08$ (17 dB), and $(a + b)/2 = 28$ (29 dB). In order to satisfy the circle criterion of Theorem 10-4 for $q = 0$, the critical circle of Fig. 10-10 corresponds to the contours here of $20 \log \left|\frac{z}{1+z}\right| = 20 \log \left|\frac{b+a}{b-a}\right|$. For the two $[(a+b)/2]$ $G(j\omega)$ loci with $(a + b)/2 = 7.08$ and $(a + b)/2 = 28$, we find that the largest $20 \log \left|\frac{b+a}{b-a}\right|$ contours that they touch are those corresponding to 5.9 dB or $\left|\frac{b+a}{b-a}\right| = 1.97$ and 9 dB or $\left|\frac{b+a}{b-a}\right| = 2.82$ respectively.

Consider first the 7.08 $G(j\omega)$ locus. For this locus, $(a + b)/2 = 7.08$. The critical boundary for this locus has been found to be one given by $\left|\frac{b+a}{b-a}\right| = 1.97$. Solving for a and b in the two equations $(a + b)/2 = 7.08$ and $\left|\frac{b+a}{b-a}\right| = 1.97$ yields $a = 3.5$ and $b = 10.7$. Thus a possible Popov sector for the 7.08 $G(j\omega)$ locus is $(u/e) \in (3.5, 10.7)$. In a similar manner we can find for the 28 $G(j\omega)$ locus a Popov sector of $(u/e) \in (18, 38)$.

By vertical shifting of the $G(j\omega)$ locus, we can obtain an entire range of possible Popov sectors. This is shown in Fig. 10-23. The region for control and output asymptoticity of degree $\alpha = 0.5\ \text{sec}^{-1}$ is also displayed in Fig. 10-23. This region was obtained in the same manner as above except that, by virtue of Theorem 10-3, $G(j\omega)$ is replaced by $G(j\omega - 0.5)$ (see Exercise 10-6).◆◆

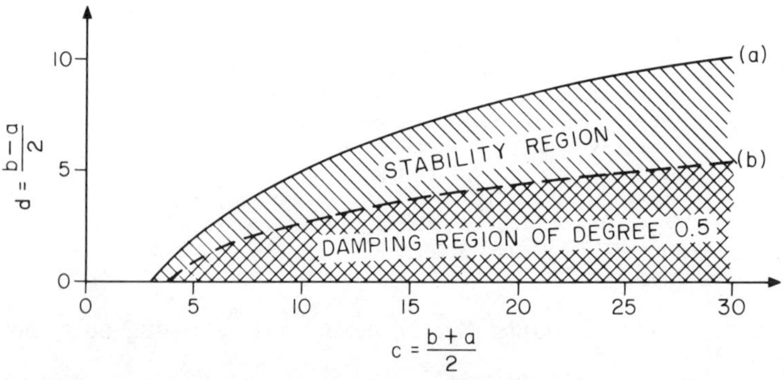

Fig. 10-23. Parameter regions of the system of Fig. 10-21 to guarantee control and output asymptoticity (region bounded by curve (a)) and control and output asymptoticity of degree $\alpha = 0.5\ \text{sec}^{-1}$ (region bounded by curve (b)).

2. The Case q $\neq 0$

So far we have discussed the interpretation of the Popov criterion for $(u/e) \in [a, b]$ and $q = 0$. Let us now consider the Popov condition for $(u/e) \in [0, K]$ and any value of q. We will now show that for $q \neq 0$, we can create a logarithmic gain-phase chart for the $KG(j\omega)$ locus that is almost as easy to use as the Nichols chart for the $q = 0$ case. The transformation of the Popov lines from the (polar) $G(j\omega)$-plane into the logarithmic $KG(j\omega)$ plane is illustrated in Fig. 10-24. How these boundaries can easily be constructed from a Nichols chart will now be explained.

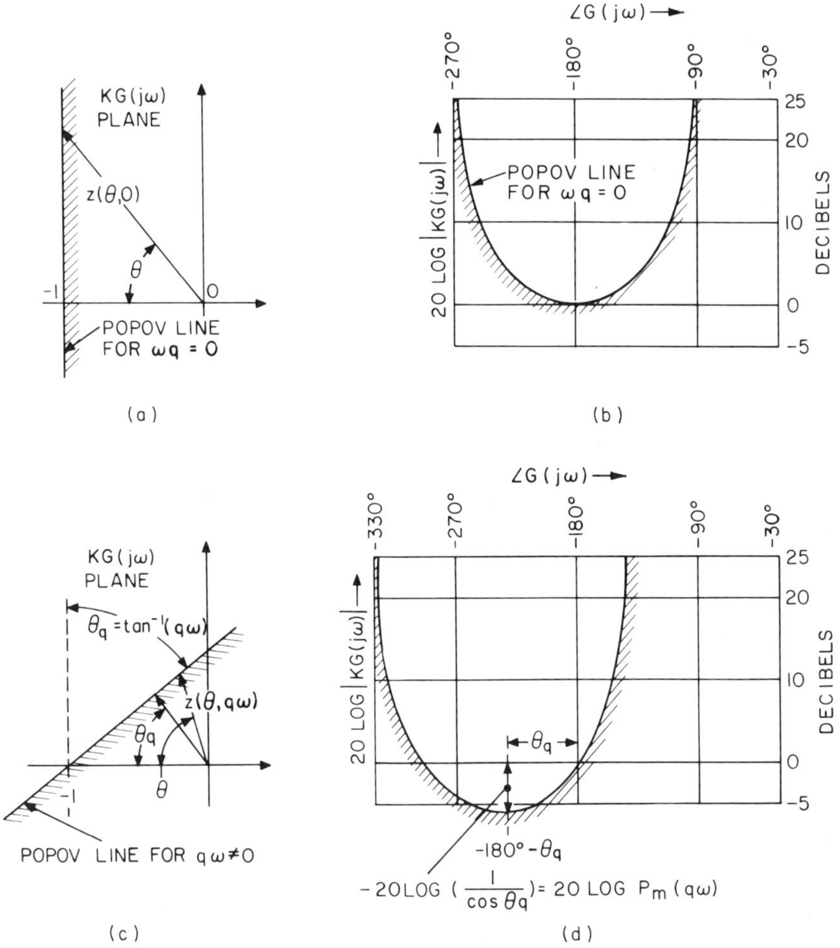

Fig. 10-24. Generation of Popov boundaries in the logarithmic $G(j\omega)$ plane from the Popov lines of the polar plane (as in Fig. 10-4). For $\omega q = 0$, the contour in (b) is a mapping of that in (a). For given $\omega q \neq 0$, the contour in (d), which is a mapping of (c), can be obtained by vertical and horizontal shifting of the contour for $\omega q = 0$ as shown.

We had shown in Sec. 10.3 that the Popov condition (10-20) defines the Popov lines of Fig. 10-4a. Let us first consider the special case $q = 0$. Here, for $(u/e) \in [0, K]$ we have a special case of the circle criterion, with $a = 0$, $b = K$. Consider Fig. 10-20, the Popov line will correspond to the boundary line in the Nichols chart for $[(b+a)/(b-a)] = K/K = 1$, or the 0 dB locus. The ordinate of the Nichols chart becomes 20 log $(K/2)|G(j\omega)|$ = 20 log $|KG(j\omega)|$-6 dB. However, we are interested in the logarithmic $KG(j\omega)$ plane, i.e., one with the coordinates 20 log $|KG(j\omega)|$ and $\angle G(j\omega)$. In order to obtain the Popov boundary line in this plane, we must shift the 0-dB axis of the Nichols chart downward by 6 dB. This yields the boundary curve shown in Fig. 10-24b.*

The mapping of the Popov line for $\omega q \neq 0$ from the original to the logarithmic $KG(j\omega)$ plane is illustrated in Figs. 10-24c and d. Here, representing the Popov line for a given product $q\omega$ in terms of $z = |z|e^{j\theta}$ as shown, we find from Fig. 10-24c that $\cos\theta_q = |z| \cos(\theta - \theta_q)$, with $\tan\theta_q \triangleq q\omega$, or

$$|z| = |z(\theta, q\omega)| = \frac{\cos\theta_q}{\cos(\theta - \theta_q)}, \qquad \theta_q = \tan^{-1} q\omega \tag{10-46}$$

From this, we obtain

$$|z(\theta, q\omega)| = \frac{|z(\theta - \theta_q, 0)|}{|z(\theta_q, 0)|}$$

or

$$20\log|z(\theta, q\omega)| = 20\log|z(\theta - \theta_q, 0)| - 20\log|z(\theta_q, 0)| \tag{10-47}$$

Thus, we can obtain the boundary curve for $q\omega \neq 0$ by vertical and horizontal shifting of the boundary curve for $q = 0$, by 20 log $|z(\theta_q, 0)|$ dB's and $\theta_q = \tan^{-1}(q\omega)$ degrees respectively. This is illustrated in Fig. 10-24d. Thus by parallel "sliding" of the boundary curve for $q\omega = 0$ such that it always passes through the point (−180°, 0 dB) we can generate a family of boundary curves for given values of the product $q\omega$. Such a family of curves is shown in Fig. 10-25. It represents the logarithmic equivalent of the family of Popov lines of Fig. 10-4b.

*A method utilizing the boundary curve for the evaluation of the Popov criterion for $q = 0$ has been proposed by Naumov [N1]. His procedure involves the plotting of a family of phase-gain loci for functions $G_q(j\omega, q) \triangleq (1 + j\omega q)G(j\omega)$ and establishing whether one of these curves lies outside the boundary curve of Fig. 10-24b. Naumov's method, however, involves more elaborate calculations than those described in the present section. A procedure along the lines of Naumov's has been proposed by Murphy [M14].

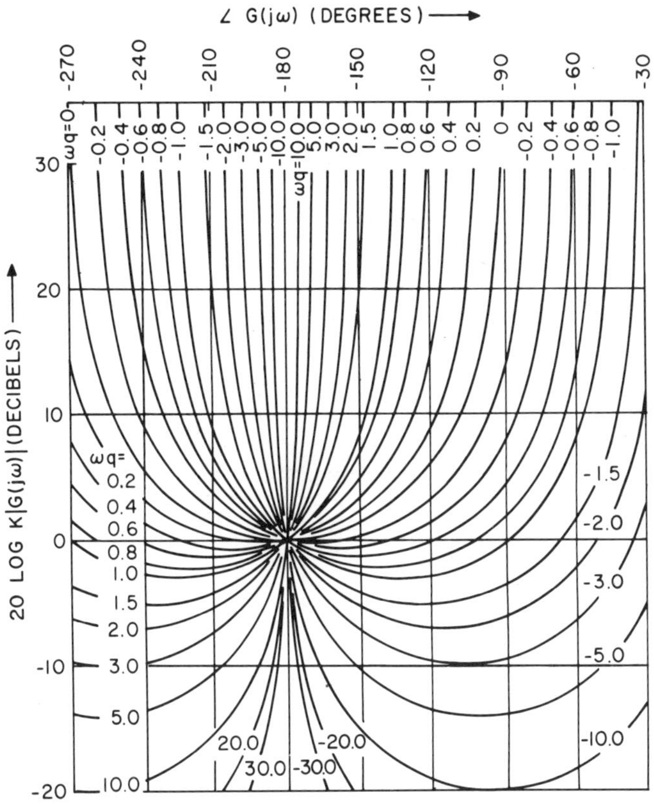

Fig. 10-25. Popov boundaries in the logarithmic $KG(j\omega)$ plane. Condition (10-19) will be satisfied if, for each $\omega \geq 0$, the point of the $KG(j\omega)$ locus lies below the respective boundary for $q\omega$. The present chart can also be used for examining the Popov criterion on the logarithmic $KG^{\star}(j\omega)$ plane. In that case, the boundaries for ωq become boundaries for q and the Popov condition will be satisfied if a q can be found such that the $KG^{\star}(j\omega)$ locus lies below the boundary for that value of q.

The application of Fig. 10-25 is clear from the following fact: *For a given* $G(j\omega)$, *the Popov condition (10-19) of Theorem 10-1 is satisfied if there exists a real value of* q *such that for every* ω, *the* $G(j\omega)$ *point lies below the respective* $q\omega$ *boundary line.**

◆◆**Example 10-14.** For a system of Fig. 10-1, with a single-valued function $u = f(e)$ and a linear plant

$$G(p) = \frac{10}{p(p+1)(p+5)}$$

*If control or output-asymptoticity of degree α is desired, then according to Theorem 10-3, $G(j\omega)$ has to be replaced by $G(j\omega - \alpha)$.

obtain the bound K of $(u/e) \in (0, K)$ so as to guarantee control and output asymptoticity of this system.

This system is the same as that in Example 10-8, except for a gain of 10. The locus for $G(j\omega)$ is shown in Fig. 10-26, superimposed with the family of boundary curves of Fig. 10-25. By vertical sliding of the $G(j\omega)$ locus, we find that for $20 \log K = 9.5$ dB or $K = 3.0$, we can find a value of q, viz. $q = 1.2$, such that for each product $q\omega = 1.2\omega$, the point

$$20 \log |KG(j\omega)| = 20 \log |G(j\omega)| + 9.5 \text{ dB}$$

lies below the respective Popov boundary.* We thus conclude that

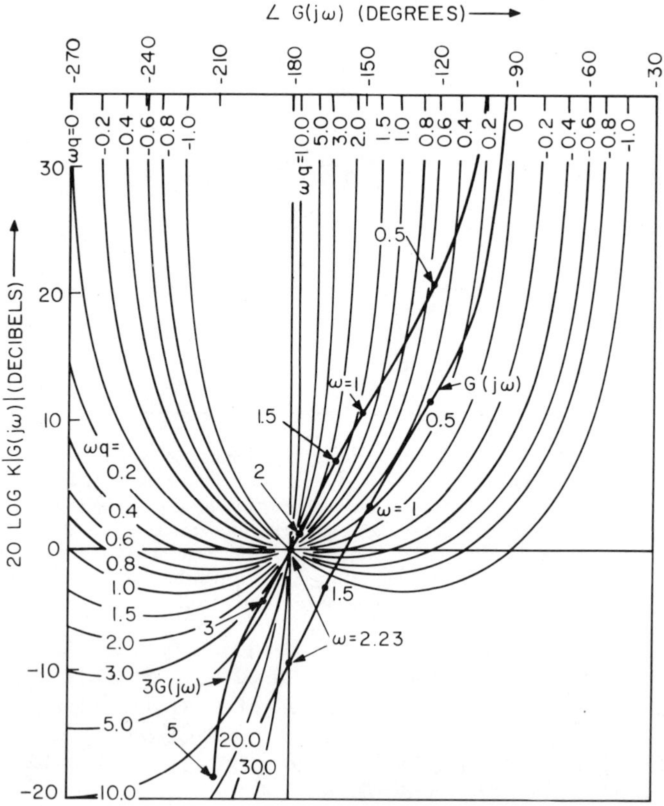

Fig. 10-26. Examination of logarithmic gain-phase locus for the system of Example 10-14. For $K = 3$, a value for q can be found, namely $q = 1.2$, for which every point of the $3G(j\omega)$ locus lies on or below the respective $q\omega$-Popov boundary. This indicates a Popov sector $(u/e) \in (0,3)$.

*The actual value of $q = 1.2$ can be found by a few trials. It can also be obtained directly in the logarithmic $KG^{\star}(j\omega)$ plane, as we shall consider below.

for a gain of $20 \log K = 9.5$ dB or $K = 3.0$, the Popov condition is satisfied. As we would expect, this is the same result as that obtained in Example 10-8 by using the $G^{\star}(j\omega)$ locus.♦♦

For increasing values of ω, the Popov boundaries in Fig. 10-25 will move downward. However, it is usually very easy to establish that the $G(j\omega)$ locus will move downward much faster than the Popov boundaries for increasing ω. To show this we first see from Fig. 10-24d that the minimum of each Popov boundary is given by $-20 \log[1/(\cos\theta_q)]$, which corresponds to a value $P_m(q\omega)$ defined as

$$P_m(q\omega) \triangleq \cos \theta_q \tag{10-48}$$

But since $\cos \theta_q = 1/\sqrt{1 + \tan^2 \theta_q}$, it follows from (10-46) and (10-48) that

$$P_m(q\omega) = \frac{1}{\sqrt{(q\omega)^2 + 1}} \tag{10-49}$$

If for a certain value of $q\omega$, $|G(j\omega)| < P_m(q\omega)$, then the point $G(j\omega)$ in the logarithmic plane will certainly lie below the respective Popov boundary. From (10-49) we can see that the minimum of the Popov boundary decreases no faster than the first power of ω. Therefore, for typical systems, where $|G(j\omega)|$ decreases by powers of ω equal or greater than 1, the $G(j\omega)$ locus will move downward as fast or faster than the Popov boundaries for increasing ω; i.e., if the $G(j\omega)$ locus lies below the minimum of the Popov boundaries for a range of ω up to a certain value, then this will be true for all values of ω.

♦♦Let us return to Example 10-14, where we had established that the $3G(j\omega)$ locus in Fig. 10-26 will always lie below the Popov boundaries with $q = 1.2$. To show that this is also true for the ranges beyond the scale shown, we note from Fig. 10-26 that for $\omega = 5$, the point of the $3G(j\omega)$ locus lies below the minimum of the Popov boundary for $q\omega = 1.2 \times 5 = 6$. Since in this example $|G(j\omega)|$ decreases with $1/\omega^3$ for increasing ω we can see that the $3G(j\omega)$ locus will move downward much faster than the minima of the Popov boundaries. Thus the Popov condition will be satisfied for all $\omega \geq 0$.♦♦

As with the polar representation, the examination of the Popov condition can be simplified when a logarithmic $KG^{\star}(j\omega)$ plane is used. Since, as illustrated in Figs. 10-24c and d, the contours in Fig. 10-25 represent the image of the Popov lines in the $G(j\omega)$ plane of Fig. 10-4, it is clear that *the image of the Popov lines in the $G^{\star}(j\omega)$ plane of Fig. 10-5 in the logarithmic $KG^{\star}(j\omega)$ plane will be identical to the contours in Fig. 10-25 except that "ωq" is replaced by "q."*

Once the logarithmic $KG^{\star}(j\omega)$ locus is drawn, one can immediately establish whether it lies below any one of the Popov boundaries (for some q). Thus, the trial and error procedure of finding q in order to establish whether the $KG(j\omega)$ locus lies below the Popov boundaries for *all* ω is not needed if the logarithmic $KG^{\star}(j\omega)$ locus is used. On the other hand, as in Example 10-14, the extra work involved in establishing the Popov condition in the logarithmic $KG(j\omega)$ plane instead of the logarithmic $KG^{\star}(j\omega)$ plane is rather small and appears to be worthwhile if this plot is to be used for the design of linear compensating networks (see Exercise 10-13). As mentioned in the beginning of this section, such a design is more difficult in the $KG^{\star}(j\omega)$ plane in view of (10-39).

10.9 Summary

Popov's method gives an exact, sufficient condition for absolute stability of closed-loop free systems in the standard form of Fig. 10-1. The power of the method stems from the fact that the condition is given in terms of the frequency response function of the linear plant. This makes the method readily applicable even for systems with high-order linear plants.

The restrictions that are to be imposed on the linear and the nonlinear elements are given in Sec. 10.1. Basically, the nonlinearity can have passive or active hysteresis and/or it can be time varying, but it must lie in a sector (Eqs. 10-2). The linear element must be output stable of degree α for some α (Definition 10-3). This requirement places few restrictions on the linear element and moreover can be relaxed in certain cases (see Theorem 10-6). Linear plants with time lag and distributed parameters are admissible.

It is meaningful to speak of the system being *absolutely control asymptotic* or *absolutely output asymptotic* (Definition 10-4). These requirements are less strict than those for absolute stability; they imply absolute stability if further restrictions are imposed on the system (Theorem 10-2).

The fundamental result is given as Theorem 10-1. The basic inequality (10-19), given in terms of the frequency response function $G(j\omega)$ of the linear plant and a real constant q, is the key of the theorem. For time-varying nonlinearities the basic inequality with $q = 0$ admits of a ready geometrical interpretation in terms of the Nyquist diagram of the linear plant. For other nonlinearities where q need not be 0, a simple geometrical test (Fig. 10-5 and Eq. 10-22) can be carried out using the modified frequency response function $G^{\star}(j\omega)$ (Eq. 10-21) of the linear plant.

The basic theorem can be extended in a number of directions. It can be extended to some systems with unstable or nonasymptotically stable plants by using the pole-shifting technique. Alternately such a system can be tested by means of the generalized circle criterion of Theorem 10-4 (and Condition 10-36)). The latter technique is particularly useful when $q = 0$, which applies to time-varying nonlinear elements.

Additional flexibility in permitting trade-off between the restrictions on the linear element and those on the nonlinear element can be achieved by means of the zero-shifting technique. The basis for this technique is given in Theorem 10-6.

All the frequency response criteria presented here can be readily extended to determine the degree of stability or the rate of convergence of a system. The key result is given by Theorem 10-3, extending the basic Theorem 10-1 and all the derived theorems to yield control asymptoticity of degree α which, in turn, represents the degree of stability or damping of the system.

The use of logarithmic frequency characteristics is discussed in Sec. 10.8. It is shown how the Nichols chart can be used for this purpose. The circle criterion for $q = 0$ can be directly transformed into appropriate contours of the Nichols chart. For $q \neq 0$, the ideas embodied in the Nichols chart can be used to create a gain-phase chart with appropriate contours that permit direct application of the Popov condition (10-19) on the original frequency characteristic $G(j\omega)$. This chart is presented in Fig. 10-25 and an analysis using it is carried out in Example 10-14.

10.10 Exercises

10-1 (Fitts) Consider the basic feedback system of Fig. 10-1 where the plant is given by

$$G(p) = \frac{p^2}{[(p + 0.1)^2 + 0.9^2][(p + 0.1)^2 + 1.1^2]}$$

a) What is the Popov sector for a time-invariant single-valued nonlinear element? Note that this system satisfies both the Kalman and Aizerman conjectures for $(u/e) \in [0, \infty]$ (see Exercise 7-3).

b) What is the Popov sector for a general time-varying nonlinear element?

10-2 Derive Eqs. (10-30) and (10-31).

10-3 For a linear element defined by its transfer function $G(s)$ and initial-condition response $-e_0(t) = -\mathcal{L}^{-1}[E_0(s)]$, show that, if both $G(s)$ and $E_0(s)$ are rational functions of s and if all of their poles lie in $\mathcal{R}e\ s < -\alpha$, then the linear element is output stable of degree α (i.e., condition (10-9) is satisfied).

10-4 In Example 10-6, the original system was transformed by the pole-shifting technique into one for which the transfer function of its linear element is given by (10-35). If the nonlinear element is time invariant and single valued or of the active hysteresis type, verify that the Popov sector will be given by $(u_a/e) \in [0, 30 - 2\epsilon]$, where $0 < \epsilon \leq 15$.

10-5 Show that transformation (10-41) maps the region outside the circle in Fig. 10-19a into the inside of the circle in Fig. 10-19b. With this, complete the proof of Bongiorno's theorem stated in the footnote on page 402.

10-6 For the damped Mathieu equation (10-45) investigated in Example 10-13, verify Fig. 10-23, i.e.

a) Obtain the entire range of Popov sectors in terms of a boundary curve $d = (b - a)/2$ vs. $c = (b + a)/2$ defining the region for which $e(t) \to 0$ as $t \to \infty$.
b) Obtain the region in the d vs. c plane for which $e^{0.5t}e(t) \to 0$ as $t \to \infty$.

10-7 Let a linear time-invariant element be defined by $\dot{\mathrm{x}}(t) = \mathrm{A}\mathrm{x}(t) + \mathrm{b}u(t)$, $e(t) = -\mathrm{c}^T\mathrm{x}(t)$. Let all eigenvalues λ_i of the matrix A satisfy $\Re\mathrm{e}\ \lambda_i < -\alpha$.

a) Show that the linear element is output stable of degree α.
b) Show that there exists a constant M_0, depending on the set of initial conditions, such that the initial-condition response satisfies $|e_0(t)| \leq M_0 \exp(-\alpha t)$.
c) For the unit-impulse response $g(t)$ of the linear element, show that there exists a constant M_g such that $|g(t)| \leq M_g \exp(-\alpha t)$. (Hint: Use Theorem 5-7 of Exercise 5-13.)

10-8 Show that the system of Exercise 5-20 is not output stable. Can linear feedback make this system output stable? Explain.

10-9 For a system in the standard form of Fig. 10-1, let the linear element be a unit delay with the transfer function $G(s) = e^{-\tau s}$ and

$$-e_0(t) = \begin{cases} e_1(t - \tau), & 0 \leq t \leq \tau \\ 0 & , \text{ elsewhere} \end{cases}$$

where $e_1(t)$ is a given function.

a) Show that the linear element is not output stable.
b) By reasonings similar to those used to prove Theorem 10-6, show that for the unit delay, the requirement of output

stability can be waived in Theorem 10-1 and other theorems derived from Theorem 10-1.

c) In the light of (b) what is the sector u/e sufficient for control and output asymptoticity of degree α of the system if the nonlinearity is a general time-varying element $u(t) = \mathcal{F}[e(t), t]$?

10-10 Consider the indirect control system with time delay given by $\dot{e}(t) = -u(t - \tau) - hu(t)$; $u(t) = \mathcal{F}[e(t), t]$, $\tau = 2$ seconds.

a) If the nonlinear element is time varying, determine the value K for the sector $(u/e) \in [0, K]$ sufficient for absolute control and output asymptoticity. Does the value of K depend on h? Explain.
b) If the nonlinear element is single-valued and time-invariant and $(u/e) \in (0, \infty]$ (but (10-3) is satisfied), what is the range of h sufficient for control and output asymptoticity?
c) For the general time-varying nonlinear element and $h = 1$, determine the range a vs. $(b - a)$ of all possible sectors $(u/e) \in [a, b]$ sufficient for absolute control and output asymptoticity.

10-11 For each of the unstable linear plants of Exercise 3-16,

a) Obtain the unit-impulse response $g(t)$ and the initial-condition response $y_0(t)$.
b) Determine whether the plant is output stable.
c) Determine the degree α of output stability.

10-12 Construct the modified frequency characteristics $G^{\star}(j\omega)$ for the following linear plants. Indicate those plants whose Hurwitz sector coincides with the Popov sector.

a) $$G(p) = \frac{10}{(p + 2)(p + 5)}$$

b) $$G(p) = \frac{10}{(p - 2)(p + 5)}$$

c) $$G(p) = \frac{p^2 - 0.5}{(p^2 + 1)(p + 1)}$$

d) $$G(p) = \frac{10}{p(p^2 + p + 100)}$$

10-13 Consider the system of Example 10-14 which is to be modified by addition of a lead-lag network

$$G_c(p) = \frac{1 + p/4}{1 + p/8}$$

into the loop. By the use of the logarithmic $G(j\omega)G_c(j\omega)$ locus, obtain the bound K of $(u/e) \in (0, K)$ so as to guarantee control and output asymptoticity of this system.

10–14 The relative temperature of a semi-infinite heat conductor is measured at some finite distance x from one end and used to control the wall temperature of the conductor at $x = 0$. The equations for this infinite heat conductor are of the distributed-parameter type and are the same as those for the infinite R–C transmission line considered in Example 3–16 of Sec. 3.9.

This system can be cast into the form of the basic feedback system of Fig. 10–1, with $g(t) = g(x, t)$ and $e_0(t) = -v_0(x, t)$, where $v_0(x, t)$ and $g(x, t)$ are expressed in (3–64) and (3–65) respectively. Also, $u(t) = v(0, t)$, where $v(x, t)$ is the variable of this distrubuted parameter element, described by (3–62) or (3–63). It can be shown that this linear element, whose transfer function $G(s) = G(x, s) = e^{-x\sqrt{s}}$ (Eq. (3–66)), is output stable.

Obtain the sector u/e to guarantee control and output asymptoticity

a) for a general nonlinearity
b) for a zero-memory nonlinearity.

Remark: In order to satisfy conditions (10–9) (for $\alpha = 0$) for $e_0(t) = -v_0(x, t)$, one must assume finite initial potential energy on the heat conductor. This will be guaranteed if $|v(x, 0)| \le V < \infty$ for $0 \le x \le L < \infty$ and $v(x, 0) = 0$ for $x > L$. The proof that all of conditions (10–9) are satisfied for the present system is however rather involved.

10–15 Let the distributed-parameter linear element of Exercise 10–14 be controlled by an actuator in the manner shown in Fig. 6–31 (here, with $x = 2.3$, we have $G(s) = e^{-2.3\sqrt{s}}$).

a) Let $R = 0$. Obtain the range of the gain K that yields control asymptoticity [with respect to $u(t)$]. Compare this result with the result of Exercise 6–9, part (c) and comment. (Suggestion: Use an approach similar to that in Example 10–14).
b) Show that the result of (a) is not changed if $R \neq 0$. (Note that, even if the system is control asymptotic with respect to $u(t)$ and output asymptotic with respect to $e(t)$, it is not output asymptotic with respect to the plant output $y(t)$).

10–16 (Neuman) A system in the standard form with

$$G(p) = \frac{p^2}{(p + a)(p^2 + bp + c)}; \quad a, b, c > 0$$

and with $u = f(e)$ is known to be output asymptotic for $(u/e) \in [0, \infty]$.

a) Show that the above result cannot be obtained from a straightforward application of Theorem 10-1.
b) Determine whether any other theorem in this chapter can be used to obtain the correct result.

10-17 (Bergen and Sapiro) for a sector $(u/e) \in [a, b]$ and $q \neq 0$ it is possible to obtain a frequency-invariant stability boundary in the $G^\star(j\omega)$ plane:

a) Show that the following inequality can be obtained directly from condition (10-36)

$$(X^\star)^2 + \frac{a+b}{ab} X^\star + \frac{1}{ab} - \frac{b-a}{ab} qY^\star + \left(\frac{Y^\star}{\omega}\right)^2 \begin{cases} >0 , & \text{if} \quad \frac{1}{a} > \frac{1}{b} \\ <0 , & \text{if} \quad \frac{1}{a} < \frac{1}{b} \end{cases}$$

where

$$X^\star = \Re\mathrm{e}\, G^\star(j\omega) \qquad Y^\star = \Im\mathrm{m}\, G^\star(j\omega)$$

Note that the above inequality implies that

$$(X^\star)^2 + \frac{a+b}{ab} X^\star + \frac{1}{ab} - \frac{b-a}{ab} qY^\star > 0 \qquad \frac{1}{a} > \frac{1}{b} \tag{10-50}$$

is a sufficient condition that the generalized circle criterion (10-36) is satisfied.

b) For the system of Fig. 10-1, with a linear plant given by (10-32) and a time-invariant nonlinear element, determine the largest sector u/e guaranteeing absolute control and output asymptoticity via the *parabola criterion* (10-50). Compare the result with that of Examples 10-6, 10-8, and 10-9.
c) Discuss the usefulness of the criterion.

10-18 Prove Corollary 10-1 (p. 388) and show how it applies to the system of Example 10-10.

10.11 References

Three texts in English, [A1], [H3], and [L10], treat the method of Popov. These texts approach the problem via the notion of absolute stability. The first text also gives a comprehensive bibliography on Popov's method and related topics up to about 1963. A more recent survey paper on stability theory that also contains an extensive bibliography is [B18].

The original result of Popov was presented in [P9]. In a number of subsequent papers (see Bibliography in [A1]) Popov also considered systems with several nonlinearities which can contain hysteresis of a special type (see also [Y1]). He also investigated the relation between his frequency domain criterion and the existence of a Lyapunov function. The last topic was later treated in depth in [Y4] and [K3]. In [K3], Kalman shows for the indirect control configuration that Popov's criterion is necessary and sufficient for the existence of a Lyapunov function that is a quadratic form in the system states plus an integral of the nonlinearity. For a comprehensive discussion of this particular subject, see [L10].

The literature is divided between emphasizing absolute stability and on asymptotic behavior of control or output variables. Popov's original proof of absolute stability [P9] (see also [A1] and [L10]) proceeded via consideration of the asymptotic behavior of the output signal. Versions of Popov's Theorem with respect to the asymptotic behavior of the output are also given in [D4] and [S6].

The circle criterion (for $q = 0$) was introduced in [B16] for a special class of systems and in [S2] in a more complete form. It is also given (without proof) in [Z3]. For later developments, see also [S5] and [Z2].

The use of the logarithmic gain-phase plot was introduced in [N1], [N2], [M14], and [M12]. In [N1], the extension of the Popov criterion to consider the degree of stability was also discussed (see Sec. 10.5 of this chapter).

Extensions to the Popov criterion to the case where the system nonlinearity $u = f(e)$ obeys bounds of the form

$$a \leq \frac{df(e)}{de} \leq b$$

are considered in [B19], [Y3], and [D6]. For a different approach to the frequency domain criterion see [P11] and [N4].

11

Stability Considerations for Systems with Inputs

In the foregoing chapters, we have dealt mostly with the stability of systems without input, though we have taken care to point out that for systems with a completely specified input, it is possible to speak of the stability of the resultant solution. We now look at some of the available results for systems with inputs.

A minimum stability requirement for a driven system is to ask that the system output be bounded whenever the system input and system initial conditions are bounded. This form of stability is known rather naturally as bounded-input bounded-output stability, which we shall abbreviate to BIBO stability.

BIBO stability takes several forms. At the lowest level is BIBO stability in the small. This in the Russian literature is known as *total stability*. It is analogous to Lyapunov stability for systems without input. It is not really satisfactory, practically speaking, because the maximum bounds on the input and the initial condition necessary to ensure a bounded output are not known.

More useful is global BIBO stability, where, whenever the input and the initial conditions are bounded, the output is guaranteed to be bounded. Theorems governing this mode of stability only exist for linear (though time-varying) systems and Popov type nonlinear systems.

An essential tool in establishing BIBO stability mathematically is the use of inequalities. Mathematical techniques involving inequalities were used to some extent in the previous chapter (and in Appendix C). In the present chapter these techniques are employed to the full. A new inequality, the Bellman-Gronwall inequality, is introduced, and an analytical technique involving inequalities, the contraction-mapping fixed-point theorem, is used to develop an iterative method to improve on the describing function solution for systems with inputs.

The practical importance of BIBO stability should not be exaggerated. The mere fact that the output is bounded when the input is bounded gives an engineer only scant comfort. An output never goes to infinity physically, but it may become large enough to burn out fuses or trip circuit breakers. Thus, in many applications, the mere assurance of BIBO stability may not be enough; usually an estimate of the exact bound on the output is required.

Thus far the mathematics of inequalities leaves much to be desired in obtaining useful bounds for engineering assessment of physical systems. These techniques in general eliminate too much useful information in order to establish general bounds. Caution and judgment therefore are called for in applying some of the techniques to physical problems.

11.1 The Bellman-Gronwall Lemma and its Application to Stability

In Chap. 10, we have gained some hint of the fact that in searching for stability and boundedness properties of dynamic systems, it is often convenient to utilize certain constraints of the system to convert the system integral equation to an integral inequality.

An important tool for dealing with integral inequalities involving nonlinear feedback control systems with a linear portion is given by the following celebrated lemma:

◆◆Lemma 11-1 (The generalized Bellman-Gronwall Lemma*). Let $v(t)$ and $w(t)$ be real functions of t. Let $w(t) \geq 0$ and c be a real constant. If

$$v(t) \leq c + \int_0^t w(\tau)\, v(\tau)\, d\tau \tag{11-1a}$$

then

$$v(t) \leq c \exp\left[\int_0^t w(\tau)\, d\tau\right] \tag{11-1b}$$ ◆◆

The lemma is readily proved. Let us define two functions $x(t)$ and $z(t)$ such that

$$x(t) \triangleq c + \int_0^t w(\tau)\, v(\tau)\, d\tau \tag{11-2}$$

*See [K12] p. 496. In the original version of the lemma (see [B6] p. 35), it was required that $v(t) \geq 0$. (This requirement is not needed in the present version.) Lemma 11-1 can be cast into even more general forms, see e.g., [H3] pp. 7-8, and [S7] pp. 11-12.

$$v(t) \triangleq x(t) - z(t) \tag{11-3}$$

If (11-1a) holds, then $z(t) \geq 0$. Moreover, $x(t)$ is continuous. Differentiating $x(t)$ and using Eq. (11-3) we have

$$\dot{x}(t) = w(t)x(t) - w(t)z(t) \tag{11-4}$$

Equation (11-4) is in a form to be integrated by the method of Example 3-6 to yield

$$x(t) = x(0) \exp\left[\int_0^t w(\tau)\,d\tau\right] - \exp\left[\int_0^t w(\tau)\,d\tau\right] \int_0^t z(\tau)w(\tau) \exp\left[-\int_0^\tau w(\mu)\,d\mu\right] d\tau \tag{11-5}$$

Since $z(t) \geq 0$ and $w(t) \geq 0$, then

$$x(t) \leq x(0) \exp\left[\int_0^t w(\tau)\,d\tau\right] \tag{11-6}$$

But from the definition of $x(t)$, we see that $x(0) = c$. Therefore, with $z(t) \geq 0$, we have, from Eq. (11-3)

$$v(t) = x(t) - z(t) \leq x(t) = c \exp\left[\int_0^t w(\tau)\,d\tau\right]$$

which proves the lemma.

With this lemma, we can immediately obtain a useful inequality relative to the single-loop nonlinear feedback system of Fig. 11-1. The system is given by the following set of equations

$$\begin{aligned} y(t) &= -e_0(t) + \int_0^t g(t-\tau)u(\tau)\,d\tau \\ u(t) &= \mathfrak{F}[e(t), t] \\ u(t) &= r(t) - y(t) \end{aligned} \tag{11-7}$$

It is identical to the system of Eq. (10-1) except that an input $r(t)$ has been added.

♦♦Theorem 11-1. Consider the system of Fig. 11-1. Assume that:

1) For the linear element, the initial conditions are chosen such that the following conditions are satisfied:

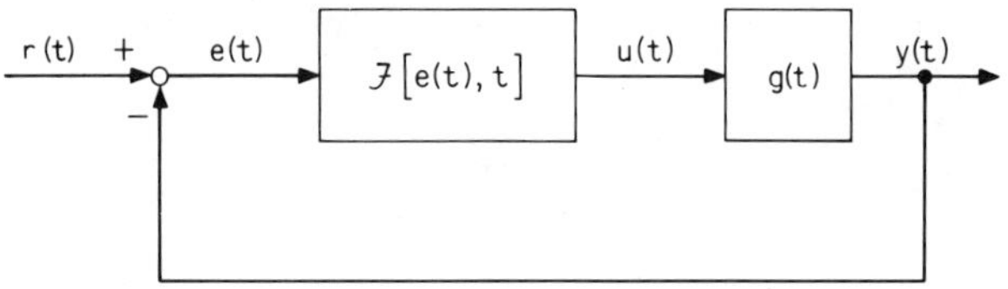

Fig. 11-1. The system of Theorem 11-1.

$$|e_0(t)| \leq c_0 e^{-\alpha t}, \quad |g(t)| \leq c_g e^{-\alpha t} \tag{11-8}$$

where c_0, c_g, and α are constants.

2) For the nonlinear element, there is a constant K such that

$$|u(t)| \leq K|e(t)| \qquad \text{for every } t \tag{11-9}$$

3) There is a constant c_r such that the input $r(t)$ obeys

$$|r(t)| < c_r e^{-\alpha t} \qquad \text{for every } t \tag{11-10}$$

If

$$\alpha > Kc_g \tag{11-11}$$

then $e(t) \to 0$ as $t \to \infty$. Moreover, $e(t)$ is bounded in the following manner

$$|e(t)| \leq (c_0 + c_r)e^{-(\alpha - Kc_g)t} \tag{11-12}$$ ◆◆

To prove the theorem, we apply (11-8) through (11-10) to the system equations (11-7) and obtain

$$|e(t)| \leq (c_r + c_0)e^{-\alpha t} + Kc_g e^{-\alpha t}\int_0^t |e(\tau)|e^{\alpha\tau}\,d\tau$$

or

$$|e(t)|e^{\alpha t} \leq (c_r + c_0) + Kc_g\int_0^t |e(\tau)|e^{\alpha\tau}\,d\tau$$

On applying Lemma 11-1, Eq. (11-12) is obtained immediately.

Theorem 11-1 yields a relatively conservative bound; however, it provides a ready tool to quickly check the stability of systems. For example, where directly applicable, it is easier to use when compared to Popov's method, though it usually gives a smaller stability boundary.

◆◆Example 11-1. Consider again the damped Mathieu equation of Example 10-13. The system equation is

$$\ddot{e}(t) + 2\dot{e}(t) + [c - 3 - d\cos\omega t]\,e(t) = 0 \qquad (11\text{-}13)$$

Thus we have, in terms of Fig. 11-1,

$$r(t) = 0, \quad u(t) = k(t)e(t), \quad G(p) = \frac{1}{(p+1)^2 + c - 4},$$

$$k(t) = d\cos\omega t \qquad (11\text{-}14)$$

The impulse response of $G(p)$ is:

$$g(t) = \frac{e^{-t}}{\sqrt{c-4}}\sin(\sqrt{c-4}\,t)$$

Therefore, we can write

$$|g(t)| \le \begin{cases} \dfrac{1}{2\sqrt{4-c}}\,e^{-(1-\sqrt{4-c})t}, & c < 4 \\[2ex] \dfrac{1}{\sqrt{c-4}}\,e^{-t}, & c > 4 \end{cases}$$

The bounds for the initial-condition response must have the same exponents. Thus, in the terminology of Theorem 11-1, we have

$$c_g = \frac{1}{2\sqrt{4-c}}, \quad \alpha = 1 - \sqrt{4-c} \qquad \text{if} \quad c < 4$$

$$c_g = \frac{1}{\sqrt{c-4}}, \quad \alpha = 1 \qquad \text{if} \quad c > 4$$

Therefore, a sufficient condition for $e(t) = 0$ as $t \to \infty$ follows from (11-11):

$$d < \begin{cases} 2(\sqrt{4-c} - 4 + c), & c < 4 \\ \sqrt{c-4}, & c > 4 \end{cases} \qquad (11\text{-}15)$$

We find that the bound for d given by (11-15) is about one half of that obtained in Example 10-13 by the frequency response method of Chap. 10 (see also Exercise 10-6). This is not surprising in view of the simplicity of the use of Theorem 11-1. However, it is this simplicity that may render the present approach attractive to the quick handling of problems where a sufficient stability condition is required whose closeness to the true stability boundary is not essential.◆◆

11.2 Stability and Boundedness of Forced Linear Time-Varying Systems

There is a good deal of intuitive appreciation of the equivalence of stability and BIBO stability in linear time-invariant systems. It turns out that this equivalence also occurs for linear time-varying systems under a mild set of conditions. Indeed we can make the above loosely stated sentence precise and comprehensive by quoting an important theorem.

Consider a general linear time-varying system given by:

$$\mathbf{x}(t) = \mathbf{\Phi}(t, t_0)\mathbf{x}(t_0) + \int_{t_0}^{t} \mathbf{\Phi}(t, \tau)\mathbf{u}(\tau)\, d\tau \tag{11-16}$$

Let us define the norm of the transition matrix as:

$$||\mathbf{\Phi}(t, t_0)|| = \sum_{i=1}^{n}\sum_{j=1}^{n} |\phi_{ij}(t, t_0)|$$

then we have [P4], [B5]:

◆◆Theorem 11-2. For the system (11-16), for every t_0, each of the properties below implies the others:

1) For every bounded input $\mathbf{u}(t)$ (i.e., there is a constant $U < \infty$ such that $||\mathbf{u}(t)|| \leq U$)* and for every finite initial condition, the state $\mathbf{x}(t)$ is bounded for all $t \geq t_0$.
2) There are positive constants b and c such that

$$||\mathbf{\Phi}(t, t_0)|| \leq b < \infty \quad \text{for every } t \geq t_0 \tag{11-17}$$

and

$$\int_{t_0}^{t} ||\mathbf{\Phi}(t, \tau)||\, d\tau \leq c < \infty \qquad \text{for every} \qquad t \geq t_0 \tag{11-18}$$

*The norm of the vector is the usual Euclidean norm

$$||\mathbf{u}(t)|| = \left(\sum_{i=1}^{r} u_i^2(t)\right)^{\frac{1}{2}}.$$

3) There exist constants $M > 0$ and $\alpha > 0$ such that

$$\|\Phi(t, t_0)\| \leq Me^{-\alpha(t - t_0)} \qquad \text{for} \qquad t \geq t_0 \tag{11-19}$$

4) For $\mathbf{u}(t) \equiv 0$, the equilibrium state $\mathbf{x} = 0$ is (globally) uniformly asymptotically stable.

Proof: To prove that (1) imples (2), we will show by contradiction that it is impossible for (1) to hold when (2) does not.

Consider a special input vector $\mathbf{u}(t) \equiv 0$, and a special initial condition vector $\mathbf{x}(t_0)$ which is 0 at every component except the kth $(0 \leq k \leq n)$ where the value of unity is assumed. Assume that there is a value of t such that the component ϕ_{jk} of Φ is unbounded, i.e., $|\phi_{jk}(t, t_0)| = \infty$; then

$$\infty = |\phi_{jk}(t, t_0)| = |x_j(t)| \leq \sum_{i=1}^{n} |x_i(t)| \leq \sqrt{n}\|\mathbf{x}(t)\|$$

which violates condition (1) of the theorem. Thus in order for $\|\mathbf{x}(t)\| < \infty$, it is necessary that $|\phi_{jk}(t, t_0)| < \infty$ for all possible j, k and for all t_0 and t; hence $\|\phi(t, t_0)\| < \infty$ for all t_0 and t.

Again if we consider a special initial condition $\mathbf{x}(t_0) = 0$ and a special input $\mathbf{u}(t)$ which is zero at every component except the kth where $u_k(t) = \operatorname{sgn}\phi_{jk}(t, \tau)$. If we assume that for the component $\phi_{jk}(t, \tau)$, $\int_{t_0}^{t} |\phi_{jk}(t, \tau)|\, d\tau = \infty$, then we have

$$\infty = \int_{t_0}^{t} |\phi_{jk}(t, \tau)| d\tau = \int_{t_0}^{t} \phi_{jk}(t, \tau) \operatorname{sgn}\phi_{ik}(t, \tau)\, d\tau = |x_j(t)| \leq \sqrt{n}\, \|\mathbf{x}(t)\|$$

Thus, in order for $\|x(t)\| < \infty$, it is necessary that $\int_{t_0}^{t} |\phi_{jk}(t, \tau)|\, d\tau < \infty$ for every j, k, which implies that (11-18) must hold.

To show that (2) implies (3), let us define the constants b and c in (11-17) and (11-18) by*

$$\max_{t, t_0} \int_{t_0}^{t} \|\Phi(t, \tau)\|\, d\tau = \max_{t, t_0} \int_{t_0}^{t} \|\Phi(\tau, t_0)\|\, d\tau \triangleq c < \infty \tag{11-20}$$

$$\max_{t, t_0} \|\Phi(t, t_0)\| \triangleq b < \infty \tag{11-21}$$

*Mathematically it is more exact to use the operation $\sup_t[\quad]$, meaning the least upper bound of the quantity that follows, but we choose to use $\max_t[\quad]$ to lessen the shock of newness to some readers. For ordinary control problems the two operations are clearly the same. This comment applies to the remainder of this book.

Furthermore, define the sequence of numbers b_n, $n = 0, 1, 2, \ldots$, by

$$b_n \triangleq \max_{t,\, t_0} (t - t_0)^n \, \|\Phi(t, t_0)\|, \qquad n = 0, 1, 2, \ldots, \; t \geq t_0 \tag{11-22}$$

where we see from (11-21) that $b_0 = b$.

Since $\Phi(t, t_0) = \Phi(t, \tau)\Phi(\tau, t_0)$ for all t_0, t, and τ, we have

$$b_n = \max_{t,\, t_0} n \int_{t_0}^{t} (t - \tau)^{n-1} \|\Phi(t, t_0)\| \, d\tau$$

$$\leq \max_{t,\, t_0} n \int_{t_0}^{t} (t - \tau)^{n-1} \|\Phi(t, \tau)\| \, \|\Phi(\tau, t_0)\| \, d\tau \leq n b_{n-1} c$$

We thus have

$$b_n \leq c n b_{n-1} \leq c^2 n(n-1) b_{n-2} \leq \cdots \leq c^n n! \, b_0 = c^n n! \, b$$

or, by (11-22)

$$(t - t_0)^n \|\Phi(t, t_0)\| \leq c^n n! \, b$$

Let us select an $\alpha > 0$ such that $\alpha c < 1$; then

$$\frac{\|\Phi(t, t_0)\|}{b} \sum_{n=0}^{\infty} \frac{1}{n!} [\alpha(t - t_0)]^n \leq \sum_{n=0}^{\infty} (\alpha c)^n$$

or

$$\frac{\|\Phi(t, t_0)\|}{b} e^{\alpha(t - t_0)} \leq \frac{1}{1 - \alpha c}$$

and condition (3) follows with $M = b/(1 - \alpha c)$.

To show that (3) implies (4), we see that for $\mathbf{u}(t) = 0$,

$$\|\mathbf{x}(t)\| \leq \|\Phi(t, t_0)\| \, \|\mathbf{x}(t_0)\| \leq M e^{-\alpha(t - t_0)} \|\mathbf{x}(t_0)\|$$

For every $\epsilon > 0$, we can pick a $\delta < \epsilon/M$ to satisfy the requirement of global Lyapunov asymptotic stability (see Definition 5-16). Since δ does not depend on t_0, we further have global uniform asymptotic stability.

To show that (4) implies (3), we see that with δ and for every μ, and the corresponding T as given in Sec. 5.6 we have, for all t_0:

$$\|\mathbf{x}(t_0 + T)\| \leq \|\Phi(t_0 + T, t_0)\| \, \|\mathbf{x}(t_0)\| \leq \|\Phi(t_0 + T, t_0)\| \, \delta \leq \mu \tag{11-23}$$

where δ does not depend on t_0. Therefore, for all t_0 and for $n = 1, 2, 3, \ldots$ we can also write

$$\|\Phi(t_0 + nT, t_0 + (n-1)T)\| \le \frac{\mu}{\delta}$$

or, since $\Phi(t_1, t_2)\Phi(t_2, t_3) = \Phi(t_1, t_3)$,

$$\begin{aligned} \|\Phi(t_0 + nT, t_0)\| &= \left\| \prod_{k=1}^{n} \Phi(t_0 + kT, t_0 + (k-1)T) \right\| \\ &\le \prod_{k=1}^{n} \|\Phi(t_0 + kT, t_0 + (k-1)T)\| \le \left(\frac{\mu}{\delta}\right)^n \end{aligned} \tag{11-24}$$

If we choose M and α such that $\mu/\delta = M\exp(-\alpha T)$ and $nT = t$, (11-24) becomes (11-19), which is condition (3) of Theorem 11-2.

It is left to the reader to show that (3) implies (2) and (2) implies (1).

11.3 Total Stability—BIBO Stability in the Small

Analogous to stability in the small, we have BIBO stability in the small. As in the case of stability in the small, BIBO stability in the small is rather restricted in its meaning but is nevertheless easy to prove because of the existence of a comprehensive theorem. In the Russian literature, the rather unfortunate name *total stability* has been given for this mode of stability [H2], [M3].

Consider a system of the following form

$$\begin{aligned} \dot{\mathbf{x}} &= \mathbf{f}(\mathbf{x}, t) + \mathbf{g}(\mathbf{x}, t), \qquad \mathbf{x}(t_0) = \mathbf{x}_0 \\ \mathbf{f}(\mathbf{0}, t) &\equiv \mathbf{0} \qquad \text{for all} \quad t > t_0 \end{aligned} \tag{11-25}$$

We note that if $\mathbf{g}$ is not dependent on $\mathbf{x}$, it may be viewed as the conventional type of input, such as is shown in Fig. 11-2a. If $\mathbf{g}$ is a function of $\mathbf{x}$ as well as t, then it may include components of undesired disturbances which enter at points inside the control loop such as shown in Fig. 11-2b.

Fig. 11-2a. A system of the form of Eq. (11-25) in which $\mathbf{g}$ is not dependent on $\mathbf{x}$.

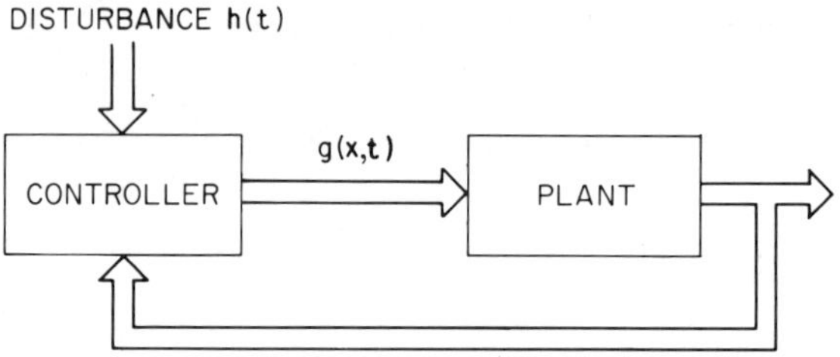

Fig. 11-2b. A system of the form of Eq. (11-25) in which **g** is dependent on **x**.

If $g(x, t) \equiv 0$ in (11–25), the system is said to be unperturbed. The unperturbed system is seen to have an equilibrium state $x = 0$.

♦♦Definition 11-1. The equilibrium state $x = 0$ of the unperturbed system $\dot{x} = f(x, t)$ is totally stable if for every $\epsilon > 0$, two positive numbers $\delta_1(\epsilon)$ and $\delta_2(\epsilon)$ can be found such that the solution $x(t)$ of the perturbed system (11–25) obeys $\|x(t)\| < \epsilon$ for $t > t_0$ provided that $\|x_0\| < \delta_1$ and $\|g(x, t)\| < \delta_2$.♦♦

The stability concept given by Definition 11–1 is in the small since it merely states that the output can be kept within an arbitrarily small neighborhood of the origin 0 provided that the input *and* the initial conditions are kept *sufficiently* small. However, the definition gives us no clue on the exact size of this smallness.

It turns out that a large class of feedback control systems with a stable linear part is totally stable.

Consider a class of feedback systems which obeys

$$\dot{x}(t) = A(t)x(t) + u(x, t), \quad u(x, t) = h\big(x(t), t\big) + r(t) \tag{11-26}$$

or equivalently, the form

$$\begin{aligned} x(t) &= \Phi(t, t_0)x(t_0) + \int_{t_0}^{t} \Phi(t, \tau)u(x, \tau)\,d\tau \\ u(x, t) &= h\big(x(t), t\big) + r(t) \end{aligned} \tag{11-27}$$

These systems, for example, may describe the linearized motion of a nonlinear system about a given trajectory. We recall that Theorem 5–2 gave a rather important result concerning the uniform asymptotic stability of systems essentially of the form of (11–26). In the light of Theorem 11–2, however, we can now bring together uniform asymptotic stability and total stability for these systems in the following way:

♦♦Theorem 11-3 [K8]. For system (11–26) or (11–27), let

$$\frac{\|h\big(x(t), t\big)\|}{\|x(t)\|} \to 0 \quad \text{uniformly as} \quad \|x(t)\| \to 0 \tag{11-28}$$

Let the linear system defined by setting $\mathrm{h}(\mathrm{x}(t), t) = 0$ satisfy any of the properties (1) to (4) of Theorem 11-2; then

1) For $\mathrm{r}(t) = 0$, the system is uniformly asymptotically stable.
2) Relative to the input $\mathrm{r}(t)$, the system is totally stable.♦♦

Proof: To prove part (1) of the theorem, we note that the condition (11-28) means that for every constant $k_1 > 0$ there is another constant k_2 depending on k_1 such that for all t,

$$||\mathrm{h}(\mathrm{x}(t), t)|| \leq k_1 ||\mathrm{x}(t)|| \qquad \text{whenever} \qquad ||\mathrm{x}(t)|| \leq k_2 \tag{11-29}$$

With $\mathrm{r}(t) \equiv 0$ in (11-27) and using the bound (11-28) as well as condition (3) of Theorem 11-2, we can then write:

$$||\mathrm{x}(t)|| e^{\alpha(t - t_0)} \leq \mathrm{M} ||\mathrm{x}(t_0)|| + Mk_1 e^{-\alpha t_0} \int_{t_0}^{t} e^{\alpha\tau} ||\mathrm{x}(\tau)|| \, d\tau$$

or

$$||\mathrm{x}(t + t_0)|| e^{\alpha t} \leq \mathrm{M} ||\mathrm{x}(t_0)|| + Mk_1 \int_{0}^{t} e^{\alpha\tau} ||\mathrm{x}(\tau + t_0)|| \, d\tau$$

On applying the Bellman-Gronwall Lemma (Lemma 11-1), we obtain

$$e^{\alpha t} ||\mathrm{x}(t + t_0)|| \leq \mathrm{M} ||\mathrm{x}(t_0)|| e^{Mk_1 t} \quad , \; t \geq 0$$

or,

$$||\mathrm{x}(t)|| \leq \mathrm{M} ||\mathrm{x}(t_0)|| e^{-(\alpha - Mk_1)(t - t_0)} \quad , \; t \geq t_0 \tag{11-30}$$

By the statement of the theorem, k_1 can be made arbitrarily small relative to the numbers α and M as $||\mathrm{x}(t)|| \to 0$. Hence, for every $\epsilon > 0$ we can pick a $\delta > 0$ such that $||\mathrm{x}(t)|| \leq \epsilon$ whenever $||\mathrm{x}(t_0)|| \leq \delta$. In particular, a suitable value for δ is $\delta = \min[(\epsilon/\mathrm{M}), \kappa]$, where κ is defined such that $k_1 < \alpha/\mathrm{M}$ for $||\mathrm{x}(t_0)|| \leq \kappa/\mathrm{M}$. Since δ is independent of t_0 and, moreover, by (11-30), $||\mathrm{x}(t)|| \to 0$ as $t \to \infty$ uniformly in t_0 and $||\mathrm{x}(t_0)||$, the equilibrium state $\mathrm{x} = 0$ is uniformly asymptotically stable.

Part (2) of Theorem 11-3 can be proved by contradiction. Let δ_1 be the bound on $||\mathrm{x}(t_0)||$ and δ_2 be the bound on $r(t)$: then for a sufficiently small $||x(t_0)||$ we can write in view of Eqs. (11-27) and

(11-29) and condition (3) of Theorem 11-2

$$\|\mathbf{x}(t)\| \leq M\delta_1 e^{-\alpha(t-t_0)} + k_1 \int_{t_0}^{t} \|\mathbf{\Phi}(t,\tau)\| \, \|\mathbf{x}(\tau)\| \, d\tau + \frac{M\delta_2}{\alpha}\left(1 - e^{-\alpha(t-t_0)}\right) \quad \text{for } t \geq 0$$

or

$$\|\mathbf{x}(t)\| \leq M\left(\delta_1 + \frac{\delta_2}{\alpha}\right) + k_1 \int_{t_0}^{t} \|\mathbf{\Phi}(t,\tau)\| \, \|\mathbf{x}(\tau)\| \, d\tau, \quad t > 0 \tag{11-31}$$

We wish to show now that if δ_1 and δ_2 are sufficiently small then $\|\mathbf{x}(t)\|$ can be made arbitrarily small. Since the integral in (11-31) is monotonically increasing with t, there is a t_0 such that

$$\|\mathbf{x}(t)\| < 2M\left(\delta_1 + \frac{\delta_2}{\alpha}\right) \quad \text{for} \quad t \geq t_0 \tag{11-32}$$

Now at $t = t_0$, (11-32) certainly holds. Assume, however, that (11-32) does not hold for all t, and let t_1 be the first time that $\|\mathbf{x}(t)\| = 2M[\delta_1 + (\delta_2/\alpha)]$. Noting that the rhs of (11-31) is monotonically increasing with t, we have

$$\max_{t_0 \leq t \leq t_1} \|\mathbf{x}(t)\| = \|\mathbf{x}(t_1)\| \leq M\left(\delta_1 + \frac{\delta_2}{\alpha}\right) + k_1 \|\mathbf{x}(t_1)\| \int_{t_0}^{t_1} \|\mathbf{\Phi}(t,\tau)\| \, d\tau$$

Since by assumption $\int_{t_0}^{t} \|\mathbf{\Phi}(t,\tau)\| \, d\tau \leq c < \infty$ for any $t \geq t_0$, we have

$$\|\mathbf{x}(t_1)\| \leq \frac{M[\delta_1 + (\delta_2/\alpha)]}{1 - Mk_1 c} \tag{11-33}$$

The quantity $Mk_1 c$ in (11-33) can be made arbitrarily small because k_1 can be made arbitrarily small in $[t_0, t_1]$ by choosing $\|\mathbf{r}(t)\|$ and $\|\mathbf{x}(t_0)\|$ small enough. In this case (11-33) contradicts the assumption that (11-32) does not hold. Part (2) of Theorem 11-3 is thus proved.

As we may perhaps expect, the close relationship between the uniform asymptotic stability of an equilibrium state of a system without input and the total stability of the same system with input covers more than systems with a linear part. In fact we have:

◆◆Theorem 11-4. Consider a system of the form (11-25). If with $\mathbf{g} \equiv 0$ the origin of the system is uniformly asymptotically stable, then the system is totally stable.◆◆

In the light of the proof for Theorem 11-3, Theorem 11-4 is perhaps believable. Because of a lack of a suitable bound for nonlinear systems that are uniformly asymptotically stable, however, there apparently does not exist a proof along the lines of the previous proofs in this chapter. There is a proof using Lyapunov functions the high points of which we list below.

To begin with, it has been proved by Massera [M4] that if system (11-25), with f satisfying a local Lipschitz condition and with $g \equiv 0$, is uniformly asymptotically stable, then there exists a Lyapunov function satisfying the conditions of Theorem 9-11 for the system. With this, the following lemma by Malkin [M3] then completes the proof.

♦♦Lemma 11-2. If a scalar function $V(x, t)$ satisfying the condition of Theorem 9-11 exists for the system (11-25) with $g \equiv 0$, then the equilibrium state $x = 0$ is totally stable.♦♦

To prove Lemma 11-2, for any $\epsilon > 0$, we must produce δ_1 and δ_2 to satisfy the conditions for total stability. Now the assumptions of the lemma mean that there exist two continuous strictly increasing functions $\phi(z)$ and $\rho(z)$ with $\phi(0) = \rho(0) = 0$ such that $V(x, t)$, the Lyapunov function for the problem, satisfies

Moreover, for the system (11-25) with $g \equiv 0$

$$\phi(\|x\|) \le V(x, t) \le \rho(\|x\|) \tag{11-34}$$

$$\dot{V}(x, t) = (\text{grad } V)^T f + \frac{\partial V}{\partial t} \le -\theta(\|x\|) \tag{11-35}$$

where $\theta(z)$ is a positive-definite (pd) function of one variable.

If we take the $V(x, t)$ above and find $\dot{V}$ along the trajectories of (11-25) with $g \neq 0$, we find that

$$\dot{V}(x, t) = (\text{grad } V)^T (f + g) + \frac{\partial V}{\partial t} \tag{11-36}$$

The difference between (11-36) and (11-35) is the term

$$(\text{grad } V)^T g = \sum_{i=1}^{n} \frac{\partial V}{\partial x_i} g_i(x, t) \tag{11-37}$$

If the g_i's were made sufficiently small, then in view of the bound in (11-35), we can always choose $\|x_0\|$ such that $\dot{V} < 0$ in (11-36). This means that V can only decrease monotonically with time in the region. With (11-34), it is implied that $\|x(t)\|$ is bounded. The remaining task is to choose $\|x_0\|$ and $\|g\|$ small enough to satisfy both the foregoing requirements and the condition that $\|x(t)\| < \epsilon$; this always can be done.

The two theorems discussed in this section are limited to total stability or BIBO stability in the small. For global BIBO stability, further restrictions are needed.* It is useful to point out that even for a time-invariant system, we still cannot say that if the origin of the (unperturbed) system $\dot{\mathbf{x}} = \mathbf{f}(\mathbf{x})$ with $\mathbf{f}(0) \equiv 0$ is globally uniformly asymptotically stable, then the driven system $\dot{\mathbf{x}} = \mathbf{f}(\mathbf{x}) + \mathbf{u}(t)$ is BIBO stable. An interesting illustration of this is given in Exercise 11-17.

11.4 Global BIBO Stability of a Class of Single-Loop Control Systems

We will use the unqualified term BIBO stability to mean BIBO stability in the global sense. The definition of BIBO stability can be given in the following way:

◆◆Definition 11-2. A dynamic system with a single input and a single output is BIBO stable if, for every $\delta_1 \geq 0$ and $\delta_2 \geq 0$, there is an $\epsilon(\delta_1, \delta_2) > 0$ such that the absolute value of the output will be bounded by ϵ whenever the absolute value of the input and the norm of the initial conditions are bounded by δ_1 and δ_2 respectively.**◆◆

This property can be ascertained for several classes of dynamic systems. Consider, for example, the linear time-varying system given by

$$\mathbf{x}(t) = \mathbf{\Phi}(t, t_0)\mathbf{x}(t_0) + \int_{t_0}^{t} \mathbf{\Phi}(t, \tau)\mathbf{b}(\tau)r(\tau)\,d\tau \qquad \text{(11-38a)}$$

$$y(t) = \mathbf{c}^T(t)\mathbf{x}(t) \qquad \text{(11-38b)}$$

where $r(t)$ is the input and $y(t)$ is the output. Equation (11-38a) is identical to (11-16), with $\mathbf{u}(t) = \mathbf{b}(t)r(t)$. Equation (11-38b) relates the state $\mathbf{x}(t)$ linearly to the output $y(t)$. For this system, the following theorem holds:

◆◆Theorem 11-5. If for system (11-38) with $r(t) = 0$, the equilibrium $\mathbf{x} = 0$ is uniformly asymptotically stable, and, if $\|\mathbf{c}^T(t)\| = \sum_{i=1}^{n} c_i^2(t) < \infty$, $\|\mathbf{b}(t)\| = \sum_{i=1}^{n} b_i^2(t) < \infty$ for all t, then the forced system (11-38) is BIBO stable.◆◆

This theorem follows directly from Theorem 11-2 (see Exercise 11-2). The applicability of Theorem 11-5 to a time-invariant

*See, e.g., [V2]; also see Sec. 11.4.

**Note the difference in the role that δ_1, δ_2 and ϵ play between Definitions 11-2 and 11-1. Definition 11-2 can easily be extended to systems with multiple inputs and outputs.

linear system is well known. For the unforced time-invariant linear system with a transfer function $G(s) = \mathbf{c}^T \Phi(s)\mathbf{b}$, where $\Phi(s) = (\mathbf{I}s - \mathbf{A})^{-1}$, the origin $\mathbf{x} = 0$ of the state space is uniformly asymptotically stable if and only if every pole of each element $\phi_{ij}(s)$ of the matrix $\Phi(s)$ lies in $\Re e\, s < 0$. In that case, the transfer function $G(s)$ has all its poles in $\Re e\, s < 0$ and it can be shown that every bounded input $r(t)$ produces a bounded output $y(t)$ (see also Exercise 11-3). Theorem 11-5 extends BIBO stability to time-varying linear systems as well.

For nonlinear systems, however, no such general theorems can be found. Results can only be obtained for the special class of systems treated in the Lur'e or the Popov problems.

Consider the single-loop control system shown in Fig. 11-1, given by (11-7):

$$y(t) = -e_0(t) + \int_0^t g(t - \tau)u(\tau)\,d\tau \tag{11-39a}$$

$$u(t) = \mathcal{F}[e(t), t] \tag{11-39b}$$

$$e(t) = r(t) - y(t) \tag{11-39c}$$

In Chap. 10, frequency-response criteria were presented for the asymptotic behavior of this system with zero-input, $r(t) = 0$. Suppose a system satisfying any one of these criteria is control asymptotic for $r(t) = 0$, we may reasonably ask whether this implies that the forced system is BIBO stable. The answer is given by the following theorem:

♦♦**Theorem 11-6.** Let the system given by (11-39) or Fig. 11-1 with $r(t) = 0$ satisfy the conditions of Theorem 10-1, 10-4, or 10-5 of Chap. 10 such that it is control asymptotic of degree ϵ for a sufficiently small $\epsilon > 0$ (see Theorem 10-3).*

1) If both $r(t)$ and $\dot{r}(t)$ are bounded for all t, then the output $y(t)$ will be bounded for all finite initial conditions.
2) The requirements in these three theorems regarding output stability of the linear element** can be waived if the linear element $G(p)$ can be obtained by zero-shifting transformation (10-38) from an element $G_c(p) = G(p) - c$ that is output stable, provided that $c \geq 0$ and $(u/e) \in [0, \infty]$.

* The requirement that the unforced system be control asymptotic of degree $\epsilon > 0$ for a sufficiently small ϵ is not very restrictive. For example, if $G(s)$ and $E_0(s)$ are rational functions of s, then the reader may show by suitable continuity arguments that if the system is control asymptotic (of degree 0) an $\epsilon > 0$ can be found such that the system is also control asymptotic of degree ϵ.

** In case of Theorems 10-4 and 10-5, this refers to the linear element obtained by negative feedback gain $a \geq 0$.

3) If the conditions of the theorems in Chap. 10 (for the unforced system) are satisfied for $q = 0$, then the boundedness requirement of $\dot{r}(t)$ can be omitted.◆◆

Theorems along the lines of Theorem 11-6 have been presented by Bergen, Iwens, and Rault [B9], and by Sandberg [S3], [S5], and [S6].*

Proof of Theorem 11-6. From (11-39a) we obtain, upon multiplying and dividing the integrand by $e^{\epsilon(t-\tau)}$, the following inequality:

$$|y(t)| \leq |e_0(t)| + \left| \int_0^t e^{\epsilon(t-\tau)} g(t-\tau) e^{-\epsilon(t-\tau)} u(\tau)\, d\tau \right|$$

Because of the conditions of the theorem, we can write:

$$\left. \begin{aligned} |r(t)| &\leq r_m < \infty \\ |\dot{r}(t)| &\leq r_m' < \infty \\ |e_0(t)| &\leq e_{0m} < \infty \end{aligned} \right\} \tag{11-40}$$

Then, using Schwarz's inequality,** the above integral inequality becomes

$$|y(t)| \leq e_{0m} + \left(\int_0^t e^{2\epsilon\tau} g^2(\tau)\, d\tau \right)^{\frac{1}{2}} \left(\int_0^t e^{-2\epsilon(t-\tau)} u^2(\tau)\, d\tau \right)^{\frac{1}{2}} \tag{11-41}$$

The major part of the proof will consist of showing that the two integrals are finite if the conditions of any of the theorems in Chap. 10 are satisfied. We shall start with the basic Theorem 10-1 (as modified by Theorem 10-3). First of all, we require output stability of degree ϵ for sufficiently small $\epsilon > 0$ of the linear element which, by (10-9), implies that there exists a constant c_g such that

$$\left(\int_0^t e^{2\epsilon\tau} g^2(\tau)\, d\tau \right)^{\frac{1}{2}} \leq c_g < \infty, \quad 0 \leq t \leq \infty \tag{11-42}$$

For the other integral expression in (11-41), the following lemma holds:

*[S3], and [S5], which consider the case of $q = 0$ where $t^n g(t) \in \mathfrak{L}_1$ and $\mathfrak{L}_2$ for $n = 0, 1, 2$ (which is more general than the result here, and may be of use for certain distributed parameter systems).

**See Section C-1, Appendix C.

♦♦Lemma 11-3. For system (11-39) with $r(t) = 0$, let all conditions of Theorem 10-1, modified by Theorem 10-3, be satisfied so that the system is control asymptotic of degree ϵ for some sufficiently small $\epsilon > 0$. Then, for the case $r(t) \neq 0$, if there are constants r_m and r_m' such that $|r(t)| \leq r_m < \infty$ and $|\dot{r}(t)| \leq r_m' < \infty$, the following holds.

$$\left(\int_0^t e^{-2\epsilon(t-\tau)} u^2(\tau)\, d\tau\right)^{\frac{1}{2}} \leq c_u < \infty \,, \quad 0 \leq t \leq \infty \tag{11-43}$$

where c_u is a constant which depends on the initial conditions.

The requirement in Theorem 10-1 that the linear element be output-stable of degree $\epsilon > 0$ can be waived if this linear element can be obtained by zero-shifting transformation (10-38) from one that is output stable of degree $\epsilon > 0$. The requirement that $|\dot{r}(t)| \leq r_m' < \infty$ can be waived for those cases for which Theorem 10-1 (for the unforced system), modified by Theorem 10-3, can be satisfied for $q = 0$.♦♦

The proof of this lemma is outlined in Sec. C-5 of Appendix C. As a result of this lemma, it follows from (11-40) to (11-43) that

$$|y(t)| \leq e_{0m} + c_g c_u < \infty \,, \quad 0 \leq t \leq \infty \tag{11-44}$$

Thus, we have proved that, if the linear element is output stable of degree $\epsilon > 0$ and the nonlinear element satisfies $(u/e) \in [0,K]$. $0 \leq K \leq \infty$,* then control asymptoticity of degree $\epsilon > 0$ of the unforced system by virtue of Theorem 10-1, modified by Theorem 10-3, implies BIBO stability.

Next, we will show that the same applies to Theorem 10-4. If the conditions of that theorem are satisfied, then the pole-shifted system shown in Fig. 10-9b will satisfy all the requirements of Theorem 10-1** (see Proof of Theorem 10-4). Since

$$\frac{1}{1 + aG(s)} = 1 - \frac{aG(s)}{1 + aG(s)} = 1 - aG_a(s) = \frac{\mathfrak{L}[r_a(t) + e_{a0}(t)]}{\mathfrak{L}[r(t) + e_0(t)]}$$

(see Fig. 10-9), we have for the initial-condition response of the

*See the conditions of Theorem 10-1 for restrictions on K, depending on the nature of the nonlinear element.

**As modified by Theorem 10-3 for control asymptoticity of degree $\epsilon > 0$.

transformed system, with (11-40),

$$|r_a(t) + e_{0a}(t)| \leq \left| r(t) + e_0(t) - a\int_0^t g_a(t-\tau)[r(\tau) + e_0(\tau)]\, d\tau \right| \tag{11-45}$$
$$\leq (r_m + e_{0m})(1 + ac_a)$$

where c_a is defined such that

$$\int_0^\infty |g_a(t)|\, dt \leq c_a < \infty \tag{11-46}$$

This integral is finite because, by the conditions of Theorem 10-4 and the requirement of Theorem 11-5, the pole-shifted linear element (of unit-impulse response $g_a(t)$) is output stable of degree $\epsilon > 0$, which also implies that

$$\left(\int_0^t e^{2\epsilon\tau} g_a^2(\tau)\, d\tau\right)^{\frac{1}{2}} \leq c_{g_a} < \infty \tag{11-47}$$

From Lemma 11-3, we have for the pole-shifted system of Fig. 10-9b,

$$\left(\int_0^t e^{-2\epsilon(t-\tau)} u_a^2(\tau)\, d\tau\right)^{\frac{1}{2}} \leq c_{u_a} < \infty, \quad 0 \leq t \leq \infty \tag{11-48}$$

so that for this system, by (11-45), (11-47), and (11-48), corresponding to (11-44), we have

$$|e(t)| = \left| r_a(t) + e_{a0}(t) - \int_0^t g_a(t-\tau) u_a(\tau)\, d\tau \right|$$
$$\leq (r_m + e_{0m})(1 + ac_a) + c_{g_a} c_{u_a} < \infty, \quad 0 \leq t \leq \infty$$

Therefore, by (11-39c), we have, for the original system

$$|y(t)| = |r(t) - e(t)| \leq r_m + (r_m + e_{0m})(1 + ac_a) + c_{g_a} c_{u_a} < \infty \quad \text{for} \quad 0 \leq t \leq \infty \tag{11-49}$$

Theorem 10-5 is a special case of Theorem 10-4 and hence, as the reader may verify, no special proof is necessary.

Suppose now that the requirement on output stability of the linear element is not satisfied. Consider first Theorem 10-1, and assume that the linear element $G(p)$ can be obtained by the zero-shifting transformation (10-38), $e_c(t) = e(t) + cu(t)$, from an element $G_c(p) = G(p) - c$ that is output stable of degree $\epsilon > 0$. This transformation is illustrated in Fig. 10-16. The unit-impulse response of the transformed element then is $g_c(t) = g(t) - c\mu_0(t)$ where $\mu_0(t)$ is the unit impulse. With this, we obtain from (11-39a) and (11-39c)

$$e(t) = r(t) - e_0(t) - \int_0^t g_c(t-\tau)\,u(\tau)\,d\tau - cu(t)$$

Therefore, with (11-40) and (11-43),

$$|e(t) + cu(t)| \leq r_m + e_{0m} + c_{g_c} c_u < \infty, \quad 0 \leq t \leq \infty \qquad (11\text{-}50)$$

where c_{g_c} is defined analogous to c_g in (11-42); i.e., for arbitrarily small $\epsilon > 0$

$$\left(\int_0^t e^{2\epsilon\tau} g_c^{\,2}(\tau)\,d\tau\right)^{\frac{1}{2}} \leq c_{g_c} < \infty, \quad 0 \leq t \leq \infty \qquad (11\text{-}51)$$

Condition (11-51) is satisfied since, by the statement of the theorem, the linear element with unit-impulse response $g_c(t)$ is output stable of degree $\epsilon > 0$. Condition (11-43) holds by virtue of Lemma 11-3.

Consider now the restrictions $c \geq 0$ and $(u/e) \in [0, \infty]$ stated in Theorem 11-6. Then $\operatorname{sgn} u = \operatorname{sgn} e$ and, therefore, $|e(t) + cu(t)| = |e(t)| + c|u(t)|$, so that (11-50) becomes

$$|e(t)| + c|u(t)| \leq r_m + e_{0m} + c_{g_c} c_u < \infty, \quad 0 \leq t \leq \infty \qquad (11\text{-}52a)$$

This means that both $u(t)$ and $e(t)$ are bounded. Therefore, from (11-39c), (11-40), and (11-41),

$$|y(t)| = |r(t) - e(t)| \leq r_m + |e(t)| \leq r_m + |e(t)| + c|u(t)|$$

$$\leq 2r_m + e_{0m} + c_{g_c} c_u < \infty, \quad 0 \leq t \leq \infty \qquad (11\text{-}52b)$$

Next, we have to prove that if Theorem 10-4 is used, then the output-stability requirement of the linear element obtained by applying feedback gain $a \geq 0$ about the original element can be waived, as long as that linear element $G_a(p) = G(p)/[1 + aG(p)]$ can be obtained by zero-shifting transformation (10-38), where the element $G_c(p)$ is output stable of degree $\epsilon > 0$. Instead of (11-45), we than have

$$|r_a(t) + e_{0a}(t)| \leq \left| r(t) + e_0(t) - a\int_0^t g_c(t-\tau)e_0(\tau)\,d\tau + cae_0(t)\right|$$

$$\leq (r_m + e_{0m})(1 + ac_c + ca) < \infty \tag{11-53}$$

where c_c is defined such that

$$\int_0^\infty |g_c(t)|\,dt \leq c_c < \infty \tag{11-54}$$

Analogous to (11-51), we have for the pole-shifted system

$$|e(t)| + c|u_a(t)| \leq (r_m + e_{0m})(1 + ac_c + ca) + c_{g_c}c_{u_a} < \infty \tag{11-55a}$$

$$|y(t)| = |r(t) - e(t)| \leq r_m + |e(t)| \leq r_m + |e(t)| + c|u_a(t)|$$

$$\leq r_m + (r_m + e_{0m})(1 + ac_c + ca) + c_{g_c}c_{u_a} < \infty \tag{11-55b}$$

As before, since Theorem 10-5 represents a special case of Theorem 10-4, no special proof is necessary for the case where the conditions of that theorem hold for the unforced system.

Finally, we come to the case where the conditions of either of the theorems in Chap. 10 can be satisfied for $q = 0$. Then, according to Lemma 11-3, condition (11-43) holds even if $\dot{r}(t)$ is not bounded. The boundedness requirement of $\dot{r}(t)$ is not needed in the rest of the proof of Theorem 11-6. The omission of this requirement holds for all cases in the theorem for which $q = 0$. This concludes the proof of Theorem 11-6.

11.5 Process Stability—The Stability of a Forced Solution

In the Russian literature, the stability of a forced solution is sometimes known as process stability [N2], [Y2]. In this section, we shall show that the process stability of a Popov-type system is relatively easy to determine by the use of perturbation analysis and by some of the theorems of Chap. 10. We shall consider a system of Fig. 11-1 with a memoryless nonlinearity $u(t) = f(e(t), t)$.

1. Linear Time-Varying System

Consider first the case where $f(e(t), t)$ is given by a time-varying gain $k(t)$. The system equation is given by

$$e(t) = e_0(t) + r(t) - \int_0^t g(t-\tau)k(\tau)e(\tau)\,d\tau \tag{11-56}$$

Suppose that $|e_0(t)| < \infty$ for $t \in (0, \infty)$, $g(t) \in \mathfrak{L}_1$ and $\mathfrak{L}_2$ and $e_0(t) \in \mathfrak{L}_2$,* each over $(0, \infty)$ and assume, moreover, that for $r(t) = 0$ and $a \leq k(t) \leq b$, the circle criterion of Theorem 10-4 is satisfied for $q = 0$, which implies that with $r(t) \equiv 0$ the unforced system is absolutely control and output asymptotic for the given range of $k(t)$.

If now an input $r(t)$ is imposed, then for a given initial condition, a system solution $e(t)$ is completely specified by Eq. (11-56).

Suppose that at $t = 0$ the set of initial conditions is changed; then $e_0(t)$ and hence $e(t)$ will be changed. Letting $e'(t) = e(t) + \Delta e(t)$ and $e'_0(t) = e_0(t) + \Delta e_0(t)$** be the perturbed values of $e(t)$ and $e_0(t)$ respectively, we have

$$e'(t) = e'_0(t) + r(t) - \int_0^t g(t-\tau)k(\tau)e'(\tau)\,d\tau \tag{11-57}$$

Subtracting Eq. (11-57) from Eq. (11-56), there remains an equation in the perturbing variables $\Delta e(t)$

$$\Delta e(t) = \Delta e_0(t) - \int_0^t g(t-\tau)k(\tau)\Delta e(\tau)\,d\tau \tag{11-58}$$

For this particular perturbation, note that $r(t)$ is subtracted out of the problem and an equivalent unforced linear system results in Eq. (11-58). As the plant is linear, $\Delta e_0(t)$ is of the same form as $e_0(t)$ and hence $|\Delta e_0(t)| < \infty$ and $\Delta e_0(t) \in \mathfrak{L}_2$. The plant $G(p)$ is unchanged and hence $g(t) \in \mathfrak{L}_1$ and $\mathfrak{L}_2$. Under the assumptions on the original system, we immediately conclude that $\Delta u(t) \in \mathfrak{L}_2$ where $\Delta u(t) = k(t)\Delta e(t)$. Then by Lemma 10-1 we can conclude that $\Delta e(t) \to 0$ as $t \to \infty$. This means that the original driven solution $e(t)$, given by Eq. (11-56), is stable in the sense that all perturbations on the initial conditions die out eventually. Moreover, the solution $e(t)$ is unique.***

In the same manner we can conclude that the system solution $e(t)$ given by Eq. (11-56) is stable under a perturbation on $r(t)$ of the form $\Delta r(t)$ provided that $|\Delta r(t)| < \infty$ and $\Delta r(t) \in \mathfrak{L}_2$.

2. Nonlinear Time Invariant System

If, instead of a gain $u(t) = k(t)e(t)$, a memoryless nonlinearity $u(t) = f\big(e(t)\big)$ is present, then the same line of argument as above can be employed to reach a useful conclusion.

With a forcing function $r(t)$, a solution $e(t)$ of the system is given by

$$e(t) = e_0(t) + r(t) - \int_0^t g(t-\tau)f\big(e(\tau)\big)\,d\tau \tag{11-59}$$

*See the second footnote on page 367. See also Appendix C.

**We use the notations $\Delta e(t)$ and $\Delta e_0(t)$ rather than $\delta e(t)$ and $\delta e_0(t)$ to indicate that the perturbation need not be small.

***This is of course not surprising in a linear system.

Under a perturbation $\Delta e_0(t)$ on the initial condition response $e_0(t)$ and a perturbation $\Delta r(t) \in \mathfrak{L}_2$ on the input $r(t)$, we then immediately have for the perturbation variables

$$\Delta e(t) = \Delta e_0(t) + \Delta r(t) - \int_0^t g(t-\tau) f_\Delta\big(e(\tau), \Delta e(\tau)\big)\, d\tau \tag{11-60}$$

where

$$f_\Delta\big(e(t), \Delta e(t)\big) \triangleq f\big(e(t) + \Delta e(t)\big) - f\big(e(t)\big) \tag{11-61}$$

We recognize that $\Delta u(t) = f_\Delta\big(e(t), \Delta e(t)\big)$ can be viewed as the output of the nonlinearity f under an input $e(t)$ and a perturbation about the input $\Delta e(t)$. Letting $\Delta u(t)$ be the perturbation on the output of the nonlinearity f, we then have a situation as described in Fig. 11-3.

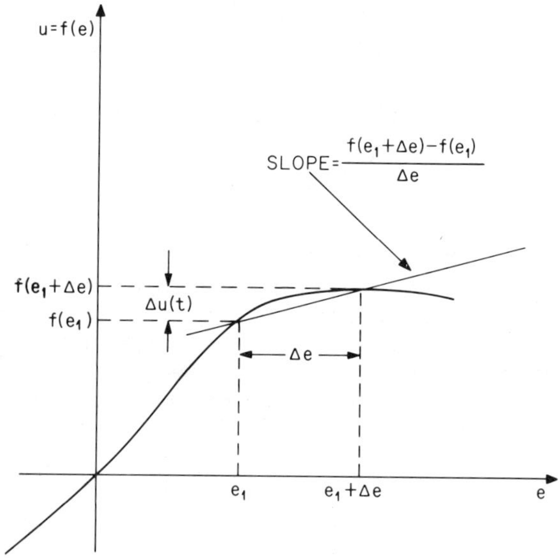

Fig. 11-3. The relationship between a change Δe about the value $e = e_1$ and the resultant change in $u = f(e)$.

Now Eq. (11-60) is the equation of a system in the standard form with the nonlinearity $f_\Delta\big(e(t), \Delta e(\tau)\big)$, which in terms of the perturbation variables alone may be viewed as a time-varying nonlinearity $f_\Delta\big(\Delta e(t), t\big)$. Thus the circle criterion of Theorem 10-4 with $q = 0$ can be applied to the system of (11-60). Let

$$\frac{\Delta u(t)}{\Delta e(t)} \in [k_1, k_2] \tag{11-62}$$

Then Theorem 10-4 dictates that the system (11-60) will be control and output asymptotic if (1) the system $G(p)/[1 + k_1 G(p)]$ is output stable and (2) the $G(j\omega)$ locus lies outside (inside) the circle centered on the real axis and passing through the points $-1/k_1$ and $-1/k_2$ if $(1/k_1) > (1/k_2)$ [if $(1/k_1) < (1/k_2)$].

In terms of the original nonlinearity, (11-62) may be written as

$$k_1 \leq \frac{f\big(e(t) + \Delta e(t)\big) - f\big(e(t)\big)}{\Delta e(t)} \leq k_2\,, \text{ for every } e(t) \text{ and } \Delta e(t) \tag{11-63}$$

or

$$k_1 \leq \frac{f(e_a) - f(e_b)}{e_a - e_b} \leq k_2\,, \text{ for every } e_a \text{ and } e_b \tag{11-64}$$

If $f(e)$ is a continuously differentiable function of e, then a necessary and sufficient condition for (11-64) to be fulfilled is that

$$k_1 \leq \frac{df(e)}{de} \leq k_2 \qquad \text{for all } e \tag{11-65}$$

Note that if $r(t) \equiv 0$ and $\Delta r(t) \equiv 0$, process stability still demands that the response to each initial condition perturbation must die out. This, however, is the original Popov problem, and Theorem 10-4 can be directly used to obtain a condition for the unforced case. Let $(u/e) \in [K_1, K_2]$, or

$$K_1 \leq \frac{u(t)}{e(t)} \leq K_2 \tag{11-66}$$

It is quite clear that for every function $f(e)$, the range of the slopes $f'(e)$ must contain the range of $f(e)/e$, i.e., we have

$$k_1 \leq K_1 \leq K_2 \leq k_2 \tag{11-67}$$

This property is illustrated in terms of the circle diagram of Fig. 11-4, where in the unforced case, a sufficient condition for the system to be output asymptotic is that the $G(j\omega)$ locus avoid the smaller circle passing through the points $-1/K_1$ and $-1/K_2$. In the forced case, in order for the perturbed system (11-60) to be control asymptotic, i.e., in order for $\Delta u(t)$ to be in $\mathcal{L}_2$, it is required that the $G(j\omega)$ locus avoid the (larger)* circle that passes through the points $-1/k_1$ and $-1/k_2$. Next, by Lemma 10-1, we can then deduce that $\Delta y(t) \to 0$ as $t \to \infty$.

3. Nonlinear Time-Varying System

The above consideration can readily be extended to the case of a time-varying nonlinear function $u = f(e, t)$. Here the key Eqs.

*The circles in Figure 11-4 are drawn for the case $k_1 > 0$. If $k_1 < 0$ and $(1/k_1) < (1/k_2)$, then the $G(j\omega)$ locus must lie inside the circle centered on the real axis and passing through the points $-1/k_1$ and $-1/k_2$ (see Theorem 10-4).

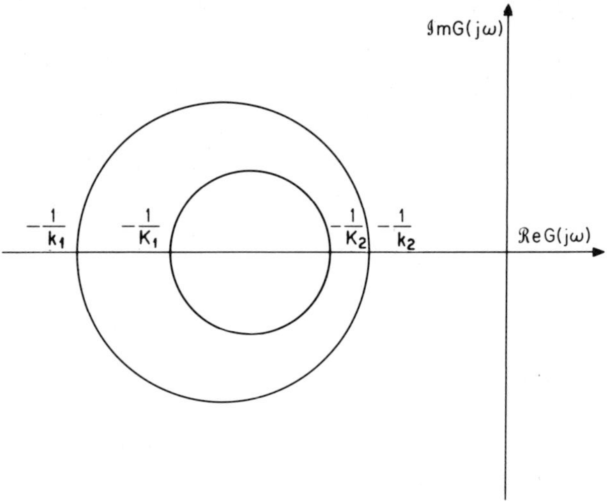

Fig. 11-4. If $(1/k_1) > (1/K_1) > (1/K_2) > (1/k_2)$, then a sufficient condition for a system to have process stability is that the $G(j\omega)$ locus not only must remain outside of the circle determined by the Popov sector $(f(e)/e) \in [K_1, K_2]$, but must also remain outside of the larger circle determined by $(df(e)/de) \in [k_1, k_2]$.

(11-64) and (11-65) become

$$k_1 \leq \frac{f(e_a, t) - f(e_b, t)}{e_a - e_b} \leq k_2, \qquad \text{for every } e_a, e_b, \text{ and } t \tag{11-68}$$

and

$$k_1 \leq \frac{\partial f(e,t)}{\partial e} \leq k_2, \qquad \text{for every } t \tag{11-69}$$

respectively.

To summarize the results of this section, we state the following theorem:

◆◆Theorem 11-7. For the system of Fig. 11-1, assume that two constants k_1 and k_2 exist such that condition (11-68) is satisfied; then, for every bounded input disturbance $\Delta r(t) \in \mathfrak{L}_2$ and for every perturbation on the initial condition of any response $y(t)$, the perturbation $\Delta y(t)$ will tend to 0 as $t \to \infty$ if

1) The linear system $G(p)/[1 + k_1 G(p)]$ is output stable.
2) The $G(j\omega)$ locus lies outside (inside) the circle centered on the negative real axis and passing through the points $-1/k_1$ and $-1/k_2$ if $(1/k_1) > (1/k_2)$ [if $(1/k_1) < (1/k_2)$].*◆◆

*Since Theorem 11-7 was derived by a direct application of Theorem 10-4, the circle criterion (10-36) with $q = 0$ applies to both cases $(1/k_1) > (1/k_2)$ and $(1/k_1) < (1/k_2)$.

The above theorem can, for example, be useful in the study of the stability of forced oscillatory responses. Suppose that $y_p(t) = y_p(t+T)$ is the periodic steady-state response of the feedback system of Fig. 11-1 due to some periodic excitation. If the conditions of Theorem 11-7 are satisfied, then for every disturbance of the initial conditions the motion $y(t)$ will return to $y_p(t)$ as $t \to \infty$ no matter how large the disturbance. This assures the uniqueness of the steady state response $y_p(t)$.

♦♦Example 11-2. Consider the feedback system with a unit limiter as the nonlinearity. In Sec. 6.5 of Chap. 6, we demonstrated, by the describing function method, that if the frequency locus $G(j\omega)$ is within a certain region (Fig. 6-19), then the *jump phenomenon* may occur. This means that certain periodic responses to periodic input may not be unique. The reader may verify by application of Theorem 11-7 that a sufficient condition for nonexistence of the jump phenomenon for that system will be given by the condition $\mathcal{R}e\, G(j\omega) > -1$ (see Exercise 11-11). This is illustrated as the dotted line in Fig. 6-19 and is seen, as expected, to be somewhat more conservative than the boundary between jump and no-jump obtained by the approximate describing function method. Indeed, it is possible to show (See Exercise 11-16) that for all zero-memory nonlinearities, the boundary for jump phenomenon determined by the method of the present section will always be more conservative than that derived from the describing function.♦♦

We have been careful in stating that if the conditions of Theorem 11-7 are satisfied, then every forced periodic solution $y(t) = y(t+T)$ is stable and unique. This may not necessarily mean that $y(t)$ is periodic with the same period as the input of the system, $r(t)$. For example, there may be subharmonic responses. However, it has been shown by Yakubovich [Y2] and by Sandberg [S5] that under certain conditions, for every periodic input of period T, there exists a unique output that is of the same period T. The conditions for which this is true include the case of a system of Fig. 11-1 with a single-valued, time-invariant nonlinearity $u = f(e)$, for which the conditions of Theorem 11-7 are satisfied. *Thus, for single-valued nonlinearities, Theorem 11-7 will yield not only a sufficient condition for stability and uniqueness of every forced solution $y(t)$ but also a sufficient condition for nonexistence of subharmonic response of periodic excitation.*

The response of single-loop, nonlinear feedback systems to periodic excitation will be expounded further in the next section.

11.6 The Stability of Periodic Solutions

We shall now show that linearization frequently can help determine the orbital asymptotic stability or asymptotic stability of a known period solution of a system.

Let us first note that when a time-invariant system $\dot{\mathbf{x}} = \mathbf{f}(\mathbf{x}, \mathbf{u})$ is driven by a periodic input $\mathbf{u}(t)$ of period T, then on expressing the system input as a function of t, the system equation can be given in a time-varying form

$$\dot{\mathbf{x}} = \mathbf{f}(\mathbf{x}, t) \tag{11-70a}$$

where $\mathbf{f}$ enjoys the property that

$$\mathbf{f}(\mathbf{x}, t) = \mathbf{f}(\mathbf{x}, t + T) \tag{11-70b}$$

Systems in the form of (11-70a) with $\mathbf{f}$ obeying (11-70b) are known as periodic systems. Another case where a periodic system can occur is when a periodically driven system undergoes forced oscillation (at the driven frequency).

By now we appreciate the fact that a periodic system as defined above need not necessarily yield an output that is periodic with the same period T. When it does, there is then a periodic solution $\mathbf{x}_p(t)$ such that

$$\mathbf{x}_p(t) = \mathbf{x}_p(t + T) \tag{11-71}$$

In Chap. 5, we have shown that by linearization about a trajectory and using Theorem 5-2, uniform asymptotic stability of a trajectory can be determined, provided that the linearized system is itself uniformly asymptotically stable with respect to the origin. There are two difficulties with Theorem 5-2. First, it is difficult to determine uniform asymptotic stability of a linear system. Second, uniform asymptotic stability is often too stringent. Sometimes, for example, orbital asymptotic stability will suffice. Some interesting results are available when the linearized system itself is periodic. The main lemma is the following.

◆◆Lemma 11-4. Consider a periodic linear system

$$\dot{\mathbf{x}} = \mathbf{A}(t)\mathbf{x} \tag{11-72}$$

where $\mathbf{A}(t + T) = \mathbf{A}(t)$ for some $T \neq 0$. Let the transition matrix for the system, $\mathbf{\Phi}(t, t_0)$, be bounded and let $\zeta_i, i = 1, \ldots, n$ be the eigenvalues of the matrix $\mathbf{\Phi}(t_0 + T, t_0)$. Then, we have

1) $\mathbf{\Phi}(t + nT, t_0 + nT) = \mathbf{\Phi}(t, t_0)$ (11-73)

2) If $|\zeta_i| < 1$ for all $i = 1, \ldots, n$, then the origin of system (11-72) is (globally) uniformly asymptotically stable.◆◆

Proof: Part (1) is clear from physical reasoning. Since $\mathbf{A}(t)$ is periodic with period T, a state $\mathbf{x}_0$ starting at a time t will experience the same velocity $\dot{\mathbf{x}}$ as one starting at a time $t + T$, or indeed one starting at a time $t + nT$ This means that if we let $x(t_0) = x_0$ and $x(t_0 + T) = x_0$, then $x(t + T) = x(t)$ for all t_0 and t. Equation (11-73) thus immediately follows.

Part (2) can be proved by use of the z-transform (see Appendix B). Let

$$\boldsymbol{\Phi}(z, t_0) \triangleq \sum_{n=0}^{\infty} \Phi(t_0 + nT, t_0) z^{-n} \tag{11-74}$$

By (B-21), Appendix B, if $\boldsymbol{\Phi}(z, t_0)$ is analytic in $|z| \geq 1$, then $\lim_{n \to \infty} ||\Phi(t_0 + nT, t_0)|| = 0$. But since $\Phi(t_0 + nT, t_0) = [\Phi(t_0 + T, t_0)]^n$, it is clear that a necessary and sufficient condition for the sequence $||\Phi(t_0 + nT, t_0)||$ to converge to zero as $n \to \infty$ is that $||\Phi(t_0 + T, t_0)|| < 1$. Hence, if $\boldsymbol{\Phi}(z, t_0)$ is analytic in $|z| \geq 1$ for all t_0, then $||\Phi(t_0 + T, t_0)|| < 1$ for all t_0.

Taking the z-transform of both sides of the identity

$$\Phi\big(t_0 + (n + 1)T, t_0\big) = \Phi(t_0 + nT, t_0)\Phi(t_0 + T, t_0)$$

we obtain (using (B-14b), Appendix B, and rearranging):

$$[z\mathbf{I} - \Phi(t_0 + T, t_0)]\boldsymbol{\Phi}(z, t_0) = z\Phi(t_0, t_0) = z\mathbf{I} \tag{11-75}$$

where $\mathbf{I}$ is the unit matrix. The characteristic equation of (11-75) is given by

$$|\Phi(t_0 + T, t_0) - \mathbf{I}\zeta| = 0 \tag{11-76}$$

Thus, if all the roots ζ_i of (11-76) obey $|\zeta_i| < 1$, then $\boldsymbol{\Phi}(z, t_0)$ is analytic in $|z| \geq 1$ which, as shown above, implies that there exists a ρ (independent of t_0) such that $||\Phi(t_0 + T, t_0)|| \leq \rho < 1$ for every t_0. Letting $t = t_0 + nT + \tau$ where $0 \leq \tau \leq T$, we have

$$\begin{aligned}\|x(t_0 + nT + \tau)\| &= \|\Phi(t_0 + nT + \tau, t_0 + nT)x(t_0 + nT)\| = \|\Phi(t_0 + \tau, t_0)x(t_0 + nT)\| \\ &= \|\Phi(t_0 + \tau, t_0)\Phi(t_0 + nT, t_0)x(t_0)\| \leq \phi_M \rho^n \|x(t_0)\|\end{aligned}$$

with $0 \leq \rho < 1$, where $\phi_M \triangleq \max_{\substack{0 \leq \tau \leq T \\ \text{all } t_0}} \|\Phi(t_0 + \tau, t_0)\|$.

Therefore, for every $\epsilon > 0$, there exists a δ, namely $\delta = \epsilon/\phi_M$ (independent of t_0) such that if $||x(t_0)|| < \delta$, then $||x(t_0 + t)|| = ||x(t_0 + nT + \tau)|| < \epsilon\rho^n < \epsilon$ with $0 \leq \rho < 1$ for every t_0, τ and n. This implies global uniform asymptotic stability.

With Lemma 11-4, it is possible to establish the following important result:*

*Theorem 11-8 represents a combination of theorems by Lyapunov (part 1) and Andronov and Witt (part 2). For statements and proofs see [C1] pp. 55-59, 96-99 and [P7] p. 264.

♦♦Theorem 11-8. For a system $\dot{\mathbf{x}} = \mathbf{f}(\mathbf{x}, t)$, let the perturbed equation about a given periodic solution $\mathbf{x}_p(t) = \mathbf{x}_p(t + T)$, $T \neq 0$, be given by

$$\delta\dot{\mathbf{x}} = \left[\frac{\partial \mathbf{f}}{\partial \mathbf{x}}\right]_p \delta\mathbf{x} + \mathbf{h}(\delta\mathbf{x}, t) \tag{11-77}$$

where $\delta\mathbf{x}(t) = \mathbf{x}(t) - \mathbf{x}_p(t)$, $[(\partial\mathbf{f}(t)/\partial\mathbf{x})]_p$ is periodic with period T and it is assumed that $\|\mathbf{h}(\mathbf{x}, t)\| / \|\delta\mathbf{x}\| \to 0$ uniformly as $\|\delta\mathbf{x}\| \to 0$. Let the linear system $\delta\dot{\mathbf{x}} = [(\partial\mathbf{f}(t)/\partial\mathbf{x})]_p\, \delta\mathbf{x}$ have a transition matrix $\mathbf{\Phi}(t, t_0)$ and let ζ_i, $i = 1, \ldots, n$ be the eigenvalues of the matrix $\mathbf{\Phi}(t_0 + T, t_0)$.

1) If the original system is of the form $\dot{\mathbf{x}} = \mathbf{f}(\mathbf{x}, t) = \mathbf{f}(\mathbf{x}, t + T)$ (i.e., the system is periodic with period T) and $|\zeta_i| < 1$ for all $i = 1, \ldots, n$, then the periodic solution $\mathbf{x}_p(t)$ is asymptotically stable.
2) If the original system is autonomous i.e., of the form $\dot{\mathbf{x}} = \mathbf{f}(\mathbf{x})$, and if $|\zeta_i| < 1$ for all $i = 1, \ldots, n$ except for one eigenvalue $\zeta_k = 1$, then the periodic solution $\mathbf{x}_p(t)$ is stable and orbitally asymptotically stable.♦♦

♦♦Example 11-3. Consider the system of Example 4-4.

$$\begin{aligned} \dot{x}_1 &= x_2 - ax_1\left(x_1^2 + x_2^2 - 1\right) \\ \dot{x}_2 &= -x_1 - ax_2\left(x_1^2 + x_2^2 - 1\right) \end{aligned} \tag{11-78}$$

In Example 4-4 we were able to show that the system (11-78) has a limit cycle which is given by

$$\mathbf{x}_p(t) = \begin{bmatrix} \sin t \\ \cos t \end{bmatrix} \tag{11-79}$$

The linearized system has a $\left[\dfrac{\partial \mathbf{f}}{\partial \mathbf{x}}(t)\right]_p$ matrix given by (show this)

$$\left[\frac{\partial \mathbf{f}}{\partial \mathbf{x}}(t)\right]_p = \begin{bmatrix} -2a\sin^2 t & 1 - 2a\sin t\cos t \\ -1 - 2a\sin t\cos t & -2a\cos^2 t \end{bmatrix} \tag{11-80}$$

It can be shown that (verify this) for the linearized system, the transition matrix is

$\mathbf{\Phi}(t, t_0) =$

$$\begin{bmatrix} e^{-2a(t-t_0)}(\sin t_0 \sin t + \cos t_0 \cos t) & e^{-2a(t-t_0)}(\cos t_0 \sin t - \sin t_0 \cos t) \\ e^{-2a(t-t_0)}(\sin t_0 \cos t - \cos t_0 \sin t) & e^{-2a(t-t_0)}(\cos t_0 \cos t + \sin t_0 \sin t) \end{bmatrix}$$

The $[\partial f/\partial x]_p$ matrix is seen to be periodic with the same period $T = 2\pi$ as the limit cycle of the original system (11-78). From (11-81) we have:

$$\Phi(t_0 + T, t_0) = \begin{bmatrix} e^{-4\pi a}(\sin^2 t_0 + \cos^2 t_0) & -(1 - e^{-4\pi a}) \sin t_0 \cos t_0 \\ -(1 - e^{-4\pi a}) \sin t_0 \cos t_0 & e^{-4\pi a}(\cos^2 t_0 + \sin^2 t_0) \end{bmatrix}$$

The characteristic equation becomes

$$|\Phi(t_0 + T, t_0) - \zeta \mathbf{I}| = \zeta^2 - (1 - e^{-4\pi a})\zeta + \frac{1}{8}(1 + e^{-8\pi a})(1 - \cos 4t_0) + \frac{1}{4} e^{-4\pi a}(3 + \cos 4t_0) = 0 \qquad (11\text{-}82)$$

The roots of (11-82) are given by

$$\begin{aligned} \zeta_1 &= \frac{1}{2}\Big(1 + \cos 2t_0 + e^{-4\pi a}(1 - \cos 2t_0)\Big) \\ \zeta_2 &= \frac{1}{2}\Big(1 - \cos 2t_0 + e^{-4\pi a}(1 + \cos 2t_0)\Big) \end{aligned} \qquad (11\text{-}83)$$

The magnitude of the ζ's is seen to be dependent on t_0 and a. For $a = +1$, it is possible to establish (show this) that at most one ζ can reach the magnitude of 1; otherwise, the magnitudes of the ζ's are always less than 1. Thus the limit cycle (11-79) is stable and orbitally asymptotically stable by part (2) of Theorem 11-8.

Similarly, we can establish (show this) that if $a = -1$, the conditions for stability of the limit cycle (11-79) cannot be satisfied. The above results check with our observation in Example 4-4.◆◆

To make use of Theorem 11-8 requires the finding of the transition matrix, which is almost equivalent to the finding of the system solution. At first glance, therefore, the theorem seems to be rather limited in utility. We should mention however, two points in favor of Theorem 11-8. First, it is possible to find the transition matrix $\Phi(t, t_0)$ numerically by integrating the matrix equation $\dot{\Phi} = [\partial f/\partial x]_p \Phi$, $\Phi(t_0, t_0) = \mathbf{I}$. Indeed to use Theorem 11-8, all we need to do is to obtain Φ for one period from t_0 to $t_0 + T$ and then find the eigenvalues ζ_i of the matrix $\Phi(t_0 + T, t_0)$. This is simpler than finding Φ for long periods of time. Second, for relay systems it is possible to express the form of the solutions conveniently. In that case Theorem 11-8 can frequently be used, as we shall now show:

♦♦Example 11-4. We will now provide the sketch of a proof for Theorem 8-4.* We will leave the reader to fill in the missing details (see Exercise 11-18).

For the system considered for Theorem 8-4, we have $y(t) = -e(t)$ and $g(0^+) = 0$. From (8-13a), with $\alpha = 1/2$ and from (8-61), we have

$$0 < \frac{|\dot{e}(\pi/\omega)|}{2U} = -\frac{\dot{e}(\pi/\omega)}{2U} = \frac{\dot{y}(\pi/\omega)}{2U} = -\mathcal{G}'(-1) \qquad (11\text{-}84)$$

so that the characteristic Eq. (8-77) becomes

$$\mathcal{G}'(z) - \mathcal{G}'(-1) = 0 \qquad (11\text{-}85)$$

But from Eqs. (11-84) and (8-61), it follows that a root $z = -1$ refers to a periodic mode of the solution of the linearized system in Fig. 8-15. By proper interpretation of Theorem 11-8 (show this), the self-oscillation of the original relay system will be orbitally asymptotically stable if all roots of (11-85) lie in $|z| < 1$ except for one single root at $z = -1$.

Consider a contour $\mathcal{C}$ defined by $|z| = 1$ except for infinitesimal half circles outside $|z| = 1$ about the point $z = -1$ and possibly the point $z = +1$ (if $\mathcal{G}'(z)$ has a pole at $z = +1$). Under the assumptions made on the linear element, the region in the z-plane outside $\mathcal{C}$ is mapped into a region of the $\mathcal{G}'(z)$ plane that encloses a neighborhood to the right of $\mathcal{G}'(-1)$. The $\mathcal{G}'(-1)$ point will not be enclosed if and only if the mapping from $z = -1 + re^{j\theta}$ with $\pi/2 \le \theta \le 3\pi/2$ and $r \to 0$ on the $\mathcal{G}'(z)$ plane will pass the $\mathcal{G}'(-1)$ point to the right. At the neighborhood $z = -1$, we have

$$\mathcal{G}'(z) = \mathcal{G}'(-1) + \left.\frac{\partial \mathcal{G}'(z)}{\partial z}\right|_{z=-1} re^{j\theta}, \quad \frac{\pi}{2} \le \theta \le \frac{3\pi}{2}, \quad r \to 0 \qquad (11\text{-}86)$$

But from (8-3), (8-62) and (8-63), we can show that $[\partial \mathcal{I}m J(\omega)/\partial\omega] = (2\pi U/\omega^2)[\partial \mathcal{G}'(z)/\partial z]_{z=-1}$ so that (11-86) becomes

$$\mathcal{G}'(-1) + \frac{\omega^2}{2\pi U}\frac{\partial \mathcal{I}m J(\omega)}{\partial\omega} re^{j\theta}, \quad \frac{\pi}{2} \le \theta \le \frac{3\pi}{2}, \quad r \to 0 \qquad (11\text{-}87)$$

Therefore, the $\mathcal{G}'(z)$ locus mapped out by $\mathcal{C}$ will pass the $\mathcal{G}'(-1)$ point to the right and will not encircle it if $[\partial \mathcal{I}m J(\omega)/\partial\omega] < 0$. This, by proper interpretation of the Nyquist's criterion, by (11-85) and by Theorem 11-8,* implies that the periodic solution of the original system is stable and orbitally asymptotically stable.♦♦

*Note that for relay systems the perturbed equations are not obtained through the usual procedure of taking partial derivatives (see the development leading to Theorem 8-2). Nevertheless, Theorem 11-8 applies to the resultant perturbed equations.

11.7 The Use of the Contraction-Mapping Fixed Point Theorem in Functional Analysis

As a last item in stability analysis, we shall mention the potentially fertile field of functional analysis. If nothing else, this section can serve to open our eyes to some new viewpoints and, perhaps to paths that lead to new and exciting results.

It is not possible to be complete in our discussion of the results in functional analysis;* therefore, we will just mention one important result in functional analysis that is relevant to stability analysis, namely, the contraction mapping fixed-point theorem. Before doing so, we need to lay the background for functional analysis to some extent.

1. Abstract Spaces and the Banach Space

As the name implies, functional analysis deals with functions. Analogous to the vector space $\mathcal{E}_n$, which is the space of n-dimensional vectors, we can define a function space in order to analyze the problem topologically. Functional analysis consists of many successful attempts to define and use precisely such spaces. In fact we have already made use of the function spaces $\mathcal{L}_1$ and $\mathcal{L}_2$ in this chapter and in Chap. 10. We now look into some of the basic requirements and structures of a particular function space, namely a linear function space.

A *linear function space* $\mathcal{V}$ is a collection of functions $v_1, v_2, \cdots$ with the following properties:

1) Two operations are defined relative to the members of $\mathcal{V}$: (i) addition of two members v_i and v_j, denoted $v_i + v_j$, and (ii) multiplication by a scalar α, denoted αv_i. It is required that such operations done on a member of the collection result in another member of the same collection. In particular $1v = v$.
2) There is a null function θ such that $v + \theta = v$ for every v in $\mathcal{V}$, and such that $0v = \theta$.
3) The multiplication and addition operations are associative in the sense that $\alpha(v_i + v_j) = \alpha v_i + \alpha v_j$, $(\alpha + \beta) v_i = \alpha v_i + \beta v_i$.

If to each member v of a function $\mathcal{V}$ a norm $\|v\|$ is defined such that (i) $\|v\| > 0$ if and only if $v \neq \theta$ and $\|v\| = 0$ if and only if $v = \theta$, (ii) $\|\alpha v\| = |\alpha| \|v\|$ and (iii) $\|v_i + v_j\| \leq \|v_i\| + \|v_j\|$, then $\mathcal{V}$ is called a normed function space.

*We may mention that functional analysis is also very useful in optimal control theory. The interested reader is referred to the tutorial chapter by Aoki [A4] and the book by Porter [P10].

A sequence of functions $\{v_1, v_2, \ldots\}$ on a normed function space $\mathcal{V}$ is said to be a *Cauchy sequence* if for each $\epsilon > 0$ there is a positive integer N such that for each positive integer m, $\|v_{n+m} - v_n\| < \epsilon$ whenever $n \geq N$. The sequence is said to converge to an element v' of $\mathcal{V}$ if for each $\epsilon > 0$ there is an N such that $\|v_n - v'\| < \epsilon$ whenever $n \geq N$.

A *complete* normed linear function space $\mathcal{V}$ is one in which every Cauchy sequence converges to an element in $\mathcal{V}$. Such a space is called a *Banach space*.

♦♦Example 11-5. Consider the set of all real-valued continuous functions $f(t)$ defined over the time interval $[t_1, t_2]$. If we define addition and multiplication by a scalar in the usual manner and introduce the norm

$$\|f_1(t) - f_2(t)\| = \max_{t_1 \leq t \leq t_2} |f_1(t) - f_2(t)|$$

we have a function space $\mathcal{C}[t_1, t_2]$. A Cauchy sequence* $\{f_1(t), f_2(t), \ldots\}$ (abbreviated to $\{f_n(t)\}$) in this space must obey the requirement that for any $\epsilon > 0$, there exists an integer N such that if $n, m > N$, then $|f_n(t) - f_m(t)| < \epsilon$ for all $t \in [t_1, t_2]$. This condition, however, implies that the sequence $\{f_n(t)\}$ converges uniformly. By the theorem concerning uniform convergence** $\{f_n(t)\}$ converges to a continuous function $f(t)$. Thus $\mathcal{C}[t_1, t_2]$ is a Banach space (see however Exercise 11-7).♦♦

For n-dimensional real and continuous vector functions of time $\mathbf{f}(t)$ defined in $[t_1, t_2]$, we may, for example, impose a norm

$$\|\mathbf{f}_a(t) - \mathbf{f}_b(t)\| = \max_{t_1 \leq t \leq t_2} \sqrt{\sum_{i=1}^{n} \left(f_{ai}(t) - f_{bi}(t)\right)^2}$$

where $f_{ai}(t)$ is the ith component of $\mathbf{f}_a(t)$. It is now readily established that the space of $\mathbf{f}(t)$ defined above is also a Banach space.

♦♦Example 11-6. Consider now the space $\mathcal{K}$ of real-valued periodic functions of t with period T which are square-integrable over a period. For an element v of this space, if we define the norm of v as its rms value

$$\|v\| = \left(\frac{1}{T} \int_0^T v^2\, dt\right)^{\frac{1}{2}}$$

*An example of a Cauchy sequence in the space $\mathcal{C}[t_1, t_2]$ may be $f_n(t) = f(t) + a^{-n}$ where $|a| > 1$ and $f(t)$ is some given member of the space.

**See any advanced calculus text.

then the reader may demonstrate to himself that $\mathcal{K}$ becomes a Banach space (see Exercise 11-9).♦♦

2. Functional Operations in Banach Spaces

Two function spaces $\mathcal{U}$ and $\mathcal{V}$ often are related by a functional equation of the form

$$\mathcal{G}u = v$$

where we mean that there is a transformation $\mathcal{G}$ which can transform (map) an element u of the space $\mathcal{U}$ into an element v of the space $\mathcal{V}$.

Of course a transformation $\mathcal{G}$ can take an element of a function space $\mathcal{V}$ into another one of the same function space; in that case we say $\mathcal{G}$ is an *operator*. For such a transformation, sometimes we are interested in finding one (or more) element of $\mathcal{V}$, denoted v^*, which is unchanged under the transformation $\mathcal{G}$. In this case we are seeking the solutions v^* such that

$$\mathcal{G}v^* = v^* \tag{11-88}$$

A function v^* that satisfies an equation of the form (11-88) is said to be a *fixed point* of the transformation $\mathcal{G}$.

♦♦Example 11-7. Consider the first-order system $\dot{x}(t) = f\big(x(t)\big)$, $x(0) = x_0$. If $f(x)$ is differentiable then the solution $x(t)$ that satisfies the differential equation and the initial condition is continuous, and $f(x)$ over an interval $t \in [0, T]$ is an element of the space $\mathcal{C}[0, T]$ defined in Example 11-5. If we define an operator $\mathcal{G}$ such that $\mathcal{G}[x(t)] = x_0 + \displaystyle\int_0^t f\big(x(\tau)\big)d\tau$, then $\mathcal{G}$ is a transformation of $\mathcal{C}[0, T]$ into itself, and any solution $x(t)$ to the system $\dot{x} = f(x)$ in the interval $[0, T]$ and satisfying the initial condition $x(0) = x_0$ is a fixed point of the operator $\mathcal{G}$.♦♦

We may mention in passing that occasionally the concept of the norm of an operator is required. The traditional definition of the norm of a linear operator $\mathcal{G}$† (defined on an appropriate Banach space $\mathcal{V}$) denoted by $\|\mathcal{G}\|$ is

$$\|\mathcal{G}\| = \max_{\substack{v \in \mathcal{V} \\ \|v\| = 1}} \|\mathcal{G}v\| \tag{11-89}$$

In words, the norm of $\mathcal{G}$ is given by the maximum value assumed

† A linear operator $\mathcal{G}$ has the property that, for any two functions in u, v in the relevant Banach space $\mathcal{V}$, and for any two scalars k_1 and k_2, $\mathcal{G}\left[k_1 v + k_2 u\right] = k_1 \mathcal{G} v + k_2 \mathcal{G} u$.

for the norm $\|\mathcal{G}v\|$ for all v's of unity norm belonging to $\mathcal{V}$. When $\|\mathcal{G}\|$ is bounded, we say $\mathcal{G}$ is a *bounded* operator.

It is clear that for all $v \in \mathcal{V}$

$$\|\mathcal{G}v\| \leq \|\mathcal{G}\| \, \|v\| \tag{11-90}$$

3. The Contraction-Mapping Fixed Point Theorem

A bounded operator $\mathcal{G}$ that maps a space $\mathcal{V}$ into self is called a contraction mapping if for any two elements v_a and v_b of $\mathcal{V}$ the following condition holds:

$$\|\mathcal{G}v_a - \mathcal{G}v_b\| \leq \rho\|v_a - v_b\|, \quad 0 < \rho < 1 \tag{11-91}$$ †

As the name implies, the "distance" between the transformed functions is less than the "distance" between the original functions.

The importance of the contraction operators in Banach space lies in the fact that there is a unique fixed point. Furthermore this fixed point may be found by successive iteration. This fact we state in the following theorems:

♦♦Theorem 11-9 (The Contraction-Mapping Fixed-Point Theorem). If $\mathcal{G}$ is a contraction mapping defined on a Banach space $\mathcal{V}$, then

1) there exists a *unique* element v^* of $\mathcal{V}$ satisfying

$$\mathcal{G}v^* = v^* \tag{11-92}$$

2) the sequence $v_1, v_2, \ldots,$ given by

$$v_{n+1} = \mathcal{G}v_n \qquad (n = 0, 1, \ldots) \tag{11-93}$$

converges to v^* for *any* initial choice of v_0 in $\mathcal{V}$,

3) the norm $\|v_n - v^*\|$ is bounded by

$$\|v_n - v^*\| \leq \frac{\rho^n}{1-\rho}\|\rho v_0 - v_0\| \tag{11-94}$$ ♦♦

The proof of the theorem follows in a straightforward manner, for we have, for any n, m with $m > n$,

$$\begin{aligned}
\|v_n - v_m\| &= \|\mathcal{G}^n v_0 - \mathcal{G}^m v_0\| \leq \rho^n\|v_{m-n} - v_0\| \\
&\leq \rho^n\{\|v_0 - v_1\| + \|v_1 - v_2\| + \cdots + \|v_{m-n} - v_{m-n+1}\|\} \\
&\leq \rho^n \, \|v_0 - v_1\|\{1 + \rho + \rho^2 + \cdots + \rho^{m-n}\} \leq \frac{\rho^n}{1-\rho}\|v_0 - v_1\| \\
&\leq \frac{\rho^n}{1-\rho}\|\rho v_0 - v_0\|
\end{aligned} \tag{11-95}$$

† Note that (11-91) is a Lipschitz condition.

Thus (11-94) is directly shown. The limit of $\mathcal{G}^n v_0$, as $n \to \infty$ exists by virtue of the completeness of a Banach space. Thus the existence of at least one limit for each choice of v_0 is clear. Let v_1^* be such a limit; it is seen then that $\mathcal{G}v_1^* = \mathcal{G} \lim_{n\to\infty} \mathcal{G}^n v_0 = \mathcal{G} \lim_{n\to\infty} v_n = \lim_{n\to\infty} v_{n+1} = v_1^*$; thus v_1^* is a fixed point under the transformation $\mathcal{G}$.

To show the uniqueness of the fixed point v^*, suppose that there exist two distinct fixed points v_1^* and v_2^*. We have

$$\|v_1^* - v_2^*\| = \|\mathcal{G}v_1^* - \mathcal{G}v_2^*\| \le \rho \|v_1^* - v_2^*\| \tag{11-96}$$

Unless the norm $\|v_1^* - v_2^*\|$ is 0, Eq. (11-96) states that it is less than itself, which is impossible. Thus $v_1^* = v_2^*$, and there is a unique fixed point.

If the contraction-mapping operator is only valid in a neighorhood of the Banach space about an element v_0, we have the following version of the contraction-mapping fixed-point theorem:

◆◆Theorem 11-10. If condition (11-91) holds only in the neighborhood $\|v - v_0\| < r$ about an element v_0 of a Banach space, then Theorem 11-9 is valid provided that ρ satisfies the further inequality

$$\|\mathcal{G}v_0 - v_0\| < (1 - \rho) r \tag{11-97}$$ ◆◆

Theorems 11-9 and 11-10 not only give the conditions under which there is one and only one solution to the functional equation $\mathcal{G}v = v$ but also provide us with what amounts to a successive approximation technique to obtain the solution. It turns out that the theorems are of wide usage, belying their simple appearances, as we can see from the following Examples.

◆◆Example 11-8 (The Proof of Theorem 3-1). The set (3-3) can be written in the integral form

$$\mathbf{x} = \mathbf{x}_0 + \int_{t_0}^{t} \mathbf{f}\big(\mathbf{x}(\tau), \tau\big)\, d\tau \tag{11-98}$$

Using a norm given by†

$$\|\mathbf{x}(t)\| = \max_{t_0 - c \le t \le t_0 + c} \left[\sqrt{\sum_{i=1}^{n} x_i^2(t)}\right] \tag{11-99}$$

†Note that even though the symbols are the same, the norm as defined in the present example is different from that used in Theorem 3-1; this, however, does not affect the generality of the proof.

we can then define

$$M = \max_{\mathcal{R}} \| \mathrm{f}(\mathrm{x}(t), t) \|$$

Taking a value ρ, $0 < \rho < 1$, we set the value a as given in Theorem 3-1 to be

$$a = \min \left\{ c, \frac{b}{M}(1 - \rho), \frac{\rho}{k} \right\}$$

where k is the Lipschitz constant for the problem. We now have a Banach space of continuous vector functions $\mathrm{x}(t)$ over the interval $|t - t_0| \leq a$ with the norm specified by (11-99). In this space, consider the operator $\mathcal{G}$ defined by

$$\mathcal{G}[x(t)] = \mathrm{x}_0 + \int_{t_0}^{t} \mathrm{f}(\mathrm{x}(\tau), \tau)\, d\tau \tag{11-100}$$

Consider any two functions $\mathrm{x}_1(t)$ and $\mathrm{x}_2(t)$ in the above Banach space satisfying $\|\mathrm{x}_1(t) - \mathrm{x}_0\| < b$ and $\|\mathrm{x}_2(t) - \mathrm{x}_0\| < b$. We clearly have

$$\mathcal{G}[\mathrm{x}_1(t)] - \mathcal{G}[\mathrm{x}_2(t)] = \int_{t_0}^{t} \left[\mathrm{f}(\mathrm{x}_1(\tau), \tau) - \mathrm{f}(\mathrm{x}_2(\tau), \tau)\right] d\tau$$

or

$$\| \mathcal{G}[\mathrm{x}_1(t)] - \mathcal{G}[\mathrm{x}_2(t)] \| \leq \int_{t_0}^{t_0 + a} \left\| \mathrm{f}(\mathrm{x}_1(\tau), \tau) - \mathrm{f}(\mathrm{x}_2(\tau), \tau) \right\| d\tau$$

Using the Lipschitz condition (3-5) on the rhs, we have

$$\|\mathcal{G}[\mathrm{x}_1(t)] - \mathcal{G}[\mathrm{x}_2(t)]\| \leq ka\|\mathrm{x}_1(t) - \mathrm{x}_2(t)\| \leq \rho\|\mathrm{x}_1(t) - \mathrm{x}_2(t)\|$$

hence $\mathcal{G}$ is a contraction operator in our Banach space in the region $\mathcal{R}$.

Also, since

$$\mathcal{G}\mathrm{x}_0 - \mathrm{x}_0 = \int_{t_0}^{t} f(\mathrm{x}_0, \tau)\, d\tau$$

we have, for $t \in (t_0, t_0 + a)$

$$\|\mathcal{G}\mathrm{x}_0 - \mathrm{x}_0\| \leq Ma \leq (1 - \rho)b$$

Thus by Theorem 11-10, there exists a unique solution $x(t)$ of (3-1) that satisfies the conditions of Theorem 3-1.♦♦

4. A Method to Improve on the Describing Function Method for Systems with Periodic Input

Using the function space $\mathcal{K}$ and the rms norm given in Example 11-6, Sandberg [S4] in studying a system with input in the standard form of Fig. 11-5 was able to employ the contraction-mapping fixed-point theorem to obtain some results concerning the response of the system under a periodic input. However, because the contraction operator permits a solution to be generated by a successive approximation procedure, a way is indicated to improve on the describing function approach as far as waveform prediction is concerned. The method, however, is only valid for systems (in the standard form) with a periodic input. Moreover, under the assumptions to be imposed, the system does not self-oscillate.

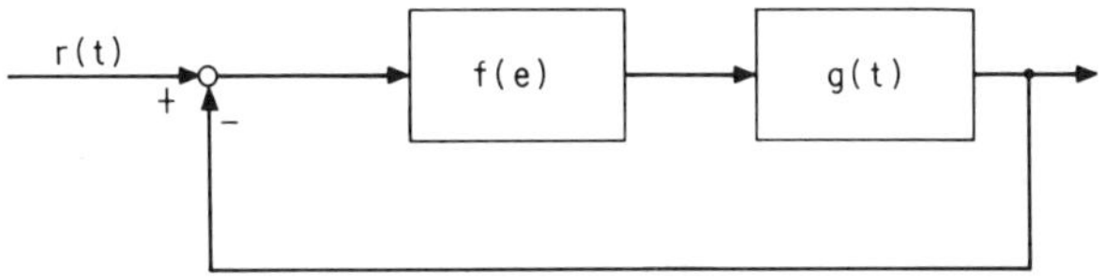

Fig. 11-5. The class of system studied in Part 4 of Sec. 11.7.

For the system of Fig. 11-5, let us pole-shift the system such that the following relations are obeyed.

1) The zero-memory nonlinearity $f(e)$ obeys the condition*

$$0 \le \frac{f(e_2) - f(e_1)}{e_2 - e_1} \le 2 \tag{11-101}$$

for any e_1 and e_2.

2) The time-invariant linear plant is completely specified by the impulse response $g(t)$ so that it operates on an element of space $\mathcal{K}$ through the operator $\mathcal{G}$ defined by the usual convolution integral

$$\mathcal{G}[v(t)] = \int_{-\infty}^{\infty} g(t - \tau)\, v(\tau)\, d\tau \tag{11-102}$$

Before proceeding to the main result, it is necessary to note two intuitively reasonable properties of the linear plant.

*Sandberg [S4] treated a more general case than is given here.

First, the norm of the operator $\mathcal{G}$ of (11-102), in accordance with Eq. (11-89), can easily be shown to obey

$$\|\mathcal{G}\| = \max_n \left| G\left(jn\frac{2\pi}{T}\right)\right| \tag{11-103}$$

This is because in the space $\mathcal{K}$, the square of the norm of $\mathcal{G}$ can be thought of as the maximum possible "power density" of the output of the linear block G when the input is chosen from the class of periodic functions of period T and of unity "power density." By Parseval's theorem, if v_n is the nth Fourier coefficient of the input $v(t) \in \mathcal{K}$, then

$$\|\mathcal{G}v\|^2 = \sum_{-\infty}^{\infty} \left| G\left(jn\frac{2\pi}{T}\right)\right|^2 |v_n|^2$$

Hence

$$\|\mathcal{G}\| \leq \max_n \left| G\left(jn\frac{2\pi}{T}\right)\right| \tag{11-104}$$

However, if $n = m$ is the index at which $|G(jn\, 2\pi/T)|$ assumes a maximum, then a $v(t)$, which is a periodic function of period T/m and of unit norm, will yield a $\|\mathcal{G}\|$ which is equal to $|G(jm\, 2\pi/T)|$. Thus (11-104) must only hold with the equal sign.

Next, let us note that as long as $|1 + G(jn\, 2\pi/T)| > \delta > 0$ for each integer n, then, for any element $u \in \mathcal{K}$ with finite norm, there always exists an element $v \in \mathcal{K}$ of finite norm such that

$$(\mathcal{I} + \mathcal{G})u = v \tag{11-105}$$

where $\mathcal{I}$ is the identity operator defined by $\mathcal{I}v = v$ for all $v \in \mathcal{K}$. When (11-105) is satisfied, we may write symbolically

$$u = (\mathcal{I} + \mathcal{G})^{-1} v \tag{11-106}$$

Indeed, we readily see that for the linear plant G

$$\|(\mathcal{I} + \mathcal{G})^{-1}\| = \max_n \left| \frac{1}{1 + G(jn\, 2\pi/T)} \right| \tag{11-107}$$

We can now state the following theorem.

◆◆Theorem 11-11 (Sandberg [S4]). For the system defined above, if the input $r(t)$ belongs to $\mathcal{K}$, and if

$$\rho = \max_n \left| \frac{G(jn\,2\pi/T)}{1 + G(jn\,2\pi/T)} \right| < 1 \tag{11-108}$$

then there exists a unique output function $y^*(t)$ that belongs to $\mathcal{K}$. Moreover, $y^*(t)$ may be obtained as the limit of the successive iterations $\lim_{n \to \infty} y_n(t)$ where

$$y_{n+1} = (\mathcal{I} + \mathcal{G})^{-1}\mathcal{G}\{f(r - y_n) + y_n\} \tag{11-109}$$

and the result of the nth iteration satisfies

$$\|y_n - y^*\| \le \frac{\rho^n}{1 - \rho}\|y_1 - y_0\| \tag{11-110}$$ ◆◆

We may note that the existence of a unique solution when (11-108) is satisfied is not surprising and can be obtained through other methods. The main result of interest is provided by formula (11-109), which, for example, can be used to improve on the result obtained using a describing function approach for systems under a sinusoidal input as given in Chap. 6 (Sec. 6.5).

Let $\hat{y}(t)$ be the sinusoidal solution obtained using the describing function method; then (11-109) indicates that we should obtain the sinusoidal solution $e(t) = r(t) - \hat{y}(t)$ and then obtain the output of the nonlinearity $f(e(t))$. This output, when operated on by a linear block with transfer function $G(s)/[1 + G(s)]$, will yield an improved solution, $y_1(t)$. This is illustrated in Fig. 11-6. The rms error of the above procedure is estimated by (11-110)

$$\|y_1 - y^*\| \le \frac{\rho}{1 - \rho}\|y_1 - \hat{y}\| \tag{11-111}$$

where $y^*(t)$ is the exact (but unknown) output of the system. In (11-111) we note that unless $\rho < 0.5$, the estimate is too conservative to be helpful.

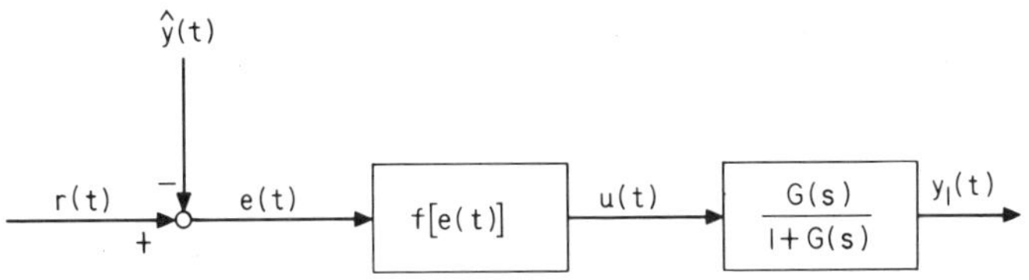

Fig. 11-6. The block diagram of an iterative process derived from Eq. (11-109). Using the output $\hat{y}(t)$ determined by describing function on the system of Fig. 11-5, an improved output waveform $y_1(t)$ can be generated. The process can be repeated by using $y_1(t)$ in place of $\hat{y}(t)$ to generate a yet better waveform $y_2(t)$, etc.

To prove Theorem 11-11, we need to construct an appropriate contraction operator. Let us write the nonlinearity $f(e)$ in the form

$$f(e) = e + f_1(e) \tag{11-112}$$

With (11-112), the functional equation of the system becomes

$$y = \mathcal{G}[f(r-y)] = \mathcal{G}[(r-y) + f_1(r-y)] = \mathcal{G}r - \mathcal{G}y + \mathcal{G}[f_1(r-y)]$$

Thus on rearranging

$$y = (\mathcal{I} + \mathcal{G})^{-1}\mathcal{G}r + (\mathcal{I} + \mathcal{G})^{-1}\mathcal{G}[f_1(r-y)] \tag{11-113}$$

The rhs of (11-113) defines an opeartor $\mathcal{M}$ in $\mathcal{K}$ such that

$$\mathcal{M}y = (\mathcal{I} + \mathcal{G})^{-1}\mathcal{G}r + (\mathcal{I} + \mathcal{G})^{-1}\mathcal{G}[f_1(r-y)]$$

for any $r \in \mathcal{K}$. Now for any two elements y_1 and y_2 in $\mathcal{K}$

$$\|\mathcal{M}y_1 - \mathcal{M}y_2\| = \|(\mathcal{I} + \mathcal{G})^{-1}\mathcal{G}[f_1(r-y_1) - f_1(r-y_2)]\|$$

by (11-90) we have

$$\|\mathcal{M}y_1 - \mathcal{M}y_2\| \le \|(\mathcal{I} + \mathcal{G})^{-1}\mathcal{G}\| \, \|f_1(r-y_1) - f_1(r-y_2)\| \tag{11-114}$$

By (11-101), it is seen that

$$\|f_1(r-y_1) - f_1(r-y_2)\| \le \|y_1 - y_2\| \tag{11-115}$$

Therefore

$$\|\mathcal{M}y_1 - \mathcal{M}y_2\| \le \|(\mathcal{I} + \mathcal{G})^{-1}\mathcal{G}\| \, \|y_1 - y_2\|$$

and $\mathcal{M}$ is a contraction operator if

$$\|(\mathcal{I} + \mathcal{G})^{-1}\mathcal{G}\| = \max_n \left| \frac{G(jn\,2\pi/T)}{1 + G(jn\,2\pi/T)} \right| < 1$$

Since $\mathcal{M}y = \mathcal{G}[f(r-y)]$, we have proved Theorem 11-11.

The reader is referred to reference [H15]* for further use of the contraction-mapping theorem for driven systems in the standard form with nonlinearities not covered by the global type of Lipschitz condition given by Eq. (11-101).

*Holtzman in [H15] also pointed out that the contraction-mapping theorem cannot be applied to autonomous systems to determine the existence of self-oscillations.

11.8 Summary

For a system that is stable without input, two further qualitative questions concerning stability arise when it is driven: first, whether the output is bounded when the input is bounded; second, whether the driven solution is stable.

There are a number of results concerning bounded-input bounded-output (BIBO) stability of feedback control systems (see Definitions 11-1 and 11-2). In this text we have shown that:

1) For a linear time-varying system, as long as $x = 0$ is uniformly asymptotically stable without input, then (except for some trivial cases) it is globally BIBO stable. In fact the converse is also true (see Theorems 11-2 and 11-5).
2) For a closed-loop control system of the form of (11-26) with a time-varying linear part, if (11-28) holds and if the unperturbed system is uniformly asymptotically stable, then the perturbed system is BIBO stable in the small (totally stable) (see Theorem 11-3).
3) For a closed-loop control system in the standard form of the Popov problem, if with no input it is output asymptotic, then under a bounded input with bounded derivative, the output will also be bounded (see Theorem 11-6).
4) For a nonlinear system of the form of (11-25), if the origin of the unperturbed system is uniformly asymptotically stable, then it is BIBO stable in the small.

Concerning the driven solution, we have the following results:

1) For a linear time-varying system whose origin is uniformly asymptotically stable without input, the driven solution is also uniformly asymptotically stable. (Show this.)
2) For a nonlinear system whose linearized equation about a solution takes the form of Eq. (11-26) with $r(t) = 0$, if (11-28) holds, then uniform asymptotic stability of the origin of the unperturbed linearized system implies that the original solution is also uniformly asymptotically stable (see Theorem 5-2).
3) For a closed-loop control system in the standard form of the Popov problem with a zero-memory nonlinearity, the driven solution will be stable in the sense given in Theorem 11-7 if the conditions given therein are satisfied.
4) For a periodic system or an autonomous system with a known periodic solution of period T, linearization about the solution can frequently be applied to determine the stability of the periodic solution. The test here becomes one of examining the magnitude of the eigenvalues of the transition matrix evaluated at the time $t_0 + T$. (See Theorem 11-8.)

In addition to the above results, two special tools are introduced; they are the Bellman-Gronwall inequality (Lemma 11-1) and the contraction-mapping fixed-point theorem (Theorem 11-9). Their usefulness is indicated by Example 11-1 and Theorem 11-11 respectively.

The mathematics of inequalities are used extensively to arrive at the results of this chapter. In many cases the results prove to be too conservative for physical systems.

The practical utility of BIBO stability is questionable if non-conservative bounds cannot be established. The use of inequalities, unfortunately, tends to give conservative bounds. The quest for meaningful bounds associated with BIBO stability promises to be an interesting research area.

The theorems concerning the stability of driven solutions are more useful. In many cases, however, only in-the-small stability information can be obtained.

11.9 Exercises

11-1 Determine if each of the following systems is BIBO stable or unstable.

a) $$\ddot{x} + a_1 \dot{x} + \left(1 + \frac{a_2}{1 + t^2}\right)x = r(t)\,, \qquad a_1, a_2 > 0$$

b) $$\ddot{x} + \left(1 + \frac{1}{1 + t^2}\right)x = r(t)$$

(Hint: consider the difference of the given system with an approximate system $\ddot{y} + y = r(t)$, and use the Bellman-Gronwall lemma.)

11-2 Prove Theorem 11-5. (Hint: this theorem follows directly from Theorem 11-2.)

11-3 For the special case where system (11-38) is time invariant, prove Theorem 11-5 independently from the general proof given in the previous problem by considering the location of the poles of the transfer function $G(s)$ between input and output.

What additional conditions, if any, must be imposed if the converse of Theorem 11-5 is to hold, i.e., if BIBO stability is to imply asymptotic stability of the unforced time-invariant system?

11-4 Consider systems of the form

$$\dot{\mathbf{x}}(t) = [\mathbf{A} + \mathbf{B}(t)]\,\mathbf{x}(t) + \mathbf{r}(t) \tag{11-116}$$

where A is a constant matrix such that a system $\dot{y}(t) = Ay(t)$ is asymptotically stable. Suppose $\int_0^t \|B(\tau)\| \, d\tau \leq d < \infty$. Prove that

a) With $r(t) \equiv 0$, all solutions $x(t)$ are bounded. (Hint: Use the Bellman-Gronwall lemma.)
b) With $r(t) \equiv 0$, all solutions $x(t) \to 0$ as $t \to \infty$.
c) With $r(t) \equiv 0$, the origin of (11-116) is uniformly asymptotically stable.
d) The system (11-116) is BIBO stable with respect to the input $r(t)$.

11-5 Show that for the linear periodic system given in Example 5-17, condition (2) of Lemma 11-4 is not satisfied.

11-6 Prove the following:

◆◆Theorem 11-12: Feedback system (11-39) is (globally) BIBO stable if (i) $|u(t)| = |\mathcal{F}[e(t), t]| \leq U < \infty$ and (ii) the linear element is output stable.◆◆

Comment on the usefulness of this theorem.

11-7 Show that the sequence $\{f_n(t)\} = \{\tan^{-1}(nt)\}$ defined in the space $\mathcal{C}[-1, 1]$ of Example 11-5 does not constitute a Cauchy sequence. Show that $\lim_{n \to \infty} f_n(t)$ is not a continuous function.

11-8 For Example 11-5, for any given element $f_1(t)$ of the Banach space $\mathcal{C}[t_1, t_2]$ create a Cauchy sequence that converges to a specific element $f(t)$.

11-9 Show that the normed function space $\mathcal{K}$ of Example 11-6 is a Banach space. (Hint: To prove that the space is complete, use the Fourier series expansion of each element of any Cauchy sequences.)

11-10 Consider a system in the standard form of Fig. 11-1 with $\mathcal{F}$ the unit limiter and $\mathcal{L}[g(t)] = 1/[(s+1)(s+10)]$. Suppose $r(t)$ is given by $R \sin 3t$, find an approximate solution for the system using describing function and then improve upon it by the technique of Sandberg (Sec. 11.7). Try to iterate once more for an even better solution.

11-11 Consider a feedback system in the standard form with a unit limiter as the nonlinearity. Show by using Theorem 11-7 that a sufficient condition for nonexistence of the jump phenomenon, i.e. for the uniqueness of every response to periodic excitation $r_p(t)$, is given by $\mathcal{R}e\, G(j\omega) > -1$.

11-12 Create a table, comparing all the theorems and lemmas in Chaps. 5, 9, 10, and 11. Do not re-state any theorem or lemma but list the following items: (1) System to which applicable, (2) Subject, (3) Theorem number and name (if applicable), (4) Scope of theorem, (5) Method to which applicable (if any).

Example: (1) Autonomous system, $\dot{x} = f(x)$, (2) Lyapunov stability of an equilibrium, (3) 5-1 (Lyapunov), (4) Relates the stability of the linearized system obtained by small perturbation about an equilibrium to the stability of that equilibrium, (5) Local linearization about an equilibrium state.

11-13 Considering the basic feedback systems of Fig. 11-1:

a) If $r(t) = 0$, what is the largest sector with $G(p) = 1/(p - 1)$ for absolute control asymptoticity of degree α if the nonlinear element is (i) time varying? and (ii) time invariant?
b) What is the largest sector of the nonlinear element in both cases (i) and (ii) for global BIBO stability with respect to an input $r(t)$ as in Fig. 11-1?

11-14 Consider the linear time-varying system:

$$\dot{e}(t) + 2e(t) + k(t)e(t) = 0\ , \quad |k(t)| < K$$

a) Using a suitable frequency response criterion, what is the value of K ensuring output asymptoticity and global asymptotic stability?
b) Determine K to ensure global asymptotic stability by application of Theorem 11-1.

11-15 Consider the feedback system given by $e(t) \doteq r(t) - y(t)$; $u(t) = \mathfrak{F}[e(t), t]$; $\dot{y}(t) = u(t - T)$; and $T = 2$:

a) For $r(t) = 0$ and a time-varying nonlinear element, what is the sector u/e guaranteeing absolute output asymptoticity?
b) Let $r(t) = 0$ and let the nonlinear element be given by $u = 0.0001e + u_1$, where

$$u_1 = \begin{cases} \dfrac{2}{e_0^{\,2}}|e|\,e, & |e| \le e_0 \\ 2 \quad , & e > e_0 \\ -2 \quad , & e < -e_0 \end{cases}$$

Determine the value for e_0 to guarantee output stability.
c) For arbitrary $r(t)$ and a nonlinear element as in (b), what is the value of e_0 that guarantees global BIBO stability?
d) For the same system as in (c), what is the value for e_0 that guarantees process stability?

11-16 Consider a single-loop system of Fig. 11-1 with a memoryless nonlinearity satisfying (11-65). In accordance with the result of Sec. 11.5, if $(1/k_1) > (1/k_2)$ the system cannot exhibit the jump phenomenon for a sinusoidal $r(t)$ if the Nyquist plot of the linear plant $G(p)$ neither encircles nor enters the circle that passes through the points $-1/k_1$ and $-1/k_2$. Show that by using describing function, a forbidden region for the Nyquist plot of $G(p)$ can be found for the avoidance of the jump phenomenon which is always contained in the circle determined above.

11-17 (Baker and Bergen). Consider a system in the form of Fig. 11-5 where the nonlinearity is given by $f(e) = 50e(1 + \sin 2\pi e)$ and where the linear plant is given by $g(p) = 1/(p + 1)^2$. Show that

a) with $r(t) \equiv 0$, the system is uniformly globally asymptotically stable;
b) however, there exist inputs satisfying $|r(t)| \leq 1$ that can cause the output to become unbounded. (Hint: Show that the system can be converted into the time-varying system given in Exercise 5-22.)

11-18 Complete the proof of Theorem 8-4 of Chap. 8 (p. 313), as outlined in Example 11-4.

11.10 References

References to the topics treated in the present chapter are well scattered. A text that includes a fair portion of the results of this chapter is [H3].

The basic references for the various topics of this chapter are as follows: The Bellman-Gronwall lemma: [K12]; Theorem 11-2: [P4], [B5], and [K8]; BIBO stability in the small: [H2]; global BIBO stability: [S3], [S5], [S6], [B9], and [V2]; process stability: [N2] and [Y2]: the stability of periodic solutions: [C1] and [P7]; and the use of contraction-mapping fixed-point theory: [K19], [S4], and [H15].

PART III

OPTIMUM SYSTEM PERFORMANCE ANALYSIS

12

Performance and Optimality

Good performance is difficult to define. Ideally, we would like to have a system carry out its commands without error. However, since this is in general not achievable, all that we can hope for is to design a system to perform as closely as possible to the ideal, subject of course to the various constraints imposed by factors such as realizability, availability of components, and economics. But what then is meant by "as closely as possible to the ideal"? This, to different designers and to different customers, certainly will mean different things.

To get around this problem, the engineer quite often sets up a mathematical performance criterion or index and then tries to find solutions that optimize this particular performance measure. Examples in this regard are criteria such as the minimization of the mean square error or of the integral square error, the minimization of the fuel used, or the minimization of the time to reach a deadbeat response.

Recently, several methods have been advanced which facilitate the finding of solutions to certain classes of problems cast in the above mathematical form. These methods are all related to calculus of variations. Among these are the maximum principle of Pontryagin and the dynamic programming of Bellman. A common earmark of all these methods is that they provide *necessary*, but usually not *sufficient*, conditions that the optimum solution must satisfy.

There are several immediate problems with optimization relative to mathematical performance criterion. First, it is not clear whether a given criterion completely describes the main goal of a particular design endeavor; furthermore, satisfying a given criterion does not necessarily imply that other basic requirements on a practical system, such as stability under disturbance, will also be guaranteed. Indeed it is rather inconceivable that for a complex system a single performance index can encompass all the qualities that are desired in an ideal system. Thus practically speaking, if a mathematical performance criterion is to be used, much thought should go into its selection, so that it fits the problem in some appropriate way. Second, the solution of these problems is exceedingly complex even with the help of the modern methods. Only fairly low-order systems can be readily attacked today either analytically or by computers. Also, since the arithmetical complexity increases extremely rapidly as the order of the system increases, the day that a sufficiently large-scaled general-purpose computer can be developed to solve the nontrivial problems encountered in practice seems quite remote, especially in view of the fact that the programming portion of the task is most likely entrusted to fallible humans. Third, in almost all of the cases, *the optimality must be defined relative to a completely specified* input history*. In particular, step-type inputs are generally specified where the duration of each step is assumed to be significantly longer than the longest time constant of the system in question. These assumptions restrict the scope of applicability of the optimal control theories to the *regulator* class of problems and thereby greatly narrow the utility of most of the recent analytical approaches.

Finally, many new approaches yield only an open-loop control solution, which is not necessarily useful practically. Thus, in many cases a solution may seem satisfactory in a mathematical sense but is not satisfactory in an engineering sense.

The above shortcomings, however, are not serious enough to render optimal control theory useless in engineering. Indeed, recently there are more and more cases where an engineering situation can approximately fit an optimal control format. Some examples may be the maximization of range for a given amount of fuel and payload in a rocket mission and the minimization of cost on some process control operations. In these cases not only can a natural mathematical criterion be found to approximately fit the design goal, but also, at least in the overall system sense, the control can be reduced to an essentially regulator-type problem.

In many instances, too, the finding of an optimum solution relative to a simplified model provides a standard of reference to which all practical designs may be compared. Sometimes it is a comforting feeling to see that a practical realization actually comes quite close in performance to the ideal. If it does not, then the designer knows there is room for improvement. The form of the optimal control function can frequently provide insight as to how one may proceed to achieve the improvement. The structure of optimal control frequently provides insight as to how suboptimal but practical systems can be designed.

*In some cases, only certain statistical properties of the input need to be specified. However, significant results here have been rather scarce for nontrivial nonlinear systems.

Lastly, while large-scale computers cannot promise the miracle of solving all the control problems once and for all, they have nevertheless made possible the solution of many hitherto numerically intractable problems. In fact, the art of making the best use of the computers as analytical or design tools is only in its infancy, and through the vehicle of the well-formulated class of optimal-control problems, there is now a growing impetus to study the nonroutine usage of the computers in control problems.

In the following chapters, we shall treat calculus of variations, the maximum principle of Pontryagin, and dynamic programming in the light of the above comments. Before doing so, however, we shall devote some time to examining the basic premises in the formulation of some typical optimal control problems. We shall examine a class of optimal control problems that have been analyzed and solved without the use of the newer techniques. We shall also see why attacking most other systems will require new mathematical tools over and above those with which we are familiar. In the historically interesting problem of achieving the fastest deadbeat response for a linear plant with power constraint (the time optimal control problem), simple physical intuition can guess at many of the solutions, though they do not allow us to prove the results conclusively. In the case of other optimal control problems even the physical intuition will be lacking, and we must look for more powerful methods of attack.

12.1 The Optimal Control Problem—Formulation and Examples

The typical classes of optimal control problems that we will treat in this section depend on the following specifications:

1) A system to be controlled optimally, $\dot{\mathbf{x}} = \mathbf{f}(\mathbf{x}, \mathbf{u}, t)$.
2) A starting time t_1, a starting state $\mathbf{x}(t_1) \triangleq \mathbf{x}_1$, an end time t_2, and an end state $\mathbf{x}(t_2) \triangleq \mathbf{x}_2$. Quite frequently the end time t_2 is only given implicitly, such as requiring that t_2 be the minimum time necessary to reach the end state $\mathbf{x}_2$. Likewise, the end state may only be required to lie on a set of points.
3) *A performance index* which defines the goal of designing the control system. It is generally of the form

$$\mathcal{J} = P(\mathbf{x}_1, \mathbf{x}_2, t_1, t_2) + \int_{t_1}^{t_2} L(\mathbf{x}, \mathbf{u}, t)\, dt \qquad \text{(12-1)*}$$

*Mathematically speaking, $\mathcal{J}$ in (12-1) is a *functional* that depends on the entire histories of $\mathbf{x}(t)$ and $\mathbf{u}(t)$ over $t_1 \le t \le t_2$ as well as on the numbers $\mathbf{x}_1$, $\mathbf{x}_2$, t_1, t_2. We should write it in the form $\mathcal{J}[\mathbf{x}(t), \mathbf{u}(t), t, \mathbf{x}_1, \mathbf{x}_2, t_1, t_2]$, but for brevity we shall simply use the letter $\mathcal{J}$ to denote all this.

4) Additional constraints to be imposed on the control $\mathbf{u}$ and/or the state $\mathbf{x}$. Typically, for example, due to limited power, there is saturation in the control vector $\mathbf{u}$ so that the constraints on $\mathbf{u}$ may take the form $\mathbf{V} \leq \mathbf{u}(t) \leq \mathbf{U}$, with $\mathbf{U}$ and $\mathbf{V}$ constant vectors. The states sometimes are also constrained to lie within a bounded region of state space due to structural vulnerability and other considerations.

With the above four conditions specified, *the goal of control is to find a control function* $\mathbf{u}$, *either in an open-loop form* $\mathbf{u}(t)$ *or a feedback form* $\mathbf{u}(\mathbf{x}, t)$, *which can drive the system from the state* $\mathbf{x}_1$ *at* t_1 *to the state* $\mathbf{x}_2$ *at* t_2 *in such a way as to minimize or maximize the performance index* $\mathcal{J}$.

Consider now some typical classes of the optimal control problems.

1. The Time-Optimal Control Problem

We are given a plant $\dot{\mathbf{x}} = \mathbf{f}(\mathbf{x}, \mathbf{u}, t)$; a starting time t_1; starting and end states $\mathbf{x}_1$, $\mathbf{x}_2$; and saturation constraints on $\mathbf{u}$, $|u_i(t)| \leq U$ $(i = 1, \ldots, r)$. We wish to drive the system from $\mathbf{x}_1$ at t_1 to $\mathbf{x}_2$ in the least possible time t^*.

For this problem the function P in (12-1) is zero, and the function L is unity. The performance index is merely

$$\mathcal{J} = \int_{t_1}^{t_2} dt \tag{12-2}$$

Note here however that the upper limit of integration is not known *a priori*, though it is implicitly given by $t_2 - t_1 = t^*$.

2. The Fuel-Optimal Problem

We are given a plant $\dot{\mathbf{x}} = \mathbf{f}(\mathbf{x}, \mathbf{u}, t)$ which may for example be a rocket where the control function $\mathbf{u}$ may be the instantaneous thrust acting on the vehicle; $\mathbf{u}$ is then a measure of the rate of fuel loss. A natural performance index is then

$$\mathcal{J} = \int_{t_1}^{t_2} \sum_{i=1}^{r} |u_i(t)|\,dt \tag{12-3}$$

or the total fuel loss. A meaningful problem is to find $\mathbf{u}(t)$ which takes the system state from $\mathbf{x}_1$ at t_1 to $\mathbf{x}_2$ at t_2 so as to minimize the fuel loss (12-3).

3. The Minimum Integral-Square Error Problem

Relative to the end state x_2, the quantity $x - x_2$ can be viewed as the instantaneous system error. If we transform the system such that x_2 becomes the origin, then the new state x is itself the error. Some investigators have advanced the argument that the integral-square error

$$\mathcal{J} = \int_{t_1}^{t_2} \sum_{i=1}^{n} (x_1)^2 \, dt = \int_{t_1}^{t_2} (\mathbf{x}^T \mathbf{x}) \, dt$$

is a reasonable measure of the system transient response from the time t_1 to t_2. To be more general, the integral of a quadratic form of the errors

$$\mathcal{J} = \int_{t_1}^{t_2} (\mathbf{x}^T \mathbf{Q} \mathbf{x}) \, dt \tag{12-4}$$

with Q a symmetric $n \times n$ positive definite matrix can be used. In this case we wish to find a u so as to drive a system state from x_1 at t_1 to the origin 0 at t_2 in such a way as to minimize a performance index of the form (12-4).

4. The Minimum Energy Problem

In some problems, $\sum_{i=1}^{r} u_i^2$ or $\mathbf{u}^T \mathbf{R} \mathbf{u}$, where R is a symmetric $r \times r$ matrix, are measures of the instantaneous rate of expenditure of energy. As an example, if u_i is the current in the ith loop of a network, then $\sum_{i=1}^{r} u_i^2 r_i$, where r_i is the resistance in the ith loop, is the total power or the total rate of energy expenditure of the network. Thus a performance index

$$\mathcal{J} = \int_{t_1}^{t_2} (\mathbf{u}^T \mathbf{R} \mathbf{u}) \, dt \tag{12-5}$$

is a meaningful one for a problem where minimization of the expended energy is the design goal.

5. The Terminal Optimal Control Problem or the Final Value Optimal Control Problem

In endeavors such as aircraft intercept by means of ground-to-air missiles the ultimate measure of goodness is the distance between interceptor and the target at a final time, say the time of detonation of the warhead of the interceptor. Here the quantity L in (12-1) is zero while the quantity P is nonzero. $\mathcal{J}$ thus will be of the form

$$\mathcal{J} = P(\mathbf{x}_2, t_2) \tag{12-6}$$

As a specific example, if x_{I1}, x_{I2}, and x_{I3} are the position coordinates of the interceptor and x_{T1}, x_{T2}, and x_{T3} are the position coordinates of the target, a good performance criterion is to minimize the distance of the interceptor from the target at the time of intercept t_2. In this case

$$P = \sum_{i=1}^{3} \left(x_{Ii}(t_2) - x_{Ti}(t_2)\right)^2$$

6. Problems with More Complex Performance Indices

Frequently a simple index by itself lead to solutions that are ambiguous or impractical. For example, as we shall show in the sequel, under certain conditions, the time-optimal, the fuel optimal, and the minimum integral-square error problems all can yield solutions that are nonunique. To overcome such ambiguity and sometimes to lend flexibility in design, it is frequently desirable to have a performance index that includes more than one of the simple indices as given above. We may for example use the index

$$\mathcal{J} = \int_{t_1}^{t_2} \left(\sum_{i=1}^{r} |u_i(t)| + k\right) dt \tag{12-7}$$

which, with t_2 unspecified *a priori*, represents a linear combination of (12-2) and (12-3), or we may use the index

$$\mathcal{J} = \int_{t_1}^{t_2} (\mathbf{x}^T \mathbf{Q} \mathbf{x} + \mathbf{u}^T \mathbf{R} \mathbf{u})\, dt \tag{12-8}$$

which represents a combination of (12-4) and (12-5).

7. Problems with More Complex End States

Often some (or all) of the end states are left unspecified. For example, in the aircraft intercept example above, the velocity of the interceptor does not appear in the performance index and it does not need to be constrained in any way at the intercept time

t_2. Indeed here it is practically not meaningful even to fix the end state *a priori*. When only some of the end states are specified, we have a *mixed* end condition.

Occasions can further arise where, for example, we are required to come within a distance ρ of a given point x_0 in state space in a minimum time. Here the end point is constrained to lie on a hypersphere given by $\|x_2 - x_0\| = \rho$. Instead of an end state, we now have an end set.

The above represents rather special classes of problems and we may expect that special tools must be developed to cope with them. Three such tools will be discussed in Chaps. 13–15 respectively. It is, however, instructive to attempt to solve some of the optimal control problems posed without resorting to special methods. The difficulties that we encounter and the feel that we thus derive can allow us to appreciate both the scope of the problem and the versatility and limitations of the methods that we will introduce.

12.2 A Frequency-Domain Technique for Optimization of a Linear Time-Invariant System

One class of problems that analysts have learned to deal with prior to the advent of the newer techniques is the finding of linear time-invariant systems that minimize the integral-square error for a specific input. The approach here was essentially inspired by the pioneering work of Norbert Wiener [W4] and the extension of his results into the frequency-domain by Bode and Shannon [B12].

The adaptation of Wiener's technique for the minimization of integral-square error in the case of deterministic system was due to G. C. Newton, et al. [N6].

The problem in its simplest form can be formulated in the following way.† For a linear system of the form of Fig. 12-1, with the plant $G(p)$ specified, and with $r(t)$ such that the square-integrability of $e(t)$ over $0 \le t \le \infty$ is assured,†† find that stable linear compensator $G_1^*(p)$ which minimizes the performance index†††

† The succinct development presented here follows that of Chang [C2]. We give the present problem a rather short treatment merely to let the reader appreciate the steps required to solve the problem in the frequency domain. In Chap. 13 we shall indicate a more comprehensive time-domain solution.

†† For example, we may require that $r(t)$ is square integrable for a general stable plant $G(p)$, or we may use an $r(t)$ that is a unit step function for a plant that has integration, etc.

††† The term $ku^2(t)$ in the integrand is to impose penalty for very large values of $u(t)$; otherwise, we will obtain the trivial result $H(p) \equiv 1$, implying an obvious solution $G_1(p) = [K/G(p)]$ with $K \to \infty$. The use of such penalty terms in the performance index will be treated in Chap. 13.

$$\mathcal{J}[e(t), u(t)] = \int_0^\infty [e^2(t) + ku^2(t)]\,dt$$

and which results in a stable closed-loop system

$$H^*(p) = \frac{G_1^*(p)\,G(p)}{1 + G_1^*(p)\,G(p)}$$

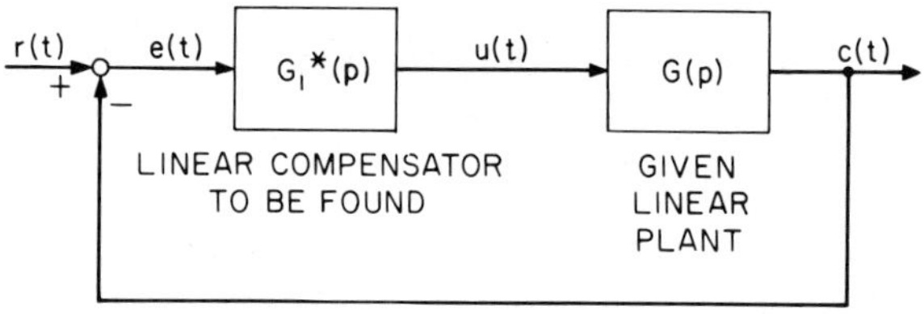

Fig. 12-1. The configuration of the system considered in Sec. 12.2. The compensator $G_1{}^*(p)$ is to be found so as to minimize a performance index of the form of Eq. (12-9) for a given square-integrable $r(t)$.

The problem can be attacked in the time domain to result in an integral equation known as a Wiener–Hopf equation [N6]. However, the analysis is much more straightforward in the frequency domain. The key is to make use of Parsavel's theorem. (See Appendix C.)

By the use of Parseval's theorem, the performance index can be expressed in the Laplace-transform domain or the s-domain via the relation

$$\mathcal{J}[e(t), u(t)] = \int_0^\infty [e^2(t) + ku^2(t)]\,dt$$
$$= \frac{1}{2\pi j}\int_{-j\infty}^{j\infty} [E(s)E(-s) + kU(s)U(-s)]\,ds \qquad \textbf{(12-9)}$$

where $E(s)$ and $U(s)$ are the Laplace transforms of $e(t)$ and $u(t)$ respectively. Letting

$$H(s) = \frac{Y(s)}{R(s)} = \frac{G_1(s)\,G(s)}{1 + G_1(s)\,G(s)}, \qquad \textbf{(12-10)}$$

we can write (12-9) in the form

$$\mathcal{J}[e(t), u(t)] = \mathcal{J}[H(s)]$$
$$= \frac{1}{2\pi j}\int_{-j\infty}^{j\infty} \left[\Big(H(s) - 1\Big)\Big(H(-s) - 1\Big) + \frac{kH(s)H(-s)}{G(s)G(-s)}\right] R(s)R(-s)\,ds \qquad \textbf{(12-11)}$$

The object then is to find a stable $H^*(s)$ so as to minimize $\mathcal{J}[H(s)]$.

To find the minimizing transfer function $H^*(s)$ we can use the following development, which is frequently invoked, to set up a problem in calculus of variation:† Let us observe first that if $H^*(s)$ were the optimum linear transfer function, then the performance index corresponding to the $H(s)$ must, by definition, have a *smaller* value than that corresponding to any other transfer functions. In particular, for some constant ϵ, the following holds

$$\mathcal{J}[H^*(s)] \le \mathcal{J}[H^*(s) + \epsilon H_1(s)] = \mathcal{J}_\epsilon[H^*(s)]$$

where $H_1(s)$ is some arbitrary stable transfer function.

Consider the quantity $\mathcal{J}[H^*(s) + \epsilon H_1(s)] \triangleq \mathcal{J}_\epsilon[H^*(s)]$ as a function of ϵ. For any arbitrarily selected $H_1(s)$, the plot of $\mathcal{J}_\epsilon[H^*(s)]$ vs. ϵ for small ϵ will look like that in Fig. 12-2. A minimum occurs at $\epsilon = 0$. Suppose $\mathcal{J}_\epsilon[H^*(s)]$ is smooth relative to ϵ at $\epsilon = 0$; then a necessary condition that $H(s)$ is the minimizing transfer function is that the dual requirements

$$\frac{d}{d\epsilon}\mathcal{J}_\epsilon[H^*(s)]\bigg|_{\epsilon=0} = 0 \tag{12-12a}$$

$$\frac{d^2}{d\epsilon^2}\mathcal{J}_\epsilon[H^*(s)]\bigg|_{\epsilon=0} \ge 0 \tag{12-12b}$$

are met.

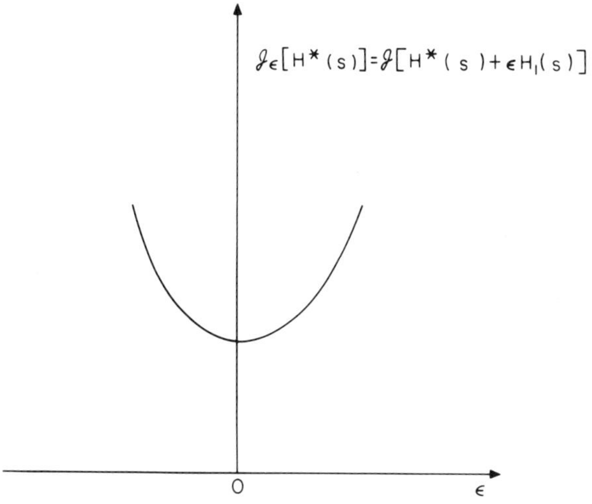

Fig. 12-2. The function $\mathcal{J}_\epsilon[H^*(s)]$ vs. ϵ for small ϵ will show a local minimum at $\epsilon = 0$.

†See Chapter 13 for further significance of this development.

Now using (12-11), we see that $\mathcal{J}_\epsilon[H^*(s)]$ can be written as:

$$\mathcal{J}_\epsilon[H^*(s)] = \mathcal{J}_a + 2\epsilon\mathcal{J}_b + \epsilon^2\mathcal{J}_c \tag{12-13}$$

where $\mathcal{J}_a = \mathcal{J}[H^*(s)]$

$$\mathcal{J}_b = \frac{1}{2\pi j}\int_{-j\infty}^{j\infty}\left[\Big(H^*(s) - 1\Big) + \frac{kH^*(s)}{G(s)G(-s)}\right]R(s)R(-s)H_1(-s)\,ds$$

$$= \frac{1}{2\pi j}\int_{-j\infty}^{j\infty}\left[\Big(H^*(-s) - 1\Big) + \frac{kH^*(-s)}{G(s)G(-s)}\right]R(s)R(-s)H_1(s)\,ds$$

and $\mathcal{J}_c$ is an integral with an integrand that is never negative. (What is it?)

Performing $\left.\dfrac{d\mathcal{J}_\epsilon[H^*(s)]}{d\epsilon}\right|_{\epsilon=0}$ and setting it to 0 readily yields $\mathcal{J}_b = 0$ as a necessary condition. We thus see that in order for $H^*(s)$ to be the minimizing transfer function, it must be such as to make $\mathcal{J}_b$ vanish relative to an arbitrary stable transfer function $H_1(s)$. Thus we have

$$\frac{1}{2\pi j}\int_{-j\infty}^{j\infty}\left[\Big(H^*(s) - 1\Big) + \frac{kH^*(s)}{G(s)G(-s)}\right]R(s)R(-s)H_1(-s)\,ds = 0 \tag{12-14}$$

Moreover, with $\mathcal{J}_c$ positive the condition (12-12b) is also satisfied.

As $H_1(s)$ is assumed stable and hence all poles of $H_1(s)$ lie in the left-half of the s plane (lhp). Then all poles of $H_1(-s)$ lie in the right-half of the s plane (rhp). Using a result in the theory of complex variables, a sufficient condition that $\mathcal{J}_b = 0$ is that the integrand of (12-14) has only poles in the rhp.† This in turn implies that the quantity

$$\left[\Big(H^*(s) - 1\Big) + \frac{kH^*(s)}{G(s)G(-s)}\right]R(s)R(-s)$$

must only have poles that lie in the rhp.

The optimum transfer function $H^*(s)$ is readily found under the above condition. The reader can demonstrate to himself that the following procedure will yield the $H^*(s)$ sought for.

†This can be shown by integrating the integrand of (12-14) over a semi-infinite contour that includes the $j\omega$ axis and a semicircle of infinite radius that encloses the lhp. (What is the condition on the integrand such that the contour integration vanishes?)

Let $A(s)$ be such that it possesses no pole or zero in the rhp and, moreover, let

$$A(s)A(-s) = \left[1 + \frac{k}{G(s)G(-s)}\right]$$

Similarly, let $B(s)$ be a function with no pole or zero in the rhp such that $B(s)B(-s) = R(s)R(-s)$. Finally, let the partial fraction expansion of the function $B(s)/A(-s)$ be written in the form $B(s)/A(-s) = C_+(s) + C_-(s)$, where $C_+(s)$ is composed of the part involving all the poles in the lhp and half of the poles on the imaginary axis. In terms of these quantities, the optimum transfer function $H^*(s)$ will be

$$H^*(s) = \frac{C_+(s)}{A(s)B(s)} \tag{12-15}$$

Once $H^*(s)$ is known, $G_1^*(s)$ can be found using (12-10). They then can be used to find the minimum value of the performance index $\mathcal{J}$ through the evaluation of the integral (12-11).†

The above method represents one of the more satisfying analytical results. The reason for the relatively simple solution is the fact that the upper limit of integration in the performance index is infinity. Since the input is completely specified and the system is linear and time invariant, the steady state response of the system can be determined. This means, with the upper limit infinity, the end condition need not be an item that enters into the optimization procedure. Thus only the initial conditions of the system can dictate the solutions. We have then essentially only a *one-point boundary value problem*, which is more readily solvable.

The method is not without its drawbacks. The application of the method usually leads to systems that do not strongly overshoot but which are sluggish with respect to small deviations from the desired output. The system step response usually exhibits a long tail. The fault here lies with the very nature of the performance index (12-9), which tends to penalize the large values of $e(t)$ and $u(t)$ more than the small values. However, as we will indicate below, any attempt to modify the integrand from a sum of the squares form quickly leads to problems which cannot be solved by the present method. The same occurs when we try to change the upper limit of integrations to a small number or to impose hard limits on the amplitude $u(t)$, thereby making the system nonlinear.

† There are tables which can facilitate the calculation of the integral (12-11); see, e.g., [N6] pp. 366-381.

We will show in Chap. 15 that such extensions can be handled using the newer theories, at the cost of more additional labor.

12.3 The Solving of Two-Point Boundary Value Problems for Linear Time-Varying Systems

When we examine the requirements for the classes of more general optimal control problems where the technique of the previous section is inapplicable, we note that the requirements can be conveniently broken into two parts. First, we must find a family of solutions that passes through two different points $\mathbf{x}_1$ and $\mathbf{x}_2$.* A solution must satisfy these two boundary conditions before it can even be considered as a candidate for the optimal trajectory. Second, having found a family of candidate solutions, we then must devise ways to sort out the optimum one(s).

The next four chapters will be devoted to methods which will allow us to find the optimal solution from the candidate solutions. Before studying the particular methods, it is fruitful to pause and consider how readily we can find families of candidate solutions for the class of *two-point boundary value problems* typical in optimal control.

As may be expected, there is currently no general method to find solutions to a two-point boundary value problem involving a differential system. If, however, the system happens to be linear, superposition comes again to the rescue and we can always find a family of possible solutions, if it exists, at least by numerical means.

To show this, consider a general nth-order linear system

$$\dot{\mathbf{x}}(t) = \mathbf{A}(t)\mathbf{x}(t) + \mathbf{B}(t)\mathbf{u}(t) \tag{12-16}$$

Suppose that $\mathbf{A}(t)$, $\mathbf{B}(t)$, and $\mathbf{u}(t)$ are specified and we wish to find a trajectory whose first p components satisfy the conditions $x_1(t_1) = x_{11}, x_2(t_1) = x_{21}, \ldots, x_p(t_1) = x_{p1}$, and $x_1(t_2) = x_{12}, x_2(t_2) = x_{22}, \ldots, x_p(t_2) = x_{p2}$ where $p = n/2$.** The other components of $\mathbf{x}$ at t_1 and t_2 are left free.

The general solution of (12-16) is

$$\mathbf{x}(t) = \mathbf{\Phi}(t, t_1)\mathbf{x}(t_1) + \int_{t_1}^{t} \mathbf{\Phi}(t, \tau)\mathbf{B}(\tau)\mathbf{u}(\tau)\,d\tau \tag{12-17a}$$

*In the system of Sec. 12.2, it is implicit that $\mathbf{x}_2$ is the equilibrium state of the plant as $t \to \infty$.

**The general solution of (12-16) has only n arbitrary constants, hence only n boundary conditions can be given. They of course do not need to be evenly distributed at the two end points. We have further assumed that n is even here, but from the foregoing considerations, there would be no difficulty in dealing with the case where n is any positive integer.

Let

$$\mathbf{x}^{(u)}(t) = \int_{t_1}^{t} \mathbf{\Phi}(t, \tau)\mathbf{B}(\tau)\mathbf{u}(\tau)\,d\tau$$

$\mathbf{x}^{(u)}(t)$ is then the nonhomogeneous part of the solution. Since $\mathbf{\Phi}(t, t_1)$ can be found from integrating the equation $\dot{\mathbf{\Phi}}(t, t_1) = \mathbf{A}(t)\mathbf{\Phi}(t, t_1)$ with the initial condition $\mathbf{\Phi}(t_1, t_1) = \mathbf{I}$, it follows that $\mathbf{x}^{(u)}(t)$ can be found for all t in $[t_1, t_2]$. What remains is to write Eq. (12-17), evaluated at $t = t_2$, as

$$\mathbf{x}(t_2) = \mathbf{\Phi}(t_2, t_1)\mathbf{x}(t_1) + \mathbf{x}^{(u)}(t_2) \tag{12-17b}$$

and match boundary conditions. We see that with $\mathbf{\Phi}(t_2, t_1)$ and $\mathbf{x}^{(u)}(t_2)$ known there remain n unknowns in (12-17b), namely $n/2$ components of the vector $\mathbf{x}(t_2)$ and $n/2$ components of the vector $\mathbf{x}(t_1)$. Since (12-17b) provides n algebraic equations, the unknowns can readily be solved for.

For nonlinear systems, there is no general way to solve two-point boundary problems. This is why most of the "solved" optimal control problems involve a linear plant.

There are numerical procedures which permit the solving of some nonlinear two-point boundary value problems through iteration. All such procedures, however, make use of local linearization so as to utilize the aforementioned desirable property of a linear system with respect to two-point boundary value problems.

Just by the result of this section, however, it may seem that the result of Sec. 12.2 should be capable of being extended considerably. The linear plant for example can be time varying, and the upper limit of integration need not be ∞, so that end points $\mathbf{x}_2$ other than 0 can be specified. These extensions will be discussed in later chapters. In the meantime let us look at some of the basic problems involved in optimal control of simple linear time-invariant plants.

12.4 The Time-Optimal Control Problem

We have had our initial acquaintance with the problem of time-optimal control of a system of the double integrator type in Chap. 4. We are now ready to consider the problem in more detail in the light of the above comments.

In Example 4-1 (Case 6) of Chap. 4, we have indicated that a reasonable conjecture would seem to be that *for time-optimal control, the maximum available power should be used at all times to either accelerate or to brake the system.* In the early days of the investigations of the class of time-optimal control systems this conjecture played an important role. For if it were true, then, for many time-invariant linear plants, the control strategy could be readily calculated mathematically and the switching lines and surfaces readily established in the state space. However, the engineers were stymied in trying to establish whether the conjecture was true. It would appear that the mathematical tools then at their disposal were not sufficient for this task. Moreover, there was always the nagging fear that the conjecture, known as the bang-bang conjecture, may not hold in special cases.

Since 1956, the conjecture has been proved to be true in almost all cases where the plant to be controlled is linear and time-invariant. We shall, however, defer discussing the proof of the conjecture until Chap. 14. In the meantime, let us investigate some properties of the control of linear constant systems assuming this conjecture to be true.

Let us first restrict our attention to the bang-bang control of linear time-invariant, second-order systems with no numerator dynamics. Let it be desired to drive the system from an arbitrary initial state to the origin in the minimum time by means of a relay with an amplitude $\pm U$.

For this class of problems the state-plane construction is a natural approach. If y is the output of the system, then in the state-plane of $\dot{y}$ vs. y we can immediately take notice of several facts. First, we see that the polarity of control relay is clearly determined in the first and third quadrant. This is because in the first quadrant, we have $y > 0$, $\dot{y} > 0$; this means the output is greater than 0 and increasing. Clearly, here $-U$ is called for. Similarly in the third quadrant $y < 0$, $\dot{y} < 0$, so that $+U$ is called for. Thus, *all the switch lines must lie in the second and fourth quadrants*.

Second, we note that not all second-order systems can be driven to the origin from an arbitrary initial state. For an inherently unstable system, for example, when the initial state is sufficiently far from the origin, the free part of the system motion will dominate over the driven part so that neither polarity of the drive can prevent the output from diverging further. Thus the unstable systems will be controllable only within a zone which contains the origin.*

Third, we note that there is a basic symmetry in the problem, so that only half of the phase plane needs to be investigated.

Finally, we note that the trajectory after the final switch must be such that it passes directly through the origin. Thus the entire trajectory through the origin, which corresponds to a drive of $+U$ and lying in the fourth quadrant will constitute half of the final switch line. The remaining half is its reflection about the origin,

*This is easily seen in a first-order system, $\dot{x} = ax + u$, $a > 0$, $u = \pm U$. When $ax_0 > |U|$, negative drive will not prevent x from increasing; however, when $ax_0 < |U|$, negative drive will bring x toward the origin. We will explore this point later in this section.

and corresponds to a drive of $-U$. If we take a hint from the double integrating system and if the final switch line effectively divides the entire phase plane into two parts, such that any state in one of the halves can always be brought to the switch line by a given polarity of the relay (see Fig. 4-8), then the final switch is the only switch line. In this case, one switch at most is sufficient for this bang-bang control problem.

One of the simplest ways by which the final switch line may be found is through the strategem of reversing time, i.e., running the problem backward. Here if we start at the origin, then half of the final switch line is automatically obtained when the input of $+U$ is used while the remaining half is obtained when $-U$ is used. The device is very commonly invoked to generate switch lines using analog computers, and it can also be profitably employed analytically.

Consider the following example:

◆◆Example 12-1. Let the plant have two real poles a, b, and no numerator dynamics, so that the system equation is

$$\ddot{y} + (a + b)\dot{y} + aby = u(t)$$

Letting $x_1 = y$ and $x_2 = \dot{y}$, we have

$$\begin{aligned} \dot{x}_1 &= x_2 \\ \dot{x}_2 &= -(a + b)x_2 - abx_1 + u \end{aligned} \tag{12-18}$$

Consider a point $\mathbf{x}_0$ on the final switch line, T seconds away from the origin; to reverse time, we set $\tau = T - t$. Let us suppose that at $t = 0$ we are at $\mathbf{x}_0$; then with time running forward, we would have reached the origin at $t = T$. With time running backward, however, if we start at the origin at $\tau = 0$, we would have reached the point $\mathbf{x}_0$ at $\tau = T$.

We note that

$$\frac{dx(t)}{dt} = -\frac{dx(\tau)}{d\tau}, \quad \frac{d^2x(t)}{dt^2} = \frac{d^2x(\tau)}{d\tau^2}$$

so that in the τ domain, the system equations become

$$\begin{aligned} x_1' &= -x_2 \\ x_2' &= (a + b)x_2 + abx_1 - u \end{aligned} \tag{12-19}$$

where $x' \triangleq dx(\tau)/d\tau$. Here we have

$$\mathbf{A} = \begin{bmatrix} 0 & -1 \\ ab & (a+b) \end{bmatrix}, \quad \mathbf{b} = \begin{bmatrix} 0 \\ -1 \end{bmatrix} \tag{12-20}$$

and the eigenvalues are now $\lambda = +a, +b$ (in contrast to $-a, -b$ for the system with the time running forward).

Starting at the origin with $u(0) = +U$, we can verify that

$$x_1(\tau) = \frac{U}{a(a-b)}(e^{a\tau} - 1) - \frac{U}{b(a-b)}(e^{b\tau-1})$$

$$x_2(\tau) = \frac{-U}{a-b}e^{a\tau} + \frac{U}{a-b}e^{b\tau}$$

(12-21)

which represents the reverse evolution of the switch line. Solving for τ, we obtain

$$\tau = \frac{1}{b}\ln\left(1 - \frac{abx_1}{U} - \frac{bx_2}{U}\right)$$

(12-22)

Substituting (12-22) into one of the equations of (12-21) we can obtain the equation for the switch line

$$\left(1 - \frac{ab}{U}x_1 - \frac{a}{U}x_2\right) - \left(1 - \frac{ab}{U}x_1 - \frac{b}{U}x_2\right)^{a/b} = 0, \qquad u = +U \qquad (12\text{-}23)$$

Similarly, for $u = -U$, we obtain

$$\left(1 + \frac{ab}{U}x_1 + \frac{b}{U}x_2\right) - \left(1 + \frac{ab}{U}x_1 + \frac{a}{U}x_2\right)^{a/b} = 0, \qquad u = -U \qquad (12\text{-}24)$$

There are several points that we can establish on inspecting the above equations. First, by Eq. (12-21) we note that if both a and b are positive, corresponding to a stable plant, then both $|x_1(\tau)|$ and $|x_2(\tau)|$ increase monotonically with τ at an ever faster rate. It follows that the entire state plane is divided into two parts by the switch line. It is also relatively clear that the optimal state portraits will be quite similar to that of Fig. 4-8. All trajectories in the $-U$ control zone will eventually intercept the $+U$ switch line and conversely. Thus when the plant is stable, all states are completely controllable even with $|u(t)| \leq U$, and one switch in $u(t)$ suffices for the optimal bang–bang control.◆◆

If one of the numbers a or b is negative, then the plant has at least one positive pole. We have intimated that here not all initial points can be driven to the origin. This can be seen most readily if we make use of the canonical coordinates.

◆◆Example 12-2. In the previous example, let $a > 0$ and $b < 0$; then the system equations in the canonical form are

$$\dot{x}_1 = -ax_1 - \frac{1}{a-b}u = -ax_1 - v$$
$$\dot{x}_2 = -bx_2 + \frac{1}{a-b}u = -bx_2 + v \qquad (12\text{-}25)$$

where $v = [1/(a-b)]u$. With $|u| \leq 1$, we will then have $|v| \leq 1/(a-b) \triangleq V$.

It is readily seen that with $u = +1$ or $v = +V$, the system equilibrium state is located at the state $(-V/a, +V/b)$. Similarly with, $v = -V$, the equilibrium state changes to $(+V/a, -V/b)$. Both states are saddle points by inspection and the system trajectories in the neighborhood of these equilibrium states are given in Fig. 12-3a and 12-3b.

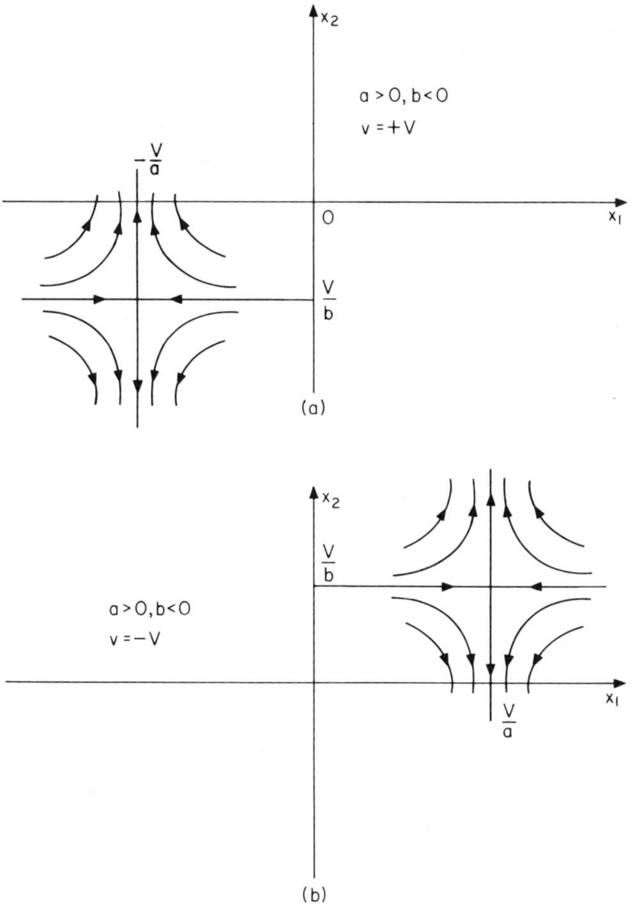

Fig. 12-3. The state-plane portrait about the system equilibrium state for the system of (12-25) for $v = +V$ and $v = -V$.

Note that when $v = -V$ (or $u = -1$), there is one and only one state trajectory that passes through the origin; let this be the curve Γ_-. Similarly, when $v = +V$, a corresponding trajectory Γ_+ passes through the origin.

Superimposing Figs. 12-3a and b, we quickly come to the conclusion that only states in the area bounded by the lines $x_2 = \pm V/b$ can be transferred to the origin. This is shown in Fig. 12-4.

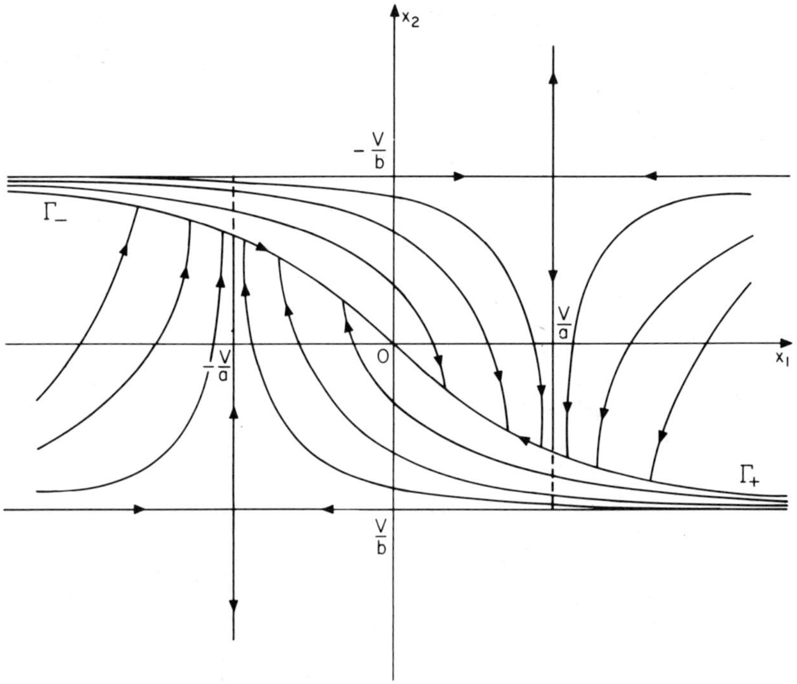

Fig. 12-4. The time-optimal trajectories from an arbitrary initial point to the origin can be determined by appropriately superimposing Figs. 12-3a and 12-3b. Note that initial states with $|x_{20}| > |V/b|$ cannot be driven to the origin.

When both a and b are negative, then the set of initial states that can be transferred to the origin is even smaller, as can be readily established. (See Exercise 12-6.)◆◆

The idea of running time backward is also useful in helping us to appreciate the time-optimal control of higher dimensional linear time-invariant plants with a single input.* Consider, for example,

*Note however that since in general we do not know the proper switching times in order to reach a particular initial state $\mathbf{x}_0$, the technique of running a system backward from the origin does not overcome the inherent two-point boundary value problem in time-optimal control.

a typical third-order stable system with real poles. Starting from the origin and running time backward, with $+U$, it is obvious that a specific trajectory Γ_+ is generated. By the uniqueness theory (Theorem 3-1), it must be the only trajectory that passes through the origin under $+U$. Conversely, with time running forward, the final segment of all optimal trajectories must lie on Γ_+ under the bang-bang conjecture. Similarly, there is a path Γ_- corresponding to $-U$ with the same properties. (See Fig. 12-5.)

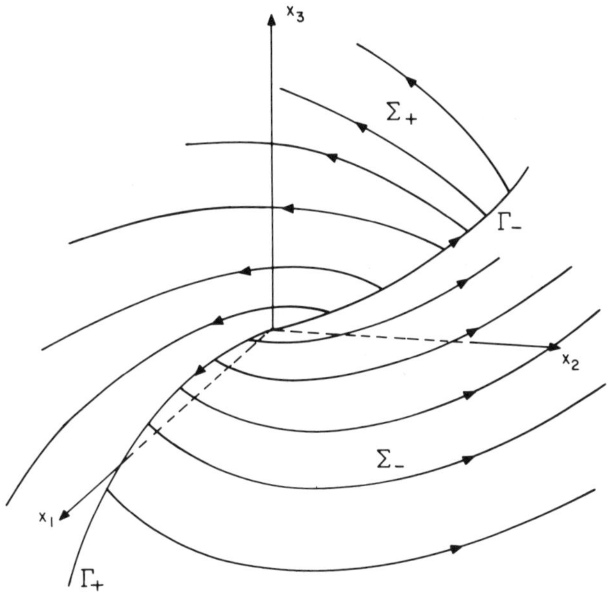

Fig. 12-5. Switching lines Γ_+ and Γ_- and switching surfaces Σ_+ and Σ_- for time-optimal control of a third-order plant.

With time running backward, and using a point x_1 on Γ_+ as the initial point, if we switch to $-U$, we generate a trajectory $\sigma_-(x_1, \tau)$. This trajectory has the property that, with time running forward, the optimal control is $u = -U$ (under the bang-bang conjecture) until the point x_1 is reached, and then the optimal control is $u = +U$ until the trajectory reaches the origin.

It is perhaps intuitive that using all possible points on Γ_+ to generate σ_- using $u = -U$, we will create a surface Σ_-. Similarly, we can create a surface Σ_+ relative to Γ_- (see Fig. 12-5). Also, it is intuitive (think in terms of the canonical coordinates) that if the plant is stable, Σ_+ and Σ_- will divide the entire three-dimensional state space into two equal halves. These half state spaces have the property that from any point in one of them, a drive of $u = +U$ will transfer it in some finite time to the surface Σ_+; from any point in the other, a drive of $u = -U$ will transfer it some finite time to the plane Σ_+. Arguing this way, we see that if a third-order linear time-invariant plant is stable, then at most two switches in $u(t)$ will suffice to transfer any initial state to the origin. The first switch must take place on the *switching surface* Σ_+ or Σ_-, and the final switch must take place on the switching line Γ_- or Γ_+. When the plant is not stable, the same arguments still hold, except that here Σ_+ and Σ_- do not extend indefinitely so that not all initial points can be transferred to the origin; but among those that can be, it appears that at most two switches of polarity in $u(t)$ are necessary.

The above reasoning can be extended to n-dimensional systems with $n > 3$. Under the bang-bang assumption it then seems reasonable that we can conjecture that: *for an n-th order, linear time-invariant system with a single input, if all the system poles are real, then at most* $n - 1$ *switches in the polarity of the control function* $u(t)$ *are necessary to transfer an initial point to the origin if such is possible.*

This $n - 1$ switchings conjecture is again difficult to prove rigorously using standard methods.

Let us note that for linear plants, under the bang-bang and the $n - 1$ switching assumptions, if the polarity of the switchings are known, then a particular time-optimal control problem can always be solved through the solving of a set of n simultaneous algebraic equations. This is because in this case only the $n - 1$ switching times and the end time are unknown; they then consitute the n quantities to be solved for.

We can infer the form of these algebraic equations. For a linear time-invariant system with real eigenvalues, the elements of the transition matrix $\Phi(t)$ will be a linear combination of exponential functions. At the optimum time t^*, we have

$$\mathbf{x}(t^*) = 0 = \Phi(t^*)\mathbf{x}_0 + \int_0^{t^*} \Phi(t^* - \tau)\mathbf{b}u(\tau)\,d\tau \tag{12-26}$$

since $\mathbf{x}_0$ is known and $u(\tau)$ is known down to $n - 1$ switching instants $t_1, t_2, \ldots, t_{n-1}$, then a set of n simultaneous algebraic equations involving exponential functions in the eigenvalues and the t_i's $(i = 1, \ldots, n - 1)$ and t^* will result. For the system of Example 12-1, it is not difficult to see that if we assume $u(\tau)$ to be of the form

$$u(\tau) = \begin{cases} -1, & 0 \le \tau < t_1 \\ +1, & t_1 \le \tau < t^* \\ 0, & t^* \le \tau \end{cases}$$

then using canonical coordinates the relevant set of algebraic equations will be

$$x_1(0) = \frac{U}{a(a - b)}\left[1 - 2e^{at_1} + e^{at^*}\right]$$

$$x_2(0) = \frac{-U}{b(a - b)}\left[1 - 2e^{bt_1} + e^{bt^*}\right] \tag{12-27}$$

and the switching time t_1 and the optimum time t^* can be solved for.

The need to solve a set of simultaneous equations, however, is an indication that we are encountering a two-point boundary value problem because boundary value matching is indicated by the simultaneous equations.

A linear time-invariant system with poles that have imaginary parts introduces a great deal more difficulty.† Even assuming that the bang-bang conjecture is correct, the method of running time backward no longer yields as much information concerning the problem unless there is further insight. Furthermore, from simple physical considerations we can show that the $n - 1$ switching conjecture does not hold for this case.

♦♦Example 12-3. Consider the time-optimal control of an undamped second-order plant $\ddot{x} + x = u(t)$ with $|u(t)| \leq U$. Suppose we start at the origin and run the system backwards through reversing time as before. With $u(t) = +U$, it is easily seen that the system trajectory in the $\dot{x}$ vs. x plane describes a circle Γ_+ with the center at $x_e = U$. With $u(t) = -U$ the system trajectory is a circle Γ_- with center at $x_e = -U$. On reflection, we can see that

1) The upper half of Γ_+ and the lower half of Γ_- should not constitute any portion of the switching curve since it should be reasonable that when $\dot{x} > 0$, $u(t) = -U$ should be used, and when $\dot{x} < 0$, $u(t) = +U$ should be used.
2) The lower half of Γ_+ and the upper half of Γ_-, however, must constitute the final segment of an optimum trajectory by the uniqueness theorem.
3) As $\dot{x}$ for the system under a constant drive periodically changes sign, it is obvious that $u(t)$ must also periodically change sign.
4) Since it is a matter of removing the energy from an oscillatory system, the number of switchings in $u(t)$ must depend on the magnitude of U and hence can be arbitrarily large.

Putting together considerations (1)-(4) actually will permit us to construct the optimal switching curve under the bang-bang

†Such systems, under the bang-bang conjecture, were first studied by Bushaw [B21].

conjecture. (See Exercise 12-3.) However, we shall see in Chap. 15 that the method of LaSalle or the maximum principle can permit us to do this much more simply and without assumptions.♦♦

12.5 The Fuel-Optimal Control Problem

The fuel-optimal control problem, when the index of performance is of the form of Eq. (12-3), turns out to be much more difficult to analyze than the time-optimal control problems discussed in the preceding section. The problem here is the possibility that there may be a lack of uniqueness in the solution.* It is also not easy to guess at the form of solution. Let us consider some examples to illustrate these points.

♦♦Example 12-4. Consider the control of a plant $\dot{x} = u$, with an input $u(t)$ subject to the constraint $|u(t)| \leq 1$. It is desired to find a $u(t)$ which drives the plant from $x = 1$ to $x = 2$ in 5 seconds and which minimizes the criterion $\int_0^5 |u(t)|\, dt$.

On studying this problem, we soon see that it has an infinite number of possible solutions because Δx, the change in the value of the state variable x, is given by

$$\Delta x = \int_0^5 u(t)\, dt \tag{12-28}$$

As long as $u(t)$ does not change sign, any control which satisfies $|u(t)| \leq 1$ and which yields $\Delta x = \int_0^5 u(t)\, dt = 1$ qualifies to be an optimal control. By (12-28) it is impossible to improve upon any of these $u(t)$. On the other hand, if $u(t)$ should change sign, it only tends to undo what it is trying to do and hence a $u(t)$ that changes sign cannot be an optimal solution.

Let us note that if we insist on maximum effort, then an optimum $u(t)$ can be one where $u(t)$ is switched to $+1$ for one second and switched to 0 for the remaining time. Since the one second "on" time can take place anytime during the five-second interval, even this type of full-on and zero control is not unique.♦♦

The problem of fuel-optimal control is even more pronounced when we consider a more complex example.

♦♦Example 12-5. Suppose the plant is now $\ddot{x} = u$, with $|u(t)| \leq 1$. The object is to drive the system from some arbitrary x_0 to the

*As we shall see, there is also the possibility of nonuniqueness in the solution in time-optimal control for systems with more than one control variable.

origin 0 in some time T so as to minimize the performance index

$$\mathcal{J} = \int_0^T |u(t)|\, dt.$$

It is immediately clear that the upper limit of time of control T plays an important role in the problem. If T is less than t^*, where t^* corresponds to the minimum time that 0 can be reached from $\mathbf{x}_0$, there cannot be any solution, for it is impossible to reach the origin in the time allotted. Thus it must be that $T \geq t^*$. On the other hand T must be bounded. A performance criterion of the form $\int_0^\infty |u(t)|\, dt$, for example, will be without meaning for certain starting conditions; this is because, as has been shown in Chap. 4, if $\dot{x}$ and x are taken to be the coordinates of the state-plane, then even when $u(t) \equiv 0$, an $\mathbf{x}_0$ in the second quadrant will drift horizontally to the right and an $\mathbf{x}_0$ in the fourth quadrant will drift horizontally twoard the left. Consider now an $\mathbf{x}_0$ on the positive x axis. To transfer it to the origin, all that is needed initially is an infinitesimal amount of $u(t)$ in the negative direction. This will drive the state to just below the x-axis, and it will then drift toward the origin at some infinitesimal speed. When it reaches a point below the origin, an infinitesimal amount of $u(t)$ in the positive direction will drive it to the origin. It is clear that the fuel expenditure in this case can be made as small as desired.

The above illustrations of nonuniqueness and/or the possibility of meaningless solutions are not serious, for they merely mean that T must be properly chosen. However, even when this is done, it is not clear what will be the form of the fuel-optimal control function.

We may heuristically suspect that, with $t^* < T < \infty$, a reasonable candidate for the fuel-optimal control function is one that includes segments of full-on, zero, and full-reverse for $u(t)$ in some suitable order. The purpose of the segments with $u(t) \equiv 0$, for example, is to take advantage of the natural tendency for the system state to drift in the right direction when it is in certain quadrants. Indeed, a not unreasonable choice would seem to be one as illustrated in Fig. 12-6 for an $\mathbf{x}_0$ in the first quadrant. Here $u(t)$ is $-U$ for T_1 seconds, 0 for T_2 seconds, and $+U$ for T_3 seconds, with $T_1 + T_2 + T_3 = T$. Because of the geometry, it is clear that there will be a unique set T_1, T_2, T_3 that satisfies the conditions of the problem.†

We can show that the above control function is better than some others. (See Exercise 12-4.) However, for particular starting

† Note during the $+U$ phase of control, the system state must necessarily be traveling on the time-optimal switching curv.e Γ_+.

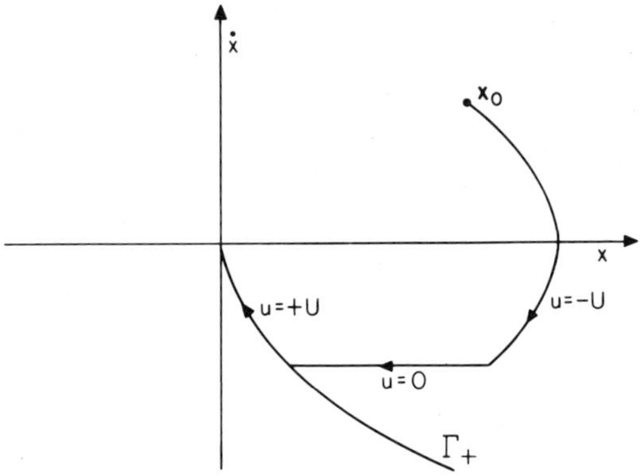

Fig. 12-6. A possible fuel-optimal trajectory for the system of Example 12-5. The trajectory features segments with $u(t) = +U$ and $-U$ as well as a segment with $u(t) = 0$.

states there are other control functions that do just as well. (See Exercise 12-5.) It is difficult to show conclusively that the solution is the best. Clearly, here the theory on the existence of unique solutions is lacking, as is the theory on the form of the optimal solution. As we shall see, the maximum principle can overcome both these shortcomings.◆◆

12.6 Some Other Types of Optimal Control Problems

We have shown that the straightforward approach to the solving of differential equations is becoming less and less useful as we proceed from minimizing the integral-square error in linear systems to the time-optimal and thence to the fuel-optimal control problems. It is not necessary to stretch the imagination too far to see that there are problems for which all the tools at our disposal thus far cannot even allow us to begin the solving of the problem. Just to clinch the point that new tools are needed, let us consider two seemingly trivial extensions of a problem considered previously, and see what further difficulties are encountered.

◆◆Example 12-6. Consider again the time-optimal control of a double integrator plant $1/p^2$. This time, however, let it be required that a $u^*(t)$ subject to $|u(t)| \leq U$ be found which drives the system from any initial state over a given time $T < t^*$ such that the distance to the origin $\|\mathbf{x}(T) - \mathbf{0}\|$ is to be minimized.

Now it is not immediately clear if the bang-bang conjecture is reasonable for this problem, and indeed it is not readily apparent how we can begin our investigation unless the solution is bang-bang.◆◆

♦♦Example 12-7. For the same plant and the same control constraint as in the previous example, suppose we now wish to take the system state from an arbitrary $\mathbf{x}(t_1)$ to an arbitrary $\mathbf{x}(t_2)$ while minimizing $\int_{t_1}^{t_2} \left(x_1^2 + x_2^2 + u^2\right) dt$.

This is close to the type of problems considered in Sec. 12.2 but with two essential differences: first, there is now a constraint on $|u(t)|$; second, the end time is finite, which then permits the specifying of an arbitrary end state $\mathbf{x}(t_2)$. As the system is now nonlinear, the method of Sec. 12.2 cannot be applied. Also as it turns out the solution $u^*(t)$ is not necessarily bang-bang for this problem. Our intuition and our tools are not adequate here and we are stymied.♦♦

Let us note further that in this chapter we have restricted ourselves only to the optimal control of linear plants. If the plants should be nonlinear, they obviously will be even more troublesome.

We will show in Chap. 13 that the techniques closely related to calculus of variations can help us solve some of these problems.

12.7 Summary

Generally speaking, the goodness of performance of a system is not easy to put in mathematical terms.

If perchance a performance criterion is adequately given in mathematical terms, then there is a possibility that some of the modern mathematical optimization tools can be used to find the best system relative to the given performance criterion.

Some of the standard formulations of optimal control systems are given in Sec. 12.1.

Linear control techniques and the techniques that have been developed thus far in the text are quite inadequate to cope with the type of systems formulated in Sec. 12.1. The only exception is the design of linear, time-invariant systems that minimize the integral-square error (over a semi-infinite range of time) which is treated in Sec. 12.2 using frequency-domain methods. Any modification of the problem, however, immediately makes it unamenable to solution using the same method.

Typical optimal control problems, such as the time-optimal and the fuel-optimal control problems, are basically problems which are of the two-point boundary value type. To find solutions to an optimal control problem then involves (1) the finding of a family of solutions that satisfies the two-point boundary conditions as well as the other imposed constraints, and (2) the determination of the optimal solutions from among the candidate solutions. Only in the case of a linear plant can (1) be solved in general, as is shown in Sec. 12.3.

When a plant is linear and time invariant, then the problems involved in optimization can be analyzed to an extent without introducing new methods provided that the performance criteria are sufficiently simple. Sections 12.4 and 12.5 are devoted to a discussion of the basic aspect of time- and fuel-optimal control of linear time-invariant plants. The solutions to these problems can be found provided that certain conjectures are assumed. The proofs, however, require new methods.

The need for new methods becomes even more apparent if we modify but slightly the formulation of some of the optimization problems. This is shown in Sec. 12.6.

12.8 Exercises

12-1 Consider the first-order system $\dot{x} = g(x) + u$ where $|u(t)| \leq U$ and $|g(x)| < U$, with $g(x)$ a continuous function of x.

a) Show that a bang-bang solution is the time-optimal solution for all initial and end states.
b) Find the time-optimal control function u^* as a function of the state; i.e., in the form $u^*(x)$.
c) Are there any complications if $|g(x)| \leq U$? Discuss.

12-2 Without resorting to mathematics, sketch the state trajectory portraits for the system of Example 12-2 using the normal coordinates.

12-3 Try to obtain the switching boundaries for the system of Example 12-3 using the considerations given in the text (and new ones that you may have discovered).

12-4 Consider the fuel-optimal control of the double integrating plant $\dot{x}_1 = x_2$, $\dot{x}_2 = u$ with $\mathcal{J} = \int_0^T |u(t)|\, dt$, $|u(t)| \leq 1$, $\mathbf{x}(0) = x_0$ arbitrary, and $\mathbf{x}(T) = 0$. Show that with $T > t^*$, a control $u_a(t)$, constrained to the values -1, or 0, or $+1$ and constituted in the manner suggested in Fig. 12-6, will yield a smaller value of $\mathcal{J}$ than a control of the form $u_b(t) = \pm b$. In the above, $b < 1$ is a positive number chosen such that one switch in $u_b(t)$ is sufficient to drive the system state from $\mathbf{x}_0$ to 0 in the time T. To minimize efforts, do the exercise only for $\mathbf{x}(0)$'s on the x_1 axis.

12-5 Show that for certain values of T obeying $t^* < T < \infty$, there exist an infinity of possible fuel-optimal controls for the system of Example 12-5. (Hint: Consider those controls which do not involve switching of polarity in $u^*(t)$.)

12-6 For time-optimal control of the system $\ddot{y} + (a, + b)\dot{y} + aby = u(t)$, $|u(t)| \leq 1$, can all initial states be driven to the origin if $a < 0$ and $b < 0$? If not, specify which ones cannot.

12-7 Consider the time-optimal control for the triple integrator $\dot{x}_1 = x_2$, $\dot{x}_2 = x_3$, $\dot{x}_3 = u$, subject to $|u| \leq U$. If the origin is the final state, find the equation for the switching line and switching surface for u^*.

12-8 Prove that the expression given in Eq. (12-15) yields the optimal $H^*(s)$ for the class of problems of Sec. 12.2.

12-9 For the plant $1/[p(p+1)(p+2)]$, find the switching times and the optimal control functions for time-optimal control of the system, in the normal coordinates, from the initial state (2, 1, 3) to the origin. Assume that $|u(t)| \leq 1$ and that the time-optimal control function $u^*(t)$ is bang-bang.

12-10 For the plant $1/[p(p+1)]$, find the optimum compensator by the approach of Sec. 12.2 that minimizes $\int_0^\infty \left(e^2(t) + u^2(t)\right) dt$ under an input $r(t) = e^{-t}$. Assume that at $t = 0$ the initial conditions of the system are all 0.

12.9 References

The material of Sec. 12.2 is thoroughly treated in [N6]. Chapter 1 of [C2] should also be consulted.

Time-optimal contol of linear second-order plants under the bang-bang assumption can be found in pp. 393-418 of [G8] and pp. 150-159 of [T4]. For high order linear systems with real eigenvalues, see [R2]. The bang-bang control of a second-order undamped plant was first solved by Bushaw; see [B21].

For time-optimal control of some third-order systems, see [B13].

13

Calculus of Variations and Optimal Control

Calculus of variations is the branch of mathematics which is concerned with the finding of trajectories that maximize or minimize a given functional. To be sure, the modern optimal control techniques such as the maximum principle of Pontryagin and dynamic programming of Bellman are derived from significantly different points of view, but it is now becoming clear that they are inspired to a great extent by the classical calculus of variations.

The advantage of calculus of variations is that it can be easily appreciated by envisioning families of trajectories in the state space. In the simplest cases, once the idea of variations of trajectories is grasped, many of the results from the maximization or minimization of a function in ordinary calculus can carry over; thus this idea has much inherent intuitive appeal. Understanding the mechanics involved in calculus of variations would also facilitate the introduction of the radically different veiwpoints needed to study the maximum principle and dynamic programming. In a way, then, the newer techniques are variations on an old theme; the variations can be appreciated much more if the theme is recalled.

In this chapter we investigate some of the aspects of calculus of variations which can be directly applied to the optimal control problem. After a review of the simplest technique, we derive the Euler-Lagrange equations as well as some other necessary conditions for optimality. From the inspection of these equations and the boundary conditions, we can develop an appreciation for the key inherent characteristics of the optimal control problem.

When the system to be controlled is nonlinear, the two-point boundary value problem that results must generally be solved by trial and error. Only when the system is linear and the performance index is an integral of quadratic functions of the state variables and the control variable is there hope of obtaining solutions analytically.

Calculus of variations can also yield insight into the necessary conditions for optimality for more general control problems. Through a special method due to Valentine, inequality type constraints on control variables can be handled. Thus we show that calculus of variations can be employed alone to solve almost all control problems.

Calculus of variations will also leave a number of questions in the reader's mind. For example, the role of the Lagrange multipliers that invariably appear is rather mystifying. The notion of strong variation beclouds the orderly world that results from only weak variations. The series of necessary conditions that a solution must satisfy can also add just enough confusion to defocus the central point of the problem. Here we must await the maximum principle and dynamic programming to shed new light on these issues.

13.1 The Euler-Lagrange Equations and the Other Necessary Conditions for a Local Minimum

Strictly speaking calculus of variations does not permit us to find an optimal solution directly. Instead it imposes a series of necessary conditions that an optimum trajectory must satisfy. In this way most non-optimum trajectories are eliminated. Sometimes, the only trajectory that remains is the optimum one.

A straightforward account of calculus of variations tends to gloss over a number of basic issues. These issues can be brought out by referring to a typical problem in optimal control.

Suppose we wish to find the optimal control $\mathbf{u}^*(t)$ which drives the system $\dot{\mathbf{x}} = \mathbf{f}(\mathbf{x}, \mathbf{u})$ over the interval $[t_1, t_2]$ from an initial point $\mathbf{x}(t_1) = \mathbf{x}_1$ to a final point $\mathbf{x}(t_2) = \mathbf{x}_2$, and, in the process, minimizes† a functional

$$\mathcal{J} = \int_{t_1}^{t_2} L(\mathbf{x}, \mathbf{u})\, dt \tag{13-1}$$

The basic issues at hand can, with license, be brought out by referring to the $\mathbf{x}$ vs. t plot of Fig. 13-1.

With each choice of $\mathbf{u}(t)$ over $[t_1, t_2]$ there is associated a trajectory $\mathbf{x}(t)$, but all trajectories must start at the point $\mathbf{x}_1 \triangleq \mathbf{x}(t_1)$ and end at the point $\mathbf{x}_2 \triangleq \mathbf{x}(t_2)$. Thus a trajectory such as $\mathbf{x}_c(t)$ in Fig. 13-1 is ruled out since it starts at $\mathbf{x}_1$ but does not end at $\mathbf{x}_2$. As we have seen from Chap. 12, to require that all trajectories begin at $\mathbf{x}_1$ is easy enough, but making certain that they end at $\mathbf{x}_2$ is not necessarily straightforward.

†Since $\min \mathcal{J} = -\max(-\mathcal{J})$, we need only concentrate on the minimization problem.

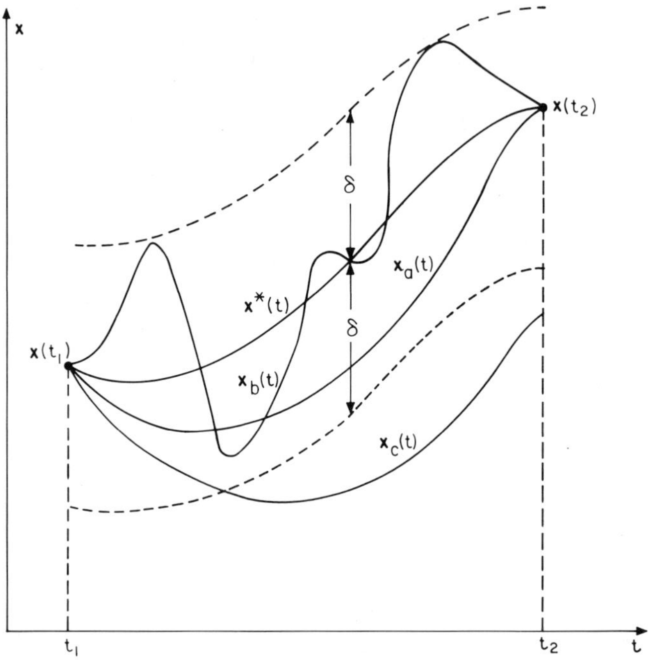

Fig. 13-1. Curve $\mathbf{x}_a(t)$ obeys $\|\mathbf{x}^*(t) - \mathbf{x}_a(t)\| \leq \delta$ and $\|\dot{\mathbf{x}}^*(t) - \dot{\mathbf{x}}_a(t)\| \leq \delta$ for $t_1 \leq t \leq t_2$; thus $\mathbf{x}_a(t)$ lies in a weak δ-neighborhood of $\mathbf{x}^*(t)$. Curve $\mathbf{x}_b(t)$ obeys $\|\mathbf{x}^* - \mathbf{x}_b(t)\| \leq \delta$, but $\|\dot{\mathbf{x}}^*(t) - \dot{\mathbf{x}}_b(t)\| > \delta$ for some t; thus $\mathbf{x}_b(t)$ only lies in a strong δ-neighborhood of $\mathbf{x}^*(t)$.

Suppose somehow we do manage to find a number of trajectories which connect x_1 to x_2 and satisfy the other stipulations of our optimal control problem. Then we still must find from among these the trajectory that yields the smallest value of $\mathcal{J}$ via (13-1). It turns out that finding the absolute minimizing trajectory is quite difficult even through the use of calculus of variations. It is much simpler to find minimizing trajectories in a local sense.

We now encounter the question of what is meant by "in a local sense." We will show that there are at least two ways to define trajectories that are "close to each other."

Suppose there is a curve $x^*(t)$ defined in an appropriate state space. We say that another curve $x_1(t)$ lies in a *weak* δ-neighborhood of $x^*(t)$ if $x_1(t)$ and $\dot{x}_1(t)$ are respectively within δ units of $x^*(t)$ and $\dot{x}^*(t)$; i.e., $\|x^*(t) - x_1(t)\| \leq \delta$, $\|\dot{x}^*(t) - \dot{x}_1(t)\| \leq \delta$. (See curve $x_a(t)$ of Fig. 13-1.)

We say that $x_1(t)$ lies in a *strong* δ-neighborhood of $x^*(t)$ if only the first condition holds, i.e., if $\|x^*(t) - x_1(t)\| \leq \delta$. (See curve $x_b(t)$ of Fig. 13-1.)

We say that a trajectory $x^*(t)$ yields a weak (strong) local minimum if there is a weak (strong) neighborhood of $x^*(t)$ such that the functional $\mathcal{J}$ corresponding to the trajectory $x^*(t)$ is smaller than that corresponding to any other qualified trajectory in the neighborhood. We see that a strong minimum is necessarily a weak minimum, whereas the converse is not necessarily true.

It turns out that weak local minima can be found by methods analogous to those used in finding extremum points in calculus. These we review below. The finding of strong local minima, however, is slightly more involved.

We shall now develop the basic results in calculus of variations. In the remaining pages of this section we will state the results. In the next sections the results will be applied to concrete cases.

1. The Finding of a Minimum Point in Calculus

In ordinary calculus, when we look for the minimum point of a twice differentiable function $f(x)$ in an open interval $x_a < x < x_b$ we first look for those points where the derivative $df(x)/dx$ vanishes. Thus, $df(x)/dx = 0$ at the point in question constitutes the first necessary condition for a minimum. It is, however, not sufficient, since the point that obeys this property may also be a maximum point, or a point of inflection. A second necessary condition is that at the point the second derivative $d^2f(x)/dx^2 \geq 0$ must also be imposed.

Now these two conditions jointly still do not guarantee that an absolute minimum point has been found. First if $d^2f(x)/dx^2 = 0$ at a point, insufficient information is provided by the above two necessary conditions; second even if $d^2f(x)/dx^2 > 0$, there may be many points with this property. This means that each such point is a minimum *locally*. In order to establish which point is the smallest one, the value of the function $f(x)$ at each of these points must be compared, and only the smallest one selected. The above can be mathematically stated as follows: Let $x_1, x_2, x_3, \ldots, x_n$ be points satisfying the first two necessary conditions for a minimum point of a function $f(x)$; then the absolute minimum point x^* must have the property that $f(x^*) \leq f(x_i)$ for all i. We may call this the third necessary condition for a minimum point.

All three of the necessary conditions together constitute a sufficient condition that a point x^* is the absolute minimum point of $f(x)$ over the interval (x_a, x_b) provided the second necessary condition is that $d^2f/dx^2 > 0$ at x^*. It is of course clear that if $f(x)$ is not twice differentiable, some or all of the above conditions cannot be applied. For example, if $f(x)$ is only once differentiable, then the first necessary condition $df(x)/dx = 0$ still holds; however, the condition $d^2f(x)/dx^2 > 0$ must be replaced by the local condition $f(x^*) \leq f(x)$ for all x in a certain neighborhood of x^*. Similarly if $f(x)$ is only piecewise differentiable (i.e., there are a finite number of points in the interval (x_a, x_b) at which $df(x)/dx$ is discontinuous), then only when the minimum point does not correspond to a point of discontinuity in $df(x)/dx$ can we make use of the first two necessary conditions at all. When $f(x)$ is "worse" than the above cases, we have only the obvious condition $f(x^*) \le f(x)$ for all x to fall back on. This last condition is of course not very useful mathematically.

Also if the minimum point of $f(x)$ is to be sought over a closed interval $[x_a, x_b]$, then the minimum point may occur at the boundary point x_a or x_b. Here even when $f(x)$ is twice differentiable, the first two conditions above are no longer necessary conditions, and a more involved search procedure must be applied.

In the case of finding a minimum point for a function of several variables $f(x_1, x_2, \dots, x_n)$, the condition will be similar though more complicated. The first necessary condition becomes one of requiring that, at each candidate point, $\partial f/\partial x_i = 0$ for each i. The second necessary condition becomes one of requiring that, at each candidate point, the matrix* $\left[f_{x_i x_j}\right]$ be positive semidefinite. (See Exercise 13-1.)

The third necessary condition carries directly over from the case of a single variable, as do the conditions related to cases where the minimum point is to be found in a closed set or where $f(x)$ is not twice continuously differentiable.

An important consideration arises when we wish to find a minimum point of a twice continuously differentiable function $f(x_1, \dots, x_n)$ under the constraint that this point is to be located on a subspace specified by a set of equations $g_1(x_1, \dots, x_n) = 0$, $g_2(x_1, \dots, x_n) = 0, \dots, g_m(x_1, \dots, x_n) = 0$.** A straightforward way to do this but one that is often technically complex is to try to eliminate m of the variables $x_1, \dots, x_n$ in the function f through the use of the m constraint equations and then proceed to minimize the resulting function of $n - m$ variables by the usual approach.

A highly useful alternative way is to use the method of Lagrange multipliers, which we briefly develop below.

Let us note that the first necessary condition can also be written as

$$df(x_1, \dots, x_n) = \sum_{i=1}^{n} \frac{\partial f}{\partial x_i} dx_i = 0 \tag{13-2}$$

and the m constraint equations imply the m equations

$$\sum_{i=1}^{n} \frac{\partial g_1}{\partial x_i} dx_i = 0, \dots, \sum_{i=1}^{n} \frac{\partial g_m}{\partial x_i} dx_i = 0 \tag{13-3}$$

*We use the conventional notation f_{xy} to denote the second partial derivative $\partial^2 f/\partial x \partial y$; thus the matrix $[f_{x_i x_j}]$. is $n \times n$ matrix with the ijth entry $\partial^2 f/\partial x_i \partial x_j$.

**Of course $m < n$; also, each of the functions g_i's is assumed to be twice continuously differentiable.

When there are no constraints, the infinitesimals dx_i can be arbitrarily taken and (13-2) will still hold. This means that $\partial f/\partial x_i = 0$ for all i as has already been mentioned. With the constraints, however, the dx_i's cannot be chosen arbitrarily but must be chosen as prescribed by Eq. (13-3).

Suppose we introduce m parameters $\psi_1, \ldots, \psi_m$, called the *Lagrange multipliers*, and form the quantity

$$\sum_{i=1}^{n} \left(\frac{\partial f}{\partial x_i} + \sum_{j=1}^{m} \psi_j \frac{\partial g_j}{\partial x_i} \right) dx_i = 0 \tag{13-4}$$

if we choose $\psi_1, \ldots, \psi_m$ so that the first m of the n terms

$$\left(\frac{\partial f}{\partial x_i} + \sum_{j=1}^{m} \psi_j \frac{\partial g_i}{\partial x_i} \right)$$

vanish, then the remaining terms in (13-4) must also individually vanish. This is because the ψ_j's are now specified and the $n - m$ remaining dx_i's can be chosen arbitrarily. This implies that in order to satisfy (13-4) the terms

$$\left(\frac{\partial f}{\partial x_i} + \sum_{j=1}^{m} \psi_j \frac{\partial g_j}{\partial x_i} \right), \quad i = m + 1, \ldots, n$$

must vanish also. We thus have

$$\frac{\partial f}{\partial x_i} + \sum_{j=1}^{m} \psi_j \frac{\partial g_j}{\partial x_i} = 0, \qquad i = 1, 2, \ldots, n$$

or

$$\frac{\partial}{\partial x_i} \left(f + \sum_{j=1}^{m} \psi_j g_j \right) = 0, \qquad i = 1, 2, \ldots, n \tag{13-5}$$

Equation (13-5), along with the m constraint equations $g_j(x_1, \ldots, x_n) = 0$, $j = 1, \ldots, m$, constitute the $m + n$ equations in $m + n$ unknowns $\psi_1, \ldots, \psi_m, x_1, \ldots, x_n$. These equations can be solved if the problem is well formulated.*

*However, see Sec. 16.1.

Let us note that *(13-5) is exactly the same as the first necessary condition for the finding of an extremum point for the composite function* $f + \sum_{j=1}^{m} \psi_j g_j$ *without regard for constraints.*

2. The First Necessary Condition in Calculus of Variations and the Euler-Lagrange Equation

The simplest problem in calculus of variations involves the minimization of a functional of the form

$$\mathcal{J} = \int_{t_1}^{t_2} L\left(x(t), \frac{dx(t)}{dt}, t\right) dt \tag{13-6}$$

through the finding of a minimizing function $x^*(t)$ satisfying some prescribed end condition of the form

$$x(t_1) = x_1, \ x(t_2) = x_2$$

Note that now instead of looking for a minimum *point*, we are looking for a minimizing *function* or trajectory. This naturally brings on many added complications. The important point to recognize, however, is that when the class of functions from among which we are seeking the minimizing function is sufficiently well behaved, many of the fundamental steps used in calculus in finding the extremum points can be carried over to aid our intuition.

Assume that the function L in (13-6) is twice differentiable relative to its arguments x, dx/dt, and t and, moreover, that a minimizing solution to the problem exists. Then the procedure for finding the first necessary condition for this problem is a relatively simple one.

Suppose we suspect that a function $x(t)$ is the minimizing function to be sought. Consider now any (almost everywhere) continuously differentiable function $\eta(t)$ with the property $\eta(t_1) = \eta(t_2) = 0$. If we form a function $x(t) + \epsilon\eta(t)$ with ϵ a parameter, it will satisfy the requisite boundary conditions; hence it belongs to the class of functions from which the function which yields a weak local minimum for $\mathcal{J}$ is to be found.† For this function, the functional $\mathcal{J}$ will take on the value

$$\mathcal{J}(\epsilon) = \int_{t_1}^{t_2} L(\dot{x} + \epsilon\dot{\eta}, x + \epsilon\eta, t)\, dt \tag{13-7}$$

†Note that for each value of ϵ, the function $x(t) + \epsilon\eta(t)$ defines a weak δ-neighborhood where $\delta = \max_{t_1 \le t \le t_2} (\epsilon\eta(t), \epsilon\dot{\eta}(t))$.

If $x(t)$ were the minimizing function, then by definition, $\mathcal{J}(\epsilon)$ will be always greater than the minimum possible value except when $\epsilon = 0$. Moreover, under the conditions given, $\mathcal{J}(\epsilon)$ will be differentiable relative to ϵ. Thus $\mathcal{J}(\epsilon)$ will have a stationary point at $\epsilon = 0$. This is the type of considerations that led to Eq. (12-12). Therefore we have

$$\left.\frac{d\mathcal{J}(\epsilon)}{d\epsilon}\right|_{\epsilon=0} = 0 \tag{13-8}$$

and the optimal function $x^*(t)$ can only be found in cases where (13-8) is satisfied.

Let $X(t) = x(t) + \epsilon\eta(t)$ and $\dot{X}(t) = \dot{x}(t) + \epsilon\dot{\eta}(t)$; then, carrying out the operation of (13-8) by differentiating the rhs of (13-7) and setting $\epsilon = 0$, we have:

$$\left.\frac{d\mathcal{J}(\epsilon)}{d\epsilon}\right|_{\epsilon=0} = \left[\int_{t_1}^{t_2}\left(\frac{\partial L}{\partial X}\frac{\partial X}{\partial \epsilon} + \frac{\partial L}{\partial \dot{X}}\frac{\partial \dot{X}}{\partial \epsilon}\right)dt\right]_{\epsilon=0}$$

$$= \int_{t_1}^{t_2}\left(\frac{\partial L}{\partial x}\eta + \frac{\partial L}{\partial \dot{x}}\dot{\eta}\right)dt = 0 \tag{13-9}$$

By an integration by parts on the second term of the integral, we obtain:

$$\left.\frac{d\mathcal{J}(\epsilon)}{d\epsilon}\right|_{\epsilon=0} = 0 = \left.\frac{\partial L}{\partial \dot{x}}\eta(t)\right|_{t_1}^{t_2} + \int_{t_1}^{t_2}\left[\frac{\partial L}{\partial x} - \frac{d}{dt}\left(\frac{\partial L}{\partial \dot{x}}\right)\right]\eta(t)\,dt \tag{13-10}$$

As $\eta(t_1) = \eta(t_2) = 0$ by definition, the first term in the rhs vanishes and hence the remaining integral must vanish for all functions $\eta(t)$. We can then show that the terms under the bracket must also vanish;† thus we arrive at the Euler-Lagrange equation:

$$\frac{\partial L}{\partial x} - \frac{d}{dt}\left(\frac{\partial L}{\partial \dot{x}}\right) = 0 \tag{13-11}$$

†Since (13-10) must hold for *every* choice of $\eta(t)$, we may choose one such that it has the same sign as the quantity $(\partial L/\partial x) - d(\partial L/\partial x)/dt$ for all t. For this choice the integrand of (13-10) is nonnegative and can be 0 only if (13-11) holds.

Equation (13-11) represents the first necessary condition for optimality in the simple calculus of variation problem under consideration.

It may be noted that if L is not explicitly a function of t, we can write

$$\frac{d}{dt}\left(L - \frac{\partial L}{\partial \dot{x}}\dot{x}\right) = \dot{x}\left(\frac{\partial L}{\partial x} - \frac{d}{dt}\left(\frac{\partial L}{\partial \dot{x}}\right)\right)$$

In view of (13-11) we have, along the optimal trajectory $x^*(t)$,

$$L - \frac{\partial L}{\partial \dot{x}}\dot{x} = \text{constant} \quad (\text{for } L \text{ independent of } t) \tag{13-12}$$

♦♦Example 13-1. Find an $x(t)$ satisfying the boundary conditions $x(0) = 0$, $x(1) = 1$, and the Euler-Lagrange equation (13-11) relative to the functional

$$\mathcal{J} = \int_0^1 \frac{1}{\dot{x}}\, dt$$

For this case $L = 1/\dot{x}$ and $\partial L/\partial x = 0$. Equation (13-11) yields $d(\partial L/\partial \dot{x})/dt = 0$ or $\partial L/\partial \dot{x} = \text{constant}$. Since $\partial L/\partial \dot{x} = -(\dot{x})^{-2}$, the above implies $\dot{x} = k$, where k is a constant. Thus $x = kt + x(0)$. The boundary condition is satisfied with $k = 1$; therefore the solution is the straight line $x = t$.♦♦

When there are several dependent variables in the problem, the function L in (13-6) will have the form $L(x_1, \ldots, x_n; \dot{x}_1, \ldots, \dot{x}_n; t)$ and

$$\mathcal{J} = \int_{t_1}^{t_2} L(x_1, \ldots, x_n; \dot{x}_1, \ldots, \dot{x}_n; t)\, dt \tag{13-13}$$

Again assuming that L is twice continuously differentiable with respect to each of its arguments, we proceed in much the same manner. We define n arbitrary functions $\eta_i(t)$, $i = 1, \ldots, n$ satisfying $\eta_i(t_1) = \eta_i(t_2) = 0$ and consider the variation about the possible optimum solution $x_i(t)$ and $\dot{x}_i(t)$ by considering what happens to the integral when

$$X_i(t) = x_i(t) + \epsilon\eta_i(t), \quad i = 1, \ldots, n$$

and (13-14)

$$\dot{X}_i(t) = \dot{x}_i(t) + \epsilon\dot{\eta}_i(t), \quad i = 1, \ldots, n$$

are substituted in the integral (13-13).

It will be clear that Eq. (13-8) still gives a necessary condition for the optimum. On applying this condition, the following is obtained:

$$\left.\frac{d\mathcal{J}(\epsilon)}{d\epsilon}\right|_{\epsilon=0} = \int_{t_1}^{t_2} \sum_{i=1}^{n} \left(\frac{\partial L}{\partial x_i}\eta_i + \frac{\partial L}{\partial \dot{x}_i}\dot{\eta}_i\right) dt = 0 \tag{13-15}$$

For each x_i, integration by parts will yield terms of the form similar to (13-10), viz.,

$$\sum_{i=1}^{n} \frac{\partial L}{\partial x_i}\eta_i \Bigg|_{t_1}^{t_2} + \int_{t_2}^{t_2} \sum_{i=1}^{n} \left[\frac{\partial L}{\partial x_i} - \frac{d}{dt}\left(\frac{\partial L}{\partial \dot{x}_i}\right)\right] \eta_i \, dt = 0 \tag{13-16}$$

We observe that, first, (13-16) must hold for all possible choices of η_i's, and, in particular, will hold when all the n_i's except one, say the jth one, are taken to be identically 0. Second, the jth term in the summation of (13-16) must be equal to 0 whatever the choices of $\eta_j(t)$ since $\eta_j(t_1) = \eta_j(t_2) = 0$. These considerations lead to the Euler-Lagrange equations for this case, namely

$$\frac{\partial L}{\partial x_i} - \frac{d}{dt}\left(\frac{\partial L}{\partial \dot{x}_i}\right) = 0, \qquad i = 1, \ldots, n \tag{13-17}$$

which represent a system of simultaneous differential equations that must be satisfied *at every point* of an optimal trajectory.

When L is independent of t, then along the optimal trajectory, corresponding to (13-12), we have

$$L - \sum_{i=1}^{n} \frac{\partial L}{\partial \dot{x}_i}\dot{x}_i = \text{constant} \quad (\text{for } L \text{ independent of } t) \tag{13-18}$$

3. Discontinuities and Jump Conditions

If we integrate each of the equations in (13-17), we obtain the Euler-Lagrange equations in the integral form:

$$\frac{\partial L}{\partial \dot{x}_i} = \int_{t_1}^{t} \frac{\partial L}{\partial x_i}\, dt + C_i, \qquad i = 1, \ldots, n \tag{13-19}$$

where the C_i's are integration constants.

It turns out that (13–19) is valid even for trajectories $x(t)$ which possess a finite number of discontinuities in $\dot{x}(t)$.* Thus while it has the same status as the Euler–Lagrange equations, it is more comprehensive in scope.

Points at which $\dot{x}(t)$ is discontinuous are known as *corners* in calculus of variations. Most of the major results can be carried over to trajectories with a finite number of corners.

There are two basic conditions that must be obeyed by optimizing trajectories. These are known as the *Weierstrass-Erdmann corner conditions*.

The first corner condition follows directly from (13–19). Since the rhs of (13–19) is continuous even at the corners, it follows that the lhs is also, thus if $t = \tau$ is a point on an optimum trajectory at which a corner occurs, one or more of the $\dot{x}_i$ must have

$$\left.\frac{\partial L}{\partial \dot{x}_k}\right|_{t=\tau^-} = \left.\frac{\partial L}{\partial \dot{x}_k}\right|_{t=\tau^+} \quad ; \quad k = 1, \ldots, n \tag{13–20}$$

The second corner condition** states that on a corner $x_k(\tau)$ of an optimal trajectory

$$\left.\left(L - \sum_{i=1}^{n} \frac{\partial L}{\partial \dot{x}_i} \dot{x}_i\right)\right|_{t=\tau^-} = \left.\left(L - \sum_{i=1}^{n} \frac{\partial L}{\partial \dot{x}_i} \dot{x}_i\right)\right|_{t=\tau^+} \tag{13–21}$$

This implies, for example, that when L is independent of t, the condition given by (13–18) still holds even for trajectories with corners.

4. Some Further Necessary Conditions in Calculus of Variations

The first necessary condition in calculus of variations as given by (13–8) is often written as

$$\delta \mathcal{J} = 0 \tag{13–22}$$

or the *first variation of* $\mathcal{J}$ is equal to 0. It is analogous to the vanishing of the first derivative for calculus.

*See, for example, [P2] pp. 29–32. Of course between the points of discontinuities of $\dot{x}(t)$ the Euler–Lagrange equations must still hold.

**See [P2] pp. 34–36. This condition will become clear when we study the maximum principle (Chapter 14).

The condition analogous to the second necessary condition in calculus is then given by a condition on the *second variation*, which we now develop.

Suppose we expand $\mathcal{J}(\epsilon)$ of (13-7) by Taylor's formula into

$$\mathcal{J}(\epsilon) = \mathcal{J} + \epsilon\delta\mathcal{J} + \frac{\epsilon^2}{2}\delta^2\mathcal{J} + \cdots \tag{13-23}$$

with

$$\mathcal{J} = \int_{t_1}^{t_2} L(x,\dot{x},t)\,dt\,, \qquad \delta\mathcal{J} = \int_{t_1}^{t_2}\left(\frac{\partial L}{\partial x}\eta + \frac{\partial L}{\partial \dot{x}}\dot{\eta}\right)dt$$

$$\delta^2\mathcal{J} = \int_{t_1}^{t_2}\left(\eta^2\frac{\partial^2 L}{\partial x^2} + 2\eta\dot{\eta}\frac{\partial^2 L}{\partial x\partial\dot{x}} + \dot{\eta}^2\frac{\partial^2 L}{\partial\dot{x}^2}\right)dt \tag{13-24}$$

For a trajectory that satisfies the Euler-Lagrange equations, by (13-9) $\delta\mathcal{J}$ vanishes. But of all the trajectories that satisfy the Euler-Lagrange equations, the minimizing one should be such that all other trajectories neighboring to it must yield a larger value of $\mathcal{J}$. This property can be brought out mathematically by stating that for a sufficiently small value of ϵ, $\mathcal{J}(\epsilon) \geq \mathcal{J}$ in (13-23). This means that when ϵ is sufficiently small, $\delta^2\mathcal{J}$ must be ≥ 0 in order that the trajectory in question will yield a *local* minimum for $\mathcal{J}$.

The Legendre condition holds that a necessary condition for $\delta^2\mathcal{J} \geq 0$ *for a given trajectory is that* $\partial^2 L/\partial\dot{x}^2 \geq 0$ *along that trajectory*. To show this result, we first recall that the function $\eta(t)$ is assumed to vanish at t_1 and t_2 but is otherwise unspecified. We can then create a particular function $\eta(t)$ in order to exhibit the Legendre condition.

If we take the function as illustrated in Fig. 13-2, i.e.,

$$\eta(t) = \begin{cases} \sqrt{h}\left(1 + \dfrac{t-\tau}{h}\right), & \tau - h \leq t \leq \tau \\ \sqrt{h}\left(1 - \dfrac{t-\tau}{h}\right), & \tau \leq t < \tau + h \\ 0, & \text{elsewhere} \end{cases} \tag{13-25}$$

where τ, $t_1 < \tau < t_2$, is picked at a point where the integrand of $\delta^2\mathcal{J}$ is regular. Using the $\eta(t)$ in $\delta^2\mathcal{J}$ and letting $h \to 0$, the Legendre condition is readily established. (Show this.)

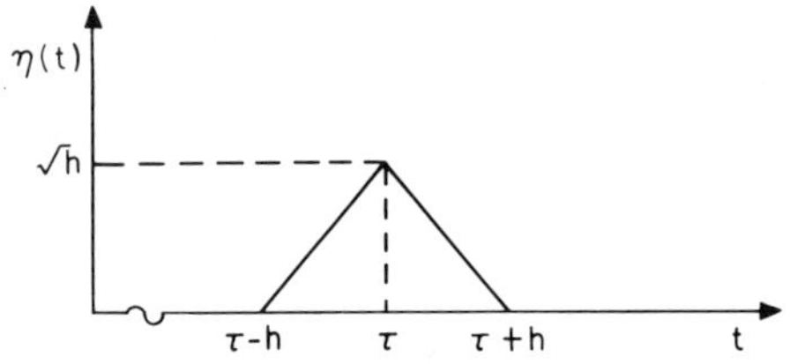

Fig. 13-2. A special $\eta(t)$ which will permit the derivation of the Legendre condition for the case of a single variable.

In the case of several dependent variables, the Legendre condition† *is that the matrix* $\left[L_{\dot{x}_i \dot{x}_j}\right]$ *is positive semidefinite along the optimal trajectory.*

If a trajectory satisfies the Legendre condition as well as the Euler-Lagrange equations, it minimizes the function $\mathcal{J}$ at least in a weak neighborhood. In order to establish that it yields a strong local minimum as well, we must impose a third necessary condition.

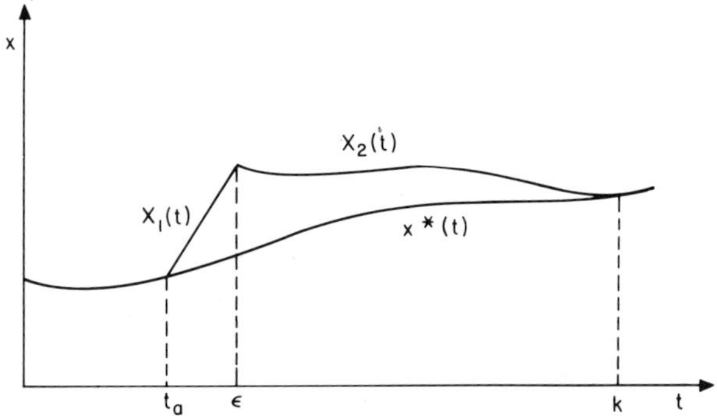

Fig. 13-3. A construction to produce curves $X_1(t)$ and $X_2(t)$ which together constitute a strong variation about $x^*(t)$. The curve $X_1(t)$ obeys Eq. (13-26) and the curve $X_2(t)$ obeys Eq. (13-27).

It is instructive at this point to construct a strong variation. Referring to Fig. 13-3, let $x^*(t)$ be a reference trajectory. We wish to perturb $x^*(t)$ in such a way as to result in a trajectory $X(t)$ that lies in a strong neighborhood of $x^*(t)$. Such a perturbation can be constructed starting at a point $x^*(t_a)$ in the following

† The Legendre condition was extended to the present class of problems by Clebsch and thus is frequently referred to as the Legendre-Clebsch condition.

way: (1) At the point $x^*(t_a)$ we create the straightline $X_1(t)$ with a finite slope m

$$X_1(t) = x^*(t_a) + m(t - t_a) \tag{13-26}$$

(2) At a point $t > t_a$, we create a function $X_2(t)$ which depends on the parameter ϵ. We require that $X_2(t) = x^*(t)$ when $\epsilon = t_a$. Such a function for example can be given by

$$X_2(t) = x^*(t) + \frac{k - t}{k - \epsilon}[x^*(t_a) + m(\epsilon - t_a) - x^*(\epsilon)] \tag{13-27}$$

where k is an arbitrary constant.

It is clear that $X_1(t)$ meets $X_2(t)$ at $t = \epsilon$, and $X_2(t)$ meets $x^*(t)$ at $t = k$. If we construct a function $X(t)$ in accordance with

$$X(t) = \begin{cases} x^*(t) \;, & t \leq t_a \text{ and } k < t \\ X_1(t) \;, & t_a < t \leq \epsilon \\ X_2(t) \;, & \epsilon < t \leq k \end{cases} \tag{13-28}$$

we see that we have created a perturbation as a function of ϵ that lies in a strong neighborhood of $x^*(t)$. This is because as $\epsilon \to 0$ we can make $|X(t) - x^*(t)|$ as small as we wish; however, since a part of $X(t)$ will always have the slope m, a fixed number, $|\dot{X}(t) - \dot{x}^*(t)|$ cannot be made as small as we wish.

Suppose $x^*(t)$ is the absolute minimizing trajectory; then besides satisfying the Euler-Lagrange equations as well as the Legendre condition relative to a functional $\mathcal{J}$, it must also be such that for any other trajectory $X(t)$ (including those which are minimizing trajectories locally) the condition

$$\Delta\mathcal{J} = \int_{t_1}^{t_2} L\big(X(t), \dot{X}(t), t\big)dt - \int_{t_1}^{t_2} L\big(x^*(t), \dot{x}^*(t), t\big)dt \geq 0 \tag{13-29}$$

must hold.

Consider the family of strong variations that we have just created. Suppose $x^*(t)$ is the minimizing trajectory, then relative to the $X(t)$ of (13-28), Eq. (13-29) holds. Moreover, in line with the consideration that led to (13-8), it is clear that we also must have

$$\left.\frac{\partial\Delta\mathcal{J}}{\delta\epsilon}\right|_{\epsilon=t_a} \geq 0 \tag{13-30}$$

If we define the so-called *Weierstrass excess function*

$$E(x^*, \dot{x}^*, \dot{x}, t) = L(x^*, \dot{x}, t) - L(x^*, \dot{x}^*, t) - (\dot{x} - \dot{x}^*)\frac{\partial L}{\partial \dot{x}}(x^*, \dot{x}^*, t) \tag{13-31}$$

where $\dot{x}$ is an arbitrary nonoptimal derivative function which for our example is equal to $\dot{X}(t)$, then we can show (see Exercise 13-12) that a necessary condition that $\Delta\mathcal{J} \geq 0$ in (13-29) is that

$$E(x^*, \dot{x}^*, \dot{x}, t) \geq 0 \tag{13-32}$$

on the trajectory $x^*(t)$ for every t. Equation (13-32) is the *Weierstrass condition*. A proof of the Weierstrass condition will be given in Chap. 14 when the maximum principle is proved.

♦♦Example 13-2. Consider the Example 13-1 again and test the solution, (i) relative to the Legendre condition and (ii) relative to the Weierstrass condition.

If the solution obtained in Example 13-1 is an optimal one at all, it must be a minimizing one from practical considerations; thus the Legendre condition becomes $\partial^2L/\partial\dot{x}^2 \geq 0$. Now $\partial^2L/\partial\dot{x}^2 = 2/\dot{x}^3$ for $L = 1/\dot{x}$; thus along the "optimal" trajectory where $\dot{x} = 1$, $\partial^2L/\partial\dot{x}^2 = 2$, and the Legendre condition is satisfied.

Applying the Weierstrass condition, however, we find that

$$E = \frac{1}{\dot{x}} - 1 + (\dot{x} - 1) = \frac{1}{\dot{x}} + \dot{x} - 2$$

and E does not satisfy the condition $E \geq 0$ if $\dot{x} < 0$. The Weierstrass condition is therefore not satisfied. Thus we have shown that the solution $x(t) = t$ for the problem of Example 13-1 yields at most a weak local minimum.

Indeed it is quite easy to construct a trajectory of the strong variation type that yields a lower value of $\mathcal{J}$ than the trajectory $x(t) = t$. Taking a hint from the requirement of $\dot{x} < 0$, which is needed to defeat the Weierstrass condition, let us consider the trajectory

$$x_1(t) = \begin{cases} -2t, & 0 \leq t < 0.1 \\ -0.2 + 2(t - 0.1), & 0.1 \leq t < 0.4 \\ t, & 0.4 < t \leq 1 \end{cases}$$

It clearly satisfies the boundary conditions given and is a piecewise, twice-differentiable function with one corner.†

It is a simple matter, however, to show that the $x_1(t)$ given above yields a value of $\mathcal{J} = 0.7$ whereas the "optimal trajectory" $x(t) = t$ yields a $\mathcal{J}$ of unity.♦♦

†At $t = 0.4$, $x_1(t)$ is to be made smooth to satisfy the corner condition.

In the multivariable case, the Weierstrass condition for a strong local minimum takes the form

$$E(\mathbf{x}^*, \dot{\mathbf{x}}^*, \dot{\mathbf{x}}, t) = L(\mathbf{x}^*, \dot{\mathbf{x}}, t) - L(\mathbf{x}^*, \dot{\mathbf{x}}^*, t) - (\dot{\mathbf{x}} - \dot{\mathbf{x}}^*)^T \frac{\partial L}{\partial \dot{\mathbf{x}}}(\mathbf{x}^*, \dot{\mathbf{x}}^*, t) \geq 0 \tag{13-33}$$

Finally, we should mention the conditions that need to be satisfied for $\delta^2 \mathcal{J}$ in (13-24) to be positive or 0. These essentially stipulate that the class of trajectories from which the minimizing one is to be sought must be well behaved in some sense. A sufficient condition for a trajectory to be well behaved is specified by the *Jacobi condition*. Because the statement and derivation of this condition would require some further concepts and, moreover, since its use is rather difficult, it will be omitted from this text. The interested reader is referred to the references.†

5. The Case of Unspecified or Variable End Points

In the general case of several dependent variables, suppose some of the end conditions $x_i(t_2)$ are left unspecified, then our minimizing procedure must be modified somewhat.††

Following the procedure of part 2 of this section in considering the variation $X_i(t) = x_i(t) + \epsilon\eta_i(t)$ for those x_i's with unspecified $x_i(t_2)$, we see that the condition $\eta_i(t_1) = 0$ can still be imposed, but we can no longer stipulate that $\eta_i(t_2) = 0$.

It is clear, however, that whatever the condition is on $\eta_i(t_2)$, Eq. (13-8) must still hold. This would still lead to the necessary conditions as given by (13-16). We observe, however, that the first term on the left side of (13-16) will now play a role.

As before, since the choice of $\eta_i(t)$ is arbitrary, then, for each i, the first and second term on the left side of (13-16) must vanish separately. The vanishing of the second term will lead to the Euler-Lagrange equations (13-17) as before, but the first term, for those variables with an unspecified end point at t_2, will lead to the so-called *transversality conditions*:

$$\left.\frac{\partial L}{\partial \dot{x}_i}\right|_{t=t_2} = 0 \quad \text{(for those } x_i(t) \text{ whose end points } x_i(t_2) \text{ are unspecified).} \tag{13-34}$$

†See, e.g., reference [E1], pp. 103-110.

††The point $\mathbf{x}(t_2)$ is sometimes referred to in the literature as the right end point, and the point $\mathbf{x}(t_1)$ is sometimes called the left end point.

When the end point is not free, but is given implicitly through specifying that it must lie on a given curve or hypersurface of the state space, the transversality conditions naturally become more involved. Consider the simplest problem in calculus of variations given in part 2 of this section. Assume that the optimum trajectory is now to be found such that its end point at t_2 is to lie on a curve

$$\rho\big(x(t_2),\ t_2\big) = 0$$

Note now that the value of t_2 is no longer specified in advance, but is now given implicitly.

Let us immediately observe that all the necessary conditions for optimality for the fixed end-point case must also apply here. This is because an optimal trajectory for the variable end-point case must also be the optimal one for the corresponding fixed end-point problem if we choose the end point found in the variable end-point case as the terminal state.

Thus the only condition that is affected is the transversality condition. To derive it, let us consider a perturbation in t_2, $x(t)$, and $\dot{x}(t)$ by amounts δt_2, $\delta x(t)$, and $\delta\dot{x}(t)$, respectively.* Consider now the change $\Delta\mathcal{J}$ in the performance index

$$\begin{aligned}\Delta\mathcal{J} &= \int_{t_1}^{t_2+\delta t_2} L(t,\ x+\delta x,\ \dot{x}+\delta\dot{x})\,dt - \int_{t_1}^{t_2} L(t,\ x,\ \dot{x})\,dt \\ &= \int_{t_2}^{t_2+\delta t_2} L(t,\ x+\delta x,\ \dot{x}+\delta\dot{x})\,dt \\ &\quad + \int_{t_1}^{t_2} [L(t,\ x+\delta x,\ \dot{x}+\delta\dot{x}) - L(t,\ x,\ \dot{x})]\,dt\end{aligned}$$

To a first order of approximation, the above can be written term-by-term as

$$\Delta\mathcal{J} \simeq L(t,\ x,\ \dot{x})\Big|_{t=t_2}\delta t_2 + \int_{t_1}^{t_2}\left(\frac{\partial L(t,\ x,\ \dot{x})}{\partial x}\,\delta x + \frac{\partial L(t,\ x,\ \dot{x})}{\partial\dot{x}}\,\delta\dot{x}\right)dt$$

Now the integral $\int_{t_1}^{t_2}\frac{\partial L}{\partial\dot{x}}\,\delta\dot{x}\,dt$ can be integrated by parts, much as

*Note that in contrast to the previous cases, we now also permit a variation δt_2. Also, we employ a slightly different point of view.

we derive (13-10), resulting in

$$\int_{t_1}^{t_2}\left(\frac{\partial L}{\partial x}\,\delta x + \frac{\partial L}{\partial \dot{x}}\,\delta\dot{x}\right)dt = \frac{\partial L}{\partial \dot{x}}\,\delta x\,\Bigg|_{t_1}^{t_2} + \int_{t_1}^{t_2}\left(\frac{\partial L}{\partial x} - \frac{d}{dt}\frac{\partial L}{\partial \dot{x}}\,\delta x\right)dt$$

Because the Euler-Lagrange equation must be satisfied along the optimal trajectory, the integrand of the rhs of the above expression must be identically zero. Moreover $\delta x = 0$ at $t = t_1$. We have then

$$\Delta\mathcal{J} \simeq \left(L\delta t_2 + \frac{\partial L}{\partial \dot{x}}\,\delta x\right)\Bigg|_{t=t_2}$$

We must now relate a change in t_2, denoted as δt_2, with a change in x at the time t_2, denoted as $\delta x|_{t=t_2}$. Let the actual change in x at the end point be denoted δx_2; then

$$\delta x_2 \simeq \delta x\,\Big|_{t=t_2} + \dot{x}(t_2)\,\delta t_2$$

Thus

$$\Delta\mathcal{J} \simeq \left(L - \dot{x}\,\frac{\partial L}{\partial \dot{x}}\right)\Bigg|_{t=t_2}\delta t_2 + \frac{\partial L}{\partial \dot{x}}\Bigg|_{t=t_2}\delta x_2$$

As δt_2 and $\delta x_2 \to 0$, $\Delta\mathcal{J} \to \delta\mathcal{J}$ and the above approximate expression becomes an equality. Moreover, since for a minimum $\delta\mathcal{J} = 0$, we then have

$$\left(L - \dot{x}\,\frac{\partial L}{\partial \dot{x}}\right)\Bigg|_{t=t_2}\delta t_2 + \frac{\partial L}{\partial \dot{x}}\Bigg|_{t=t_2}\delta x_2 = 0 \qquad (13\text{-}35)$$

subject to the boundary condition $\rho(x(t_2), t_2) = 0$. This means δt_2 and δx_2 cannot be chosen independently but must be such that the equation

$$\frac{\partial \rho}{\partial x_2}\,\delta x_2 + \frac{\partial \rho}{\partial t_2}\,\delta t_2 = 0 \qquad (13\text{-}36)$$

is observed.

Equations (13-35) and (13-36) jointly constitute the requisite transversality conditions.

6. Equality-type Constraints and Lagrange Multipliers

Following the development of a maximization or minimization problem in calculus it is quite straightforward to see that equality-type constraints in calculus of variations can be similarly handled. If we wish to find the extremal of a functional of the form (13-13) under the associated stipulated conditions, but with the further constraints that the trajectories must satisfy the m twice-differentiable relations

$$\phi_k\big(x_1(t), \ldots, x_n(t); \dot{x}_1(t), \ldots, \dot{x}_n(t)\big) = 0, \qquad k = 1, \ldots, m \text{ and } m < n \tag{13-37}$$

then Lagrange multipliers can again be used to advantage. As in the case of calculus, through the introduction of m Lagrange variables, which will now in general be functions of t, $\psi_1(t)$, $\psi_2(t)$, ..., $\psi_m(t)$, the problem of finding the minimizing solution to (13-13) subject to the constraining conditions (13-37) can alternately, and generally more advantageously, be treated as a problem of minimizing the functional

$$\mathcal{J}_1 = \int_{t_2}^{t_2} \left(L + \sum_{k=1}^{m} \psi_k \phi_k\right) dt$$

without regard to the constraints.

If a minimizing trajectory satisfies the requisite boundary conditions, then $\mathcal{J}_1$ is stationary relative to variations in the Lagrange variables. Thus in the expression for the first variation of $\mathcal{J}_1$ the coefficient of each ψ_i vanishes, and therefore the stationary value of $\mathcal{J}_1$ also corresponds to a stationary value of $\mathcal{J}$. We then have the so-called multiplier rule, which in a more general form, may be stated:†

♦♦Theorem 13-1 *(The multiplier rule)*. Consider the problem of minimizing a performance index of the form (13-13) subject to m constraints of the form (13-37). For every piecewise smooth†† minimizing trajectory $x^*(t)$, there exist a constant c and functions $\psi_1(t)$, ..., $\psi_m(t)$, with c, ψ_1, ..., ψ_m not all identically zero, such

†For a rigorous proof, see [M8]. The multiplier rule can also be proved in the way we prove the maximum principle in the next section.

††A piecewise smooth curve is one which has piecewise continuous derivatives.

that the Euler–Lagrange equations (13–17), the Legendre condition (p. 505), and the Weierstrass condition (13–33) are all satisfied at every point (excepting the corners) of $x^*(t)$, provided that the function L in the conditions is replaced by the function

$$L_1 = cL + \sum_{k=1}^{m} \psi_k \phi_k$$

◆◆

Theorem 13-1 thus permits us to treat a minimizing problem with constraints by converting it to one without constraint. This is done through the creation of the auxiliary function L_1 which depends on the multipliers $c, \psi_1(t), \ldots, \psi_m(t)$.

As it turns out in most practical problems, $c \neq 0$, in which case one can always scale c and the ψ's such that $c = 1$.†

To indicate how Theorem 13-1 may be arrived at, consider a first-order case in which we wish to minimize $\mathcal{J} = \int_{t_1}^{t_2} L(x, \dot{x}, t)\, dt$ subject to the constraint $\phi(x, \dot{x}, t) = 0$. We must first of all have by (13–9)

$$\left.\frac{d\mathcal{J}(\epsilon)}{d\epsilon}\right|_{\epsilon=0} = \int_{t_1}^{t_2} \left(\frac{\partial L}{\partial x}\eta + \frac{\partial L}{\partial \dot{x}}\dot{\eta}\right) dt = 0 \qquad (13\text{–}38)$$

However, $x(t)$ is constrained also to satisfy the equation $\phi(x, \dot{x}, t) = 0$; this means $\eta(t)$ cannot be chosen arbitrarily. In fact it must be chosen such that

$$\phi(x + \epsilon\eta, \dot{x} + \epsilon\dot{\eta}, t) = 0 \qquad (13\text{–}39)$$

Equation (13–39) implies $\left.\frac{d\phi}{d\epsilon}\right|_{\epsilon=0} = 0$, or on setting $x + \epsilon\eta = X$ and $\dot{x} + \epsilon\dot{\eta} = \dot{X}$ as before, we have

$$\frac{\partial \phi}{\partial X}\frac{\partial X}{\partial \epsilon} + \frac{\partial \phi}{\partial \dot{X}}\frac{\partial \dot{X}}{\partial \epsilon} = \frac{\partial \phi}{\partial x}\eta + \frac{\partial \phi}{\partial \dot{x}}\dot{\eta} = 0 \qquad (13\text{–}40)$$

Now (13–38) and (13–40), through the introduction of a multiplier $\psi(t)$, may be combined to form the single necessary condition

†See, however, Sec. 16.1.

$$\int_{t_1}^{t_2} \left[\left(\frac{\partial L(x, \dot{x}, t)}{\partial x} + \psi(t)\,\frac{\partial \phi(x, \dot{x}, t)}{\partial x}\right)\eta(t) + \left(\frac{\partial L(x, \dot{x}, t)}{\partial \dot{x}} + \psi(t)\,\frac{\partial \phi(x, \dot{x}, t)}{\partial \dot{x}}\right)\dot{\eta}\right] dt = 0 \tag{13-41}$$

At each time t, if $\psi(t)$ is chosen such that the term multiplying $\dot{\eta}(t)$ vanishes, the first term in the integral must also vanish, since $\eta(t)$ is arbitrary.

Comparing with (13-9) we see that (13-41) corresponds to a problem of finding trajectories, without constraints, that satisfy the boundary conditions $x(t_1) = x_1$, $x(t_2) = x_2$ and minimize the performance index $\mathcal{J}_1 = \int_{t_1}^{t_2} (L + \psi\phi)\,dt$. We see also that the Lagrange multipliers $\psi_k (k = 1, \ldots, m)$ must in general be functions of time, since only then will they have the required property for the problem throughout the time interval $t_1 \leq t \leq t_2$.

13.2 A Special Class of Optimal Linear Control Problems

The techniques of calculus of variations introduced in the previous section can be directly applied to a special class of optimal linear control systems. This class of optimal linear control systems is characterized by the following:

1) The plant to be controlled is linear and takes the general form $\dot{\mathbf{x}} = \mathbf{A}(t)\mathbf{x} + \mathbf{B}(t)\mathbf{u}$.
2) The goal of control is to find a control function $\mathbf{u}(t)$ that drives the system state from a point $\mathbf{x}_1$ at the time t_1 to a point $\mathbf{x}_2$ at the time t_2 in such a way that a scalar performance index

$$\mathcal{J} = \int_{t_2}^{t_2} L(\mathbf{x}, \mathbf{u}, t)\,dt \tag{13-42}$$

is minimized.
3) The criterion function $L(\mathbf{x}, \mathbf{u}, t)$ is of the special form of a quadratic form in the state variables plus a quadratic form in the control functions. The coefficients of the quadratic forms however can be time varying.

In the general time-varying case where $\mathbf{A}$, $\mathbf{B}$, and L are all functions of time, the application of calculus of variations will lead to a two-point boundary value problem which can be solved by the method of Sec. 12.3, though in general not in closed form. When all the coefficients are time-invariant, however, closed-form solutions, and in some particular cases even closed-loop solutions, can be found.

So as to minimize unnecessary details, let us examine a system with a single control variable of the form $\dot{\mathbf{x}} = \mathbf{A}(t)\mathbf{x} + \mathbf{b}(t)u$ and a criterion function

$$L = \sum_{k=1}^{n} c_k(t) x_k^2 + d(t) u^2$$

In the light of calculus of variations, the system equations may be regarded as a set of n constraints of the form*

$$\phi_k(\mathbf{x}, \dot{\mathbf{x}}, u) = \dot{x}_k - \sum_{j=1}^{n} a_{kj}(t) x_j - b_k(t) u = 0, \qquad k = 1, \ldots, n \tag{13-43}$$

In accordance with the discussion of the previous section, if we define a set of n Lagrange multipliers $\psi_1, \psi_2, \ldots, \psi_n$, then the minimization problem posed above becomes the same as that of the minimization without constraint of an equivalent functional

$$\mathcal{J}_1 = \int_{t_1}^{t_2} \left(L + \sum_{k=1}^{n} \psi_k \phi_k \right) dt = \int_{t_1}^{t_2} L_1 \, dt \tag{13-44a}$$

where

$$L_1 \triangleq L + \sum_{k=1}^{n} \psi_k \phi_k \tag{13-44b}$$

The solution sought should appear in the form of a relation among the x_i's and the u, which will then be the required closed-loop solution.

Comparing our problem with that of the case of several variables treated in Sec. 13.1, we note that aside from the x_i's and the $\dot{x}_i$'s, an added variable u appears. To handle this extra variable within the context of the techniques of the previous section we can define an extra variable x_{n+1} where

*We can tolerate n constraints because there is now an extra variable $u(t)$.

$$x_{n+1}(t) = \int_{t_1}^{t} u(\tau)\,d\tau \ , \quad x_{n+1}(t_1) = 0 \ , \quad x_{n+1}(t_2) \text{ is free}$$

Then we have

$$\dot{x}_{n+1}(t) \equiv u(t) \tag{13-45}$$

and the Euler-Lagrange equations become

$$\frac{\partial L_1}{\partial x_k} - \frac{d}{dt}\left(\frac{\partial L_1}{\partial \dot{x}_k}\right) = 0, \qquad k = 1, \ldots, n+1$$

For the problem at hand we have

$$\begin{aligned} &\frac{\partial L_1}{\partial \dot{x}_k} = \psi_k \ , \quad \frac{\partial L_1}{\partial x_k} = 2c_k(t)x_k - \sum_{j=1}^{n} a_{jk}(t)\psi_j \ , \qquad k = 1, \ldots, n \\ &\frac{\partial L_1}{\partial \dot{x}_{n+1}} = \frac{\partial L_1}{\partial u} = 2d(t)u - \sum_{j=1}^{n} b_j(t)\psi_i, \qquad \frac{\partial L_1}{\partial x_{n+1}} = 0 \end{aligned} \tag{13-46}$$

The Euler-Lagrange equations will then yield

$$\dot{\psi}_k = -\sum_{j=1}^{n} a_{jk}(t)\psi_j + 2c_k(t)x_k, \qquad k = 1, \ldots, n \tag{13-47a}$$

and

$$2d(t)u - \sum_{j=1}^{n} b_j(t)\psi_j = \text{constant}$$

The value of the constant in the last equation can be obtained from considering the transversality condition for $x_{n+1}(t)$ at $t = t_2$. Using (13-34), we obtain

$$\left.\frac{\partial L_1}{\partial \dot{x}_{n+1}}\right|_{t=t_2} = 0$$

Thus the constant is 0 and the equation below (13-47a) becomes

$$2d(t)u - \sum_{j=1}^{n} b_j(t)\psi_j = 0 \tag{13-47b}$$

To (13-47a) and (13-47b) we add the system equation

$$\dot{x}_k = \sum_{j=1}^{n} a_{kj}(t)x_j + b_k(t)u, \quad k = 1, \ldots, n \tag{13-47c}$$

Equations (13-47) constitute a set of $2n$ simultaneous differential equations in $\mathbf{x}$ and $\boldsymbol{\psi}$ that are linear but time varying. The imposed boundary conditions $\mathbf{x}(t_1) = \mathbf{x}_1$, $\mathbf{x}(t_2) = \mathbf{x}_2$ provide us with the requisite $2n$ conditions. The method of Sec. 12.3 can now be invoked to solve these equations numerically (see also Exercise 13-8).

In the case of linear time-invariant differential systems with a time-invariant quadratic performance index, provided a solution exists, the solving of a two-point boundary value problem is no more difficult than a one-point boundary value problem. This is because the form of the solution is already known and what remains is to solve for the constants of the solution by utilizing the boundary values.

In this case, using (13-47b) in (13-47c), we can rewrite the set (13-47) in the following form:

$$\dot{x}_k = \sum_{j=1}^{n} a_{kj}x_j + \frac{b_k}{2d}\sum_{j=1}^{n} b_j\psi_j, \qquad \dot{\psi}_k = -\sum_{j=1}^{n} a_{jk}\psi_j + 2c_k x_k \tag{13-48}$$

$$k = 1, \ldots, n$$

The characteristic equation of the linear system (13-48) is then given by the determinant

$$\Delta(\lambda) = \begin{vmatrix} a_{11}-\lambda & a_{12} & \cdots & a_{1n} & \dfrac{b_1^2}{2d} & \cdots & \dfrac{b_1 b_n}{2d} \\ \cdot & & & & & & \\ \cdot & & & & & & \\ \cdot & & & & & & \\ a_{n1} & \cdot & \cdot\ \cdot & a_{nn}-\lambda & \dfrac{b_n b_1}{2d} & \cdots & \dfrac{b_n^2}{2d} \\ 2c_1 & 0 & \cdots & 0 & -a_{11}-\lambda & \cdots & -a_{n1} \\ \cdot & \cdot & & & & & \\ \cdot & \cdot & & & & & \\ \cdot & \cdot & & & & & \\ 0 & \cdot & \cdot\ \cdot & 2c_n & -a_{1n} & \cdots & -a_{nn}-\lambda \end{vmatrix} \tag{13-49a}$$

This determinant is represented more simply in terms of the determinant of the following partitioned matrix:

$$\Delta(\lambda) = \left| \begin{bmatrix} \mathbf{A} - \lambda\mathbf{I} & \frac{1}{2d}[\mathbf{b}\mathbf{b}^T] \\ 2\mathbf{C} & -\mathbf{A}^T - \lambda\mathbf{I} \end{bmatrix} \right| \tag{13-49b}$$

where $\mathbf{C} = \text{diag}[c_1, \ldots, c_n]$.

Making use of the facts that $(1/2d)\mathbf{b}\mathbf{b}^T$ and $2\mathbf{C}$ are both symmetric matrices and, moreover, that the determinant of a matrix is the determinant of its transpose, (13-49b) can be manipulated into the form (exercise for the reader)

$$\Delta(\lambda) = \left| \begin{bmatrix} \mathbf{A} + \lambda\mathbf{I} & \frac{1}{2d}[\mathbf{b}\mathbf{b}^T] \\ 2\mathbf{C} & -\mathbf{A}^T + \lambda\mathbf{I} \end{bmatrix} \right| \tag{13-50}$$

By inspecting (13-49b) and (13-50), we conclude that if λ_1 is a solution of $\Delta(\lambda) = 0$, $-\lambda_1$ is also a solution. Thus the poles of the system are seen to be symmetrically disposed relative to the imaginary as well as the real axis in the complex plane.

Let us assume that the system has only simple roots whose real parts are nonzero, and assume further that $\lambda_1, \lambda_2, \ldots, \lambda_n$ are the n roots with negative real parts; then the general solution of the system equations will be a linear combination of exponentials of the form $\alpha_k e^{\lambda_k t}$ and $\beta_k e^{-\lambda_k t}$ $(k = 1, \ldots, n)$. These contain $2n$ arbitrary constants $\alpha_1, \ldots, \alpha_n; \beta_1, \ldots, \beta_n$ which constitute the $2n$ unknowns to be solved for. The $2n$ boundary conditions given will then provide the $2n$ equations that render a solution possible. Equation (13-47b) will allow elimination of n.

When the boundary condition is imposed only at t_1, so that $\mathbf{x}(t_1) = \mathbf{x}_1$ but $\mathbf{x}(t_2)$ is left free, then in accordance with the discussion above, in addition to the initial boundary values, we also have the transversality condition (13-34). This will yield

$$\left.\frac{\partial L_1}{\partial \dot{x}_i}\right|_{t=t_2} = \psi_i(t_2) = 0, \quad i = 1, \ldots, n \tag{13-51}$$

Therefore, *when the right end point is left free, the value of the Lagrange multipliers will automatically become zero at the right end point*. However, we still have a two-point boundary value problem and we can proceed to solve it by the usual way.

In some cases, the upper limit of integration t_2 is infinite; thus the minimization problem is to be achieved over the semi-infinite time interval. This is meaningful only if the final boundary conditions are the system equilibrium states as $t \to \infty$, which in the linear case must be the origin 0; thus $\mathbf{x}(\infty) = \mathbf{0}$.* Here it becomes obvious that the coefficients β_k for the exponentials with positive real parts must vanish. Or

$$\beta_k = 0, \qquad k = 1, \ldots, n \tag{13-52}$$

In the above case we will have $2n$ equations for n unknowns. We can then eliminate the n functions $\alpha_k e^{\lambda_k t}$, with $k = 1, \ldots, n$, from these equations to result in expressions which define each ψ_i as a linear combination of the n x_j's. Then by virtue of (13-47b) u can be made a linear combination of the x_j's. Here we can readily achieve an optimal feedback controller, i.e., we can express u as a function of the instantaneous state $\mathbf{x}$.

The reader should have no difficulty in demonstrating to himself that the coefficients for the x_j's will all be constants.

♦♦Example 13-3. Consider the linear optimal control of the system $1/(p^2 + 1)$ with respect to the performance index

$$\mathcal{J} = \int_0^\infty \left(x_1{}^2 + x_2{}^2 + (1/9)\,u^2\right) dt$$

with boundary conditions $\mathbf{x}(0) = \mathbf{x}_0$ and $\mathbf{x}(\infty) = \mathbf{0}$.

If we let the output be x_1 and $\dot{x}_1 = x_2$ the system equation is

$$\dot{x}_1 = x_2, \qquad \dot{x}_2 = -x_1 + u$$

Then by (13-44b)

$$L_1 = x_1{}^2 + x_2{}^2 + \frac{u^2}{9} + \psi_1(\dot{x}_1 - x_2) + \psi_2(\dot{x}_2 + x_1 - u)$$

Thus the Euler-Lagrange equations are

$$\dot{x}_1 = x_2, \qquad \dot{x}_2 = -x_1 + u, \qquad \dot{\psi}_1 = +2x_1 + \psi_2, \qquad \psi_2 = +2x_2 - \psi_1$$

with an auxiliary equation $u = 9\psi_2/2$ obtained from (13-47b).

Eliminating u by using the auxiliary equation, we have in matrix form

*This case is close to the form of the class of problems considered in Sec. 12.2.

$$\begin{bmatrix} \dot{x}_1 \\ \dot{x}_2 \\ \dot{\psi}_1 \\ \dot{\psi}_2 \end{bmatrix} = \begin{bmatrix} 0 & 1 & 0 & 0 \\ -1 & 0 & 0 & \frac{9}{2} \\ 2 & 0 & 0 & 1 \\ 0 & 2 & -1 & 0 \end{bmatrix} \begin{bmatrix} x_1 \\ x_2 \\ \psi_1 \\ \psi_2 \end{bmatrix}$$

for which the characteristic equation is $\lambda^4 - 7\lambda^2 + 10 = 0$ and the roots are $\lambda = \pm\sqrt{2}, \pm\sqrt{5}$. By our previous comments, we can assume a form for x_1 as follows:

$$x_1 = \alpha_1 e^{-\sqrt{2}\,t} + \alpha_2 e^{-\sqrt{5}\,t}$$

Then, since $x_2 = \dot{x}_1$, and by virtue of the equations defining the ψ's, we have

$$x_2 = \dot{x}_1 = -\sqrt{2}\,\alpha_1 e^{-\sqrt{2}\,t} - \sqrt{5}\,\alpha_2 e^{-\sqrt{5}\,t}$$

$$\psi_2 = \frac{2}{9} u = \frac{2}{9} (\dot{x}_2 + x_1) = \frac{2}{3} \alpha_1 e^{-\sqrt{2}\,t} + \frac{4}{3} \alpha_2 e^{-\sqrt{5}\,t}$$

We wish to express ψ_2 in terms of the x's. This can be done first through the elimination of the quantities $\alpha_1 e^{-\sqrt{2}\,t}$ and $\alpha_2 e^{-\sqrt{5}\,t}$ from the equations for x_1 and x_2, and we obtain

$$\alpha_1 e^{-\sqrt{2}\,t} = \frac{1}{\sqrt{5} - \sqrt{2}} (\sqrt{5}\,x_1 + x_2)$$

$$\alpha_2 e^{-\sqrt{5}\,t} = \frac{-1}{\sqrt{5} - \sqrt{2}} (\sqrt{2}\,x_1 + x_2)$$

With this, the above expression for ψ_2 becomes, to three decimal places

$$\psi_2 = -0.445x_1 - 0.406x_2$$

and therefore

$$u = \frac{9}{2} \psi_2 = -2.00\,x_1 - 1.83\,x_2$$

and the final configuration of the optimal feedback controller is as shown in Fig. 13-4.

The system designed in this case, as should be relatively obvious, is automatically stable.◆◆

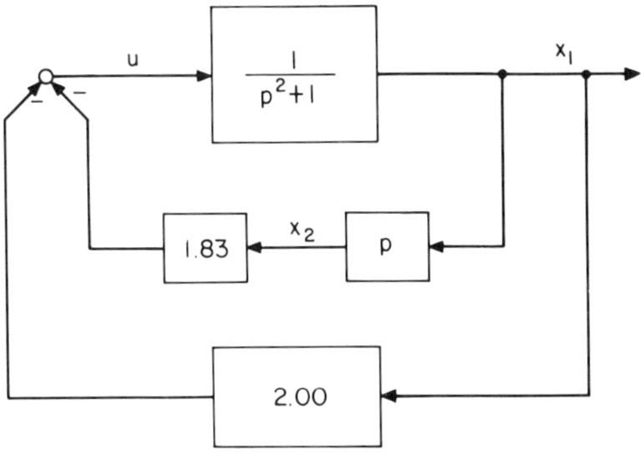

Fig. 13-4. The optimal feedback control system of Example 13-3.

For the class of problems considered above, we have thus far only made use of the Euler-Lagrange equations, which represent the first necessary conditions for optimality. As it turns out, this class of systems is contrived to yield a unique optimal solution. It is nevertheless instructive to consider the other necessary conditions, as these yield some insights which serve to improve our understanding of Pontryagin's maximum principle which we will introduce later.

The Legendre-Clebsch condition dictates that the $(n+1) \times (n+1)$ matrix $\left[L_{\dot{x}_i \dot{x}_j}\right]$ be positive semi-definite, where $x_{n+1} \equiv u(t)$. Applying this, we readily find that the Legendre condition in this instance reduces to

$$\frac{\partial^2 L_1}{\partial u^2} \geq 0 \tag{13-53}$$

For Example 13-3, we have $\partial^2 L_1 / \partial u^2 = 2/9$ and hence the Legendre condition is satisfied.

Next consider the Weierstrass condition which for a minimum dictates that the function E of (13-31) must be nonnegative along an optimal trajectory. In the present problem, the function E is also a function of the control $u(t)$, which would, by definition, be optimum when $\mathbf{x}(t)$ and $\dot{\mathbf{x}}(t)$ assume optimum values. Thus we can write†

$$E = L_1(\mathbf{x}^*, \dot{\mathbf{x}}, u, t) - L_1(\mathbf{x}^*, \dot{\mathbf{x}}^*, u^*) - \sum_{i=1}^{n} (\dot{x}_i - \dot{x}_i^*) \frac{\partial L_1}{\partial \dot{x}_i}(\mathbf{x}^*, \dot{\mathbf{x}}^*, u^*, t) \tag{13-54}$$

†Recall that $\partial L_1^* / \partial u \equiv 0$ by the Euler-Lagrange equations, where $L_1^* \triangleq L_1(\mathbf{x}^*, \dot{\mathbf{x}}^*, \mathbf{u}^*, t)$.

With

$$f_k(\mathbf{x}, u, t) = \sum_{j=1}^{n} a_{kj}(t)\, x_j + b_k(t)\, u$$

we have

$$L_1 = L + \sum_{k=1}^{n} \psi_k [\dot{x}_k - f_k(\mathbf{x}, u, t)]$$

and thus

$$E = L - L^* + \sum_{k=1}^{n} \psi_k \{(\dot{x}_k - \dot{x}_k^*) - [f_k(\mathbf{x}^*, u, t) - f_k(\mathbf{x}^*, u^*, t)] - (\dot{x}_k - \dot{x}_k^*)\}$$

$$= L - L^* - \sum_{k=1}^{n} \psi_k [f_k(\mathbf{x}^*, u, t) - f_k(\mathbf{x}^*, u^*, t)] \qquad (13\text{-}55)$$

where $L^* \triangleq L(\mathbf{x}^*, u^*, t)$.

For a minimum, we need $E \geq 0$; this implies that u^* must be chosen so that

$$\sum_{k=1}^{n} \psi_k f_k(\mathbf{x}^*, u^*, t) - L^* \geq \sum_{k=1}^{n} \psi_k f_k(\mathbf{x}^*, u, t) - L \qquad (13\text{-}56)$$

In words, (13-56) indicates that u^* must be chosen so that the function

$$H = \sum_{k=1}^{n} \psi_k f_k(\mathbf{x}^*, u, t) - L \qquad (13\text{-}57)$$

(which on the trajectory $\mathbf{x}^*$ depends only on u) takes on the maximum value at each point of the optimal trajectory $\mathbf{x}^*$. As we shall see in the next chapter, this is a statement of the maximum principle for the particular problem being considered.

Since in our present problem there are no constraints on u, we can find u^* by taking the partial derivative of the quantity H of (13-57) with respect to u and setting it to 0. This yields the same equation as (13-47b); thus, the solution also satisfies the Weierstrass condition.

Note further that, in order for H to be a maximum, we also must have

$$\left.\frac{\partial^2 H}{\partial u^2}\right|_{u=u^*} \leq 0$$

which interestingly enough yields the Legendre condition (13-53) independently. Indeed, the Weierstrass condition always implies the Legendre condition for the class of problems considered in this section.

13.3 Terminal Control Problems—The Problem of Mayer

Quite frequently, a control problem arises where the final state alone determines the goodness of control. Such problems occur, for example, in missile gudiance, where the minimum miss-distance is the only suitable figure of merit in certain intercept problems.

A terminal control problem is closely related to the classical *problem of Mayer* in calculus of variations. In contradistinction, the type of control problem considered in Sec. 13.2, where the performance index is an integral of the form of (13-42), is known as the *problem of Lagrange*.*

Let us try to obtain the necessary conditions associated with the problem of Mayer by making use of the multiplier rule of Theorem 13-1.

Consider again a first-order system given by $\phi(x, \dot{x}, t) = 0$, to be driven from $x(t_1) = x_1$ over a fixed-time interval $[t_1, t_2]$ so as to minimize the function $\mathcal{J} = P(x_2)$. The end point $x_2 = x(t_2)$ is assumed free.

Since there is no integral to be minimized, the quantity L in the multiplier rule given by Theorem 13-1 is identically equal to zero. Thus we may suppose that the present problem is equivalent to one of finding the trajectory $x(t)$ satisfying the given boundary conditions and which minimizes the (equivalent) performance index

$$\mathcal{J}_1 = P(x_2) + \int_{t_1}^{t_2} \psi(t)\, \phi(x, \dot{x}, t)\, dt \tag{13-58}$$

Suppose we again consider variations of the form $X(t) = x(t) + \epsilon\, \eta(t)$, with $\eta(t_1) = 0$; we find that

$$\mathcal{J}_1 = P\Big(x(t_2) + \epsilon\, \eta(t_2)\Big) + \int_{t_1}^{t_2} \psi(t)\, \phi\Big(x + \epsilon\, \eta,\ \dot{x} + \epsilon\, \dot{\eta}(t),\ t\Big) dt$$

*The problems of Lagrange and Mayer may be transformed into one another. (See Exercise 13-15.) However, such transformations often lead to equations in an unnecessarily cumbersome form; hence it is meaningful to treat these problems individually.

Performing $\left.\dfrac{d\mathcal{J}_1}{d\epsilon}\right|_{\epsilon=0} = 0$, and integrating by parts in the same manner as in Sec. 13-1, we obtain the Euler-Lagrange equation along the optimal trajectory

$$\frac{\partial L_1}{\partial x} - \frac{d}{dt}\left(\frac{\partial L_1}{\partial \dot{x}}\right) = 0 \tag{13-59}$$

where

$$L_1 = \psi(t)\ \phi(x, \dot{x}, t) \tag{13-60}$$

along with the further boundary condition that

$$\left.\frac{\partial P(x)}{\partial x}\eta(t)\right|_{t=t_2} + \left.\frac{\partial L_1(x, \dot{x}, t)}{\partial \dot{x}}\eta(t)\right|_{t=t_2} = 0$$

Since $\eta(t_2)$ is arbitrary, this leads to the following transversality condition

$$\left.\frac{\partial P(x)}{\partial x}\right|_{t=t_2} = \left.\frac{-\partial L_1(x, \dot{x}, t)}{\partial \dot{x}}\right|_{t=t_2} \tag{13-61}$$

In addition to the conditions (13-59) and (13-61), the Weierstrass condition $E \geq 0$ must also be satisfied, where, from (13-31) and (13-60),

$$E = \psi(t)\ \phi(x^*, \dot{x}, t) - \psi(t)\ \phi(x^*, \dot{x}^*, t) - (\dot{x} - \dot{x}^*)\ \psi(t) \tag{13-62}$$

When there are n variables $x_1, x_2, \ldots, x_n$ and n differential equations $\phi_1, \phi_2, \ldots, \phi_n$, we can define n-dimensional vectors $\mathbf{x}$ and $\dot{\mathbf{x}}$ such that each ϕ_i will be specifically dependent on them as well as t, and P will be a function of $\mathbf{x}(t_2) = \mathbf{x}_2$. The first necessary conditions for optimality here are the set of Euler-Lagrange equations along the optimal trajectory

$$\frac{\partial L_1}{\partial x_i} - \frac{d}{dt}\left(\frac{\partial L_1}{\partial \dot{x}_i}\right) = 0, \qquad i = 1, \ldots, n \tag{13-63a}$$

where

$$L_1 = \sum_{i=1}^{n} \psi_i(t)\ \phi_i(\mathrm{x}, \dot{\mathrm{x}}, t) \qquad \text{(13-63b)}$$

In addition, we have the set of transversality conditions

$$\left.\frac{\partial P}{\partial x_i}\right|_{t=t_2} = -\left.\frac{\partial L_1}{\partial \dot{x}_i}\right|_{t=t_2} \qquad \text{(13-64)}$$

and the Weierstrass condition

$$E = \sum_{i=1}^{n} \psi_i(t)\ \phi_i(\mathrm{x}^*, \dot{\mathrm{x}}, t) - \sum_{i=1}^{n} \psi_i(t)\ \phi_i(\mathrm{x}^*, \dot{\mathrm{x}}^*, t) - \sum_{i=1}^{n} (\dot{x}_1 - \dot{x}_1{}^*)\ \psi_i(t) \qquad \text{(13-65)}$$

When P is also a function of end time t_2, indicating that the end time t_2 is not specified in advance, (13-58) becomes

$$\mathcal{J}_1 = P(x_2, t_2) + \int_{t_1}^{t_2} \psi(t)\ \phi(x, \dot{x}, t)\, dt \qquad \text{(13-66)}$$

This means that t_2 permits a variation δt_2 as well and must be taken into account. Here we can make use of the approach of Part 5 of Sec. 13.1 and readily derive that the appropriate transversality condition at the end point is

$$\left.\left(\frac{\partial P(x, t)}{\partial t} + L_1 - \dot{x}\,\frac{\partial L_1}{\partial \dot{x}}\right)\right|_{t=t_2} \delta t_2 + \left.\left(\frac{\partial P(x, t)}{\partial x} + \frac{\partial L_1}{\partial \dot{x}}\right)\right|_{t=t_2} \delta x_2 = 0 \qquad \text{(13-67)}$$

(exercise for the reader).

In the case of n variables, the transversality condition becomes

$$\left.\left(\frac{\partial P(\mathrm{x}, t)}{\partial t} + L_1 - \sum_{i=1}^{n} \dot{x}_i\,\frac{\partial L_1}{\partial \dot{x}_i}\right)\right|_{t=t_2} \delta t_2 + \sum_{i=1}^{n} \left.\left(\frac{\partial P(\mathrm{x}, t)}{\partial x_i} + \frac{\partial L_1}{\partial \dot{x}_i}\right)\right|_{t=t_2} \delta x_{2i} = 0 \qquad \text{(13-68)}$$

where δx_{2i} is the ith component of the vector $\delta \mathrm{x}_2$.

Among the class of problems that the present formulation can treat is the class of time-optimal control problems mentioned in the previous chapter.† For this class of problems $P(\mathbf{x}_2, t_2) = t_2$ and $\mathcal{J}_1 = t_2 + \int_{t_1}^{t_2} L_1(\mathbf{x}, \dot{\mathbf{x}}, t)\,dt$ with t_2 unknown and to be found.

To properly view the minimum time problem, we note that the necessary conditions here must be identical to those for a corresponding fixed-time problem if the minimum time is chosen as the terminal time. When we do this, however, t_2 in $\mathcal{J}_1$ becomes a constant and does not play any role in the minimization. This means that the necessary conditions for the minimum-time problem, with $\mathcal{J}_1 = t_2 + \int_{t_1}^{t_2} L_1(\mathbf{x}, \dot{\mathbf{x}}, t)\,dt$, must be the same as those for a fixed-time problem with $\mathcal{J}_1 = \int_{t_1}^{t_2} L_1(\mathbf{x}, \dot{\mathbf{x}}, t)\,dt$. The only difference must come via the transversality condition (13-68). In particular, if the end point $\mathbf{x}(t_2)$ is fixed, $\delta\mathbf{x}_2 \equiv 0$, then by (13-68) we obtain, for the minimum time problem, the important condition

$$\left.\left(\sum_{i=1}^{n} \dot{x}_i \frac{\partial L_1}{\partial \dot{x}_i} - L_1\right)\right|_{t=t_2} = 1\,, \quad \text{if } \mathbf{x}(t_2) \text{ is fixed} \tag{13-69}$$

If ϕ_i is of the form $\phi_i = \dot{x}_i - f_i(\mathbf{x}, \mathbf{u}, t) = 0$, then (13-69) further reduces to

$$\left.\left[\sum_{i=1}^{n} \psi_i(t)\dot{x}_i(t) - \sum_{i=1}^{n} \psi_i(t)\phi_i(\mathbf{x}, \dot{\mathbf{x}}, t)\right]\right|_{t=t_2} = 1$$

or

$$\left.\sum_{i=1}^{n} \psi_i(t) f_i(\mathbf{x}^*, \mathbf{u}^*, t)\right|_{t=t_2} = 1 \tag{13-70}$$

Indeed, if $L_1(\boldsymbol{\psi}, \mathbf{x}, \dot{\mathbf{x}}, \mathbf{u}) = \sum_{i=1}^{n} \psi_i[\dot{x}_i - f_i(\mathbf{x}, \mathbf{u})]$ is not an explicit

†If the problem requires inequality constraints on the control variable, then we will need the approach of Valentine, which will be treated in Sec. 13.5.

function of time, then by (13-18), (13-69), and (13-70), it follows that in our case

$$\sum_{i=1}^{n} \psi_i(t) f_i(\mathbf{x}^*, \mathbf{u}^*) \equiv 1 , \quad t_1 \le t \le t_2 \tag{13-71}$$

This is true if $\mathbf{f}(\mathbf{x}, \mathbf{u})$ does not depend explicitly on time. Let us now apply the necessary conditions developed above to a nontrivial nonlinear system. We will see that in contrast to the linear case of Example 13-3 the necessary conditions can only yield a two-point boundary value problem involving a set of $2n$ nonlinear simultaneous differential equations.

♦♦Example 13-4.† The dynamics of an idealized jet aircraft flying in a vertical plane can be approximately given by the following set of five simultaneous first-order differential equations:

$$\begin{aligned}
\dot{x}(t) &= v(t)\cos\gamma(t) \triangleq f_1\\
\dot{z}(t) &= v(t)\sin\gamma(t) \triangleq f_2\\
\dot{v}(t) &= \frac{g}{w(t)}\left[T\cos\alpha(t) - D\big(v(t), \alpha(t)\big) - k\frac{v(t)}{g}\right] - g\sin\gamma(t) \triangleq f_3\\
\dot{\gamma}(t) &= \frac{g}{v(t)\,w(t)}\left[T\sin\alpha(t) + L\big(v(t), \alpha(t)\big)\right] - \frac{g}{v(t)}\cos\gamma(t) \triangleq f_4\\
\dot{w}(t) &= -k \triangleq f_5
\end{aligned} \tag{13-72}$$

where $x(t)$ and $z(t)$ are the horizontal and vertical coordinates of the aircraft; $v(t)$ is the magnitude of the aircraft's velocity vector, which has an angle that is $\gamma(t)$ radians from the horizontal; T is the constant thrust developed by the jet; g is the magnitude of the gravitational acceleration, also assumed constant; $w(t)$ is the weight of the aircraft, assumed to be independent of the height z; D and L are respectively the drag and lift forces which are, in general, functions of v and α; and the constant k is the rate of loss of the weight of the jet fuel. The geometry of the problem is as given in Fig. 13-5.

The problem is to find the necessary conditions governing the minimum time-of-flight problem, using $\alpha(t)$ as the control variable; that is, find $\alpha(t)$ such that, starting at the position (x_1, z_1) at the time $t = 0$, the aircraft can arrive at a final position (x_2, z_2) in a minimum time t_2^*.

† See [H9]. Hestenes apparently was the first to treat time-optimal problems within the context of the problem of Mayer.

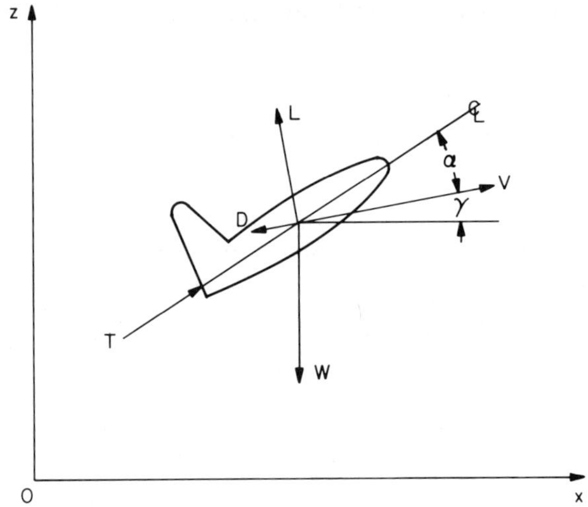

Fig. 13-5. An idealized jet aircraft flying in a vertical plane.

As in Sec. 13.2, to handle the control variable $\alpha(t)$, we introduce an auxiliary variable $\mu(t)$ such that

$$\dot{\mu}(t) = \alpha(t), \qquad \mu(0) = 0 \tag{13-73}$$

We can now define a 6-dimensional state vector $\mathrm{x}(t)$ with components $x(t)$, $z(t)$, $v(t)$, $\gamma(t)$, $w(t)$, and $\mu(t)$. The differential equation constraints are then $\phi_1 = \dot{x} - f_1 = 0$, $\phi_2 = \dot{z} - f_2 = 0$, $\phi_3 = \dot{v} - f_3 = 0$, $\phi_4 = \dot{\gamma} - f_4 = 0$, and $\phi_5 = \dot{w} + k = 0$.

Introducing the multipliers $\psi_1(t), \ldots, \psi_5(t)$, we form $L_1 = \sum_{i=1}^{5} \psi_i(t)\, \phi_i(\mathrm{x}, \dot{\mathrm{x}})$.

By means of the multiplier rule, we then transform the problem into one of finding $\mathrm{x}(t)$ without constraint over the time interval $[0, t_2]$ so as to minimize the performance index $\int_0^{t_2} L_1(\mathrm{x}, \dot{\mathrm{x}}, t)\, dt$. The necessary conditions are

1) *The Euler-Lagrange equations*. Developing the equations corresponding to (13-63a), we find:

$$\dot{\psi}_1(t) = 0\,, \quad \dot{\psi}_2(t) = 0$$

$$\dot{\psi}_3(t) = -\psi_1 \cos\gamma - \psi_2 \sin\gamma + \frac{\psi_3}{w}\left[k + g\,\frac{\partial D(v, \alpha)}{\partial v}\right]$$

$$-\psi_4\,\frac{g}{vw}\left[\frac{-T}{v}\sin\alpha + \frac{\partial L}{\partial v} - \frac{1}{v}(L - w\cos\gamma)\right]$$

$$\dot{\psi}_4(t) = +\psi_1 v \sin\gamma - \psi_2 v \cos\gamma + \psi_3 g \cos\gamma - \psi_4 \frac{g}{v} \sin\gamma$$

$$\dot{\psi}_5(t) = \psi_3 \frac{g}{w^2}\left[T \cos\alpha - D(v, \alpha) + \frac{kv}{g}\right] + \psi_4 \frac{g}{vw^2}[T \sin\alpha + L(v, \alpha)]$$

and

$$\frac{\partial L_1}{\partial \alpha} = +\frac{g}{w}\left[\psi_3\left(T \sin\alpha + \frac{\partial D}{\partial \alpha}\right) - \psi_4\left(\frac{T}{v}\cos\alpha + \frac{1}{v}\frac{\partial L}{\partial \alpha}\right)\right] = 0 \quad (13\text{-}74)$$

The last equation follows from the considerations that led to Eq. (13-47b).

2) *The Weierstrass conditions*. Equation (13-32), when applied to the present problem readily yields

$$\sum_{i=1}^{5} \psi_i f_i(\mathrm{x}^*, \alpha^*) \geq \sum_{i=1}^{5} \psi_i f_i(\mathrm{x}^*, \alpha) \quad (13\text{-}75)$$

(exercise for the reader). This implies that the optimal angle of attack history $\alpha^*(t)$, for all t, should be chosen such that the quantity $\sum_{i=1}^{5} \psi_i f_i(\mathrm{x}^*, \alpha)$ is maximized. Since only f_3 and f_4 depend on α, then the Weierstrass condition dictates that α must be chosen such that

$$h(v, \alpha) \triangleq \psi_3(t) \frac{g}{w}[T \cos\alpha - D(v, \alpha)] + \psi_4(f) \frac{g}{vw}[T \cos\alpha + L(v, \alpha)] \quad (13\text{-}76)$$

is maximized.

If there is no constraint on the value of α, then a necessary condition for this case is

$$\left.\frac{\partial h(v, \alpha)}{\partial \alpha}\right|_{\alpha=\alpha^*} = 0 \quad (13\text{-}77)$$

3) *The transversality conditions*. For this problem, only $x(t_2)$ and $z(t_2)$ are fixed. This means δx_2 and δz_2 must be 0. Moreover, as δt_2 and δx_2 can vary independently, their arguments must separately vanish; thus we have, from (13-68)

$$\psi_3^*(t_2) = \psi_2^*(t_2) = \psi_5^*(t_2) = 0 \quad (13\text{-}78)$$

and

$$\left.\left(\sum_{i=1}^{5} \psi_i^* f_i^* - 1\right)\right|_{t=t_2} = 0 \qquad (13\text{-}79)^\dagger$$

Since the f_i's do not explicitly depend on t, then Eq. (13-79) further implies, in line with the reasoning that leads to (13-71), that

$$\sum_{i=1}^{5} \psi_i^* f_i^* - 1 \equiv 0 \qquad \text{for all } t \in [0, t_2] \qquad (13\text{-}80)$$

To obtain a possible solution to the problem, the $2n$ differential equations (13-72) and (13-74) must be solved, making use of (13-77) through (13-80). There is no hope in finding a closed-form solution. In general, numerical solutions must be resorted to. Some of the numerical methods will be treated in Chap. 17.◆◆

13.4 More General Optimal Control Problems—The Problem of Bolza

The calculus of variations has been developed far enough to treat a rather large class of optimal control problems. The most general class of such problems can for our purposes be formulated in the following way:

Consider systems of the form

$$\dot{\mathbf{x}} = \mathbf{f}(\mathbf{x}, \mathbf{u}, t), \quad \mathbf{x}(t_1) = \mathbf{x}_1 \qquad (13\text{-}81)$$

It is desired to find a control function $\mathbf{u}^*(t)$ over $t_1 \le t \le t_2$ so as to (1) drive the system state to one at t_2 which observes the relationship

$$\rho\big(\mathbf{x}(t_2), t_2\big) = 0 \qquad (13\text{-}82)$$

and (2) minimize a performance index of the form

$$\mathcal{J} = P\big(\mathbf{x}(t_2), t_2\big) + \int_{t_1}^{t_2} L(\mathbf{x}, \mathbf{u}, t)\, dt \qquad (13\text{-}83)$$

†Here, we define $f_i^* \triangleq f_i(\mathbf{x}^*, \alpha^*)$.

Let us further impose an equality-type constraint on the driving function $\mathbf{u}$ of the form $\zeta(\mathbf{u}) = 0$; for example, $\sum_{i=1}^{r} u_i^2 - k = 0$, with k a constant.

The problem in calculus of variations that uses a general performance index of the form of (13-83) and differential equation constraints of the form $\Phi(\mathbf{x}, \dot{\mathbf{x}}, t) = 0$ is called the *problem of Bolza.* It can be transformed to the form of either Lagrange or Mayer, though often it is more convenient to attack it directly without transformation.

The optimal control $\mathbf{u}(t)$ is found by much the same procedure as before. If $\mathbf{u}$ is r-dimensional, we first form r auxiliary states $x_{n+1}, \ldots, x_{n+r}$ and r auxiliary differential equations $\dot{x}_j = u_{j-n}(t)$, $x_j(t_1) = 0$, $j = n+1, \ldots, n+r$; then we form

$$L_2(\mathbf{x}, \dot{\mathbf{x}}, \mathbf{u}, \boldsymbol{\psi}, t) = L(\mathbf{x}, \mathbf{u}, t) + \sum_{i=1}^{n} \psi_i(t)\,\phi_i(\mathbf{x}, \dot{\mathbf{x}}, \mathbf{u}, t) + \lambda(t)\,\zeta(\mathbf{u})$$

$$= L_1(\mathbf{x}, \dot{\mathbf{x}}, \mathbf{u}, \boldsymbol{\psi}, t) + \lambda(t)\,\zeta(\mathbf{u}) \qquad (13\text{-}84)$$

where $\phi_i = \dot{x}_i - f_i(\mathbf{x}, \mathbf{u}, t)$ for $i = 1, \ldots, n$ and the n ψ_i's are the usual Lagrange multipliers, λ is an extra multiplier to handle the equality constraint on $\mathbf{u}(t)$, and $L_1 = L + \sum_{i=1}^{n} \psi_i \phi_i$.

1) *The Euler-Lagrange equations.* Writing the equations $[(\partial L_2/\partial x_i) - d(\partial L_2/\partial \dot{x}_i)/dt] = 0$ explicitly, we obtain

$$\dot{\psi}_k = \frac{\partial L}{\partial x_k} - \sum_{i=1}^{n} \psi_i \frac{\partial f_i}{\partial x_k} \quad ; \quad k = 1, \ldots, n$$

$$\frac{\partial L_2}{\partial u_j} = 0 \quad ; \quad j = 1, \ldots, r \qquad (13\text{-}85)$$

These $n + r$ equations along with the n system equations (13-79) and the equation of the constraint on u, $\zeta(\mathbf{u}) = 0$, provide $2n + r + 1$ equations for the $2n + r + 1$ unknowns $x_1, \ldots, x_n, \psi_1, \ldots, \psi_n, u_1, \ldots, u_r$, and λ.

When L_1 is not an explicit function of time, then corresponding to Eq. (13-18), we have the condition

$$-L_1 + \sum_{i=1}^{n} \frac{\partial L_1}{\partial \dot{x}_i}\dot{x}_i = \text{constant} \qquad (13\text{-}86)$$

which reduces to

$$-L + \sum_{i=1}^{n} \psi_i f_i = \text{constant} \tag{13-87}$$

2) *The Legendre–Clebsch condition.*

$$\left[L_{2_{u_i u_j}}\right] \geq 0 \qquad \text{for } \mathcal{J} \text{ to be a minimum.} \tag{13-88}$$

3) *The Weierstrass condition.* From (13-33), (13-84) and considering (13-85), we get

$$-L(\mathbf{x}^*, \mathbf{u}^*, t) + \sum_{i=1}^{n} \psi_i f_i(\mathbf{x}^*, \mathbf{u}^*, t) - \lambda\zeta(\mathbf{u}^*)$$

$$\geq -L(\mathbf{x}^*, \mathbf{u}, t) + \sum_{i=1} \psi_i f_i(\mathbf{x}^*, \mathbf{u}, t) - \lambda\zeta(\mathbf{u}) \tag{13-89}$$

This implies that $\mathbf{u}^*$ *must be so chosen that the quantity* $H = -L + \sum_{i=1}^{n} \psi_i f_i - \lambda\zeta$ *is maximized at every point of the optimal trajectory.* This, under the differentiability assumption, implies that at every point along the optimal trajectory the following condition must hold

$$\left.\left(-\frac{\partial L}{\partial u_l} + \sum_{i=1}^{n} \psi_i \frac{\partial f_i}{\partial u_l} - \lambda \frac{\partial \zeta}{\partial u_l}\right)\right|_{u_l = u_l^*} = 0, \qquad l = 1, \ldots, r \tag{13-90}$$

Equations (13-90) correspond to the last r of the Euler-Lagrange equations (13-85). In addition, the requirement $\left.\frac{\partial^2 H}{\partial u^2}\right|_{\mathbf{u}=\mathbf{u}^*} \leq 0$ yields the Legendre-Clebsch condition (13-86) above.

4) *The transversality conditions.* When the functions P and ρ are both independent of the end time t_2, then if we let $R = P + \alpha\rho$, where α is a constant multiplier, the transversality condition at t_2 is

$$\left.\frac{\partial R}{\partial x_i}\right|_{t=t_2} = -\left.\frac{\partial L_1}{\partial \dot{x}_i}\right|_{t=t_2} \tag{13-91}$$

If P and ρ do depend on t_2, we shall have (show this)

$$\left[\delta R + \left(L_2 + \sum_{i=1}^{n} \frac{\partial L_1}{\partial \dot{x}_i} \dot{x}_i\right) \delta t + \sum_{i=1}^{n} \frac{\partial L_1}{\partial \dot{x}_i} \delta x_i\right]\Bigg|_{t=t_2} = 0 \qquad \text{(13-92)}$$

for all infinitesimal changes in δx_i and δt consistent with the constraint $\rho\left(\mathbf{x}(t_2), t_2\right) = 0$. In (13-92), $\delta R = \sum_{i=1}^{n} \frac{\partial R}{\partial x_i} \delta x_i + \frac{\partial R}{\partial t} \delta t$.

Let us point out one important boundary condition arising from the transversality condition (13-91). For the class of problems where $L \equiv 0$ and P is independent of $\mathbf{x}_2$ and where the end point must lie on a surface $\rho(\mathbf{x}) = 0$,

$$\frac{\partial \rho}{\partial x_i}\bigg|_{t=t_2} = -\frac{\partial L_1}{\partial \dot{x}_i}\bigg|_{t=t_2} \qquad \text{with } L_1 = \sum_{i=1}^{n} \psi_i \phi_i$$

If now $\phi_i = \dot{x}_i - f_i$, we have

$$\frac{\partial \rho}{\partial x_i}\bigg|_{t=t_2} = -\psi_i(t_2) \qquad \text{(13-93)}$$

This means the gradient vector of $\rho(\mathbf{x})$ must point in a direction opposite to $\boldsymbol{\psi}(t_2)$. To put it in another way, for this class of problems, a boundary condition is that $\boldsymbol{\psi}(t_2)$ is normal to the hypersurface $\rho(\mathbf{x}_2)$.

An example of this class of problems is the class of time-optimal problems. Specifically, consider:

♦♦Example 13-5. Suppose, in a dog fight, the jet aircraft of Example 13-4 must go from a point $\left(x(0), z(0)\right)$ into a cloud given parametrically by $\rho(x, z) = 0$ in a minimum time t_2^*; find the boundary conditions necessary for the solution of the problem.

The starting conditions $x(0)$, $z(0)$, $v(0)$, $\gamma(0)$, and $w(0)$ presumably are given. By (13-73), we have $\mu(0) = 0$. Further, Eqs. (13-74), (13-75), and (13-77) must also hold here. This means that ψ_1 and ψ_2 are constants.

The first part of Eq. (13-68) still holds since ρ is independent of time; thus (13-79) still holds. The second part needs a slight modification since (13-93) must be satisfied. This yields (13-78) since ρ is independent of the variables v, γ, w, and μ, but, in addition, we have $\psi_1(t^*) = -(\partial\rho/\partial x)$, $\psi_2(t^*) = -(\partial\rho/\partial z)$ which helps to fix the relative values of the constants ψ_1 and ψ_2.

The above considerations yield the 11 boundary conditions for the 11 variables of the problem.♦♦

13.5 Inequality Constraints on the Control Variable

Very frequently, we encounter problems in which the constraint on the control variable $u(t)$ is of the inequality type: $-U' \leq u \leq U$, with $U, U' > 0$. This type of constraint can be handled approximately by the so-called penalty function method and exactly by the use of a special approach due to Valentine [V1].

1. The Penalty Function Approach

The basic concept of the penalty function approach is to introduce additional terms in the performance index that is to be minimized such that violation of the inequality constraints by the control variables will bring about large values for the performance index. After such terms are introduced, the optimization problem is then solved without regard for the inequality constraints on the state.

As an example, consider a problem in which a trajectory for $\dot{x} = f(x, u, t)$ connecting x_1 and x_2 is to be found so as to minimize a performance index $\mathcal{J} = \int_{t_1}^{t_2} L(x, u, t)\,dt$. Suppose that the single control variable $u(t)$ must satisfy the constraint $-1 \leq u \leq 1$.

In the penalty function formulation, we consider a new performance index

$$\mathcal{J}_1 = \mathcal{J} + \int_{t_1}^{t_2} g(u)\,dt$$

where $g(u)$, the penalty function, is a function which is small when $|u(t)| < 1$ but increases sharply when $|u(t)| > 1$. We then proceed to find a solution that minimizes $\mathcal{J}_1$ without regard to the constraint $|u| \leq 1$.

The penalty function approach is particularly useful in some of the numerical schemes for finding optimal solutions. As will be discussed in Chap. 17, the numerical schemes frequently require linearization about trajectories and control functions. There is generally no convenient way to handle inequality constraints. Penalty function offers one meaningful way to cope with the problem.

2. The Method of Valentine

Valentine [V1] showed in 1937 that by introducing some extra variables, the inequality constraints on the control variables are converted into equality constraints.*

Suppose that in a system $\dot{x} = f(x, u, t)$ there are r components u_j, $j = 1, \ldots, r$, each of which is subjected to the inequality constraint

$$-U_j' \le u_j \le U_j; \quad U_j, U_j' \ge 0 \tag{13-94}$$

We can convert these to a set of equality constraints through introducing r extra variables $\nu_j(t)$, $j = 1, \ldots, r$, and stipulating that at each time t, $t_1 \le t \le t_2$, the expression

$$\left(u_j(t) + U_j'\right)\left(U_j - u_j(t)\right) - \nu_j^2(t) = 0 \tag{13-95}$$

is satisfied. Note that $\nu_j(t)$ is a variable which is forced to vanish whenever $u_j(t)$ reaches either of its limits $-U_j'$ or U_j. When $u_j(t)$ lies in between these limits, then $\nu_j(t)$ assumes finite values and in a sense takes up the slack created by the $u_j(t)$'s not reaching their limits. For example, $u_j(t) = 0$, $\nu_j(t)$ has the magnitude of $\sqrt{U_j'U_j}$.

Having specified $\nu_j(t)$ as in (13-95) and thereby creating an equality-type constraint, the remaining steps involved in producing the Euler-Lagrange equations are quite straightforward. In particular, we can introduce r extra variables $x_{n+r+1}, \ldots, x_{n+2r}$ such that

$$\dot{x}_{n+r+j} = \nu_j(t), \quad j = 1, \ldots, r \tag{13-96}$$

In addition, we can define r quantities $\zeta_j(u_j)$,

$$\zeta_j(u_j) = \left(u_j(t) + U_j'\right)\left(U_j - u_j(t)\right) - \nu_j^2(t) = 0, \; j = 1, \ldots, r \tag{13-97}$$

When this is done, these quantities become similar to the quantity $\zeta(u)$ of the previous section and we should then be able to handle them accordingly. Thus, we can introduce, in addition to the usual n Lagrange multipliers $\psi_1(t), \ldots, \psi_n(t)$, another r multipliers $\lambda_1(t), \ldots, \lambda_r(t)$, and we construct the function

$$L_2 = L + \sum_{i=1}^{n} \psi_i \phi_i + \sum_{j=1}^{r} \lambda_j \zeta_j$$

*As will be shown in the next chapter, the inequality constraints on the control variables are readily handled through the use of the maximum principle. It is not even necessary to introduce extra variables. In reference [D3], another possible method is offered.

and proceed to obtain theEuler-Lagrange equations, etc., much as in the case of the previous section.

Since the u_j's may sometimes reach their upper or lower limit for a finite length of time, the variational investigation can become quite involved. Valentine, however, has shown that the various necessary conditions still hold whenever the problem remains nonsingular.† In particular, the Weierstrass condition holds in the form of (13-89) and leads almost directly to the Pontryagin maximum principle which constitutes the subject of the next chapter.

♦♦Example 13-6. For the aircraft of Example 13-4, suppose that to prevent it from stalling, the magnitude of the angle of attack must be constrained such that $|\alpha(t)| \leq \alpha_{max}$. Find the necessary conditions for the minimum time-of-flight problem.

Here, introducing an additional variable $\nu(t)$ and a multiplier $\lambda(t)$, we define a new derivative $\dot{x}_7 = \nu(t)$, $x_7(0) = 0$ and a constraining relationship

$$\zeta(\alpha, \nu) = \left(\alpha(t) + \alpha_{max}\right)\left(\alpha_{max} - \alpha(t)\right) - \nu^2(t) = 0 \tag{13-98}$$

From these, we form

$$L_2 = \sum_{i=1}^{5} \psi_i \phi_i + \lambda\zeta(\alpha, \nu).$$

On carrying out the calculations we find that the first five Euler-Lagrange equations remain unchanged from those of (13-47). In addition, we have two further equations

$$\left.\frac{\partial L_2}{\partial \alpha}\right|_{\alpha=\alpha*} = 0 \quad \text{and} \quad \left.\frac{\partial L_2}{\partial \nu}\right|_{\nu=\nu*} = 0 \tag{13-99}$$

The second equation in (13-99) yields

$$\lambda^*(t)\,\nu^*(t) \equiv 0, \quad 0 \leq t \leq T \tag{13-100}$$

in view of which, we see that the transversality condition will not change from that given in Example 13-4.

From (13-100), let us note that over a given section of a trajectory, three possibilities exist:

1) $\lambda^* \equiv 0$ and $\nu^* \neq 0$
2) $\lambda^* \equiv 0$ and $\nu^* \equiv 0$
3) $\lambda^* \neq 0$ and $\nu^* \equiv 0$

†See Chap. 16 for a discussion of the singular problem in control.

In the first case, from the definition of the variable $\nu(t)$, we see that $\alpha(t)$ must assume a value between α_{max} and $-\alpha_{max}$. In cases (2) and (3), $\alpha(t)$ is either equal to $+\alpha_{max}$ or $-\alpha_{max}$, and a bang-bang solution is indicated.

The question of which of the modes of control should apply over a given time interval must be settled by a more detailed look at the system solution. Frequently the Weierstrass condition can be helpful. (See Exercise 13-9.)

When a bang-bang solution is indicated, then at each switching instant, the variable $\alpha(t) = \dot{\mu}(t)$ in (13-73) becomes discontinuous. By the development in Part 3 of Sec. 13.1 we note that a *corner* occurs for the problem. At each corner, we know that the Weierstrass-Erdmann corner conditions must be satisfied. In the present problem, these conditions take the exact form of (13-20) and (13-21) except that L in the equations must be replaced by L_2, and n is replaced by $n + 2$. The first corner condition stipulates that each $\psi_i(t)$, $i = 1, \ldots, 5$, as well as that the quantity $\lambda(t)\nu^*(t)$ be continuous at the corners.

The second corner condition (13-21) yields the condition (show this) that the quantity $H = \sum_{i=1}^{5} \psi_i^* f_i(x^*, \alpha^*)$ must be continuous at the corners.

The reader may further convince himself that in the present case the Weierstrass condition reduces to

$$H \triangleq \sum_{i=1}^{5} \psi_i^* f_i(\mathbf{x}^*, \alpha^*) \geq \sum_{i=1}^{5} \psi_i^* f_i(\mathbf{x}^*, \alpha) \tag{13-101}$$

subject to the constraining equation (13-98), which is merely a statement of the requirement that $|\alpha(t)| \leq \alpha_{max}$. The Weierstrass condition thus implies that the rhs of (13-101) must be maximized subject to $|\alpha(t)| \leq \alpha_{max}$. This turns out to be a statement of the maximum principle as we shall see in the next chapter.

The fact that $\sum_{i=1}^{5} \psi_i^* f_i(\mathbf{x}^*, \alpha^*) \equiv 1$ as given in (13-80) is also frequently useful. The appearance of extra variables $\lambda(t)$ and $\nu(t)$ adds complexity to the problem. In the maximum principle formulation in the next chapter, we shall show that these variables need not be used. ♦♦

13.6 Summary

A large class of optimal control problems can be attacked by calculus of variations, which furnishes a series of necessary conditions to be satisfied by the optimal trajectories. The necessary conditions are (1) the Euler-Lagrange equations (Eq. (13-11) or (13-17)), (2) the Legendre condition (pp. 505 and 506), (3) the Weierstrass condition (pp. 508 and 509), and (4) the Jacobi condition, which is not considered in this text. Of these, the Euler-Lagrange equations and the Legendre condition must be satisfied by a trajectory that yields a weak local minimum (Sec. 13.1). The Weierstrass condition must be satisfied by a trajectory that yields a strong local minimum.

The necessary conditions can serve to narrow the search for the optimal trajectories. In most cases, the Euler-Lagrange equations, the Weierstrass condition (which implies the Legendre condition), and the Jacobi condition constitute a sufficient condition that a piecewise smooth function $\mathbf{x}(t)$ is an optimal trajectory.*

Calculus of variations can be extended to problems involving systems of differential equations through the use of the multiplier rule of Euler-Lagrange (Theorem 13-1). The classical treatment of calculus of variations does not admit a control variable u. This can, however, be remedied by defining an extra variable $x_{n+1}(t)$ such that $\dot{x}_{n+1}(t) = u(t)$. By this device, the class of linear optimal control problems with a performance index that is an integral of a quadratic positive definite function in $\mathbf{x}$ and $\mathbf{u}$ can now be solved. Section 13.2 deals with this class of systems.

The optimal control problems involving performance indices that are integrals are known as the problem of Lagrange; this class of problems can be treated by calculus of variations. In addition, calculus of variations can be employed to attack the class of final value optimal control problems known as the problem of Mayer (Sec. 13.3), as well as the class of problems with the combined features of the problem of Lagrange and the problem of Mayer, known as the problem of Bolza.

When the control variables are bounded in accordance with Eq. (13-94), a method proposed by Valentine can be used. Basically the method calls for the introduction of a sufficient number of "slack" variables in accordance with Eq. (13-96) and (13-97). From then on, the usual approaches can be used. Whether or not the control variables reach the limits can generally be determined from the Weierstrass condition.

On applying the various necessary conditions on a nontrivial problem, we obtain a two-point boundary value problem involving $2n$ differential equations. Only in rare instances can they be solved outright. Usually, numerical methods must be employed.

13.7 Exercises

13-1 The function of two variables $f(x_1, x_2)$ possess partial derivatives up to the third order with respect to its arguments.

*This point is not brought out in the text proper as we will consider sufficient conditions for optimality again in the next chapter.

Show that at each local minimum point not located on a boundary of f, the matrix $\left[\partial^2 f/\partial x_i \partial x_j\right]$ must be positive semi-definite.

13-2 The function $f(u) = \psi u - |u|$ is valid over the range $-1 \le u \le 1$. Find the value of u in this range at which $f(u)$ takes on its maximum value. Do this as a function of ψ. (We will use the result in the next chapter.)

13-3 Find the trajectory passing through the points $x(0) = 1$ and $x(1) = 0$ that minimizes the functional

$$\mathcal{J} = \int_0^1 \frac{\sqrt{1 + \dot{x}^2}}{x}\, dt$$

Test the result relative to the Legendre and the Weierstrass conditions.

13-4 Find a trajectory satisfying the Euler-Lagrange equation relative to the functional

$$\mathcal{J} = \int_0^1 (\dot{x}^4 - 6\dot{x}^2)\, dt$$

and satisfying the boundary conditions $x(0) = 0$, $x(1) = 0$. Does the resultant trajectory satisfy the Weierstrass condition? If not, find a trajectory that does.

13-5 A uniform rope of per unit density ρ is suspended from two fixed points (x_1, y_1) and (x_2, y_2) such that it is only acted upon by gravity.

a) Show that the potential energy of the rope is given by

$$\phi = \rho g \int_{x_1}^{x_2} y \sqrt{1 + \frac{dy^2}{dx}}\, dx$$

where $y(x)$ gives the height of the rope as a function of the horizontal distance x.

b) The equilibrium position $y^*(x)$ of the rope is one that minimizes the potential energy ϕ. Find $y^*(x)$ under the constraint that the length of the rope is L.

13-6 For the problem given in Exercise 13-5, if the right end of the rope must lie on a line with slope $-m$, $m > 0$, find the slope at which the rope meets the line.

13-7 For the first-order plant $\dot{x} = -ax + bu, \quad a, b > 0$

a) Set up the Euler-Lagrange equations relevant to the problem of finding the optimum control function $u^*(t)$ that minimizes

$$\mathcal{J} = \int_0^\infty (x^2 + u^2)\, dt$$

for arbitrary initial conditions.

b) Find the optimum feedback control function $u^*(x)$.

13-8 For the system of Exercise 13-7, suppose

$$\mathcal{J} = \int_0^T (x^2 + u^2)\, dt$$

where T is finite and the final state is free; discuss the possibility of finding the optimum feedback control function in this case through the finding of a function $p(t)$ such that $u(t) = -p(t)x(t)$, $0 \leq t \leq t$.

a) Find the functional form of $p(t)$.

b) Find a differential equation that $p(t)$ must satisfy. Specify the boundary conditions.

13-9 Consider again the time-optimal control of the system $\ddot{x} = u$ from an arbitrary x_0 to the origin with $|u(t)| \leq 1$

a) Using the method of Valentine, set up the necessary conditions derived from the Euler-Lagrange equations.

b) Go as far as practicable toward solving the equations.

c) Check the corner conditions if the need arises.

13-10 (The sounding rocket problem or the Goddard problem). The equation of motion of a vertically launched rocket is approximated by $\ddot{x} + kx^2 + g = u(t)$, $k, g > 0$, where x is the height of the rocket from the launch pad. The thrust u is constrained to $0 \leq u \leq U$ and, moreover, there is a total fuel constraint

$$\int_0^T u(t)\, dt = b$$

where T is free. The goal of control is to find $u(t)$ for $0 \leq t \leq T$ so as to maximize the velocity of the rocket at the time T.

a) Set up the problem in the form suitable for the methods considered in this chapter.
b) Find the Euler-Lagrange equation, the Weierstrass condition, and the transversality condition for the problem.

13-11 For the first-order system $\dot{x} = u^2$, $|u| \leq 1$, a time optimal solution to any state is clearly $u = +1$.

a) Show that the given solution does not satisfy the Weierstrass condition for $L_1 = \psi(\dot{x} - u^2)$.
b) Show, however, that if $L_1 = \psi(\dot{x} - u^2) + \lambda(1 - u^2 - \nu^2)$ (which results if the approach of Valentine is used) then the Weierstrass condition will be satisfied.

13-12 Show that the Weierstrass condition, Eq. (13-32) is satisfied for the strong variation (13-28).

13-13 Suppose an optimization problem in the Lagrange form is such that a trajectory must start from a surface $\rho_1(\mathbf{x}_1) = 0$ and end on a surface $\rho_2(\mathbf{x}_2) = 0$; find the relevant transversality condition for

a) a first-order system
b) an nth-order system.

13-14 (Zermelo's problem). Consider a motorboat moving on a stream with coordinates x_1, x_2 whose current is such that the x_1 and x_2 components of the velocity are describable by the functions $f_1(x_1, x_2, t)$ and $f_2(x_1, x_2, t)$. Assume that the boat travels with a constant velocity V with respect to the water. The only variable that can be manipulated instantaneously is the angle θ of the velocity vector with respect to the x_1 axis. Thus the equations of motion are

$$\dot{x}_1 = f_1(x_1, x_2, t) + V \cos\theta, \qquad \dot{x}_2 = f_1(x_1, x_2, t) + V \sin\theta$$

Determine explicitly the Euler-Lagrange equations and the Weierstrass condition for the problem if the boat is to move from the point $\mathbf{x}_0$ to the point $\mathbf{x}_f$ in the minimum time. Do this for

a) no constraints on the magnitude of θ
b) $|\theta(t)| \leq \theta_{max}$
c) $\dot{\theta}(t) = 0$ (i.e., choose a constant θ^* to satisfy the conditions of the problem)

13-15 Show that the problem of Lagrange can be transformed to a problem of Mayer and vice versa.

13-16 It can be shown that the velocity v_{b0} (at second-stage burnout) of a vertically ascending two-stage rocket can be given by

$$v_{b0} = k_1 ln \frac{1}{l_1 + s_1} + k_2 ln \frac{1}{l_2 + s_2}$$

where l_i and s_i, $i = 1, 2$, are the respective ratios of the mass of the useful portion and of the useless portion (i.e., that portion taken up by structural members, fuel, etc.) of the payload to the full mass for the ith stage. Find the value of l_1, subject to $l_1 l_2 =$ constant, that maximizes v_{b0}. What is the physical meaning of the constraint $l_1 l_2 =$ constant?

13-17 Consider a plant given by $\ddot{y}(t) = k_1 u(t)$; design a feedback control for the plant such that the integral-square error

$$\int_0^\infty \left(r(t) - y(t)\right)^2 dt$$

is minimized relative to a $r(t)$ which is a step input applied at $t = 0$. The solution must be such that the constraint

$$\int_0^\infty u^2(t)\, dt = k_2$$

is observed.

13.8 References

Two of the best elementary books on calculus of variations are [E1] and [P2]. A deeper treatment which includes a statement and proof of the multiplier rule for the problem of Lagrange is [A2]. A comprehensive and definitive treatment of calculus of variations as applied to control problems is [H9].

An enlightening treatment of the problem of Mayer from an intuitive viewpoint can be found in [C4].

Many stimulating examples that can be solved by calculus of variations can be found in [L12]. [T3] also includes a good treatment of calculus of variations for engineers.

For the theoretical development of calculus of variation as applied to differential systems, the reader should consult [M8]. McShane in the paper proved the multiplier rule in a general form. The mathematical techniques used foreshadowed the proof of the maximum principle by Pontryagin, et al. [H9] consolidates most of the results of these papers.

For other theoretical background and a comprehensive treatment of the problem of Bolza, refer to the rather difficult treatise [B11].

14

The Maximum Principle of Pontryagin

In 1956 Bellman, Glicksberg, and Gross [B7] treated the time-optimal control problem for a linear plant in a novel geometrical way. They considered the problem in the state space in terms of the set of reachable points. By showing that these sets are convex in shape and expanding with time, they were able to prove that the optimal solution for the problem must of necessity be bang-bang in form. They also proved that for a plant with real negative poles each component of the control function can have at most $n - 1$ switches in polarity, where n as usual is the order of the linear plant to be controlled. While the problem treated by Bellman, et al. was not the most general one in optimal control, they did manage to indicate a very fruitful path for subsequent research. Using essentially the same line of reasoning, LaSalle extended the results to the case of the time-varying linear plant. Finally, Halkin and others showed that the maximum principle of Pontryagin can also be derived through using this approach.

As it happened, the maximum principle was advanced in 1956 by Pontryagin in Russia. It is particularly useful in treating problems such as the time-optimal types, which are relatively difficult to handle using calculus of variations.

In this chapter we try to bring together the geometrical approaches of Bellman et al., and LaSalle and the results of the maximum principle.* We feel that in this way we not only can view the optimal control problem from a radically different and perhaps more natural viewpoint than that obtained from the calculus of variation approach, but can also gain greater appreciation of the result of Pontryagin.

Our exposition begins with a consideration of the approach of Bellman et al. Next we mention the many contributions of LaSalle.

*Our approach is strongly influenced by the work of Halkin.

Finally we shall treat the maximum principle of Pontryagin and indicate its applications for many types of problems.

The derivation of the maximum principle to be used here employs only strong variations. This bypasses the typical, partly weak-variation and partly strong-variation derivations for classical calculus of variations. Aside from this, it introduces a Hamiltonian point of view, which is advantageous in that many extraneous variables and equations can now be avoided. Such a viewpoint is not new,* but, by the compact statement of the maximum principle, the theorems are streamlined and rendered more succinct. Finally, more geometrical insight is imparted to the problem, giving further perspective to the resultant two-point boundary value problem.

14.1 Solution of a Special Time-Optimal Control Problem and Its Geometric Interpretation

Consider the linear time-invariant plant

$$\dot{\mathbf{x}} = \mathbf{A}\mathbf{x} + \mathbf{B}\mathbf{u} \tag{14-1}$$

with initial condition $\mathbf{x}(t_1) = \mathbf{x}_1$.

Assume that $\mathbf{A}$ *has nonrepeating real and negative eigenvalues. Assume further that* $\mathbf{B}$ *is an* $n \times n$ *nonsingular matrix* $[b_{ij}]$ *and thus* $\mathbf{u}(t)$ *is an* n *vector.* Without loss of generality, let us further assume that $t_1 = 0$, and, moreover, that the problem is suitably scaled so that the constraint $|u_i| \leq 1$ is imposed on the control function $\mathbf{u}(t)$.

The problem is to find a $\mathbf{u}^*(t)$ subject to the above constraint such that the state $\mathbf{x}(t)$, starting at $\mathbf{x}_1$ with $t = 0$, reaches the origin in the (absolute) minimum time. When this $\mathbf{u}^*(t)$ is found, we call it the *time-optimal* control function.

We first cast the system into the canonical form. Here, $\mathbf{A}$ becomes the diagonal matrix of the eigenvalues Λ. Corresponding to this system, the solution will be:

$$x_i(t) = x_i(0)e^{\lambda_i t} + e^{\lambda_i t}\int_0^t e^{-\lambda_i \tau} \sum_{j=1}^{n} b_{ij}u_j(\tau)\,d\tau\,, \quad i = 1, \ldots, n \tag{14-2}$$

With $\mathbf{B}$ nonsingular, it is possible to establish that the problem does have a solution, that is, there exists an *admissible control*

*Hestenes uses the Hamiltonian point of view in 1949 on minimum time problems as cited in Sec. 13.3 of the previous chapter.

function (i.e., one which satisfies the constraint $|u_i| \le 1$) which can carry out the stipulations of the problem.

By inspection of (14-2) we see that the existence of an admissible control function $\mathbf{u}(t)$ which can drive the state from $\mathbf{x}_1$ to 0 is equivalent to the existence of functions $u_i(t)$ for $0 \le t \le t_2$, and $i = 1, \ldots, n$ satisfying the constraint $|u_i(t)| \le 1$ and the existence of a time t_2 such that

$$x_i(t_2) = 0 = x_i(0)e^{\lambda_i t_2} + e^{\lambda_i t_2} \int_0^{t_2} e^{-\lambda_i \tau} \sum_{j=1}^{n} b_{ij} u_j(\tau)\, d\tau \qquad i = 1, \ldots, n \tag{14-3}$$

or, equivalently,

$$-x_i(0) = \int_0^{t_2} e^{-\lambda_i \tau} \sum_{j=1}^{n} b_{ij} u_j(\tau)\, d\tau\,, \quad i = 1, \ldots, n \tag{14-4}$$

It is readily established that, as $\mathbf{B}$ is nonsingular, for every $\mathbf{x}(0)$, there exist constant admissible values of $u_j(t)$ ($|u_j| \le 1$) and a time t_2 that can fulfill (14-4).

With the existence of an admissible control function for the problem thus assured, the next task is to find the best admissible control function for the problem. In our case we wish to find an optimal control function such that t_2 in (14-4) is minimized.

Let the range of values that all admissible control functions $\mathbf{u}(t)$ can assume be designated by the set $\mathfrak{U}$ which in our case can be visualized as an n-dimensional cube $|u_i| \le 1$ in an n-dimensional Euclidean space.

A cube of any dimension has the property that any two points within it can be joined by a straight line every point of which also lies in the cube. Any set of points with this property is called a *convex set*.

Mathematically a convex set is a set of points such that if points $\mathbf{a}$ and $\mathbf{b}$ lie in the set, then all the points on the line $\alpha\mathbf{a} + (1 - \alpha)\mathbf{b}$ for all α obeying $0 \le \alpha \le 1$ also belong to the set. Thus in Fig. 14-1, (a) and (b) are two-dimensional convex sets, and (c) is not a convex set. In the following, convex sets defined in suitable spaces will play important roles.

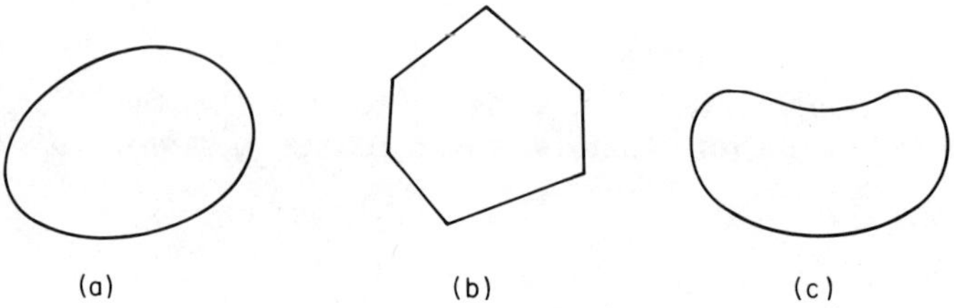

Fig. 14-1. The sets (a) and (b) are convex, the set (c) is not convex.

For simplicity in notation let us also designate the set of all admissible $\mathbf{u}(t)$ defined over the closed-time interval from 0 to t as the set Ω_t.

Consider Eq. (14-4). For each choice of an admissible $\mathbf{u}(\tau)$ over $0 \leq \tau \leq t_2$, a vector $\mathbf{x}(0)$ will result, which represents the initial state which can be driven to the origin by the particular choice of $\mathbf{u}(\tau)$. For all possible choices of admissible $\mathbf{u}(\tau)$ over $0 \leq \tau \leq t_2$, then, it is *possible* to visualize that the totality of corresponding vectors $\mathbf{x}(0)$ will form a *reachable set* $\mathcal{C}(t_2)$ in the system state space. Viewed in another way, $\mathcal{C}(t_2)$ may be regarded as the result of a transformation (14-4) which takes all $\mathbf{u}(\tau)$ from the admissible set Ω_t to the n-dimensional Euclidean state space.

We can make use of a standard shorthand notation and write $\mathcal{C}(t_2)$ as

$$\mathcal{C}(t_2) = \left\{ -\int_0^{t_2} e^{-\Lambda\tau} \mathbf{B}\, \mathbf{u}(\tau)\, d\tau \; : \; \mathbf{u} \in \Omega_{t_2} \right\} \tag{14-5}$$

where the rhs of (14-5) reads: "the set of all points generated by $-\int_0^{t_2} e^{-\Lambda\tau} \mathbf{B}\, \mathbf{u}(\tau)\, d\tau$ with $\mathbf{u}$ belonging to the set Ω_{t_2}."

We can now show that *with* $\mathbf{u}(\tau)$ *chosen from the admissible set* Ω_{t_2} *the reachable set* $\mathcal{C}(t_2)$ *will be convex*. This is so because if $\mathbf{p}_1(t_2)$ and $\mathbf{p}_2(t_2)$ are points reachable through the choice of $\mathbf{u}_1(\tau)$ and $\mathbf{u}_2(\tau)$ $(0 \leq \tau \leq t_2)$ respectively, i.e., if the components of $\mathbf{p}_1(t_2)$ and $\mathbf{p}_2(t_2)$ are defined by

$$p_{1i}(t_2) = \int_0^{t_2} e^{-\lambda_i\tau} \sum_{j=1}^{n} b_{ij} u_{1j}(\tau)\, d\tau\,, \quad i = 1, \ldots, n$$

$$p_{2i}(t_2) = \int_0^{t_2} e^{-\lambda_i\tau} \sum_{j=1}^{n} b_{ij} u_{2j}(\tau)\, d\tau\,, \quad i = 1, \ldots, n \tag{14-6}$$

then the points lying in the line joining $\mathbf{p}_1(t_2)$ and $\mathbf{p}_2(t_2)$ are those with coordinates

$$\alpha p_{1i}(t_2) + (1-\alpha) p_{2i}(t_2) = \int_0^{t_2} e^{-\lambda_i\tau} \sum_{j=1}^{n} b_{ij}[\alpha u_{1j}(\tau) + (1-\alpha) u_{2j}(\tau)]\, d\tau$$

$$i = 1, \ldots, n$$

or

$$\alpha \mathbf{p}_1(t_2) + (1-\alpha)\mathbf{p}_2(t_2) = \int_0^{t_2} e^{-\Lambda\tau}\mathbf{B}[\alpha\mathbf{u}_1(\tau) + (1-\alpha)\mathbf{u}_2(\tau)]\, d\tau \tag{14-7}$$

for all $0 \leq \alpha \leq 1$. The function $\alpha \mathbf{u}_1(\tau) + (1 - \alpha)\mathbf{u}_2(\tau)$ is clearly an admissible control for all α, thus proving our assertion.

Examining now the set $\mathcal{C}(t)$ as a function of t, we see that at $t = 0$ it consists only of the point $\mathbf{0}$, but as t increases, $\mathcal{C}(t)$ grows monotonically. (Show this.) At any time t, the set $\mathcal{C}(t)$ then consists of all those initial points $\mathbf{x}(0)$ which can be transferred to the origin in time t or less by some choice of admissible control function $\mathbf{u}(\tau)$ where $0 \leq \tau \leq t$.

As $\mathcal{C}(t)$ is a monotonically growing set, then for a particular initial condition $\mathbf{x}(0)$, the minimum time must be that time t^* such that the set $\mathcal{C}(t^*)$ just touches the point $\mathbf{x}(0)$.†

For a given admissible control function $\mathbf{u}(\tau)$, $0 \leq \tau \leq t$, let $\mathbf{x}(\mathbf{u}, t) = -\int_0^t e^{-\Lambda t}\mathbf{B}\mathbf{u}(\tau)\,d\tau$. From (14-5) $\mathbf{x}(\mathbf{u}, t) \in \mathcal{C}(t)$. It is a consequence of the growing closed and convex set $\mathcal{C}(t)$ that, when $\mathcal{C}(t)$ does not contain $\mathbf{x}(0)$, one can always find a vector $\boldsymbol{\eta}_t$ such that for any point $\mathbf{x}(\mathbf{u}, t)$ of $\mathcal{C}(t)$, the following inequality holds:

$$\left(\boldsymbol{\eta}_t^T \mathbf{x}(\mathbf{u}, t)\right) \leq \left(\boldsymbol{\eta}_t^T \mathbf{x}(0)\right) \tag{14-8}$$

In particular, geometrically $\boldsymbol{\eta}_t$ can be the vector that is the outward normal to the supporting plane of $\mathcal{C}(t)$ at the point where the vector $\mathbf{x}(0)$ pierces the convex set $\mathcal{C}(t)$.†† (See Fig. 14-2a.)

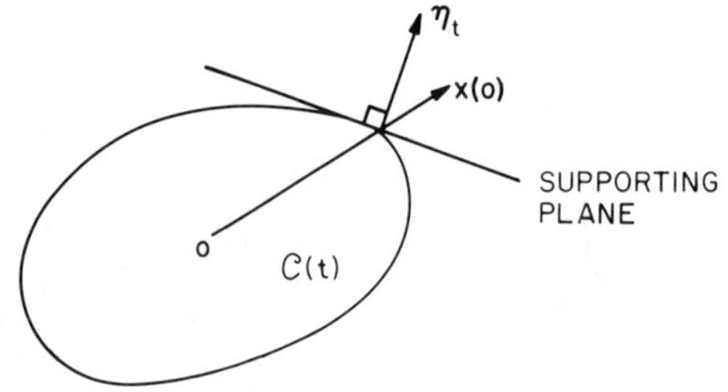

Fig. 14-2a. The geometry of the reachable set $\mathcal{C}(t)$ and the point $\mathbf{x}(0)$ when $\mathcal{C}(t)$ does not contain $\mathbf{x}(0)$. Here Eq. (14-8) will be seen to hold.

†To be mathematically correct it must be shown that the set $\mathcal{C}(t)$ is a closed set in order to guarantee that $\mathbf{x}(t)$ will at some time just "touch" $\mathbf{x}(0)$. Basically, a closed set is one which contains all of its boundary points where the boundary points of a set $\mathcal{C}(t)$ are all those points $\mathbf{p}$ in $\mathcal{E}_n$ such that for any number ϵ, however small, there is a point $\mathbf{p}_1$ in $\mathcal{C}$ and a point $\mathbf{p}_2$ not in $\mathcal{C}$ such that $||\mathbf{p}_1 - \mathbf{p}||$ and $||\mathbf{p}_2 - \mathbf{p}||$ are both less than ϵ. Bellman et al., proved that $\mathcal{C}(t)$ is closed through the use of a theorem concerning Banach space. For our case from practical considerations, it is perhaps quite plausible that $\mathcal{C}(t)$ is closed.

††The reader can demonstrate to himself that through each point on the boundary of a convex set at least one supporting plane, defined as a plane so positioned that the entire convex set lies wholly on one side of the plane, can always be passed. An outward normal to the supporting plane is that normal which points toward the side of the plane that contains no point of the convex set.

In the limit as $t \to t^*$, the minimum time, we will still have

$$\left(\eta_{t^*}{}^T x(u, t^*)\right) \leq \left(\eta_{t^*}{}^T x(0)\right) \qquad (14\text{-}9)$$

Now since $x(u^*, t^*) = x(0)$ by definition, we will have

$$\left(\eta_{t^*}{}^T x(u, t^*)\right) \leq \left(\eta_{t^*}{}^T x(u^*, t^*)\right) \qquad (14\text{-}10)$$

where η_{t^*}, following the above, is seen to be the vector which is the outward normal to the supporting plane of the convex set $\mathcal{C}(t^*)$ at the point $x(0)$. (See Fig. 14-2b.) We will henceforth designate the vector η_{t^*} as η.

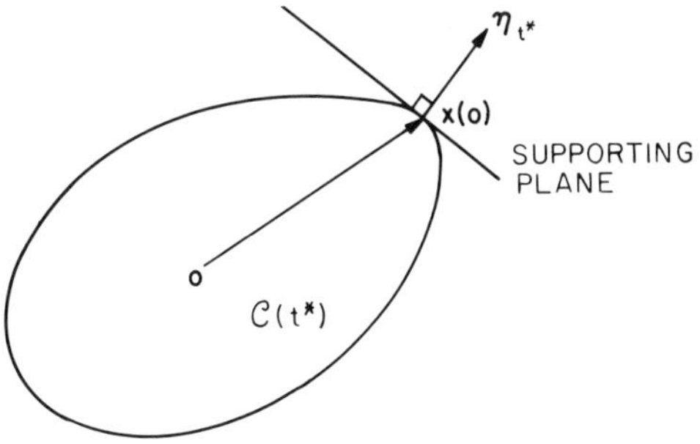

Fig. 14-2b. When $\mathcal{C}(t)$ just touches $x(0)$, Eq. (14-9) holds. The vector $\eta_t{}^*$ is the outward normal to the supporting plane of the convex set $\mathcal{C}(t)$ at the point $x(0)$.

From (14-10) and (14-4) we reach the important conclusion that the time-optimal control function is that control function $u^*(t)$ which maximizes

$$\sum_{i=1}^{n} \eta_i \int_0^{t^*} e^{-\lambda_i \tau} \sum_{j=1}^{n} b_{ij} u_j(\tau)\, d\tau \qquad (14\text{-}11)$$

By an interchanging of summation and integration, (14-11) becomes

$$\sum_{j=1}^{n} \int_0^{t^*} \left(\sum_{i=1}^{n} \eta_i b_{ij} e^{-\lambda_i \tau} \right) u_j(\tau) d\tau \qquad (14\text{-}12)$$

which is maximized only when

$$u_j^*(\tau) = \operatorname{sgn} \left[\sum_{i=1}^{n} \eta_i b_{ij} e^{-\lambda_i \tau} \right], \quad j = 1, \ldots, n$$

or

$$\mathbf{u}^*(t) = \operatorname{sgn}\left[\eta^T e^{-\Lambda\tau}\mathbf{B}\right]^T \tag{14-13}$$

Thus, whenever none of the components of the vector $\mathbf{g}(\tau) \triangleq (\eta^T e^{-\Lambda\tau}\mathbf{B})^T$ *becomes identically zero for any finite length of time,* $\mathbf{u}^*(\tau)$ *is a bang-bang control function.*

Now each component of the vector function $\mathbf{g}(\tau)$ is seen to consist of a linear combination of n decaying exponentials; then, by a result sometimes known as Descartes' rule, each component of $\mathbf{g}(\tau)$ can have at most $n - 1$ real zeros.† Thus each $u_i^*(t)$ will switch at most $n - 1$ times for distinct real roots.

Let us pause at this point to note that two important conjectures of the time-optimal control problem as mentioned in Chap. 12, namely, (i) the bang-bang conjecture and (ii) the $n - 1$ switching conjecture for a linear plant with real eigenvalues, have been readily shown for our particular case by the above geometrical reasoning. But we should, at the same time, note that the system considered in this section is a rather restrictive one. In particular $\mathbf{u}(t)$ is assumed to be n-dimensional and $\mathbf{B}$ is required to be nonsingular. This condition is violated, for example, by the simplest control system such as one with a single driving function controlling an nth order plant. Finally, we note that the approach is only useful for an nth order system with negative nonrepeating real roots.

It remained for J. P. LaSalle [L5] to remove these restricting assumptions and to shed important light on the aspects of controllability and uniqueness of controls. We consider some of his main results in the next section.

14.2 Time-Optimal Control for the General Linear System

In the previous section the assumption that $\mathbf{B}$ is an $n \times n$ nonsingular matrix is only needed to prove the existence of an admissible solution. If this restrictive assumption is removed with the hope that we can establish existence of control functions through some other means, we can significantly generalize our treatment of time-optimal control problems for linear systems [L5].

Consider the general time-invariant nth order linear system

$$\dot{\mathbf{x}} = \mathbf{A}\mathbf{x} + \mathbf{B}\mathbf{u}, \quad \mathbf{x}(0) = \mathbf{x}_0$$

†For an inductive proof see [P8] p. 122.

where we now let B be an aribitrary $n \times r$ constant matrix and $|u_j(t)| \leq 1,\ j = 1, \ldots, r$. In the canonical form corresponding to (14-4) then, we have

$$-x_i(0) = \int_0^{t_2} e^{-\lambda_i \tau} \sum_{j=1}^{r} b_{ij} u_j(\tau)\, d\tau \ , \qquad i = 1, \ldots, n \qquad \text{(14-14)}$$

Skipping over the existence question, we can parallel the development of the previous section to show that the reachable set $\mathcal{C}(t)$ in this case is also convex. (Show this.) Indeed using the same line of argument the convexity of $\mathcal{C}(t)$ can even be established for a time-varying system. Again we can merely say that it is plausible that the set $\mathcal{C}(t)$ should be closed.

LaSalle addressed himself to the time-optimal control of the general time-varying linear system

$$\dot{\mathbf{x}} = \mathbf{A}(t)\mathbf{x} + \mathbf{B}(t)\mathbf{u} \ , \quad \mathbf{x}(0) = \mathbf{x}_0 \qquad \text{(14-15)}$$

with $\mathbf{B}(t)$ an arbitrary $n \times r$ time-varying matrix. One of LaSalle's main contributions is to prove that $\mathcal{C}(t)$, even in the case of a time-varying linear system, besides being convex, is also closed. Moreover, he showed that the reachable set of the system with $\mathbf{u}(t)$'s which are exclusively bang-bang is exactly the same as that for the $\mathbf{u}(t)$'s which merely obey the saturation constraint $|u_j(t)| \leq 1,\ j = 1, \ldots, r$.

Using these results, it is not too difficult to prove:

◆◆Theorem 14-1. For the system (14-15), if of all bang-bang control functions which are piecewise continuous†, there is one that drives $\mathbf{x}_0$ to 0 in the least time, then it is a time-optimal control function.◆◆

◆◆Theorem 14-2. If a time-optimal control function exists, then there is always a piecewise continuous bang-bang control function that is time optimal. Moreover, all optimal control functions are of the form

$$\mathbf{u}^*(t) = \operatorname{sgn}\,[\eta^T \Phi^{-1}(t, 0)\, \mathbf{B}(t)]^T \qquad \text{(14-16)}$$

where η is an n-dimensional vector that is not identically equal to the null vector 0.◆◆

Physically, η is again the outward normal to the supporting plane of the convex reachable set $\mathcal{C}(t^*)$ at the point $\mathbf{x}(0)$.

There remain the questions of existence and uniqueness of solutions. It turns out that the question of uniqueness of solutions

†We are quoting results of LaSalle as extended by H. Halkin; see [H4].

can be answered with greater degree of generality than that of existence of solutions.

We note that if *none* of the n-components of the quantity $[\eta^T \Phi^{-1}(t, 0) B(t)]$ should vanish over a finite interval of time when $\eta \neq 0$, then the optimal control $u^*(t)$ can be determined uniquely through (14-16). We shall designate such systems as being controllable in the sense of LaSalle or L-controllable.†

It is instructive to consider time-invariant systems that are L-controllable. Here we require that for $\eta \neq 0$ no component of $\eta^T e^{-At} B$ vanish identically. It turns out, as we will show in Chap. 16, that this is completely equivalent to the condition that *each system state can be directly influenced by each component of the control function.* This is a stronger requirement than complete controllability as given in Chap. 3. A time-invariant system that is completely controllable as we recall has the property that each system state can be directly influenced by at least one component of the control function. This is equivalent to requiring that not all of the n-components of $[\eta^T \Phi^{-1}(t, 0) B(t)]$ vanish identically. Complete controllability is not sufficient to guaranteee the uniqueness of a time-optimal control. This we will discuss further in Chap. 16.

We may note that a linear, completely controllable system with a single input $(r = 1)$ is also L-controllable. Thus if any linear, completely controllable system with a single input has a time optimal solution, it will be unique.

As for the question of existence of solutions, the only meaningful result we can quote pertains to systems with linear time-invariant plants. For this class of systems, LaSalle proved that if the plants are stable and completely controllable, then there always exist time-optimal solutions; this fact we have hinted at in Chap. 12.

The results of LaSalle permit us to see the general form of solutions for stable, completely controllable systems with imaginary eigenvalues; this, as may be recalled, we had difficulty in doing in Chap. 12 using intuitive reasonings.

♦♦Example 14-1. Consider the time-optimal control of an oscillating plant with no damping $\ddot{y} + y = u$. Here, as there is only a single input, and since the system is completely controllable, it is also L-controllable.

Let u be constrained by $|u| \leq U$. With $x_1 = y$ and $x_2 = \dot{y}$, we readily find that

$$\mathbf{A} = \begin{bmatrix} 0 & 1 \\ -1 & 0 \end{bmatrix}, \quad \mathbf{b} = \begin{bmatrix} 0 \\ 1 \end{bmatrix}$$

†This type of system is called normal by LaSalle. Since this use of the terms is different from the calculus of variations usage, we choose not to follow the terminology.

and thus the transition matrix is

$$\Phi(t, 0) = e^{\mathbf{A}t} = \begin{bmatrix} \cos t & \sin t \\ -\sin t & \cos t \end{bmatrix}$$

As the system is stable, it has unique bang-bang time-optimal control of the form (14-16).

Since $g(t) = \eta^T \Phi^{-1}(t, 0)\mathbf{b} = -\eta_1 \sin t + \eta_2 \cos t$, where η_1 and η_2 are the components of the vector η, we have

$$u^*(t) = U \operatorname{sgn}[g(t)] = \begin{cases} +U & \text{if} \quad -\eta_1 \sin t + \eta_2 \cos t > 0 \\ -U & \text{if} \quad -\eta_1 \sin t + \eta_2 \cos t < 0 \end{cases} \tag{14-17}$$

Equation (14-17) seemingly solves the optimal control problem at hand. Unfortunately, since we do not know the shape of $\mathcal{C}(t)$ at each time t, we do not know, for each given $\mathbf{x}(0)$, the value of the components η_1 and η_2 of η. Thus our achievement is somewhat illusory. If we are interested in finding the time-optimal control function $u^*(t)$ as a function of time, given an initial state $\mathbf{x}(0)$, we still have to undertake the following steps:

1) Guess a value of η.
2) Use the control law (14-17) to drive the system from the given point $\mathbf{x}(0)$.
3) If the resulting trajectory passes through the origin $\mathbf{0}$, then it is indeed the optimal control $\mathbf{u}^*(t)$ and hence η is the correct choice.
4) If the resulting trajectory does not pass through the origin, then the η chosen is incorrect and another choice must be made.

Thus we did not succeed in taking the trial and error out of the inherent two-point boundary value problem.

The control law (14-17), however, can help us determine the switching curves for the problem if we make use of the idea developed in Chap. 12, namely, running the system backward from the origin using the optimal control. This, as we have indicated, amounts to the presolving of the optimal control problem.†

The reverse-time system is (with τ as the backward time parameter $\tau = -t$)

†The idea of running time backwards is most useful for second-order systems where all the switching is determined by a switching curve. It is of decreasing usefulness as the order of the system increases.

$$\begin{bmatrix} \dfrac{dx_1}{d\tau} \\ \\ \dfrac{dx_2}{d\tau} \end{bmatrix} = \begin{bmatrix} 0 & -1 \\ \\ 1 & 0 \end{bmatrix} \begin{bmatrix} x_1(\tau) \\ \\ x_2(\tau) \end{bmatrix} + \begin{bmatrix} 0 \\ \\ -1 \end{bmatrix} u(\tau)$$

and the corresponding optimal reverse-time control function is

$$u^*(\tau) = \begin{cases} -U & \text{if} \quad \eta_1 \sin \tau + \eta_2 \cos \tau > 0 \\ +U & \text{if} \quad \eta_1 \sin \tau + \eta_2 \cos \tau < 0 \end{cases} \tag{14-18}$$

If we initially choose $\eta_1 < 0$, $\eta_2 = 0^+$, at $\tau = 0$, then $u^*(0) = +U$. Driving the reverse-time system, we obtain the last portion of the switching curve shown as the curve Γ_1 in Fig. 14-3. It is a circular arc with the point $(U, 0)$ as center. This portion is not surprising, as we have already obtained it with heuristic reasoning in Chap. 12.

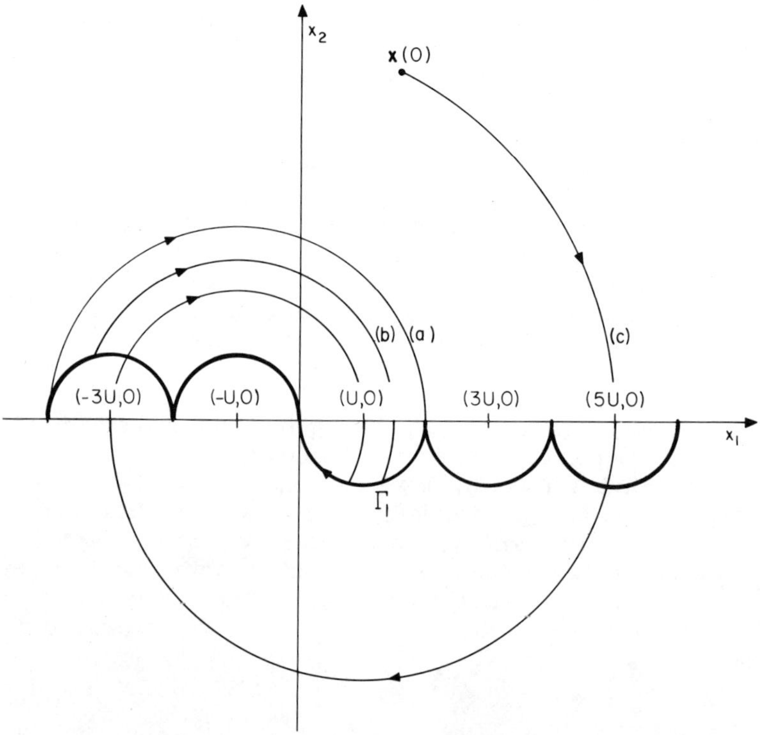

Fig. 14-3. The optimal switching curves of the system of Example 14-1 are the heavy semicircles shown. Above the switching curves $u^* = +U$, below the switching curves $u^* = -U$. Three typical optimal trajectories (a), (b), and (c) are shown.

But at the point $\tau = \pi$ where the backward system state reaches the x_1 axis, $\eta_1 \sin \tau$ changes sign and $u^*(\tau)$ will then switch, and what results will be the semicircle labeled (a) in Fig. 14-3 with the point $(-U, 0)$ as center.

If we choose $\eta_1, \eta_2 < 0$, $\eta_2 < \eta_1$, then initially, the curve Γ_1 will be followed by the system trajectory, but a switching will occur before it returns to the x_1 axis. A typical trajectory after the first switch will be like trajectory (b). As in the case of trajectory (a), the trajectory (b) is a circle with the point $(-U, 0)$ as center.

Two observations can be shown by examining (14-18):

1) The time interval between switching in $u^*(\tau)$ is π seconds.
2) The resulting time-optimal trajectory consists of circular arcs which alternately center about the points $(+U, 0)$ and $(-U, 0)$.

These observations permit us to completely construct the switching boundaries for the reverse time case. To the right of the x_2 axis, the boundaries are seen to be composed of semicircles which lie wholly below the x_1 axis. The centers of the circles are the points $(U, 0)$, $(3U, 0)$, $(5U, 0)$, etc. To the left of the x_2 axis, the switching boundaries lie wholly above the x_1 axis and are composed of semicircles with centers at $(-U, 0)$, $(-3U, 0), \ldots$. The optimal control is such that if the system state lies above the switching boundary, then initially $u^* = -U$; if the system state lies below the switching boundary, then initially $u^* = +U$.

We further see that the number of switchings in $u^*(t)$ in this case is dependent on $\mathbf{x}(0)$.

A typical optimal trajectory from a point $\mathbf{x}(0)$ in forward time is shown as trajectory (c) in Fig. 14-3.

Before leaving this example, it is instructive to examine the uniqueness aspect of the time-optimal solution as given by Eq. (14-17). As we have remarked before, the system under consideration is completely controllable and has only one input variable; it is therefore L-controllable. Thus we expect the solution given by (14-17) to be unique. Let us see if it is indeed so.

We see that $u^*(t) = U \operatorname{sgn}[g(t)]$, with $g(t) = -\eta_1 \sin t + \eta_2 \cos t$. Ambiguity in the sign of $g(t)$ can only arise if $g(t) = 0$ over a finite time interval. But this is possible only if $\eta_1 = \eta_2 = 0$ which violates the requirement that $\boldsymbol{\eta}$ cannot be the zero vector. This latter fact also is clear geometrically since the zero vector $\mathbf{0}$ does not consitute an outward normal vector to any supporting plane of a convex set. ♦♦

14.3 The Maximum Principle of Pontryagin

1. Preliminaries

The topological approaches of Bellman, et al. and LaSalle place us in a position to appreciate the maximum principle of Pontryagin.

The maximum principle was postulated by Pontryagin in 1956. Subsequently the maximum principle was proved by Pontryagin and his co-workers Boltyanskii and Gamkrelidze in a number of papers. Much of these results are now collected in a book [P8].

The maximum principle is useful to the engineer, first, because of the universality of its formulation. Optimization problems of various types are in a sense normalized such that their structures can be examined from a common point of view. This leads, for example, to the derivation of some important sufficiency proofs of the maximum principle.

The second benefit of the maximum principle is derived directly from the first. Once there is community of formulation, whatever insight derived from the examination of one member problem can be extended to apply to the entire class. In particular, using the Bellman-LaSalle-Halkin line of development, we develop added geometrical insight. An important consequence of this is the strong light the maximum principle sheds on the role of the adjoint variable in optimal control studies. It now becomes clear, for example, that the Lagrange multipliers in the calculus of variations and the rather mysterious η vectors in the Bellman-LaSalle formulation of time-optimal control problems are all related to the adjoint vectors. More important still, the geometrical orientation of the adjoint vectors at the end of the control interval always provides the requisite boundary conditions. Finally, the behavior of the adjoint vectors during the control interval generally dictates whether there is abnormal or singular modes of control.

As far as results are concerned, there is, strictly speaking, no important advance over the classical calculus of variations result.* However, through the adoption of the Hamiltonian viewpoint, the maximum principle represents a more efficient procedure than the classical calculus of variations for keeping track of the myriad of necessary and transversality conditions. Efficiency, of course, is a matter of prime concern to the engineers.

2. Formulation of the Problem

Let us at the outset consider a slightly more general version of the problem than that which has been studied in the previous chapter. In particular, for the general nth order system

$$\dot{\mathbf{x}} = \mathbf{f}(\mathbf{x}, \mathbf{u}, t), \quad \mathbf{x}(t_1) = \mathbf{x}_1 \tag{14-19}$$ **

*Except possibly some of the sufficiency proofs as previously noted.

**We assume that $\mathbf{f}(\mathbf{x}, \mathbf{u}, t)$ in (14-19) is a continuous function of $\mathbf{u}$, a piecewise continuous function of t, and is twice continuously differentiable with respect to $\mathbf{x}$. It is possible to prove the maximum principle even when $\mathbf{f}$ is once continuously differentiable with respect to $\mathbf{x}$; however; the proof will be more involved than the one used here.

a control function $\mathbf{u}(t)$ is to be chosen for $t_1 \le t \le t_2$ such that:

1) $\mathbf{u}(t)$ is amplitude constrained in each component. Without loss of generality we can restrict $\mathbf{u}(t)$ to take on the values in or on the r-dimensional unit cube u given by $|u_i(t)| \le 1$, $i = 1, \ldots, r$.
2) The system state vector is to be transferred from the state $\mathbf{x}_1$ at time t_1 to one at the time t_2 where the first m components of the state vector $x_1, \ldots, x_m$ coincide with the m components of a target state $s_1, \ldots, s_m$, $m \le n$ in such a way that a functional

$$\mathcal{J} = \int_{t_1}^{t_2} L(\mathbf{x}, \mathbf{u}, t)\,dt \tag{14-20}$$

is minimized.*

In the formulation above, we have made allowance for certain state variables (namely $x_{m+1}, \ldots, x_n$) to be left free at the end time t_2. As we shall see in some examples, this class of problems is quite common in practice.

Now the above problem can be made even more general by directly incorporating (14-20) into (14-19). This is done by defining an additional state variable x_0 where

$$\dot{x}_0 \equiv L(\mathbf{x}, \mathbf{u}, t) \qquad (14\text{-}21)^{**}$$

Adding (14-20) to (14-19), we can define two augmented $(n+1)$ dimensional vectors $\mathbf{x}'$ and $\mathbf{f}'$ with components $x_0, x_1, \ldots, x_n$, and $L, f_1, f_2, \ldots, f_n$ respectively. We can write the augmented system equations as

$$\dot{\mathbf{x}}' = \mathbf{f}'(\mathbf{x}', \mathbf{u}, t) \tag{14-22}$$

Consider the coordinate x_0, the initial condition for it, in view of (14-20), is $x_0(t_1) = 0$. At $t = t_2$, we have $x_0(t_2) = \mathcal{J}$.

The optimization problem considered in the augmented state space of $n + 1$ dimension can now be stated as follows:

In the $(n+1)$dimensional state space with coordinates x_0, $x_1, \ldots, x_n$ find the admissible control $\mathbf{u}^*(t)$ $(t_1 \le t \le t_2)$ which transfers the system state from its initial position $x_0 = 0$, $\mathbf{x} = \mathbf{x}_1$ to a final state in such a way that $x_i(t_2) = s_i$ for $i = 1, \ldots, m$ and $x_0(t_2)$ takes on its smallest possible value.

*L is assumed to have the same properties as $\mathbf{f}$ in (14-19), see the second footnote on the previous page.

**Note that by Eq. (14-21) we have managed to change a problem of Lagrange to a problem of Mayer.

By the above stratagem, we have evidently transformed an optimal control problem into one which can be considered topologically. Moreover, apparently different problems can now also be transformed into similar problems.

In the above formulation, we note also that the time t_2 can either be given explicitly or be defined implicitly. For example, consider the time-optimal control problem. Here $L \equiv +1$, so that $\mathcal{J}$ becomes $t_2 - t_1$, but t_2 is only defined implicitly.

3. The Statement of the Maximum Principle

Let us introduce an $(n+1)$ dimensional vector† $\boldsymbol{\psi}(t)$ and form the following Hamiltonian function of the four variables $\mathbf{x}'$, $\mathbf{u}$, t, $\boldsymbol{\psi}'$,

$$H(\mathbf{x}', \mathbf{u}, t, \boldsymbol{\psi}') \triangleq \boldsymbol{\psi}'^T(t)\mathbf{f}'(\mathbf{x}', \mathbf{u}, t) \tag{14-23}$$

The maximum principle can now be stated as follows:

◆◆Theorem 14-3 (The Maximum Principle of Pontryagin). Relative to the problem formulated above, if $\mathbf{u}^*(t)$ is the optimal control function of the problem defined in the previous section, and $\mathbf{x}'^*(t)$ is the optimal trajectory corresponding to $\mathbf{u}^*(t)$ via (14-22), then there is a nonzero continuous vector function $\boldsymbol{\psi}'(t)$ such that

1) At any time t (except possibly at points where $\mathbf{f}'$ or $\mathbf{u}$ is discontinuous) the Hamiltonian function evaluated along $\mathbf{x}'^*(t)$ corresponding to the optimal control $\mathbf{u}^*(t)$ is at least as large as that corresponding to any other admissible control function $\mathbf{u}(t)$. That is:

$$H(\mathbf{x}'^*, \mathbf{u}^*, t, \boldsymbol{\psi}') \geq H(\mathbf{x}'^*, \mathbf{u}, t, \boldsymbol{\psi}')$$

2) At any time t (except possibly at points where $\mathbf{f}'$ or $\mathbf{u}$ is discontinuous) the vector $\boldsymbol{\psi}'(t)$ is generated by

$$\dot{\boldsymbol{\psi}}'(t) = -\left.\frac{\partial H(\mathbf{x}', \mathbf{u}^*, t, \boldsymbol{\psi}')}{\partial \mathbf{x}'}\right|_{\mathbf{x}' = \mathbf{x}'^*(t)} \tag{14-24}$$

3) $\psi_i(t_2) = 0$ for $i = m+1, \ldots, n$
4) $\psi_0(t_2) \leq 0$. ◆◆

From (14-24), it is seen that the equation in ψ_0 is of the form $\dot{\psi}_0 = 0$ as none of the functions f_i's are dependent on the coordinate

†$\boldsymbol{\psi}'(t)$ is sometimes called the co-state vector or the covariant vector.

x_0. Thus by condition (4) of the maximum principle above, $\psi_0(t)$ will be a constant with a value that is negative or 0.

In the event that the final time t_2 is not specified in advance, we need an additional condition to be imposed on the system in order to ensure solution. This condition is

$$H(\mathbf{x}'^*, \mathbf{u}^*, t_2, \boldsymbol{\psi}') = 0 \qquad \text{(for } t_2 \text{ not specified in advance)} \tag{14-25}$$

That is, the Hamiltonian function corresponding to the optimal control must vanish at the (unspecified) time t_2.

For this, we may infer another interesting fact for the case where H is independent of time. This will be so if the system to be controlled and the criterion function L are both time-invariant.

Let us denote the Hamiltonian function corresponding to the optimal $\mathbf{u}$ as $H^*(\mathbf{x}', \boldsymbol{\psi}', t)$ and let us consider $[dH^*(\mathbf{x}', \boldsymbol{\psi}', t)]/dt$ along the optimal trajectory

$$\frac{dH^*}{dt} = \sum_{i=0}^{n} \frac{\partial H^*}{\partial x_i} \dot{x}_i^* + \sum_{i=0}^{n} \frac{\partial H^*}{\partial \psi_i} \dot{\psi}_i + \frac{\partial H^*}{\partial t} \tag{14-26}$$

From (14-23) and (14-24), we have

$$\frac{\partial H^*}{\partial x_i} = -\dot{\psi}_i \,, \qquad \frac{\partial H^*}{\partial \psi_i} = +\dot{x}_i^* \tag{14-27}$$

Substituting (14-27) into (14-26) we have, in general

$$\frac{dH^*}{dt} = \frac{\partial H^*}{\partial t} \tag{14-28}$$

If both L and $\mathbf{f}$ are not explicit functions of time, then $\partial H^*/\partial t = 0$, and it is clear that for such systems H^* is a constant; moreover, for the class of systems in which the end time is not specified in advance we know that $H^* = 0$ at the end time. Thus if these systems are, in addition, time invariant we will then have $H^* \equiv 0$.† We shall summarize the above in terms of the following corollaries:

1) For time-invariant augmented systems, H^* is a constant.
2) For time-invariant augmented systems whose end time t_2 is not specified in advance, H^* is identically zero.

An important class of problems which falls under (2) is the time-optimal control problem with a time-invariant plant.

†This is another way of arriving at Eq. (13-71) for the class of problems treated in Sec. 13.3.

4. Remarks and Illustrations

Let us pause first to consider the vector ψ'. From (14-24), the defining equations for ψ' is seen to be a set of linear and homogeneous differential equations. The components of $\psi'(t)$ are determined only to within a common constant multiplier. Thus without loss of generality, we can arbitrarily fix one of these. From the statement of the maximum principle, this is most easily done on the component ψ_0 which is a constant throughout. By statement (4) of the maximum principle, we know that $\psi_0 \le 0$. Following custom, we shall affix the value of ψ_0:†

$$\psi_0 \equiv -1 \tag{14-29}$$

In the case of a linear plant of the form

$$\dot{\mathbf{x}} = \mathbf{A}\,\mathbf{x} + \mathbf{B}\,\mathbf{u}\,, \quad \mathbf{x}(t_1) = \mathbf{x}_1 \tag{14-30a}$$

with

$$\dot{x}_0 = L(\mathbf{x}, \mathbf{u})\,, \quad x_0(t_1) = 0 \tag{14-30b}$$

Eq. (14-24) along $\mathbf{x}^*(t)$ becomes

$$\dot{\psi}_0 = 0 \tag{14-31a}$$

$$\dot{\psi} = -\mathbf{A}^T\psi - \psi_0 \frac{\partial L}{\partial \mathbf{x}} \tag{14-31b}$$

where ψ is the vector with components $\psi_1, \ldots, \psi_n$. With $\psi_0 \equiv -c$, Eq. (14-31b) is seen to be the same as the equations for the Lagrange multipliers in the Euler-Lagrange equations of Chap. 13. Thus the ψ_i's, $i = 1, \ldots, n$, are identified as the Lagrange multipliers in the classical formulation.

We can go a step further in our search for identity for the ψ_i's. Consider the time-optimal control problem for linear systems. Here $L(\mathbf{x}, \mathbf{u}) \equiv 1$, and thus (14-31b) reduces to $\dot{\psi} = -\mathbf{A}^T\psi$, which is seen to be the system adjoint to (14-30a) in accordance with our definition of Chap. 3. Thus we see that the Lagrange multipliers turn out to be none other than the adjoint variables in the linear case. Furthermore because of the identification of the ψ vector with the adjoint vector in the time-optimal control case, the augmented ψ' vector in the case of the general nonlinear system as defined by Eq. (14-24) will also be referred to as the adjoint vector.

†This can be done provided that $\psi_0 \neq 0$. When $\psi_0 \equiv 0$, the corresponding trajectory is said to be *abnormal*. This will be briefly discussed in Chap. 16.

We can now also establish the identity of the η vector which appeared in the expression for time-optimal control in the previous sections.

The Hamiltonian function for the system of (14-30) is

$$H = -L(\mathbf{x}, \mathbf{u}) + \psi^T(\mathbf{A}\,\mathbf{x} + \mathbf{B}\,\mathbf{u}) \tag{14-32}$$

In the case of time-optimal control, since $L(\mathbf{x}, \mathbf{u}) \equiv 1$,

$$H = -1 + \psi^T(\mathbf{A}\,\mathbf{x} + \mathbf{B}\,\mathbf{u})$$

By statement (1) of the maximum principle H is to be maximized by choosing $\mathbf{u}$. Now the only part of H that explicitly contains $\mathbf{u}$ is the part $\psi^T\mathbf{B}\,\mathbf{u}$. When $|u_i| \le U_i$, to maximize this quantity, we see that since

$$\psi^T\mathbf{B}\,\mathbf{u} = \sum_{i=1}^{n} \psi_i \sum_{j=1}^{r} b_{ij}u_j = \sum_{j=1}^{r} u_j \sum_{i=1}^{n} b_{ij}\psi_i \tag{14-33}$$

we must have

$$u_j^* = U_j \operatorname{sgn} \sum_{i=1}^{n} b_{ij}\psi_i$$

or

$$\mathbf{u}^*(t) = \operatorname{sgn}[\mathbf{B}^T\psi] \tag{14-34}$$

whenever the quantity $\sum_{i=1}^{n} b_{ij}\psi_i$ does not vanish over any finite interval. If the latter condition is satisfied, then each u_i will be bang-bang in form, the actual switching times being dependent on the set of adjoint variables. This seems in a way to echo the results of LaSalle as given in Sec. 14.2.

Compare now (14-34) with (14-16), where we had

$$\mathbf{u}^*(t) = \operatorname{sgn}\left[\eta^T\Phi^{-1}(t, t_1)\mathbf{B}\right]^T$$

From the material of Chap. 3 (Sec. 3.8) $\mathbf{B}^T\psi(t)$ can be written as $\mathbf{B}^T\Psi(t, t_1)\psi(t_1)$ where $\Psi(t, t_1)$ is the transition matrix for the adjoint system. Also since $\Phi^{-1}(t, t_1) = \Psi^T(t, t_1)$ when the elements of the transition matrices are real, we have

$$\left[\eta^T\Phi^{-1}(t, t_1)\mathbf{B}\right]^T = \mathbf{B}^T\Psi(t, t_1)\eta^T$$

Since (14-34) and (14-16) must yield the same result, then by the nature of the sgn function, the quantities $B^T\Psi(t) = B^T\Psi(t, t_1)\psi(t_1)$ and $B^T\Psi(t, t_1)\eta^T$ must yield vectors that at all times lie in the same direction and differ in magnitude at most by a constant factor. This means that η *must be a vector that has the same sense as the adjoint vector* ψ *at the initial time* t_1. Since the magnitude of η is not of importance in our formulations we can suitably scale η so that $\eta = \psi(t_1)$.

Since the time-optimal problem can be reduced to one of finding η, we now see that it is really a matter of finding the initial value of the adjoint vector. As soon as $\psi(t_1)$ is known, the time-optimal control problem for the linear L-controllable plant can be solved, since the value of $\psi(t)$ for $t_2 \geq t \geq t_1$ is completely determined by $\dot{\psi} = -A^T\psi$ if $\psi(t_1)$ is given.

A pictorial summary of this procedure is shown in Fig. 14-4. The difficulty in the above procedure, of course, is that in the general case† it is not at all obvious how to go about finding $\psi(t_1)$. One possible way is to try to make use of whatever topological insight provided by the maximum principle and of the other necessary conditions and to devise numerical iterative procedures. We will discuss some of these procedures in Chap. 17.

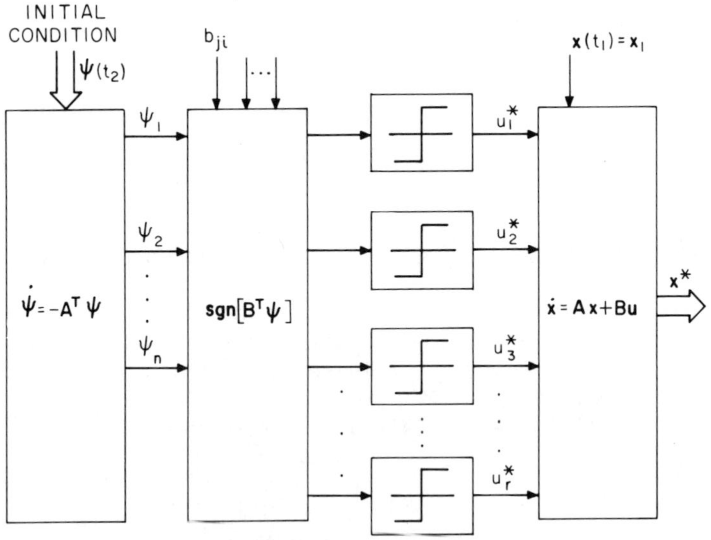

Fig. 14-4. The generation of the time-optimal control of a plant $\dot{x} = Ax + Bu$ if $\psi(t_2)$ were known and if $\mathrm{sgn}[B^T\psi]$ were well defined.

†If the plant is linear, $\psi(t_1)$ can sometines be found by using the procedure of Sec. 12.3.

If we compare the statements of Theorem 14-3 with the results derived in Chap. 13 by using calculus of variation, we find that

1) Statement (1) in Theorem 14-3 is essentially the Weierstrass condition when the Valentine method is applied to take care of the inequality constraints on the $\mathbf{u}(t)$.
2) Statement (2) corresponds to the Euler-Lagrange equations.
3) Statements (3) and (4) give the transversality conditions for the class of problem considered.
4) The fact that $\psi'(t)$ is held to be continuous implies that the corner condition (13-20) is automatically satisfied.

Thus Theorem 14-3 embodies almost all of the known necessary conditions as derived in Chap. 13 by calculus of variations. From this, we can appreciate the succinctness and power of the present formulation.

The maximum principle also readily applies to cases where there are no amplitude constraints imposed on the control function $\mathbf{u}(t)$. For these cases, we expect that the maximum principle will yield results which are identical to those obtainable by using the classical calculus of variations.

Let us consider some examples:

◆◆Example 14-2. (Time-Optimal Control of Satellite of Example 4-1). Here we have

$$\dot{x}_1 = x_2 \,, \quad \dot{x}_2 = u \,, \quad |u(t)| \leq 1$$

thus

$$\mathbf{A} = \begin{bmatrix} 0 & 1 \\ 0 & 0 \end{bmatrix}, \quad \mathbf{b} = \begin{bmatrix} 0 \\ 1 \end{bmatrix}$$

If we use calculus of variations for this example, we need to define, in accordance with the method of Valentine, a variable $\nu(t)$ and a constraining relationship

$$\zeta(u, \nu) = \Big(u(t) + 1\Big)\Big(1 - u(t)\Big) - \nu^2(t) = 0$$

The performance index $\mathcal{J}_2$, by the multiplier rule, is

$$\mathcal{J}_2 = t_2 + \int_0^{t_2} \left(\sum_{i=1}^{2} \psi_i \phi_i + \lambda\zeta\right) dt = t_2 + \int_0^{t_2} L_1\, dt$$

where

$$L_1 = \psi_1(\dot{x}_1 - x_2) + \psi_2(\dot{x}_2 - u) + \lambda\zeta$$

Since $\partial L_1/\partial \dot{x}_1 = \psi_1$, $\partial L_1/\partial x_1 = 0$, $\partial L_1/\partial \dot{x}_2 = \psi_2$, and $\partial L_1/\partial x_2 = -\psi_1$, the Euler-Lagrange equations yield

$$\dot{\psi}_1 = 0 , \quad \dot{\psi}_2 = -\psi_1 \tag{14-35}$$

In addition we have $\partial L_1/\partial \nu = -2\lambda\nu = 0$ and $\partial L_1/\partial u = -\psi_2 - 2\lambda u = 0$, or

$$\lambda(t)\,\nu^*(t) \equiv 0 \tag{14-36}$$

and

$$-\psi_2(t) = 2\lambda(t)\,u^*(t) \tag{14-37}$$

The functions $\lambda(t)$, $\nu(t)$, and $u^*(t)$ can all be found from the Weierstrass condition, which dictates that $u^*(t)$ must be such that at each time t the maximum value of H results. Since $H = \psi_1 x_2 + \psi_2 u - 1$ in this case, we have

$$u^*(t) = \operatorname{sgn}[\psi_2(t)] \tag{14-38}$$

The optimal control function $u^*(t)$ will be unique, provided that ψ_2 does not identically vanish.

From (14-35) we see that the solution for the ψ's are

$$\psi_1 = C = \text{constant} , \quad \psi_2 = -Ct + \psi_2(0) \tag{14-39}$$

and ψ_2 cannot vanish unless ψ_1 vanishes. But $\psi_1 = \psi_2 \equiv 0$ is not possible as we see from the transversality condition (13-70)

$$\left(\sum_{i=1}^{2} \psi_i f_i - 1\right)\Bigg|_{t=t_2} = \left(\psi_1 x_2 + \psi_2 u - 1\right)\Bigg|_{t=t_2} = 0 \tag{14-40}$$ †

By (13-87) and (14-40) we see that $H^* = \psi_1 x_2^* + \psi_2 u^* - 1 \equiv 0$ for all t. Thus we see that a bang-bang solution must always result. Moreover, since ψ_2 in (14-39) can only change sign once, there will only be a single switch of polarity in the bang-bang solution. By (14-37) and (14-38), we see that $\lambda(t) = -(1/2)\,|\psi_2(t)|$ and hence, by (14-36), we have $\nu(t) \equiv 0$.

Calculus of variations, of course, yields the correct answer. But if we use the maximum principle, we see that the same result can be obtained without the use of the auxiliary variables $\nu(t)$ and $\lambda(t)$. To proceed, we immediately construct

$$H = -1 + \psi_1 x_2 + \psi_2 u$$

where ψ_1 and ψ_2 evolve in accordance with

†Eq. (14-40) of course confirms Eq. (14-25).

$$\begin{bmatrix} \dot{\psi}_1 \\ \dot{\psi}_2 \end{bmatrix} = \begin{bmatrix} 0 & 0 \\ -1 & 0 \end{bmatrix} \begin{bmatrix} \psi_1 \\ \psi_2 \end{bmatrix}$$

or

$$\psi_1 = c_1 , \quad \psi_2 = -\psi_1 t + c_2 = -c_1 t + c_2$$

If the constraint is $|u| \leq 1$, then the maximum principle (Statement (1) of Theorem 14-3) immediately indicates that the solution is

$$u^*(t) = \operatorname{sgn} \psi_2(t)$$

Note that since $\psi_2(t) = c_2 - c_1 t$, $\psi_2(t)$ can change sign at most once; thus u^* can change sign at most once.

From (14-25), we also will have $H^* \equiv 0$ or $x_2 \psi_1 + \psi_2 u^* \equiv 1$; hence the case $\psi_1 = \psi_2 = 0$ is impossible.

Thus far, only the form of the solution is found. As in the case of Example 14-1, determination of the optimal control function as a function of time for a specific initial condition requires essentially that the initial value of the adjoint vector $\psi(t_1)$ be found; as usual, we have no logical procedure to do this.

We can again run the system backwards from the origin using the optimal control function $u^* = \operatorname{sgn} \psi_2$. Here, by taking arbitrary values of ψ_1 and ψ_2 to begin with (it is the value of $\psi(t_2)$ that we pick) and running the system backward, we can actually obtain the optimal initial value $\psi(t_1)$ for every point through which the system trajectory passes. Indeed, by letting $\tau = -t$, the backward $\psi(\tau)$ corresponding to each $x(\tau)$ that the backward system trajectory passes is actually the $\psi(t_1)$ for that initial state for the forward system (show this). This procedure at first glance would seem to have overcome the two-point boundary value problem. In reality, however, this is not so, because there is no direct way for us to calculate $\psi(t_2)$ such that we are assured of going through a given $x(t_1)$ with one backward trajectory.◆◆

For time-optimal control of time-invariant linear plants, if the control variable enters linearly, the maximum principle always seems to indicate a bang-bang control. But if the control variable appears in a nonlinear fashion, i.e., of the form $\dot{x} = A x + g(u)$, the solution need not be bang-bang in form. This is shown in the following example:

◆◆Example 14-3.† The motion of a certain missile is approximated by the following set of equations after thrust termination

$$\ddot{y} = \frac{c_1 q \alpha}{m} , \quad \ddot{x} = -\frac{c_1 q \alpha^2}{m}$$

†This example is due to J. A. Norton and H. Halkin.

where m is the mass of the missile, α is its angle of attack (see Example 5-5), x and y are respectively the horizontal and vertical coordinates of the missile, and $c_1 > 0$ is a proportionality constant. The quantity q, the dynamic pressure $\rho/2(\dot{x}^2 + \dot{y}^2)$, will here be approximated by a function of time only, $q(t)$.

The problem is to find the form of α as a function of time, subject to the constraint $|\alpha| \leq \alpha_{\max}$ so as to permit the missile to go from an initial point (x_1, y_1) to a terminal point (x_2, y_2) in the minimum time.

Letting $x_1 = x, x_2 = \dot{x}, x_3 = y, x_4 = \dot{y}$, $u = c_1 q(t)\alpha/m$, and $K_1 = m/c_1$, the system state equation is

$$\dot{x}_1 = x_2, \quad \dot{x}_2 = -\frac{K_1 u^2}{q(t)}, \quad \dot{x}_3 = x_4, \quad \dot{x}_4 = u$$

This is in the form $\dot{\mathbf{x}} = \mathbf{A}\,\mathbf{x} + \mathbf{g}(\mathbf{u})$ where

$$\mathbf{A} = \begin{bmatrix} 0 & 1 & 0 & 0 \\ 0 & 0 & 0 & 0 \\ 0 & 0 & 0 & 1 \\ 0 & 0 & 0 & 0 \end{bmatrix}, \qquad \mathbf{g}(\mathbf{u}) = \begin{bmatrix} 0 \\ \dfrac{K_1 u^2}{q(t)} \\ 0 \\ u \end{bmatrix}$$

The constraint on u is now $|u| \leq K_2 q(t)$ where $K_2 = c_1 \alpha_{\max}/m$. Applying the maximum principle, we find

$$H = \psi_1 x_2 + \psi_3 x_4 - \psi_2 \frac{K_1 u^2}{q(t)} + \psi_4 u - 1$$

To maximize H, let us consider two cases:

1) $|u| < K_2 q(t)$. Here H can be maximized by taking its derivative with respect to u and setting it to 0 or

$$\left.\frac{\partial H}{\partial u}\right|_{u=u^*} = -2\psi_2 K_1 \frac{u^*}{q(t)} + \psi_4 = 0$$

This yields

$$u^* = \frac{\psi_4 q(t)}{2\psi_2 K_1}$$

To find ψ_2 and ψ_4 we consider the adjoint system, and it is easy to determine that, since $\psi_2(t_2) = \psi_4(t_2) = 0$,† ψ_2 and ψ_4 will be of the form

$$\psi_2 = c_2(t_2 - t), \quad \psi_4 = c_3(t_2 - t)$$

where c_2 and c_3 are constants. Therefore,

$$u^* = \frac{c_3 q(t)}{2c_2 K_1} \quad \text{if} \quad \frac{c_3}{2c_2 K_1} < K_2 \quad \text{or} \quad \frac{c_3}{2c_2} < K_1 K_2 = \alpha_{\max}$$

Thus in this regime, u should be proportional to q which means that $\alpha = mu/(c_1 q)$ should be constant.

2) $|u| = K_2 q(t) = u_{\max}$ (or $\alpha = \alpha_{\max}$). This is so if $c_3/(2c_2) = K_1 K_2 = \alpha_{\max}$ so that instead of the above expression, we have

$$u^* = \operatorname{sgn}\left[\frac{c_3}{c_2}\right] K_2 q(t) \quad \text{or} \quad \alpha^* = \operatorname{sgn}\left[\frac{c_3}{c_2}\right]\alpha_{\max}$$ ◆◆

In all examples considered thus far in this section, we must be mindful of the fact that the maximum principle provides only a necessary but not sufficient condition for optimality. Thus in the light of our discussion of Chap. 13, what we have found may well be only a local minimum, or not a minimum at all. Fortunately in many cases the maximum principle provides a sufficient condition for optimality as well. This we will discuss in the next section.

14.4 The Maximum Principle as a Sufficient Condition

The maximum principle is often said to provide a set of strong necessary conditions, i.e., a set of necessary conditions which are also in some sense "close to" being sufficient. It turns out that when the plant to be controlled is linear, the maximum principle often can be shown to be sufficient as well.

A reasonably general form of a theorem concerning the sufficiency of the maximum principle for optimal control of a linear plant is the following††

◆◆Theorem 14-4. For the system

$$\dot{\mathbf{x}} = \mathbf{A}(t)\mathbf{x} + \mathbf{g}(\mathbf{u}, t) \tag{14-41}$$

let the performance index be provided by the auxiliary differential

†Since $x_2 = \dot{x}$ and $x_4 = \dot{y}$ are not fixed at $t = t_2$, it follows from statement (3) of Theorem 14-3 that $\psi_2(t_2) = \psi_4(t_2) = 0$.

††For a proof see, e.g., [L7].

equation

$$\dot{x}_0 = f_0(\mathbf{x}, t) + g_0(\mathbf{u}, t) \tag{14-42}$$

where A, f_0, g_0, and g are continuous in all arguments and f_0 is a single-valued convex function† of x for each t. Let the goal of control be as specified in Part 2 of Sec. 14.3. If a $\mathbf{u}^*(t)$ obeying the maximum principle is found which satisfies the conditions of the problem, then it is an optimal control function.♦♦

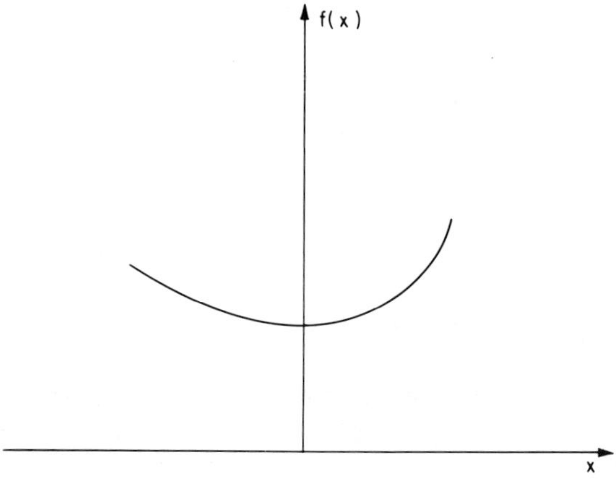

Fig. 14-5. A convex function $f(x)$.

We see that $\mathbf{u}^*(t)$ found in each of the examples in Sec. 14.3 indeed constitutes an optimal control.

14.5 A Sketch of the Proof of the Maximum Principle

In this section we will indicate how we can make use of the insight provided by the convex reachable-set approach of Bellman et al., and LaSalle, to construct a proof for the maximum principle for a particular class of linear systems. From there we will indicate the steps needed to extend the proof to the general case. The steps we use follow those of Halkin [H5]. For complete rigor, the reader should consult the original reference.

†A function f(x) is convex if for any two points $\mathbf{x}_1$, $\mathbf{x}_2$; $f(\alpha\mathbf{x}_1 + (1-\alpha)\mathbf{x}_2) \leq \alpha f(\mathbf{x}_1) + (1-\alpha)f(\mathbf{x}_2)$ for all values of $0 \leq \alpha \leq 1$. A convex function of one variable $f(x)$ will then be as shown in Fig. 14-5. A straight line connecting any two points of the function always lies above the function.

1. A Proof of the Maximum Principle for a Particular Class of Linear Systems

The particular problem that we will consider in this section will have an augmented form that is *linear*

$$\dot{\mathbf{x}}' = \mathbf{A}'(t)\mathbf{x}' + \mathbf{g}'(\mathbf{u}, t) \tag{14-43}$$

although as noted here $\mathbf{u}$ is allowed to enter in a general nonlinear fashion. As before let $|u_i| \leq 1$.

In (14-43), without loss of generality, we can assume that the coordinates have been translated so that $\mathbf{x}'(t_1) = \mathbf{0}$. This will locate the initial point of the augmented system at the origin of the $\mathcal{E}_{n+1}$ space.

Let the object of control be the same as that stated in Part 2 of Sec. 14.3, except that at the time t_2 we wish to bring the system state to one where $x_i = s_i$ for $i = 1, \ldots, m$ and in the process minimize the coordinate $x_0(t_2)$.

To avoid complicated notations, in this section we will drop the primes in denoting the augmented vectors. Thus we write (14-43) as

$$\dot{\mathbf{x}} = \mathbf{A}(t)\mathbf{x} + \mathbf{g}(\mathbf{u}, t) \tag{14-44}$$

with the understanding that $\mathbf{x}$ and $\mathbf{g}$ are $(n + 1)$-dimensional vectors with components $x_0, \ldots, x_n$ and $g_0, \ldots, g_n$ respectively and $\mathbf{A}$ is an $(n + 1) \times (n + 1)$ matrix.

To follow the development of the proof, it is instructive to visualize an illustrative optimization problem in a three-dimensional augmented state space with coordinates x_0, x_1, x_2. Here, let it be desired to control a third-order linear system of the form (14-44) from $x(t_1) = 0$ in such a way that at $t = t_2$, $x_1(t_2) = s_1$, and $x_0(t_2)$ is minimized. The state x_2 is left free at t_2.

To begin the proof, define, as before, the *reachable set* $\mathcal{C}(t_2)$ as the set of all points in $\mathcal{E}_{n+1}$ reachable by the system (14-44) by choosing $u(t)$ from the admissible set Ω, i.e.,

$$\mathcal{C}(t_2) = \left\{ \int_{t_1}^{t_2} \Phi(t_2, \tau)\, \mathbf{g}\big(\mathbf{u}(\tau), \tau\big)\, d\tau : u \in \Omega \right\} \tag{14-45)*$$

Since $\mathbf{g}(\mathbf{u}, t)$ may not be of the traditional form $\mathbf{B}(t)\mathbf{u}(t)$, it is not immediately clear whether the set $\mathcal{C}(t_2)$ is now convex or not.

An important result in Halkin's proof of the maximum principle is the following [H5].

*In contrast to Sec. 14.1 where $\mathcal{C}(t_2)$ was defined in terms of backward mapping from $\mathbf{x}(t_2) = \mathbf{0}$, we define $\mathcal{C}(t_2)$ here in terms of a forward mapping from $\mathbf{x}(t_1) = \mathbf{0}$. The result will be the same, since we can always transform the state such that $\mathbf{x}(t_1) \neq \mathbf{0}$ and $\mathbf{x}(t_2) = \mathbf{0}$.

◆◆Lemma 14-1. In (14-44), if $A(t)$ is piecewise continuous with respect to t, and $g(u, t)$ is continuous with respect to u and piecewise continuous with respect to t, then the set $\mathcal{C}(t_2)$ is convex.◆◆

Knowing that $\mathcal{C}(t_2)$ is convex, we can make use of the type of argument which permitted us to derive results in the time-optimal control case, provided that we make proper modifications for our more complicated terminal set. Note however that Lemma 14-1 has nothing to say about whether $\mathcal{C}(t_2)$ is closed or not.

In the time-optimal control case, the terminal set is the end point x_2. As soon as the closed and convex set $\mathcal{C}(t)$ touches x_2 for the first time, the problem is solved and by examining the geometry of the situation, we can derive some necessary conditions for the time-optimal control.

In our more general case, as $\mathcal{C}(t_2)$ is not necessarily closed, we cannot blithely speak of $\mathcal{C}(t_2)$ "touching" any point.† However, we can speak of points that do or do not belong to the set $\mathcal{C}(t_2)$.

Let us suppose that an optimal control function $u^*(t)$ has been found. Let the corresponding optimal trajectory resulting from the application $u^*(t)$ be $x(u^*(t), t)$. By definition, $x(u^*(t), t_2)$ is a point of $\mathcal{C}(t_2)$. Indeed it is reasonable that:

◆◆Lemma 14-2. (Principle of Optimal Evolution).†† For every t in $[t_1, t_2]$, $x(u^*, t)$ is a boundary point of the set $\mathcal{C}(t)$.◆◆

Let us define the (open) set $\mathcal{S}$ as the set of all points x such that $x_i = s_i$, $i = 1, \ldots, m$, and, moreover, $x_0 < x_0(u^*, t_2)$. The set $\mathcal{S}$ is convex, and is, intuitively, a convex set that is "just missed" by $\mathcal{C}(t_2)$.

For our example, the set $\mathcal{S}$ is seen to be the semi-infinite space given by $x_1 = s_1$ and $x_0 < x_0(u^*, t_2)$. The cross-sectional view of this set is shown in Fig. 14-6, which represents a view of the geometry of the example when a plane is passed through the point $x(u^*, t_2)$ parallel to the x_0—x_1 plane.

Let us in addition define the set $\bar{\mathcal{S}}$ as the set of all states x in $\mathcal{E}_{n+1}$ space where $x_i = s_i$, for $i = 1, \ldots, m$, and, moreover, $x_0 \leq x_0(u^*, t_2)$. Thus $\bar{\mathcal{S}}$ is the set $\mathcal{S}$ plus its boundary plane $x_0 = x_0(u^*, t_2)$. For our example, $\bar{\mathcal{S}}$ is the set $\mathcal{S}$ plus its boundary plane defined by $x_0 = x_0(u^*, t_2)$ and $x_1 = s_1$.

By definition the sets $\mathcal{C}(t_2)$ and $\mathcal{S}$ have no point in common, for otherwise we would violate our assumption that u^* is an optimal control.

Since both $\mathcal{C}(t_2)$ and $\mathcal{S}$ are convex and have no point in common, then there exists at least one hyperplane separating them in the sense that $\mathcal{C}(t_2)$ lies wholly to one side of this hyperplane and $\mathcal{S}$ lies wholly to the other side. For the example, the edge view

†If $A(t)$ is continuous with respect to t and $g(u, t)$ is continuous with respect to u and t, then for $|u_i| \leq 1$ $\mathcal{C}(t_2)$ is both closed and convex. See [N5].

††For proof, see, e.g., [F2].

of this plane is shown as indicated in Fig. 14-6. The plane here is in fact a supporting plane to the set $\mathcal{C}(t_2)$ at $x(u^*, t_2)$.

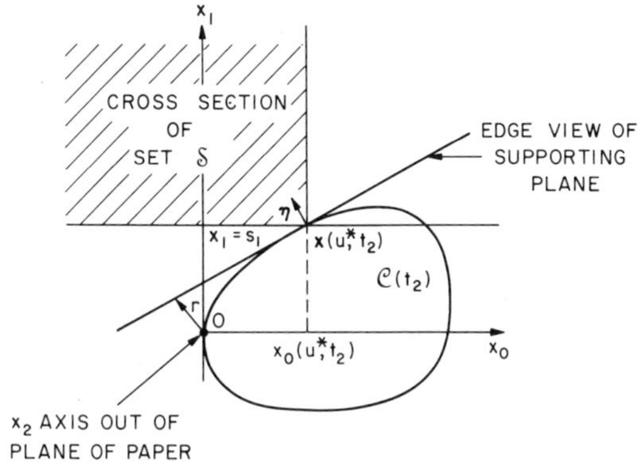

Fig. 14-6. The geometry of the convex reachable set $\mathcal{C}(t_2)$ relative to the set $\mathcal{S}$ for the special class of systems of Eq. (14-43).

Let the distance of this plane from the origin be given as the Euclidean distance r. Then the outward normal η of the supporting hyperplane (outward in the sense of pointing away from $\mathcal{C}(t_2)$) enjoys the following properties

$$\frac{(x^T\eta)}{\|\eta\|} \leq r \qquad \text{for all } x \in \mathcal{C}(t_2)$$

$$\frac{x^T\eta}{\|\eta\|} > r \qquad \text{for all } x \in \mathcal{S} \tag{14-46}$$

$$\frac{x^T\eta}{\|\eta\|} \geq r \qquad \text{for all } x \in \bar{\mathcal{S}}$$

Since $x(u^*, t_2)$ belongs to both $\mathcal{C}(t_2)$ and $\bar{\mathcal{S}}$, we have

$$\frac{x^T(u^*, t_2)\eta}{\|\eta\|} \leq r \leq \frac{x^T(u^*, t_2)\eta}{\|\eta\|} \tag{14-47}$$

which means

$$\frac{x^T(u^*, t_2)\eta}{\|\eta\|} = r \tag{14-48}$$

We can see from the example that any translation of the point $x\left(u^*(t), t_2\right)$ parallel to the x_2 axis will result in another point in $\bar{\mathcal{S}}$

(where x_2 is marked by the fact that it is the coordinate that is left free at the end time t_2). This fact extended to the general $\mathcal{E}_{n+1}$ space can be used to prove that

$$\eta_i = 0 \qquad \text{for } i = m+1, \ldots, n$$

and

$$\eta_0 \leq 0$$

To show this, let $\mathbf{e}_i$ be a unit vector parallel to the ith axis; then from the foregoing consideration, we will have both $\mathbf{x}(\mathbf{u}^*, t_2) + \mathbf{e}_i$ and $\mathbf{x}(\mathbf{u}^*, t_2) - \mathbf{e}_i$ belonging to $\bar{\mathcal{S}}$ for $i = m+1, \ldots, n$. Then from (14-46) and (14-48) we have

$$\left(\mathbf{x}(\mathbf{u}^*, t_2) + \mathbf{e}_i\right)^T \boldsymbol{\eta} \geq \mathbf{x}^T(\mathbf{u}^*, t_2)\boldsymbol{\eta} \tag{14-49a}$$

and

$$\left(\mathbf{x}(\mathbf{u}^*, t_2) - \mathbf{e}_i\right)^T \boldsymbol{\eta} \geq \mathbf{x}^T(\mathbf{u}^*, t_2)\boldsymbol{\eta}, \qquad i = m+1, \ldots, n \tag{14-49b}$$

This means $-0 \leq \mathbf{e}_i^T\boldsymbol{\eta} \leq 0$, or

$$\mathbf{e}_i^T\boldsymbol{\eta} = 0, \qquad i = m+1, \ldots, n \tag{14-50}$$

which is possible only if $\eta_i = 0$, $i = m+1, \ldots, n$

Also, clearly $\mathbf{x}(\mathbf{u}^*, t_2) - \mathbf{e}_0$ belongs to the set $\bar{\mathcal{S}}$. Therefore, by (14-46) we have

$$\left(\mathbf{x}(\mathbf{u}^*, t_2) - \mathbf{e}_0\right)^T \boldsymbol{\eta} \geq \mathbf{x}^T(u^*, t_2)\boldsymbol{\eta} \tag{14-51}$$

Hence, $-\mathbf{e}_0^T\boldsymbol{\eta} \geq 0$ which implies that

$$\eta_0 \leq 0$$

It can now be shown that if we generate the (augmented) adjoint vectors $\boldsymbol{\psi}(t)$ by

$$\boldsymbol{\psi}(t) = [\boldsymbol{\Phi}^{-1}(t, t_2)]^T\boldsymbol{\eta} = \boldsymbol{\Psi}(t, t_2)\boldsymbol{\eta} \tag{14-52}$$

for $t_1 \leq t \leq t_2$ we can prove statements (1) and (2) of the maximum principle. In (14-52), $\boldsymbol{\Phi}(t, t_2)$ is the transition matrix for the augmented system, and $\boldsymbol{\Psi}(t, t_1)$ is the transition matrix for the corresponding adjoint system.

First we can prove that (see Exercise 14-14)

$$\left(\Phi^{-1}(t, t_2)\,\mathbf{g}(\mathbf{u}^*, t)\right)^T\eta \geq \left(\Phi^{-1}(t, t_2)\,\mathbf{g}(\mathbf{u}, t)\right)^T\eta \qquad (14\text{-}53)$$

which implies

$$\mathbf{g}^T(\mathbf{u}^*, t)\Psi(t, t_2)\eta \geq \mathbf{g}^T(\mathbf{u}, t)\Psi(t, t_2)\eta \qquad (14\text{-}54)$$

In view of (14-52), the above becomes

$$\mathbf{g}^T(\mathbf{u}^*, t)\psi(t) \geq \mathbf{g}^T(\mathbf{u}, t)\psi(t) \qquad (14\text{-}55)$$

Adding $\left(\mathbf{A}(t)\mathbf{x}^*(t)\right)^T\psi(t)$ to both sides of the above inequality gives

$$\left(\mathbf{A}(t)\,\mathbf{x}^*(t) + \mathbf{g}(\mathbf{u}^*, t)\right)^T\psi(t) \geq \left(\mathbf{A}(t)\,\mathbf{x}^*(t) + \mathbf{g}(\mathbf{u}, t)\right)^T\psi(t)$$

or

$$H(\mathbf{x}^*, \mathbf{u}^*, t, \psi) \geq H(\mathbf{x}^*, \mathbf{u}, t, \psi) \qquad \text{for all } t \in [t_1, t_2] \qquad (14\text{-}56)$$

which is part (1) of the statement of the maximum principle.

From (14-52) moreover, we have for all $t \in [t_1, t_2]$

$$\frac{d\psi(t)}{dt} = \frac{d}{dt}\Psi(t, t_2)\eta = -\mathbf{A}^T(t)\Psi(t, t_2)\eta = -\mathbf{A}^T(t)\psi(t) \qquad (14\text{-}57)$$

Equation (14-57) is part (2) of the statement of the maximum principle. It also indicates that $\psi(t)$ is the (augmented) adjoint vector. Moreover as $\Psi(t_2, t_2) = \mathbf{I}$, then, from (14-52), we arrive at the conclusion that $\eta = \psi(t_2)$. Thus $\eta_i = 0$ for $i = m + 1, \ldots, n$ and $\eta_0 \leq 0$. These prove conditions (3) and (4) of the maximum principle for the present case.

2. A Proof of the Maximum Principle for the Nonlinear Case

For the general case, the proof is mathematically somewhat more involved. However, with the insight gained in our "proof" for the linear case, we can savor the flavor of the proof for the general case as well, for it will make liberal use of the properties of local linearized trajectories neighboring on an optimal trajectory and of the topological properties associated with them.

For the problem and system as defined in Sec. 14.3, Part 2, suppose we let $\mathbf{x}(\mathbf{u}^*, t)$ be the optimal augmented trajectory (abbreviated to $\mathbf{x}^*(t)$), and let $\mathbf{x}(\mathbf{u}, t)$ (abbreviated to $\mathbf{x}(t)$) be the trajectory resulting from the application of any other admissible control function $u(t)$. The difference $\delta x(u, t) \triangleq x(t) - x^*(t)$, called the variational trajectory and abbreviated to $\delta x(t)$, will propagate in accordance with

$$\delta\dot{x} = f(x, u, t) - f(x^*, u^*, t)$$

Suppose as in Chap. 5 we define the Jacobian matrix

$$\frac{\partial f}{\partial x}(x^*, u^*, t) \triangleq \begin{bmatrix} \frac{\partial f_1}{\partial x_1} & \cdots & \frac{\partial f_1}{\partial x_n} \\ \cdot & & \\ \cdot & & \\ \cdot & & \\ \frac{\partial f_n}{\partial x_1} & \cdots & \frac{\partial f_n}{\partial x_n} \end{bmatrix}_{\substack{\text{evaluating along} \\ x(t) = x^*(t) \\ u(t) = u^*(t)}} = \left[\frac{\partial f}{\partial x}(t)\right]^*$$

and let

$$g(u, t) \triangleq f(x^*, u, t) - f(x^*, u^*, t)$$

Then in terms of $\left[\frac{\partial f}{\partial x}(t)\right]^*$ and $g(u, t)$, we have

$$\delta\dot{x}(t) = \left[\frac{\partial f}{\partial x}(t)\right]^* \delta x(t) + g(u, t) + h(x, u, t) \tag{14-58}$$

where $h(x, u, t)$ is seen to be

$$h(x, u, t) = f(x, u, t) - f(x^*, u^*, t) - g(u, t) - \left[\frac{\partial f}{\partial x}(t)\right]^* \delta x(t)$$

and it is clear that $h(x, u, t)$ will be "small" if $u(t) - u^*(t)$ and $x(t) - x^*(t)$ are "small."

Now since $\delta x(t_1) = 0$, δx can be solved for exactly in terms of the transition matrix $\Phi(t, t_1)$ appropriate to $\delta\dot{x} = \left[\frac{\partial f}{\partial x}(t)\right]^* \delta x$; therefore,

$$\delta x(u, t) = \Phi(t, t_1) \int_{t_1}^{t} \Phi(t_1, \tau)\big(g(u, \tau) + h(x, u, \tau)\big)\, d\tau$$

Suppose, however, we define an *approximate* variational trajectory $\delta x_1(t)$ as that generated by

$$\delta\dot{x}_1(u, t) = \left[\frac{\partial f}{\partial x}(t)\right]^* \delta x_1(t) + g(u, t) \tag{14-59}$$

In essence δx_1 is the deviation in $x(t)$ produced by neglecting the effect of $h(x, u, t)$ in (14-58). By definition $\delta x_1(t_1) = 0$; hence

$$\delta x_1(u, t) = \int_{t_1}^{t} \Phi(t, \tau)\, g(u, \tau)\, d\tau$$

Let $\mathcal{C}_1(t_2)$ be the reachable set for the system $x = f(x, u, t)$, or

$$\mathcal{C}_1(t_2) = \{x^*(t_2) + \delta x(u, t_2) : u \in \Omega\} = \{x(u, t_2) : u \in \Omega\} \tag{14-60}$$

Because of the fact that the system is now nonlinear; the set $\mathcal{C}_1(t_2)$ is not necessarily convex.†

Consider however the reachable set $\mathcal{C}(t_2)$ for the approximate variational trajectory relative to the point $x^*(t_2)$, or

$$\mathcal{C}(t_2) = \{x^*(t_2) + \delta x_1(u, t_2) : u \in \Omega\}$$

$\mathcal{C}(t_2)$ is convex in view of the fact that the set $\{\delta x_1(u, t_2) : u \in \Omega\}$ is convex.

In addition to the sets $\mathcal{C}_1(t_2)$ and $\mathcal{C}(t_2)$, we also need the set $\mathcal{S}$ as defined in part 1 of this section.

Clearly, if we wish to obtain any result concerning the maximum principle we must try to infer properties of the set $\mathcal{C}_1$ from properties that we already know concerning the set $\mathcal{C}$. This was achieved by Halkin through proving the following fundamental lemma:

◆◆Lemma 14-3. If there is no hyperplane separating the convex sets $\mathcal{S}$ and $\mathcal{C}(t_2)$, then the sets $\mathcal{S}$ and $\mathcal{C}_1(t_2)$ have at least one point in common.◆◆

Now by definition the sets $\mathcal{S}$ and $\mathcal{C}_1(t_2)$ cannot have a point in common, for otherwise the assumed optimality of the control $u^*(t)$ is violated. By Lemma 14-3, there will then be a hyperplane separating $\mathcal{S}$ and $\mathcal{C}$.

Having established this, we no longer require the set $\mathcal{C}_1$ to prove the maximum principle but can work exclusively with $\mathcal{C}$. As $\mathcal{C}$ is the reachable set for an augmented linear system of the form (14-43), and $x^*(t_2)$ belongs to both $\mathcal{C}_1$ and $\mathcal{C}$, all of the steps used in

†See [R5] for a sufficient condition under which $\mathcal{C}_1(t)$ is closed and convex for a class of nonlinear plants.

the previous section can be directly carried over to derive the four conditions of the maximum principle. These derivations we leave for the reader.

In view of the above, we can now develop an intuitive geometrical appreciation of the main statement of the maximum principle as given by statement (1) of Theorem 14-3.

Referring to Eq. (14-23) and noting that (i) ψ' has the interpretation as the outward normal to an appropriate reachable set $\mathcal{C}(t)$ and (ii) $\mathbf{f}'$ by virtue of the augmented system equations $\dot{\mathbf{x}}' = \mathbf{f}'$ essentially give the local velocity of the system trajectory, we see that *statement (1) of the maximum principle dictates that an optimal trajectory should be such that, at every point, the local velocity* $\dot{\mathbf{x}}$ *in the direction of the outward normal of the reachable set* $\mathcal{C}(t)$ *should be maximized.*

14.6 The Application of the Maximum Principle to Some Specific Classes of Problems

1. The Fuel-Optimal Control Problem

Let us now see how the fuel-optimal control problem can be attacked by the maximum principle. Consider first the linear plant

$$\dot{\mathbf{x}} = \mathbf{A}(t)\mathbf{x} + \mathbf{B}(t)\mathbf{u} \tag{14-61}$$

with $\mathbf{x}(t_1) = \mathbf{x}_1$ and $\mathbf{x}(t_2) = \mathbf{x}_2$, $|u_j| \leq 1$ for $j = 1, \ldots, r$, and the fuel-optimal performance index

$$\mathcal{J} = \int_{t_1}^{t_2} \left(\sum_{j=1}^{r} |u_j(t)| \right) dt \tag{14-62}$$

It is of course assumed that a solution exists and hence the time interval $t_2 - t_1$ is longer (or equal to) the time t^* for time optimal control.

In accordance with the maximum principle, we form

$$H = -\left(\sum_{j=1}^{r} |u_j(t)| \right) + \psi^T \mathbf{A}\mathbf{x} + \psi^T \mathbf{B}\mathbf{u} \tag{14-63}$$

where the adjoint vector ψ obeys $\dot{\psi} = -\mathbf{A}^T(t)\psi$. To maximize H with respect to $\mathbf{u}$, we see that each component of $\mathbf{u}$ in H is in a form

$$-|u_i(t)| + \left(\sum_{j=1}^{n} \psi_j b_{ji} \right) u_i, \quad i = 1, \ldots, r \tag{14-64}$$

Setting $q_i = \sum_{j=1}^{n} \psi_i b_{ji}$, we see that to maximize the quantity in (14-64) for each i yields the solution (see Exercise 13-2)

$$u_i^* = \begin{cases} +1, & q_i > 1 \\ 0, & -1 < q_i < 1 \\ -1, & q_i < -1 \end{cases} \qquad (i = 1, \ldots, r) \tag{14-65}$$

The switching function (14-65), as depicted in Fig. 14-7, reminds us of the dead-zone characteristics (see nonlinearity (17) in Table 6-2). Following Athans and Falb [A8], we shall call it the dead-zone function dez q_i, or

$$u_i^* = \text{dez } q_i \quad [\text{if } u_i^* \text{ satisfies (14-65)}], \quad i = 1, \ldots, r \tag{14-66}$$

We further define the vector dead zone function

$$\mathbf{u}^* = \text{dez } \mathbf{q} \tag{14-67}$$

to represent (14-66) in a compact fashion.

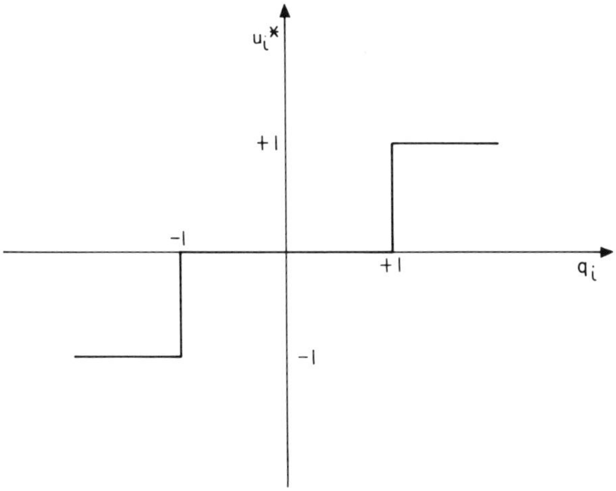

Fig. 14-7. The function $u_i^* = \text{dez } q_i$.

Let us note that the function dez q_i is not defined if $q_i \equiv +1$ or $q_i \equiv -1$. This brings about a singular case which we will consider in Chap. 16. Let us simply note that singular cases occur for Examples 12-4 and 12-5, as we may suspect already.

◆◆**Example 14-4.** Reconsider the system of Example 12-4, with $\dot{x} = u$, $x(0) = 1$, $x(5) = 2$, $|u(t)| \leq 1$, and $\mathcal{J} = \int_0^5 |u(t)| \, dt$. Here $H = -|u(t)| + \psi u$, where $\psi = 0$. Maximizing H yields

$$u^* = \text{dez } \psi$$

Now the solution for ψ is that ψ = constant.

Thus $\psi = +1$ or -1 is certainly legitimate for some initial conditions and we see that singular (i.e., nonunique) optimal control is possible. The same consideration holds for the system of Example 12-5.◆◆

◆◆**Example 14-5.** Consider however the plant

$$\dot{x}_1 = -x_1 + u$$
$$\dot{x}_2 = -2x_2 - u$$

which is essentially the plant $u(t) = (p^2 + 3p + 2) y(t)$ cast in the canonical form.

Let $x(0) = x_1$. $x(T) = 0$, and $|u(t)| \leq 1$. With

$$\mathcal{J} = \int_0^T |u(t)| \, dt$$

we quickly obtain

$H = -|u(t)| + \psi_1(t) [-x_1(t) + u(t)] + \psi_2(t) [-2x_2(t) - u(t)]$ with $\psi(t)$ satisfying

$$\dot{\psi}_1(t) = -\frac{\partial H}{\partial x_1} = \psi_1, \qquad \dot{\psi}_2 = -\frac{\partial H}{\partial x_2} = 2\psi_2$$

Thus, we have

$$u^*(t) = \text{dez}\,[\psi_1(t) - \psi_2(t)]$$

Now the solution for $\psi_1(t)$ and $\psi_2(t)$ are

$$\psi_1(t) = c_1 e^t, \quad \psi_2(t) = c_2 e^{2t}$$

and it is not possible to have $|\psi_1(t) - \psi_2(t)| = 1$ for a finite interval of time. Thus, singular control will not occur.◆◆

It turns out that singular control in fuel-optimal control of linear time-invariant plants depends on whether the plant has integration. This point will be made clear in Chap. 16.

When we have established that singular control does not exist, then the form of the solution is completely determined by (14-65) or (14-66) and it is possible to solve the two-point boundary value problem at least for linear plants represented by time-invariant ordinary differential equations.

Let us note that even if the plant is nonlinear, if $\mathbf{u}$ enters in a linear fashion, a dead-zone type of solution will still be implied by the maximum principle. For example, consider systems of the form

$$\dot{\mathbf{x}} = \mathbf{f}(\mathbf{x}, t) + \mathbf{G}(\mathbf{x}, t)\mathbf{u}$$

with $\mathbf{G}$ an appropriate matrix. We then have

$$H = -\sum_{j=1}^{r} |u_j(t)| + \boldsymbol{\psi}^T(\mathbf{f} + \mathbf{G}\mathbf{u})$$

The $\mathbf{u}$ dependent portion of H is $-\sum_{j=1}^{r} |u_j(t)| + \boldsymbol{\psi}^T\mathbf{G}\mathbf{u}$. It is clear that maximizing H relative to each component of $\mathbf{u}$ will yield (see Exercise 14-12)

$$\mathbf{u}^* = \operatorname{dez}[\mathbf{G}^T(\mathbf{x}, t)\boldsymbol{\psi}]$$

Here, with $\mathbf{G}$ as a function of $\mathbf{x}$, the problem becomes more involved.†

2. Problems Where the Trajectories End on Smooth Hypersurfaces

Sometimes the end point of the optimal control problem is not given specifically, but instead it is only stipulated that the trajectory must end on a smooth†† hypersurface $\rho(x_1, x_2, \ldots, x_n) = 0$, $(m \leq n)$. This class of problems has already been considered in the previous chapter. We recall that if the hypersurface $\rho(x_1, x_2, \ldots, x_m)$ is not a function of time, then the requisite transversality condition is that the projection of the vector $\boldsymbol{\psi}(t)$ into the m-dimensional $x_1, \ldots, x_m$ space at the end time t_2 (i.e., the time that the trajectory $\mathbf{x}^*(t)$ reaches the hypersurface $\rho(\mathbf{x}) = 0$) must be normal to the hypersurface at the point where the optimal trajectory $\mathbf{x}^*(t)$ touches the hypersurface.

†See, e.g., [A7].

††It can sometimes be a piecewise smooth hypersurface; see Example 14-6 below.

This result is not difficult to see using the geometrical development of the previous section, for it merely requires that the set $\mathcal{S}$ be altered so that $\mathcal{S} = \{\mathbf{x}: \rho(x_1, \ldots, x_m) = 0,\ x_0 < x_0(\mathbf{u}^*, t_2)\}$. If $\rho(\mathbf{x})$ is such that the altered set $\mathcal{S}$ is convex, then the result follows immediately. A vector η normal to a supporting hyperplane separating the convex sets $\mathcal{C}(t_2)$ and $\mathcal{S}$ at the point $\mathbf{x}^*(t_2)$ would enjoy the property that its projection into the m-dimensional space will be normal to the hypersurface $\rho(x_1, \ldots, x_m) = 0$. In particular, if we take the η vector to be the outward normal vector to $\mathcal{C}(t_2)$, then it is clear that its projection onto the $(x_1, \ldots, x_m)$ space would be an *inward* normal to the hypersurface $\rho(x_1, \ldots, x_m) = 0$.

In fact we can see that this result will hold even if the smooth hypersurface $\rho(x_1, \ldots, x_m) = 0$ is such that $\mathcal{S}$ is not convex. Thus *the transversality condition for the optimization problems where the trajectories are constrained to end on a smooth hypersurface* $\rho(x_1, x_2, \ldots, x_m) = 0$ *is that the vector formed by the first m components of* $\psi(t_2)$ *lies in the direction of an inward normal to the hypersurface* $\rho(x_1, \ldots, x_m) = 0$ *at the point* $\mathbf{x}^*(t_2)$.

Because the gradient $\nabla\rho$ evaluated at a point $(x_1, \ldots, x_m)$ is normal to the hypersurface $\rho = 0$ at that point, another way to characterize the result above is to state that the projection of $\psi(t_2)$ onto the $(x_1, \ldots, x_m)$ space must lie along the gradient vector $\nabla\rho$ at the point $\mathbf{x}^*(t_2)$.

◆◆**Example 14-6.** Consider the time-optimal control of the double integrating plant from an arbitrary initial state $\mathbf{x}_1$ to an end set given by the "diamond" $|x_1| + |x_2| \leq 1$.

Referring to Fig. 14-8, on sides a and b of the "diamond" the inward normal vector ψ must be such that ψ_2 is negative. Since by the maximum principle the optimal solution is given by $u^* = \operatorname{sgn}\psi_2$, we see that along the sides a and b all optimal trajectories must be incoming with the drive -1. Similarly at sides c and d, all optimal trajectories must be incoming with the drive $+1$. The change in the polarity of optimum drive u^* must occur at the corners $|x_1| = 1$. It is readily seen from the maximum principle that only one switch of the polarity of the optimal control function is permitted. Thus we conclude that the switching lines Γ_+ and Γ_- can be constructed in the manner shown in Fig. 14-8 to exhibit completely the optimal control function.◆◆

3. Problems Involving Time-Varying Systems

In Sec. 14.3, we have given the maximum principle for a general time-varying system. Let us note that a time-varying optimization problem can always be converted to an equivalent time-invariant one.† Using this, some special relationship involving

†However, a linear time-varying system will be converted into a nonlinear time-invariant system.

the necessary and transversality conditions for optimality can be derived.

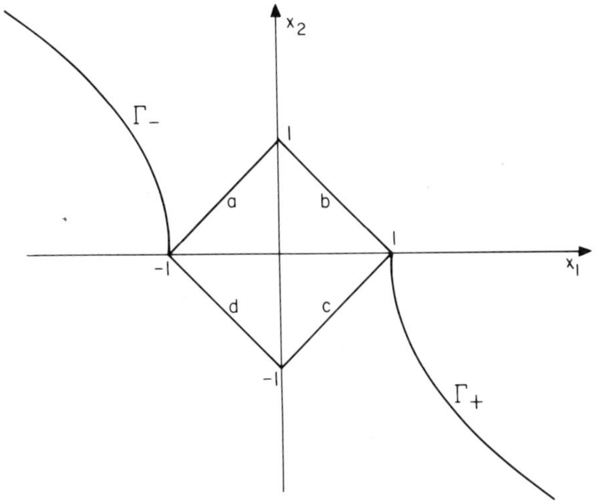

Fig. 14-8. The switching lines for the system of Example 14-6.

Suppose we introduce an extra "state" $x_{n+1} = t$; this means for the formulation of Sec. 14.3 we have an extra state equation

$$\dot{x}_{n+1} = 1, \quad x_{n+1}(t_1) = t_1 \tag{14-68}$$

In this case in an $(n + 2)$-dimensional Euclidean space with coordinates $(x_0, x_1, \ldots, x_{n+1})$, the system equations and the performance index become respectively

$$\dot{\mathbf{x}} = \mathbf{f}(\mathbf{x}, \mathbf{u}), \quad \mathcal{J} = \int_{t_1}^{t_2} L(\mathbf{x}, \mathbf{u})\, dt \tag{14-69}$$

where $f_{n+1} = 1$ and we have an equivalent time-invariant system.

If we define an $(n + 2)$-dimensional vector $\boldsymbol{\psi}(t)$ and an enhanced Hamiltonian H_1 for this $(n + 2)$-order system in the usual way, then we have

$$\dot{\psi}_i(t) = -\sum_{j=0}^{n+1} \frac{\partial f_j(\mathbf{x}, \mathbf{u})}{\partial x_i} \psi_j(t), \quad i = 0, \ldots, n + 1$$

$$H_1 = \sum_{i=0}^{n+1} \psi_i(t) f_i(\mathbf{x}, \mathbf{u}) \tag{14-70}$$

Here H_1 is not explicitly a function of time, so that by (14-28) we have $H_1^* = \text{constant}$. However, note that the "regular" Hamiltonian, $H = \sum_{i=0}^{n} \psi_i f_i$, is related to the enhanced Hamiltonian H_1 by

$$H_1 = H + \psi_{n+1}(t) \tag{14-71}$$

Suppose the end time t_2 is free, then a condition to be satisfied by the "regular" Hamiltonian along the optimal trajectory must be that at any time t

$$H(\mathbf{x}^*, \mathbf{u}^*, t) \triangleq H^*(t) = -\psi_{n+1}(t) \tag{14-72}$$

Further we have the transversality condition

$$\psi_{n+1}(t_2) = 0 \tag{14-73}$$

Corresponding to (14-27) we have

$$\left.\frac{\partial H_1}{\partial x_{n+1}}\right|_{\substack{\mathbf{x}=\mathbf{x}^* \\ \mathbf{u}=\mathbf{u}^*}} = -\dot{\psi}_{n+1}(t) = \left.\frac{\partial H^*}{\partial t}\right|_{\substack{\mathbf{x}=\mathbf{x}^* \\ \mathbf{u}=\mathbf{u}^*}} \tag{14-74}$$

Then in view of (14-74) and (14-73), (14-72) becomes

$$H^*(t) = -\int_{t_1}^{t_2} \left.\frac{\partial H^*(t)}{\partial t}\right|_{\substack{\mathbf{x}=\mathbf{x}^* \\ \mathbf{u}=\mathbf{u}^*}} dt \tag{14-75}$$

which is a relation that must be satisfied for a optimal time-varying Hamiltonian.

4. Problems of the Mayer Form

In Chap. 13, we have discussed the problem of Mayer, namely an optimization problem with a cost that is dependent only on the terminal point. As may be expected, problems in the Mayer form can also be attacked by the maximum principle; although, this class of problems is in general more difficult than those considered previously in this chapter.

In a problem of the Mayer form, the performance index is given by $\mathcal{J} = P(\mathbf{x}(t_2), t_2)$. Let us first note that if P possesses second partial derivatives, the above can be readily converted into one of the Lagrange form, namely, one with a performance index of the form $\mathcal{J} = \int_{t_1}^{t_2} L(\mathbf{x}, \mathbf{u}, t)\,dt$.

We first write

$$P\left(\mathbf{x}(t_2), t_2\right) = P_1 + \int_{t_1}^{t_2} \dot{P}(\mathbf{x}, t)\, dt = P_1 + \int_{t_1}^{t_2} \left(\sum_{i=1}^{n} \frac{\partial P}{\partial x_i} f_i + \frac{\partial P}{\partial t}\right) dt$$

where $P_1 = P(\mathbf{x}(t_1), t_1)$. Since P_1 is a constant it does not enter into the minimization problem; thus, we need only to consider minimizing the integral $\mathcal{J}' = \int_{t_1}^{t_2} \left(\sum_{i=1}^{n} \frac{\partial P}{\partial x_i} f_i + \frac{\partial P}{\partial t}\right) dt$. This is the equivalent problem of Lagrange.

If we directly use $\mathcal{J}'$ for a typical minimization problem under inequality constraints on $\mathbf{u}$, we have (assuming $\psi_0 \neq 0$ so that we set $\psi_0 = -1$)

$$H = -\nabla P^T \mathbf{f} - \frac{\partial P}{\partial t} + \boldsymbol{\psi}^T \mathbf{f} \tag{14-76}$$

Along the optimal trajectory, we have

$$\dot{\boldsymbol{\psi}}(t) = -\left.\frac{\partial H}{\partial \mathbf{x}}\right|_{\substack{\mathbf{x}=\mathbf{x}^* \\ \mathbf{u}=\mathbf{u}^*}}$$

$$= \left[\frac{\partial}{\partial \mathbf{x}}(\nabla P^T \mathbf{f}) + \frac{\partial^2 P}{\partial \mathbf{x}\partial t} - \left(\frac{\partial \boldsymbol{\psi}}{\partial \mathbf{x}}\right)^T \mathbf{f} - (\boldsymbol{\psi})^T \frac{\partial \mathbf{f}}{\partial \mathbf{x}}\right]_{\substack{\mathbf{x}=\mathbf{x}^* \\ \mathbf{u}=\mathbf{u}^*}}$$

As $(\partial \boldsymbol{\psi}/\partial \mathbf{x}) \equiv 0$, we have

$$\dot{\boldsymbol{\psi}}(t) = \left[\frac{\partial}{\partial \mathbf{x}}(\nabla P^T \mathbf{f}) + \frac{\partial^2 P}{\partial \mathbf{x}\partial t} - \boldsymbol{\psi}^T \frac{\partial \mathbf{f}}{\partial \mathbf{x}}\right]_{\substack{\mathbf{x}=\mathbf{x}^* \\ \mathbf{u}=\mathbf{u}^*}} \tag{14-77a}$$

Moreover, since the end state in the problem of Mayer must be free, we also have

$$\boldsymbol{\psi}(t_2) = 0 \tag{14-77b}$$

To find the optimal control, we will then maximize the Hamiltonian of (14-76) subject to the constraint on $\mathbf{u}$.

It turns out that the above can be further simplified, as we may suspect from the discussion in Chap. 13. It can be readily shown that the above minimization problem is identical to one with an equivalent Hamiltonian (see Exercise 14-8)

$$H_a' = \psi_a^T \mathbf{f} \tag{14-78a}$$

where

$$\psi_a = \psi - \frac{\partial P}{\partial \mathbf{x}} \tag{14-78b}$$

Equation (14-77b) implies that $\psi_a(t_2) = -\left.\frac{\partial P}{\partial \mathbf{x}}\right|_{t=t_2}$. We can write, in summary:

◆◆Theorem 14-5. Consider the problem of finding an optimal control $\mathbf{u}^*(t)$ over $[t_1, t_2]$ that minimizes a performance index $P(\mathbf{x}(t_2), t_2)$ for the system $\dot{\mathbf{x}} = \mathbf{f}(\mathbf{x}, \mathbf{u}, t)$. Assume that the starting state is fixed at $\mathbf{x}(t_1) = \mathbf{x}_1$ and the control function $\mathbf{u}(t)$ is subject to the inequality constraint $|\mathbf{u}(t)| \leq \mathrm{U}$ with U a constant vector. The maximum principle in this case is equivalent to one with a Hamiltonian $H_a = \psi_a^T \mathbf{f}$ where ψ_a is generated by $\dot{\psi}_a = -\partial H_a/\partial \mathbf{x}$ with the boundary condition† $\psi_a(t_2) = -\left.\frac{\partial P}{\partial \mathbf{x}}\right|_{t=t_2}$ ◆◆

Even with Theorem 14-5, we are still left with a nontrivial two-point boundary value problem as we can see from the following:

◆◆Example 14-7. Find an optimal control $u^*(t)$ subject to $|u(t)| < 1$ that drives a double integrating plant $1/p^2$ from the origin over a time interval $[0, T]$ so as to minimize the Euclidian distance of the end point $\mathbf{x}(T)$ to a given target point $\mathbf{x}_2$.

In the Mayer formulation, the performance index is given by

$$P(\mathbf{x}(T)) = \left(x_1(T) - x_{21}\right)^2 + \left(x_2(T) - x_{22}\right)^2$$

Clearly, the problem is meaningful only if $\mathbf{x}_2$ is not "reachable" from the origin in T seconds. We shall assume this to be so.

Making use of Theorem 14-5 we have (on dropping the subscript a)

$$H = \psi_1 x_2 + \psi_2 u$$

$$\dot{\psi}_1 = 0, \quad \dot{\psi}_2 = -\psi_1, \qquad \text{and} \qquad u^*(t) = \operatorname{sgn}[\psi_2(t)]$$

The boundary conditions are

†When we write $\partial P/\partial \mathbf{x}$ we mean that $P(\mathbf{x}(t_2), t_2)$ is to be treated like a general function $P(\mathbf{x}(t), t)$.

$$x_1(0) = x_2(0) = 0$$

$$\psi_1(T) = -\left.\frac{\partial P}{\partial x_1}\right|_{t=T} = -2[x_1(T) - x_{21}]$$

$$\psi_2(T) = -\left.\frac{\partial P}{\partial x_2}\right|_{t=T} = -2[x_2(T) - x_{22}]$$

The solution of the adjoint system satisfying the above boundary conditions is

$$\psi_1(t) = 2[x_{21} - x_1(T)]$$

$$\psi_2(t) = 2[x_{22} - x_2(T)] + 2[x_{21} - x_1(T)](T - t)$$

We see that the adjoint vector depends on the unknown end values of the state vector. However, a bang-bang solution is clearly indicated. This together with the fact that the end time T is fixed gives us clear indications on how to solve the problem.

As an example, assume that the point $\mathbf{x}_2$ lies in the first quadrant and, further, that it lies to the right of the trajectory that starts from the origin under the control $u = +1$. It is then clear that $u^*(t)$ must be such that initially it is +1; moreover, at most one switch can occur. Assume a $u^*(t)$ of the form $u^*(t) = +1$ for $0 \le t < t_1$ and $u^*(t) = -1$ for $t_1 \le t \le T$. We can then solve for the end point of the optimal trajectory $\mathbf{x}^*(T)$ as a function of t_1 over $0 < t_1 \le T$ by the system equation and the initial condition $\mathbf{x}(0) = 0$. On substituting the resultant expression for $\mathbf{x}^*(T)$ in the performance index $P(\mathbf{x}(T))$, we then merely need to find the minimum of the expression as a function t_1.

We shall leave the detail of these calculations to the exercises (See Exercise 14-11.)◆◆

If the reachable zone $\mathcal{C}(T)$ can be found graphically (implying that a second-order system is under consideration), then the solution to terminal control problems can sometimes be found graphically. If the double integrator is under consideration, then $\mathcal{C}(T)$ has the general appearance as shown in Fig. 14-9. The radius of the largest circle, centered at $\mathbf{x}_2$, that just touches the set $\mathcal{C}(T)$ yields the minimum distance at time t. The point at which the circle and $\mathcal{C}(T)$ touch is the end point of the optimal trajectory. Figures 14-9a and 14-9b show the cases where $u^*(t)$ has no switching and one switching respectively. (Why?)

Let us note that for a linear (even time-varying) system, the shape and size of $\mathcal{C}(t)$ are invariant with the initial point $\mathbf{x}_1$. (Show this.) Using this fact a larger set of problems can be attacked.

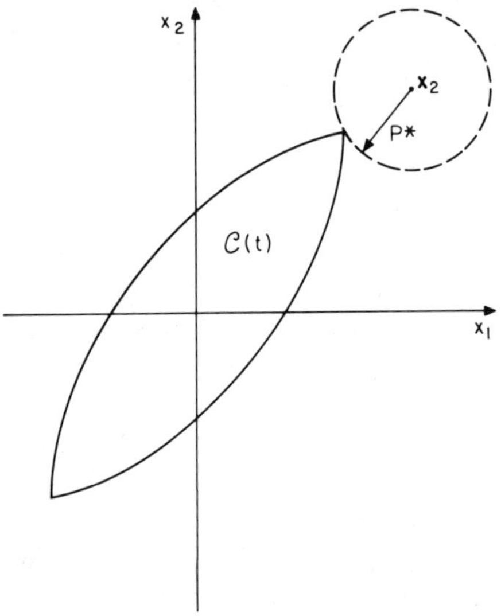

Fig. 14-9a. The geometry of the problem of Example 14-7 where no switching of polarity of $u^*(t)$ is needed.

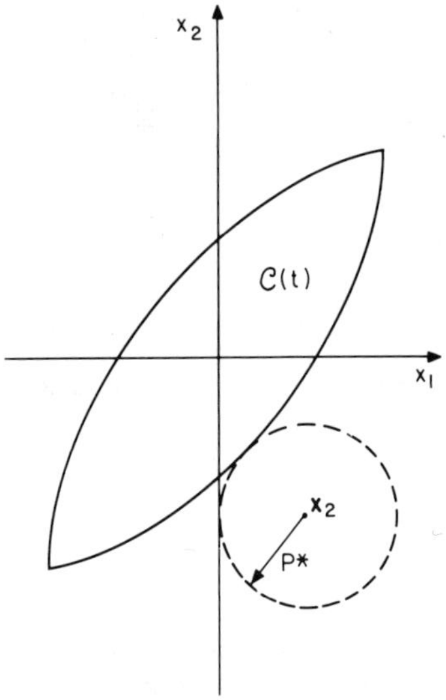

Fig. 14-9b. The geometry of the problem of Example 14-7 where one switching of polarity of $u^*(t)$ is needed.

14.7 Some Further Extensions

We shall mention briefly two areas where the maximum principle has been extended to treat problems that are unconventional.

1. Problems with Inequality Constraints on the State Variables

Sometimes the state space in which the optimal trajectory is to be found is restricted to a *closed* subspace of the Euclidean n-space, such as one defined by an inequality $g(\mathbf{x}) \leq 0$.

If the optimal trajectory lies in the interior of the bounded subspace, the maximum principle as given above is, of course, satisfied. However, if part of the optimal trajectory lies on the boundary $g(\mathbf{x}) = 0$ of the subspace, then the canonical equations must be modified by an extra term. The extra term is such that at a point where the optimal trajectory hits the boundary $g(\mathbf{x}) = 0$, a discontinuous jump in $\psi(t)$ takes place. This "jump condition" was first proved by Gamkrelidze (see [P7], Chap. 7). Problems with inequality constraints on the state variables often occur in practice. A jet plane, for example, must not go below the ground level in executing a landing, and most tracking antennae have velocity and acceleration limits that restrict their ability to track fast targets. When these problems are encountered, care must be exercised in order that the necessary conditions are not violated.

A possible way to bypass the aforementioned difficulties is again to employ penalty functions. The basic concept in using penalty functions to handle inequality constraints on the control variables has been considered in Chap. 13. The extension of the method to state variables is in principle straightforward. Again we introduce extra terms in the performance index to be minimized such that large contributions to the index are accrued when the state inequality constraints are violated. We thus try to force a solution that observes the constraints as far as is possible. When the penalty function is properly chosen, we expect the solution to be close to the exact solution. For some results indicating the propriety of using the penalty function approach, see [R7] and [O2].

2. Differential Games *

An interesting class of problems where an extension of the maximum principle can sometimes be used is the class in which two sets of control variables (and sometimes two differential systems) are involved. The goal of one of the sets of control variables (or system) is to minimize a certain index, whereas the goal of the other set is to maximize the index. As a concrete example, consider the case of a destroyer stalking a submarine. At the time of the dropping of the depth charges, the destroyer likes to be as near as possible to the submarine. The same sentiment, however, is not shared by the latter, who wishes to be far away from the destroyer at the fateful time.

Suppose the composite system is given by a vector differential equation of the form

$$\dot{\mathrm{x}} = \mathrm{f}(\mathrm{x}, \mathrm{u}, \mathrm{v}, t)$$

where u and v represent the control variables at the disposal of the respective adversaries. Further, let there be the usual types of boundary conditions and constraints on the problem. Consider a

*The best reference on differential games is [I2]. Because of its individual viewpoint and unconventional notation, the reader is advised to read the comprehensive review of the book by Y. C. Ho [H11].

performance index in the Lagrange form to be

$$\mathcal{J} = \int_{t_1}^{t_2} L(\mathbf{x}, \mathbf{u}, \mathbf{v}, t)\,dt$$

Assume that the adversary A controlling $\mathbf{u}(t)$ wishes to minimize the index $\mathcal{J}$ while the adversary B controlling $\mathbf{v}(t)$ wishes to maximize the same index. If both A and B have perfect knowledge of each other's location, then from the point of view of the adversary A, a sound strategy is to choose a $\mathbf{u}^*(t)$ to minimize $\mathcal{J}$ *in spite of the best efforts of the adversary* B. This means A wishes to define $\mathbf{u}^*(t)$ such that it yield a $\mathcal{J}^*$ defined by

$$\mathcal{J}^* = \min_{\mathbf{u}} \max_{\mathbf{v}} \int_{t_1}^{t_2} L(\mathbf{x}, \mathbf{u}, \mathbf{v}, t)\,dt$$

This yields a *minimax* control function.

Under certain conditions the above control function can be found by taking the usual Hamiltonian function and finding $\mathbf{u}^*$, $\mathbf{v}^*$ such that

$$H^* = \min_{\mathbf{u}} \max_{\mathbf{v}} H$$

The conditions for the above condition to hold are however nontrivial and we are not prepared to state them here. The interested reader is referred to the literature.†

We may mention that the minimax and other viewpoints associated with the class of problems mentioned here are derived from the *theory of games*. The fact that systems described by differential equations are involved suggests the name *differential games*.

14.8 Summary

By the maximum principle of Pontryagin, a significant class of optimal control problems can be attacked in a neat way. The analyst needs to concern himself only with a minimum of variables and a minimum of necessary conditions.

Through a geometrical viewpoint by way of reachable zones, optimization problems involving differential systems are readily handled by the maximum principle. Moreover, only strong variations need be of concern. Thus the maximum principle enjoys several advantages over classical calculus of variations. The succinctness of the statement of the maximum principle and the universality of its formulation make the setting-up of a large class of optimal control problems almost routine.

†See the bibliography on differential games as given in [A6].

Theorem 14-3 summarizes the maximum principle as a necessary condition for optimality. Theorem 14-4 provides a reasonable broad set of conditions under which the maximum principle is a sufficient condition for optimality as well. Example 14-2 illustrates the advantage the maximum principle enjoys over the classical calculus of variations formulation. Sections 14.6 and 14.7 indicate many classes of problems where the maximum principle can be employed. Section 14.5 provides a proof of the principle.

One area where the classical calculus of variations still enjoys an advantage over the maximum principle is in the theory of the second variation for which the maximum principle offers no counterpart. Second variation will be discussed in Chaps. 16 and 17.

14.9 Exercises

14-1 Find the switching boundaries for time-optimal control of the system of Example 14-1 if

a) $-V \leq u \leq U,\ U > V > 0$.
b) $|u(t)| \leq U$, but the plant is now of the form $\ddot{x} + b\dot{x} + cx = u$; $b,\ c > 0$; and $b^2 - 4c < 0$ (i.e., a lightly damped, oscillating plant).
c) Same as (b) except that $b < 0$.

14-2 Explain why η in Secs. 14.1 and 14.2 turns out to be the initial $\psi(t_1)$, while η in Sec. 14.5 turns out to be the final adjoint vector $\psi(t_2)$.

14-3 For the double integrator plant with $|u(t)| \leq 1$, find the switching curve for the time-optimal control of the plant from an initial point to

a) The unit circle centered about the origin.
b) The unit square $|x_1| \leq 1,\ |x_2| \leq 1$.

14-4 Repeat Exercise 14-3 for the plant of Example 14-1.

14-5 Using the maximum principle, find the switching curves for the time-optimal control of the system

$$\dot{x}_1 = x_2 + u_1$$

$$\dot{x}_2 = -x_1 + u_2$$

from an arbitrary $\mathbf{x}(0)$ to the origin subject to $|u_1| \leq 1,\ |u_2| \leq 2$. Give the polarity of the controls u_1 and u_2 for the various sections of the state space bounded by the switching curves.

14-6 Set up the sounding rocket problem (Exercise 13-10) by means of the maximum principle. Find the adjoint equations and the form of the optimal control $u^*(t)$. Discuss the possibility for nonunique or nonbang-bang solutions.

14-7 Find the transversality condition for the optimal control problem in which a system $\dot{\mathrm{x}} = \mathrm{f}(\mathrm{x}, \mathrm{u})$ is to be controlled from $\mathrm{x}(t_1) = \mathrm{x}_1$ to hit a moving end state $\mathrm{x}_2(t)$ in the minimum time, subject to $|u| \le U$.

14-8 Prove Eqs. (14-78a) and (14-78b).

14-9 Plot to scale the reachable sets $\mathcal{C}(t)$, starting from an arbitrary state x_1 and with $|u(t)| \le 1$

a) The double integrating plant $\ddot{x} = u$
b) The undamped oscillator $\ddot{x} + x = u$

Do this for $t = 1$, $t = \pi$, $t = 5$. Use the same sheet for all three plots involving the same plant.

14-10 Use the result of Exercise 14-9 and solve graphically the problem of minimizing the performance index $P = |x_1(T)| + |x_2(T)|$ for a starting state $x(0) = \begin{bmatrix} -2 \\ -4 \end{bmatrix}$ and a final time $T = 1$. Do this for each plant in Exercise 14-9.

14-11 Complete Example 14-7 for

a) $x_2 = \begin{bmatrix} 2 \\ 4 \end{bmatrix}, \quad T = 1$

b) $x_2 = \begin{bmatrix} 4 \\ 0 \end{bmatrix}, \quad T = 2$

14-12 The angular rates of a satellite with one axis of symmetry is given by

$$\dot{\omega}_1 + A\omega_2\omega_3 = u_1$$

$$\dot{\omega}_2 - A\omega_1\omega_3 = u_2$$

$$\dot{\omega}_3 = u_3$$

Assume $|u_1(t)|,\ |u_2(t)| \leq U;\ |u_3(t)| \leq V$

a) For time-optimal control of the satellite from $\omega(0)$ to 0, find (i) the Hamiltonian of the system, (ii) the canonical equations, (iii) the form of the optimal control function $\mathbf{u}^*(t)$, and (iv) the transversality conditions.
b) Repeat for fuel-optimal control of the satellite from $\omega(0)$ to 0 in a time $T > t^*$.

14-13 Set up the problem of Zermelo (Exercise 13-14) using the maximum principle. Find a solution if f_1 and f_2 are both constants. Repeat if $f_1(x_1, x_2, t) = -kx_2,\ k > 0$ and $f_2(x_1, x_2, t) = 0$. For the second case, construct the optimal trajectory if $V = 1,\ k = 1$ and $\mathbf{x}_0^T = [3, -1]$ and $\mathbf{x}_f^T = [0, 0]$.

14-14 Prove Eq. (14-53).

14-15 Find a closed form feedback control function $u(x)$ that minimizes the functional $\mathcal{J} = \int_0^T u^2(t)\,dt$ relative to the system $\dot{x} = ax + bu$, where a, b, and T are fixed positive constants. Find the expression for the optimal trajectory and for $\mathcal{J}^*$.

14-16 (The time-optimal control of a linear plant with numerator dynamics). Note that all of the plants for time-optimal control that have been considered in this text has so far been those with no numerator dynamics (i.e., no zeros). For a second-order time-invariant plant with numerator dynamics of the form $(p + a)(p + b)y(t) = (p + c)(p + d)u(t),\ |u(t)| \leq 1$,

a) Show that for time optimal control from an arbitrary point $y(0),\ \dot{y}(0)$ to $y = 0,\ \dot{y} = 0$, a bang-bang solution is indicated in the interval $0 \leq t \leq t^*$ if $a \neq b \neq c \neq d$.
b) Show that for $t > t^*$, a nonzero $u(t)$ is needed to maintain y and $\dot{y}$ at 0.
c) Show that it may not always be possible to find a $u(t)$ to maintain y and $\dot{y}$ at 0 for $t > t^*$.
d) Solve the specific case with $a = b = 0,\ c = 1,\ d = 3$. (Hint: Use a transformation (see Sec. 2.5) to arrive at an equivalent set of system equations in which the derivatives of $u(t)$ do not appear. Show that with the transformation, the end state $y = 0,\ \dot{y} = 0$ is transformed into a end set in the state plane of the transformed variables.)

14.10 References

As we have indicated, the approaches and results of Secs. 14.1 and 14.2 are derived directly from [B7] and [L5]. Consult also [S13].

The original work on the maximum principle by Pontryagin et al. are brought together in the carefully written book [P8]. The proof of the maximum principle in [P8], however, is quite different from that used in the text, which is derived from [H5].

A reference that is less rigorous mathematically as compared with [P8] and [H5] but which nevertheless sheds interesting insight on the subject is [R6]. In addition, numerous examples and many additional pointers can be found in [A8].

Further geometrical insight can be gained from [L11].

For some idea of the difficulties involved in applying the maximum principle to obtain the switching boundaries for third- or foruth-order systems see, e.g., [F3] and [S11].

For the use of the maximum principle in linear systems with time delay, see [C3].

An excellent overall summary of the results in optimal control as of 1965 is given in [A6]. The reference contains a comprehensive bibliography.

15

Dynamic Programming

Dynamic programming, which was developed by the mathematician Richard Bellman in the early 1950's, is important for the studying of optimal control problems for at least two reasons. The first is it provides further intuitive appreciation for the structure of the optimal control problem—or more appropriately the properties of the optimal performance index—as a function of the various starting states and times. The second is that, because dynamic programming yields basically a feedback solution to the optimal control problem, it is capable of attacking—at least in theory—problems which cannot be solved by other approaches; among these problems are those of stochastic control.

The basic result of dynamic programming is a partial differential equation known as Bellman's equation. It can be derived heuristically with ease provided certain assumptions, not always met in practice, are made. Recent works have shown, however, that Bellman's equation remains valid even when these restrictive assumptions are removed. It is therefore an important necessary condition for optimality. The validity of Bellman's equation as a sufficient condition for optimality has also been shown in the latter cases.

Dynamic programming was foreshadowed by the researches of C. Carathéodory, whose main works were published in the mid-1920's through mid-1930's. Indeed, in terms of mathematical physics, the maximum principle formulation of the optimization problem is akin to the Hamiltonian formulation of physical problems; on the other hand, the dynamic programming formulation is akin to approaching physics via the Hamilton-Jacobi equation.* It is not surprising then that, for some problems, applying both viewpoints proves helpful.

*For an introductory exposition of these approaches in physics see, e.g., [G7].

15.1 An Intuitive Approach to Solving Optimal Control Problems with the Digital Computer

Consider a one-dimensional optimization problem of minimizing the index $\mathcal{J} = \int_0^T L(x, u)\,dt$ relative to the time-invariant system $\dot{x} = f(x, u)$. The initial condition is $x(0) = x_0$ with the final state $x(T)$ left free. The constraint on the control function is $|u| \leq 1$.

Let it be assumed that the functions $f(x, u)$ and $L(x, u)$ are sufficiently complex that a closed-form solution of the system is not possible. However, let us suppose that there is available a large-scale digital computer which can be used to provide us with a numerical solution. In the interest of obtaining this solution efficiently, let us first analyze what would constitute an efficient computational procedure and, further, whether we can find some general properties of the procedure.

In order to tackle the problem digitally, we must first convert the system into a discrete form. There are a number of ways of doing this, and indeed there exist numerous special programs to solve differential equations numerically. For the sake of simplicity, let us approximate the system by dividing the interval $[0, T]$ into N equal steps,* $t_0, t_1, t_2, \ldots, t_N$, with interval $\Delta t = T/N$. Labeling the values of the state variable and the control variables at the time t_n as x_n and u_n respectively, we approximate the performance index as

$$\mathcal{J} = \sum_{n=0}^{N-1} L(x_n, u_n)\Delta t \tag{15-1a}$$

and the system as

$$x_{n+1} - x_n = f(x_n, u_n)\Delta t, \qquad n = 0, 1, \ldots, N \tag{15-1b}$$

Letting $f(x_n, u_n)\,\Delta t + x_n = g(x_n, u_n)$, (15-1b) is further converted into

$$x_{n+1} = g(x_n, u_n) \tag{15-2}$$

Let us quantize the control function u in the interval $[-1, +1]$ into $2P + 1$ values of size ϵ: $-P\epsilon, (-P + 1)\epsilon, \ldots, P\epsilon$, with $P\epsilon = 1$. We shall denote this set of $2P + 1$ values of u as $\{u_\epsilon\}$. Let us further

*It should be obvious that N must be large enough to make the incurred error negligible when the system is converted into a discrete form.

quantize each state variable in such a way that (15-2) is made consistent with respect to the set $\{u_\epsilon\}$.

One way to create a possible routine for the digital computer is to reason iteratively in the following manner.

Suppose the interval $[0, T]$ is so small that one step is sufficient; then $\Delta t = T$ and $N = 1$. Thus by (15-1) and (15-2)

$$\mathcal{J} = L(x_0, u_0)\Delta t \qquad \text{and} \qquad x_1 = g(x_0, u_0)$$

Our only latitude for optimization for each x_0 is to choose the control variable u_0 so as to minimize $\mathcal{J}$. This is readily accomplished on a digital computer. Let $\mathcal{J}_1^*(x_0)$ be the *optimal value of* $\mathcal{J}$ *for this one step control problem, with* x_0 *as the starting state*; we then have

$$\mathcal{J}_1^*(x_0) = \min_{u_0 \in \{u_\epsilon\}} [L(x_0, u_0)\Delta t] \tag{15-3}$$

where the operation $\min_{u_0 \in \{u_\epsilon\}} [L(x_0, u_0)\Delta t]$ means the finding of the smallest value of the quantity in the bracket over the $2P + 1$ possible values of u_0.

Suppose $N = 2$, i.e., two steps are necessary; then, letting $\mathcal{J}_2$ be the performance index for a two-step control problem, we have $\mathcal{J}_2 = L(x_0, u_0)\Delta t + L(x_1, u_1)\Delta t$. Two values of the control function, namely that of u_0 and u_1, must be chosen and the solutions are no longer so obvious. However, if we pause to consider what must hold true at the intermediate step t_1, we may intuitively arrive at the following hypothesis:

The optimal control sequence for a two-step process $\{u_0^*, u_1^*\}$ should be such that whatever value u_0^* and hence the value x_1^* has, the choice of u_1^* must still be optimal with respect to the state x_1^*.

If the hypothesis is true then we can proceed to solve the two-step optimization problem in the following manner:

For each possible state x_1 at time t_1, find the optimal control u_1^* as if it were a one-step control problem. Store each control $u_1^*(x_1)$ along with its optimum performance index $\mathcal{J}_1^*(x_1)$.

Next, from each state x_0, we calculate the value of the optimal control $u_0^*(x_0)$ which will transfer the state x_0 to each state x_1 *optimally*; i.e., along an optimal trajectory. This is done for each x_0 by calculating for each value of u_0 the resulting state x_1 and then computing the function $\mathcal{J}_2(x_0) = L(x_0, u_0)\Delta t + \mathcal{J}_1^*(x_1)$. The value of $u_0^*(x_0)$ will be that quantized value of u_0 which minimizes the function $\mathcal{J}_2(x_0)$. The above, expressed in the form of an equation, is

$$\mathcal{J}_2^*(x_0) = \min_{u_0 \in \{u_\epsilon\}} [L(x_0, u_0)\Delta t + \mathcal{J}_1^*(x_1)] \tag{15-4}$$

Since $\mathcal{J}_1^*(x_1)$ has been found and stored, the finding of $\mathcal{J}_2^*(x_0)$ via

(15-4) requires only direct comparison and is no more involved than finding $\mathcal{J}_1^*(x_1)$. Now inasmuch as $x_1 = g(x_0, u_0)$, we can write

$$\mathcal{J}_2^*(x_0) = \min_{u_0 \epsilon \{u_\epsilon\}} \left[L(x_0, u_0)\Delta t + \mathcal{J}_1^*\left(g(x_0, u_0)\right)\right] \tag{15-5}$$

We again store the values of $u_0^*(x_0)$ and $\mathcal{J}_2^*(x_0)$ for each x_0.

To find the optimal control function for a particular value of x_0, we retrieve from the storage the function $u_0^*(x_0)$, use it in (15-2) to calculate x_1, then retrieve from storage the value $u_1^*(x_1)$. The sequence $\{u_0^*(x_0), u_1^*(x_1)\}$ will then constitute the optimal control sequence, *provided that the hypothesis stated previously is correct*.

Indeed, if the hypothesis were correct, it can readily be generalized to read: The optimal control sequence for an N-step process $\{u_0^*, u_1^*, \ldots, u_{N-1}^*\}$ should be such that, whatever the value u_0^* and hence the value x_1^* is, the choice of the remaining values of the sequence $\{u_1^*, \ldots, u_{N-1}^*\}$ must remain optimal with respect to the state x_1^*.

Setting $N = 3$, and making use of the hypothesis, one is easily led to the conclusion that

$$\begin{aligned}\mathcal{J}_3^*(x_0) &= \min_{u_0 \epsilon \{u_\epsilon\}} [L(x_0, u_0)\Delta t + \mathcal{J}_2^*(x_1)] \\ &= \min_{u_0 \epsilon \{u_\epsilon\}} \left[L(x_0, u_0)\Delta t + \mathcal{J}_2^*\left(g(x_0, u_0)\right)\right]\end{aligned} \tag{15-6}$$

and in general

$$\mathcal{J}_N^*(x_0) = \min_{u_0 \epsilon \{u_\epsilon\}} \left[L(x_0, u_0)\Delta t + \mathcal{J}_{N-1}^*\left(g(x_0, u_0)\right)\right] \tag{15-7}$$

where $\mathcal{J}_N^*(x_0)$ for each N is the optimal value of $\mathcal{J}$ for an N-step control problem with x_0 as the starting state.

Equations (15-3) and (15-7) constitute a set of recurrent formulas in the optimum performance index value. To avoid subsequent confusion let us drop the subscript 0 in u_0 in (15-3) and (15-7) so that we have

$$\mathcal{J}_1^*(x_0) = \min_{u \epsilon \{u_\epsilon\}} \left[L(x_0, u)\Delta t\right] \tag{15-8a}$$

$$\mathcal{J}_N^*(x_0) = \min_{u \epsilon \{u_\epsilon\}} \left[L(x_0, u)\Delta t + \mathcal{J}_{N-1}^*\left(g(x_0, u)\right)\right], \quad N = z, \ldots \tag{15-8b}$$

Equations (15-8) then will allow us to find the optimal control sequence for an aribtrary integer N. The steps are as follows:

1) At time t_{N-1}, treat each possible quantized value of the state x_{N-1} as an initial state, and treat the optimization problem as a one-step problem from x_{N-1} to x_N. From (15-8a) calculate $u^*_{N-1} = u^*(x_{N-1})$ and $\mathcal{J}^*_1(x_{N-1})$, and store both quantities for each value of x_{N-1}.
2) At time t_{N-2}, use (15-8b) to calculate and store $\mathcal{J}^*_2(x_{N-2})$ and $u^*(x_{N-2})$ for each possible value of x_{N-2}. In the process, the stored values of $\mathcal{J}^*_1$ must be used. Here we treat the optimization problem as a two-step problem from x_{N-2}.
3) At time t_{N-3}, use (15-8b) to calculate and store $\mathcal{J}^*_3(x_{N-3})$ and $u^*(x_{N-3})$ for each possible value of x_{N-3}. Using the stored values of $\mathcal{J}^*_2$ in the process.
4) Continue the above process until time t_0 is reached.
5) To find the optimal sequence from an arbitrary starting point x_0, retrieve the stored value $u^*(x_0)$. It is the first value of the optimal sequence u^*_0. Using this value, generate x_1 by means of (15-2).
6) Retrieve $u^*(x_1)$. It is the value of u^*_1 in the optimal sequence. Using this value, generate x_2 by means of (15-2).
7) Continue the process to obtain the entire optimal control sequence $\{u^*_0, u^*_1, \ldots, u^*_{N-1}\}$ as well as the optimal trajectory sequence $\{x^*_0, x^*_1, \ldots, x^*_N\}$.
8) The optimum performance index for the problem is given by $\mathcal{J}^*_N(x_0)$ which can be retrieved from the computer memory.

Note that while the treatment in this section involves dynamical systems, the system dynamics, introduced via Eq. (15-2), adds but an incidental complication to the dynamic programming formulation. A system without dynamics can also be treated by dynamic programming where (i) alternate configurations (corresponding to states in dynamic systems), (ii) choice of such configurations (corresponding to control functions in dynamic systems), (iii) a cost function as a function of the configurations and choices, and (iv) a performance criterion can be defined. A set of recurrent equations such as those given by (15-8) can also be specified.†

15.2 The Principle of Optimality

Let us pause to remark on the procedure just given in the previous section.

We must admit at once that the discretizing procedure has very little to recommend it. Indeed in the exposition some important computational questions have been neatly "swept under the rug." However the section does leave us at least two important points

†The reader is urged to attempt Exercises 15-1 through 15-3 at this point.

to ponder. These are

1) The intuitive hypothesis used concerning the optimal control sequence.
2) The functional equations (15-8) which can be derived from the application of the hypothesis.

The reader with computational experience in solving differential equations will be able to see that these two points can be arrived at independently of the discretizing scheme or of the computational method involved.

The intuitive hypothesis is seen to be the backbone of the whole approach. It is called *the principle of optimality* by Bellman. We repeat its statement below:

The optimal control sequence for an N-step process $\{u_0^*, u_1^*, \ldots, u_{N-1}^*\}$ is such that, whatever value the first choice u_0^* and hence the value x_1^* is, the choice of the remaining $N-1$ values in the sequence $\{u_1^*, \ldots, u_{N-1}^*\}$ must constitute the optimal control sequence relative to the state x_1^* (which is now viewed as an initial state).

The principle can easily be proved by contradiction: Suppose that $\{u_0^*, u_1^*, \ldots, u_{N-1}^*\}$ is the optimal control sequence, and suppose by the application of u_0^* the system state is driven from x_0 to x_1^*; if the principle of optimality is false, then starting at x_1^* there exists a sequence $\{u_1^{**}, u_2^{**}, \ldots, u_{N-1}^{**}\}$ which will yield a lower value of $\mathcal{J}$ than the sequence $\{u_1^*, u_2^*, \ldots, u_{N-1}^*\}$. This means the sequence $\{u_0^*, u_1^{**}, \ldots, u_{N-1}^{**}\}$ will result in a lower value of $\mathcal{J}$ than the optimal sequence $\{u_0^*, u_1^*, \ldots, u_{N-1}^*\}$, which is impossible.

Let us examine now the form of the functional equations (15-8), repeated below

$$\mathcal{J}_1^*(x_0) = \min_{u \in \{u_\epsilon\}} [L(x_0, u)\Delta t] \tag{15-8a}$$

$$\mathcal{J}_N^*(x_0) = \min_{u \in \{u_\epsilon\}} \Big[L(x_0, u)\Delta t + \mathcal{J}_{N-1}^*\big(g(x_0, u)\big)\Big] \tag{15-8b}$$

We note first that the functional equations permit us to proceed stagewise starting at $N = 1$. The problem in other words has been reduced to an N-step one, at each step of which a single choice of u is made to minimize the quantity $\Big[L(x_0, u)\Delta t + \mathcal{J}_{N-1}^*\big(g(x_0, u)\big)\Big]$. This represents a distinct improvement over procedures which blithely try out all possible paths by direct comparison.

This point, however, should not be overemphasized since it merely indicates the difference between a "blind" approach and a "thoughtful" approach. If computational efficiency is the goal, we can sometimes devise even more efficient approaches than that given in Sec. 15.1.†

The advantage of dynamic programming lies in the insight it provides into the properties of the optimal control function and the optimal performance index. It provides us with an interesting new way of looking at the optimal control problem.

Equation (15-8), for example, is a relationship which gives the optimal performance index $\mathcal{J}^*$ as a function of the starting point x_0. This means with each starting point x_0, a value of the optimal performance index $\mathcal{J}^*$ is automatically associated. We can thus visualize a $\mathcal{J}^*$ hypersurface defined over the state space of the problem. On such a "surface," in view of the performance criteria given, it would be natural that we choose the control u^* which, as far as possible, allows us to proceed in the direction of the maximum decrease of $\mathcal{J}^*$. Upon reflection, it will not be difficult to convince ourselves that the above is exactly what (15-8) is saying.

Note that dynamic programming seems to offer us more than what we have bargained for. Rather than giving us a specific sequence $\{u^*\}$ and a specific $\mathcal{J}^*$, we, through (15-8), can now compute these quantities for all possible starting points. This indeed is the *imbedding feature* inherent in dynamic programming. By imbedding our original, specific problem with a particular starting point in the general class of similar problems, we are able to determine the general pattern of behavior for $\mathcal{J}^*$ and hence are able to deduce what the optimum sequence $\{u^*\}$ must be.

Let us note further that each u^* at each step is generated in terms of the immediate state in which the system finds itself; in other words, inherent in dynamic programming is the ability to generate a closed-loop type control function.

It is perhaps clear that the "backward" dynamic programming procedure, described in the previous section, is not the only way to make use of the principle of optimality. We may just as well proceed "forward." For the forward dynamic programming, the relevant version of principle of optimality can be phrased as follows: The optimal control sequence $\{u_0^*, u_1^*, \ldots, u_{N-1}^*\}$ for an N-step process must be such that whatever value u_{N-1}^* and hence the state x_{N-1}^* has, the first N values in the sequence $\{u_0^*, u_1^*, \ldots, u_{N-1}^*\}$ must still constitute the optimal control sequence relative to the state x_{N-1}^*, viewed as a final state.

This new viewpoint permits us to proceed forward from a given starting point x_0. We now treat every other point as if it were an

†Indeed applying dynamic programming in the manner given in Sec. 15.1 can quickly lead to intractability. Any nontrivial problem can readily exhaust the memory capacity of even the largest computer today. However, sophisticated approaches to the application of dynamic programming in numerical computation exist; see, e.g., [L2] and [L3].

end point and we proceed much as we did in the previous section. If we define a function $\mathcal{J}_N^*(x_N)$ as the value of the optimal performance index for the point x_N, treated as the end point when the optimal process is started at the point x_0, we can then quickly arrive at the functional equations

$$\mathcal{J}_1^*(x_1) = \min_{u \in \{u_\epsilon\}} [L(x_1, u)\Delta t]$$

$$\mathcal{J}_N^*(x_N) = \min_{u \in \{u_\epsilon\}} \left[\mathcal{J}_{N-1}^*\left(g(x_{N-1}, u)\right) + L(x_{N-1}, u)\Delta t\right] \tag{15-9}$$

(Show these.) With this formulation, closed-loop control and the imbedding of a large class of solutions are still inherent in the solution.

It is not surprising that the new viewpoint provided by dynamic programming can further improve our understanding of the optimization problem. It is quite possible, for example, to derive most of the important results of classical calculus of variations by a simple and straightforward application of dynamic programming.† By the same token, some of the more mysterious points of the maximum principle can be simply resolved by looking at the problem from the dynamic programming point of view. To appreciate some of these points, it is necessary for us to first consider the method as applied to continuous-time systems.

15.3 Continuous-Time Dynamic Programming—The Equation of Bellman

Let us now apply the principle of optimality to the optimal control of continuous-time systems. We shall show that we can derive a partial differential equation that corresponds to the functional equations (15-8). This equation is called Bellman's equation.††

Consider the following problem in the Lagrange form: For a system $\dot{\mathbf{x}} = \mathbf{f}(\mathbf{x}, \mathbf{u}, t)$ starting from an initial state $\mathbf{x}(t_1) = \mathbf{x}_1$, find an input $\mathbf{u}(t)$, restricted to a certain admissible class of functions $\Omega(t)$ and defined over a given time interval $[t_1, t_2]$, which minimizes a performance index $\mathcal{J} = \int_{t_1}^{t_2} L(\mathbf{x}, \mathbf{u}, t)\,dt$, where *the function* $L(\mathbf{x}, \mathbf{u}, t)$

†See [D10] or [D11].

††The derivation we use here is essentially that first employed by Tchamran [T2]. This derivation does not require the continuity of the function $\partial\mathcal{J}^*/\partial\mathbf{x}$. As we shall show in Sec. 15.6, the requirement that $\partial\mathcal{J}^*/\partial\mathbf{x}$ is continuous would render dynamic programming invalid for many common optimal control problems.

is assumed to be continuous with respect to t. The terminal state $\mathbf{x}(t_2) = \mathbf{x}_2$ is assumed to be free. The vector space $\Omega(t)$, as before, is distinguished by the fact that all vector functions $\mathbf{u}(t)$ belonging to it are amplitude-limited such that at any time t, $|u_j(t)| \le U_j$. The set of points $|u_j| \le U_j$, $j = 1, \ldots, r$ in an r-dimensional Euclidean space is denoted $\mathcal{U}$.

The performance index $\mathcal{J}$ for a fixed value of t_2 is a function of $\mathbf{u}(t)$, $\mathbf{x}_1$, and t_1. Note that the optimal value of $\mathcal{J}$, however, depends only on the initial state $\mathbf{x}_1$ and the initial time t_1. We thus denote the optimal value of $\mathcal{J}$ by $\mathcal{J}^*(\mathbf{x}_1, t_1)$.

In the light of the foregoing, to appreciate the derivation to come, it is helpful first to formulate the following mental picture. Once a meaningful optimal control problem is posed, then immediately, to each point in the state space $\mathbf{x}_1$ treated as a starting point (for a given starting time t_1), a value of the optimal performance index is associated. The function $\mathcal{J}^*(\mathbf{x}_1, t_1)$ then defines a hypersurface in an $(n+1)$-dimensional space. The hypersurface, of course, is not explicitly known to an investigator, but from certain properties of this surface, relating for example its rate of change with respect to $\mathbf{x}$ and t, he can try to deduce some necessary conditions that must be imposed on the optimal control function $\mathbf{u}^*(t)$.

Let $\mathbf{x}\big(\mathbf{u}(t), t\big)$ be the trajectory resulting from the application of $\mathbf{u}(t)$ on the system $\dot{\mathbf{x}} = f(\mathbf{x}, \mathbf{u}, t)$ starting from the state $\mathbf{x}_1$ at $t = t_1$. Clearly $\mathcal{J}^*$ is given by

$$\mathcal{J}^*(\mathbf{x}_1, t_1) = \min_{\substack{\mathbf{u}(t) \in \Omega(t) \\ t_1 \le t \le t_2}} \left[\int_{t_1}^{t_2} L\big(\mathbf{x}(\mathbf{u}, t), \mathbf{u}, t\big)\, dt \right] \tag{15-10}$$

which can be written for some time t' between t_1 and t_2 as

$$\mathcal{J}^*(\mathbf{x}_1, t_1) = \min_{\substack{\mathbf{u}(t) \in \Omega(t) \\ t_1 \le t \le t_2}} \left[\int_{t_1}^{t'} L\big(\mathbf{x}(\mathbf{u}, t), \mathbf{u}, t\big)\, dt + \int_{t'}^{t_2} L\big(\mathbf{x}(\mathbf{u}, t), \mathbf{u}, t\big)\, dt \right] \tag{15-11}$$

Equation (15-11) is in a form suitable for the application of the principle of optimality. In the continuous-time case given here, its statement can take the form: The optimal control function $\mathbf{u}^*(t)$ over $[t_1, t_2]$ has the property that, for any t' such that $t_1 < t' < t_2$, regardless of what the value of $\mathbf{u}^*(t)$ may be over $[t_1, t']$ and hence, regardless of the value of $\mathbf{x}^*(t')$, it must still remain optimal with respect to the state $\mathbf{x}^*(t')$ over the time interval $(t', t_2]$.

Applying the principle of optimality, we can convert (15-11) into the form

$$\mathcal{J}^*(\mathbf{x}_1, t_1) = \min_{\substack{\mathbf{u}(t) \in \Omega(t) \\ t_1 \le t \le t'}} \left[\int_{t_1}^{t'} L\big(\mathbf{x}(\mathbf{u}, t), \mathbf{u}, t\big)\, dt + \mathcal{J}^*\big(\mathbf{x}(t'), t'\big) \right] \tag{15-12}$$

where $\mathbf{x}(t')$ is the state resulting from the application of $\mathbf{u}(t)$ over the interval $[t_1, t']$, starting from $\mathbf{x}_1$ at t_1.†

With $\mathbf{u}(t) = \mathbf{u}^*(t)$, the optimal control function, then in $[t_1, t']$, we have

$$\mathcal{J}^*(\mathbf{x}_1, t_1) = \int_{t_1}^{t'} L\big(\mathbf{x}(\mathbf{u}^*, t), \mathbf{u}^*(t), t\big)dt + \mathcal{J}^*\big(\mathbf{x}(t'), t'\big) \quad \text{(15-13)}$$

Rearranging and dividing by $t' - t_1$, we have,

$$-\frac{\mathcal{J}^*\big(\mathbf{x}(t'), t'\big) - \mathcal{J}^*(\mathbf{x}_1, t_1)}{t' - t_1} = \frac{1}{t' - t_1}\int_{t_1}^{t'} L\big(\mathbf{x}(\mathbf{u}^*, t), \mathbf{u}^*(t), t\big)dt \quad \text{(15-14)}$$

As $t' \to t_1$, (15-14) becomes††

$$\lim_{t' \to t_1}\left[-\frac{\mathcal{J}^*\big(\mathbf{x}(t'), t'\big) - \mathcal{J}^*(\mathbf{x}_1, t_1)}{t' - t_1}\right] = L\big(\mathbf{x}_1, \mathbf{u}^*(t_1), t_1\big) \quad \text{(15-15)}$$

If the limit of the lhs of (15-15) exists, we can then define the quantity

$$\left[\frac{d\mathcal{J}^*}{dt}\right]_{\mathbf{u}^*, t_1} \triangleq \lim_{t' \to t_1}\left[\frac{\mathcal{J}^*\big(\mathbf{x}(t'), t'\big) - \mathcal{J}^*(\mathbf{x}_1, t_1)}{t' - t_1}\right] \quad \text{(15-16)}$$

The quantity $\left[\frac{d\mathcal{J}^*}{dt}\right]_{\mathbf{u}^*, t_1}$ is a certain time derivative of $\mathcal{J}^*$ at t_1. By the rhs of (15-16) we see that the derivative is to be evaluated along the trajectory that is generated by the control function $\mathbf{u}^*$, starting at $\mathbf{x}$.††† We can thus write

$$\left[\frac{d\mathcal{J}^*}{dt}\right]_{\mathbf{u}^*, t_1} + L\big(\mathbf{x}_1, \mathbf{u}^*(t_1), t_1\big) = 0 \quad \text{(15-17)}$$

†At this point, if we assume that the $\mathcal{J}^*$ possesses continuous first partial derivatives, both with respect to $\mathbf{x}$ and t, then Bellman's equation can be easily arrived at. (See [B3] and [D11].) However, as we shall see below, this assumption is not satisfied for a large class of optimal control problems. Our proof given here, based on [T2], does not use the above assumption.

††The mean value theorem for integrals (see [A5] p. 213) is used to obtain the rhs of (15-15) as the limit of the rhs of (15-14).

†††To appreciate this, visualize the following picture. For a given problem, $\mathcal{J}^*(\mathbf{x}, t)$ is fully defined for any starting state $\mathbf{x}$ and starting time t. Let $\mathbf{x}\big(\mathbf{u}(t), t\big)$ be a trajectory generated by the control function $\mathbf{u}(t)$; then along any such trajectory, $\mathcal{J}^*(\mathbf{x}, t)$ will vary with time at a rate given by $\left[\frac{d\mathcal{J}^*}{dt}\right]_{u, t}$. Specifically, it will vary at the rate $\left[\frac{d\mathcal{J}^*}{dt}\right]_{u^*, t}$ along the optimal trajectory.

Let us note that for $\mathbf{u}(t) \neq \mathbf{u}^*(t)$ in the integral of (15-13), we must by definition have

$$\mathcal{J}^*(\mathbf{x}_1, t_1) \leq \int_{t_1}^{t'} L\big(\mathbf{x}(\mathbf{u}(t), t), \mathbf{u}(t), t\big)dt + \mathcal{J}^*\big(\mathbf{x}(t'), t'\big) \qquad (15\text{-}18)$$

Following the steps involved in (15-14) through (15-17), (15-18) can be developed into the form

$$\left[\frac{d\mathcal{J}^*}{dt}\right]_{\mathbf{u}, t_1} + L\big(\mathbf{x}_1, \mathbf{u}(t_1), t_1\big) \geq 0 \qquad (15\text{-}19)$$

Combining (15-17) and (15-19), we obtain

$$\left[\frac{d\mathcal{J}^*}{dt}\right]_{\mathbf{u}, t_1} + L\big(\mathbf{x}_1, \mathbf{u}(t_1), t_1\big) \geq \left[\frac{d\mathcal{J}^*}{dt}\right]_{\mathbf{u}^*, t_1} + L\big(\mathbf{x}_1, \mathbf{u}^*(t_1), t_1\big) = 0 \qquad (15\text{-}20)$$

or we can write

$$\min_{\mathbf{u}(t_1)\in\mathcal{U}} \left\{\left[\frac{d\mathcal{J}^*}{dt}\right]_{\mathbf{u}, t_1} + L\big(\mathbf{x}_1, \mathbf{u}(t_1), t_1\big)\right\} = 0 \qquad (15\text{-}21)$$

Equation (15-21) clearly holds at any time in the interval $[t_1, t_2]$ as well, so that we can write, for any time t and any state $\mathbf{x}$ on the trajectory $\mathbf{x}^*(t)$ treated as an initial state,

$$\min_{\mathbf{u}(t)\in\mathcal{U}} \left\{\left[\frac{d\mathcal{J}^*}{dt}\right]_{\mathbf{u}, t} + L\big(\mathbf{x}(\mathbf{u}, t), \mathbf{u}, t\big)\right\} = 0 \qquad (15\text{-}22)$$

Equation (15-22) is *Bellman's functional equation* in a general form. It represents a necessary condition for optimality.

At any state $\mathbf{x}$ and a time t where $\partial\mathcal{J}^*/\partial t$, $\partial\mathcal{J}^*/\partial\mathbf{x}$, and $\mathbf{f}(\mathbf{x}, \mathbf{u}, t)$ are all continuous in $\mathbf{x}$ and t, the total derivative $\left[\frac{d\mathcal{J}^*}{dt}\right]_{\mathbf{u}, t}$ can be expressed by the chain rule as

$$\left[\frac{d\mathcal{J}^*}{dt}\right]_{\mathbf{u}, t} = \left(\frac{\partial\mathcal{J}^*}{\partial\mathbf{x}}\right)^T \mathbf{f}(\mathbf{x}, \mathbf{u}, t) + \frac{\partial\mathcal{J}^*}{\partial t} \qquad (15\text{-}23)$$

Since $\partial\mathcal{J}^*/\partial t$ is independent of $\mathbf{u}$ (why?), Eq. (15-22) can now be given in the form

$$-\frac{\partial \mathcal{J}^*}{\partial t} = \min_{\mathbf{u}(t)\in\mathcal{U}} \left[L\big(\mathbf{x}(\mathbf{u}, t), \mathbf{u}, t\big) + \left(\frac{\partial \mathcal{J}^*}{\partial \mathbf{x}}\right)^T \mathbf{f}(\mathbf{x}, \mathbf{u}, t) \right] \tag{15-24}$$

Equation (15-24) represents a special case of (15-22), though it is frequently called the Bellman's functional equation. Where it is applicable it provides a necessary condition for optimality.† Equation (15-24) is an interesting form of partial differential equation, since a minimization operation is involved.

Let us consider initially only Eq. (15-24). We see that it is a first-order (and, in general, nonlinear) partial differential equation in one variable $\mathcal{J}^*$. It is a one-point boundary value type with the boundary condition given by

$$\lim_{t_1 \to t_2} \left[\mathcal{J}^*(\mathbf{x}_1, t_1)\right] = \lim_{t_1 \to t_2} \int_{t_1}^{t_2} L(\mathbf{x}^*, \mathbf{u}^*, t)\, dt = 0 \tag{15-25}$$

We further see that it actually provides information on three conditions. First, it tells us how to carry out our search for the optimal $\mathbf{u}(t)$, namely, at any time t it must be one which minimizes the bracketed quantity in (15-24). Second, if the optimal control function $\mathbf{u}^*(t)$ is found, then (15-24) reduces to an equation without the minimization operation

$$-\frac{\partial \mathcal{J}^*}{\partial t} = L\Big(\mathbf{x}\big(\mathbf{u}^*(t), t\big), \mathbf{u}^*, t\Big) + \left(\frac{\partial \mathcal{J}^*}{\partial \mathbf{x}}\right)^T \mathbf{f}\Big(\mathbf{x}\big(\mathbf{u}^*(t), t\big), \mathbf{u}^*(t), t\Big) \tag{15-26}$$

which must be obeyed by the function $\mathcal{J}^*(\mathbf{x}, t)$ for all t in $[t_1, t_2]$. Finally, as (15-24) and (15-25) are valid for all starting states, the imbedding feature alluded to in the previous section is still present in the continuous case.

If there is no constraint on the magnitude of $\mathbf{u}$, and if L and $\mathbf{f}$ possess first partial derivatives with respect to $\mathbf{u}$, then $\mathbf{u}^*(t)$ can be found by differentiating the bracketed quantity in (15-24) and setting the result to 0. This yields the condition

$$\left[\frac{\partial L}{\partial \mathbf{u}} + \sum_{i=1}^{n} \frac{\partial \mathcal{J}^*}{\partial x_1} \frac{\partial f_i}{\partial \mathbf{u}}\right]_{\mathbf{u}=\mathbf{u}^*} = 0 \qquad \text{for all } t \in [t_1, t_2] \tag{15-27}$$

†For all the problems to be treated in this chapter, Eq. (15-24) is always valid in a specific sense; this will be brought out in Sec. 15.6.

If the performance index is of the Mayer type, namely $\mathcal{J} = P(\mathbf{x}(t_2), t_2)$, then following essentially along the lines of the above reasoning, we obtain the corresponding Bellman's equation (see Exercise 15-6)

$$\min_{\mathbf{u}(t) \in \mathcal{U}} \left[\frac{d\mathcal{J}^*}{dt}\right]_{\mathbf{u},\, t} = 0 \tag{15-28a}$$

and the boundary condition

$$\lim_{t_1 \to t_2} \mathcal{J}^*(\mathbf{x}(t_1), t_1) = P(\mathbf{x}(t_2), t_2) \tag{15-28b}$$

Where $\partial\mathcal{J}^*/\partial t$, $\partial\mathcal{J}^*/\partial \mathbf{x}$ and $\mathbf{f}(\mathbf{x}, \mathbf{u}, t)$ are all continuous in $\mathbf{x}$ and t, we further have

$$-\frac{\partial\mathcal{J}^*}{\partial t} = \min_{\mathbf{u}(t) \in \mathcal{U}} \left[\left(\frac{\partial\mathcal{J}^*}{\partial \mathbf{x}}\right)^T \mathbf{f}(\mathbf{x}, \mathbf{u}, t)\right] \tag{15-29}$$

with the same boundary condition (15-28b).

Note that the type of boundary condition at the end state plays no role in the derivation. Thus Bellman's equation (15-22) or (15-24) is also valid for the problem of this section even if the end state $\mathbf{x}_2$ is fixed and the end time t_2 free. Here, (15-25) is still valid and no change needs to be made anywhere in the derivation.

15.4 The Optimal Control of Linear Feedback Systems with Integrated Quadratic Performance Criteria

We have indicated that dynamic programming has the property that any optimal control function $\mathbf{u}^*$ found by using the method is usually in a feedback form, i.e., one that's expressed as a function of the state $\mathbf{x}$. However, to use dynamic programming requires that we must somehow solve the resulting Bellman equation. Indeed, in an effort to obtain feedback solutions, we have gone from a set of $2n$ differential equations (as would be obtained if we use calculus of variations or the maximum principle) with two-point boundary conditions to a single partial differential equation with one-point boundary conditions. Whatever gain we have achieved is not immediately apparent.

We can, however, derive an appreciation for the utility of dynamic programming by considering first a case where the

Bellman equation is directly solvable. Such a case is given by the optimal control of a linear plant using a performance index that is the integral of quadratic forms in $\mathbf{x}$ and $\mathbf{u}$. This type of problem has been briefly discussed in Chap. 13. We shall see that through the use of dynamic programming, the issues involved in this class of problems can be brought more sharply into focus.

Before considering this problem in its general form, it is instructive to consider a specific example.

♦♦Example 15-1. Consider the first-order plant $\dot{x} = -ax + bu$. The performance index to be minimized is $\mathcal{J} = \int_0^T (c_1x^2 + c_2u^2)dt$. It is desired to find the optimal linear feedback control over the time interval $[0, T]$ of the form $u(t) = -q(t)x(t)$ which is valid for any initial point $x(0)$. The terminal point is free.

For this problem, Bellman's equation (15-24) becomes

$$-\frac{\partial \mathcal{J}^*}{\partial t} = \min_u \left[c_1x^2 + c_2u^2 + \frac{\partial \mathcal{J}^*}{\partial x}(-ax + bu)\right] \tag{15-30}$$

Since there is no constraint on the magnitude of $u(t)$, to minimize the rhs of Bellman's equation we can differentiate with respect to u. By setting the result to 0, we obtain

$$u^* = -\frac{b}{2c_2}\frac{\partial \mathcal{J}^*}{\partial x} \tag{15-31}$$

Substituting Eq. (15-31) into Eq. (15-30) gives

$$\frac{\partial \mathcal{J}^*}{\partial t} + \frac{\partial \mathcal{J}^*}{\partial x}\left(-ax - \frac{b^2}{2c_2}\frac{\partial \mathcal{J}^*}{\partial x}\right) + \left[c_1x^2 + c_2\left(-\frac{b}{2c_2}\frac{\partial \mathcal{J}^*}{\partial x}\right)^2\right] = 0 \tag{15-32}$$

The boundary condition for the problem, by Eq. (15-25), is $\lim_{t \to T} \mathcal{J}^*(x, t) = 0$.

The simplest approach to the solution of a partial differential equation of the type encountered here is to attempt a separable solution; namely, try to use as a trial solution one of the form $\mathcal{J}^*(x, t) = p(t)r(x)$. From (15-31) and the requirement that $u(t)$ is to be of the form $q(t)x(t)$, we deduce that a suitable form for $r(x)$ should be x^2.

Substituting $\mathcal{J}^* = p(t)x^2(t)$ into Eq. (15-32), we obtain

$$\frac{dp}{dt}x^2 + 2xp\left(-ax - \frac{b^2}{2c_2}2xp\right) + \left[c_1x^2 + c_2\left(\frac{b}{2c_2}2xp\right)^2\right] = 0$$

or we find that $p(t)$ satisfied the nonlinear differential equation

$$\frac{dp}{dt} - 2ap - \frac{b^2p^2}{c_2} + c_1 = 0 \tag{15-33}$$

with the boundary condition $\lim_{t \to T} \mathcal{J}^*(t, x) = \lim_{t \to T} p(t)x^2 = 0$, from which we obtain

$$p(T) = 0 \tag{15-34}$$

This means that $\mathcal{J}^* = p(t)x^2$ will be a solution to Eq. (15-32) provided that there exists a solution $p(t)$ to Eq. (15-33) subject to the boundary condition (15-34).

Equation (15-33) is a differential equation that is similar in form to the classical Riccati equation;† in this particular case, it can be integrated by separation of variables

$$\frac{(c_2/b^2)\,dp}{p^2 + (2c_2a/b^2)p - c_1c_2/b^2} = dt \tag{15-35}$$

If p_1 and p_2 are the roots of the denominator polynomial $p^2 + (2c_2a/b^2)p - c_1c_2/b^2 = 0$, then the general solution for (15-35) is

$$\frac{p(t) - p_1}{p(t) - p_2} = k \exp\left[\frac{b^2}{c_2}(p_1 - p_2)t\right] \tag{15-36}$$

or

$$p(t) = \frac{-p_2k \exp\left[(b^2/c_2)(p_1 - p_2)t\right] + p_1}{1 - k \exp\left[(b^2/c_2)(p_1 - p_2)t\right]} \tag{15-37}$$

Applying the boundary condition $p(T) = 0$, we find

$$k = \frac{p_1}{p_2 \exp\left[(b^2/c_2)(p_1 - p_2)T\right]} \tag{15-38}$$

Thus we have $\mathcal{J}^*(x, t) = p(t)x^2$ for any starting point x and starting

†See, e.g., [I1] p. 23.

time t; whence, from (15-31), we obtain

$$u^*(t) = -\frac{b}{2c_2}\frac{\partial \mathcal{J}^*}{\partial x} = -\frac{bp(t)}{c_2}x \tag{15-39}$$

The resultant feedback control system is shown in Fig. 15-1. It is linear but time varying.

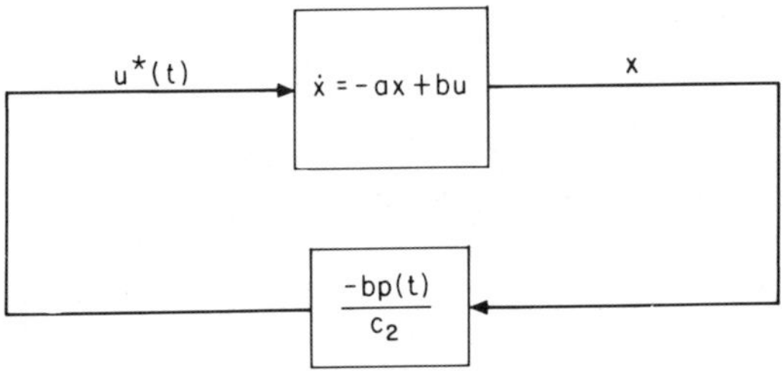

Fig. 15-1. The optimal control system of Example 15-1, with $p(t)$ given by (15-37) and (15-38).

When the final time T is infinite, then we recall from Chap. 13 that the optimal feedback control function is a constant matrix times the instantaneous state. In our one-dimension case we expect that the optimal feedback control will be a constant times the output. This we can show by the following consideration.

We expect that as $T \to \infty$ both the state x and the control function u must go to 0, for otherwise $\mathcal{J}$ will be infinite. With $\lim_{t\to\infty} x(t) = 0$, however, the value of $p(t)$ cannot be determined by the boundary condition $\lim_{t\to\infty} \mathcal{J}^*(x, t) = p(t)x^2 = 0$, and we must look elsewhere for clues.

From Eq. (15-38), if $p_1 > p_2$, then as $T \to \infty$, $k \to 0$; thus Eq. (15-36) suggests that $p(t) = p_1$. On the other hand, if $p_2 > p_1$, then as $T \to \infty$, $k \to \infty$, and Eq. (15-36) suggests that $p(t) = p_2$. Thus, $\lim_{T\to\infty} p(t) = \max(p_1, p_2)$, and this limit is a constant. It then follows that $dp/dt = 0$.

We have therefore shown that as $T \to \infty$ the optimal linear feedback function becomes $u^*(t) = px(t)$ where the constant p is the larger of the two roots of the polynomial $p^2 + (2c_2a/b^2)p - c_1c_2/b^2 = 0$.◆◆

The general problem of the above type, which we may call the general regulator problem, has been treated by Merriam [M9] and Kalman [K2], [K6], and others. The problem is the following: Given a linear time-varying plant $\dot{\mathbf{x}} = \mathbf{A}(t)\mathbf{x} + \mathbf{B}(t)\mathbf{u}$, with initial condition $\mathbf{x}(t_1) = \mathbf{x}_1$ and with $\mathbf{x}(t_2)$ unspecified, find the optimal control function $\mathbf{u}^*(t)$ over $[t_1, t_2]$ which minimizes the performance index

$$\mathcal{J} = \frac{1}{2}x_2{}^T M x_2 + \frac{1}{2}\int_{t_1}^{t_2} [x^T(\tau)Q(\tau)x(\tau) + u^T(\tau)R(\tau)u(\tau)]\,d\tau \qquad (15\text{-}40)$$

where M, $Q(t)$, and $R(t)$ are symmetric matrices, with $Q(t)$ and $R(t)$ positive definite and possess continuous second derivatives with respect to t, and M is a nonnegative definite constant matrix (so as to guarantee a unique minimum).

The above is a problem of the Bolza type, but the considerations given in Sec. 15.3 are sufficient to attack this problem as well.

We can parallel the steps in Example 15-1. The Bellman equation is

$$-\frac{\partial \mathcal{J}^*}{\partial t} = \left[\frac{1}{2}x^T(t)Q(t)x(t) + \frac{1}{2}u^{*T}(t)R(t)u^*(t) + \left(\frac{\partial \mathcal{J}^*}{\partial x}\right)^T \left(A(t)x + B(t)u^*\right)\right] \qquad (15\text{-}41)$$

The boundary condition from Eqs. (15-25) and (15-28b) is

$$\lim_{t \to t_2} \mathcal{J}^*(x, t) = \frac{1}{2}x^T(t_2)M\,x(t_2) \qquad (15\text{-}42)$$

The minimization procedure will result in

$$\left.\frac{\partial L}{\partial u}\right|_{u=u^*} + \left.\frac{\partial}{\partial u}\left[\left(\frac{\partial \mathcal{J}^*}{\partial x}\right)^T \left(A(t)x + B(t)u\right)\right]\right|_{u=u^*} = 0 \qquad (15\text{-}43)$$

where L is the integrand in Eq. (15-40).

This yields (show this)

$$u^*(t) = -R^{-1}(t)B^T(t)\left(\frac{\partial \mathcal{J}^*}{\partial x}\right) \qquad (15\text{-}44)$$

If we wish to have a linear feedback control, it suggests that $\mathcal{J}^*$ should be of the quadratic form

$$\mathcal{J}^*(x, t) = \frac{1}{2}x^T P(t)x \qquad (15\text{-}45)$$

with $P(t)$ an $n \times n$ symmetric matrix.

Substituting (15-44) and (15-45) into the Bellman equation (15-41), we obtain a *matrix Riccati equation*

$$-\frac{dP(t)}{dt} = -P(t)B(t)R^{-1}(t)B^T(t)P(t) + P(t)A(t) + A^T(t)P(t) + Q(t) \qquad (15\text{-}46)$$

subject to the boundary condition at $t = t_2$

$$\mathrm{P}(t_2) = \mathrm{M} \tag{15-47}$$

The matrix $\mathrm{P}(t)$ can in theory be found by integrating Eq. (15-46) *backward* from the final condition (15-47). When $\mathrm{P}(t)$ has been found, since it is symmetric, then by (15-44), in view of (15-45), we obtain

$$\mathrm{u}^*(\mathrm{x}, t) = -\mathrm{R}^{-1}(t)\,\mathrm{B}^T(t)\,\mathrm{P}(t)\,\mathrm{x}(t) \tag{15-48}$$

Thus there will be a unique absolute minimum of (15-40) only if the matrix Riccati equation (15-46) has a unique solution. On this, Kalman has proved the following useful theorem.†

♦♦Theorem 15-1 [K6]. Under the assumptions stated in this section, Eq. (15-46) with the boundary condition (15-47) has a unique solution for $\mathrm{P}(t)$. With this $\mathrm{P}(t)$ the feedback control function (15-48) is *the* optimal control function, yielding the optimal performance index (15-45).♦♦

In other words, the Bellman equation (15-41) provides a *sufficient* condition for optimality for this case.

An area where the results of this section can be fruitfully used is in the design of small-signal guidance loops in endeavors such as orbital insertion of a satellite. In such problems, there is a nominal trajectory that a booster is to follow. But because of booster and atmospheric parameter variations, a given booster seldom follows the nominal trajectory exactly. To correct for small deviations about the nominal trajectory, we can, for example, linearize the booster dynamics about the nominal trajectory. After this, if a performance criterion of the form (15-40) can be chosen†† then the design can proceed using the formalism of the present section.

♦♦Example 15-2.††† A simplified and linearized missile guidance loop may be expressed in the form

$$\dot{x}_1 = x_2, \qquad \dot{x}_2 = \frac{k_1}{k_2 - t}\,x_3, \qquad \dot{x}_3 = u$$

where x_1 is the lateral deviation from a "nominal trajectory," x_2

†The proof of this theorem will become apparent when we come to Sec. 15.7.

††One situation where a performance criterion of the form (15-40) arises naturally is when the second variation is employed on a performance index which originally is not in the form (15-40). This will be made clear in the next two chapters.

†††This example is by courtesy of H. Heffes, J. M. Holtzman, and S. Horing of Bell Telephone Laboratories. Their study, in an unpublished memorandum, included the effect of noise.

is the velocity of the deviation, and x_3 is the thrust angle. The relationship between laterial thrust and lateral acceleration is given through a time-varying gain $k_1/(k_2 - t)$, which accounts for the loss of mass during thrust. The one stage of integration between x_3 and u is used to represent a linearized actuator.

Assuming that $x_1(t)$, $x_2(t)$, and $x_3(t)$ can all be faultlessly measured, we can device a feedback control scheme to guide the missile optimally with respect to a given performance index. Let the index

$$\mathcal{J} = \frac{1}{2}\int_0^T \left(\mathbf{x}^T(\tau)\,\mathbf{Q}(\tau)\,\mathbf{x}(\tau) + ru^2\right)dt$$

be used, where $r = 10$, $T = 250$ sec, and

$$\mathbf{Q}(t) = \frac{1}{(300 - t)^2}\begin{bmatrix} 5 \times 10^{-7} & 0 & 0 \\ 0 & 10^{-3} & 0 \\ 0 & 0 & 10^3 \end{bmatrix}$$

and let the initial conditions be $x_1(0) = 3000$ ft, $x_2(0) = 800$ ft/sec, $x_3(0) = 12$ milliradians.

In the notation of the present section, we then have

$$\mathbf{A}(t) = \begin{bmatrix} 0 & 1 & 0 \\ 0 & 0 & \dfrac{k_1}{k_2 - t} \\ 0 & 0 & 0 \end{bmatrix}, \qquad \mathbf{b} = \begin{bmatrix} 0 \\ 0 \\ 1 \end{bmatrix}$$

and we must solve the matrix Riccati equation (15-46) with the boundary condition $\mathbf{P}(T) = \mathbf{0}$.

If we inspect the form of the feedback solution (15-48), since $r^{-1}\mathbf{b}^T = [0 \quad 0 \quad 1/10]$, only the last row of the symmetric matrix $\mathbf{P}(t) = [p_{ij}(t)]$, $(i, j = 1, 2, 3)$ will be needed, as we have $\mathbf{u}^*(\mathbf{x}, t) = -(1/10)[p_{13} \quad p_{23} \quad p_{33}]\,\mathbf{x}(t)$. However, due to the coupled nature of Eq. (15-46), we can readily demonstrate that we must solve the following six coupled nonlinear differential equations with boundary conditions at one point (show this)

$$\dot{p}_{11}(t) = \frac{1}{10}\,p_{13}{}^2(t) - \frac{5 \times 10^{-7}}{(300 - t)^2}$$

$$\dot{p}_{12}(t) = \frac{1}{10}\,p_{13}(t)\,p_{23}(t) - p_{11}(t)$$

$$\dot{p}_{13} = \frac{1}{10} p_{13}(t)\, p_{33}(t) - \frac{k_1}{k_2 - t} p_{12}(t)$$

$$\dot{p}_{22} = \frac{1}{10} p_{23}{}^2(t) - 2p_{12}(t) - \frac{10^{-3}}{(300 - t)^2}$$

$$\dot{p}_{23} = \frac{1}{10} p_{23}(t)\, p_{33}(t) - \frac{k_1}{k_2 - t} p_{22}(t) - p_{13}(t)$$

$$\dot{p}_{33} = \frac{1}{10} p_{33}{}^2(t) - 2\frac{k_1}{k_2 - t} p_{23}(t) - \frac{10^3}{(300 - t)^2}$$

The set can at least be solved numerically backward from $t = T$, with the boundary value $\mathbf{P}(T) = 0$. In Fig. 15-2a, the three quantities $p_{13}(t)$, $p_{23}(t)$, $p_{33}(t)$ with the appropriate multipliers are plotted for $k_1 = 9380$, $k_2 = 315$. In Fig. 15-2b, the optimal trajectory $\mathbf{x}^*(t)$ is plotted. (See Exercise 15-8.)◆◆

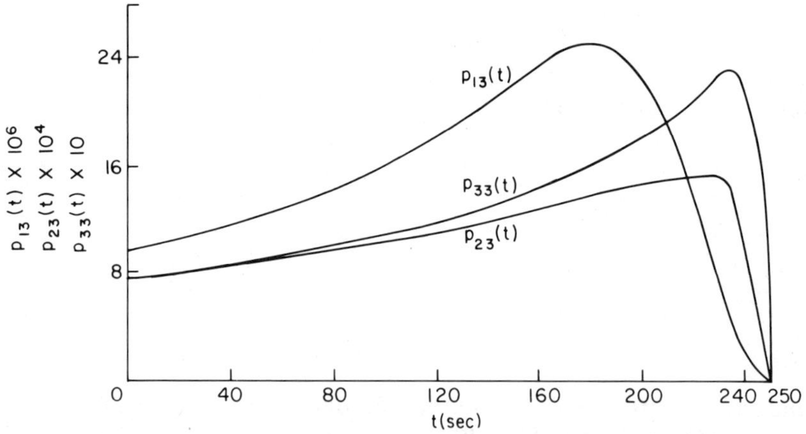

Fig. 15-2a. The optimal feedback gain functions for system of Example 15-2.

When $T \to \infty$, Kalman has further shown that, for a linear time-invariant system that is completely controllable and with a performance index that is of the form

$$\mathcal{J} = \frac{1}{2}\int_0^\infty \left(\mathbf{x}^T(\tau)\mathbf{Q}\,\mathbf{x}(\tau) + \mathbf{u}^T(\tau)\mathbf{R}\mathbf{u}(\tau)\right) d\tau$$

with $\mathbf{Q}$ and $\mathbf{R}$ both symmetrical positive-definite constant matrices, the condition $\lim_{T \to \infty} \dot{\mathbf{P}}(t) = 0$ holds, and thus the matrix Riccati

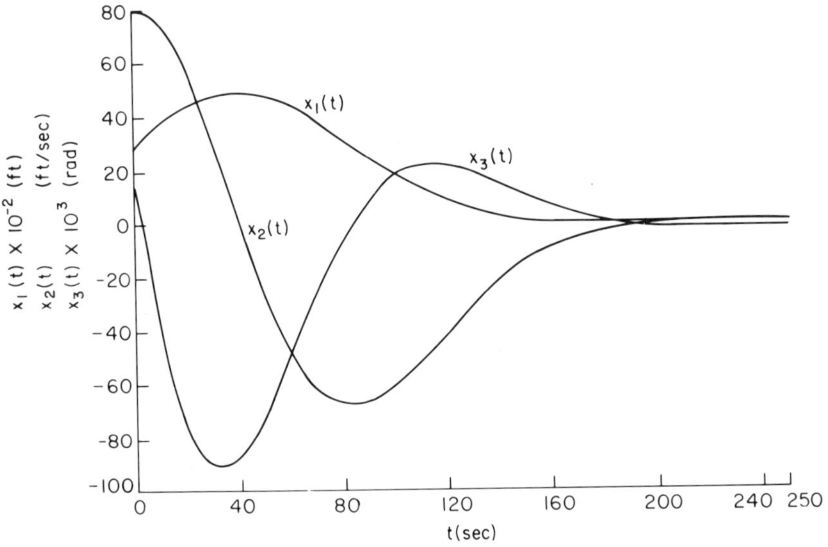

Fig. 15-2b. The optimal trajectory for the system of Example 15-2.

equation (15-46) is reduced to a nonlinear matrix algebraic equation

$$-\mathbf{P}\,\mathbf{B}\,\mathbf{R}^{-1}B^T\mathbf{P} + \mathbf{P}\,\mathbf{A} + \mathbf{A}^T\mathbf{P} + \mathbf{Q} = 0 \tag{15-49}$$

The solution of this equation will yield a constant matrix P which is the matrix for the optimal feedback function $\mathbf{u}^*(\mathbf{x}, t) = -\mathbf{R}^{-1}\mathbf{B}^T\mathbf{P}\,\mathbf{x}$.

The result above is of course identical to that given in Sec. 13.2, although (15-49) is a neat way to indicate the usual relations that must be satisfied by the feedback matrix P.

Note that the form $\mathbf{u}^*(\mathbf{x}, t) = -\mathbf{R}^{-1}\mathbf{B}\,\mathbf{P}\,\mathbf{x}$ indicates that in general all states are to be fed back. This implies that up to the $(n-1)$th derivative of the system output must be measured accurately. This is usually a difficult undertaking.

In fact for the case of a single control variable, Kalman [K7] has further shown that for the above problem, where Eq. (15-49) gives the constant feedback matrix P, there is a ready and stringent frequency domain result that must be satisfied.

Let the plant given by $\dot{\mathbf{x}} = \mathbf{A}\,\mathbf{x} + \mathbf{b}\,u$ be completely controllable. (See Sec. 3.6.) Let the optimal control function relative to a performance index of the form†

$$\mathcal{J} = \frac{1}{2}\int_0^\infty \left(\mathbf{x}^T(t)\,\mathbf{Q}\,\mathbf{x}(t) + r\,u^2(t)\right)dt$$

†Q is assumed to be p.d. and $r > 0$.

be given by $u^* = -(1/r)\mathbf{b}^T\mathbf{P}\,\mathbf{x} = -\mathbf{k}^T\mathbf{x}$ when $\mathbf{k}^T = \mathbf{b}^T\mathbf{P}/r$. Then the overall open-loop transfer function of the optimal control system is (see Sec. 3.5)

$$F^*(s) = \mathbf{k}^T(s\mathbf{I} - \mathbf{A})^{-1}\mathbf{b} \tag{15-50}$$

We can now show that *the function* $F^*(s)$ *enjoys the property that at all frequency* ω,

$$|1 + F^*(j\omega)| > 1 \tag{15-51}$$

To prove this we first note that in our case,

$$\mathcal{J} = \int_0^\infty (\mathbf{x}^T\mathbf{Q}\,\mathbf{x} + r\,u^2)\,dt$$

and it is possible to normalize $\mathcal{J}$ such that $r = 1$ without loss of generality. Thus (15-49) becomes†

$$-\mathbf{P}\,\mathbf{A} - \mathbf{A}^T\mathbf{P} = \mathbf{Q} - \mathbf{P}\,\mathbf{b}\,b^T\mathbf{P} \tag{15-52}$$

On adding and subtracting $s\mathbf{P}$ on the lhs of (15-52) we obtain

$$P(s\mathbf{I} - \mathbf{A}) + (-s\mathbf{I} - \mathbf{A}^T)\mathbf{P} = \mathbf{Q} - \mathbf{P}\,\mathbf{b}\,\mathbf{b}^T\mathbf{P} \tag{15-53}$$

The transfer function of the plant from u to $\mathbf{x}$ is given by $\mathbf{H}(s) = (s\mathbf{I} - \mathbf{A})^{-1}\mathbf{b}$.

If we premultiply each side of (15-53) by $\mathbf{H}^T(-s)$ and postmultiply each side of (15-53) by $\mathbf{H}(s)$ we obtain

$$\mathbf{H}^T(-s)\,\mathbf{P}\,\mathbf{b} + \mathbf{b}^T\mathbf{P}\,H(s) = \mathbf{H}^T(-s)[\mathbf{Q} - \mathbf{P}\,\mathbf{b}\,\mathbf{b}^T\mathbf{P}]\mathbf{H}(s)$$

or

$$\mathbf{H}^T(-s)\mathbf{P}\,\mathbf{b} + \mathbf{H}^T(-s)\mathbf{P}\,\mathbf{b}\,\mathbf{b}^T\mathbf{P}\,\mathbf{H}(s) + \mathbf{b}^T\mathbf{P}\,\mathbf{H}(s) = \mathbf{H}^T(-s)\mathbf{Q}\,\mathbf{H}(s) \tag{15-54}$$

since the positive definite matrix $\mathbf{Q}$ can be diagonalized into a form $\mathbf{Q} = \mathbf{D}^T\mathbf{\Lambda}\,\mathbf{D}$ where $\mathbf{D}$ is real and $\mathbf{\Lambda}$ is real, positive definite, and diagonal.†† Equation (15-54) can be put into the form (in view of the fact that $\mathbf{k} = \mathbf{P}\,\mathbf{b}$)

$$\left(1 + \mathbf{H}^T(-s)\,\mathbf{k}\right)\left(1 + \mathbf{k}^T\mathbf{H}(s)\right) = 1 + \mathbf{H}^T(-s)\,\mathbf{D}^T\mathbf{\Lambda}\,\mathbf{D}\,\mathbf{H}(s) \tag{15-55}$$

†For the case of a single control variable $\mathbf{R}$ in (15-49) is the scalar r.

††See [B4] p. 54.

In view of the fact that $\mathbf{k}^T\mathbf{H}(s) = F^*(s)$, we have, with $s = j\omega$

$$|1 + F^*(j\omega)|^2 = 1 + \mathbf{H}^T(-j\omega)\,\mathbf{D}^T\Lambda\;\mathbf{D}\;\mathbf{H}(j\omega) \tag{15-56}$$

Since the last term of (15-56) is always positive, (15-51) follows naturally.

Condition (15-51) can be translated into a "circle criterion": *The Nyquist plot for $F^*(j\omega)$ should not touch or enter the unit circle centered at the $-1 + j0$ point.* This means, whatever the original transfer function $G(s)$ of the plant, the optimal linear controller will compensate it into an $F^*(j\omega)$ with the above properties. Needless to say, due to the stringency of condition (15-51), we will find it difficult to implement the optimal control for nontrivial plants.

While the above results apply only to regulator type systems or systems without a reference input, they can quite readily be extended to systems with reference inputs that belong to a certain class.

Consider a linear time-invariant plant with a single input and a single output given by

$$\dot{\mathbf{x}} = \mathbf{A}\,\mathbf{x} + \mathbf{b}\,u \qquad \text{with output} \qquad y = \mathbf{c}^T\mathbf{x}$$

Let $z(t)$ be the reference input which we like the output $y(t)$ to follow. Specifically, we wish to find a feedback control function u so as to minimize the performance index

$$\mathcal{J} = \int_0^\infty \left(qe^2(t) + ru^2(t)\right)dt \tag{15-57}$$

where $e(t) = z(t) - y(t)$.

In general, since $z(t)$ is a time-varying function, we would expect to have a time-varying feedback function $u(\mathbf{x}, t)$ even when the upper limit of integration for the performance index is ∞ and when the plant is time-invariant. However, let the linear plant be completely controllable and observable (see Sec. 3.6) given in the operator form $G(p) = [M(p)/L(p)]$ such that $L(p)y(t) = M(p)u(t)$ (see Sec. 2.3). If $z(t)$ obeys

$$L(p)\,z(t) = 0 \tag{15-58}$$

then we can write

$$L(p)\,e(t) = -M(p)\,u(t) \tag{15-59}$$

which may be viewed as an equivalent plant with input $-u(t)$ and output $e(t)$. Here, if we choose any convenient set of state variables to characterize the equivalent plant (15-59), (for example

$e(t)$ and its $n-1$ derivatives), we can effectively transform the problem into a regulator form. Thus the problem considered in Sec. 12.2 using a frequency-domain approach can now be fully treated in the time domain.

15.5 The Relationship between the Maximum Principle and Dynamic Programming

The careful reader may note a marked resemblance between the expression such as that given in (15-22) or (15-24) and one involving the maximization of the Hamiltonian function in the maximum principle formulation of the optimal control problem. In fact, since for any function F, we have $\max(-F) = -\min F$, then for (15-24) we can just as well write

$$\frac{\partial \mathcal{J}^*}{\partial t} = \max_{\mathbf{u}(t) \in \mathcal{U}} \left[-L\big(\mathbf{x}(\mathbf{u}, t), \mathbf{u}, t\big) - \left(\frac{\partial \mathcal{J}^*}{\partial \mathbf{x}}\right)^T \mathbf{f} \right] \tag{15-60}$$

Along a specific optimal trajectory, if we identify $-\partial \mathcal{J}^*/\partial \mathbf{x}$ as the adjoint vector $\boldsymbol{\psi}$, then the square-bracketed quantity of Eq. (15-60) is identified as the Hamiltonian H for the maximum principle. In that case the quantity $\partial \mathcal{J}^*/\partial t$ is clearly the quantity $H(\mathbf{x}^*, \mathbf{u}^*, t, \boldsymbol{\psi})$. We can also show the correspondence between the quantity $-\partial \mathcal{J}^*/\partial \mathbf{x}$ and the adjoint vector $\boldsymbol{\psi}(t)$, and show that condition (2) of the maximum principle (Theorem 14-3) is satisfied (see Exercise 15-13). Under these conditions we have

$$-\frac{\partial \mathcal{J}^*}{\partial \mathbf{x}} = \boldsymbol{\psi}(t) \tag{15-61a}$$

$$\frac{\partial \mathcal{J}^*}{\partial t} = H^* \triangleq H(\mathbf{x}^*, \mathbf{u}^*, t, \boldsymbol{\psi}) \tag{15-61b}$$

We then have an interesting geometric interpretation; namely, *the adjoint vector corresponding to the optimal trajectory is one which points away from the gradient of the optimal performance index* $\mathcal{J}^*$. Since the gradient vector points toward the direction of fastest spatial change in a function, $\boldsymbol{\psi}$ then points in the direction of the fastest change of the optimal performance index at all times.

We can indeed go another step and develop further intuitive appreciation for the maximum principle. In the augmented form of Sec. 14.3, we have $H = \boldsymbol{\psi}'^T \dot{\mathbf{x}}'$; but in the augmented form, the principle of optimality will still yield $-\partial \mathcal{J}^*/\partial \mathbf{x}' = \boldsymbol{\psi}'$. Thus the statement

$\max_{\mathbf{u} \in \mathcal{U}} H$ in the maximum principle simply means that *in the augmented* $n + 1$ *dimensional space,* $\mathbf{u}^*$ *should be so chosen that at any instant of time, the component of the vector* $\dot{\mathbf{x}}$*, in the direction of the maximum (spatial) decrease of* $\mathcal{J}^*$ *should be as large as possible (subject to the constraint* $\mathbf{u}^* \in \mathcal{U}$*).*

From (15-61b), we arrive at the interpretation that *the optimal Hamiltonian* H^* *is equal to the rate of change of the optimal performance index with starting time at a particular starting point.*

From the above, we can immediately appreciate why, in the case of the time-optimal control of a time-invariant plant, H^* must necessarily vanish identically. This is seen by considering the quantity $\partial\mathcal{J}^*(\mathbf{x}, t)/\partial t$. We recall that t in the argument of $\mathcal{J}^*(\mathbf{x}, t)$ is the starting time. With the starting point ($\mathbf{x}$ in the argument of $\mathcal{J}^*(\mathbf{x}, t)$) fixed, it is clear that the optimal time to reach any given point is independent of the starting time for a time-invariant plant; thus $H^* \equiv 0$.

Indeed, reasoning as in the case above, we see that whenever the plant and the cost function L are both not dependent on time explicitly, and whenever the final time t_2 is not fixed, $\partial\mathcal{J}^*/\partial t$ will always vanish and hence $H^* \equiv 0$ for all these cases.

In terms of the Hamiltonian H, Bellman's equation can be written in the form

$$\frac{\partial \mathcal{J}^*}{\partial t} - H\left(\mathbf{x}^*, \mathbf{u}^*, t, \frac{\partial \mathcal{J}^*}{\partial \mathbf{x}}\right) = 0 \tag{15-62}$$

This is in the form of a classical Hamilton-Jacobi equation.†

Knowing the relationship between the maximum principle and dynamic programming, we can make use of it by extending the result of the previous section.

Suppose we wish to find the optimal linear feedback control for a system with an input $z(t)$ that is completely specified. The goal of control is to keep the output close to the input, without expending too much energy in the process. This can be formulated in the following way.

Let the output of a plant $\dot{\mathbf{x}} = \mathbf{A}(t)\mathbf{x} + \mathbf{B}(t)\mathbf{u}$ be given by $\mathbf{y}(t) = \mathbf{C}(t)\mathbf{x}(t)$ where $\mathbf{x}$ and $\mathbf{y}$ are respectively n and m dimensional. Let the input be $z(t)$, an m-vector, and define the error function $\mathbf{e}(t) = \mathbf{z}(t) - \mathbf{y}(t)$. A convenient performance index is

$$\mathcal{J} = \mathbf{e}^T(t_2)\mathbf{M}\,\mathbf{e}(t_2) + \frac{1}{2}\int_{t_1}^{t_2}\left(\mathbf{e}^T(\tau)\mathbf{Q}(\tau)\mathbf{e}(\tau) + \mathbf{u}^T(\tau)\mathbf{R}(\tau)\mathbf{u}(\tau)\right)d\tau \tag{15-63}$$

†For this reason, the Bellman equation is frequently called the Hamilton-Jacobi equation by some writers.

which is to be minimized through the finding of an optimal feedback control law $u^*(x, t)$.

Using the result of this section, we first obtain the Hamiltonian

$$H = -\frac{1}{2}\big(z(t) - C(t)x(t)\big)^T Q(t)\big(z(t) - C(t)x(t)\big) - \frac{1}{2}\big(u(t)^T R(t)u(t)\big) + \big(A(t)x(t)\big)^T \psi(t) + \big(B(t)u(t)\big)^T \psi(t) \tag{15-64}$$

The optimal control function $u^*(t)$ is obtained from setting $\left.\frac{\partial H}{\partial u}\right|_{u=u^*} = 0$, by which we have

$$u^*(t) = -R^{-1}(t)B^T(t)\psi(t) = -R^{-1}(t)B^T(t)\frac{\partial \mathcal{J}^*(x, t)}{\partial x} \tag{15-65}$$

which is well defined provided $R^{-1}(t)$ exists for all t.

Now if we insist on a linear control configuration, it is reasonable to expect from the superposition principle that the optimal linear feedback control $u^*(x, t)$ will be composed of the sum of two parts, one part depending only on the input (and on the system configuration), and the other part depending on the output. This suggests the configuration of Fig. 15-3a.

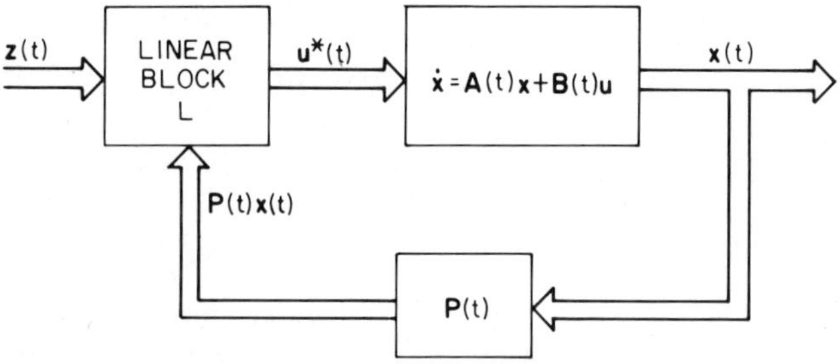

Fig. 15-3a. The configuration for a general optimal control system which controls a linear plant so as to minimize the performance index of the form of Eq. (15-53), where $e(t) = z(t) - C(t)x(t)$.

In particular, taking a hint from the case of $z(t) \equiv 0$, for a linear control system, there is no loss of generality in assuming the following form for the block marked "Linear Block L":

$$u^*(t) = R^{-1}(t)B^T(t)\big(w(t) - P(t)x(t)\big) \tag{15-66}$$

where $w(t)$, an n-vector, is a function of time which is generated by a linear operation on $z(t)$, an m-vector. In some sense, (15-66) then is in the form of an "error-actuated controller."

With $u^*(t)$ in the form (15-66), $\mathcal{J}^*(x, t)$ must take the general form

$$\mathcal{J}^*(x, t) = \frac{1}{2}x^T(t)P(t)x(t) + w^T(t)x(t) + \frac{1}{2}v(t) \tag{15-67}$$

where $v(t)$ is a scalar function of time introduced to provide a purely time-varying component for $\mathcal{J}^*(x, t)$. The boundary condition on $\mathcal{J}^*(x, t)$ from (15-25) and (15-28b) is

$$\mathcal{J}^*(x, t_2) = e^T(t_2)M\,e(t_2) \tag{15-68}$$

Substituting (15-67) and (15-68) into the Bellman equation (15-62), and after some algebraic manipulations (exercise for the reader) we arrive at the conclusion that an optimal linear control law of the form (15-66) is possible if:

1) The symmetric $n \times n$ matrix $P(t)$ satisfies the matrix Riccati equation (15-46).
2) The n-vector $w(t)$ satisfies the *linear* vector-matrix differential equation

$$\frac{dw(t)}{dt} = -[A(t)^T - B(t)R^{-1}(t)B^T(t)P(t)]^T w(t) - C^T(t)Q(t)z(t) \tag{15-69}$$

with the boundary condition imposed at the *end* time t_2

$$w(t_2) = C(t_2)M\,z(t_2) \tag{15-70}$$

3) The scalar function $v(t)$ is obtained as the solution of the differential equation

$$-\frac{dv}{dt} = z^T(t)Q(t)z(t) - \left(B^T(t)w(t)\right)^T R^{-1}(t)\left(B^T(t)w(t)\right) \tag{15-71}$$

with the boundary condition imposed at the *end* time t_2

$$v(t_2) = 2z^T(t_2)Mz(t_2) \tag{15-72}$$

Kalman has succeeded in showing that results (1), (2), and (3), above, are not only sufficient for the linear optimal control, but necessary as well.†

†See Sec. 15.7, Theorem 15-2, which encompasses Kalman's result.

The realization of the above optimal control law is as sketched in Fig. 15-3b.

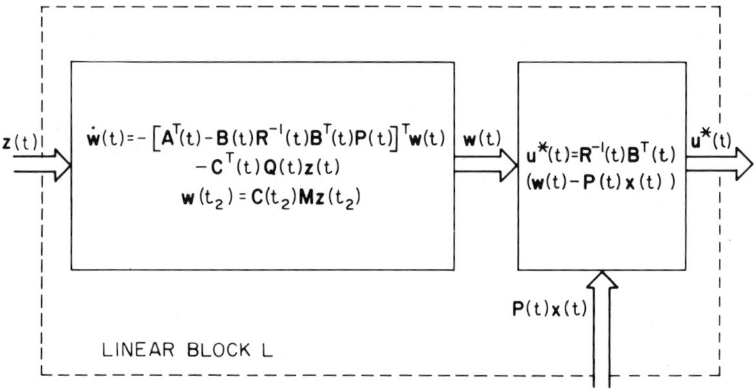

Fig. 15-3b. The details of the block L of Fig. 15-3a.

It is appropriate to make a few remarks concerning optimal linear control systems. While the theory concerning this class of systems seems to be neatly wrapped up it does not mean that practical systems can be forced into the necessary form and the formulas of Secs. 15.4 and 15.5 used blithely, for there are some basic difficulties related to this class of problems.

First, the performance index (15-40) is sometimes suspect. For typical problems there is generally no intelligent way to choose the correct weighting matrices $\mathbf{M}$, $\mathbf{Q}(t)$, and $\mathbf{R}(t)$. Quite frequently the situation becomes one where the proper $\mathbf{M}$, $\mathbf{Q}(t)$, and $\mathbf{R}(t)$ are arrived at by trial and error, the most satisfying transient response being picked by eye. This is a travesty of an optimal procedure.

Second, the optimal feedback control law is obtained by making use of all states, which usually implies that the output and its $n - 1$ derivatives all have to be measured faultlessly. This is generally impossible for most realistic systems.

Third, in the case with no input, the feedback matrix $\mathbf{P}(t)$ must be obtained by solving the nonlinear set of equations (15-46). Generally this has to be done numerically. This procedure is not very satisfactory from an engineering standpoint not only because for high-order systems the amount of labor and computation involved can be very large, but also because the result is a set of $n(n+1)/2$ time functions representing the feedback gains. For time-varying systems there is very little feeling at present concerning the correctness of these gains, and any attempt to check the result by making use of Bellman's equation can be most laborious. (See Exercise 15-8.) Further, condition (15-51), which is essential for optimality in the time-invariant case, is extremely stringent and is practically nearly impossible to implement for nontrivial systems.

Fourth, for systems with input, the matrix $P(t)$ must be evaluated as before, but in addition, the time functions $w(t)$ and $v(t)$ have to be evaluated backwards using the value $z(t_2)$ in accordance with (15-69) through (15-72). This means we must know all future input history. Thus the result cannot be used in on-line type applications.

15.6 Dynamic Programming in Cases where $\partial \mathcal{J}^*(x, t)/\partial x$ is Discontinuous

In Secs. 15.4 and 15.5 we have made use of the particular version of Bellman's equation that is given as Eq. (15-24). As we have seen in Secs. 15.3 through 15.5, (15-24) is easy to apply relative to a linear plant without constraint on u and with a performance index that is an integral of quadratic forms in x and u. Equation (15-24), however, is predicated on the assumption that $\mathcal{J}^*$ possesses continuous first-partial derivatives with respect to both x and t.† It is readily seen that even in a seemingly simple problem, e.g., time optimal control of a linear, time-invariant plant, there are regions in which the first partial derivatives of $\mathcal{J}^*(x, t)$ are discontinuous with respect to x.

♦♦Example 15-3. Consider the time-optimal control of the double integrating plant $1/p^2$. The switching boundary is reproduced as the curve $\Gamma_\pm$ in Fig. 15-4.

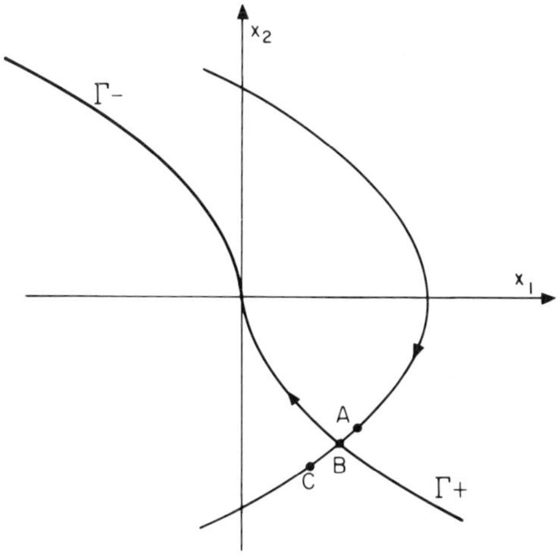

Fig. 15-4. The function $\mathcal{J}^*(x, t) = t^*$ for Example 15-3 is not continuously differentiable with respect to x along a switch line $\Gamma_\pm$.

† In Sec. 15.5, in order to relate the functional equation of dynamic programming with condition (1) of the maximum principle we further required the existence and continuity of the second partial derivative of $\mathcal{J}^*$.

The quantity $\mathcal{J}^*$, in this case, is the minimum time to reach the origin. Over the trajectory ABC it will vary as shown in Fig. 15-5. Thus it is clear that $\partial\mathcal{J}^*/\partial x$ will not be continuous at the point B. Further reasoning will show that $\partial\mathcal{J}^*/\partial x$ will be discontinuous all along the optimal switch line $\Gamma_\pm$ (see Exercise 15-4).

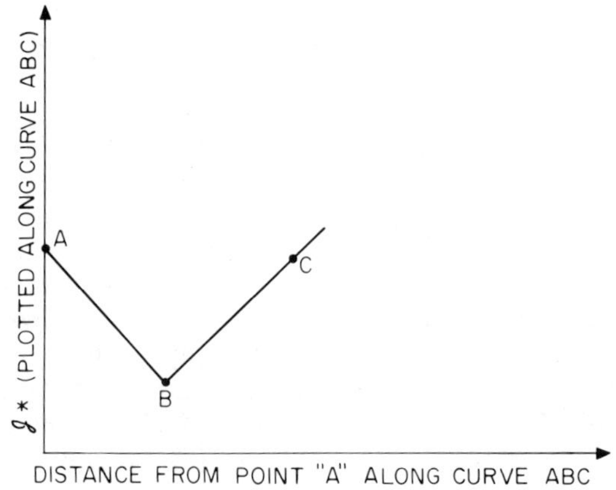

Fig. 15-5. The function $\mathcal{J}^*(x, t) = t^*$ for Example 15-3 along a typical trajectory crossing the switch line Γ_+ of Fig. 15-4. The points A, B, and C correspond to the points on the trajectory shown in Fig. 15-4.

In the case above, however, let us note that the optimal trajectory never crosses the line of discontinuity in $\partial\mathcal{J}^*/\partial x$. In the half plane above the switching line $\Gamma_\pm$, if we designate $(\partial\mathcal{J}^*/\partial x)_+$ as the value of $(\partial\mathcal{J}^*/\partial x)$ when the switch line Γ_+ is approached from above, then (see Exercise 15-4) we see that if we only use $(\partial\mathcal{J}^*/\partial x)_+$ in the half plane there is continuity in $(\partial\mathcal{J}^*/\partial x)$ along any optimal trajectory. A similar limit can be defined for the other half plane. Using these limits, the quantity $d(\partial\mathcal{J}^*/\partial x)/dt$ can be defined along the optimal trajectory and will also be continuous.

Also we have seen that in this case $(\partial\mathcal{J}^*/\partial t) \equiv 0$ everywhere; thus Bellman's equation (15-24) will hold if the proper limit of $(\partial\mathcal{J}^*/\partial x)$ is taken.♦♦

The cases where $\partial\mathcal{J}^*/\partial x$ is discontinuous in the manner of Example 15-3 can be handled by the more general Bellman equation (15-22). Let us note that while $\partial\mathcal{J}^*/\partial x$ is discontinuous along the switching line in the previous example, the quantity $\left[\dfrac{d\mathcal{J}^*}{dt}\right]_{u^*,\,t}$, which represents the total derivative of $\mathcal{J}^*$ with respect to time along an optimal trajectory, is continuous (See Exercise 15-4).

Indeed, even if $\partial \mathcal{J}^* / \partial \mathbf{x}$ and $\mathbf{f}(\mathbf{x}, \mathbf{u}, f)$ are not continuous on a trajectory $\mathbf{x}^*(t)$ at a point $\mathbf{x}^*(\tau)$, as long as

$$\lim_{t \to \tau^+} \left[\left(\frac{\partial \mathcal{J}^*}{\partial \mathbf{x}} \right)^T \mathbf{f}(\mathbf{x}, \mathbf{u}, t) \right] = \lim_{t \to \tau^-} \left[\left(\frac{\partial \mathcal{J}^*}{\partial \mathbf{x}} \right)^T \mathbf{f}(\mathbf{x}, \mathbf{u}, t) \right] \qquad (15\text{-}73)$$

$\left[\dfrac{d\mathcal{J}^*}{dt} \right]_{\mathbf{u},\, t}$ will still be continuous at $t = \tau$.

The legitimacy of Bellman's equation in the general case has been studied by Berkovitz [B10], Boltyanskii [B14], and Tchamran [T2]. It was established that under very general conditions (including those for all the solved optimal control problems in this text), as long as Bellman's equation is satisfied by a control function $\mathbf{u}^*$ away from the switching line and switching surfaces where $\partial \mathcal{J}^* / \partial \mathbf{x}$ is not defined, then $\mathbf{u}^*$ is the optimal control function. Further, if the proper one-sided limits are taken for $\partial \mathcal{J}^* / \partial \mathbf{x}$, then it can be associated with the adjoint vector $\boldsymbol{\psi}$ in the entire space in which $\boldsymbol{\psi}$ is defined.

15.7 Dynamic Programming as a Sufficient Condition for Optimality

The derivation given in Sec. 15.3 has made it clear that Bellman's equation consitutes a necessary condition for optimality. We shall now state and prove a general theorem concerning dynamic programming as a sufficient condition.

♦♦Theorem 15-2 [T2]. Consider the system stated in Sec. 15.3, let the end state be a set $\mathcal{S}$, and let the end time t_2 be free. Let $\mathcal{O}$ be an open region in the state space in which a function $V(\mathbf{x}, t)$ is defined such that:

1) $\partial V / \partial t$ is continuous in $\mathbf{x}$ and t, $\partial V / \partial \mathbf{x}$ is either continuous in $\mathbf{x}$ and t or satisfies

$$\lim_{t \to \tau^+} \left[\left(\frac{\partial V}{\partial \mathbf{x}} \right)^T \mathbf{f} \right] = \lim_{t \to \tau^-} \left[\left(\frac{\partial V}{\partial \mathbf{x}} \right)^T \mathbf{f} \right]$$

at any instance $t = \tau$ where $\partial V / \partial \mathbf{x}$ and/or $\mathbf{f}(\mathbf{x}, \mathbf{u}, t)$ is discontinuous.

2) For every $\mathbf{x}$ in $\mathcal{O}$ at each t, the Hamiltonian function $H(\mathbf{x}, \mathbf{u}, t, \partial V / \partial \mathbf{x})$ has an absolute minimum $u = u^*$ with respect to all admissible control functions. Moreover, the application of $\mathbf{u}^*(t)$ results in a unique system trajectory $\mathbf{x}^*(t)$.

3) On the end set $\mathcal{S}$, $V(\mathbf{x}, t) = 0$.

Then $V(\mathbf{x}, t) = \mathcal{J}^*(\mathbf{x}, t)$ relative to all admissible control functions that takes $\mathbf{x}_1$ to $\mathcal{S}$ without leaving $\mathcal{O}$; further the optimal feedback control function $\mathbf{u}^*(\mathbf{x}, t)$ can be obtained by solving the relevant Bellman's equation. ♦♦

We can prove Theorem 15-2 in the following way: By conditions (1) and (2) of the theorem, we can write

$$\frac{\partial V}{\partial t}(\mathbf{x}, t) + \left[\left(\frac{\partial V}{\partial \mathbf{x}}\right)^T \mathbf{f}(\mathbf{x}, \mathbf{u}^*, t) + L(\mathbf{x}, \mathbf{u}^*, t)\right] = 0$$

$$< \frac{\partial V}{\partial t}(\mathbf{x}, t) + \left[\left(\frac{\partial V}{\partial \mathbf{x}}\right)^T \mathbf{f}(\mathbf{x}, \mathbf{u}, t) + L(\mathbf{x}, \mathbf{u}, t)\right] \tag{15-74}$$

On integrating the lhs of (15-74) along $\mathbf{x}^*(t)$ from t_1 to the optimal final time t_2^* we obtain:

$$\int_{t_1}^{t_2^*} \left[\frac{\partial V(\mathbf{x}^*, t)}{\partial t} + \left(\frac{\partial V(\mathbf{x}^*, t)}{\partial \mathbf{x}}\right)^T \mathbf{f}(\mathbf{x}^*, \mathbf{u}^*, t)\right] dt + \int_{t_1}^{t_2^*} L(\mathbf{x}^*, \mathbf{u}^*, t)\, dt$$

$$= \int_{t_1}^{t_2^*} \left[\frac{dV}{dt}\right]_{\mathbf{u}^*, t} dt + \int_{t_1}^{t_2^*} L(\mathbf{x}^*, \mathbf{u}^*, t)\, dt = 0 \tag{15-75}$$

where the notation $\left[\frac{dV}{dt}\right]_{\mathbf{u}^*, t}$ is as defined in Sec. 15.3.

Consider now the integral

$$W = \int_{t_1}^{t_2^*} \left[\frac{\partial V}{\partial t} + \left(\frac{\partial V}{\partial \mathbf{x}}\right)^T \mathbf{f}(\mathbf{x}, \mathbf{u}, t) + L(\mathbf{x}, \mathbf{u}, t)\right] dt \tag{15-76}$$

We now assert that the combination $\mathbf{u}^*$ and $\mathbf{x}^*$ is the only one that can cause W to reach its absolute minimum, which by (15-75) is 0. If this assertion is not true, there will be a $\mathbf{u}(t) \neq \mathbf{u}^*(t)$ and a $\mathbf{x}(t) \neq \mathbf{x}^*(t)$ that causes (15-76) to become 0. However, by (15-74) the integrand of (15-76) is always positive; thus to cause W to be 0 would require that the integrand vanish identically over $[t_1, t_2^*]$. By (15-74), only the pair $\mathbf{u}^*(t)$ and $\mathbf{x}^*(t)$ can do this. Thus Theorem 15-2 is proved.

We see that Theorem 15-2 lends legitimacy to all of the examples that we have investigated in this chapter.

Lest we become overly impressed by our ability to solve optimization problems using the maximum principle or dynamic programming, we may point out that by only slightly changing the conditions of the problems of the previous section, we can arrive at one which has not been completely solved.

♦♦Example 15-4.† Consider again the double integrating plant $\dot{x}_1 = x_2$, $\dot{x}_2 = u$. This time, take a performance index

$$\mathcal{J} = \frac{1}{2}\int_0^\infty \left(x_1^2 + x_2^2 + c^2u^2\right)dt$$

furthermore, let there be a constraint on u of the form $|u(t)| \leq 1$.

We see that if $u(t)$ is not constrained, the method of the last section is applicable, and we can find the optimal solution (see part (a) of Exercise 15-7)

$$u^*(t) = -\frac{1}{c}\left(x_1 + \sqrt{1 + 2c}\; x_2\right) \tag{15-77}$$

where by Eq. (15-49), the matrix P is

$$\mathbf{P} = \begin{bmatrix} \sqrt{1 + 2c} & c \\ c & c\sqrt{1 + 2c} \end{bmatrix} \tag{15-78}$$

When $u(t)$ has an inequality type constraint, however, the problem becomes more involved. The solution (15-77) should of course be correct over the region where $u^*(t)$ does not become saturated. This led a number of authors to assume that for our problem the optimal solution should be†† $u^*(t) = \text{sat}\,[(-1/c)(x_1 - \sqrt{1 + 2c}\; x_2)]$. This solution, however, is wrong, as will be demonstrated below.

Bellman's equation in this example becomes (see Exercise 15-7)

$$\left(\frac{\partial \mathcal{J}^*}{\partial x_1}\right)x_2 - \frac{1}{2c^2}\left(\frac{\partial \mathcal{J}^*}{\partial x_2}\right)^2 + \frac{1}{2}\left(x_1^2 + x_2^2\right) = 0, \qquad \text{if } \frac{1}{c^2}\left|\frac{\partial \mathcal{J}^*}{\partial x_2}\right| \leq 1 \tag{15-79}$$

† See [J3]. This reference contains two other interesting examples.

$$\dagger\dagger\ \text{sat}[x] = \begin{cases} +1, & x > 1 \\ x, & |x| \leq 1\,. \\ -1, & x < -1 \end{cases}$$

$$\left(\frac{\partial \mathcal{J}^*}{\partial x_1}\right)x_2 - \left|\frac{\partial \mathcal{J}^*}{\partial x_2}\right| + \frac{c^2}{2} + \frac{1}{2}\left(x_1^2 + x_2^2\right) = 0, \qquad \text{if } \frac{1}{c^2}\left|\frac{\partial \mathcal{J}^*}{\partial x_2}\right| \geq 1 \tag{15-79 (cont'd)}$$

and $u^*(\mathbf{x})$ has the functional form

$$u^*(\mathbf{x}) = \text{sat}\left[-\frac{1}{c^2}\frac{\partial \mathcal{J}^*}{\partial x_2}\right] \tag{15-80}$$

which gives the exact solution (see the next section) except for the fact that $\partial \mathcal{J}^* / \partial \mathbf{x}$ is not known *a priori*.

Now a control function of the form (15-77) is certainly optimal if it never exceeds the limit set by the constraint. All the states reachable by such a control then define unequivocably a zone when the linear control (15-77) is optimal. This zone $\mathcal{L}$ is seen to be one bounded by the two lines for which $u^*(t) = \pm 1$, or

$$-\frac{1}{c}\left(x_1 + \sqrt{1 + 2c}\; x_2\right) = \pm 1 \tag{15-81}$$

and by the two trajectories generated by $u = \pm 1$ tangent to these lines. Zone $\mathcal{L}$ is shown in Fig. 15-6.

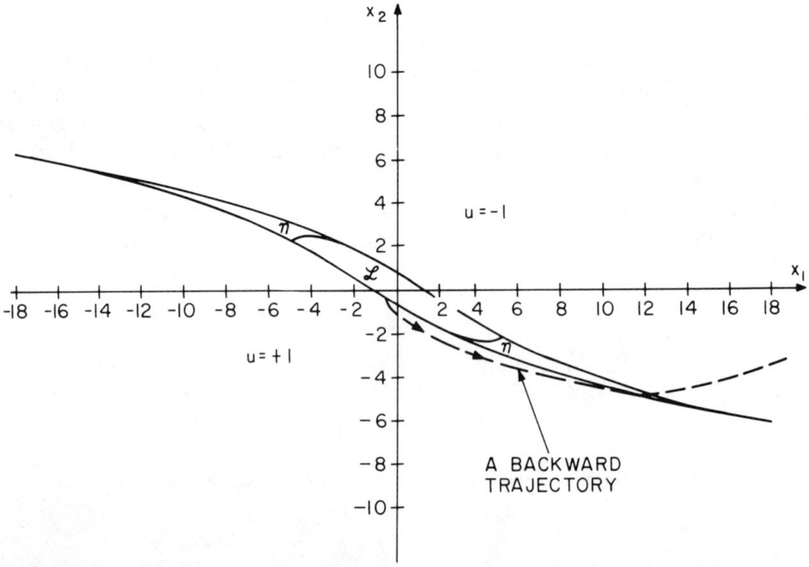

Fig. 15-6. The regions in the x_2 vs. x_1 plane in which different modes of optimal control holds for the system of Example 15-4. $\mathcal{L}$ denotes a linear control region, η denotes control regions; outside of $\mathcal{L}$ and η, bang-bang control is the optimal control.

We cannot say at this point, however, that outside of the zone $\mathcal{L}$, a bang-bang solution obtains, since there may well be other regions where the argument of the sat function in (15-80) falls below unity.

To find other zones where a nonbang-bang solution holds, we can trace an optimal trajectory backwards in time starting from the boundary of $\mathcal{L}$. To do this, first find the canonical equations as given by the maximum principle. In the present case these are

$$\dot{x}_1 = x_2, \quad \dot{x}_2 = \text{sat}\left[\frac{1}{c^2}\psi_2(t)\right] \qquad \text{(15-82)}$$
$$\dot{\psi}_1 = x_1, \quad \dot{\psi}_2 = x_2 - \psi_1$$

Since for an initial point in the region $\mathcal{L}$ we have, by (15-82), $\mathcal{J}^*(\mathbf{x}, t) = (1/2)\mathbf{x}^T\mathbf{P}\mathbf{x}$, then in $\mathcal{L}$,

$$\boldsymbol{\psi} = -\frac{\partial \mathcal{J}^*}{\partial \mathbf{x}} = -\mathbf{P}\mathbf{x} \qquad \text{(15-83)}$$

On reversing time in (15-82) and using as starting states points on the boundary of $\mathcal{L}$, it is possible to trace an optimal trajectory backwards to find zones where $|u^*| < 1$ again holds.

The result of the backward tracing done by Johnson and Wonham [J3] indicates that $|u^*| < 1$ also in a zone η shown in Fig. 15-6. As η has nonlinear boundaries, it is clear that a simple control function such as $u^*(\mathbf{x}) = \text{sat}[(-1/c)(x_1 - \sqrt{1 + 2c}\, x_2)]$ cannot be the correct solution. However, the explicit boundary for η has thus far not been determined.

Outside of $\mathcal{L}$ and η, u^* is bang-bang as indicated in Fig. 15-6.♦♦

15.8 Summary

Dynamic programming of Bellman is rather easy to appreciate in that the basic functional equation involved (Eqs. (15-22) and (15-24)) can be derived simply via the principle of optimality, which holds that any portion of an optimal trajectory (and its associated control function) must of itself be optimal.

The basic functional equation that obtains in dynamic programming, commonly called Bellman's equation, is a first-order nonlinear partial differential equation involving the optimal performance index $\mathcal{J}^*$. This is given as Eq. (15-24). The boundary condition is given at one point. Typically, the equation holds in all state space except on a set of lower dimensionality in the state space such as a switching line or a switching plane. A more general form of Bellman's equation which holds in the entire state space of a given problem is given as Eq. (15-22).

To appreciate the various conditions derived through dynamic programming, it is helpful to visualize an $(n + 1)$-dimensional space of $\mathcal{J}^*$ vs. $\mathbf{x}$. In this light, noting the equivalence of the maximum principle and dynamic programming under rather general conditions (Sec. 15.5), we can gain further appreciation of the maximum principle and hence the general optimization process.

Dynamic programming is convenient to use in the solving of the class of linear control systems involving performance indices that are an integral of a sum of quadratic forms in $\mathbf{x}$ and $\mathbf{u}$ (Sec. 15-4). In other problems, it is generally less useful than the maximum principle, inasmuch as a partial differential equation must be solved.

In cases where $\partial\mathcal{J}^*/\partial\mathbf{x}$ is not continuous with respect to $\mathbf{x}$, the more general form of Bellman's equation given in Eq. (15-22) is needed. Typically, Eq. (15-22) must be invoked when there are inequality constraints on the control variable $\mathbf{u}(t)$.

A fairly general sufficient condition (Sec. 15.7) lends strength to the dynamic programming approach.

15.9 Exercises

15-1 Among N balls with identical appearance one is slightly lighter than the rest. We wish to formulate a predetermined strategy to find this lighter ball by the least number of weighings using an equal-arm balance. Let $\mathcal{J}_N^*$ be this optimum (minimum) number of weighings, show that

$$\mathcal{J}_N^* = 1 + \min_{0 \le j \le \frac{N}{2}} \max \left[\mathcal{J}_j^*, \mathcal{J}_{N-2j}^*\right]$$

through the use of the principle of optimality. Find $\mathcal{J}_N^*$.

15-2 It is desired to choose 4 nonnegative quantities $x_1, \ldots, x_4$ so as to maximize the index $\mathcal{J} = \sum_{i=1}^{4} a^{x_i}$. An additional constraint on the x_i's is that $\sum_{i=1}^{4} x_i = 20$. Find the general allocation rule as a function of a, assuming that $a > 0$; do this first via ordinary calculus and second via the principle of optimality.

15-3 A certain airline wishes to map an economical route from the West Coast to the East Coast with three intermediate stops. There are three possible West Coast terminals A, B, or C and three possible East Coast terminals L, M, or N. In addition cities D, E, or F are possible sites for the first stop; G or H are possible sites for the second stop; and I, J, or K are possible sites for the third stop. The costs of going from each city to the next are given by Fig. 15-7.

Find the most economical route, and its cost, by

a) Backward dynamic programming. State the principle of optimality for this case.
b) Forward dynamic programming. Also state the principle of optimality.
c) Direct enumeriation of all possibilities.

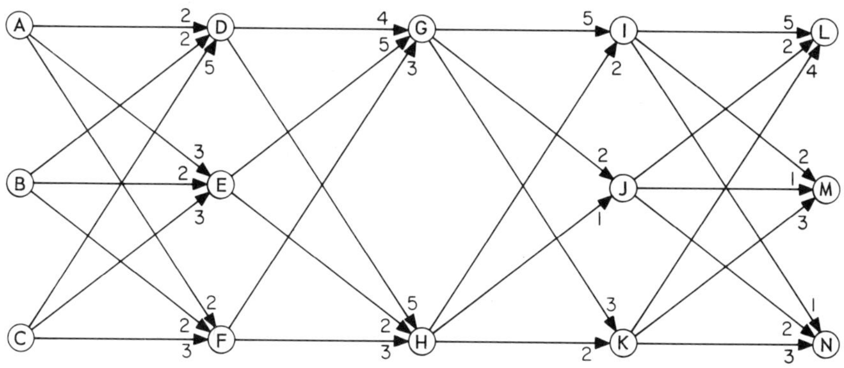

Fig. 15-7. Exercise 15-3: The cost of flying from cities on the west coast to cities on the east coast via intermediate stops. The number above each arrowhead indicates cost of travelling between cities connected by the arrow.

15-4 For time-optimal control of the double integrating plant $\dot{x}_1 = x_2$, $\dot{x}_2 = u$, with $|u(t)| \leq 1$;

a) Show that $t^*(\mathrm{x})$, the minimum time required to take a state x to the origin, is given by

$$t^*(\mathrm{x}) = \begin{cases} x_2 + \sqrt{4x_1 + 2x_2^2}, & x_1 > -\frac{1}{2}x_2|x_2| \\ -x_2 + \sqrt{-4x_1 + 2x_2^2}, & x_1 < -\frac{1}{2}x_2|x_2| \\ |x_2|, & x_1 = -\frac{1}{2}x_2|x_2| \end{cases}$$

b) Show that $t^*(\mathrm{x})$ satisfies the appropriate Bellman's equation, and that $\partial t^*/\partial \mathrm{x}$ yield the appropriate adjoint variables if the proper limits are taken. (Note that $\partial t^*/\partial t = 0$.)

15-5 For the problem considered in Sec. 15.3, derive a partial differential equation analogous to (15-24) using "forward dynamic programming"; at each step, define each term and symbol used.

15-6 Derive Eqs. (15-28) and (15-29). Hint: Note that for the problem of Mayer, the optimal performance index $\mathcal{J}^*$ is constant along the entire optimal trajectory.

15-7 Consider the class of systems with a single control component $\dot{x} = \mathrm{A}\mathrm{x} + \mathrm{b}u$. Suppose it is desired to find a control $u^*(t)$, subject to $|u(t)| \leq 1$, that takes the system state from an arbitrary initial state $\mathrm{x}(0) = \mathrm{x}_0$ to the origin so as to minimize

$$\mathcal{J} = \frac{1}{2}\int_0^\infty [\mathrm{x}^T\mathrm{Q}\mathrm{x} + cu^2]\,dt$$

a) Find the optimum feedback control function $u^*(\mathrm{x})$ if the constraint $|u(t)| < 1$ is removed.

b) Show that the optimum feedback control function is given by

$$u^*(\mathrm{x}) = \mathrm{sat}\left[\frac{1}{c}\left(-\left(\frac{\partial\mathcal{J}^*}{\partial\mathrm{x}}\right)^T\mathrm{b}\right)\right]$$

where

$$\mathrm{sat}\ x = \begin{cases} x\ , & |x| \leq 1 \\ \mathrm{sgn}\ x, & |x| \geq 1 \end{cases}$$

c) Show that Bellman's equation, under the optimal control function given above, reduces to

$$\left(\frac{\partial\mathcal{J}^*}{\partial\mathrm{x}}\right)^T\mathrm{A}\mathrm{x} - \frac{1}{2c}\left(\left(\frac{\partial\mathcal{J}^*}{\partial\mathrm{x}}\right)^T\mathrm{b}\right)^2 + \frac{1}{2}(\mathrm{x}^T\mathrm{Q}\mathrm{x}) = 0$$

if $|u| < 1$

and

$$\left(\frac{\partial\mathcal{J}^*}{\partial\mathrm{x}}\right)^T\mathrm{A}\mathrm{x} - \left|\left(\frac{\partial\mathcal{J}^*}{\partial\mathrm{x}}\right)^T\mathrm{b}\right| + \frac{c}{2} + \frac{1}{2}(\mathrm{x}^T\mathrm{Q}\mathrm{x}) = 0$$

if $|u| = 1$

15-8 The type of optimal control problems involving a time-varying linear plant and a performance index of the form of (15-40) ultimately can be reduced to a matrix Riccati equation which frequently must be solved by computers. One question that arises in this case is whether the computer program is correct. Using practical reasoning, determine whether the solution to Example 15-2, as given by Figs. 15-2 is reasonable. Be as complete as possible.

15-9 Show that the class of optimal linear control problems that can be reduced to the solution of (15-49) with **P** positive definite is globally, asymptotically stable under the action of the optimal control $u^*(\mathbf{x})$ (Hint: Does $\mathcal{J}^*(\mathbf{x})$ qualify as a Lyapunov function?)

15-10 Find Bellman's equation for the systems of

a) Example 14-1
b) Exercise 14-12
c) Exercise 13-14
d) Example 13-4

Comment on the possibility of solving the equations.

15-11 Repeat Exercise 12-9, using the time-domain approach given in Sec. 15.4.

15-12 For the system $\ddot{y} + y = u$,

a) Determine the optimal feedback control that minimizes the performance index

$$\mathcal{J} = \frac{1}{2}\int_0^\infty \left(y^2(t) + ru^2(t)\right)dt \qquad \text{with} \qquad r > 0$$

b) Plot the locus of eigenvalues of the optimal closed-loop system as r varies.
c) Plot the Nyquist diagram of the optimal transfer function $F^*(s)$ (see Eq. (15-50)) for $r = 0.1, 1.0, 10.0$.

Repeat steps (a) through (c) above relative to the plant $\ddot{y} - y = u$.

15-13 For the class of problems that led to Eq. (15-60), consider a specific optimal trajectory. Along such a trajectory, by the dynamic programming formalism, $\mathbf{u}^*$ can be expressed in a feedback form $\mathbf{u}^*(\mathbf{x},t)$, and (15-60) can be written as

$$\frac{\partial \mathcal{J}^*}{\partial t} + L\left(\mathbf{x}, \mathbf{u}^*(\mathbf{x},t), t\right) + \left(\frac{\partial \mathcal{J}^*}{\partial \mathbf{x}}\right)^T \mathbf{f}\left(\mathbf{x}, \mathbf{u}^*(\mathbf{x}, t), t\right) = 0$$

Using the above equation, and assuming that $\partial^2\mathcal{J}^*/\partial t\partial x_i$ and $\partial^2\mathcal{J}^*/\partial x_i\partial x_j$ exist for each i and j, show that condition (2) of Theorem 14-3 is satisfied if we set $\partial\mathcal{J}^*/\partial\mathbf{x}$ equal to the adjoint vector $\boldsymbol{\psi}(t)$.

15-14 For the system $\ddot{y} + y = u$, determine the optimal feedback control function that minimizes the performance index

$$\mathcal{J} = \frac{1}{2}\int_0^T u^2(t)\,dt$$

from an arbitrary initial state to the final state $y(T) = \dot{y}(T) = 0$, where T is finite.

15-15 For the system $\ddot{y} + y = u$, determine the optimal feedback control function that minimizes the performance index

$$\mathcal{J} = \frac{1}{2}y(T)^2 + \frac{1}{2}\int_{t_0}^T u^2\,dt$$

If $y(t_0)$, $\dot{y}(t_0)$, t_0, and T are given and the final state is free.

15.10 References

The term "dynamic programming" was coined in the early 1950s by R. Bellman, who then proceeded to indicate its potential usefulness in various fields in a large number of papers. The results up to 1957 are collected in the book [B3]. The application of dynamic programming to control and optimization can be found in [B2]. A valuable complement to [B2] is [D11].

The earliest work in optimal linear feedback system was apparently derived for a sampled data system in [K10]. Merriam carried the idea further to include continuous time systems and systems with a known input. His results are given in [M9]. The theoretical foundations of the linear optimal systems were considered in [K2] and [K6].

The legitimacy of Bellman's equation for optimal control systems is studied in [B10], [B14], and [T2].

16

Abnormal and Singular Control Problems

The basic necessary conditions such as those given by the maximum principle should be applied with some care. There are classes of problems for which careless application of the maximum principle can lead to the wrong result. Representative of this class is the class of *abnormal* optimal control problems.

There are further classes of problems for which even the correct application of the maximum principle is insufficient to permit the solution to be found. Representative of this class of problems is the class of *singular* optimal control problems.

The abnormal and singular optimal control problems are treated in this chapter.

16.1 Abnormal Optimal Control Problems

We have shown in Chap. 13 that in ordinary calculus, the Lagrange multiplier method can be used when we wish to find the minimum point of a twice differentiable function of two variables $f(x_1, x_2)$, subject to the twice differentiable constraint $g(x_1, x_2) = 0$. We introduce a multiplier ψ and form the function $h(x_1, x_2) \triangleq f(x_1, x_2) + \psi g(x_1, x_2)$ and proceed to find the minimum point as if there were no constraints. This leads to the vector condition

$$\left.\frac{\partial h}{\partial \mathbf{x}}\right|_{\mathbf{x} = \mathbf{x}^*} = \left.\frac{\partial f}{\partial \mathbf{x}}\right|_{\mathbf{x} = \mathbf{x}^*} + \psi \left.\frac{\partial g}{\partial \mathbf{x}}\right|_{\mathbf{x} = \mathbf{x}^*} = 0 \qquad (16\text{-}1)$$

Inspecting (16-1), we immediately see that if

$$\left.\frac{\partial g}{\partial \mathbf{x}}\right|_{\mathbf{x}=\mathbf{x}^*} = 0 \tag{16-2}$$

but $\partial f/\partial \mathbf{x}|_{\mathbf{x}=\mathbf{x}^*} \neq 0$ then there is in general no finite value of ψ which can yield the correct result, since it will then mean that $\mathbf{x}^*$ can be found from $\partial f/\partial \mathbf{x}|_{\mathbf{x}=\mathbf{x}^*}$ alone.

◆◆**Example 16-1.** Find the minimum point of $f(x_1, x_2) = ax_1^{\,2} + bx_2^{\,2}$, with $a > b > 0$, subject to $g(x_1, x_2) = 2\left(x_1^{\,2} + x_2^{\,2}\right) - \left(x_1^{\,2} + x_2^{\,2}\right)^2 - 1 = 0$. By examining the equations we can see that as g can be written in polar coordinates in the form $2r^2 - r^4 - 1$, $\partial g/\partial \mathbf{x}$ vanishes at $x_1^{\,2} + x_2^{\,2} = 1$. But $x_1^{\,2} + x_2^{\,2} = 1$ also satisfies the constraining relationship $g = 0$. We then have a situation which renders (16-1) not useful. Writing (16-1) out in full for the present problem, we have

$$\begin{aligned} 2ax_1^* + 4\psi x_1^*\left[1 - \left(x_1^{*2} + x_2^{*2}\right)\right] &= 0 \\ 2bx_2^* + 4\psi x_2^*\left[1 - \left(x_1^{*2} + x_2^{*2}\right)\right] &= 0 \end{aligned} \tag{16-3}$$

We see that with the vanishing of the bracketed quantity in the above equations, a finite value of ψ yields $2ax_1^* = 0$, $2bx_2^* = 0$ which leads to $x_1^* = x_2^* = 0$, an impossible solution since it does not satisfy the constraint. On the other hand, if $\psi = \infty$, the second term of each equation in (16-3) becomes indeterminant and $\mathbf{x}^*$ cannot be found.

It is however obvious that the problem posed does have a solution $x_1^* = 1$, $x_2^* = 0$ (or $x_1^* = 0$, $x_2^* = 1$) as the reader can establish by direct substitution.

To guard against the possibility of occurrence of (16-2) we can introduce two Lagrange multipliers ψ_0 and ψ_1, and form the quantity

$$h(x_1, x_2) = \psi_0 f(x_1, x_2) + \psi_1 g(x_1, x_2) \tag{16-4}$$

Now if we perform (16-1), even if g satisfies (16-2), the problem can still be solved with $\psi_0 = 0$.◆◆

In the general case of minimizing a function of n variables $f(x_1, \ldots, x_n)$ with m constraints $g_i(x_1, \ldots, x_n)$, ($i = 1, \ldots, m$ and $n > m$), we first form $h(\mathbf{x}) = \psi_0 f + \sum_{i=1}^{m} \psi_i g_i$. It can be shown [H1] that if at the minimum point $\mathbf{x}^*$ the rank of the $n \times m$ matrix $[\partial g_i/\partial x_j]$

is less than m, and if the vector $\partial f/\partial \mathbf{x}$ does not vanish at the point $\mathbf{x}^*$, then $\psi_0 = 0$ is a necessary condition that there exist m multipliers $\psi_1, \ldots, \psi_m$, not all 0, that satisfy

$$\left.\frac{\partial h}{\partial \mathbf{x}}\right|_{\mathbf{x} = \mathbf{x}^*} = 0$$

We shall refer to the case where $\psi_0 = 0$ as the *abnormal* case.

The abnormal optimal control problem is the analog of the abnormal case in calculus.

Consider the Hamiltonian function for a typical optimal control problem

$$H = \psi_0 L + \boldsymbol{\psi}^T \mathbf{f} = \psi_0 L + H' \tag{16-5}$$

Suppose there is a problem such that the optimal trajectory $\mathbf{x}^*(t)$ and the optimal control $\mathbf{u}^*(t)$ satisfy all the necessary conditions relative to a reduced Hamiltonian function $H' = \boldsymbol{\psi}^T \mathbf{f}$. Then in order for the Hamiltonian (16-5) to yield the optimal solution as well, the condition $\psi_0 = 0$ must hold. An optimal trajectory $\mathbf{x}^*(t)$ along which $\psi_0 = 0$ is called an *abnormal* optimal trajectory. A control problem yielding an abnormal optimal trajectory will be called an abnormal optimal control problem.

A possible class of abnormal control problems is one in which the solution is independent of the function L. This class of problems is ill-formulated, since the solution will not affect the performance index $\mathcal{J}$. We can, however, obtain from this case some geometrical insights that are helpful in visualizing other abnormal and singular control problems.

Let us note that ψ_0^* will vanish identically if the reachable zone $\mathcal{C}$ at the end point in the $n + 1$ dimensional space is such that the x_0 axis is parallel to the supporting plane of $\mathcal{C}$ at the end point. In such a case, the vector $\boldsymbol{\psi}$, which has been shown to be the outward normal to the reachable zone $\mathcal{C}$, will then have a ψ_0 component that vanishes.

To dramatize the above let us study the following rather transparent example:

◆◆Example 16-2.† Consider the first-order system $\dot{x} = u$. It is desired to find a control function $u^*(t)$ over the time interval $[0, 1]$, subject to $0 \le u(t) \le 1$ that takes the system state from $x(0) = 0$ to $x(1) = 1$ while maximizing the performance criterion††

$$\mathcal{J} = \int_0^1 \sqrt{1 - u(t)}\, dt$$

†This example is by courtesy of J. M. Holtzman.

††It is understood that the positive square root is to be used in this problem.

Since $\max \mathcal{J} = -\min(-\mathcal{J})$, the above problem can also be solved by minimizing $\int_0^1 -\sqrt{1 - u(t)}\, dt$ and then reversing the sign of the optimal performance index found.

The problem is not well formed since there is only one control function, namely $u(t) \equiv 1$ which can take $x(t)$ from 0 to 1 in the alloted time interval; hence $u^*(t) \equiv 1$. We can now show that for this problem ψ_0 must vanish in order to satisfy the maximum principle.

The Hamiltonian for the problem is

$$H(\psi_0, \psi_1, x, u, t) = -\psi_0\sqrt{1 - u(t)} + \psi_1 u(t) \tag{16-6}$$

By the maximum principle, we thus have

$$H^*(t) \triangleq H(\psi_0, \psi_1, x^*, u^*, t) \geq H(\psi_0, \psi_1, x^*, u, t)$$

With $u^*(t) \equiv 1$, (16-6) becomes

$$\psi_1 \geq -\psi_0\sqrt{1 - u(t)} + \psi_1 u(t) \tag{16-7}$$

which must be satisfied for all admissible $u(t)$.

Since $\partial H/\partial x = 0$, ψ_1 is a constant. We recall that the maximum principle also provides that ψ_0 is a constant with a nonpositive value and that ψ_0 and ψ_1 cannot vanish together. If $\psi_0 = 0$, Eq. (16-7) can be satisfied with a positive value of ψ_1. If $\psi_0 < 0$, however, no ψ_1 can be found to satisfy (16-7) for all admissible $u(t)$. Thus we see that $\psi_0 = 0$ is the only valid solution and the solution is therefore abnormal.

The fact that ψ_0 vanishes can also be established by inspecting the reachable set for the problem. With $x_0 = \mathcal{J}$, the reader can demonstrate to himself that the reachable set in the x_0 vs. x_1 plane takes on the aspect of the region shown on Fig. 16-1. At the point

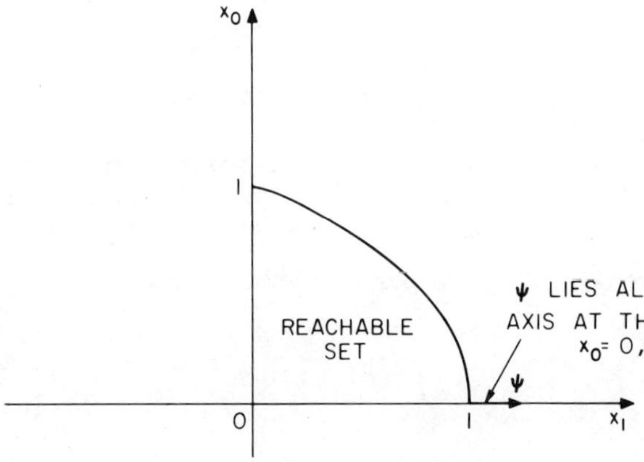

Fig. 16-1. The reachable set of the system of Example 16-2.

$x = x_1$, the outward normal of the reachable set must lie along the x_1 axis; hence $\psi_0 = 0$.◆◆

Of course abnormal control problems need not be as transparent as Example 16-2, but apparently nontrivial abnormal control problems have not been seriously studied.

16.2 Singular Controls in Time-Optimal Control Problems

For an optimal control problem, a trajectory is said to be *singular* if along it the necessary conditions for optimality such as those provided by the maximum principle are satisfied in a trivial manner. In these cases, in spite of the application of the usual necessary condtiions, no useful information is derived. Other methods must then be invoked to find the optimal trajectory. An optimal control problem in which an optimal singular trajectory is found will be referred to as a singular optimal control problem.

For time-optimal control of a linear time-invariant plant, the only manifestation of singular control is nonuniqueness in $\mathbf{u}^*(t)$. This we have hinted at in Chap. 14 and we can now exploit it in more detail.

We have shown in Chap. 14 that for time-optimal control problems with a linear plant, under the constraint $|u(t)| \leq U$, the maximum principle dictates that the optimal control must be of the form

$$\mathbf{u}^*(t) = U \operatorname{sgn}[\mathbf{B}^T \boldsymbol{\psi}(t)]$$

If the ith row of the matrix $\mathbf{B}^T$ is represented by the row vector $\mathbf{b}_i^T$ (i.e., $\mathbf{b}_i$ is the ith column vector of $\mathbf{B}$), we have

$$u_i^*(t) = U \operatorname{sgn}\left[\mathbf{b}_i^T \boldsymbol{\psi}(t)\right]$$

In general, if the quantity $\mathbf{b}_i^T \boldsymbol{\psi}(t)$ crosses 0 only at isolated instants of time such as shown in Fig. 16-2a, then the ith component of $\mathbf{u}^*(t)$ is given by a bang-bang function whose polarity is determined by a switching function made up of a linear combination of the components of the adjoint vector $\boldsymbol{\psi}(t)$.

If for some index i, the scalar product $\mathbf{b}_i^T \boldsymbol{\psi}(t)$ should become identically zero for a finite interval of time as shown in Fig. 16-2b, then we have $u_i^*(t) = \operatorname{sgn} 0$, which is undefined. The maximum principle thus does not provide enough information for us to solve the problem and we must look elsewhere for guidance.

In Chap. 14, we have indicated that L-controllable systems are those where no component of the switching function $\mathbf{B}^T \boldsymbol{\psi}(t)$ vanishes over a finite time-interval. Thus we see that *L-controllable systems cannot have singular time-optimal solutions*.

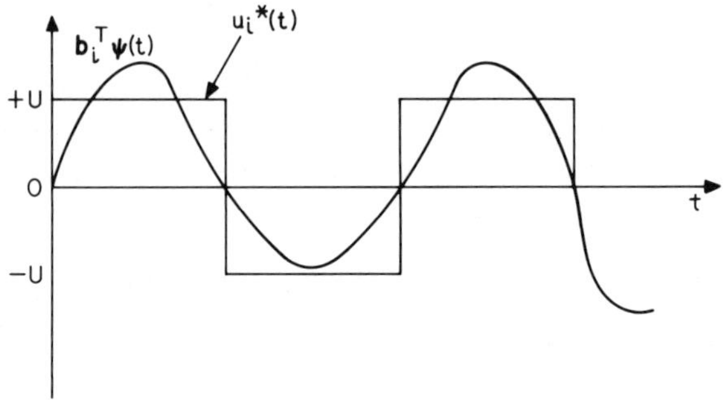

Fig. 16-2a. A case in which $u_i^*(t)$ is well defined by $\text{sgn}[\mathbf{b}_i^T\boldsymbol{\psi}(t)]$.

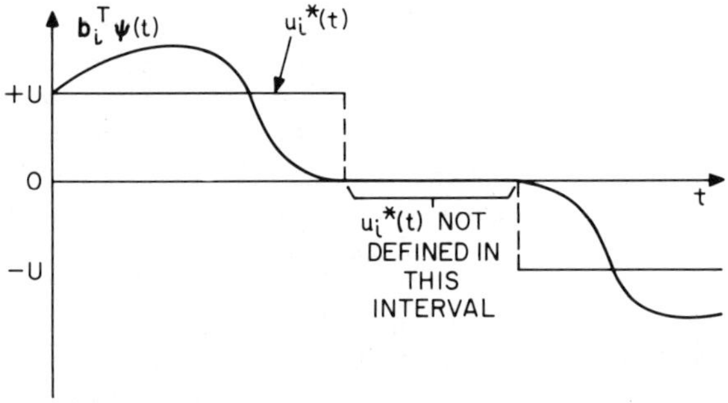

Fig. 16-2b. A case in which $u_i^*(t)$ is not completely defined by $\text{sgn}[\mathbf{b}_i^T\boldsymbol{\psi}(t)]$.

We can readily appreciate why systems that are not L-controllable can yield singular controls, as we can see from the following example:

◆◆Example 16-3. Consider a second-order system which in the canonical form is given by

$$\dot{x}_1 = \lambda_1 x_1 + u_1, \qquad \dot{x}_2 = \lambda_2 x_2 + u_2$$

This system is thus completely decoupled in this form. As a "second-order system," however, it is clearly completely controllable, but not L-controllable. Assume that the λ's are real and let $0 > \lambda_1 > \lambda_2$, assume that $|u_1| \le 1$ and $|u_2| \le 1$. Consider now initial states on the line $x_1(0) = x_2(0)$. Taking the systems involving x_1 and x_2 separately; since each first-order system is L-controllable, there is a unique bang-bang time-optimal control which takes each system to the origin. With $x_1(0) = x_2(0)$, it is clear that the system with the shorter time constant or larger value of λ can be taken to the origin faster. Let the optimal time to take x_1 and x_2 to the origin be T_1 and T_2 respectively; since $\lambda_1 > \lambda_2$, we see that $T_1 < T_2$.

Consider the systems involving x_1 and x_2 together as a second-order system; however, since the stipulation of time-optimal control is that x_1 and x_2 must *simultaneously* arrive at the origin, then the component first-order system with the *longer* time-constant clearly dictates the optimal control time. It is seen here that the optimal time must be T_2. Therefore *any* u_1 which can drive x_1 to the origin in a time T_2 greater than the minimum time T_1 (for x_1) can still qualify to be an optimal control. Thus u_1 is nonunique; in fact, it need not even be bang-bang.

A more meaningful second-order system that is not L-controllable but is completely controllable are those which are reducible to

$$\dot{x}_1 = \lambda_1 x_1 + b_{11} u_1, \qquad \dot{x}_2 = \lambda_2 x_2 + b_{21} u_1 + b_{22} u_2$$

Here the same line of argument as above can be used to show nonuniqueness of time-optimal control. (See Exercise 16-5.)◆◆

It is instructive to study some of the properties of L-controllable systems.

If we let $\mathbf{b}_i$ be the ith column vector of $\mathbf{B}$, we have the following theorem:

◆◆Theorem 16-1. A linear time-invariant system $\dot{\mathbf{x}} = \mathbf{A}\mathbf{x} + \mathbf{B}\mathbf{u}$ is L-controllable if and only if the vectors $\mathbf{b}_i, \mathbf{A}\mathbf{b}_i, \mathbf{A}^2\mathbf{b}_i, \ldots, \mathbf{A}^{n-1}\mathbf{b}_i$ are linearly independent for each i, $(i = 1, \ldots, r)$.◆◆

To prove the theorem, we first note that since $\boldsymbol{\psi}(t) = \boldsymbol{\Psi}(t,0)\boldsymbol{\psi}(0) = (e^{-\mathbf{A}t})^T \boldsymbol{\psi}(0)$, we can write $[\mathbf{B}^T \boldsymbol{\psi}(t)]$ as $[\boldsymbol{\psi}^T(0) e^{-\mathbf{A}t}\mathbf{B}]^T$. Suppose over some time interval the jth component of the switching function vanishes; this means that in this interval

$$\mathbf{b}_j^T \boldsymbol{\psi}(t) = \boldsymbol{\psi}^T(0) e^{-\mathbf{A}t}\mathbf{b}_j = 0$$

$$\frac{d}{dt}\left(\mathbf{b}_j^T \boldsymbol{\psi}(t)\right) = -\boldsymbol{\psi}^T(0)\mathbf{A}e^{-\mathbf{A}t}\mathbf{b}_j = -\boldsymbol{\psi}^T(0) e^{-\mathbf{A}t}\mathbf{A}\mathbf{b}_j = 0$$

$$\frac{d^2}{dt^2}\left(\mathbf{b}_j^T \boldsymbol{\psi}(t)\right) = \boldsymbol{\psi}^T(0)\mathbf{A}^2 e^{-\mathbf{A}t}\mathbf{b}_j = \boldsymbol{\psi}^T(0) e^{-\mathbf{A}t}\mathbf{A}^2\mathbf{b}_j = 0$$

$$\vdots$$

$$\frac{d^{n-1}}{dt^{n-1}}\left(\mathbf{b}_j^T \boldsymbol{\psi}(t)\right) = \boldsymbol{\psi}^T(0)(-\mathbf{A})^{n-1} e^{-\mathbf{A}t}\mathbf{b}_j = \boldsymbol{\psi}^T(0) e^{-\mathbf{A}t}(-\mathbf{A})^{n-1}\mathbf{b}_j = 0 \tag{16-8}$$

(16-8)*

*In arriving at (16-8) we make use of the fact that $\mathbf{A}e^{-\mathbf{A}t} = e^{-\mathbf{A}t}\mathbf{A}$, which was to be shown in Exercise 3-11.

Now the set (16-8) can be expressed as the matrix equation

$$\mathbf{K}_j^T e^{-\mathbf{A}t} \boldsymbol{\psi}(0) = 0 \tag{16-9}$$

where $\mathbf{K}_j$ is the $n \times n$ matrix with $\mathbf{b}_j$, $\mathbf{A}\mathbf{b}_j$, $\mathbf{A}^2\mathbf{b}_j, \ldots, \mathbf{A}^{n-1}\mathbf{b}_j$ as columns.

Since $e^{-\mathbf{A}t}$ is nonsingular and $\boldsymbol{\psi}(0)$ is in general non-null, for (16-9) to be satisfied means that $\mathbf{K}_j$ must be singular. Put in another way (see Appendix A), this means that the columns of $\mathbf{K}_j$ cannot be linearly independent. Thus linear independence of the column vectors of $\mathbf{K}_j$ is a necessary condition for the nonvanishing of any components of the switching function $(\mathbf{B}^T \boldsymbol{\psi}(t))$.

The sufficient part of the theorem is perhaps readily believable unless chattering or other unconventional behaviors occur. Inspecting the form of the switching function, we see that these behaviors will not be possible if none of the components of the switching function vanish over any finite time interval.

We can appreciate the nonuniqueness in $u^*(t)$ better by invoking the geometrical picture which was constructed in Chap. 14. For the system of Example 16-3 the reachable set $\mathcal{C}$ relative to the origin in the three-dimensional space with x_1, x_2, and t^* as coordinates will take on the aspect of an inverted tetrahedron with curved sides (show this). On reflection it will be clear that the projection on the x_1 vs. x_2 plane of the set $\mathcal{C}$ will be sufficient to deduce the orientation of the vector $\boldsymbol{\eta}$ or $\boldsymbol{\psi}^*(t_1)$. On the x_1 vs. x_2 plane it is clear that the projection of the set $\mathcal{C}$ is a rectangle with sides parallel to the principal axis.

Now by virtue of the presence of the flat sides of the rectangle, it is seen that all along each side, the vector $\boldsymbol{\psi}^*(t_1)$, which is the outward normal to $\mathcal{C}$, must be the same. Furthermore, since the sides of the rectangle are parallel either to the x_1 or the x_2 axis, one of the components of $\boldsymbol{\psi}^*(t_1)$ must be 0. From the adjoint equations $\dot{\psi}_1 = -\lambda_1 \psi_1$, and $\dot{\psi}_2 = -\lambda_2 \psi_2$, we know that if one of the components of $\boldsymbol{\psi}$ is 0 at t_1, it will remain 0 henceforth, bringing about a singular condition.

A flat side in the reachable zone $\mathcal{C}$ then offers a clue to the possibility of singularity. Of course it is only a sufficient but not a necessary condition for singularity.

Interesting cases of singular control for time-optimal control of some fourth-order linear time-invariant systems is found in [S11].

16.3 Singular Controls in Fuel-Optimal Control Problems

For fuel-optimal control of linear time-invariant plants, singular control again implies nonuniqueness. The conditions for singularity, however, are expected to be less stringent than in time-optimal control problems. For example, we have already seen from Chap. 12 that both the single and double integrators can have nonunique fuel-optimal solutions, although the systems $\dot{x} = u$ and $\ddot{x} = u$ are obviously L-controllable and hence cannot have singular time-optimal controls.

Let us note that plants with one or more stages of integration will always result in nonuniqueness for some initial states if the performance index is of the form $\mathcal{J} = \int_0^T |u|\, dt$ with $T > t^*$. To show this we simply follow the steps in Example 12-5 (and Exercise 12-5) and pick a starting point which requires a $\mathbf{u}^*$ that does not change polarity. It is immediately seen that there are an infinite number of ways to choose $\mathbf{u}^*$ to result in the same $\mathcal{J}^*$.

We are therefore not surprised to find the following theorem:

♦♦Theorem 16-2. The fuel-optimal control of a linear plant $\dot{\mathbf{x}} = \mathbf{A}\mathbf{x} + \mathbf{B}\mathbf{u}$ will be nonsingular if $|\mathbf{A}\mathbf{K}_j| \neq 0$ for $j = 1, \ldots, r$, where $\mathbf{K}_j$ is the same matrix as that in Eq. (16-9).♦♦

Since $|\mathbf{A}\mathbf{K}_j| = |\mathbf{A}|\,|\mathbf{K}_j|$, then $|\mathbf{A}\mathbf{K}_j| = 0$ implies either $|\mathbf{A}| = 0$ or $|\mathbf{K}_j| = 0$, or both. When $|\mathbf{K}_j| = 0$ it means the plant is not L-controllable. When $|\mathbf{A}| = 0$ on the other hand it means that at least one of the eigenvalues of $\mathbf{A}$ is 0, or the plant has at least one stage of integration.

Let us try to show the plausibility of Theorem 16-2 mathematically.

It is known from Chap. 14 that the solution of the fuel-optimal problem with a linear plant is of the form

$$u_j^*(t) = -\operatorname{dez}\left(\mathbf{b}_j^T \boldsymbol{\psi}(t)\right), \qquad j = 1, \ldots, r \tag{16-10}$$

Thus, $u_i^*(t)$ becomes undefined only if the corresponding switching function $\left(\mathbf{b}_j^T \boldsymbol{\psi}(t)\right)$ becomes identically equal to +1 or -1 over some finite time interval

Now when $\left(\mathbf{b}_j^T \boldsymbol{\psi}(t)\right)$ is identically equal to +1 or -1 we have

$$\begin{aligned}
\frac{d}{dt}\left(\mathbf{b}_j^T \boldsymbol{\psi}(t)\right) &= \mathbf{b}_j^T \dot{\boldsymbol{\psi}}(t) = \mathbf{b}_j^T\left(-\mathbf{A}^T \boldsymbol{\psi}(t)\right) = -(\mathbf{A}\,\mathbf{b}_j)^T \boldsymbol{\psi}(t) = 0 \\
\frac{d^2}{dt^2}\left(\mathbf{b}_j^T \boldsymbol{\psi}(t)\right) &= \left(\mathbf{A}^2 \mathbf{b}_j\right)^T \boldsymbol{\psi}(t) = 0 \\
&\ \ \vdots \\
\frac{d^n}{dt^n}\left(\mathbf{b}_j^T \boldsymbol{\psi}(t)\right) &= (-1)^n \left(\mathbf{A}^n \mathbf{b}_i\right)^T \boldsymbol{\psi}(t) = 0
\end{aligned} \tag{16-11}$$

With the $n \times n$ matrix $\mathbf{K}_j$ as defined in the previous section, (16-11) can be written as

$$(\mathbf{AK}_j)^T \boldsymbol{\psi}(t) = 0 \tag{16-12}$$

As $\boldsymbol{\psi}(t) \not\equiv 0$ the condition of Theorem 16-2 follows.

It is again useful to consider the geometrical relationships afforded by the developments in Chap. 14.

♦♦**Example 16-4.** For a system $\dot{x} = au$ with $\mathcal{J} = \int_0^T b\,|u|\,dt$ and $|u| \le U$, the reachable set $\mathcal{C}(t)$ in the $\mathcal{J}$ vs. x plane is seen to be an inverted isosceles triangle as shown in Fig. 16-3. The sides of the triangle have a slope of b/a.

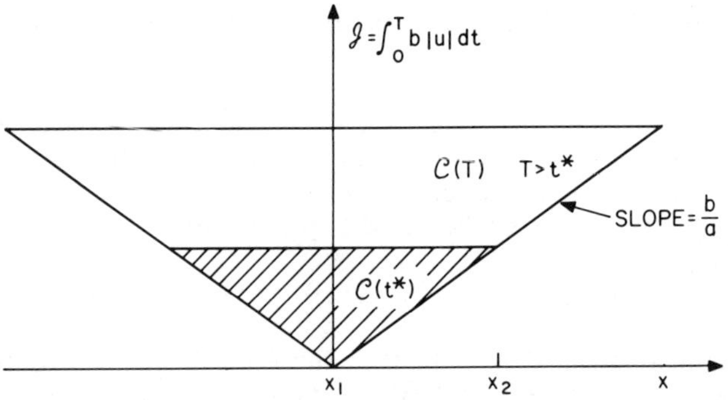

Fig. 16-3. The reachable set $\mathcal{C}(t)$ at $t = t^*$ and $t = T > t^*$ for the system of Example 16-4.

We assume that at $t = 0$, x is at the state x_1. Consider now the end state x_2. For $t < t^*$, the optimal time, it is not possible to reach x_2 by any admissible control and hence there is no solution. At the time $t = t^*$, $\mathcal{C}(t^*)$ just touches x_2 and the time-optimal and the fuel-optimal solutions are equal to each other. In fact the point $x = x_2 = aU$, $\mathcal{J} = bU$ is a corner point of the triangle $\mathcal{C}(t^*)$ (see Fig. 16-3), and there is ambiguity in what the outward normal $\psi(t^*)$ should be.† This ambiguity is resolved through the application of the maximum principle, by which we readily deduce that $\psi(t^*) = b/a$ must hold.

When $T > t^*$, then by Fig. 16-3 we see that the fuel-optimum point $x = x_2$, $\mathcal{J} = bU$ lies on the side of the triangle $\mathcal{C}(T)$ and admits a unique value for $\psi(t_2)$, namely $\psi(t_2) = b/a$.

Applying the maximum principle we see that $u^*(t) = U$ dez $[\psi(t)\,a/b]$ is the fuel-optimal solution, and singular control occurs for $\psi(t)\,a/b \equiv +1$ or $\psi(t) \equiv b/a$. This situation is clearly indicated by the geometric construction given whenever $T > t^*$.

†This type of ambiguity occurs also for the $\mathcal{C}(t^*)$ of Example 16-3, as the reader can readily verify.

Again in this case we see that a flat side in the convex set $\mathcal{C}(T)$ yields the necessary clue.♦♦

16.4 Singular Controls in Other Optimal Control Problems

In other types of optimal control problems, considerations other than nonuniqueness arise when a singular control is encountered. This will be true even for the simplest linear time-invariant plants.

♦♦Example 16-5. Find the optimal control $u^*(t)$ subject to $|u(t)| \leq 1$ that drives the single integrator plant $\dot{x} = u$ from $x = 3$ to $x = 2$ in 8 seconds while minimizing the integral $\int_0^8 x^2\, dt$.

Invoking the maximum principle, we find

$$H = -x^2 + \psi u \tag{16-13}$$

with

$$\dot{\psi} = 2x \tag{16-14}$$

and

$$\dot{x} = u \tag{16-15}$$

From $H^* = \max_u H$, we see that the optimal control must be of the form

$$u^* = \operatorname{sgn}\psi \tag{16-16}$$

whenever $\psi \neq 0$.

Inspecting the problem we can immediately see two points: (i) a bang-bang control is quite unreasonable for the particular set of numbers given, and (ii) ψ can become identically zero whenever $x = 0$ (and hence $\dot{\psi} = 0$). When $\psi \equiv 0$, the maximum principle as such does not yield sufficient information and hence we must use other methods to obtain the solution. Fortunately, in this case the true solution can be easily obtained using simple physical reasoning.

We note that $\psi(0)$ cannot be positive since this will result in x increasing without bound. Some thought will also convince us that $\psi(0)$ cannot be 0. (Why?) Thus $\psi(0)$ must be negative. However, by (16-14), $\dot{\psi}(0)$ is positive. We thus know that $u^*(t)$ must be -1 over the time interval $0 \leq t < 3$.

At $t = 3$, however, physical reasoning would show that ψ must become 0 and stay there. At $t = 6$, physical reasoning again indicates that in order to meet the boundary condition, ψ must become positive, causing $u^*(t)$ to become $+1$, which then takes x^* from 0 to 2 in 2 seconds.

The functions $x^*(t)$, $\psi(t)$, and $u^*(t)$ are plotted as functions of t in Fig. 16-4. Note that by (16-14), $\dot{\psi}$ must be continuous; hence ψ must possess continuous first derivatives at $t = 3$ and $t = 6$.◆◆

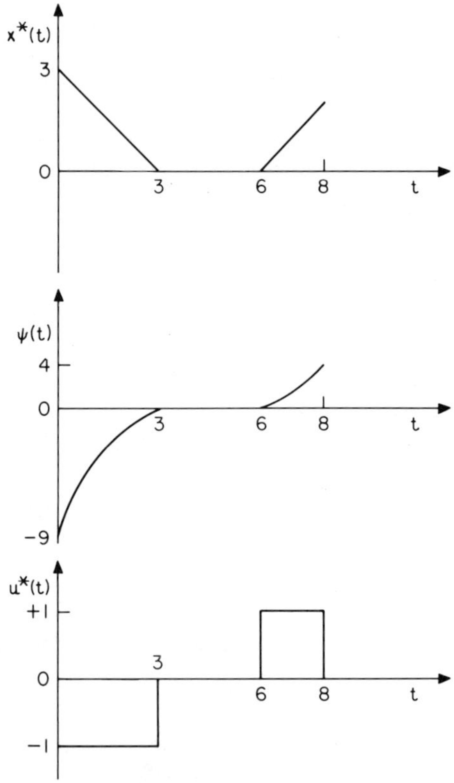

Fig. 16-4. The functions $x^*(t)$, $\psi(t)$, and $u^*(t)$ of the system of Example 16-4.

Another possible situation that gives rise to singular control problems is where the functional $\mathcal{J}$ becomes only a function of the end points. This situation can occur if the integrand L in a Problem of Lagrange is an exact integral. A differential equation

$$\frac{dx}{dt} = \frac{f(x,t)}{g(x,t)} \tag{16-17}$$

is said to be exact if

$$\frac{\partial f}{\partial x} = -\frac{\partial g}{\partial t} \tag{16-18}$$

With an exact equation, if we identify a function $h(x, t)$ such that

$$\frac{\partial h}{\partial t} = f(x, t), \qquad \frac{\partial h}{\partial x} = -g(x, t) \tag{16-19}$$

then we have

$$dh = \frac{\partial h}{\partial x} dx + \frac{\partial h}{\partial t} dt = -g(x, t)\, dx + f(x, t)\, dt = 0 \tag{16-20}$$

Equation (16-20) implies that an exact differential equation of the form (16-17) is equivalent to an equation $dh = 0$ and hence can be integrated to yield $h(x, t) = c$ with c a constant.

In calculus of variation, we may encounter a problem such as the following:

♦♦**Example 16-6.** Find a trajectory that satisfies the boundary conditions $x(t_1) = x_1$ and $x(t_2) = x_2$ and that minimizes the index

$$\mathcal{J} = \int_{t_1}^{t_2} (3x^2 \dot{x} t + x^3)\, dt$$

Since,

$$(3x^2 \dot{x} t + x^3)\, dt = 3x^2 t dx + x^3 dt = d(x^3 t)$$

we see that $\mathcal{J}^* = x_2{}^3 t_2 - x_1{}^3 t_1$ *for any trajectory that meets the boundary conditions*.♦♦

We may suppose that the above class of problems is rather pathological. This, however, is not necessarily so for two reasons. First, for problems involving differential equations, if the differential equation is free, then because of the uniqueness theorem, there is at most only one trajectory that can satisfy the boundary condition. This at least removes the nonuniqueness in the optimal solution. Second, in multivariable problems, singular control usually occurs only on special hypersurfaces; elsewhere the solution is nonsingular. Determining these singular surfaces and establishing that the singular solutions are optimal then constitute the main task.

Both of the conditions mentioned above occur in a class of systems considered by Wonham and Johnson [W7].

Consider a linear time-invariant plant that is completely controllable and which has a single input. Without loss of generality then we can write the system equation in the normal form $\dot{\mathbf{x}} = \mathbf{A}\mathbf{x} + \mathbf{b}u$ with

$$\mathbf{A} = \begin{bmatrix} 0 & 1 & 0 & \cdots & 0 \\ 0 & 0 & 1 & \cdots & 0 \\ \cdot & & & & \\ \cdot & & & & \\ \cdot & & & & \\ 0 & 0 & 0 & \cdots & 1 \\ a_1 & a_2 & a_3 & \cdots & a_n \end{bmatrix}, \quad \mathbf{b} = \begin{bmatrix} 0 \\ 0 \\ \cdot \\ \cdot \\ \cdot \\ 1 \end{bmatrix}$$

Let it be desired to find an optimal control $u^*(t)$, subject to $|u(t)| \leq 1$, which takes the system from some arbitrary initial state $\mathbf{x}_0$ to the origin $\mathbf{0}$ in some time T (T is free) so as to minimize the performance index $\mathcal{J} = \frac{1}{2}\int_0^T \left(\mathbf{x}^T(t)\mathbf{Q}\mathbf{x}(t)\right)dt$, where $\mathbf{Q}$ is a diagonal matrix: $\mathbf{Q} = \operatorname{diag}(q_1, \ldots, q_n)$, with $q_i \geq 0$, $i = 1, \ldots, n$.

Applying the maximum principle, we have

$$H = \boldsymbol{\psi}^T \mathbf{A}\mathbf{x} + (\boldsymbol{\psi}^T \mathbf{b})u - \frac{1}{2}\mathbf{x}^T \mathbf{Q}\mathbf{x}$$

whereby we immediately obtain the condition

$$u^*(t) = \operatorname{sgn}\left(\psi_n(t)\right) \quad \text{whenever} \quad \psi_n(t) \neq 0 \tag{16-21}$$

The singular cases therefore are to be found when $\psi_n(t)$ vanishes over some finite interval of time. Let us consider what must be the consequences when $\psi_n(t) \equiv 0$.

The canonical equations in $\dot{x}_i$ are

$$\begin{aligned} \dot{x}_1 &= x_2 \\ \dot{x}_2 &= x_3 \\ &\vdots \\ \dot{x}_{n-1} &= x_n \\ \dot{x}_n &= \sum_{i=1}^{n} a_i x_i + u \end{aligned} \tag{16-22}$$

and those in $\dot{\psi}_i$ are

$$\begin{aligned} \dot{\psi}_1 &= -a_1\psi_n + q_1 x_1 \\ \dot{\psi}_2 &= -\psi_1 - a_2\psi_n + q_2 x_2 \\ &\vdots \\ \dot{\psi}_{n-1} &= -\psi_{n-2} - a_{n-1}\psi_n + q_{n-1}x_{n-1} \\ \dot{\psi}_n &= -\psi_{n-1} - a_n\psi_n + q_n x_n \end{aligned} \tag{16-23}$$

When $\psi_n \equiv 0,\ \dot{\psi}_n \equiv 0$, then from the last equation of (16-23) we have

$$\psi_{n-1} = q_n x_n \quad \text{or} \quad \dot{\psi}_{n-1} = q_n \dot{x}_n \tag{16-24}$$

Using (16-24), the last equation of (16-22) yields

$$u = -\sum_{i=1}^{n} a_i x_i - \frac{1}{q_n}(\psi_{n-2} + a_{n-1}\psi_n - q_{n-1}x_{n-1}) \tag{16-25}$$

which is valid whenever the rhs has an absolute value less than 1. In the latter case u is a function of some of the x_i's and the ψ_i's and the last equations of both (16-22) and (16-23) are reduced to algebraic relations and can be eliminated from considerations when we analyze the differential equations (16-22) and (16-23).

Now the first $(n-1)$ equations of (16-22) and the first $(n-1)$ equations of (16-23) along with (16-24) yield a $2(n-1)$th order *free* linear time-invariant system. The behavior of this $2(n-1)$th order free system is such that the first $(n-1)$ equations of (16-22) sweep out a hypersurface in state space. This hypersurface is *singular* since $\psi_n(t) \equiv 0$ on the surface. Moreover, with $u^*(\mathbf{x})$ of the form of (16-25), a state originally on the hypersurface can be kept on the hypersurface.

The motion of the $2(n-1)$th order free system can be readily determined. In view of the results of Sec. 13.2, we see that the eigenvalues of this system must again be symmetrically disposed with respect to the imaginary axis of the complex plane. Indeed, the characteristic equation is seen to be

$$\sum_{i=1}^{n} (-\lambda)^{i-1} \lambda^{i-1} q_i = 0 \tag{16-26}$$

and thus if λ_k is an eigenvalue, $-\lambda_k$ is one also. Let us assume now that the λ_i's are distinct.

Suppose we choose a set of $(n-1)\ \lambda_i$'s such that $\mathcal{R}e\ \lambda_i < 0$ for each. Relative to this set, there is a solution to the $2(n-1)$th order free system above of the form

$$\begin{aligned} x_1 &= \sum_{j=1}^{n-1} k_j e^{\lambda_j t} \\ x_2 &= \dot{x}_1 = \sum_{j=1}^{n-1} k_j \lambda_j e^{\lambda_j t} \\ &\ \ \vdots \\ x_n &= \dot{x}_{n-1} = \sum_{j=1}^{n-1} k_j \lambda_j^{n-2} e^{\lambda_j t} \end{aligned} \tag{16-27}$$

The set (16-27) contains $n - 1$ arbitrary constants $k_1, \ldots, k_{n-1}$, depending on the particular solution. Another way to characterize the set is to write (16-27) in the form

$$(\mathbf{c}^T \mathbf{x}) = 0 \tag{16-28}$$

where $\mathbf{c}^T$ is a constant n-vector. By (16-27) and (16-28), $\mathbf{c}$ is defined by (why?)

$$\sum_{i=1}^{n} c_i \lambda_k^{i-1} = 0, \qquad k = 1, \ldots, n - 1 \tag{16-29}$$

The solution (16-27) will converge to the origin since $\mathcal{Re}\, \lambda_j < 0$ for $j = 1, \ldots, n - 1$ and hence it is a candidate for the optimal solution. By the last equation of (16-22) we can find a $u(t)$ which can maintain the solution on the hypersurface given by (16-27) or (16-28). By the consideration in Sec. 13.2, such a u can be expressed in a linear feedback form

$$u(\mathbf{x}) = \mathbf{d}^T \mathbf{x} \tag{16-30}$$

where by the last equation of (16-22), we have

$$\sum_{i=1}^{n-1} d_i x_i = \dot{x}_n - \sum_{i=1}^{n} x_i a_i$$

or

$$\sum_{i=1}^{n-1} d_i \lambda_k^{i-1} = \lambda_k{}^n - \sum_{i=1}^{n} a_i \lambda_k^{i-1} \tag{16-31}$$

With a particular choice of the λ's and hence $u(\mathbf{x})$ (inasmuch as the singular hypersurface is swept out by essentially a free system) then because of the uniqueness theorem we would expect that on the hypersurface the functional $\mathcal{J}$ depends only on the initial and final states. Now the final state is the origin $\mathbf{0}$, which also is seen to lie on the singular hypersurface. Thus, on the hypersurface, through each point there is a unique trajectory that ultimately leads to the origin.

If now we can establish that there is no better way to transfer states on the singular hypersurface to the origin, then the optimality of the singular control as given by (16-30) is assured. This was proved by Wonham and Johnson through demonstrating that the value of $\mathcal{J}$ as determined by (16-30) for points on the singular hypersurface cannot be improved upon.

The optimal solution for initial states not on the singular hypersurface will involve a control u^* which is $+1$ or -1 until the singular hypersurface is reached. Note that depending on where the optimal trajectory hits the singular hypersurface, the function u may or may not suffer a discontinuity on reaching the hypersurface.

We may note in passing that whereas in Example 16-5, the function sgn 0 ultimately yielded a value of 0, in the present case, as $u(\mathrm{x})$ is linear, sgn 0 yields a continuously changing value between $+1$ or -1 and 0.

♦♦Example 16-7 (Wonham and Johnson). Let the plant be the double integrator $\dot{x}_1 = x_2$, $\dot{x}_2 = u$, and let $\mathcal{J} = \frac{1}{2}\int_0^T \left(x_1^2 + x_2^2\right) dt$.

Here we have the canonical equations

$$\dot{x}_1 = x_2, \qquad \dot{x}_2 = u, \qquad \dot{\psi}_1 = x_1, \qquad \dot{\psi}_2 = -\psi_1 + x_2 \tag{16-32}$$

and by the maximum principle, we have $u^* = \operatorname{sgn}\psi_2$ whenever $\psi_2 \neq 0$.

When $\psi_2 \equiv 0$, then the last equation of (16-32) yields $\dot{\psi}_2 = 0 = -\psi_1 + x_2$; thus $x_2 = \psi_1$. The first and third equations of (16-32) then give

$$\dot{x}_1 = \psi_1, \qquad \dot{\psi}_1 = x_1 \tag{16-33}$$

(16-33) is equivalent to $\ddot{x}_1 - x_1 = 0$; thus the eigenvalues of (16-33) are $\lambda_1 = -1$, $\lambda_2 = +1$. By (16-31), moreover, we obtain $d_1 = 1$, $d_2 = 0$. Thus with λ_1 in (16-29), and by (16-30), we obtain the equation for the set of all singular trajectories as

$$x_1 + x_2 = 0, \qquad |x_1| \leq 1 \tag{16-34}$$

which is a straight line segment passing through the origin. It is shown as the segments Ω_+ and Ω_- in Fig. 16-5.

The lines Σ_+ and Σ_- are respectively the trajectories under the controls $u = +1$ and $u = -1$ that pass through the points $(1, -1)$ and $(-1, 1)$.

On the set (16-34) (i.e., on the set $\Omega_\pm$), the optimal control is the linear one

$$u^*(\mathrm{x}) = x_1 \tag{16-35}$$

Elsewhere, the optimal contol is bang-bang, and all resultant trajectories except two will intersect either the segment Ω or the switching line Σ. The two exceptions are the two bang-bang trajectories that meet the origin. These are marked as Γ_+ and Γ_-. Thus for all starting states not lying on $\Gamma_\pm$, a portion of the optimal trajectories will be singular. A typical trajectory of this type is trajectory A as shown in Fig. 16-5. The optimal control for the

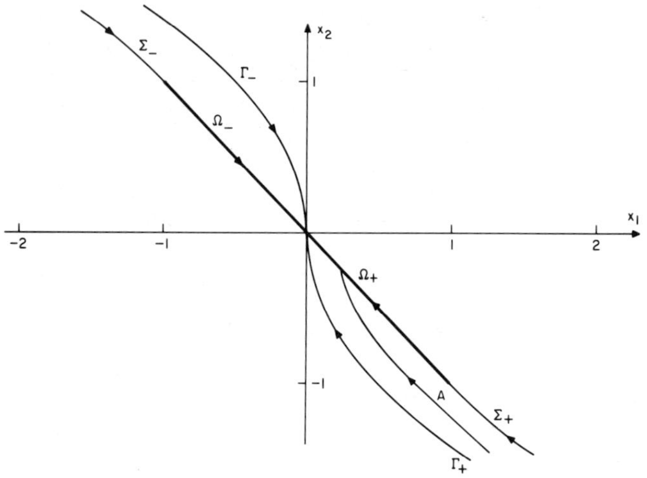

Fig. 16-5. The different optimal control regions of the system of Example 16-7. Only the trajectories following Γ_+ and Γ_- will have strictly bang-bang control. The other trajectory (such as the trajectory A shown) will be under linear control when it reaches the line segment Ω_+ or Ω_-.

trajectory is +1 until the line Ω_+ is reached. Since the line Ω_+ intersects trajectory A at a point with the x_1 coordinate less than unity, then by (16-35), at the point of intersection $u^*(t)$ undergoes a discontinuous jump. ◆◆

There are also many known examples of singular control involving nonlinear systems. Probably the most well known of these is the sounding rocket problem (see Exercise 16-6). For this problem, somewhat contrary to intuition, a thrust program that is not always full-on is sometimes needed in order for the missile to reach the maximum height.

16.5 The Meaning of Singularity

Having explored some of the manifestations of singularity, it will be fruitful to see some of the theoretical aspects of this class of problems.

We have already noted that for singular controls, the maximum principle is satisfied in an ambiguous way, such as sgn 0, which is not defined. It will be instructive to investigate the singular case with respect to the other necessary conditions for optimality.

For the sake of simplicity, let us consider a typical problem with a single control variable u. Let us further note that in the classes of problems considered so far in this chapter, *the control variable u has entered the problem linearly*, i.e., the system equations can be written in the form

$$\dot{\mathbf{x}} = \mathbf{f}(\mathbf{x}, t) + \mathbf{g}(\mathbf{x}, t)u \tag{16-36}$$

and the performance criterion can be written in the form

$$\mathcal{J} = \int_{t_1}^{t_2} \left(f_0(\mathbf{x}, t) + g_0(\mathbf{x}, t)u\right) dt \qquad (16\text{-}37)^*$$

In each of the classes of problems considered, moreover, $u(t)$ is constrained to

$$|u(t)| \leq U \qquad (16\text{-}38)$$

Let us now formulate the problem using the approach of Sec. 13.5.** Accordingly, we define the functions $\nu(t)$ and $\zeta(u,\nu)$ so that

$$\zeta(u,\nu) = \left(u(t) + U\right)\left(U - u(t)\right) - \nu^2(t) = 0 \qquad (16\text{-}39)$$

and further, we define the multipliers $\boldsymbol{\psi}$ and ν and form

$$L_2(\mathbf{x}, \dot{\mathbf{x}}, \boldsymbol{\psi}, u, \nu, \lambda, \zeta) = \left(f_0(\mathbf{x}, t) + g_0(\mathbf{x}, t)u\right) + \boldsymbol{\psi}^T\left(\dot{\mathbf{x}} - \mathbf{f}(\mathbf{x}, t) - \mathbf{g}(\mathbf{x}, t)u\right) + \lambda\zeta(u,\nu) \qquad (16\text{-}40)$$

Suppose we test the expression (16-40) with respect to the Legendre-Clebsch condition (Eq. (13-53)) $\partial^2 L_2/\partial u^2 \geq 0$; we obtain

$$\frac{\partial^2 L_2}{\partial u^2} = \lambda \frac{\partial^2 \zeta}{\partial u^2} \geq 0 \qquad (16\text{-}41)$$

However, we note that for singular control, it is possible that $u^*(t)$ is not bang-bang, i.e., $|u(t)| < U$. In this case we have shown in Sec. 13.4 that the multiplier λ must vanish. This means that $\partial^2 L_2/\partial u^2 \equiv 0$. We have thus shown that for the class of problems considered in this chapter, *an optimal singular trajectory is characterized by the fact that the Legendre-Clebsch condition is trivially satisfied along the trajectory.*

The fact that $\partial^2 L_2/\partial u^2 \equiv 0$ actually comes about because u enters only linearly in the function L_1 (as defined in Chap. 13). For our problem

$$L_1(\mathbf{x}, \dot{\mathbf{x}}, \boldsymbol{\psi}, u) = \left(f_0(\mathbf{x}, t) + g_0(\mathbf{x}, t)u\right) + \boldsymbol{\psi}^T\left(\dot{\mathbf{x}} - \mathbf{f}(\mathbf{x}, t) - \mathbf{g}(\mathbf{x}, t)u\right) \qquad (16\text{-}42)$$

and it is clear that $\partial^2 L_1/\partial u^2 \equiv 0$. Indeed the Hamiltonian in this

*For the fuel-optimal control, the integrand for the performance index is a function of $|u|$; however, we recall that for that class, singular control occurs only for $u(t)$'s that do not change sign.

**We assume that the problem is not abnormal.

case is

$$H(\mathbf{x}, \boldsymbol{\psi}, u) = -f_0(\mathbf{x}, t) - g_0(\mathbf{x}, t)u + \boldsymbol{\psi}^T\big(\mathbf{f}(\mathbf{x}, t) - \mathbf{g}(\mathbf{x}, t)u\big) \tag{16-43}$$

and it is also true that $\partial^2 H/\partial u^2 \equiv 0$. When $\partial^2 L_1/\partial u^2 = \partial^2 H/\partial u^2 \equiv 0$, we may then be alerted for the possible occurrence of singular controls.

A further property of a singular trajectory is that, along it, the Weierstrass excess function vanishes or

$$E(\mathbf{x}^*, \dot{\mathbf{x}}, \dot{\mathbf{x}}^*, u, u^*) \equiv 0 \tag{16-44}$$

The proof for the class of systems given by (16-36) and (16-37) is left to the reader.

16.6 A Necessary Condition for Optimality of Singular Solutions

Thus far we see that it is frequently feasible to obtain possible singular optimal solutions; however, a readily applicable test is lacking—a test which can differentiate between the truly optimal singular solutions and the nonoptimal ones.

It is reasonable to return to calculus of variations to find such a test. In fact, since many of the necessary conditions obtained through taking the first variation in calculus of variations are satisfied in a trivial manner by singular solutions it becomes sensible to seek a test using the second variation. Such a test has been found by Kelley [K14]. Tait [T1], further extended its use.

To develop Kelley's result, consider a typical Mayer problem in which a system with a single control variable $\dot{\mathbf{x}} = \mathbf{f}(\mathbf{x}, u)$ is to be controlled from the initial state $\mathbf{x}(t_1) = \mathbf{x}_1$ such that a function of the final state $P\big(\mathbf{x}(t_2)\big)$ is to be minimized. To avoid details of no consequence, let us assume that the system is time invariant and that x_0, t_1, and t_2 are fixed.

Suppose an optimal singular solution $\mathbf{x}^*(t)$ and an optimal singular control $u^*(t)$ are found over $t_1 \leq t \leq t_2$; let us determine the conditions that must be satisfied by these functions.

If we use the multiplier rule (Theorem 13-1), the problem above is equivalent to one of minimizing a functional

$$\mathcal{J}_1 = P\big(\mathbf{x}(t)\big)\big|_{t=t_2} + \int_{t_1}^{t_2} \boldsymbol{\psi}^T(\dot{\mathbf{x}} - \mathbf{f})\,dt$$

without regard to the system equations $\dot{\mathbf{x}} = \mathbf{f}$.

Suppose that we perturb $\mathbf{x}^*(t)$ and $u^*(t)$ by $\delta\mathbf{x}(t)$ and $\delta u(t)$ respectively; we have, to terms in the first degree,

$$\mathcal{J}_1 + \delta\mathcal{J}_1 = P\left(\mathbf{x}^*(t)\right)_{t=t_2} + \left(\frac{\partial P}{\partial \mathbf{x}}\right)^T \delta\mathbf{x}\Bigg|_{t=t_2} + \int_{t_1}^{t_2}\left(\boldsymbol{\psi}^T(\dot{\mathbf{x}} - \mathbf{f}) - \boldsymbol{\psi}^T\left(\frac{\partial \mathbf{f}}{\partial \mathbf{x}}\,\delta\mathbf{x} + \frac{\partial \mathbf{f}}{\partial u}\,\delta u\right) + \boldsymbol{\psi}^T\,\delta\dot{\mathbf{x}}\right)dt \quad (16\text{–}45)$$

Thus

$$\delta\mathcal{J}_1 = \left(\frac{\partial P}{\partial \mathbf{x}}\right)^T \delta\mathbf{x}\Bigg|_{t=t_2} - \int_{t_1}^{t_2}\left(\boldsymbol{\psi}^T\left(\frac{\partial \mathbf{f}}{\partial \mathbf{x}}\,\delta x + \frac{\partial \mathbf{f}}{\partial u}\,\delta u\right) - \boldsymbol{\psi}^T\,\delta\dot{\mathbf{x}}\right)dt \quad (16\text{–}46)$$

Since by assumption, the reference trajectory and control about which all derivatives are to be taken are optimal, $\delta\mathcal{J}_1 = 0$. As the optimal trajectory is singular, moreover, the vanishing of $\delta\mathcal{J}_1$ does not yield enough useful information.

Let us go one step further to obtain the second variation. For this it is convenient to take the Hamiltonian $H \triangleq \boldsymbol{\psi}^T\mathbf{f}$ and to write $\mathcal{J}_1$ in the form $\mathcal{J}_1 = P\left(\mathbf{x}(t)\right)_{t=t_2} + \int_{t_1}^{t_2}(\boldsymbol{\psi}^T\dot{\mathbf{x}} - H)\,dt$. Expanding the terms to second degree, and noting that along the optimal trajectory the term $\delta\mathcal{J}_1$, given by (16–46), vanishes, we have

$$\mathcal{J}_1 + \delta\mathcal{J}_1 + \tfrac{1}{2}\delta^2\mathcal{J}_1 = \left(P\left(x^*(t)\right) + \tfrac{1}{2}\,\delta\mathbf{x}^T\,\frac{\partial^2 P}{\partial \mathbf{x}^2}\,\delta\mathbf{x}\right)_{t=t_2} + \int_{t_1}^{t_2}\left((\boldsymbol{\psi}^T\dot{\mathbf{x}} - H) - \tfrac{1}{2}\left(\delta\mathbf{x}^T\,\frac{\partial^2 H}{\partial \mathbf{x}^2}\,\delta\mathbf{x} + 2\,\delta\mathbf{x}^T\,\frac{\partial^2 H}{\partial \mathbf{x}\partial u}\,\delta u + \frac{\delta^2 H}{\delta u^2}\,\delta u^2\right)\right)dt$$

(16–47)

or

$$\delta^2\mathcal{J}_1 = \delta\mathbf{x}^T\,\frac{\partial^2 P}{\partial \mathbf{x}^2}\,\delta\mathbf{x}\Bigg|_{t=t_2} - \int_{t_1}^{t_2}\left(\delta\mathbf{x}^T\,\frac{\partial^2 H}{\partial \mathbf{x}^2}\delta\mathbf{x} + 2\,\delta\mathbf{x}^T\,\frac{\partial^2 H}{\partial \mathbf{x}\partial u}\,\delta u + \frac{\delta^2 H}{\delta u^2}\delta u^2\right)dt$$

(16–48)

where $\partial^2 P/\partial\mathbf{x}^2$ is the matrix $[\partial^2 P/\partial x_i\partial x_j]$ and $\partial^2 H/\partial\mathbf{x}\partial u$ is a vector with the ith element $\partial^2 H/\partial x_i\partial u$ etc.

If $\mathbf{x}^*(t)$ and $u^*(t)$ were the minimizing solutions, then it is necessary that $\delta^2 \mathcal{J}_1 \geq 0$ for any perturbations $\delta\mathbf{x}$ and δu that satisfy the first-degree system approximation equation

$$\delta\dot{\mathbf{x}} = \left(\frac{\partial \mathbf{f}}{\partial \mathbf{x}}\right)^T \delta\mathbf{x} + \frac{\partial \mathbf{f}}{\partial u}\delta u \tag{16-49}$$

with

$$\delta\mathbf{x}(t_1) = \delta\mathbf{x}(t_2) = 0 \tag{16-50}$$

Through the use of a special δu in the following form

$$\delta u = \begin{cases} 0 \ , & t \leq \tau \\ k/\Delta \ , & \tau < t \leq \tau + \Delta \\ -k/\Delta \ , & \tau + \Delta < t \leq \tau + 2\Delta \\ 0 \ , & \tau + 2\Delta < t \end{cases} \tag{16-51}$$

and letting Δ become sufficiently small, it can be shown [K14] that a necessary condition for $\delta^2 \mathcal{J} \geq 0$ is that along the optimal trajectory,

$$\frac{\partial}{\partial u}\left(\frac{d^2}{dt^2}\left(\frac{\partial H}{\partial u}\right)\right) \geq 0 \tag{16-52}$$

In the event that the optimization problem is in the Bolza form, so that $\mathcal{J} = P\big(x(t_2)\big) + \int_{t_1}^{t_2} L(\mathbf{x}, \mathbf{u}, t)\,dt$ is to be minimized, then we can readily show that the necessary condition remains in the form (16-52) where $H = -L + \boldsymbol{\psi}^T \mathbf{f}$.

The power of the test lies in the ease with which it can be applied. Consider the following:

♦♦**Example 16-8.** Applying the test (16-52) to the problem of Example 16-5 we have: $H = -x^2 + \psi u$, $\dfrac{\partial H}{\partial u} = \psi$, $\dfrac{d^2}{dt^2}\left(\dfrac{\partial H}{\partial u}\right) = \dfrac{d}{dt}\dot{\psi} = 2\dot{x} = 2u$, $\dfrac{\partial}{\partial u}\left(\dfrac{d}{dt^2}\left(\dfrac{\partial H}{\partial u}\right)\right) = 2 > 0$. Thus the test is satisfied, and any singular solution satisfying the boundary conditions of the problem is also optimal.♦♦

♦♦**Example 16-9.** Applying the test (16-52) to the problem of Example 16-7, we have

$$H = -\frac{1}{2} x_1^2 + \dot{x}_2 + \psi_1 x_2 + \psi_2 u$$

$$\frac{\partial H}{\partial u} = \psi_2, \qquad \frac{d^2}{dt^2}\left(\frac{\partial H}{\partial u}\right) = -\dot{\psi}_1 + \dot{x}_2 = -x_1 + u$$

and again, any singular solution satisfying the boundary condition is optimal.♦♦

16.7 Summary

Abnormal and singular situations can occur in optimal control problems to trap the unwary.

Abnormal optimal control problems are characterized by the fact that the component of the adjoint vector ψ_0^* (in the maximum principle formulation of the problem) vanishes. Abnormal optimal control problems occur for a system with a Hamiltonian of the form (16-5) when there is an optimal trajectory along which all the necessary conditions are satisfied by the H' portion of the given Hamiltonian. Abnormal optimal control problems can be better appreciated when we study the analog of such problems in calculus (Sec. 16.1, beginning).

Aside from the ill-formed case where the performance index is independent of the solutions, abnormal control problems have not been seriously studied.

Singular optimal control occurs when most of the necessary conditions derived from first variations are trivially satisfied. Some of the manifestations of singular control are:

1) Nonuniqueness in solution.
2) Solutions that are not bang-bang or not on-off in situations where bang-bang or on-off optimal controls are apparently called for.
3) The existence of hypersurfaces in state space on which the integrand of the performance index becomes an exact integral.

An important class of problems where singular control can occur is the class in which u enters linearly in both the system equation and the integrand of the performance index (see Eqs. (16-36) and (16-37)). For such a class $\partial^2 H/\partial u_i^2 \equiv 0$ for all i.

The main points developed in this chapter concerning singular control are:

1) In time-optimal control of linear time-invariant plants, the manifestation of singularity is nonuniqueness in the optimal control. Singularity can only occur for systems that are not L-controllable.

2) In fuel-optimal control of linear time-invariant plants, singularity again means nonuniqueness. Singularity can occur for systems that have one or more stages of integration and/or systems which are not L-controllable.
3) In amplitude limited control of linear time-invariant plants whose performance index has an integrand that is a quadratic form in the states alone (the control function is not involved), singular hypersurfaces in the state space can appear on which the optimum control is not bang-bang.

The manner in which the various necessary conditions in optimal control are trivially satisfied is indicated in Sec. 16.5.

A useful test for the optimality of singular control functions is given in Sec. 16.6 (Eq. (16.52)).

16.8 Exercises

16-1 Solve the following minimization problems in calculus through the use of Lagrange multipliers. Indicate the abnormal cases if any. (The functions $f(x_1, x_2)$ and $g(x_1, x_2)$ used below are the same as those employed in Sec. 16.1.)

a) $f(x_1, x_2) = x_1^2 - 2(x_1 + x_2) + 6$

$g(x_1, x_2) = (x_1 + x_2)^2 - 4 = 0$

b) $f(x_1, x_2) = x_1^2 + 2x_1 x_2 + 4x_2^2$

$g(x_1, x_2) = \sin^2(x^2 + y^2) - 1 = 0$

c) $f(x_1, x_2) = (x_1 - x_2)^2$

$g(x_1, x_2) = \exp\left((x - 3)^2 + (y - 4)^2\right) - 1 = 0$

16.2 Consider the fuel-optimal control of the system $p(p + 1)y = u$ with $\mathcal{J} = \int_0^T |u(\tau)|\, d\tau$ from an arbitrary point to the origin. For $T = 2$, find and sketch

a) The reachable zone $\mathcal{C}(T)$
b) The zones where singular control occurs
c) The zones where nonsingular control occurs

16-3 Find the zones in the state plane for singular control for the system

$$\dot{x}_1 = 3x_2 + u, \qquad \dot{x}_2 = -2u$$

with $\mathcal{J} = \int_0^\infty x_1^2(\tau)\,d\tau$ and arbitrary $\mathbf{x}(0)$. Assume $|u(t)| \le U$. Establish the optimality of the singular control.

16-4 (Snow). Consider the problem of fuel-optimal control of the time-varying plant

$$\dot{x}_1 = x_2, \qquad \dot{x}_2 = -a_1(t)x_1 - a_2(t)x_2 + u$$

from a reachable set $\mathcal{C}(T)$ to the origin subject to $|u(t)| \le 1$. Show that if $a_1(t) = d(a_2(t))/dt$, singular control can exist.

16-5 Consider the time-optimal control (to the origin) of the plant

$$\dot{x}_1 = -2x_1 + u_1, \qquad \dot{x}_2 = -x_2 + u_1 + u_2$$

Identify and sketch the zones in the state plane where nonunique solutions exist. For those zones where the optimal solution is unique, identify the polarity sequence of the optimal control function.

16-6 For the sounding rocket of Exercise 13-10, suppose it is now desired to maximize the height $x(t)$ at the (unspecified) final time T; show that, for this case, singular control can occur. Find the singular control and motion, and give physical explanation for the result.

16-7 For the satellite with one axis of symmetry given in Exercise 14-12, consider the possibility of singular solutions for time-optimal control (from an arbitrary $\boldsymbol{\omega}(0)$ to 0) by

a) Using physical reasoning
b) Using mathematics

16-8 Repeat Exercise 16-7 for fuel-optimal control of the satellite.

16-9 A useful application of the second variation method of Sec. 16.6 for certain space navigational problems is the following: An optimal open-loop solution $\mathbf{x}^*(t)$ and $\mathbf{u}^*(t)$ for a given problem can usually be found *a priori*, at least numerically. For a variety of reasons, however, the space vehicle can stray off-course. Assume at time t_1, the space vehicle has strayed from $\mathbf{x}^*(t_1)$ by $\delta\mathbf{x}(t_1)$; a meaningful approach is to find an incremental "optimal" feedback control $\delta\mathbf{u}^*(\delta\mathbf{x}, t)$ to minimize the second variation $\delta^2\mathcal{J}_1$.

Let a space vehicle be represented by $\dot{\mathbf{x}} = \mathbf{f}(\mathbf{x}, \mathbf{u})$, let the performance index be $P(\mathbf{x}(t_2))$, and let the end time t_2 be fixed; find the explicit expression for $\delta\mathbf{u}(\delta\mathbf{x}, t)$ in terms of the various parameters in the second variation expansion.

16.9 References

The abnormal cases in calculus of variations are treated briefly in [P2], pp. 224-226, and more extensively in [B11], pp. 210-219.

Singular controls in time-optimal problems were first treated in [L5]. [A8] is also a good source book.

An active worker on the singular control problem is C. D. Johnson; see [J2] and [W7]. A concise review article is [J1].

The material of Sec. 16.6 is based on [K14]. The second-variation test is generalized in [T1].

17

Applications and Potentialities of Optimal Control

Having studied many of the known details of optimal control, we might examine the field and ask exactly what these tools can do for us in practical situations.

By now we are knowledgeable in optimal control of first- and second-order linear time-invariant plants, particularly the double integrator. However, we are not likely to encounter problems with such simple plants in practice. We are reasonably conversant with the problems involved in the optimal control of many time-invariant linear plants, particularly those of low order. Here our knowledge is beginning to be useful, for while most practical plants are not linear, they can be considered to be approximately linear for sufficiently small signals. Finding an optimal solution for a plant that approximates the true one then yields a near-optimal solution that may be reasonably good.

When we are faced with plants that are nonlinear or time varying, we have essentially only one recourse, namely, to linearize the system relative to some known nominal trajectory and to carry out optimization relative to the linearized system. This presupposes two conditions: (1) linearization is warranted and (2) a nominal trajectory can be found. If either of these conditions is not met, we are apparently stymied.

Indeed, if we look into some of the typical complex problems that are being faced by industry, we will find them seemingly intractable. First, most problems cannot readily be fit into an optimization format, for the choice of a suitable performance criterion is not apparent. Second, many problems are not in the regulator form in that the input, and hence the end conditions for optimal control are not specified *a priori*. The solutions, moreover, frequently must be formed in real time, which precludes the use of many techniques.

If we utilize optimization techniques only in accordance with a literal interpretation of the theory, we soon conclude that the role that optimal control can play in practice is small. If, however, we interpret the theory in accordance with the inherent spirit, there are several ways we can extend the utility of the results.

First, with the number of necessary conditions at our disposal, we may try numerical methods to find nominal solutions, letting the computer handle some of the complexity in routine computation.

Second, we can intelligently carry out a trade-off study, possibly with the aid of the computer, to determine (1) the best that can be achieved in certain situations and (2) the consequences of different weighting factors in the performance index. This can lead to a determination of whether practical suboptimal designs are good enough.

Third, with our knowledge concerning the properties of optimal systems, we might back up one step and try to design near-optimal systems that provide us with leeway in other less tangible directions.

Finally, and perhaps most important, while there exist a large number of systems that defy exact analysis by the existing optimization techniques, we may make use of our total knowledge in control to analyze these sophisticated control systems approximately. In so doing we may perhaps develop clearer understanding of the fundamental problems of these systems and evolve a new theory for this class of systems.

In this final chapter we indicate the areas of engineering where modern optimal control theory can yield useful answers, and those areas were full analysis is not yet possible.

17.1 Numerical Methods for Finding Optimal Solutions

Since only relatively simple problems in optimal control can be solved analytically, numerical solution of these problems takes on added importance. As of now, the computational aspects of these problems are not trivial and straightforward, since there is no general method which can be counted upon to yield the optimal solution unerringly. The engineer thus needs to be aware of the advantages and pitfalls of the several numerical methods enjoying favor in recent years.

We should first point out that even in the case of a one-point boundary value problem or initial value problem, the numerical computational questions are far from being completely answered.

The most common one-point boundary value problem is encountered in the simulation of a differential system. Here the system equations are programmed on a digital computer and, given an input function and a set of initial conditions, the response of the system is to be determined.

Other one-point boundary value problems occur when we attempt to solve optimal control problems. For example, we have already seen in Chap. 15 that a matrix Riccati equation results when dynamic programming is applied to a certain class of problems. As we will show later, many two-point boundary value problems can also be solved iteratively as a series of one-point boundary value problems.

An immediate problem with solving one-point boundary value problems on a digital computer is that while the physical system itself evolves in continuous time and in a parallel manner—i.e., all the states evolve simultaneously—the common digital computer carries out mathematical operations in discrete time, and in a serial manner. For a system operating this way, two potential areas of error are at once apparent. First, there is a source of error in approximating a continuous time system by a discrete time system. Second, in any simulation of a continuous time system operating in a closed loop, the resultant simulated system has at least one step of delay around the loop.

As is well known, the closeness of the approximation (and the amount of delay), all else being equal, is a function of the step size chosen for the discrete system approximation. In practice we cannot usually choose a step size that is one or two orders of magnitude lower than necessary since the computation time (and hence cost) will be excessive. Furthermore, the round-off error, due to the fact that the computer uses only a finite number of digits to represent each number, may become too large.

While recognizing the need to estimate the proper step size, the actual finding of it is sometimes quite difficult. Moreover, the proper step size for one part of the problem may be far too large for another part. This is because the step size must be smaller during periods of strong system transients than for periods of quiescent operation. The system transient behavior, in turn, will depend largely on the magnitude of the drive or the control variable. Thus, we may expect that the local gain, or the local Lipschitz constant, will generally dictate the choice of step size.

Since the proper step size is not a constant throughout the duration of simulation, it is natural to select digital integration routines that can adjust their own step size in accordance with some internal estimates of the local errors. The class of routines that incorporate predictor-corrector features [H6] will indeed do just that. However, these routines, while overcoming some problems, also introduce some of their own.

First, we note that, for nonlinearities such as relays, the local Lipschitz constant approaches infinity when it is switching, on the other hand, when it is not switching, the Lipschitz constant is zero. The step size can change over several orders of magnitude, and *so does the delay around each loop* as previously mentioned. If we are not careful in reducing the error due to the changing Lipschitz constant down to a small level we may unwittingly incur a large error due to the delay.

Second, because of the step size changing features, the predictor-corrector program has a closed loop of its own which can go unstable under the mutual interaction with the simulated system. The instability phenomenon here is not well understood and is the subject of avid research by numerical analysts.

Third, almost all existing integrating routines use a polynomial extrapolation to obtain the value of the system state for the next step. Unfortunately, very frequently the system state can change discontinuously. For example, in a typical system with output rate and output acceleration saturation, as soon as the output reaches saturation, the output rate must be reset to zero. The same goes for the second derivative of the output when the output rate saturates. Discontinuous states of this type are not possible to approximate by a polynomial using previous history without added refinement.

Thus, to obtain good solutions, even in a straightforward digital simulation of a one-point boundary value problem, we still cannot be too careful.

A hybrid computer can, in theory, overcome many of the above difficulties. Up to the present, however, the experience in using hybrid computers is too limited to permit judging their performance.

To numerically solve two-point boundary value problems involving differential equations, all the problems mentioned above that are associated with one-point boundary-value problems still remain. In addition, new problems also arise in relation to storage requirements and convergence. Much art in programming is frequently required to reduce a program and its running time to manageable proportions.

Three techniques for solving optimization problems will be discussed; they are the method of gradient, the method of second variation, and the generalized Newton-Raphson method. The only common feature of all three methods is that linearization of the system equations is used to permit ease in matching boundary conditions.

1. The Method of Gradient or Steepest Descent

It is well known in calculus that a function of n variables $f(x_1, x_2, \ldots, x_n)$ undergoes the maximum change in magnitude in a direction given by a vector whose ith component is $\partial f/\partial x_i$. This vector is the gradient vector and is denoted by ∇f.

If we visualize $f(\mathrm{x})$ as some "mountain range" in an $(n + 1)$-dimensional space, then the ∇f will locally provide, at any given point x_0, the direction of steepest ascent; whereas, $-\nabla f$ provides the direction of steepest descent. It is clear that if the direction of the local gradient vector is continuously followed, a relative peak in the mountain range will eventually be reached.

Similarly if the direction opposed to the local gradient vector is followed, a relative low point will be reached.

The method of steepest descent is a computational method that makes use of the above property of the gradient so as to obtain an extremum in a variational problem by proceeding iteratively, and always in a direction to maximize the decrease (or increase) of the performance index.

Consider, for simplicity, a system with a single control variable

$$\dot{x} = f(x, u) \tag{17-1}$$

Suppose we wish to find a $u^*(t)$ that transfers the system state from x_1 at t_1 to some state x_2 at t_2 so as to minimize the function

$$P = P(x_2) \tag{17-2}$$

In the above, we assume x_1, t_1, and t_2 are given and x_2 is free. For the present, let us assume that there is no constraint on the control function.

Taking a hint from the consideration of gradients, we could formulate the following general approach:

1) We attempt a trial solution $u^{(1)}(t)$ which allows us to obtain a solution $x^{(1)}(t)$ from the proper starting point x_1 at t_1; neither of these functions is optimal, though $x^{(1)}$ must fit the boundary conditions given. This nonoptimal solution will result in a value of the performance index $P^{(1)}$.
2) We perform local linearization of system (17-1) about $x^{(1)}(t)$ and $u^{(1)}(t)$ in the manner of Chap. 5. This gives an approximate description of the behavior of the system about the solution $x^{(1)}(t)$ and $u^{(1)}(t)$.
3) From the linearized equation, determine a $\delta u^{(1)}(t)$ which is the correction to $u^{(1)}(t)$ consistent with the imposed constraint, so as to decrease P about $P^{(1)}$ in the fastest manner. For this step, a calculation akin to that of the gradient determination is carried out.
4) Set $u^{(2)}(t) = u^{(1)}(t) + \delta u^{(1)}(t)$ and repeat the process to obtain successively $u^{(3)}(t)$, $u^{(4)}(t)$, ...
5) Stop the process when $\delta u^{(n)}(t)$ is uniformly smaller than some prespecified amount, or when the change in performance index δP is small enough.

This rather reasonable approach has been formulated by Kelley [K13] and Bryson et al. [B20], among others.

To be more specific, assume that we have managed to obtain a trial solution $u^{(1)}(t)$, $t_1 \le t \le t_2$; then integrating (17-1), we obtain an $x^{(1)}(t)$. On linearizing about $x^{(1)}(t)$ and $u^{(1)}(t)$ in accordance with the development of Chap. 5, we have

$$\delta\dot{x} = \frac{\partial f^{(1)}}{\partial x}(t)\,\delta x + \frac{\partial f^{(1)}}{\partial u}(t)\,\delta u \tag{17-3}$$

where $\partial \mathrm{f}^{(1)}(t)/\partial \mathrm{x}$ and $\partial \mathrm{f}^{(1)}(t)/\partial u$ are respectively the matrix $\partial \mathrm{f}/\partial \mathrm{x}$ and the vector $\partial \mathrm{f}/\partial u$ evaluated along $\mathrm{x}^{(1)}(t)$ and $u^{(1)}(t)$.

Let $\Phi^{(1)}(t, t_1)$ be the transition matrix associated with the linear Eq. (17-3), the solution of which is then

$$\delta \mathrm{x}(t) = \Phi^{(1)}(t, t_1)\,\delta \mathrm{x}(t_1) + \int_{t_1}^{t} \Phi^{(1)}(t, \tau)\,\frac{\partial \mathrm{f}^{(1)}}{\partial u}(\tau)\,\delta u(\tau)\,d\tau \qquad (17\text{-}4)$$

Since from the boundary condition $\mathrm{x}(t_1) = \mathrm{x}_1$, $\delta \mathrm{x}(t_1)$ will be 0, then at the time t_2 we have

$$\delta \mathrm{x}(t_2) \triangleq \delta \mathrm{x}_2 = \int_{t_1}^{t_2} \Phi^{(1)}(t_2, \tau)\,\frac{\partial \mathrm{f}^{(1)}}{\partial u}(\tau)\,\delta u(\tau)\,d\tau \qquad (17\text{-}5)$$

Equation (17-5) yields an approximate estimate of the change in the final state $\delta \mathrm{x}(t_2)$ as the input function $u(t)$ in (17-1) is perturbed by an amount $\delta u(t)$. The approximation here is done through linearization.

The task that remains is to choose $\delta u(t)$ for each t in such a way that $\delta \mathrm{x}(t_2)$ lies in the most desirable direction.

Now in terms of small changes in x_2, the resultant change in the performance index is, to a first approximation,

$$\delta P = \left(\frac{\partial P}{\partial \mathrm{x}_2}\right)^T \delta \mathrm{x}_2 \qquad (17\text{-}6)$$

By (17-5) we have

$$\delta P = \int_{t_1}^{t_2} \left(\frac{\partial P}{\partial \mathrm{x}_2}\right)^T \Phi^{(1)}(t_2, \tau)\,\frac{\partial \mathrm{f}^{(1)}}{\partial u}(\tau)\,\delta u(\tau)\,d\tau \qquad (17\text{-}7)$$

The goal of steepest descent is to find δu so as to maximize δP. Of course δu must be in some sense small, so that the local linearization approximation remains valid; thus we impose a constraint of the form

$$\int_{t_1}^{t_2} \left(\delta u(\tau)\right)^2 d\tau = k \qquad (17\text{-}8)$$

with a suitably chosen value of k.

Now the maximizing of (17-7) through choosing a $\delta u(t)$, subject to the constraint (17-8), is a simple problem in calculus of variations. The solution $\delta u^{(1)}$ is readily found to be

$$\delta u^{(1)}(t) = -C\left(\frac{\partial P}{\partial x_2}\right)^T \Phi^{(1)}(t_2, t)\,\frac{\partial f^{(1)}}{\partial u}(t) \tag{17-9a}$$

where

$$C = \left\{\frac{1}{k}\int_{t_1}^{t_2}\left[\left(\frac{\partial P}{\partial x_2}\right)^T \Phi^{(1)}(t_2, \tau)\,\frac{\partial f^{(1)}}{\partial u}(\tau)\right]^2 d\tau\right\}^{1/2} \tag{17-9b}$$

(show this).

Now by Eq. (3-58) we have

$$\Psi^T(t, t_2) = \Phi(t_2, t) \tag{3-58}$$

where $\Psi(t, t_2)$ is the transition matrix of the adjoint system to that of Eq. (17-3). As we can find the matrix $\Psi(t, t_2)$ for (17-3) by integrating the system

$$\dot{\Psi}(t, t_2) = -\left[\frac{\partial f^{(1)}}{\partial x}(t)\right]^T \Psi(t, t_2) \tag{17-10}$$

backward from the final condition

$$\Psi(t_2, t_2) = I \tag{17-11}$$

we can find $\Phi(t_2, t)$. Thus we see that the computational steps to be taken in the steepest descent approach when there is no constraint on $u(t)$ should be:

1) Take the trial solution $u^{(1)}(t)$, and with it integrate numerically Eq. (17-1). At each step store the values of $x^{(1)}(t)$.
2) At the end of integration, evaluate the performance index $P^{(1)} = P(x_2^{(1)}(t_2))$ and the vector $\partial P^{(1)}/\partial x_2$.
3) Integrate the adjoint system (17-10) backward from $t = t_2$, using the boundary condition (17-11), and evaluate the necessary values of $\partial f^{(1)}(t)/\partial x$ and $\partial f^{(1)}(t)/\partial u$ for each t by using the stored values of $x^{(1)}(t)$ and $u^{(1)}(t)$. At each step backward, moreover, evaluate $\delta u^{(1)}$ via Eqs. (17-9); evaluate the new trial control function at each t, $u^{(2)}(t) = u^{(1)}(t) + \delta u^{(1)}(t)$.
4) Repeat the process.

If at a given iteration, say the nth, $P^{(n)} < P^{(n+1)}$, it usually means that the step size taken is too large. The constant k in Eq. (17-8) then must be decreased.

Suppose $u(t)$ is subjected to an inequality constraint of the form

$$\beta(t) \le u(t) \le \alpha(t) \tag{17-12}$$

We could use the penalty function approach as mentioned in Chap. 13 and proceed to find the solution in an inexact manner. After n iterations we could then obtain a $u^{(n)}(t)$ satisfying (17-12) by means of the following truncation

$$\text{if} \quad u^{(n)}(t) - C\left(\frac{\partial P}{\partial \mathrm{x}_2}\right)^T \Phi^{(n)}(t_2, t)\frac{\partial \mathrm{f}^{(n)}}{\partial u}(t) \geq \alpha(t)$$

$$\text{set} \quad \delta u^{(n)}(t) = \alpha^{(n)}(t) - u^{(n)}(t)$$

$$\text{if} \quad u^{(n)}(t) - C\left(\frac{\partial P}{\partial \mathrm{x}_2}\right)^T \Phi^{(n)}(t_2, t)\frac{\partial \mathrm{f}^{(n)}}{\partial u}(t) \leq \beta(t) \tag{17-13}$$

$$\text{set} \quad \delta u_n(t) = u_n(\tau) - \beta(t)$$

$$\text{if} \quad \beta(t) < u^{(n)}(t) - C\left(\frac{\partial P}{\partial \mathrm{x}_2}\right)^T \Phi^{(n)}(t_2, t)\frac{\partial \mathrm{f}^{(n)}}{\partial u}(t) < \alpha(t)$$

use Eq. (17-9)

A more time-consuming method but one which offers hope of obtaining a solution that is closer to the exact one is not to stop at step (17-13). Instead, at that point, we remove the terms in the performance index associated with the penalty functions and then proceed to apply the method of steepest descent in such a way that only the portion of $u^{(n)}(t)$ that is not truncated is varied in accordance with (17-9). After a few iterations using this refinement, we expect to obtain a much better solution than that given by the penalty function method.

Some of the problems associated with the steepest descent approach are:

1) When the dimensionality of x is large or when the integration interval is long, storage may become a problem.
2) The forward and backward equations must have steps that coincide; otherwise, interpolation must be involved.
3) The convergence of the approach tends to be very slow as the optimum trajectory is approached.*

Also the method is most convenient to apply to a problem of the Mayer type. This would then entail transforming the given problem into the Mayer form by change of variables such as that used in Chap. 14.

*A new method employing the properties of gradients, called the conjugate gradient method, overcomes this convergence problem. See, e.g., L. S. Lasdon, S. K. Mitter, and A. D. Waren, The Conjugate Gradient Method for Optimal Control Problems, *IEEE Trans. on Automatic Control,* Vol. AC-12, No. 2, pp. 132-138, April, 1967.

As with all of the methods mentioned in this section, the gradient approach only seeks out a local minimum point. However, unlike the other two methods to be mentioned, the gradient approach should converge to a singular solution if one exists,* because the necessary conditions for optimality as given by the Euler-Lagrange equations or the maximum principle are not used.

When there are inequality constraints on the state variables, the penalty function method, mentioned in Chap. 14, can sometimes be used to advantage.

2 Optimization Using the Method of the Second Variation

An optimization technique based on the theory of the second variation in calculus of variations has the advantage of fast convergence near the optimal trajectory [B17], [K20]. In return it requires considerable programming complexity, and the method may not even yield a local minimum if it is started too far from the optimal trajectory.

In view of our discussions in Chap. 16 concerning the second variation approach, the basic idea can be given in a straightforward manner.

Consider the same class of problems as given in the previous section, except that there is no inequality type of constraints on the control variable.** Instead of proceeding with the gradient approach, we may do the following:

1) Find a trial solution $u^{(1)}(t)$ and generate via (17-1) a trial trajectory $\mathrm{x}^{(1)}(t)$ from the given starting point. $\mathrm{x}^{(1)}(t)$ is generally not optimal.
2) Find the linearized system equation (17-3) about this trajectory.
3) Using the linearized system we find an approximate optimal incremental control $\delta u^{(1)}$ which maximizes an approximate functional $\Delta \mathcal{J}_1$, where $\Delta \mathcal{J}_1$ represents the change in augmented function $\mathcal{J}_1 = P(\mathrm{x}_2) + \int_{t_1}^{t_2} \psi^T(\dot{\mathrm{x}} - \mathrm{f})\,dt$ as it is expanded in accordance with the method of second variations. (See Sec. 16.6).
4) Creating $u^{(2)}(t) = u^{(1)}(t) + \delta u^{(1)}(t)$, repeat the process.

To be specific, suppose that x_0, t_1, and t_2 are fixed; then we can expand $\mathcal{J}_1$ in the same way as we have done in Sec. 16.6. Thus the

* The convergence, however, tends to be slow.

** It is very difficult at present to use the second variation approach with constraints.

immediate problem is to find $\delta u^{(1)}(t)$ which drives the system (17-3) so as to minimize the approximate functional

$$\Delta \mathcal{J}_1 = \delta \mathcal{J}_1 + \frac{1}{2}\delta^2 \mathcal{J}_1$$

subject to the boundary condition $\delta \mathbf{x}(t_1) = \delta \mathbf{x}_1 = 0$.

The terms $\delta \mathcal{J}_1$ and $\delta^2 \mathcal{J}_1$ are given in Sec. 16.6. Specifically, we have

$$\delta \mathcal{J}_1 = \left(\frac{\partial P}{\partial \mathbf{x}}\right)^T \delta \mathbf{x}\bigg|_{t=t_2} - \int_{t_1}^{t_2} \left(\boldsymbol{\psi}^T\left(\frac{\partial \mathbf{f}}{\partial \mathbf{x}}\delta \mathbf{x} + \frac{\partial \mathbf{f}}{\partial u}\delta u\right) - \boldsymbol{\psi}^T \delta \dot{\mathbf{x}}\right) dt \tag{16-46}$$

Since there is no assurance that the trajectory resulting from the nth iteration $\mathbf{x}^{(n)}(t)$ is an optimal trajectory, then, in contrast to the case in Sec. 16.6, $\delta \mathcal{J}_1$ now does not necessarily vanish and hence must be taken into account in our optimization process.

When the last term in the integral of (16-46) is integrated by parts, the equation becomes

$$\delta \mathcal{J}_1 = \left(\left(\frac{\partial P}{\partial \mathbf{x}}\right)^T \delta \mathbf{x} + \boldsymbol{\psi}^T \delta \mathbf{x}\right)\bigg|_{t=t_2} - \int_{t_1}^{t_2} \left(\left(\dot{\boldsymbol{\psi}}^T + \boldsymbol{\psi}^T \frac{\partial \mathbf{f}}{\partial \mathbf{x}}\right)\delta \mathbf{x} + \boldsymbol{\psi}^T \frac{\partial \mathbf{f}}{\partial u}\delta u\right) dt \tag{17-14}$$

Now if we define the nominal adjoint function $\boldsymbol{\psi}(t)$ in the nth iteration as that satisfying $\dot{\boldsymbol{\psi}} = -(\partial \mathbf{f}/\partial \mathbf{x})^T \boldsymbol{\psi}$ or $\dot{\boldsymbol{\psi}}^T = -\boldsymbol{\psi}^T(\partial \mathbf{f}/\partial \mathbf{x})$ (subject to the appropriate transversality condition $\boldsymbol{\psi}(t_2) = -(\partial P/\partial \mathbf{x})_{t_2}$), then the term $(\dot{\boldsymbol{\psi}}^T + \boldsymbol{\psi}^T(\partial \mathbf{f}/\partial \mathbf{x}))\,\delta \mathbf{x}$ and the term $[(\partial P/\partial \mathbf{x})^T \delta \mathbf{x} + \boldsymbol{\psi}^T \delta \mathbf{x}]|_{t=t_2}$ in the integrand of (17-14) both vanish. Thus we are left with

$$\delta \mathcal{J}_1 = -\int_{t_1}^{t_2} \left(\frac{\partial H}{\partial u}\delta u\right) dt \tag{17-15}$$

along the nominal trial trajectory where $H \triangleq \boldsymbol{\psi}^T \mathbf{f}$.

The term $\delta^2 \mathcal{J}_1$ is unchanged from that given in (16-48). The net result then is a performance index $\Delta \mathcal{J}_1$ of the form

$$\Delta \mathcal{J}_1 = \delta \mathcal{J}_1 + \frac{1}{2}\delta^2 \mathcal{J}_1$$

$$= \left(\frac{1}{2}\delta \mathbf{x}^T \frac{\partial^2 P}{\partial \mathbf{x}^2}\delta \mathbf{x}\right)\bigg|_{t=t_2}$$

$$- \int_{t_1}^{t_2} \left(\frac{\partial H}{\partial u}\delta u + \frac{1}{2}\left(\delta \mathbf{x}^T \frac{\partial^2 H}{\partial \mathbf{x}^2}\delta \mathbf{x} + 2\delta \mathbf{x}^T \frac{\partial^2 H}{\partial \mathbf{x}\partial u}\delta u + \frac{\partial^2 H}{\partial u^2}\delta u\right)\right) dt \tag{17-16}$$

Now the approximation or auxiliary optimization problem is well characterized. We wish to find a solution $\delta \mathbf{x}^{(1)}(t)$, $t_1 \leq t \leq t_2$, satisfying (17-3) and the boundary condition $\delta \mathbf{x}(t_1) = 0$ that minimizes (17-16).

To find $\delta \mathbf{x}^{(1)}(t)$ numerically, we can for example invoke the maximum principle. Here in accordance with the development of Chap. 14 we define the (auxiliary) adjoint variables $\delta \boldsymbol{\psi}$ and create the (auxiliary) Hamiltonian

$$h \triangleq \delta \boldsymbol{\psi}^T \left(\left(\frac{\partial \mathbf{f}}{\partial \mathbf{x}} \right)^T \delta \mathbf{x} + \frac{\partial \mathbf{f}}{\partial u} \delta u \right) + \frac{1}{2} \left(2 \frac{\partial H}{\partial u} \delta u + \delta \mathbf{x}^T \frac{\partial^2 H}{\partial \mathbf{x}^2} \delta \mathbf{x} + 2 \delta \mathbf{x}^T \frac{\partial^2 H}{\partial \mathbf{x} \partial u} \delta u + \frac{\partial^2 H}{\partial u^2} \delta u \right) \tag{17-17}$$

The auxiliary adjoint variable $\delta \boldsymbol{\psi}$ must satisfy

$$\delta \dot{\boldsymbol{\psi}} = -\frac{\partial h}{\partial \delta \mathbf{x}} = -\frac{\partial \mathbf{f}}{\partial \mathbf{x}} \delta \boldsymbol{\psi} - \frac{\partial}{\partial \delta \mathbf{x}} \left(\delta \mathbf{x}^T \frac{\partial^2 H}{\partial \mathbf{x}^2} \delta \mathbf{x} + 2 \delta \mathbf{x}^T \frac{\partial^2 H}{\partial \mathbf{x} \partial u} \delta u \right) \tag{17-18}$$

with the transversality condition (why?)

$$\delta \boldsymbol{\psi}(t_2) = -\frac{\partial^2 P}{\partial \mathbf{x}^2} \delta \mathbf{x} \bigg|_{t = t_2} \tag{17-19}$$

and the auxiliary optimal incremental control $\delta u^{(1)}$ is to be found from the condition

$$\frac{\partial h}{\partial \delta u} = 0 \tag{17-20}$$

Collecting the above results, we can now describe the optimization procedure more specifically in the following steps:

1) Take a trial control function $u^{(1)}(t)$; with it, integrate the system equation (17-1) numerically to obtain the trajectory $\mathbf{x}^{(1)}(t)$.
2) Find the adjoint variables $\boldsymbol{\psi}^{(1)}(t)$ corresponding to $\mathbf{x}^{(1)}(t)$ by integrating a set $\dot{\boldsymbol{\psi}} = -(\partial \mathbf{f}/\partial \mathbf{x})^T \boldsymbol{\psi}$ backward from $t = t_2$ with the boundary condition

$$\boldsymbol{\psi}(t_2) = -\frac{\partial P}{\partial \mathbf{x}} \bigg|_{t = t_2}$$

3) Find $\delta \mathbf{x}^{(1)}(t)$ and $\delta \boldsymbol{\psi}^{(1)}(t)$ obeying Eqs. (17-3) and (17-18) with the boundary conditions

$$\delta \mathbf{x}^{(1)}(t_1) = 0, \quad \delta \boldsymbol{\psi}^{(1)}(t_2) = \frac{\partial^2 P}{\partial \mathbf{x}^2} \bigg|_{t = t_2}$$

and with $\delta u^{(1)*}(t)$ found from condition (17-20). This problem in a $2n$-dimensional state space is the same as that considered in Sec. 12.3 and can be solved numerically.

4) The control function for the next iterative becomes $u^{(2)}(t) = u^{(1)}(t) + \delta u^{(1)}(t)$. Repeat the process for the next iteration.

It is often advantageous to solve the above minimization problem by means of the optimal linear feedback scheme discussed in Chap. 15. The implementation, at least in principle, is straightforward [B17], [M10].

There are a number of practical problems associated with the second variation approach just described. The first is the obvious complexity involved in programming. Step (3) above, for example, while simply stated, is fairly laborious to implement. The second is that there is usually no assurance that the Legendre condition and the Jacobi condition are satisfied.* Finally, since the method relies on some of the necessary conditions for optimality which become trivially satisfied in the case of singular control, the method of second variations cannot find singular trajectories.

The advantage of the method lies in its superior convergence properties as compared to the gradient method when a local optimum solution is near.

3. The Generalized Newton-Raphson Method

In numerical analysis, an effective way to find a root for the one-dimensional algebraic equation

$$f(x) = 0 \tag{17-21}$$

is to proceed in the following way: a first guess at a solution $x^{(1)}$ is made, then successive solutions are found in accordance with the sequence

$$x^{(n+1)} = x^{(n)} - \frac{f\left(x^{(n)}\right)}{\dfrac{df}{dx}\left(x^{(n)}\right)}, \qquad n = 1,2,\ldots \tag{17-22a}$$

which can be written as

$$f\left(x^{(n)}\right) + \frac{df}{dx}\left(x^{(n)}\right)[x^{(n+1)} - x^{(n)}] = 0 \tag{17-22b}$$

* When the conditions are not satisfied, it often leads to finite escape time in the matrix Ricatti equation when we attempt to find feedback solution, See, e.g. [M10].

On a graph of $f(x)$ vs. x, the iterative process described by (17-22b) may be displayed as shown in Fig. 17-1. We see that if $f(x)$ is sufficiently well behaved and df/dx exists and does not vanish in some neighborhood of the solution, then $x^{(n+1)}$ will be closer to the true solution than $x^{(n)}$. Convergence however need not take place if $x^{(1)}$ is not well chosen or if $f(x)$ is irregular in the range between $x^{(1)}$ and the true solution x^*. (Show this.)

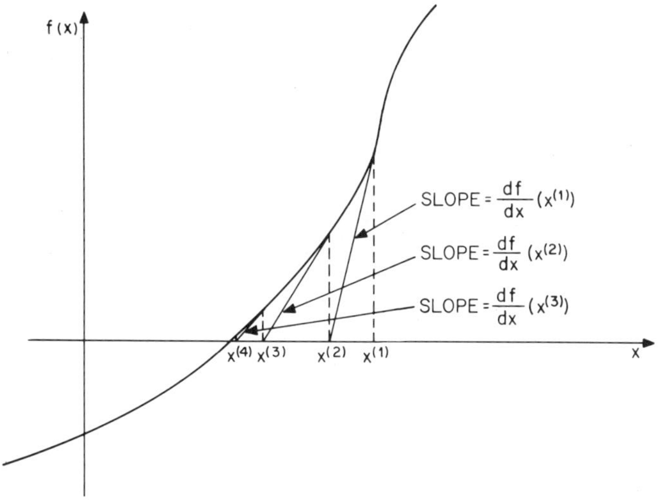

Fig. 17-1. The Newton-Raphson method for iteratively solving for the root of $f(x) = 0$.

The method embodied in Eqs. (17-22) was apparently first discovered by Sir Isaac Newton and is commonly known as the Newton-Raphson method.

It is possible to arrive at rigorous sufficient conditions for the convergence of the sequence (17-22).† The method can further be extended to the vector case, where the zero of the vector algebraic equation

$$\mathbf{f}(\mathbf{x}) = 0 \tag{17-23}$$

is to be found. Here a generalization of the Newton-Raphson method leads to the sequence

$$\mathbf{x}^{(n+1)} = \mathbf{x}^{(n)} - \left[\left(\frac{\partial \mathbf{f}}{\partial \mathbf{x}}\right)_{\mathbf{x}=\mathbf{x}^{(n)}}\right]^{-1} \mathbf{f}\left(\mathbf{x}^{(n)}\right) \tag{17-24a}$$

† See [O4] p. 43.

or

$$\mathrm{f}\left(\mathrm{x}^{(n)}\right) + \left[\left(\frac{\partial \mathrm{f}}{\partial \mathrm{x}}\right)_{\mathrm{x} = \mathrm{x}^{(n)}}\right]\left(\mathrm{x}^{(n+1)} - \mathrm{x}^{(n)}\right) = 0 \qquad \text{(17-24b)}$$

Sufficient conditions for convergence in the vector case have also been given in [O4].

Kantorovish and Akilov [K11] have shown that it is quite possible to extend the Newton-Raphson method to solve vector functional equations of the form

$$\mathcal{P}(\mathrm{x}) = 0 \qquad \text{(17-25)}$$

where $\mathcal{P}$ for our purpose may be considered to be a bounded operator which transforms elements of a Banach space $\mathcal{X}$ into another element of the same space (see Sec. 11.7).

For an element x_0 of the Banach space $\mathcal{X}$, if the limit

$$\lim_{h \to 0} \frac{\mathcal{P}(\mathrm{x}_0 + h\mathrm{x}) - \mathcal{P}(\mathrm{x}_0)}{h} \triangleq \mathcal{P}'(\mathrm{x}_0)\,\mathrm{x} \qquad \text{(17-26)}$$

exists for every x in $\mathcal{X}$, then $\mathcal{P}'(\mathrm{x}_0)$ is said to be the derivative of the operator $\mathcal{P}$ at x_0.† Kantorovich and Akilov have shown that if an initial guess $\mathrm{x}^{(1)}$ is made sufficiently close to the solution x^*, then a functional equation of the form (17-25) can be solved iteratively by the generalized Newton-Raphson sequence

$$\mathrm{x}^{(n+1)} = \mathrm{x}^{(n)} - \left[\mathcal{P}'\left(\mathrm{x}^{(n)}\right)\right]^{-1} \mathcal{P}\left(\mathrm{x}^{(n)}\right), \qquad n = 1, 2, \ldots \qquad \text{(17-27)}$$

Let us note that (17-27) immediately suggests a way to solve a two-point boundary value problem of the form

$$\dot{\mathrm{x}} = \mathrm{f}(\mathrm{x}, t), \qquad \mathrm{x}(t_1) = \mathrm{x}_1, \qquad \mathrm{x}(t_2) = \mathrm{x}_2 \qquad \text{(17-28)}$$

where f has continuous first partial derivatives with respect to x. In the Banach space of real-valued continuous vector function of time with a norm as defined in Example 11-5, if we define an operator $\mathcal{P}$ as

$$\mathcal{P} = \frac{d}{dt} - \mathrm{f} \triangleq \mathcal{P}_1 - \mathcal{P}_2 \qquad \text{(17-29)}$$

† As defined we have what is known as the Gateaux or the weak derivative of the operator $\mathcal{P}$. If (17-26) converges uniformly with respect to all $\mathrm{x} \in \mathcal{X}$ with unit norm, then we have the Fréchet or the strong derivative. See [K11].

where $\mathcal{P}_1$ is the operator d/dt and $\mathcal{P}_2$ is the operator defined by $\mathcal{P}_2(x) = f(x, t)$, then (17-28) can be written as the functional equation $\mathcal{P}(x) = 0$ with the attendant boundary conditions. Now d/dt is an unbounded operator, but formally, we can show that [K15]

$$\mathcal{P}_1'(x_0)x = \frac{d}{dt} \tag{17-30}$$

and

$$\mathcal{P}_2'(x_0) = \left[\frac{\partial f}{\partial x}\right]_{x = x_0} = \left[\frac{\partial f}{\partial x}(x_0)\right] \tag{17-31}$$

Hence heuristally we have, by (17-27), the iterative sequence

$$x^{(n+1)} = x^{(n)} - \left[\frac{d}{dt} - \frac{\partial f}{\partial x}(x^{(n)})\right]^{-1}\left(\frac{dx^{(n)}}{dt} - f\left(x^{(n)}, t\right)\right) \tag{17-32}$$

By multiplying through by the operator $\left[\frac{d}{dt} - \frac{\partial f}{\partial x}(x^{(n)})\right]$ and rearranging we arrive at the vector iterative sequence [K15]

$$\frac{dx^{(n+1)}}{dt} = \left[\frac{\partial f}{\partial x}(x^{(n)})\right]\left(x^{(n+1)} - x^{(n)}\right) + f\left(x^{(n)}, t\right) \tag{17-33}$$

with the boundary condition $x(t_1) = x_1$, $x(t_2) = x_2$. We can now solve (17-28) iteratively by first picking a trial solution $x^{(1)}(t)$ that satisfies the boundary conditions. Since $\left[\frac{\partial f}{\partial x}(x^{(n)})\right]$ is the Jacobian matrix for the system of (17-28), it is seen that (17-33) is linear for each index n and can be solved for the given boundary condition using the technique as described in Sec. 12.3.

By using the necessary conditions as provided by calculus of variations, the maximum principle, or dynamic programming, we have seen that we can always reduce a standard optimal control problem involving an nth-order plant to a form involving $(2n + 1)$ differential equations of the form $\dot{y} = f(y, t)$* and a set of m algebraic

*i.e., n system equations, the equation relating the performance index, and n adjoint equations.

equations of the form $g(z, t) = 0$.* The boundary conditions are given at two points and are of the form $y(t_1) = y_1$, $y(t_2) = y_2$. We thus see that the generalized Newton–Raphson method given above can be used to solve the $2n + m + 1$ equations iteratively. For the $(2n + 1)$ differential equations, we use the iteration given by (17-33). For the m algebraic equations, the iterative sequence is given by (17-24)

$$y^{(n+1)} = y^{(n)} - \left[\frac{\partial g(y^n, t)}{\partial y}\right]^{-1} g\left(y^{(n)}, t\right) \tag{17-34}$$

The iteration can proceed along the following lines:

1) A trial solution $y^{(1)}(t)$ is obtained satisfying the boundary conditions.
2) The control variables are solved for from the algebraic Eqs. (17-34) in terms of the first $(2n + 1)$ state variables in the $(2n + 1)$ differential equations.
3) The $(2n + 1)$ differential equations in the form (17-33) are solved by the method of Sec. 12.3 to obtain the first $(2n + 1)$ components of the vector $y^{(2)}(t)$.
4) The solutions obtained in step (3) are used to obtain the last m components of the vector $y^{(2)}(t)$.
5) Repeat the process until the norm of the difference $y^{(n+1)} - y^{(n)}$ falls below a prespecified value.

The generalized Newton–Raphson method is again more difficult to program when compared to say the gradient method. It is however of about the same degree of complexity as the second variation method. Also, since some of the necessary conditions for optimality are used, singular trajectories and solutions cannot be found by the technique.

There appears to be relatively little practical experience in using the Newton–Raphson method. Generally speaking while there are theorems giving sufficient conditions for convergence, they are too restrictive to be helpful. Thus one must proceed without much *a priori* assurance of convergence. Preliminary indications, however, seem to be encouraging [K15], [M6].

In addition to the methods mentioned, there are at least two more less comprehensive methods that can be cited. The first is a method based on a straightforward application of the principles inherent in dynamic programming (see Sec. 15.1). Here

*The m algebraic equations may, for example, appear from applying the technique of Valentine to a problem with amplitude constraints on the control variable. In this case m is the number of control variables with amplitude constraint.

the problems involved are storage space and programming complexity, though a number of devices [L3] can be employed to lessen the demands in these areas. The method, however, is limited to relatively low-order systems.

The second class of numerical methods is the class of indirect methods. This class of methods makes use of the necessary conditions and the imposed boundary values to arrive at the usual nonlinear two-point boundary value problem. Through the arbitrary choice of say the free adjoint variables and by integrating backward, an optimal trajectory but to a wrong set of initial boundary conditions is obtained. A systematic variation of the initial condition is then attempted in order to solve the proper boundary value problem. Unfortunately, because of the fact that the normal optimal control problem is generally extremely sensitive to the initial condition, indirect methods have not been completely successful.

17.2 The Study of the Structure of Optimal Control

Even when a problem obviously fits the format for optimal control, the application of the theory is still not necessarily straightforward because the optimal control theory takes for granted that a performance index already exists for a given problem. In practice, however, the desired goal of a control system is given in a vague way, and the designer often must find a performance index that, in his opinion, fits the requirements of the system in the best way.

If a single performance index is adequate, then the structure or the pattern of optimal control should be examined. Such questions as the sensitivity of system performance to system parameter variations should be investigated. The computer can be made use of where necessary.

Often a single index of performance is inadequate or cannot be found *a priori* because the many considerations that dictate the system performance cannot be simply expressed in terms of a single number. In that case a trade-off type study may be necessary to determine whether a sensible combination of the system requirements can represent a reasonable measure of system performance. Again, the computer can be helpful.

There are of course many possible ways to study the basic structure of an optimal control problem; in this section, we will discuss an approach proposed by W. L. Nelson [N3].

♦♦Example 17-1. Consider, for the sake of simplicity, the case of pitch angle control of a satellite. It is desired that an antenna mounted on a satellite acquire the signal from an earth station in an efficient manner through pitch attitude control.

We must first define the meaning of the phrase "in an efficient manner," which, typically, represents the wish of a customer.

First, it is clear that jet fuel must be conserved. However, as we have learned from the foregoing chapters, fuel-optimal control without a time restriction may mean infinite acquisition time. This violates our concept of the word "efficient." Thus for the particular problem, we must balance the dual requirements of minimizing fuel and minimizing time of acquisition.

The equation of motion is

$$I \frac{d^2\theta}{dt^2} = L(t), \qquad L(t) \leq U \tag{17-35}$$

Through the introduction of the following normalized variables

$$x_1(t) \equiv \frac{I}{U}\theta(t), \qquad x_2(t) \equiv \frac{I}{U}\dot{\theta}(t), \qquad u(t) \equiv \frac{L(t)}{U}$$

we obtain the familiar set

$$\dot{x}_1 = x_2, \qquad \dot{x}_2 = u(t), \qquad |u(t)| \leq 1 \tag{17-36}$$

The goal of control is to drive the satellite from an arbitrary initial condition $\mathbf{x} = \mathbf{x}_0$ to the origin $\mathbf{x} = 0$ in time T, x while minimizing a performance index of the form

$$\mathcal{J} = \int_0^T |u(\tau)|\, d\tau \tag{17-37}$$

On reflection, we see that because in real life a value of θ, say θ_1, is indistinguishable from $\theta_1 + 2n\pi$ for any integer n, we have here a slightly more difficult control problem than a straightforward one involving the double integrating plant. There is no loss in generality, however, if we cast the problem in a form such that we consider all possible initial states

$$\begin{aligned} \theta(0) &= \theta_0 + 2n\pi, \qquad n = 0, \pm 1, \pm 2, \ldots \\ \dot{\theta}(0) &= \dot{\theta}_0 \end{aligned} \tag{17-38a}$$

where θ_0 and $\dot{\theta}_0$ are the the true initial states, and evolve "efficient" control to transfer the system to the single final state $\theta = \dot{\theta} = 0$. The best solution is then picked.

Alternately, we can cast the problem in a form to consider optimal solutions to the possible final states

$$\begin{aligned} \theta &= 2n\pi, \qquad n = 0, \pm 1, \pm 2, \ldots \\ \dot{\theta} &= 0 \end{aligned} \tag{17-38b}$$

from a given initial state.

In terms of the variables x_1 and x_2 of (17-36), the set of initial states given by (17-38a) becomes

$$\begin{aligned} x_1(0) &= x_{10} + 2k\pi\left(\frac{I}{U}\right), \qquad k = 0, \pm 1, \pm 2, \ldots \\ x_2(0) &= x_{20} \end{aligned} \tag{17-39}$$

Now the solution of the problem from each equivalent initial state to the origin is straightforward. In particular, to avoid nonuniqueness of singular solutions it can be shown that for each initial state, if we let

$$u(t) = \begin{cases} 1, & \psi_2(t) > 1 \\ 0, & -1 \le \psi_2(t) \le 1 \\ -1, & \psi_2(t) < -1 \end{cases} \tag{17-40}$$

with

$$\psi_2(t) = \nu \frac{T - \nu x_{20} - 2t}{\left(T^2 - x_{20}^2 + 2\nu T x_{20} + 4\nu x_{10}\right)^{1/2}} \tag{17-41}$$

where

$$\nu = \operatorname{sgn}\left(x_{10} + \tfrac{1}{2}x_{20}\,|x_{20}|\right) \tag{17-42}$$

then a fuel-optimal control function is specified for that particular initial state. (Show this.)

The desired solution for the satellite attitude control problem is of course the solution that corresponds to the equivalent initial state that yields the smallest value for the fuel expenditure.

For the particular problem under study, two quantities are of concern, the time interval of control T and the fuel expenditure in this interval $\int_0^T |u(\tau)|\,d\tau = \mathcal{J}$. These two quantities then constitute meaningful outputs as we vary the initial conditions.

Choosing a value of the torque-to-inertia ratio U/I of $\pi/5$ rad/sec^2 and an initial state (2, 1), we find that $\mathcal{J}$ and T under the minimum fuel strategy vary in accordance with Fig. 17-2a. These curves can be readily explained. The two bounding lines $\mathcal{J} = T$ and $\mathcal{J} = |x_{20}|$ are rather self-evident. The former represents the case where the given control time T is equal to t^*, the minimum time required to reach the origin from the given initial state. The latter represents the minimum possible value of fuel expenditure

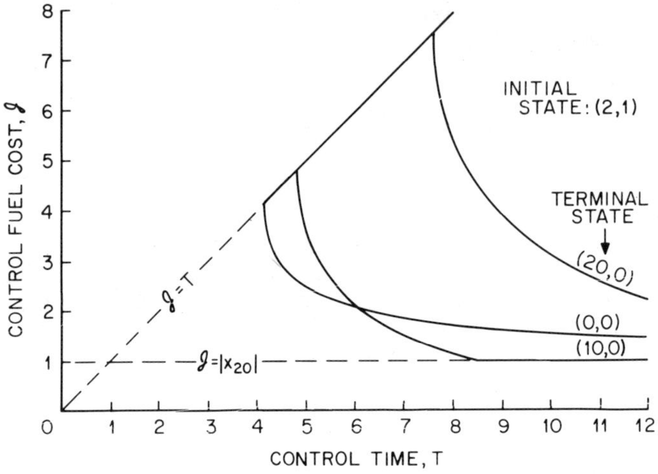

Fig. 17-2a. The curves $\mathcal{J}$ vs. T for the system of Sec. 17.2 under the standard fuel-optimal control for the various final states. The initial state is the state (2, 1).

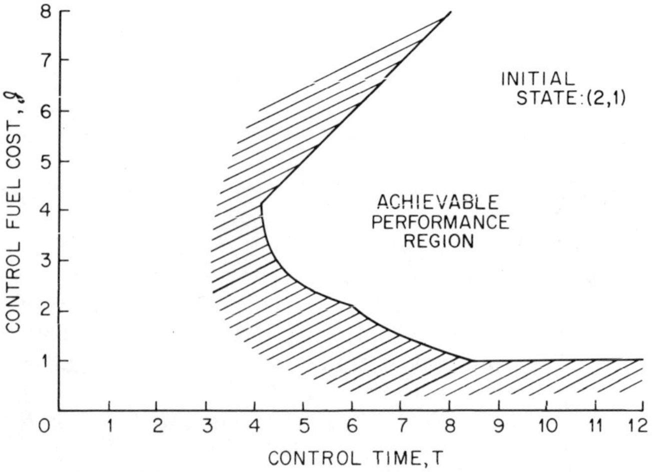

Fig. 17-2b. The composite curve derived from Fig. 17-2a. It delineates an achievable performance region, shown unshaded.

from the given initial state to the origin. An interesting aspect of Fig. 17-2a is that for the terminal state (0, 0), the $\mathcal{J} = |x_{20}|$ line is only approached asymptotically by the minimum fuel curve while for the equivalent final state (10, 0), the line is actually reached by the curve. This can be explained through Fig. 17-3. From the initial state (2, 1) it is possible to reach the final state (0, 0) only through a control sequence $u = -1, 0, +1$, and it is not possible to reach the origin while expending the minimum amount of fuel $|x_{20}|$ in a finite amount of time. However, for the equivalent final state (10, 0), whenever the control time T is long enough to permit the system state to drift from (2, 1) to the switch line Γ_2 before $u = -1$ is turned on, the $\mathcal{J} = |x_{20}|$ condition can always be obtained. The same consideration applies to the equivalent fuel state (20, 0).

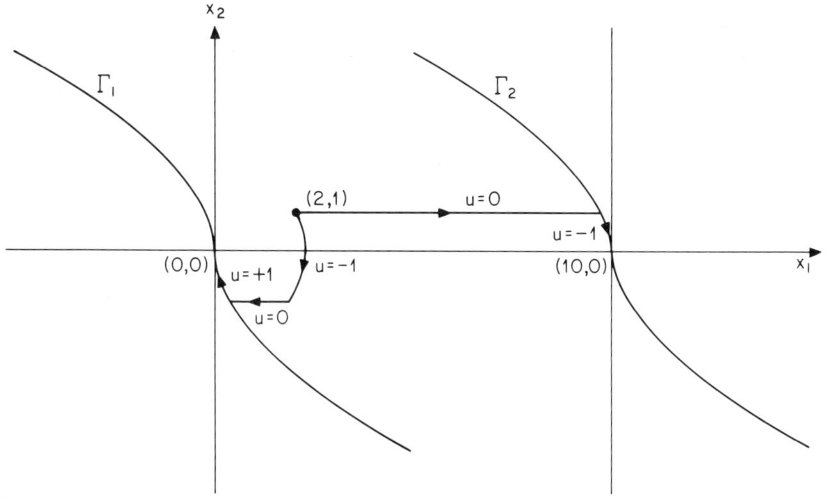

Fig. 17-3. State-plane diagram showing the final state (10, 0) can be reached from (2, 1) through the expenditure of the minimum amount of fuel $\mathcal{J} = |x_{20}|$ in a finite time while the final state (0, 0) cannot be reached

We see that for the initial state (2, 1), the equivalent final states $(-10n, 0)$, $n = 1, 2, \ldots$, need not be considered, as it is obvious that the resultant fuel expenditure cannot be less than that for (0, 0). Similarly we see that the final states beyond (10, 0) do not have to be considered.

Taking the portions of the $\mathcal{J}$ vs. T curves that give the minimum $\mathcal{J}$ for a given T, we arrive at the composite optimum curves of Fig. 17-2b. Each point on the optimum performance curves is a different optimum design. A practical system can only yield performance points that lie in the unshaded region of the figure.*

By holding the initial velocity x_{20} at a constant value and varying the initial position x_{10}, we can obtain a family of optimum performance curves for a range of initial states which can be displayed as shown in Fig. 17-4.

*Note the lack of convexity of the achievable performance region. This raises problems in applying composite scalar performance criteria.

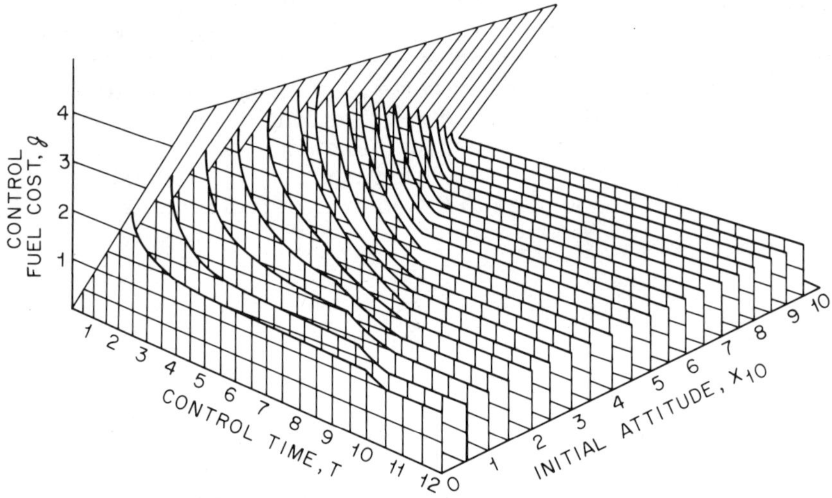

Fig. 17-4. The optimum performance surface for the system of Example 17-1 with $x_{20} = 1$ and $0 \leq x_{10} \leq 10$.

The performance of various practical designs of attitude control systems can be directly plotted on Fig. 17-4. The extent to which the practical design approaches the ideal provides us with a measure of the soundness of the design.

In [N3] some near optimal approaches to practical design are offered.◆◆

17.3 Nearly Optimal Control Systems

When a problem can be readily formulated into an optimal control format, then an open-loop or a closed-loop solution will indicate to us how good performance can be achieved. In practice, however, due to a variety of causes, the optimal control system is generally difficult to instrument precisely. A number of compromise steps need to be taken; thus we arrive at a suboptimal design.

It is of course desirable to evolve a suboptimal design that is nearly optimal. To measure the soundness of a suboptimal design then calls for examining such factors as: how closely the spirit of optimal design is preserved in a practical sense, how readily the design can be implemented by practical components, and how sensitive the design is to parameter and environmental changes.

The above factors tend to be subjective and, for this reason, are difficult to discuss intelligently. Nevertheless, two strong reasons prompt us to attempt a discourse on suboptimal control systems. First, subjectivity is an inescapable reality in practice; however, even in this nebulous realm, there are clear norms of desirability or excellence which can separate indifferent designs from outstanding ones. Second, in spite of the large amounts of published results on optimal control, linear design methods still are the rule in large sectors of the industry. Linear design often leads to poor large-signal behavior. This, however, can be remedied if we modify the design while adhering to the spirit of optimal control, which is suitable for large-signal situations.

One of the essentials in any control system is insensitivity to parameter changes. The issue of sensitivity or insensitivity represents a burgeoning area of investigation which we are not prepared to treat at length [D9] [H16]; nevertheless, some of the basic ideas can be readily inferred, as we can see from the following example.

◆◆Example 17-2. To create a system that can control a plant optimally, we need to instrument the optimal switching line or switching surface. This we can do through the use of function generators or other means. Suppose that there is inaccuracy in the instrumentation of the switch line or that the plant characteristics change over a period of time; we must then determine the consequences and the specific steps to be taken to gain a measure of insensitivity.

Consider the double integrator plant. The system that will achieve time-optimal control with this plant is shown in Fig. 4-9. A function generator is needed to create the switching function $-\left(\frac{1}{2}\,|x_2|\,x_2 + Ux_1\right)$. Suppose now due to system parameter variations, the instrumented switching line causes early switching. This will result in "sliding motion" along the switching line* (see Chap. 4) as shown in Fig. 17-5a. On the other hand, if the switching line is such that late switching takes place, then the "under-damped" motion shown in Fig. 17-5b will occur.

Of these two suboptimal cases, the case with sliding motion is more independent of the system parameters and depends only on the instrumented switching line. It is therefore good practice to design the switching line such that sliding motion due to early switching takes place.

The ideas just presented can be extended to the suboptimal control of other, possibly nonlinear, plants. Let us now illustrate an approach to sound suboptimal design for a simplified missile autopilot.

*We recall that in practice, the "sliding motion" is given by chatter about the switching line at a (high) frequency and (small) amplitude dictated by the higher-order dynamics in the system neglected in the analysis.

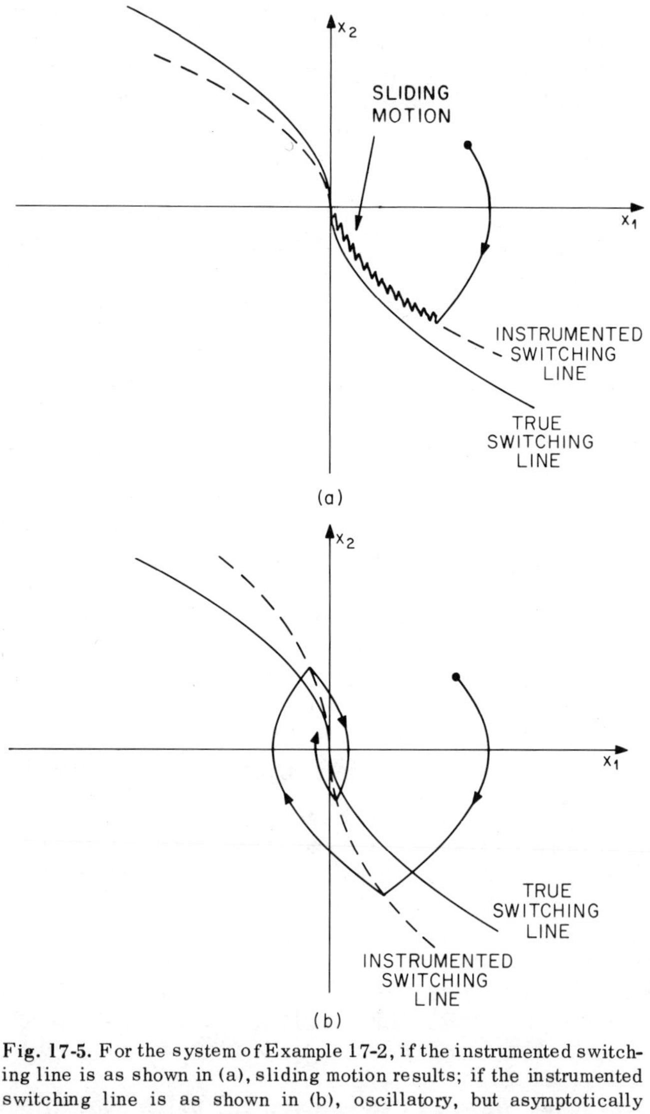

Fig. 17-5. For the system of Example 17-2, if the instrumented switching line is as shown in (a), sliding motion results; if the instrumented switching line is as shown in (b), oscillatory, but asymptotically stable motion ensues. The system in case (a) is less sensitive to parameter changes.

♦♦**Example 17-3.** Consider the two-dimensional model of the fin-controlled missile discussed in Chap. 5 (Examples 5-6 and 5-8). The equations of motion are given by (5-15) and can be written as

$$\dot{\omega}(t) = \frac{Al}{I} Q C_M(\alpha, \delta) \tag{17-43a}$$

$$\dot{\alpha}(t) = \omega - \frac{A}{mV} Q C_L(\alpha, \delta) \tag{17-43b}$$

$$a_N(t) = \frac{A}{mg} Q C_N(\alpha, \delta) \tag{17-43c}$$

where $\omega = \dot{\theta}$ is the rate of change of the pitch angle, α is the angle of attack, and a_N is the normal acceleration of the missile which is to be controlled. The control variable is the fin angle δ. The nonlinear functions are the aerodynamic coefficients $C_M(\alpha, \delta)$, $C_L(\alpha, \delta)$, and $C_N(\alpha, \delta)$, determined from wind tunnel tests. The parameters A, l, I, m, g, and Q are all as defined in Example 5-6. It should be noted that the dynamic pressure Q may vary considerably over the range of possible flight regimes.

A commonly used design procedure is based on local linearization, as was shown in Example 5-8, leading to Eqs. (5-20) and (5-21). A typical autopilot based on linear design is shown in Fig. 17-6. There is an inner rate loop, in which the body rate $\dot{\theta}$, measured by a rate gyro, is compensated by an amplifier whose gain varies as $1/Q$ (to offset the Q dependence from δ to θ) and a linear filter. The poles or zeros of the compensator may possibly be made Q-dependent so as to "track" those of the missile. In the outer acceleration loop, the missile lateral acceleration is measured by an accelerometer and is directly fed back to be subtracted from the input. This signal is also acted upon by a linear compensator whose gain and/or dynamics may be Q-dependent.

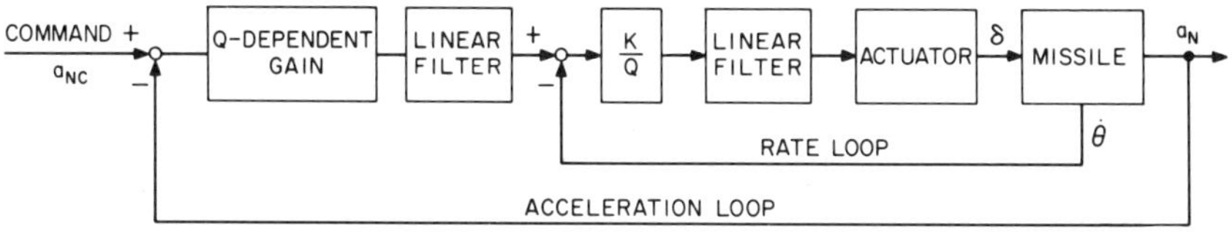

Fig. 17-6. A typical autopilot for a missile based on linear design principles.

When the compensators are properly chosen, the missile output a_N will follow the missile input a_{NC} in a reasonable manner, at least for small signals, as dictated by small values of α.

Missiles designed in the above manner have been known to perform well in many noncritical situations. Where high performance is the goal, however, the missiles designed in accordance with linear principles often are found unequal to the task.

We now show how some fundamental points from optimal control can be used to design autopilots for better large signal performance of the missile.

The basic requirements of a high-performance missile are:

1) Maneuverability in the sense of fast response to large commands.
2) Stability or recoverability of the missile from the effects of not only large commands but also from large disturbances.
3) Insensitivity of the large-signal behavior with respect to aerodynamic and environmental variation (e.g., large variation in the dynamic pressure Q).
4) Simplicity of design.

We of course need a performance criterion. Looking at the needs of the system we see that time optimality in response appears to be a reasonable criterion except for the following qualifications: (1) Minimum dead-beat response to a step command is less meaningful than fast initial rise-time with a tolerable amount of overshoot. (2) It also goes without saying that in the interest of creating a near-optimal design, as many state variables as it is physically possible to measure should be utilized.

Under large signal conditions, the behavior of the actuator, as has been pointed out in Chap. 6 (Sec. 6.6), can be approximated by a nonlinear first-order feedback system (see Fig. 6-20). The actuator and the missile together then constitute a third-order system. In addition to the state variables a_N and θ, we also have the fin deflection angle δ, which can for example be measured by a differential transformer.

With three measurable state variables in a third-order system, we can theoretically construct a true optimal control system. Aside from the obvious computational difficulty involved in trying to arrive at an optimal control function valid for all possible initial conditions, we note that the optimal control will depend on some aerodynamic and environmental parameters which are rather inaccurately known. It is therefore more meaningful to create a near-optimal controller which is simple to instrument and which is not sensitive to variations in the aerodynamic and environmental parameters.

It is reasonable to proceed under the following guidelines.

1) Since it is still desirable to command lateral acceleration, we may retain the unity negative feedback path from the measured lateral acceleration a_N.
2) It can be shown from simulation that the trajectories in the ω vs. $(a_N - a_{NC})$ plane for a typical missile under the constraint $|\delta| \leq \delta_M$ are quite similar in the shape to those of the ideal double integrator of Example 4-1. It is reasonable then to feed the signal $\omega(t)$ back in a manner similar to that of Fig. 4-9. A relay is further inserted in the forward path.
3) It can be shown that the projection of the switching surface in a plane can be approximated by a switching line. By

feeding back $\delta(t)$ through appropriate gains the effective switching line can be shifted.

4) The effect of the dynamic pressure Q on the above switching line can be reduced by making some of the gains Q-dependent.
5) We adjust the various gains in such a way that the instrumented switching line causes sliding motion over all flight regimes. This will result in a high degree of insensitivity to aerodynamic and environmental changes.

The resultant autopilot configuration is as shown in Fig. 17-7.

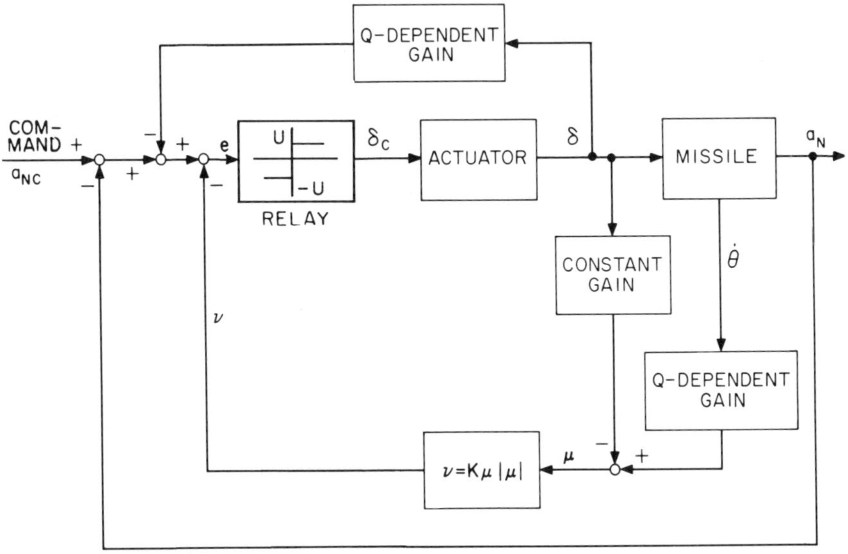

Fig. 17-7. A possible design of a nonlinear autopilot.

A design evolved with the aid of analog simulation for an experimental system shows responses that are significantly better than those from a system evolved using standard linear aerospace techniques.◆◆

17.4 A Class of Modern Control Systems

When we look into the sophisticated man-made control systems of today, we discover that most of them do not conform to a form amenable to treatment by optimal control theory. When we look further, we may even begin to question the usual impression that theory is ahead of practice because these modern systems boast of more components than the theory can accommodate; but they perform, and usually meet the design specifications. The theoreticians, up to now, have not been able to explain, to an acceptable degree of rigor, why and under what conditions these systems should work. Having amassed the known facts concerning modern control systems theory, let us now consider a class of systems that is challenging our analytical ability to the full.

A common feature of most realistic systems is that the system input is usually incompletely known or characterized. Further, most of the plants to be controlled are highly complex. A combination of these two factors makes it impractical or impossible to make use of the existing optimization theory or even the stochastic optimization theory in a routine manner.

To deal with such systems and make use of all available theoretical knowledge, the modern engineer usually designs a control system with the following features:

1) The input is measured and predicted to some future time.
2) The plant output is also predicted to the future time; however, since the plant output depends on the plant input, outputs are predicted for a set of admissible inputs. Further, since it is usually impossible to calculate the response of the true system for the various inputs in the time allotted even with the aid of a computer, a simplified model of the system must suffice.
3) A decision is made as to which of a set of control functions is the best one. This necessitates one or more performance indices.
4) The best input is then selected and applied for one sampling period, after which the entire procedure is repeated.

The above four points, while easily stated, introduce some rather difficult problems. First is the problem of prediction. Basically the theoretical development in the field of prediction in a sense parallels the situation in control theory. True understanding of the problem only exists where the system is linear and/or the input process enjoys good statistical properties. Thus our ability to predict is by no means beyond criticism.

The modeling of a complex plant presents further problems. There is no satisfactory theory today governing the modeling of high-order complex plants by low-order ones, and, therefore, no experience in determining how the liberty that is taken in modeling will affect the result.

Also, the problem of decision making cannot be reduced to quantitative terms until a decision criterion, akin to a performance index, is introduced. This point then raises most of the same questions as those raised when a performance index is to be found.

Finally, there is no clear-cut rule that governs the duration of each cycle determined by the four steps mentioned before. This frequently involves some trade-off considerations such as hardware costs (e.g., computer cost) vs. accuracy in control.

To lend concreteness to the problem, consider the problem of guiding a missile against an evasive target. The system, in the block diagram form, is as shown in Fig. 17-8.

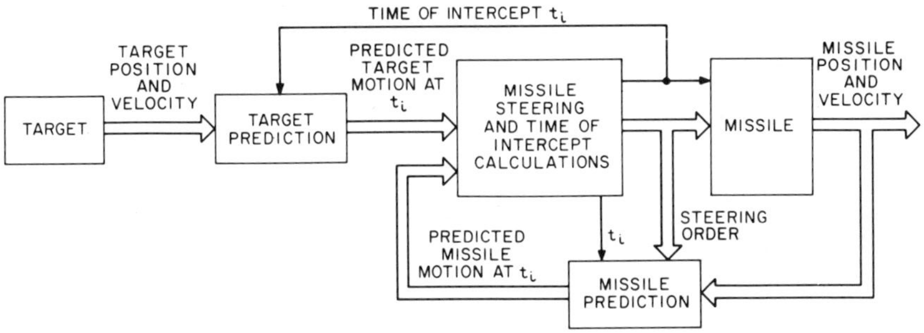

Fig. 17-8. A typical missile guidance loop.

The motion of the target, as sensed by, for example, a radar, corresponds to the input to the system. Inasmuch as the target can undergo evasive motion, however, our ability to predict its future motion is limited.

The guided missile is the plant to be controlled and its motion, as sensed by a radar, is the plant output. Prediction of the missile's motion depends on our ability to foresee the (instantaneous) directions we wish to command it to take; but the command, in turn, depends on the evasive action that the target chooses to execute. Quite frequently the dynamics of both the target and the missile may be modeled by differential equations. Predicting them usually involves fast-time solutions of differential equations and hence the use of a computer.

The problem of intercept is complicated by the so-called time loop. This is indicated in Fig. 17-8. Typically, the warhead of the missile will be detonated when the distance between the target and the missile is at a minimum. The instant when this occurs is called the intercept time and labeled t_i. Clearly, at each cycle, the target and the missile positions and velocities must all be predicted to the time t_i. At that time, from geometrical and other considerations, command to the missile, as well as a new t_i, must be calculated. Due to the consideration of the intercept time, the loop that generates t_i and the loop that generates the command to the missile are intercoupled as shown. Moreover, because of the time loop, the target information, as measured by a radar, does not constitute a pure input.

In addition, in order to give a quantitative measure of the tactical choices at our disposal, a performance index is required. For the problem at hand, it is conceivable that a decision can be implemented to minimize the miss-distance based on either (1) the assumption that the enemy will make the most unfavorable maneuvers from the point of view of the missile (a minimax strategy) or (2) the assumption that the enemy uses the most likely evasive action (a maximum likelihood strategy).

Finally, a simple plan must be devised for choosing the best input, consistent with the performance criteria adopted. For the present problem, for example, we may assume that the input waveform to the missile will always be of the same form, (e.g., full-on or full-off) and only one parameter is to be changed (e.g., the time at which the input is cut off). The parameter is then chosen so as to minimize the miss-distance at the time of intercept.

In putting the loop together, however, we must be mindful of stability considerations. It is very common for a guidance loop of the type described to become less and less stable as the missile approaches the target because of the unavoidable fact that the sensitivity of the control action to the evasive motion of the target increases monotonically as the missile approaches the target. The missile's capability per unit time in reducing miss-distance at the intercept time, for example, will decrease as the intercept time is approached.

At the present state of development, it is clear that neither the stability theory nor the optimal control theory are yet prepared to cope with the class of problems outlined above.

The possibilities in sophistication need not end here. It is, for example, possible to visualize control loops with learning or adaptation abilities. Such loops introduce further problems for our control loop and open new horizons to challenge us.

17.5 Summary

Optimal control today is represented by a body of mathematical theorems. It is not obvious that they are applicable to most of the current control problems.

There are, however, several ways that optimal control theory can further our understanding of physical systems.

Where the format fits the requirements of a physical system, but the problem proves to be too difficult to solve by analytical means, we can resort to numerical solutions by means of computers. Section 17.1 is devoted to this aspect of the application of the control theory.

Even when the format fits the requirements of a physical system, quite frequently it is not obvious what performance criterion should be used. This necessitates trade-off type studies. Section 17.2 discusses this problem by means of an example due to Nelson.

Quite frequently the optimal control format is not directly applicable due to sensitivity and other considerations, but some type of near-optimal behavior is desired. Here the knowledge gained from the studying of optimal control systems often permits us to evolve near-optimal designs that improve upon the classical designs. Section 17.3 gives an up-to-date example of a near-optimal design.

However, there are many systems in existence which are difficult to analyze using the existing theory. This indicates that the existing theory rather lags behind the existing practice for the above systems. Section 17.4 challenges us with a class of systems which thus far has defied analysis. To be completely useful, modern control theory needs to be considerably extended.

17.6 References

The basic references on the method of steepest descent are [K13] and [B20]. In the former, a penalty function approach is used. See also [D1] for extension to cases with inequality constraints.

The second-variation approach is discussed in [B17], [K15], and [K20].

The generalized Newton-Raphson method is first mentioned in [K11] and adopted for use with differential systems in [M6] and [K15].

Section 17.2 is based on [N3] as well as on published material by Nelson.

The material discussed in Secs. 17.3 and 17.4 is based on unpublished works done by the authors.

Appendix A

Vectors and Matrices*†

A-1 Preliminaries

An $n \times m$ *matrix* is an orderly arrangement of nm quantities in a rectangular array with n rows and m columns. We use a boldface uppercase letter to represent a matrix. A matrix whose entry at the ith row and the jth column is a_{ij} is written as $[a_{ij}]$. Thus

$$\mathbf{A} = \begin{bmatrix} a_{11} & a_{12} & \cdots & a_{1m} \\ a_{21} & a_{22} & \cdots & a_{2m} \\ \vdots & & & \\ a_{n1} & {}_{n2} & \cdots & a_{nm} \end{bmatrix} = [a_{ij}] \tag{A-1}$$

Each entry a_{ij} is known as an *element* of the matrix $\mathbf{A}$. $n \times m$ is known as the order of the matrix.

The *transpose* of a matrix $\mathbf{A}$, labeled $\mathbf{A}^T$, is that matrix which is formed through the interchanging of the rows and columns of $\mathbf{A}$, for the $\mathbf{A}$ matrix above, its transpose is

$$\mathbf{A}^T = \begin{bmatrix} a_{11} & a_{21} & \cdots & a_{n1} \\ a_{12} & a_{22} & \cdots & a_{n2} \\ \vdots & & & \\ a_{1m} & a_{2m} & \cdots & a_{nm} \end{bmatrix} = [a_{ji}] \tag{A-2}$$

It is thus an $m \times n$ matrix.

*The authors are indebted to Dr. M. A. Murray-Lasso for reviewing this section and suggesting most of the lesser known results.

†Some of the important references on matrices include [H10], [F4], [P5], [G1].

A-2 Types of Matrices

An $n \times 1$ matrix is called a *column vector* or simply a *vector*. It is represented by a boldface lowercase letter, e.g., $\mathbf{x}$. The transpose of such a matrix is a $1 \times n$ matrix called a *row vector*. In this book a row vector will be written in the form $\mathbf{x}^T$. A 1×1 matrix is called a scalar and is represented by an ordinary lowercase letter, e.g., a.

A matrix whose number of rows is equal to the number of columns is called a square matrix. An $n \times n$ square matrix is said to be of order n. Many matrix operations are defined only relative to a square matrix.

The elements a_{ii}, $i = 1, \ldots, n$ of an $n \times n$ square matrix are called the *diagonal* elements; the remaining elements, characterized by a_{ij} with $i \neq j (i, j = 1, \ldots, n)$ are known as the *off-diagonal* elements.

The sum of the diagonal elements of a square matrix $\mathbf{A}$ is called the *trace* of the matrix $\mathbf{A}$ and is denoted $\mathrm{Tr}(\mathbf{A})$.

A square matrix whose off-diagonal elements are all 0 is called a *diagonal* matrix. A diagonal matrix with $a_{ii} = c_i$, $i = 1, \ldots, n$ is sometimes labeled diag $(c_1, \ldots, c_n)$.

A diagonal matrix with all of its diagonal elements unity (i.e. the matrix diag $(1, 1, \ldots, 1)$) is known as the identity (or unit) matrix. It is represented by the symbol $\mathbf{I}$.

A matrix with every element 0 is called a *null* or *zero matrix*; it is labeled $\mathbf{0}$.

An $n \times n$ square matrix whose off-diagonal elements are such that $a_{ij} = a_{ji}$ for $i \neq j, (i, j = 1, \ldots, n)$ is called a *symmetric matrix*. If such a matrix is given by $\mathbf{A}$, then $\mathbf{A}^T = \mathbf{A}$.

If a square matrix $\mathbf{A}$ has complex numbers as elements, then its *conjugate transpose matrix*, labeled $\mathbf{A}^\dagger$, is the matrix formed by replacing every element of the matrix $\mathbf{A}^T$ by its complex conjugate. A matrix $\mathbf{A}$ with the property that $\mathbf{A}^\dagger = \mathbf{A}$ is known as a *hermitian* matrix.

A square matrix $\mathbf{A}$ whose determinant $|\mathbf{A}|$ is 0 is called a *singular* matrix. Otherwise it is nonsingular.

The *determinant* of a square matrix $\mathbf{A}$ is a number associated with the matrix and is usually written

$$\begin{vmatrix} a_{11} & \cdots & a_{1n} \\ \vdots & & \\ a_{n1} & \cdots & a_{nn} \end{vmatrix}$$

The determinant of a matrix $\mathbf{A}$ is also written $|\mathbf{A}|$ or $|[a_{ij}]|$.

The determinant $|[m_{ij}]|$ of the $(n-1)\times(n-1)$ matrix that results when the ith row and the jth column are removed from an $n \times n$

matrix A is called the *minor* of the element a_{ij} of A. The minor of a_{ij} multiplied by $(-1)^{i+j}$ yields the *cofactor* of the element a_{ij}.

The value of a determinant can be obtained by the so-called *Laplace expansion formula*

$$
\begin{aligned}
|[a_{ij}]| &= \sum_{j=1}^{n} (-1)^{i+j} a_{ij} \, |[m_{ij}]| \qquad \text{for any integer } i \quad 1 \le i \le n \\
&= \sum_{i=1}^{n} (-1)^{i+j} a_{ij} \, |[m_{ij}]| \qquad \text{for any integer } j \quad 1 \le j \le n
\end{aligned}
\tag{A-3}
$$

(A-3)*

Since each determinant $|[m_{ij}]|$ in (A-3) can be further expanded by means of the Laplace expansion formula, the value of the determinant of any order is uniquely given if we define the value of a 1×1 and a 2×2 determinant.

These are defined as follows

$$|a| = a \tag{A-4a}$$

$$\begin{vmatrix} a_{11} & a_{12} \\ a_{21} & a_{22} \end{vmatrix} = a_{11} a_{22} - a_{21} a_{12} \tag{A-4b}$$

The *adjoint matrix* of a square matrix A, labeled adj A, is the matrix obtained by replacing each element a_{ij} of A by its cofactor and then transposing

◆◆Example A-1. For the matrix

$$A = \begin{bmatrix} 1 & 0 & 1 \\ 2 & 3 & 1 \\ 0 & 1 & 4 \end{bmatrix}$$

the element a_{21} is 2, the minor of this element is the determinant $\begin{vmatrix} 0 & 1 \\ 1 & 4 \end{vmatrix} = -1$, and the cofactor of this element is $(-1)^{2+1} \begin{vmatrix} 0 & 1 \\ 1 & 4 \end{vmatrix} = +1$.

The adjoint matrix of A is given by

*In words, the value of a determinant is given by the sum of the product of the elements of any one row or column with their cofactors

$$\text{adj } \mathbf{A} = \begin{bmatrix} \begin{vmatrix} 3 & 1 \\ 1 & 4 \end{vmatrix} & -\begin{vmatrix} 2 & 1 \\ 0 & 4 \end{vmatrix} & \begin{vmatrix} 2 & 3 \\ 0 & 1 \end{vmatrix} \\ -\begin{vmatrix} 0 & 1 \\ 1 & 4 \end{vmatrix} & \begin{vmatrix} 1 & 1 \\ 0 & 4 \end{vmatrix} & -\begin{vmatrix} 1 & 0 \\ 0 & 1 \end{vmatrix} \\ \begin{vmatrix} 0 & 1 \\ 3 & 1 \end{vmatrix} & -\begin{vmatrix} 1 & 1 \\ 2 & 1 \end{vmatrix} & \begin{vmatrix} 1 & 0 \\ 2 & 3 \end{vmatrix} \end{bmatrix}^T$$

$$= \begin{bmatrix} 11 & -8 & 2 \\ 1 & 4 & -1 \\ -3 & 1 & 3 \end{bmatrix}^T = \begin{bmatrix} 11 & 1 & -3 \\ -8 & 4 & 1 \\ 2 & -1 & 3 \end{bmatrix}$$

The determinant of $\mathbf{A}$ is

$$|\mathbf{A}| = 1\begin{vmatrix} 3 & 1 \\ 1 & 4 \end{vmatrix} - 2\begin{vmatrix} 0 & 1 \\ 1 & 4 \end{vmatrix} = (12 - 1) - 2(-1) = 13$$ ◆◆

A-3 Basic Matrix Operations

Two matrices $\mathbf{A} \triangleq [a_{ij}]$ and $\mathbf{B} \triangleq [b_{ij}]$ are equal if and only if (1) their orders are equal and (2) their corresponding elements are equal, i.e., $a_{ij} = b_{ij}$ for all i and j. When $\mathbf{A}$ and $\mathbf{B}$ are equal, we write $\mathbf{A} = \mathbf{B}$.

Two matrices $\mathbf{A} \triangleq [a_{ij}]$ and $\mathbf{B} \triangleq [b_{ij}]$ whose orders are the same can be added or subtracted to result in new matrices $\mathbf{C} \triangleq [c_{ij}]$ and $\mathbf{D} \triangleq [d_{ij}]$ respectively; the elements of $\mathbf{A}$, $\mathbf{B}$, $\mathbf{C}$, and $\mathbf{D}$ are related by

$$c_{ij} = a_{ij} + b_{ij}, \qquad d_{ij} = a_{ij} - b_{ij} \tag{A-5}$$

When a matrix $\mathbf{A} \triangleq [a_{ij}]$ is multiplied by a scalar k, a new matrix, whose element is ka_{ij} results.

Two matrices $\mathbf{A}$ and $\mathbf{B}$ can be multiplied to form the product matrix $\mathbf{AB} = \mathbf{C}$ if and only if the number of columns of $\mathbf{A}$ is equal to the number of rows of $\mathbf{B}$. When this holds, $\mathbf{A}$ and $\mathbf{B}$ are said to be conformable with regard to multiplication. If $\mathbf{A}$ is $n \times m$ and $\mathbf{B}$ is $m \times l$, then the resulting matrix $\mathbf{C} = \mathbf{AB}$ will be $n \times l$ and has elements

$$c_{ij} = \sum_{k=1}^{m} a_{ik} b_{kj} \tag{A-6}$$

Note that in the above, if $n \neq l$, then the product BA is not possible. It is also easy to show that even if $n = l$, the matrix multiplication is not commutative, so that in general $AB \neq BA$. However, it is readily seen that for any square matrix A of the same dimensions as I, $AI = IA = A$.

It can also be demonstrated that

$$A[\text{adj}\,A] = |A|\,I = [\text{adj}\,A]\,A \tag{A-7}$$

To define an operation that resembles division, the concept of the *inverse* of a square matrix is necessary. Relative to a square matrix A that is nonsingular, its inverse A^{-1} is given by the relation

$$AA^{-1} = A^{-1}A = I \tag{A-8}$$

On premultiplying Eq. (A-7) by A^{-1} and simplifying, it is seen that A^{-1} is given by

$$A^{-1} = \frac{\text{adj}\,A}{|A|} \tag{A-9}$$

♦♦Example A-2. For the matrix A given in Example A-1 as $|A| = 13$, we have

$$\begin{bmatrix} 1 & 0 & 1 \\ 2 & 3 & 1 \\ 0 & 1 & 4 \end{bmatrix}^{-1} = \frac{1}{13}\begin{bmatrix} 11 & 1 & -3 \\ -8 & 4 & 1 \\ 2 & -1 & 3 \end{bmatrix} = \begin{bmatrix} \frac{11}{13} & \frac{1}{13} & -\frac{3}{13} \\ -\frac{8}{13} & \frac{4}{13} & \frac{1}{13} \\ \frac{2}{13} & -\frac{1}{13} & \frac{3}{13} \end{bmatrix}$$

Also, since

$$\begin{bmatrix} 1 & 0 & 1 \\ 2 & 3 & 1 \\ 0 & 1 & 4 \end{bmatrix}\begin{bmatrix} 11 & 1 & -3 \\ -8 & 4 & 1 \\ 2 & -1 & 3 \end{bmatrix} = \begin{bmatrix} 13 & 0 & 0 \\ 0 & 13 & 0 \\ 0 & 0 & 13 \end{bmatrix} = \begin{bmatrix} 11 & 1 & -3 \\ -8 & 4 & 1 \\ 2 & -1 & 3 \end{bmatrix}\begin{bmatrix} 1 & 0 & 1 \\ 2 & 3 & 1 \\ 0 & 1 & 4 \end{bmatrix},$$

the validity of Eq. (A-7) is demonstrated for this case.♦♦

Frequently some advantage may be gained in matrix operations if *partitioning* is used. Partitioning is the process of subdividing a matrix into submatrices. When the dimensions of these submatrices are compatible, the rules of matrix algebra directly carry over if we treat the submatrices as the element of a matrix. As an example, if a 9×8 matrix A and an 8×6 matrix B are respectively written in the form

$$\mathrm{A}=\left[\begin{array}{c|c}\mathrm{P} & \mathrm{Q}\\ \hline \mathrm{R} & \mathrm{S}\end{array}\right], \qquad \mathrm{B}=\left[\begin{array}{c|c}\mathrm{K} & \mathrm{L}\\ \hline \mathrm{M} & \mathrm{N}\end{array}\right]$$

where in A, the submatrix P is 5×6, Q is 5×2, R is 4×6, and S is 4×2 and in B, K and L are each 6×3 and M and N are each 2×3, then these partitioned matrices are conformable relative to multiplication and the product AB is a 9×6 matrix given by*

$$\mathrm{AB}=\left[\begin{array}{c|c}\mathrm{PK}+\mathrm{QM} & \mathrm{PL}+\mathrm{QN}\\ \hline \mathrm{RK}+\mathrm{SM} & \mathrm{RL}+\mathrm{SN}\end{array}\right] \tag{A-10}$$

Partitioning is particularly fruitful if one or more of the submatrices have only 0s as elements. It is further useful in the computing of inverses for large matrices, which if we adopt the straightforward process using Eq. (A-7) is likely to be highly tedious and time consuming.

To illustrate the latter point we can develop a formula for the inverse of a $2n\times 2n$ matrix A which. when partitioned into four $n\times n$ matrices, takes the form

$$\mathrm{A}=\left[\begin{array}{c|c}\mathrm{B} & \mathrm{C}\\ \hline \mathrm{D} & \mathrm{E}\end{array}\right]$$

Let A^{-1} take the form

$$\mathrm{A}^{-1}=\left[\begin{array}{c|c}\mathrm{F} & \mathrm{G}\\ \hline \mathrm{H} & \mathrm{J}\end{array}\right]$$

where again the submatrices are $n\times n$. Since $\mathrm{AA}^{-1}=\mathrm{I}$, we obtain

$$\begin{aligned}\mathrm{BF}+\mathrm{CH}&=\mathrm{I}_n, &\quad \mathrm{BG}+\mathrm{CJ}&=0,\\ \mathrm{DF}+\mathrm{EH}&=0, &\quad \mathrm{DG}+\mathrm{EJ}&=\mathrm{I}_n\end{aligned} \tag{A-11}$$

*Note that the order of multiplication of the submatrices must be carefully preserved.

where I_n is the $n \times n$ identity matrix. Solving for F, G, H, and J from the four equations in (A-11), we obtain

$$F = (B - CE^{-1}D)^{-1}, \qquad H = -E^{-1}DF,$$
$$J = (E - DB^{-1}C)^{-1}, \qquad G = -B^{-1}CJ \tag{A-12}$$

(Show this.)

A-4 Linear Independence and Rank

The *rank* of an $n \times m$ matrix A is defined as the order of the largest square array whose determinant does not vanish. The square array is formed through removing appropriate rows and columns of A.

It can be shown that the rank of A is not changed by any of the following operations:

1) The interchange of any two rows or two columns of A.
2) The multiplication of the elements of any row or column by a nonzero number.
3) The addition to the elements of a row (column) of k times the corresponding elements of another row (column).

The rank of a matrix has the following significance:

◆◆Theorem A-1. If from an $n \times m$ matrix A of rank l ($n \geq m > l$) a set of l rows (or columns) which together forms a submatrix of rank l is selected, then any other row (column) in A can always be expressed as a linear combination of these l rows (columns).◆◆

Consider a set of m vectors $a_1, a_2, \ldots, a_m$, each with n components $n > m$; if there exists a set of m constants $c_1, c_2, \ldots, c_m$ at least one of which is nonzero, such that the linear combination

$$c_1 a_1 + c_2 a_2 + \cdots + c_m a_m = \sum_{i=1}^{m} c_i a_i = 0 \tag{A-13}$$

then the set of m vectors $x_1, \ldots, x_m$ are said to be *linearly dependent*; otherwise they are said to be linearly *independent*.

Now $\sum_{i=1}^{m} c_i a_i = 0$ can also be written as

$$Ac = 0 \tag{A-14}$$

where A is the $n \times m$ matrix whose ith column is occupied by the vector a_i and c is the vector with components c_i. In the context of the vector-matrix equation (A-14), we have the result that $a_1, \ldots, a_m$ are linearly independent if and only if the matrix A defined above is of rank m.

In the above light, if an $m \times m$ square matrix A is of rank $l < m$, then its determinant $|A|$ vanishes. This is also true if there is an $n \times n$ square matrix A and a nonzero n-vector x that satisfies $Ax = 0$. Since this can be written as $\sum_{i=1}^{n} x_i a_i = 0$ where x_i are the components of x and a_i are the columns of A, we see that $Ax = 0$ is only possible if $|A| = 0$.

A-5 Eigenvalues and Eigenvectors of a Square Matrix

An equation of the form $Ax = y$ may be viewed as a linear transformation of a vector x to a vector y. Relative to such an equation, the matrix A can be viewed as a mapping which can take any vector in the space in which x was defined to one in the space where y is defined. If A is a square matrix, then x and y have the same number of components, and indeed in this case we may view A as an operator which takes any vector x in a given space and transforms it to another one in the same space.

Occasions often arise where one needs to find vectors x and values of scalars λ such that the equation (see for example Sec. 3.4)

$$Ax = \lambda x \tag{A-15}$$

is satisfied for a given square matrix A. The values of scalar λ's that are found to satisfy (A-15) are called the eigenvalues of the square matrix A.

Writing (A-15) in the form

$$(A - \lambda I)x = 0 \tag{A-16}$$

we see that

$$|A - \lambda I| = 0 \tag{A-17}$$

is a necessary and sufficient condition for the existence of nontrivial λ's that satisfy (A-15).

Expanding the determinant (A-17), we obtain an nth degree polynomial in λ which is called the *characteristic equation* of A. The n values of $\lambda, \lambda_1, \ldots, \lambda_n$ (which need not be either real or distinct) can then be solved for as the roots of the characteristic equation.

For each value of λ, say λ_i, there is associated a vector v_i which satisfies (A-15); i.e., $Av_i = \lambda_i v_i$. Vector v_i is called the eigenvector corresponding to the eigenvalue λ_i.

♦♦Example A-3. For the matrix

$$A = \begin{vmatrix} 0 & 1 & 0 \\ 0 & 0 & 1 \\ -8 & -14 & -7 \end{vmatrix}$$

$$|A - \lambda I| = \begin{vmatrix} -\lambda & 1 & 0 \\ 0 & -\lambda & 1 \\ -8 & -14 & -7-\lambda \end{vmatrix} = \lambda^3 + 7\lambda^2 + 14\lambda + 8 = 0.$$

The eigenvalues are then $\lambda_1 = -1$, $\lambda_2 = -2$, $\lambda_3 = -4$. Corresponding to λ_1 we have $A v_1 = -v_1$. This yields the set of equations $v_{12} = -v_{11}$, $v_{13} = -v_{12} = v_{11}$, $-8v_{11} - 14v_{12} - 7v_{13} = -v_{13}$, where v_{11}, v_{12}, v_{13} are the components of the vector v_1. This set is homogeneous and hence is determined down to a multiplicative constant. Letting $v_{11} = 1$, we have the solution

$$v_1 = \begin{bmatrix} 1 \\ -1 \\ 1 \end{bmatrix}$$

In a similar manner, we can find

$$v_2 = \begin{bmatrix} 1 \\ -2 \\ 4 \end{bmatrix} \quad \text{and} \quad v_3 = \begin{bmatrix} 1 \\ -4 \\ 16 \end{bmatrix}$$ ♦♦

The characteristic equation of a real matrix may turn out to have complex roots appearing in conjugate pairs. Here the eigenvectors may also have complex components. It may be shown however that if a matrix is hermitian, then the eigenvalues must be real. A real symmetric matrix, being a particular case of hermitian matrices, has therefore real eigenvalues and eigenvectors.

A-6 The Diagonalization of a Square Matrix

For a square matrix A, there are often occasions where we are called upon to find, if possible, another square matrix P such that the matrix equation

$$P^{-1}AP = \Lambda \qquad \text{(A-18)}$$

is observed. (See, for example, Sec. 3.4.) Here Λ is the square matrix diag $(\lambda_1, \ldots, \lambda_n)$, where $\lambda_1, \ldots, \lambda_n$ are the n eigenvalues of the matrix A.

From the result of the previous section, it is clear that a candidate matrix P for this is one whose first through the nth columns are taken up respectively by the eigenvectors $v_1, \ldots, v_n$. A proviso here is of course that P^{-1} exists, or P is nonsingular, for then (A-18) is defined and we can simply write it in the form

$$AP = P\Lambda \tag{A-19}$$

and the result follows immediately.

◆◆Example A-4. For the matrix A of Example A-3, a matrix P that diagonalizes A in accordance with (A-18) is one whose columns are made up by the vectors v_1, v_2, and v_3 found in Example A-3. Thus

$$P = \begin{bmatrix} 1 & 1 & 1 \\ -1 & -2 & -4 \\ 1 & 4 & 16 \end{bmatrix}$$

With this it is easy to demonstrate that

$$P^{-1}AP = \begin{bmatrix} -1 & 0 & 0 \\ 0 & -2 & 0 \\ 0 & 0 & -4 \end{bmatrix}$$ ◆◆

As it turns out, if the eigenvalue λ_i's of A are distinct, the matrix P constructed in the above way is always nonsingular.

To show this, we suppose that $|P| = 0$; then by the result of Sec. A-4, the columns of P are linearly dependent. We can then write

$$\sum_{i=1}^{n} c_i v_i = 0 \tag{A-20}$$

for some set of constants $c_1, \ldots, c_n$ not all of which are 0.

If we premultiply both sides of (A-20) by I, A, $A^2, \ldots, A^{n-1}$ successively we have by (A-19)

$$\begin{aligned} \sum_{i=1}^{n} c_i v_i &= 0 \\ \sum_{i=1}^{n} c_i \lambda_i v_i &= 0 \\ &\vdots \\ \sum_{i=1}^{n} c_i \lambda_i^{n-1} v_i &= 0 \end{aligned} \tag{A-21}$$

Let the vector v_i have the components $v_{i1}, \ldots, v_{in}$, then for a nontrivial solution for c_i to occur for one of these components (which is implied by the conditions of the problem, why?) we must have

$$\begin{vmatrix} 1 & 1 & \cdots & 1 \\ \lambda_1 & \lambda_2 & \cdots & \lambda_n \\ \lambda_1^2 & \lambda_2^2 & \cdots & \lambda_n^2 \\ \cdot & & & \\ \cdot & & & \\ \cdot & & & \\ \lambda_1^{n-1} & \lambda_2^{n-1} & \cdots & \lambda_n^{n-1} \end{vmatrix} = 0 \tag{A-22}$$

However, it is known that the above Vandermonde determinant can be expressed in the form $\prod_{1 \leq i < j \leq n} (\lambda_j - \lambda_i)$ [B4] and hence can vanish if and only if $\lambda_j = \lambda_i$ for some $j \neq i$. As our original assumption is contradicted, $|\mathrm{P}| \neq 0$ and hence P is nonsignular.

When the λ's are not distinct, we are no longer guaranteed that a P that diagonalizes A via (A-18) can be found. The best that can be done is the finding of a nonsingular P that reduces A to the Jordan canonical form Λ_J via $\mathrm{P}^{-1}\mathrm{A}\mathrm{P} = \Lambda_J$, where Λ_J is given by Eq. (2-25) in the text.*

A-7 Quadratic Forms and the Positive Definiteness of a Square Matrix

An expression such as

$$q(x_1, \ldots, x_n) = \sum_{i=1}^{n} \sum_{j=1}^{n} k_{ij} x_i x_j \tag{A-23}$$

involving terms of second degree in x_i and x_j is known as a *quadratic form* of n variables.

It is clear that a quadratic form can be compactly expressed in a vector-matrix form as:

$$q(x_1, \ldots, x_n) = \sum_{i=1}^{n} \sum_{j=1}^{n} k_{ij} x_i x_j = \mathbf{x}^T \mathrm{Q} \mathbf{x} \tag{A-24}$$

*An exception to this case occurs for a matrix A that commutes with its transpose (i.e., $\mathrm{A}\mathrm{A}^T = \mathrm{A}^T\mathrm{A}$). Such a matrix can always be diagonalized by $\mathrm{P}^{-1}\mathrm{A}\mathrm{P}$. A particular case of this is a symmetric matrix.

where

$$\mathbf{Q} = \begin{bmatrix} k_{11} & \dfrac{k_{12}+k_{21}}{2} & \cdots & \dfrac{k_{1n}+k_{n1}}{2} \\ \dfrac{k_{12}+k_{21}}{2} & k_{22} & & \\ \cdot & & \cdot & \\ \cdot & & & \cdot \\ \cdot & & & \cdot \\ \dfrac{k_{1n}+k_{n1}}{2} & & & k_{nn} \end{bmatrix} = [q_{ij}] = \mathbf{Q}^T \tag{A-25}$$

A quadratic form is said to be positive (negative) definite if $q = 0$ for $\mathbf{x} = 0$ and $q > 0$ ($q < 0$) for $\mathbf{x} \neq 0$. It is said to be positive semidefinite (negative semidefinite) if $q = 0$ for $\mathbf{x} = 0$ and $q \geq 0$ ($q \leq 0$) for $\mathbf{x} \neq 0$.

An important test of the positive definiteness of a quadratic form is given by the following theorem, [G1], [B4].

◆◆Theorem A-2. A quadratic form $q(\mathbf{x}) = \mathbf{x}^T\mathbf{Q}\mathbf{x}$ is positive (negative) definite if an only if the n determinants $|\mathbf{Q}_1|, \ldots, |\mathbf{Q}_n|$ are all positive (negative), where

$$|\mathbf{Q}_1| = |q_{11}|, \qquad |\mathbf{Q}_2| = \begin{vmatrix} q_{11} & q_{12} \\ q_{12} & q_{22} \end{vmatrix}, \qquad |\mathbf{Q}_3| = \begin{vmatrix} q_{11} & q_{12} & q_{13} \\ q_{12} & q_{22} & q_{23} \\ q_{13} & q_{23} & q_{33} \end{vmatrix}$$

$$|\mathbf{Q}_m| = |[q_{ij}]|, \begin{matrix} i = 1, \ldots, m \leq n \\ j = 1, \ldots, m \leq n \end{matrix}, \qquad |\mathbf{Q}_n| = |\mathbf{Q}| \tag{A-26}$$ ◆◆

A-8 The Cayley-Hamilton Theorem

An important result in the theory of matrices is the Cayley-Hamilton Theorem.

◆◆Theorem A-3. Let $f(\lambda) = 0$ be the characteristic equation of an arbitrary square matrix $\mathbf{A}$; then $f(\mathbf{A}) = 0$ (i.e., $\mathbf{A}$ satisfies its own characteristic equation).◆◆

For the case of distinct eigenvalues, the theorem is easy to prove; for in this case, we know that a nonsingular matrix $\mathbf{P}$ can be found such that $\mathbf{P}^{-1}\mathbf{A}\mathbf{P} = \mathbf{\Lambda}$ or $\mathbf{A}\mathbf{P} = \mathbf{P}\mathbf{\Lambda}$. This implies that by premultiplying in turn by $\mathbf{A}, \mathbf{A}^2, \ldots, \mathbf{A}^n$ we have $\mathbf{A}^2\mathbf{P} = \mathbf{P}\mathbf{\Lambda}^2, \ldots, \mathbf{A}^n\mathbf{P} =$

$\mathbf{P}\Lambda^n$. This means for any polynomial $g(x) = \sum_{i=1}^{n} a_i x^i$, we have $g(\mathbf{A})\mathbf{P} = \mathbf{P}g(\Lambda)$. In particular, this holds for the characteristic polynomial; thus

$$f(\mathbf{A})\mathbf{P} = \mathbf{P}f(\Lambda) \tag{A-27a}$$

However

$$f(\Lambda) = \text{diag}\left(f(\lambda_1), \ldots, f(\lambda_n)\right) \tag{A-27b}$$

but $f(\lambda_i) \triangleq 0$ for each i; hence by (A-27a) as $\mathbf{P}$ is nonsingular, we have $f(\mathbf{A}) = 0$.

For a proof for the general case, see [G1] and [B4].

A-9 Some Useful Relationships

1. Some Matrix Identities

The reader may wish to verify the following useful matrix relations:

a) $[\mathbf{AB}\ldots\mathbf{MN}]^T = \mathbf{N}^T\mathbf{M}^T\ldots\mathbf{B}^T\mathbf{A}^T$
b) $[\mathbf{AB}\ldots\mathbf{MN}]^{-1} = \mathbf{N}^{-1}\mathbf{M}^{-1}\ldots\mathbf{B}^{-1}\mathbf{A}^{-1}$, if each of the inverse matrices exists
c) $|\mathbf{AB}\ldots\mathbf{MN}| = |\mathbf{A}||\mathbf{B}|\ldots|\mathbf{M}||\mathbf{N}|$
d) For an $n\times n$ matrix partitioned into $\left[\begin{array}{c|c}\mathbf{A} & \mathbf{B}\\ \hline \mathbf{C} & \mathbf{D}\end{array}\right]$ with $\mathbf{A}$ an $m\times m$ matrix and $\mathbf{D}$ an $(n-m)\times(n-m)$ matrix, then

$$\left[\begin{array}{c|c}\mathbf{A} & \mathbf{B}\\ \hline \mathbf{C} & \mathbf{D}\end{array}\right]^{-1} = \left[\begin{array}{c|c}\mathbf{I}_m & -\mathbf{A}^{-1}\mathbf{B}\\ \hline 0_{(n-m)\times m} & \mathbf{I}_m\end{array}\right]\left[\begin{array}{c|c}\mathbf{A}^{-1} & 0_{m\times(n-m)}\\ \hline 0_{(n-m)\times m} & (\mathbf{D}-\mathbf{C}\mathbf{A}^{-1}\mathbf{B})^{-1}\end{array}\right]\left[\begin{array}{c|c}\mathbf{I}_m & 0_{m\times(n-m)}\\ \hline -\mathbf{C}\mathbf{A}^{-1} & \mathbf{I}_m\end{array}\right]$$

where $0_{r\times s}$ is an $r\times s$ matrix composed entirely of 0s.

2. The Calculation of the Determinant of a High-Order Matrix

To find the determinant of a high-order (e.g., $n > 10$) matrix requires an enormous amount of computation time if the Laplace expansion formula of Sec. A-2 is used. However the following theorem holds.

◆◆Theorem A-4. The determinant of a matrix is unchanged if to the elements of any row (column) are added k times the corresponding elements of any row (column). ◆◆

With Theorem A-4, the determinant of a matrix can be manipulated into a *triangular* form in which all elements above (or below) the main diagonals are zero. By the Laplace expansion formula, *the value of the determinant of a triangular matrix is given by the product of the elements of the main diagonal.*

3. The Finding of the Values of Analytic Functions of Matrices

Let $\lambda_1, \lambda_2, \ldots, \lambda_n$ be the eigenvalues of a square matrix $\mathbf{A}$ of order n. Corresponding to these eigenvalues, let $\mathbf{v}_1, \mathbf{v}_2, \ldots, \mathbf{v}_n$ be *distinct* unit length eigenvectors of $\mathbf{A}$ and let $\mathbf{u}_1, \mathbf{u}_2, \ldots, \mathbf{u}_n$ be *distinct* unit length eigenvectors of $\mathbf{A}^T$. It can be shown that square matrices $\mathbf{v}_i\mathbf{u}_i^T$, called the *spectral set* of $\mathbf{A}$, are each of rank 1 and are *idempotent*; that is

$$\left[\mathbf{v}_i\mathbf{u}_i^T\right]^N = \mathbf{v}_i\mathbf{u}_i^T \qquad \text{for each } i \text{ and for} \quad N = 1, 2, \ldots \tag{A-28}$$

Further, for any polynomial $P(x)$ we have

$$P(\mathbf{A}) = \mathbf{v}_1\mathbf{u}_1^T P(\lambda_1) + \mathbf{v}_2\mathbf{u}_2^T P(\lambda_2) + \cdots + \mathbf{v}_n\mathbf{u}_n^T P(\lambda_n) \tag{A-29}$$

and for any *analytic* functions $F(\mathbf{A})$ of matrices which are defined by the same power series that defines the corresponding functions of a scalar (e.g., $e^{\mathbf{A}t}$), we have

$$F(\mathbf{A}) = \mathbf{v}_1\mathbf{u}_1^T F(\lambda_1) + \mathbf{v}_2\mathbf{u}_2^T F(\lambda_2) + \cdots + \mathbf{v}_n\mathbf{u}_n^T F(\lambda_n) \tag{A-30}$$

wherever the series converges for each of the λ_i's.*

If the eigenvalues of $\mathbf{A}$ are not distinct, then the following extension of Cauchy's formula may be used

$$F(\mathbf{A}) = \frac{1}{2\pi j}\int_{\mathcal{C}} F(z)(z\mathbf{I} - \mathbf{A})^{-1}\,dz \tag{A-31}$$

where z is a complex variable, $\mathcal{C}$ is the boundary of a region (not

*The functions of the matrices may be defined elsewhere by analytic continuation of the functions of the eigenvalues.

necessarily singly connected) in the complex plane containing all the eigenvalues of A.*

♦♦Example A-5. The matrix $A = \begin{bmatrix} 3 & 2 \\ 2 & 3 \end{bmatrix}$ has eigenvalues $\lambda_1 = 5$, $\lambda_2 = 1$. Here

$$v_1 = u_1 = \frac{1}{\sqrt{2}}\begin{bmatrix} 1 \\ 1 \end{bmatrix}, \quad v_2 = u_2 = \frac{1}{\sqrt{2}}\begin{bmatrix} 1 \\ -1 \end{bmatrix}$$

Hence the spectral set is

$$v_1 u_1^T = \begin{bmatrix} \frac{1}{2} & \frac{1}{2} \\ \frac{1}{2} & \frac{1}{2} \end{bmatrix}, \quad v_2 u_2^T = \begin{bmatrix} \frac{1}{2} & -\frac{1}{2} \\ -\frac{1}{2} & \frac{1}{2} \end{bmatrix}$$

With the spectral set and using Eqs. (A-28) and (A-29), it becomes extremely simple to calculate such quantities as A^{23}, A^{-1}, e^{At}, $\cos At$. By (A-28)

$$A^{23} = \begin{bmatrix} \frac{1}{2} & \frac{1}{2} \\ \frac{1}{2} & \frac{1}{2} \end{bmatrix} 5^{23} + \begin{bmatrix} \frac{1}{2} & -\frac{1}{2} \\ -\frac{1}{2} & \frac{1}{2} \end{bmatrix} 1^{23}$$

$$A^{-1} = \begin{bmatrix} \frac{1}{2} & \frac{1}{2} \\ \frac{1}{2} & \frac{1}{2} \end{bmatrix} \frac{1}{5} + \begin{bmatrix} \frac{1}{2} & -\frac{1}{2} \\ -\frac{1}{2} & \frac{1}{2} \end{bmatrix} 1$$

By (A-29)

$$e^{At} = \begin{bmatrix} \frac{1}{2} & \frac{1}{2} \\ \frac{1}{2} & \frac{1}{2} \end{bmatrix} e^{5t} + \begin{bmatrix} \frac{1}{2} & -\frac{1}{2} \\ -\frac{1}{2} & \frac{1}{2} \end{bmatrix} e^{t}$$

$$\cos At = \begin{bmatrix} \frac{1}{2} & \frac{1}{2} \\ \frac{1}{2} & \frac{1}{2} \end{bmatrix} \cos 5t + \begin{bmatrix} \frac{1}{2} & -\frac{1}{2} \\ -\frac{1}{2} & \frac{1}{2} \end{bmatrix} \cos t$$

♦♦

*It is assumed that $F(z)$ is analytic in the region bounded by $\mathcal{C}$, that $\mathcal{C}$ consists of a finite number of closed curves, and that it is traversed in the positive sense with respect to the areas enclosing the eigenvalues.

◆◆Example A-6. The matrix $A = \begin{bmatrix} 1 & 1 \\ 0 & 1 \end{bmatrix}$ has only one distinct eigenvector (show this). To find e^{At}, we must use (A-31), which leads to

$$e^{At} = \frac{1}{2\pi j} \int_{\mathcal{C}} e^{zt} \begin{bmatrix} \dfrac{1}{(1-z)} & -\dfrac{1}{(1-z)^2} \\ 0 & \dfrac{1}{1-z} \end{bmatrix} dz = \begin{bmatrix} -e^t & -te^t \\ 0 & -e^t \end{bmatrix}$$

◆◆

4. Calculation of the Characteristic Equation from the Traces of the Power of a Matrix

The following method is useful for digital computer calculation without a language that can manipulate symbols algebraically.

Let the characteristic equation be

$$|A - \lambda I| = (-1)^n \left(\lambda^n + a_1 \lambda^{n-1} + a_2 \lambda^{n-2} + \cdots + a_n\right) \tag{A-32}$$

then

$$\begin{aligned} a_1 &= \mathrm{Tr}(A), \qquad a_2 = -\tfrac{1}{2}\left[a_1 \mathrm{Tr}(A) + \mathrm{Tr}(A^2)\right] \\ a_3 &= -\tfrac{1}{3}\left[a_2 \mathrm{Tr}(A) + a_1 \mathrm{Tr}(A^2) + \mathrm{Tr}(A^3)\right] \\ &\ \vdots \\ a_n &= -\frac{1}{n}\left[a_{n-1} \mathrm{Tr}(A) + a_{n-2} \mathrm{Tr}(A^2) + \cdots + a_1 \mathrm{Tr}(A^{n-1}) + \mathrm{Tr}(A^n)\right] \end{aligned} \tag{A-33}$$

5. Calculation of the Inverse of a Matrix by the Coefficients of the Characteristic Equation

If the characteristic equation of A is given by (A-32) above, then

$$\begin{aligned} |A| &= (-1)^n a_n \\ \mathrm{adj}\, A &= (-1)^{n+1}\left[A^{n-1} + a_1 A^{n-2} + \cdots + a_{n-2} A + a_{n-1} I\right] \\ A^{-1} &= \frac{\mathrm{adj}\, A}{|A|} \end{aligned} \tag{A-34}$$

Appendix B

The z-Transform and the Advanced z-Transform

B-1 Introduction

The z-transform has long been used to solve linear difference equations. With the advent of discrete control systems, it has become an important tool for control engineers. For the convenience of treating the difference equations governing discrete systems, the z-transform was later generalized to the so-called "advanced z-transform."

The advanced z-transform also has other uses; for example, the investigation of existence and stability of periodic motion in relay control systems (Chap. 8).

B-2 Basic Definitions

1. The Advanced z-Transform of a Function

Consider an absolutely integrable function $g(t)$. Suppose there are real constants M and β such that for a set of values of t, namely $t = (k + m)T$, where $m \geq 0$, $T > 0$, $k = 0,1,2 \ldots,$

$$|g(t)| < Me^{\beta t} \tag{B-1}$$

For this function, the advanced z-transform is defined as

$$\mathcal{Z}_A[g(t)] \triangleq \mathcal{G}(z,m) = \sum_{k=0}^{\infty} g[(k+m)T^+]z^{-k} \tag{B-2)*†}$$

for $|z| \geq e^{\beta T}$ and real numbers $m \geq 0$ and $T > 0$.

Condition (B-1) implies that there is some real $\delta > 0$ such that we can write $|g(t)| \leq Me^{(\beta - \delta)t}$. Using this in (B-2), we obtain

$$|\mathcal{G}(z,m)| \leq M \sum_{k=0}^{\infty} e^{(k+m)(\beta-\delta)T^+} |z|^{-k}$$

$$= Me^{(\beta-\delta)mT} \lim_{N\to\infty} \frac{1 - (e^{(\beta-\delta)T}|z|^{-1})^N}{1 - e^{(\beta-\delta)T}|z|^{-1}}$$

From the above inequality, we see** that for every m for which (B-1) holds, $\mathcal{G}(z,m)$ will converge absolutely if $|z| \geq e^{\beta T}$.

2. The z-Transform of a Function

The z-transform is a special case of the advanced z-transform. The z-transform of a function $g(t)$ satisfying condition (B-1) is defined as

$$\mathcal{Z}[g(t)] \triangleq \mathcal{G}(z) \triangleq \lim_{m\to 0} \mathcal{G}(z,m) = \mathcal{G}(z,0)$$
$$= \sum_{k=0}^{\infty} g(kT^+)z^{-k}; \qquad |z| \geq e^{\beta T} \tag{B-3}$$

As before, $\mathcal{G}(z)$ will converge absolutely for $|z| \geq e^{\beta T}$.

*The superscript + in $g[(k+m)T^+]$ means $\lim_{\epsilon\to 0} g[(k+m+\epsilon)T]$ where the limit is to be taken from the side $\epsilon > 0$.

† Also used is the "modified z-transform," which is defined by

$$\mathcal{G}_M(z,m) \triangleq \sum_{k=0}^{\infty} g[(k+m)T^+]z^{-(k+1)}$$

It is clear that $\mathcal{G}_M(z,m) = z^{-1}\mathcal{G}(z,m)$. Throughout this book, the advanced z-transform is used.

**If $|z| \geq e^{\beta T}$, then, for $\delta \geq 0$,

$$\lim_{N\to\infty} \left(e^{(\beta-\delta)T}|z|^{-1}\right)^N \leq \lim_{N\to\infty} e^{-N\delta T} = 0$$

3. The z-Transform of an Infinite Sequence of Numbers

The z-transform can also be defined for an infinite sequence of numbers.

Let

$$\{g_k\} \triangleq \{g_0, g_1, g_2, \dots\} \tag{B-4a}$$

be an infinite sequence of numbers. Let there be real constants $M > 0$ and $T > 0$ such that

$$|g_k| < Me^{\beta Tk}, \qquad k = 0, 1, 2, \dots \tag{B-4b}$$

The z-transform for this sequence is defined as

$$\mathcal{Z}\{g_k\} \triangleq \mathcal{G}(z) \triangleq \sum_{k=0}^{\infty} g_k z^{-k}, \qquad |z| \geq e^{\beta T} \tag{B-5}$$

4. Some Useful Relations

From the defining equations (B-2) and (B-3) we arrive at the relations

$$\mathcal{G}(z,1^+) = \left(\mathcal{G}(z) - g(0^+)\right) z \tag{B-6a}$$

$$\mathcal{G}(z,1^-) = \mathcal{G}(z,1^+) \quad \text{if} \quad g(kT^+) = g(kT^-) \quad \text{for} \quad k = 1,2,3, \dots \tag{B-6b}^*$$

It is often useful to express the advanced z-transform in terms of the z-transform of a shifted function

$$\mathcal{G}(z,m) = \mathcal{Z}_A[g(t)] = \mathcal{Z}[g(t + mT)] \tag{B-7}$$

(B-7) follows directly from (B-2) and (B-3). Indeed, the advanced z-transform derives its name from this property.

The advanced z-transform and the z-transform for a few common functions are presented in Table B-1. For more comprehensive tables, the reader is referred to [J6] and [T5].

*In most practical cases, $g(t)$ is continuous at $t = kT$, $k = 1,2,3, \dots$, but not necessarily at $t = 0$.

Table B-1. Some Important Advanced z-Transform Pairs*

$G(s)$	$g(t)$**	$\mathcal{G}(z,m);\ 0 \le m < 1$	Region of Validity
$\frac{1}{s}$	1	$\frac{z}{(z-1)}$	$\lvert z \rvert > 1$
$\frac{1}{s^2}$	t	$\left[\frac{m}{(z-1)} + \frac{1}{(z-1)^2}\right] Tz$	$\lvert z \rvert > 1$
$\frac{1}{s^3}$	$\frac{1}{2}t^2$	$\frac{zT^2}{2}\left[\frac{m^2}{(z-1)} + \frac{2m+1}{(z-1)^2} + \frac{2}{(z-1)^3}\right]$	$\lvert z \rvert > 1$
$\frac{1}{s+a}$	e^{-at}	$\frac{ze^{-amT}}{z-e^{-aT}}$	$\lvert z \rvert > e^{-aT}$
$\frac{1}{(s+a)^2}$	te^{-at}	$zTe^{-amT}\left[\frac{m}{z-e^{-aT}} + \frac{e^{-aT}}{(z-e^{-aT})^2}\right]$	$\lvert z \rvert > e^{-aT}$
$\frac{1}{(s+a)^3}$	$\frac{1}{2}t^2e^{-aT}$	$\frac{1}{2}zT^2e^{-amT}\left[\frac{m^2}{z-e^{-aT}} + \frac{(2m+1)e^{-aT}}{(z-e^{-aT})^2} + \frac{2e^{-2aT}}{(z-e^{-aT})^3}\right]$	$\lvert z \rvert > e^{-aT}$
$\frac{b}{(s+a)^2+b^2}$	$e^{-at}\sin bt$	$ze^{-amT}\left[\frac{z\sin mbT + e^{-aT}\sin\left((1-m)bT\right)}{z^2 - 2ze^{-aT}\cos bT + e^{-2aT}}\right]$	$\lvert z \rvert > e^{-aT}$

$\dfrac{s+a}{(s+a)^2+b^2}$	$e^{-at}\cos bt$	$ze^{-amT}\left[\dfrac{z\cos mbT - e^{-aT}\cos\left((1-m)bT\right)}{z^2-2ze^{-aT}\cos bT+e^{-2aT}}\right]$	$\lvert z\rvert > e^{-aT}$
$\dfrac{a}{s^2-a^2}$	$\sinh at$	$z\left[\dfrac{z\sinh maT + \sinh\left((1-m)aT\right)}{z^2-2z\cosh aT+1}\right]$	$\lvert z\rvert > e^{\lvert a\rvert T}$
$\dfrac{s}{s^2-a^2}$	$\cosh at$	$z\left[\dfrac{z\cosh maT - \cosh\left((1-m)aT\right)}{z^2-2z\cosh aT+1}\right]$	$\lvert z\rvert > e^{\lvert a\rvert T}$
$\dfrac{a^2}{s^2(s+a)}$	$at-(1-e^{at})$	$z\left[\dfrac{aT}{(z-1)^2}+\dfrac{(amT-1)}{z-1}+\dfrac{e^{-amT}}{z-e^{-aT}}\right]$	$\lvert z\rvert > \max\left[1, e^{-aT}\right]$
$\dfrac{a^2+b^2}{s[(s+a)^2+b^2]}$	$1-e^{-at}\dfrac{\cos(bt-\phi)}{\cos\phi}$, $\phi=\tan^{-1}(a/b)$	$\dfrac{z}{z-1}-\dfrac{ze^{-amT}\left[z\cos(mbT-\phi)-e^{-aT}\cos\left((1-m)bT+\phi\right)\right]}{\cos\phi[z^2-2ze^{-aT}\cos bT+e^{-2aT}]}$	$\lvert z\rvert > \max\left[1, e^{-aT}\right]$

*The z-transform is given by $\mathcal{G}(z) = \mathcal{G}(z,0)$.

**It is understood that $g(t) = 0$ for $t < 0$.

B-3 Inversion of the Advanced z-Transform*

Every power series is analytic within its region of convergence [K17]. Since the power series defined in Eq. (B-2) is of the form $\sum_{k=0}^{\infty} a_k (1/z)^k$, where $|1/z| < \exp(-\beta T)$, the region defined by $|z| > \exp(\beta T)$ represents the region of convergence for the series. Therefore, the defining equation (B-2) implies that the advanced z-transform $\mathcal{G}(z,m)$ is analytic in $|z| \geq \exp(\beta T)$. Conversely, any function $\mathcal{G}(z,m)$ that is analytic in $|z| \geq \exp(\beta T)$ can be uniquely represented by the Laurent expansion**

$$\mathcal{G}(z,m) = \sum_{k=0}^{\infty} \left[\frac{1}{2\pi j} \oint_{\mathcal{C}} \mathcal{G}(\xi,m)\, \xi^{k-1} d\xi \right] z^{-k} \tag{B-8}$$

where $\mathcal{C}$ is any closed counterclockwise path in $|z| > \exp(\beta T)$.

Comparing (B-8) with (B-2) yields the inverse advanced z-transform

$$\mathcal{Z}_A^{-1}[\mathcal{G}(z,m)] = g\left((m+k)T^+\right) = \frac{1}{2\pi j} \oint_{\mathcal{C}} \mathcal{G}(z,m) z^{k-1} dz \tag{B-9}$$

Thus, we conclude:

♦♦Theorem B-1. If $\mathcal{G}(z,m)$ is analytic in $|z| \geq \exp(\beta T)$, then its inverse advanced z-transform $g\left((k+m)T^+\right) (k = 0,1,2, \ldots)$ exists and is uniquely represented by (B-9).♦♦

If, for example, $\mathcal{G}(z,m)$ is a rational function of z, then all its singularities are poles and (B-9) can be evaluated by the residue theorem [K17] yielding

$$g\left((k+m)T^+\right) = \sum_{\substack{\text{all poles}\\ \text{of } \mathcal{G}(z,m)}} [\text{Residues of } z^{k-1}\mathcal{G}(z,m)] \tag{B-10}$$

The use of (B-9) or (B-10) does not always constitute the simplest procedure for evaluating the inverse advanced z-transform (or inverse z-transform in the case $m = 0$). Because of the uniqueness of the power-series representation of analytic functions, we can use any available method to expand $\mathcal{G}(z,m)$ into a power series with

*Since the z-transform can be regarded as a special case of the advanced z-transform, only the latter will be discussed in the sequel.

**See [K17] pp. 117-122. Since $\mathcal{G}(z,m)$ is analytic in $|z| \geq \exp(\beta T)$, its Laurent expansion has only descending powers of z.

descending powers of z and obtain the inverse, $g\left((k+m)T^+\right)$, simply as the multiplying factor of the term with z^{-k} in this series [J6], [T5]. There also exists other ingenious methods [B1].

B-4 Further Properties

The advanced z-transform enjoys the following properties

1. Linearity

$$\mathcal{Z}_A[g_1(t) + g_2(t)] = \mathcal{Z}_A[g_1(t)] + \mathcal{Z}_A[g_2(t)] \qquad \text{(B-11)}$$

$$\mathcal{Z}_A[kg(t)] = k\mathcal{Z}_A[g(t)], \qquad k \text{ a constant}$$

2. The Shifting Properties

Let $g(t) = 0$ for $t < 0$. Then we have

$$\mathcal{Z}_A[g(t-\lambda T) = \begin{cases} \mathcal{G}(z,m-\lambda), & \lambda \le m \\ z^{-1}\mathcal{G}(z,1+m-\lambda), & -(1-\lambda) \le m < \lambda \end{cases} \qquad \text{(B-12)}$$

$$\mathcal{Z}_A[g(t-nT) = z^{-n}\,\mathcal{G}(z,m), \qquad 0 \le m < 1, \quad n = 0,1,2,\ldots \qquad \text{(B-13a)}$$

$$\mathcal{Z}_A[g(t+nT) = z^{n}\mathcal{G}(z,m) - \sum_{k=0}^{n-1} g\left((m+k)T^+\right) z^{n-k}, \qquad m \ge 0, \quad n = 1,2,\ldots \qquad \text{(B-13b)}$$

For the sequence $\{g_k\}$ and its z-transform, $\mathcal{G}(z) = \mathcal{Z}[\{g_k\}]$, defined by (B-5), Eqs. (B-13), for $m = 0$ and $g_k = g(kT^+)$, become

$$\mathcal{Z}[\{g_{k-n}\}] = z^{-n}\mathcal{G}(z), \qquad n = 0,1,2,\ldots \qquad \text{(B-14a)}$$

$$\mathcal{Z}[\{g_{k+n}\}] = z^{n}\mathcal{G}(z) - \sum_{k=0}^{n-1} g_k z^{n-k}, \qquad n = 1,2,3,\ldots \qquad \text{(B-14b)}$$

3. The Multiplication of $g(t)$ by $e^{\alpha t}$

From (B-2) it follows directly that for any real α

$$\mathcal{Z}_A[e^{\alpha t} g(t)] = e^{\alpha T m}\,\mathcal{G}(e^{-\alpha T}z,m), \qquad |z| \ge e^{(\alpha+\beta)T} \qquad \text{(B-15a)}$$

From (B-4), we can obtain a corresponding relation for any real constant C and an infinite sequence of numbers $\{g_k\}$

$$\mathcal{Z}\left[\left\{C^k g_k\right\}\right] = \mathcal{G}\left(\frac{z}{C}\right), \qquad |z| \geq Ce^{\beta T} \tag{B-15b}$$

4. Analyticity

The analyticity of $\mathcal{G}(z,m)$, already discussed in Sec. B-3, leads to the important property

$$\lim_{z \to 1} \mathcal{G}(z,m) = \sum_{k=0}^{\infty} g\left((m+k)T^{+}\right) \qquad \text{if } \mathcal{G}(z,m) \text{ is analytic in } \quad |z| \geq 1 \tag{B-16}$$

This property follows from the fact that any function that is analytic in $|z| \geq 1$ can always be uniquely expanded into a power-series of descending powers of $|z|$.

Property (B-16) is used for obtaining closed-form expressions for certain infinite series from the available tables of advanced z-transforms. (This is done in Chap. 8.)

5. Real Convolution

Consider the following z-transform and advanced z-transform expressions

$$\mathcal{F}(z,0) = \mathcal{F}(z) = \mathcal{Z}[f(t)], \qquad |z| \geq e^{\beta_f T}$$

$$\mathcal{G}(z,m) = \mathcal{Z}_A[g(t)], \qquad |z| \geq e^{\beta_g T} \tag{B-17a}$$

$$\mathcal{H}(z,m) = \mathcal{Z}_A[h(t)], \qquad |z| \geq e^{\beta_h T}$$

If

$$h(t) = \sum_{k=0}^{\infty} f(kT^{+})g(t-kT) \tag{B-17b}$$

then

$$\mathcal{H}(z,m) = \mathcal{F}(z)\mathcal{G}(z,m), \qquad |z| \geq e^{\beta_h T}, \qquad 0 \leq m < 1$$

$$\beta_h = \max(\beta_f, \beta_g) \tag{B-17c}$$

which follows directly from the defining equations (B-2) and (B-3). For $m = 0$ by (B-3), (B-17c) becomes

$$\mathcal{H}(z) = \mathcal{F}(z)\mathcal{G}(z), \qquad |z| \geq e^{\beta_h T} \tag{B-17d}$$

$$\beta_h = \max(\beta_f, \beta_g)$$

Equation (B-17d) is meaningful when (B-17b) is expressed with $t = nT$, i.e.,

$$h(nT) = \sum_{k=0}^{\infty} f(kT^+)\, g\big((n-k)T\big) \tag{B-18a}$$

or, in terms of the sequence $\{g_k\}$, $\{f_k\}$ and $\{h_k\}$ defined in (B-4a),

$$h_n = \sum_{k=0}^{\infty} f_k g_{n-k} \tag{B-18b}$$

Expressions (B-18) represent a convolution sum whose z-transform expression, (B-17d), is analogous to the Laplace-transform expression of convolution integrals. Convolution sums of the forms of (B-17b) and (B-18) play an important role in sampled-data control systems. This will be discussed later in Secs. B-5 and B-6.

6. Complex Convolution

Consider the product

$$p(t) = f(t + \lambda T)\, g(t + \nu T), \qquad \lambda \geq 0, \quad \nu \geq 0. \tag{B-19a}$$

Using (B-2), (B-3), (B-7), and (B-9), we obtain

$$\mathcal{P}(z) = \mathcal{Z}[f(t+\lambda T)\, g(t + \nu T)]$$

$$= \frac{1}{2\pi j} \oint_{\mathcal{C}_g} \mathcal{G}(\xi, \nu)\, \mathcal{F}\left(\frac{z}{\xi}, \lambda\right) \xi^{-1}\, d\xi, \qquad |z| \geq e^{(\beta_f + \beta_g)T} \tag{B-19b}$$

$$= \frac{1}{2\pi j} \oint_{\mathcal{C}_f} \mathcal{G}\left(\frac{z}{\xi}, \nu\right) \mathcal{F}(\xi, \lambda)\, \xi^{-1} d\xi, \qquad |z| \geq e^{(\beta_f + \beta_g)T} \tag{B-19c}$$

where $|z| \geq e^{\beta_f T}$ and $|z| \geq e^{\beta_g T}$ are the regions in which $\mathcal{F}(z,m) = \mathcal{Z}_A[f(t)]$ and $\mathcal{G}(z,m) = \mathcal{Z}_A[g(t)]$ respectively are analytic and where

$\mathcal{C}_g$ and $\mathcal{C}_f$ are any counterclockwise paths in $|\xi| > e^{\beta_g T}$ and $|\xi| > e^{\beta_f T}$ respectively.

7. Initial Value Relations

From (B-2) and (B-3) we immediately have

$$\begin{aligned} g(mT^+) &= \lim_{z \to \infty} \mathcal{G}(z,m) \\ g(0^+) &= \lim_{z \to \infty} \mathcal{G}(z) \end{aligned} \tag{B-20}$$

8. Asymptotic Behavior

From the discussion in Sec. B-3, we can show that if $\mathcal{G}(z,m)$ is analytic in $|z| \geq 1$, then

$$\lim_{k \to \infty} g\big((m + k)T^+\big) = 0 \tag{B-21}$$

Moreover, we can show that if $\mathcal{G}(z,m)$ is not analytic in $|z| > 1$, then if $\mathcal{G}(z,m)$ has a pole at $|z| > 1$, we have

$$\left| g\big((m + k)T^+\big) \right| \to \infty \qquad \text{for some } k \tag{B-22)*}$$

These asymptotic properties are of importance in the study of linear discrete systems, as we shall see below.

9. Final Value Relation

One case of practical importance not covered by the asymptotic expressions above is that for which $\mathcal{G}(z,m)$ has a pole at $z = 1$. In this case, if $(z-1)\mathcal{G}(z,m)$ is analytic in $|z| \geq 1$, we have

$$\lim_{z \to 1} (z - 1)\mathcal{G}(z,m) = \lim_{N \to \infty} g\big((m + N)T^+\big) \tag{B-23}$$

This can be proved by considering the advanced z-transform for $g(t + T) - g(t)$. (Show this.)

*Usually $\left|g\big((m + k)T^+\big)\right| \to \infty$ as $k \to \infty$.

B-5 The Advanced z-Transform and the Laplace Transform

A frequently used alternate expression for the advanced z-transform may be obtained from (B-2); here the advanced z-transform is expressed in terms of a Laplace transform.

We recall that a $g(t)$ satisfying (B-1) has a Laplace transform $G(s)$ that is absolutely convergent for $\Re e\ s \geq \alpha$. Furthermore, the inverse of $G(s)$ will be given by*

$$\frac{1}{2\pi j}\int_{C-j\infty}^{C+j\infty} e^{pt}G(p)\,dp = \begin{cases} \frac{1}{2}[g(t^+) + g(t^-)], & t > 0 \\ \frac{1}{2}g(0^+), & t = 0 \\ 0, & t < 0 \end{cases} \qquad \text{(B-24)}$$

where $C \geq \alpha$.

It will be assumed now that $g(t)$ is continuous at $t = (k+m)T$ $(k = 1, 2, 3, \ldots)$ but not necessarily at $t = mT$ $(m \geq 0)$. Setting (B-24) in (B-2) and with $z = e^{sT}$, we obtain

$$\mathcal{G}(e^{sT},m) = \frac{1}{2\pi j}\sum_{k=0}^{\infty}\int_{C-j\infty}^{C+j\infty} G(p)e^{mTp+(p-s)Tk}\,dp + \frac{1}{2}[g(mT^+) - g(mT^-)]$$

$$m \geq 0, \quad \alpha \leq C < \Re e\ s \qquad \text{(B-25)}$$

Under the conditions given, the interchanging of the summation and integration is permissible; then summing under the integration sign leads to

$$\mathcal{G}(e^{sT},m) = \frac{1}{2\pi j}\int_{C-j\infty}^{C+j\infty} G(p)\frac{e^{mTp}\,dp}{1-e^{(p-s)T}} + \frac{1}{2}[g(mT^+) - g(mT^-)] \qquad \text{(B-26)}$$

$$m \geq 0, \quad \alpha \leq C < \Re e\ s$$

The corresponding z-transform is therefore

$$\mathcal{G}(e^{sT}) = \frac{1}{2\pi j}\int_{C-j\infty}^{C+j\infty} \frac{G(p)\,dp}{1-e^{(p-s)T}} + \frac{1}{2}g(0^+) \qquad \text{(B-27)}$$

*[D8], p. 212.

Now, the above $G(s)$ is analytic in $\Re\text{e}\ s \geq \alpha$. The only singularities of the integrand of (B-26) and (B-27) in the region are simple poles at $p = s + j\dfrac{2\pi n}{T}$, $n = 0, \pm 1, \pm 2, \ldots$. Therefore, using the residue theorem [K17] on (B-26) and (B-27), we have

$$\mathcal{G}(e^{sT},m) = \frac{1}{T} \sum_{n=-\infty}^{\infty} G\left(s + j\frac{2\pi}{T}n\right) e^{(sT + j2\pi n)m} + \frac{1}{2}[g(mT^{+}) - g(mT^{-})]$$

$$\Re\text{e}\ s > \alpha, \qquad 0 \leq m < 1 \qquad \text{(B-28a)*}$$

and, for $m = 0$,

$$\mathcal{G}(e^{sT}) = \frac{1}{T} \sum_{n=-\infty}^{\infty} G\left(s + j\frac{2\pi}{T}n\right) + \frac{1}{2}g(0^{+}), \quad \Re\text{e}\ s > \alpha \qquad \text{(B-28b)}$$

Another interesting relation can be derived between $\mathcal{G}(z,m)$ and $G(s)$. Because of the assumptions made on $g(t)$ (in Sec. B-2), it follows from Eq. (B-2) that

$$\begin{aligned}\lim_{T\to 0} T\mathcal{G}(e^{sT},m) &= \lim_{T\to 0} \sum_{k=0}^{\infty} g\big(mT^{+} + (kT)\big) e^{-s(kT)}T \\ &= \int_0^{\infty} e^{-sT} g(t)\,dt \qquad \text{(B-29)} \\ &= G(s), \quad \Re\text{e}\ s \geq \alpha\end{aligned}$$

Since the operation in (B-29) is independent of m, it is equally valid if $\mathcal{G}(z)$ is used instead of $\mathcal{G}(z,m)$.

B-6 Linear Difference Equations with Constant Coefficients

A linear difference equation with constant coefficients can be written as

$$\sum_{i=0}^{n} a_i y_{k+i} = \sum_{i=0}^{m} b_i e_{k+i} \qquad \text{(B-30)}$$

*The validity of using the residue theorem on the integral in (B-26) requires that $0 \leq m < 1$.

where $\{e_i\}$ is a given input sequence and $\{y_i\}$ is the unknown output sequence. To solve (B-30), we take the z-transform of both sides. Using the shifting property (B-14b), we have

$$\left(\sum_{i=0}^{n} a_i z^i\right)\mathcal{Y}(z) - \sum_{i=1}^{n}\sum_{j=0}^{i-1} y_j z^{i-j} = \left(\sum_{i=0}^{m} b_i z^i\right)\mathcal{E}(z) - \sum_{i=1}^{m}\sum_{j=0}^{i-1} e_j z^{i-j}$$

or

$$\mathcal{Y}(z) = \mathcal{G}(z)\,\mathcal{E}(z) + \mathcal{Y}_0(z) \qquad \text{(B-31a)}$$

where

$$\mathcal{G}(z) = \frac{\sum_{i=0}^{m} b_i z^i}{\sum_{i=0}^{n} a_i z^i} \qquad \text{(B-31b)}$$

and

$$\mathcal{Y}_0(z) = \frac{\sum_{i=1}^{n}\sum_{j=0}^{i-1} y_j z^{i-j} - \sum_{i=1}^{m}\sum_{j=0}^{i-1} e_j z^{i-j}}{\sum_{i=0}^{n} a_i z^i} \qquad \text{(B-31c)}$$

Here $\mathcal{G}(z)$ may be viewed as the transfer function in the z-domain between the input sequence $\{e_k\}$ and the output sequence $\{y_k\}$; also, $\mathcal{Y}_0(z)$ is the output response due to the initial values of the sequences. The system given by (B-31) may be viewed as a linear discrete system, and we may note the analogy between the z-transform of a discrete system and the Laplace transform of a linear continuous system.

The output sequence $\{y_k\}$ can be obtained by the inverse z-transform of $\mathcal{Y}(z)$.

From (B-31b) and (B-31c), we see that $\mathcal{G}(z)$ and $\mathcal{Y}_0(z)$ have the same poles. It follows that we can infer the stability of the linear system (B-30) from the location of these poles when there is no input.

The system (B-30) is said to be *output stable* if with $e_k = 0$ for all k, $\lim_{k \to \infty} y_k = 0$ for every set of initial conditions $\{y_0, y_1, \ldots, y_{n-1}\}$, and that $|y_k|$ is finite for all k. With this definition, we can then show from (B-21), (B-22), and (B-31) that

◆◆Theorem B-2. The linear discrete system (B-30) is output stable if and only if all poles of $\mathcal{G}(z)$ lie in $|z| < 1$.◆◆

B-7 Linear Sampled-Data Systems

The dynamic behavior of many discrete systems, such as computer-controlled systems, can be represented in terms of linear continuous elements being excited by "samplers." For a sampler input $e(t)$, the sampler output $e^*(t)$ is defined as

$$e^*(t) \triangleq \sum_{k=0}^{\infty} e(kT^+)\, \mu_0(t - kT) \tag{B-32}$$

where $\mu_0(t)$ represents the unit impulse. This is indicated in Fig. B-1a. The sampler-output $e^*(t)$ will excite a linear element such that the output of the linear element becomes

$$y(t) = y_0(t) + \sum_{k=0}^{\infty} e(kT^+)\, g(t - kT) \tag{B-33}$$

where $y_0(t)$ is the initial-condition response and $g(t)$ is the unit-impulse response of the linear element.

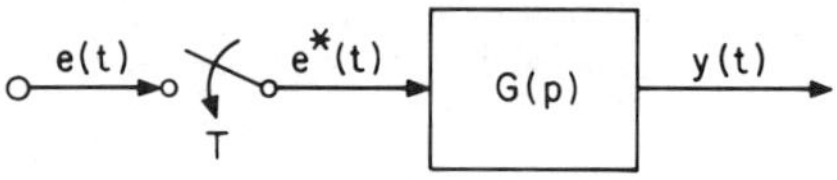

Fig. B-1a. An open-loop sampled-data system.

Using the real convolution property (B-17), the advanced z-transform of the expression in (B-33) becomes

$$\mathcal{Y}(z,m) = \mathcal{Y}_0(z,m) + \mathcal{E}(z)\mathcal{G}(z,m) \tag{B-34}$$

For a closed-loop sampled-data system illustrated in Fig. B-1b, we have the additional relation $e(t) = r(t) - y(t)$ which has the advanced z-transform

$$\mathcal{E}(z,m) = \mathcal{R}(z,m) - \mathcal{Y}(z,\, m) \tag{B-35}$$

Since $\mathcal{E}(z,0) = \mathcal{E}(z)$, $\mathcal{R}(z,0) = \mathcal{R}(z)$, and $\mathcal{Y}_0(z,0) = \mathcal{Y}_0(z)$, we obtain from (B-34) and (B-35)

$$\mathcal{E}(z) = \frac{\mathcal{R}(z) - \mathcal{Y}_0(z)}{1 + \mathcal{G}(z)} \tag{B-36}$$

Using this in (B-34), we obtain for the output

$$\mathcal{Y}(z,m) = \frac{\mathcal{Y}_0(z,m)}{1+\mathcal{G}(z)} + \frac{\mathcal{G}(z)\,\mathcal{Y}_0(z,m) - \mathcal{G}(z,m)\,\mathcal{Y}_0(z)}{1+\mathcal{G}(z)} + \frac{\mathcal{G}(z,m)}{1+\mathcal{G}(z)}\,\mathcal{R}(z) \tag{B-37a}$$

For the special case $m = 0$, we have

$$\mathcal{Y}(z) = \frac{\mathcal{Y}_0(z)}{1+\mathcal{G}(z)} + \frac{\mathcal{G}(z)}{1+\mathcal{G}(z)}\,\mathcal{R}(z) \tag{B-37b}$$

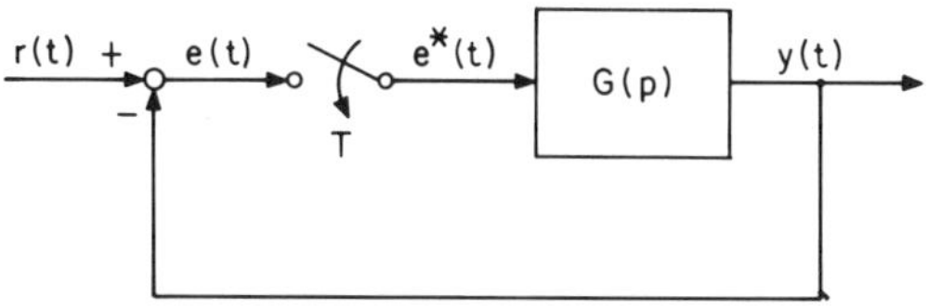

Fig. B-1b. A closed-loop sampled-data system.

From (B-34) or (B-37a), we can obtain the output-response $y(t) = y\big((m+k)T^+\big)$ of the open-loop and closed-loop system respectively by taking the inverse transform of $\mathcal{Y}(z,m)$. If we are only interested in the response at sampling instants $t = kT^+$, then (B-37b) can be used.

For stability analysis of linear sampled-data systems, we may investigate the asymptotic behavior of $y(t)$. Analogous to the definition given in Sec. B-5 we say that a linear sampled data system is *output stable with respect to* m if $\lim_{k\to\infty} y\big((m+k)T^+\big) = 0$ for every set of initial conditions and for the given value of m, when the system is unforced (i.e., $e(t) \equiv 0$ for the open-loop system and $r(t) \equiv 0$ for the closed-loop system), provided that $|y\big((m+k)T^+\big)| < \infty$ for every k.

Analogous to Theorem B-2, we then have from (B-21) and (B-37a)

♦♦Theorem B-3. The closed-loop sampled-data system of Fig. B-1b is output stable with respect to m if, for that m, the expression

$$\frac{\mathcal{Y}_0(z,m)}{1+\mathcal{G}(z)} + \frac{\mathcal{G}(z)\,\mathcal{Y}_0(z,m) - \mathcal{G}(z,m)\,\mathcal{Y}_0(z)}{1+\mathcal{G}(z)}$$

is analytic in $|z| \geq 1$.♦♦

When the linear element is given by an ordinary differential equation, then we can prove the following.

♦♦Theorem B-4. Consider a closed-loop sampled-data system in the form of Fig. B-1b. Let the linear element of the system be given by an ordinary time-invariant linear differential equation, whose states are completely controllable and completely observable (see Chap. 3).

1) The system will be output stable with respect to $m = 0$ if all zeros of $1 + \mathcal{G}(z) = 0$ lie in $|z| < 1$. If any of these zeros lie in $|z| > 1$, the system will not be output stable with respect to $m = 0$.
2) The system will be output stable with respect to every m if all poles of $\mathcal{G}(z,m)/[1 + \mathcal{G}(z)]$ lie in $|z| < 1$ for every m. If any of these poles lies in $|z| > 1$, then the system will not be output stable with respect to every m.
3) If all poles of $\mathcal{G}(z,m)/[1 + \mathcal{G}(z)]$ lie in $|z| < 1$ for every m, then the origin of the state space representing the system will be asymptotically stable. If any of these poles lies in $|z| > 1$ then the origin will be unstable. ♦♦

In Theorem B-4, Case 3 implies Case 2. Case 1 is a special case of Case 2. The requirement in (1) guarantees only that the output variable approaches 0 with time during sampling instants. The additional requirements in (2) and (3) preclude any possibility of "hidden oscillation" which can occur if the linear element is unstable; then it is possible that with sampled-data feedback, the system output is well behaved at the sampling instants but swings to significant amplitudes between the sampling instants. Hidden oscillation will not occur if the linear element is stable.

Observe, however, that the origin of the state space of the closed-loop sampled-data system may be asymptotically stable even if the linear element is unstable. This will be so if (i) all zeros of $1 + \mathcal{G}(z) = 0$ lie in $|z| < 1$ and (ii) the poles of $\mathcal{G}(z) = \mathcal{G}(z,0)$ are identical to those of $\mathcal{G}(z,m)$ for every m. The last condition is almost always satisfied.

Appendix C

Mathematical Background of Chapters 10 and 11

C-1 Important Mathematical Terms and Relations Used*

1. Classes of Functions in $\mathfrak{L}_1$ and $\mathfrak{L}_2$

This notation is finding increasing use in the engineering literature.

A function $f(x)$ is said to belong to the class $\mathfrak{L}_1$ on $[a, b]$ or $\mathfrak{L}_2$ on $[a, b]$ if $\int_a^b |f(x)|\,dx < \infty$ or $\int_a^b |f(x)|^2\,dx < \infty$, respectively. We write: "$f(x) \in \mathfrak{L}_1$ on $[a, b]$" or "$f(x) \in \mathfrak{L}_2$ on $[a, b]$."

Strictly speaking, it should be required that $f(x)$ is *measurable*, a property usually satisfied in functions related to the physical world. If the interval $[a, b]$ is finite, then a function that belongs to $\mathfrak{L}_2$ on $[a, b]$ also belongs to $\mathfrak{L}_1$ on $[a, b]$. However, this is not necessarily true if the range $[a, b]$ is infinite.

2. Schwarz's Inequality

If $f(x)$ and $g(x)$ both belong to $\mathfrak{L}_2$ on $[a, b]$, then $f(x)\,g(x)$ belongs to $\mathfrak{L}_1$ on $[a, b]$ and

$$\int_a^b |f(x)\,g(x)|\,dx \le \left[\left(\int_a^b |f(x)|^2\,dx\right)\left(\int_a^b |g(x)|^2\,dx\right)\right]^{\frac{1}{2}}$$

*See [W5].

3. Minkowski's Inequality

If $f(x)$ and $g(x)$ both belong to $\mathfrak{L}_2$ on $[a, b]$, then so does $f(x) + g(x)$, and

$$\int_a^b |f(x) + g(x)|^2\, dx \le \left[\left(\int_a^b |f(x)|^2\, dx\right)^{\frac{1}{2}} + \left(\int_a^b |g(x)|^2\, dx\right)^{\frac{1}{2}}\right]^2$$

4. Plancherel's Theorem

If $f(t)$ belongs to $\mathfrak{L}_2$ on $(-\infty, \infty)$ then the function*

$$F(j\omega) = \underset{A\to\infty}{\text{l.i.m.}} \int_{-A}^{A} e^{-j\omega t} f(t)\, dt$$

known as the Fourier transform of $f(t)$, exists and also belongs to $\mathfrak{L}_2$. Moreover,

$$\frac{1}{2\pi}\int_{-\infty}^{\infty} |F(j\omega)|^2\, d\omega = \int_{-\infty}^{\infty} |f(t)|^2\, dt$$

and

$$f(t) = \underset{A\to\infty}{\text{l.i.m.}} \frac{1}{2\pi}\int_{-A}^{A} e^{j\omega t} F(j\omega)\, d\omega$$

Plancherel's theorem represents one of the most fundamental theorems concerning Fourier transforms.

5. Parseval's Theorem

If $F_1(j\omega)$ and $F_2(j\omega)$ are Fourier transforms of real functions $f_1(t)$ and $f_2(t)$ respectively, then

$$\int_{-\infty}^{\infty} f_1(t) f_2(t)\, dt = \frac{1}{2\pi}\int_{-\infty}^{\infty} F_1(j\omega) F_2(-j\omega)\, d\omega$$

*The notation "l.i.m." means "limit in the mean." We say l.i.m. $f_n(t) = f(t)$ on $[a, b]$ if $\lim_{n\to\infty} \int_a^b |f_n(t) - f(t)|^2\, dt = 0$. See [W5] pp. 27-28.

6. Boundedness of Solution of the Basic Feedback System (10-1)

♦♦Lemma C-1. For any set of initial conditions of the basic feedback system (10–1), whose linear element is output-stable and, for whose nonlinear element, condition (10–3) holds, the solution $u(t)$ is bounded for all *finite* time, i.e., for $0 \leq t < \infty$.♦♦

We will sketch a proof of this lemma. Note first that condition (10–3) implies that there exists a nondecreasing function $h(|e|)$ such that

$$|u(t)| = |\mathfrak{F}[e(t), t]| \leq h\left(|e(t)|\right) < \infty \quad \text{for} \quad |e(t)| < \infty \tag{C-1}$$

From (10–1), we can write the following inequality

$$|e(t)| \leq |e_0(t)| + \int_0^t |g(t - \tau)|\,|u(\tau)|\,d\tau \tag{C-2}$$

Let us define bounds $e_m(t)$ and $u_m(t)$ as follows

$$\left.\begin{aligned} |e(\tau)| &\leq e_m(t) \\ |u(\tau)| &\leq u_m(t) \end{aligned}\right\} \quad \text{for} \quad 0 < \tau \leq t \tag{C-3}$$

Since the function $h(|e|)$ is defined to be nondecreasing, we have

$$u_m(t) = h\left(e_m(t)\right) < \infty \quad \text{if} \quad e_m(t) < \infty \tag{C-4}$$

Since the linear element is assumed to be output stable, we can define a constant c_0 and a function $G(t)$ such that

$$|e_0(t)| \leq c_0 \tag{C-5}$$

$$G(t) \triangleq \int_0^t |g(\tau)|\,d\tau \tag{C-6}$$

We will now show that for each c_0 there exists a time T_1 and bounds $u_m(t)$ for $0 \leq t \leq T_1$ such that

$$\left.\begin{aligned} |u(\tau)| &\leq u_m(t) = h\left(e_m(t)\right) \\ |e(\tau)| &\leq e_m(t) = c_0 + G(t)\,u_m(t), \end{aligned}\right. \quad 0 \leq \tau \leq t \leq T_1 \tag{C-7a}$$

From (C–7a), we can write

$$u_m(t) = h\left(e_m(t)\right) = \frac{e_m(t) - c_0}{G(t)}, \quad 0 \leq t \leq T_1 \tag{C-7b}$$

Since $G(0) = 0$ and $G(t)$ is a nondecreasing function and since $h(e_m(t)) < \infty$ for $e_m(t) < \infty$, it follows that there exists a time T_1 such that (C-7b) has a solution for $e_m(t)$. This is illustrated in Fig. C-1. It follows from (C-2), (C-4) to (C-6) and (C-7b) that

$$|e(\tau)| \leq c_0 + \frac{G(\tau)}{G(t)}[e_m(t) - c_0] \leq e_m(t)$$

$$|u(\tau)| \leq h\big(e_m(t)\big), \qquad 0 \leq \tau \leq t \leq T_1$$

In particular, for each c_0, there exist finite positive values T_1 and $e_m(T_1)$ such that

$$\begin{aligned} |e(t)| &\leq e_m(T_1) < \infty \\ |u(t)| &\leq h\big(e_m(T_1)\big) = u_m(T_1) < \infty, \qquad 0 \leq t \leq T_1 \end{aligned} \tag{C-8}$$

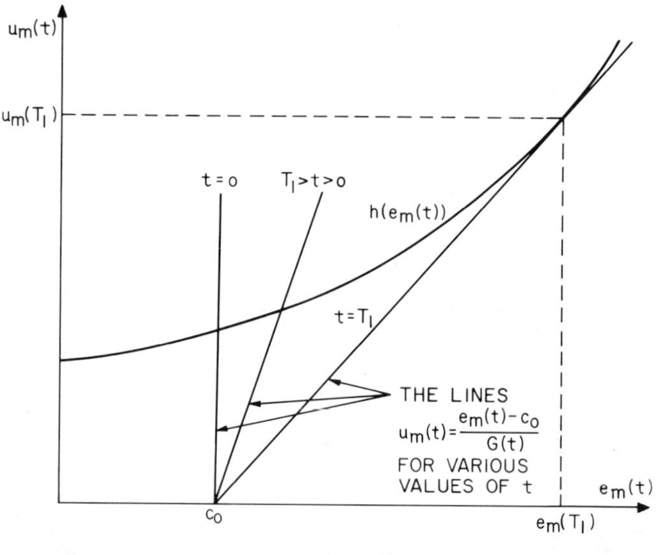

Fig. C-1 Construction showing a relationship between the bounds $e_m(t)$ and $u_m(t)$ defined in Eq. (C-3). There is always at least one value of time T_1 such that Inequality (C-7b) is satisfied in view of the fact that $G(t)$ defined in Eq. (C-6) is a nondecreasing function of t.

Repeating the same reasoning for successive intervals

$$[T_1, T_1 + T_2], \ldots, \left[\sum_{i=1}^{n-1} T_i, \sum_{i=1}^{n} T_i\right], \ldots,$$

we can show that for $\sum_{i=1}^{n-1} T_i \le t \le \sum_{i=1}^{n} T_i$, $n = 1, 2, 3, \ldots$

$$
\begin{aligned}
|e(t)| &\le e_m\left(\sum_{i=1}^{n} T_i\right) < \infty \\
|u(t)| &\le h\left(e_m\left(\sum_{i=1}^{n} T_i\right)\right) = u_m\left(\sum_{i=1}^{n} T_i\right) < \infty;
\end{aligned}
\tag{C-9}
$$

As for $n = 0$ the validity of (C-9) is based on the finiteness of bounds c_n on the "initial-condition responses" $e_{0n}(t_n)$ of the system obtained by time-shifting the original system (10-1) by $t_n = t - \sum_{i=1}^{n} T_i$. It can be shown (exercise for the reader) that these bounds are given by

$$
\begin{aligned}
c_n &= c_{n-1} + u_m\left(\sum_{i=1}^{n} T_i\right) G(\infty) \\
&= c_0 + G(\infty) \sum_{i=1}^{n} u_m\left(\sum_{j=1}^{i} T_j\right); \qquad n = 1, 2, 3, \ldots
\end{aligned}
\tag{C-10}
$$

Since each $u_m\left(\sum_{i=1}^{n} T_i\right) < \infty$, we have for each finite number n of intervals $T_i (i = 1, \ldots, n)$ a finite value c_n by (C-10). This provides the basis for (C-9) to hold for finite n, i.e., $|e(t)| < \infty$, $|u(t)| < \infty$ for $0 \le t < \infty$.

C-2 Proof of Lemma 10-1

Let $|e^{\alpha t} u(t)| \ge \epsilon_k > 0$ for a countably infinite set of intervals $t_k \le t \le t_k + \delta_k$, $0 \le \delta_k < t_{k+1} - t_k < \infty$, and $t \ge t_0$, where $k = 0, 1, 2, \ldots$; then

$$
\int_{t_0}^{\infty} [e^{\alpha t} u(t)]^2 \, dt \ge \lim_{N \to \infty} \sum_{k=0}^{N-1} \epsilon_k^2 \delta_k = \infty \quad \text{if} \quad \sum_{k=0}^{\infty} \epsilon_k^2 \delta_k \quad \text{diverges}
$$

This contradicts the assumption of the lemma. Therefore, in order for $\int_0^{\infty} [e^{\alpha t} u(t)]^2 \, dt < \infty$, it is necessary either that $e^{\alpha t} u(t) \to 0$ for

$t \to \infty$, or that the products $\epsilon_k^2 \delta_k > 0$ constitute a sequence of diminishing values such that the series $\sum_{k=0}^{\infty} \epsilon_k^2 \delta_k$ converges. This implies that the "pulse-areas" $\epsilon_k \delta_k$ must approach 0 with $k \to \infty$, i.e., it can be that $u(t) \neq 0$ for $t \to \infty$ only in (infinitesimal) neighborhoods of countably infinite values of t.

Thus, if $u(t)$ does not go to 0 for all $t \to \infty$, then $u(t)$ can be only represented in terms of an infinite sequence of pulses of diminishing pulse-areas $a_k > \epsilon_k \delta_k$ such that the series $\sum_{k=0}^{\infty} \epsilon_k^2 \delta_k$ converges. This means that there exists a positive number T such that

$$|e^{\alpha t} u(t + T)| \leq \sum_{k=0}^{\infty} a_k \left[\mu_{-1}(t - t_k) - \mu_{-1}(t - t_k - \delta_k)\right] \quad \text{for} \quad t \geq T$$

where $\mu_{-1}(t)$ is the unit-step function. For the response of the linear element to this signal $u(t + T)$, we can then write

$$|e^{\alpha t} e(t + T)| \leq \sum_{k=0}^{\infty} G_{\alpha k}(t - t_k)$$

where

$$G_{\alpha k}(t) \triangleq \int_{t-t_k-\delta_k}^{t-t_k} a_k \, |e^{\alpha \tau} g(\tau)| \, d\tau$$

We note that, because of the output stability of the linear element (Conditions (10-9)), we have

$$G_{\alpha k}(t) \to 0 \begin{cases} \text{for } t - t_k \to \infty, & \delta_k > 0, & \text{and} & a_k > 0 \\ \text{for } t - t_k > 0, & \delta_k \to 0, & \text{and} & a_k > 0 \\ \text{for } t - t_k > 0, & \delta_k > 0, & \text{and} & a_k \to 0 \end{cases}$$

Therefore, since we have already established that the product $a_k \delta_k \to 0$ as $k \to \infty$, it follows that

$$\lim_{t\to\infty} |e^{\alpha t} e(t + T)| = \lim_{t\to\infty} |e^{\alpha t} e(t)| = 0$$

Thus, Lemma 10-1 is proved.

C-3 Proof of the Fundamental Theorem of Chapter 10 (Theorem 10-1)

The proof consists of showing that for the system with the given restrictions, condition (10-19) is sufficient for (10-10) to hold with $\alpha = 0$, i.e., for every set of initial conditions, we have

$$\int_0^\infty u^2(t)\,dt < \infty$$

When this is satisfied, then the system is control asymptotic, moreover, from the conditions of Theorem 10-1 and from Lemma 10-2, the system is also output asymptotic. Let us define the following truncated functions

$$u_T(t) = \begin{cases} u(t), & 0 \le t \le T \\ 0, & t < 0,\ t > T \end{cases}$$
$$e_{0T}(t) = \begin{cases} e_0(t), & 0 \le t \le T \\ 0, & t < 0,\ t > T \end{cases} \tag{C-11}$$

where T is some finite value of time and $e_0(t)$ is the initial-condition response of the linear element due to a given set of initial conditions. Let the linear element of our system be excited by these functions. Then, its output, $-e_T(t)$, will be given by

$$e_T(t) = e_{0T}(t) - \int_0^T g(t-\tau)\,u_T(\tau)\,d\tau \tag{C-12}$$

where $g(t)$ represents the unit impulse of the linear element.

By the conditions of Theorem 10-1 and by (10-9) and (C-11) with $\alpha = 0$, $e_{0T}(t)$ and $g(t)$ are both square-integrable functions over $0 \le t \le \infty$, i.e., $e_{0T}(t) \in \mathfrak{L}_2$ and $g(t) \in \mathfrak{L}_2$.* The same is true for $u_T(t)$ as defined in (C-11) because of its truncated nature, and the boundedness of $u(t)$ for finite time (Lemma C-1); i.e., $u_T(t) \in \mathfrak{L}_2$. Therefore, by Plancherel's theorem,* the three functions $e_{0T}(t)$, $g(t)$ and $u(t)$ have Fourier transforms $E_{0T}(j\omega)$, $G(j\omega)$, and $U_T(j\omega)$, respectively,

*See Sec. C-1.

each of which belongs to $\mathcal{L}_2$. The Fourier transform of (C-12) is

$$E_T(j\omega) = E_{0T}(j\omega) - G(j\omega)U_T(j\omega) \qquad \text{(C-13)*}$$

Let us now introduce the following integral

$$I = \frac{1}{2\pi}\int_{-\infty}^{\infty}\left[\frac{1}{K} - \delta + \mathcal{R}e[(1 + j\omega q)G(j\omega)]\right]|U_T(j\omega)|^2\,d\omega \qquad \text{(C-14a)}$$

$$= \frac{1}{2\pi}\int_{-\infty}^{\infty}\left[\frac{1}{K} - \delta + (1 + j\omega q)G(j\omega)\right]|U_T(j\omega)|^2\,d\omega \qquad \text{(C-14b)}$$

where $\delta > 0$. The two expressions (C-14a) and (C-14b) are equivalent because the imaginary part of $(1 + j\omega q)G(j\omega)$ is an odd function of ω; hence, its integral over $-\infty \leq \omega \leq \infty$ vanishes.

The Popov condition (10-19) of Theorem 10-1 implies that $I \geq 0$; that is,**

$$I \geq 0 \qquad \text{if (10-19) is satisfied} \qquad \text{(C-15)}$$

Considering that $|U_T(j\omega)|^2 = U_T(j\omega)U_T(-j\omega)$ and using (C-13) in (C-14b) yields

$$I = \frac{1}{2\pi}\int_{-\infty}^{\infty}\left[\left(\frac{1}{K} - \delta\right)U_T(j\omega) - (1 + j\omega q)E_T(j\omega) + (1 + j\omega q)E_{0T}(j\omega)\right]U_T(-j\omega)\,d\omega \qquad \text{(C-16)}$$

*To show that $E_T(j\omega) \in \mathcal{L}_2$, we note first from (C-11) and Lemma C-1 that

$$|U_T(j\omega)| = \left|\int_0^T e^{-j\omega t}u(t)\,dt\right| \leq \int_0^T |u(t)|\,dt < \infty$$

Therefore

$$\int_{-\infty}^{\infty}|G(j\omega)U_T(j\omega)|^2\,d\omega \leq \left[\int_0^T |u(t)|\,dt\right]^2 \int_{-\infty}^{\infty}|G(j\omega)|^2\,d\omega$$

Since $G(j\omega) \in \mathcal{L}_2$, then $G(j\omega)U_T(j\omega) \in \mathcal{L}_2$. Finally, because $E_{0T}(j\omega) \in \mathcal{L}_2$, it follows from (C-13) and Minkowski's inequality (see Sec. C-1) that $E_T(j\omega) \in \mathcal{L}_2$.

**We can write (10-19) as

$$\frac{1}{K} - \delta + \mathcal{R}e\left[(1 + j\omega q)G(j\omega)\right] \geq 0.$$

Theorem 10-1 requires that this inequality be satisfied only for $\omega \geq 0$. However, because of the basic property of Fourier transforms that $\mathcal{R}e\,G(-j\omega) = \mathcal{R}e\,G(j\omega)$ and $\mathcal{I}m\,G(-j\omega) = -\mathcal{I}m\,G(j\omega)$, it follows that the lhs of the above inequality (or the rhs of (C-14a)) will be unchanged if ω is replaced by $-\omega$. Hence if the above inequality is satisfied for $\omega \geq 0$ then it follows from (C-14a) that $I \geq 0$.

Using Parseval's relation on (C-16) yields

$$I = \int_0^\infty \left[\left(\frac{1}{K} - \delta\right)u_T(t) - e_T(t) - q\dot{e}_T(t) + e_{0T}(t) + q\dot{e}_{0T}(t)\right] u_T(t)\,dt \tag{C-17}$$

Note from (C-11) and (C-12) that

$$e_T(t) = e(t) \quad \text{for} \quad 0 \le t \le T \tag{C-18}$$

Therefore, we can write

$$I = \int_0^T \left[\left(\frac{1}{K} - \delta\right)u(t) - e(t)\right] u(t)\,dt - q\int_0^T \dot{e}(t)\,u(t)\,dt$$
$$+ \int_0^T \left[e_0(t) + q\dot{e}_0(t)\right] u(t)\,dt \tag{C-19}$$

If the Popov condition (10-19) holds, then, because of (C-15), we obtain from (C-19)

$$\int_0^T \left[e(t) - \left(\frac{1}{K} - \delta\right)u(t)\right] u(t)\,dt + q\int_0^T u(t)\,\dot{e}(t)\,dt$$
$$\le \int_0^T \left[e_0(t) + q\dot{e}_0(t)\right] u(t)\,dt \tag{C-20}$$

Now, from the requirements in Theorem 10-1, we have $(u/e) \in [0, K]$. Therefore, since $0 \le K \le \infty$, we have

$$\left[e - \left(\frac{1}{K} - \delta\right)u\right]u \ge u^2\,\delta \tag{C-21}$$

Using (C-21) on the lhs and Schwarz's inequality on the rhs of (C-20) and then multiplying both sides of (C-20) by $1/\delta$ yields

$$\int_0^T u^2(t)\,dt + q\,\frac{1}{\delta}\int_0^T u(t)\,\dot{e}(t)\,dt \le \frac{1}{\delta}\int_0^T \left[e_0(t) + q\dot{e}_0(t)\right] u(t)\,dt$$
$$\le \frac{1}{\delta}\left(\int_0^T \left[e_0(t) + q\dot{e}_0(t)\right]^2 dt\right)^{\frac{1}{2}} \left(\int_0^T u^2(t)\,dt\right)^{\frac{1}{2}}$$

or

$$J_u^2(T) - q\frac{1}{\delta}I_\Gamma(T) \leq \frac{1}{\delta}J_0(T)\,J_u(T) \tag{C-22}$$

where

$$J_u(T) \triangleq \left(\int_0^T u^2(t)\,dt\right)^{\frac{1}{2}} \tag{C-23a}$$

$$I_\Gamma(T) \triangleq -\int_0^T u(t)\,\dot{e}(t)\,dt = -\int_{\Gamma\; e(0)}^{e(T)} u(t)\,de(t) \tag{C-23b}$$

and

$$J_0(T) \triangleq \left(\int_0^T \left[e_0(t) + q\dot{e}_0(t)\right]^2 dt\right)^{\frac{1}{2}} \tag{C-23c}$$

where $I_\Gamma(T)$ represents the line integral over the path Γ representing the functional relation $u(t) = \mathcal{F}[e(t), t]$ for $0 \leq t \leq T$, and $J_0(T)$ depends only on the set of initial conditions.

We seek to find the conditions for control asymptoticity, i.e., the conditions for which $J_u(T) < \infty$ for $T = \infty$. Adding the (positive) quantity $[J_0(T)/2\delta]^2$ to both sides of (C-22) gives

$$\left[J_u(T) - \frac{1}{2\delta}J_0(T)\right]^2 - q\frac{1}{\delta}I_\Gamma(T) \leq \frac{1}{4\delta^2}J_0^2(T) \tag{C-24}$$

Note from (C-23) that $J_0(T) \leq J_0(\infty)$. Therefore, from (C-24), we have

$$\left[J_u(T) - \frac{1}{2\delta}J_0(T)\right]^2 - q\frac{1}{\delta}I_\Gamma(T) \leq \frac{1}{4\delta^2}J_0^2(\infty)$$

Since the rhs of the above inequality is independent of T, the lhs holds for every T including $T = \infty$. Thus, we can write

$$\left[J_u(\infty) - \frac{1}{2\delta}J_0(\infty)\right]^2 - q\frac{1}{\delta}I_\Gamma(\infty) \leq \frac{1}{4\delta^2}J_0^2(\infty) \tag{C-25}$$

Inequality (C-25) is of fundamental importance. By it, we can prove the individual cases in Theorem 10-1, corresponding to the different types of nonlinear elements. First, we shall note from (10-9), (C-23), and the use of Minkowski's inequality that, for every set of initial conditions

$$J_0(\infty) \leq \left(\int_0^\infty e_0^2(t)\,dt\right)^{\frac{1}{2}} + |q|\left(\int_0^\infty \dot{e}_0^2(t)\,dt\right)^{\frac{1}{2}} < \infty \qquad \text{(C-26)}$$

Thus, if we can show that the expression $-qI_\Gamma(\infty) \geq 0$, then it follows from (C-25) that $J_u(\infty) < \infty$, which defines control asymptoticity. Let us now consider the different cases considered in Theorem 10-1.

1. General Case: $q = 0,\ u(t) = \mathcal{F}[e(t), t]$

For $q = 0$, (C-25) reduces to

$$\left(J_u(\infty) - \frac{1}{2\delta} J_0(\infty)\right)^2 \leq \left(\frac{1}{2\delta} J_0(\infty)\right)^2$$

or, with (C-26) for $q = 0$

$$J_u(\infty) \leq \frac{1}{\delta} J_0(\infty) \leq \frac{1}{\delta}\left(\int_0^\infty e_0^2(t)\,dt\right)^{\frac{1}{2}} < \infty \qquad \text{(C-27)}$$

By Lemma 10-2, it now follows that both $u(t)$ and $e(t)$ are square integrable, which proves the case $q = 0$ in Theorem 10-1 is valid for the general functional relation $u(t) = \mathcal{F}[e(t), t]$.

2. Special Case: $0 \leq q < \infty$, Active Hysteresis or Time-Invariant Function $u(t) = \mathcal{F}[e(t)]$

Active hysteresis is defined by condition (10-4b) in Definition 10-2. Though it is not of practical importance, the results for this case will be used in the proof of the theorem for the more important cases of passive hysteresis and the single-valued function $u = f(e)$.

With (10-4b) and (C-23), inequality (C-25) becomes

$$\left[J_u(\infty) - \frac{1}{2\delta} J_0(\infty)\right]^2 + q\frac{1}{\delta}\int_{0\ \Gamma_0+\Gamma_\infty}^{e(\infty)} u(t)\,de(t)$$

$$\leq q\frac{1}{\delta}\int_{0\ \Gamma_0}^{e(0)} u(t)\,de(t) + \frac{1}{4\delta^2} J_0^2(\infty) \quad \text{(C-28)}$$

where Γ_0 is any one of the possible paths (no closed path) on the functional relation $u = \mathfrak{F}[e(t)]$ from 0 to $e(0)$ and Γ_∞ is any one possible path from $e(0)$ to $e(\infty)$. Because $(u/e) \in [0, K]$, both line integrals in (C-28) must be ≥ 0. Furthermore, the rhs of (C-28) depends only on the set of initial conditions and is finite. Therefore, the lhs of (C-28) is finite. Since it is also nonnegative, it follows that

$$J_u(\infty) < \infty \quad \text{and} \quad J_e(\infty) \triangleq \int_0^\infty e^2(t)\,dt < \infty \qquad \text{(C-29)*}$$

Thus, the system is both control and output asymptotic, which was to be shown.

A special subclass of the case of active hysteresis is the important class of single-valued functions** $u = f(e)$; we have thus also proved the part of Theorem 10-1 for single-valued functions and $0 \leq q < \infty$. The part of the proof for single-valued functions and $-\infty < q \leq 0$ will be presented next, as a subcase of that for passive hysteresis.

3. Special Case: $-\infty < q \leq 0$, Passive Hysteresis or Time-Invariant Function $u(t) = \mathfrak{F}[e(t)]$

If $0 < K < \infty$, then we can easily transform a system of the form (10-1) with passive hysteresis into an equivalent system of the same form (10-1) with active hysteresis, so that the results obtained for that case can be applied (see for example Fig. 10-2 p. 366). Let this transformation be defined by

$$u(t) = (K + \epsilon)e(t) - u_1(t) \qquad \text{(C-30)}$$

for some arbitrarily small $\epsilon > 0$.

*From (C-28) it actually follows that $J_u(\infty) < \infty$ and $|e(\infty)| < \infty$; however, because of the assumption in Theorem 10-1 that the linear element is output stable, control asymptoticity implies output asymptoticity (by Lemma 10-2).

**For single-valued functions $u = f(e)$, the paths Γ_0 and Γ_∞ of the line integrals in (C-28) are each unique.

This transformation is illustrated in Fig. C-2. The linear element of the transformed system is characterized by its transfer-function $G_1(s)$ and its initial-condition response, $e_{01}(t)$, given by

$$\mathcal{L}[g_1(t)] = G_1(s) = \frac{-G(s)}{1 + (K + \epsilon)G(s)} \tag{C-31a}$$

$$e_{01}(t) = e_0(t) + (K + \epsilon)\int_0^t g_1(t - \tau)e_0(\tau)d\tau \tag{C-31b}$$

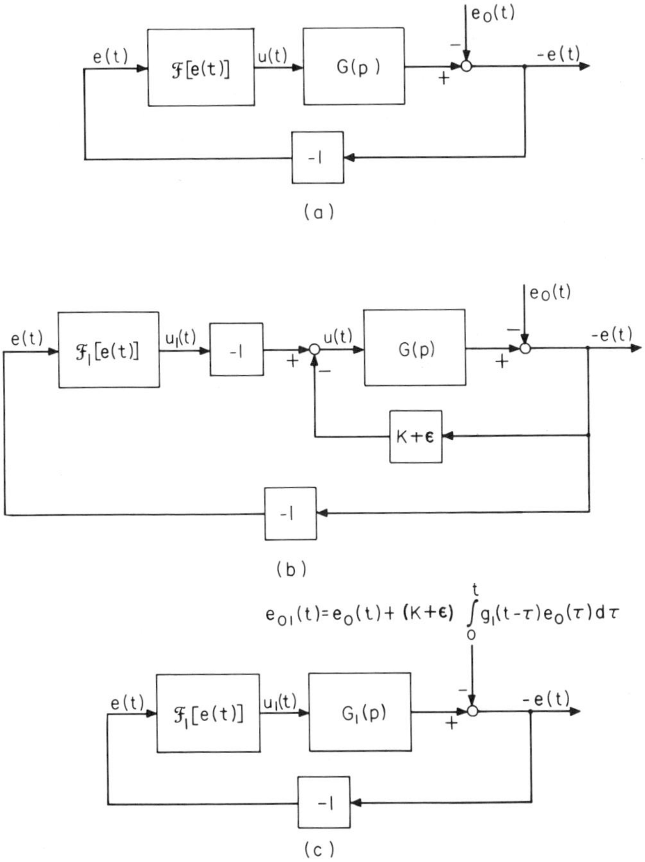

Fig. C-2 Transformation illustrating how a system with passive hysteresis can be converted into one with active hysteresis. (a) is the original system in which $\mathcal{F}[e(t)]$ is a nonlinear element with passive hysteresis. By Eq. (C-30) the system in (a) is changed to that in (b); By (C-31) it is further changed into that in (c). In both (b) and (c), the nonlinear element $\mathcal{F}_1[e(t)]$ has active hysteresis.

The Fourier transforms of these expressions are given by

$$G_1(j\omega) = \frac{-G(j\omega)}{1 + (K + \epsilon)G(j\omega)}, \qquad E_{01}(j\omega) = \frac{E_0(j\omega)}{1 + (K + \epsilon)G(j\omega)} \tag{C-32}$$

The following two lemmas hold:

♦♦Lemma C-2. If Theorem 10-1 holds for some value of q $(-\infty < q < \infty)$, then for a sufficiently small $\epsilon > 0$, the linear element obtained by transformation (C-30) has all of properties (10-9) for output stability except possibly for the condition $\int_0^\infty |g(t)|dt < \infty$.♦♦

Proof of Lemma C-2. Choose δ_1 such that $\delta > \delta_1 > 0$ and $(1/K) - \delta = [1/(K + \epsilon)] - \delta_1$. Because of the Popov condition (10-19), there exists a number $\mu > 0$ such that $|1 + (K + \epsilon)G(j\omega)| \geq \mu > 0$. Therefore, we obtain from (C-32) $|G_1(j\omega)| \leq \frac{1}{\mu}|G(j\omega)|$ and $|E_{01}(j\omega)| \leq \frac{1}{\mu}|E_0(j\omega)|$. Also, $|j\omega E_{01}(j\omega)| \leq \frac{1}{\mu}|j\omega E_0(j\omega)|$.

Since the original linear element is output stable, it follows from (10-9) and from Plancherel's theorem (see Sec. C-1) that the right sides of the above three inequalities are square-integrable over $-\infty \leq \omega \leq \infty$. The left sides are also, and it follows again from Plancherel's theorem that $g_1(t) \in \mathfrak{L}_2$, $e_{01}(t) \in \mathfrak{L}_2$, and $\dot{e}_{01}(t) \in \mathfrak{L}_2$ over $(0, \infty)$. The proof of the remaining condition follows from (C-31b) and Schwarz's inequality:

$$|e_{01}(t)| \leq |e_0(t)| + (K + \epsilon)\left(\int_0^\infty g_1^2(t)dt\right)^{\frac{1}{2}}\left(\int_0^\infty e_0^2(t)dt\right)^{\frac{1}{2}} < \infty$$

This expansion is finite because $g_1(t) \in \mathfrak{L}_2$ and the original element satisfies (10-9).

♦♦Lemma C-3. If the Popov condition (10-19) holds for $G(j\omega)$ with $q \leq 0$, then it will also hold for $G_1(j\omega)$, expressed in (C-32), with $q \geq 0$.*♦♦

Because of Lemmas C-2 and C-3, satisfying the requirements in Theorem 10-1 on the linear element of the original system implies the same for the transformed system. We must now investigate to what extent this holds for the nonlinear element. The answer is presented in the following lemma:

*It can be shown that if $(1/K) + \Re e[(1+j\omega q)G(j\omega)] \geq \delta > 0$, then $[1/(K+\epsilon)] + \Re e[(1-j\omega q)G_1(j\omega)] \geq \delta_1 > 0$, with δ and δ_1 as defined on this page (left as an exercise for the reader). From this, Lemma C-3 follows.

♦♦Lemma C-4. If the nonlinear element of the original system obeys $(u/e) \in [0, K]$, then the transformed element obeys $(u_1/e) \in [\epsilon, K + \epsilon]$. Moreover, transformation (C-30) transforms a nonlinear element with passive hysteresis into one with active hysteresis and vice versa, as defined in Definition 10-2.♦♦

The proof of Lemma C-4 follows from applying (C-30) to (10-2) and (10-4) (left as an exercise for the reader). From Lemmas C-1*, C-2, and C-4, it follows that satisfaction of the requirements of Theorem 10-1, including the Popov condition (10-19) with $q \leq 0$ for the original system with passive hysteresis, will imply control asymptoticity of the transformed system, i.e.,

$$J_{u1}(\infty) \triangleq \left(\int_0^\infty u_1^2(t)\,dt\right)^{\frac{1}{2}} < \infty \tag{C-33}$$

therefore, since $\epsilon e^2(t) \leq u_1^2(t)$, we have

$$J_e(\infty) \triangleq \left(\int_0^\infty e^2(t)\,dt\right)^{\frac{1}{2}} < \infty \tag{C-34}$$

for every set of initial conditions.

Hence, by (C-30), (C-33), (C-34), and Minkowski's inequality, we have

$$J_u^2(\infty) = \int_0^\infty u^2(t)\,dt = \int_0^\infty \left[(K+\epsilon)e(t) - u_1(t)\right]^2 dt$$

$$\leq \left[(K+\epsilon)J_e(\infty) + J_{u1}(\infty)\right]^2 < \infty \tag{C-35}$$

Thus, we have concluded the proof of the part of Theorem 10-1 for passive hysteresis.

4. Special Case: $-\infty < q < \infty$, Single-Valued, Time-Invariant Function $u = f(e)$

A single-valued, time-invariant function $u = f(e)$ may be considered a special case of a hysteresis function, namely, one for which the functional relationship between e and u is unique. Hence, a system with a single-valued, time-invariant function $u = f(e)$, satisfying all other requirements of Theorem 10-1, will be control and output asymptotic if the Popov condition (10-19) is satisfied either for $q \geq 0$ (special case of active hysteresis) or for $q \leq 0$ (special case of passive hysteresis), and hence for $-\infty < q < \infty$. This holds for $0 < K < \infty$. Since for $-\infty < q < 0$ the theorem does not extend to the case $K = \infty$, it follows that for $K = \infty$, q must be restricted to $0 \leq q < \infty$.

*Note that the proof for $u(t) \in \mathfrak{L}_2$ over $(0, \infty)$ given in this appendix does not require that $|g(t)| \in \mathfrak{L}_1$ over $(0, \infty)$. This applies here for $u_1(t)$ and $g_1(t)$.

C-4 Proof of Theorem 10-2

To prove Theorem 10-2, we will need the following lemma:

◆◆**Lemma C-5.** If the conditions of Theorem 10-2 are satisfied, then there exists a real number $K_{u\alpha}$ such that

$$J_u(\infty) = \left(\int_0^\infty u^2(t)\,dt\right)^{\frac{1}{2}} \leq K_{u\alpha}\|\mathbf{x}(0)\| \qquad \text{(C-36)}◆◆$$

Proof of Lemma C-5. From (10-8a), we have

$$e_0(t) = -\mathbf{c}^T\mathbf{\Phi}(t)\mathbf{x}(0) \qquad \text{(C-37a)}$$

The time-derivative of $e_0(t)$ is

$$\dot{e}_0(t) = -\mathbf{c}^T\dot{\mathbf{\Phi}}(t)\mathbf{x}(0) \qquad \text{(C-37b)}$$

Now, by the proposition of Theorem 10-2, all eigenvalues $\lambda_i(i = 1, \ldots, n)$ of the matrix $\mathbf{A}$ have negative real parts. This means that there exists a value $\alpha > 0$ such that $\Re e\, \lambda_i \leq \alpha$ for all $i = 1, \ldots, n$. It follows then (see Exercise 5-14) that there exist numbers M, M' such that

$$\begin{aligned}\|\mathbf{\Phi}(t)\| &\triangleq \left(\sum_{i,j=1}^{n} \phi_{ij}^2(t)\right)^{\frac{1}{2}} \leq Me^{-\alpha t}\\ \|\dot{\mathbf{\Phi}}(t)\| &\triangleq \left(\sum_{i,j=1}^{n} \dot{\phi}_{ij}^2(t)\right)^{\frac{1}{2}} \leq M'e^{-\alpha t}\end{aligned} \qquad \text{(C-38)}$$

Thus, from (C-37) and (C-38), we can obtain the following inequalities

$$|e_0(t)| \leq cMe^{-\alpha t}\|\mathbf{x}(0)\|, \qquad |\dot{e}_0(t)| \leq cM'e^{-\alpha t}\|\mathbf{x}(0)\| \qquad \text{(C-39)}$$

where

$$c \triangleq \|\mathbf{c}\| = \left(\sum_{i=1}^{n} c_i^2\right)^{\frac{1}{2}} \qquad \text{(C-40)}$$

(i.e., c is a norm of the constant vector $\mathbf{c}$). Therefore, it follows from (C-23c) and (C-39) that

$$J_0(\infty) \leq M_{0\alpha}\|\mathbf{x}(0)\| \qquad \text{(C-41)}$$

where

$$M_{0\alpha} = \left(M + |q| M'\right) \frac{c}{\sqrt{2\alpha}} < \infty \tag{C-42}$$

For $0 \le q < \infty$, inequality (C-28) is valid. Since the conditions of Theorem 10-1 must be satisfied, we have $0 \le u(t) e(t) \le K e^2(t)$. Because of Lemma 10-1, $e(\infty) = 0$; therefore, we obtain for the two line integrals in (C-28)

$$\int_{0\;\Gamma_0+\Gamma_\infty}^{e(\infty)} u(t)\, de(t) = 0, \qquad \int_{0\;\Gamma_0}^{e(0)} u(t)\, de(t) \le \frac{K}{2} e^2(0) \le \frac{K}{2} c^2 \| \mathbf{x}(0) \|^2 \tag{C-43}$$

The last inequality follows from the assumption that $u/e \in [0, K]$ with $0 < K < \infty$ and from (10-24) and (C-40). With (C-41) and (C-42), inequality (C-28) becomes

$$J_u(\infty) \le \frac{1}{2\delta} M_{0\alpha} \| \mathbf{x}(0) \| + \left[q \frac{K_c^{\;2}}{2\delta} + \frac{1}{4\delta^2} M_{0\alpha}^2 \right]^{\frac{1}{2}} \| \mathbf{x}(0) \|$$

from which (C-36) follows, with

$$K_{u\alpha} = \frac{1}{2\delta} M_{0\alpha} + \left(q \frac{K_c^{\;2}}{2\delta} + \frac{1}{4\delta^2} M_{0\alpha}^2 \right)^{\frac{1}{2}} < \infty \tag{C-44}$$

Proof of Theorem 10-2. With (C-38) we can write

$$\| \mathbf{x}(t) \| \le M e^{-\alpha t} \| \mathbf{x}(0) \| + bM \int_0^t e^{-\alpha(t-\tau)} | u(\tau) |\, d\tau \tag{C-45}$$

where

$$b \triangleq \|\mathbf{b}\| = \left(\sum_{i=1}^{n} b_i^{\;2} \right)^{\frac{1}{2}}$$

Using Schwarz's inequality and (C-36), we have

$$\| \mathbf{x}(t) \| \le M e^{-\alpha t} \| \mathbf{x}(0) \| + \frac{bM}{\sqrt{2\alpha}} \left(\int_0^\infty u^2(t)\, dt \right)^{\frac{1}{2}}$$

or

$$\| \mathbf{x}(t) \| \leq M \left[e^{-\alpha t} + \frac{bK_{u\alpha}}{\sqrt{2\alpha}} \right] \| \mathbf{x}(0) \| \tag{C-46}$$

From (C-46), it follows that for every $\epsilon > 0$, there exists a $\delta(\epsilon) > 0$, namely

$$\delta(\epsilon) = \frac{\epsilon}{M \left[1 + \dfrac{bK_{u\alpha}}{\sqrt{2\alpha}} \right]}$$

such that $\| \mathbf{x}(0) \| < \delta$ implies that $\| \mathbf{x}(t) \| < \epsilon$ for all $t \geq 0$. Thus, the origin $\| \mathbf{x} \| = 0$ is Lyapunov stable. To prove that it is also globally asymptotically stable, we must show that $\mathbf{x}(t) \to 0$ as $t \to \infty$ for every $\mathbf{x}(0)$. From (C-41) and by using Minkowski's inequality, Parseval's relation, and (C-36), we obtain

$$\left(\int_0^\infty \| x(t) \|^2 dt \right)^{\frac{1}{2}} \leq M \| \mathbf{x}(0) \| \left(\int_0^\infty e^{-2\alpha t} dt \right)^{\frac{1}{2}} + bM \left(\frac{1}{2\pi} \int_{-\infty}^{\infty} \frac{|U(j\omega)|^2}{|j\omega + \alpha|^2} d\omega \right)^{\frac{1}{2}}$$

$$\leq \frac{M}{\sqrt{2\alpha}} \| \mathbf{x}(0) \| + bM \left(\sup_{-\infty \leq \omega \leq \infty} \frac{1}{|j\omega + \alpha|} \right) \left(\int_0^\infty u^2 dt \right)^{\frac{1}{2}}$$

$$\leq M \left[\frac{1}{\sqrt{2\alpha}} + \frac{bK_{u\alpha}}{\alpha} \right] \| \mathbf{x}(0) \| < \infty \tag{C-47}$$

Equation (C-47) can only be satisfied if $\| x(t) \| \to 0$ as $t \to \infty$ which, in turn, is only possible if $\mathbf{x}(t) \to 0$ as $t \to \infty$ (exercise for the reader). This concludes the proof of the theorem.

C-5 An Outline of the Proof of Lemma 11-3

In the interest of brevity, we shall only give a detailed proof of this lemma for the general case $q = 0$, $u(t) = \mathcal{F}[e(t), t]$, and $0 < K \leq \infty$. For the other cases, an outline is presented.

Since the linear element is output stable of degree ϵ for a sufficiently small $\epsilon > 0$, there exists an $\epsilon_1 > 0$ such that $e^{\epsilon_1 t} g(t) \in \mathcal{L}_1$ and $\mathcal{L}_2$ over $(0, \infty)$ (see Sec. C-1 and Definition 10-3). Let us now choose an ϵ $(0 < \epsilon < \epsilon_1)$ and transform the system variables as follows

$$e_\epsilon(t) \triangleq e^{\epsilon t} e(t), \qquad u_\epsilon(t) \triangleq e^{\epsilon t} u(t), \qquad g_\epsilon(t) \triangleq e^{\epsilon t} g(t), \text{ for } 0 < \epsilon < \epsilon_1 \quad \text{(C-48)}$$

Also, let

$$e_{0_\epsilon}(t) \triangleq e^{\epsilon t}\left[e_0(t) + r(t)\right], \qquad 0 < \epsilon < \epsilon_1 \quad \text{(C-49)}$$

Then, system (11-39) can be expressed as

$$e_\epsilon(t) = e_{0_\epsilon}(t) - \int_0^t g_\epsilon(t-\tau)\, u_\epsilon(\tau)\, d\tau, \qquad u_\epsilon(t) = \mathcal{F}\left[e_\epsilon(t), t\right] \quad \text{(C-50)}$$

As in Sec. 10.5, if $u/e \in [a, b]$, then $u_\epsilon/e_\epsilon \in [a, b]$. Let all conditions of Theorem 10-1 be satisfied for the unforced system. Then, the Popov condition (10-19) is satisfied which implies that there exists a $\delta_0 > 0$ such that

$$\mathcal{Re}\left[(1 + j\omega q)\, G(j\omega)\right] + \frac{1}{K} \geq \delta_0 > 0$$

Now, since $e^{\epsilon_1(t)} g(t) \in \mathcal{L}_1$ and $\mathcal{L}_2$, the Laplace transform $\mathcal{L}\left[e^{\epsilon_1 t} g(t)\right] = G(s - \epsilon_1)$ exists and is analytic in $\mathcal{Re}\, s \geq 0$. Therefore, $G(s) = \mathcal{L}[g(t)]$ is analytic in $\mathcal{Re}\, s \geq -\epsilon_1$ which implies that $G(s)$ is continuous in $\mathcal{Re}\, s \geq -\epsilon_1$. Therefore, there exists an ϵ $(0 < \epsilon < \epsilon_1)$ such that

$$\mathcal{Re}\left[(1 + j\omega q)\, G(j\omega - \epsilon)\right] + \frac{1}{K} \geq \delta > 0 \quad \text{(C-51)}$$

where $0 < \delta \leq \delta_0$. Since $G(s - \epsilon) = \mathcal{L}[g_\epsilon(t)]$, condition (C-51) is the Popov condition for the transformed system (C-50).

It is now possible to parallel the proof of Theorem 10-1, presented in Sec. C-3, for the system (C-50), keeping in mind, however, that the term $e_{0\epsilon}(t)$, defined in (C-49), does not satisfy the requirements of Theorem 10-1, since $|e_{0\epsilon}(t)| \to \infty$ as $t \to \infty$.

It can be readily verified that for system (C-50), with (C-51), every step in Sec. C-3 is valid, up to condition (C-24). Without any loss of generality, we can replace T by t in (C-24) so that, in terms of system (C-50), Eq. (C-24) becomes

$$\left(J_{u\epsilon}(t) - \frac{1}{2\delta} J_{0\epsilon}(t)\right)^2 - \frac{q}{\delta} I_{\Gamma\epsilon}(t) \leq \frac{1}{4\delta^2} J_{0\epsilon}^2(t) \quad \text{(C-52)}$$

where, from (C-23), (C-48), and (C-49),

$$J_{u\epsilon}(t) \triangleq \left(\int_0^t u_\epsilon(\tau)\, d\tau\right)^{\frac{1}{2}} = \left(\int_0^t e^{2\epsilon\tau} u^2(\tau)\, d\tau\right)^{\frac{1}{2}} \quad \text{(C-53a)}$$

$$I_{\Gamma\epsilon}(t) \triangleq -\int_0^t u_\epsilon(\tau)\,\dot{e}_\epsilon(\tau)\,d\tau = -\int_{\Gamma\; e_\epsilon(0)}^{e_\epsilon(t)} u_\epsilon(\tau)\,de_\epsilon(\tau) \tag{C-53b}$$

$$J_{0\epsilon}(t) \triangleq \left(\int_0^t e^{2\epsilon\tau}\left[e_0(\tau) + q\dot{e}_0(\tau) + r(\tau) + q\dot{r}(\tau)\right]^2 d\tau\right)^{\frac{1}{2}} \tag{C-53c}$$

and Γ is the path representing the functional relation between $u_\epsilon(\tau)$ and $e_\epsilon(\tau)$ during $0 \leq \tau \leq t$. Multiplying both sides of (C-52) and (C-53) by $e^{-2\epsilon t}$ yields

$$\left[J'_{u\epsilon}(t) - \frac{1}{2\delta} J'_{0\epsilon}(t)\right]^2 - \frac{q}{\delta} I'_{\Gamma\epsilon}(t) \leq \frac{1}{4\delta^2} J'^2_{0\epsilon}(t) \tag{C-54}$$

where

$$J'_{u\epsilon}(t) \triangleq \left(\int_0^t e^{-2\epsilon(t-\tau)} u^2(\tau)\,d\tau\right)^{\frac{1}{2}} \tag{C-55a}$$

$$I'_{\Gamma\epsilon}(t) \triangleq -e^{-2\epsilon t} \int_{\Gamma\; e_\epsilon(0)}^{e_\epsilon(t)} u_\epsilon(\tau)\,de_\epsilon(\tau) \tag{C-55b}$$

$$J'_{0\epsilon}(t) \triangleq \left(\int_0^t e^{-2\epsilon(t-\tau)}\left[e_0(\tau) + q\dot{e}_0(\tau) + r(\tau) + q\dot{r}(\tau)\right]^2 d\tau\right)^{\frac{1}{2}} \tag{C-55c}$$

Let us now consider the properties of the three integrals defined in (C-55). Using Minkowski's inequality we obtain from (C-55c)

$$J'_{0\epsilon}(t) \leq \left(\int_0^t e^{-2\epsilon(t-\tau)}\left[e_0(\tau) + q\dot{e}_0(\tau)\right]^2 d\tau\right)^{\frac{1}{2}}$$

$$+ \left(\int_0^t e^{-2\epsilon(t-\tau)}\left[r(\tau) + q\dot{r}(\tau)\right]^2 d\tau\right)^{\frac{1}{2}}$$

Since $\epsilon > 0$ and $|r(t)| \leq r_m < \infty$, $|\dot{r}(t)| \leq r'_m < \infty$, we obtain from the above inequality

$$J'_{0\epsilon}(t) \le J_0(t) + (r_m + qr'_m)\left(\frac{1 - e^{-2\epsilon t}}{2\epsilon}\right)^{\frac{1}{2}} \le J_0(\infty) + \frac{r_m + qr'_m}{\sqrt{2\epsilon}} < \infty \qquad \text{(C-56)}$$

where $J_0(t) < \infty$ is the same as that defined in (C-23c), with $T = t$.

For $q = 0$, (C-54) reduces to

$$J'_{u\epsilon}(t) \le \frac{1}{\delta} J'_{0\epsilon}(t) < \infty \qquad \text{(C-57)}$$

Because of (C-56), the above expression is finite. Moreover, since with $q = 0$ the term involving r'_m drops out, it follows that the requirement $|\dot{r}(t)| \le r'_m < \infty$ can be waived for the case $q = 0$.

For the other cases, the proof for the finiteness of $J'_{u\epsilon}(t)$ for all $t \ge 0$ is accomplished by continuing to parallel the proof of Theorem 10-1. Thereby, inequality (C-54) serves as the fundamental relation much as (C-25) served to prove Theorem 10-1. The second part of Lemma 11-3, which states that the linear element need not be output stable if it can be obtained by the zero-shifting transformation (10-38) from an element that is output stable, can be proved in the same manner as Theorem 10-6.

Bibliography

A1 Aizerman, M. A., and F. R. Gantmacher: "Absolute Stability of Regulator Systems," 1963 (in Russian); English translation, Holden-Day, Inc., San Francisco, 1964.

A2 Akhiezer, N. I.: "The Calculus of Variations," 1955 (in Russian); English translation, Blaisdell Publishing Company, New York, 1962.

A3 Andronov, A. A., and C. E. Chaikin: "Theory of Oscillations," 1937 (in Russian); English translation, Princeton University Press, Princeton, N. J., 1949.

A4 Aoki, M.: "Minimum Norm Problems and Some Other Control System Optimization Techniques," in C. T. Leondes (ed.), *Modern Control Systems Theory*, chap. 8, McGraw-Hill Book Company, New York, 1965.

A5 Apostol, T. M.: "Mathematical Analysis; a Modern Approach to Advanced Calculus," Addison-Wesley Publishing Company, Inc., Reading, Mass., 1957.

A6 Athans, M.: The Status of Optimal Control Theory and Applications for Deterministic Systems, *IEEE International Convention Record*, vol. 14, pt. 6, pp. 100–124, 1966.

A7 Athans, M., and M. D. Canon: On the Fuel-Optimal Singular Control of Nonlinear Second-Order Systems, *IEEE Trans. on Automatic Control*, vol. AC-9, no. 4, pp. 360–370, 1964.

A8 Athans, M., and P. L. Falb: "Optimal Control; an Introduction to the Thoery and Its Applications," McGraw-Hill Book Company, New York, 1966.

B1 Badgett, L. R.: A New Method of Obtaining Inverse z-Transforms, *Proc. of the IEEE*, vol. 54, no. 7, pp. 1010–1011, July 1966.

B2 Bellman, R.: "Adaptive Control Processes: A Guided Tour," Princeton University Press, Princeton, N. J., 1961.

B3 Bellman, R.: "Dynamic Programming," Princeton University Press, Princeton, N. J., 1957.

B4 Bellman, R.: "Introduction to Matrix Analysis," McGraw-Hill Book Company, New York, 1960.

B5 Bellman, R.: On an Application of a Banach-Steinhaus Theorem to the Study of the Boundedness of Solutions of Nonlinear Differential and Difference Equations, *Ann. of Math.*, (2) vol. 49, no. 3, pp. 515-522, July 1948.

B6 Bellman, R.: "Stability Theory of Differential Equations," McGraw-Hill Book Company, New York, 1953.

B7 Bellman, R., I. Glicksberg, and O. Gross: On the "Bang-Bang" Control Problem, *Quart. Appl. Math.*, vol. 14, pp. 11-18, April 1956.

B8 Bendixson, I.: Sur les Courbes Définies par des Equations Différentielles, *Acta Mathematica*, vol. 24, pp. 1-88, 1901.

B9 Bergen, A. R., R. P. Iwens, and A. J. Rault: On Input-Output Stability of Nonlinear Feedback Systems, *IEEE Trans. on Automatic Control*, vol. AC-11, no. 4, pp. 742-744, October 1966.

B10 Berkovitz, L. D.: Variational Methods in Problems of Control and Programming, *J. of Math. Analysis and Applications*, vol. 3, no. 1, pp. 145-169, August 1961.

B11 Bliss, G. A.: "Lectures on the Calculus of Variations," The University of Chicago Press, 1946.

B12 Bode, H. W., and C. E. Shannon: A Simplified Derivation of Linear Least Square Smoothing and Prediction Theory, *Proc. of the IRE*, vol. 38, no. 4, pp. 417-425, April 1950.

B13 Bogner, I., and L. F. Kazda: An Investigation of the Switching Criteria for Higher Order Contactor Servomechanisms, *Trans. AIEE*, vol. 73, pt. II, pp. 118-126, 1954.

B14 Boltyanskii, V. G.: Sufficient Conditions for Optimality and the Justification of the Dynamic Programming Method, *SIAM Jour. on Control*, vol. 4, no. 2, pp. 326-361, May 1966.

B15 Bonenn, Ze'ev: Frequency Response of Feedback Relay Amplifiers, *IEEE Proc. (British)*, vol. 108, pt. C, pp. 287-295, 1961.

B16 Bongiorno, J. J., Jr.: Real-Frequency Stability Criteria for Linear Time-Varying Systems, *Proc. of the IEEE*, vol. 52, no. 7, pp. 832-841, July 1964. (Correction in vol. 52, no. 10, pp. 1127-1128, October 1964.)

B17 Breakwell, J. V., J. L. Speyer, and A. E. Bryson: Optimization and Control of Nonlinear Systems Using the Second Variation, *J. SIAM on Control*, Ser. A, vol. 1, no. 2, pp. 193-223, 1963.

B18 Brockett, R. W.: The Status of Stability Theory for Deterministic Systems, *IEEE Trans. on Automatic Control*, vol. AC-11, no. 3, pp. 596-606, July 1966.

B19 Brockett, R. W., and J. W. Willems: Frequency Domain Stability Criteria, *IEEE Trans. on Automatic Control*, pt. I, vol. AC-10, no. 3, pp. 255-261, July 1965; pt. II, vol. AC-10, no. 4, pp. 407-413, October 1965.

B20 Bryson, A. E., F. J. Carroll, K. Mikami, and W. F. Denham: Determination of the Lift or Drag Program That Minimizes Re-Entry Heating with Acceleration or Range Constraints Using a Steepest Descent Computation Procedure, *Institute of the Aerospace Sciences 29th Annual Meeting*, New York City, Paper 61-6, 1961.

B21 Bushaw, D.: "Optimal Discontinuous Forcing Terms" in S. Lefschetz (ed.), *Contributions to the Theory of Nonlinear Oscillations*, vol. 4 (Annals of Mathematics Studies, no. 41), Princeton University Press, Princeton, N. J., pp. 29-52 (based on Ph.D. dissertation of 1953).

B22 Butenin, N. V.: "Elements of the Theory of Nonlinear Oscillations" (in Russian); English translation, Blaisdell Publishing Company, New York, 1965.

C1 Cesari, L.: "Asymptotic Behavior and Stability Problems in Ordinary Differential Equations," Academic Press, Springer-Verlag, 2nd ed., 1963.

C2 Chang, S. S. L.: "Synthesis of Optimum Control Systems," McGraw-Hill Book Company, New York, 1961.

C3 Chyung, D. H., and E. B. Lee: Linear Optional Systems with Time Delay, *SIAM Jour. on Control*, vol. 4, no. 3, pp. 548-575, August 1966.

C4 Cicala, P.: "An Engineering Approach to the Calculus of Variations," Levrotto and Bella, Torino, Italy, 1964. (Revised second impression.)

C5 Coddington, E. A., and N. Levinson: "Theory of Ordinary Differential Equations," McGraw-Hill Book Company, New York, 1955.

C6 Coppel, W. A.: "Stability and Asymptotic Behavior of Differential Equations," D. C. Heath and Company, Boston, 1965.

C7 Cunningham, W. J.: "Introduction to Nonlinear Analysis," McGraw-Hill Book Company, New York, 1958.

D1 Denham, W. F., and A. E. Bryson, Jr.: Optimal Programming Problems with Inequality Constraints. II: Solution by Steepest Descent, AIAA Jour., vol. 2, no. 1, pp. 25-34, January 1964.

D2 DeRusso, P. M., R. J. Roy, and C. M. Close: "State Variables for Engineers," John Wiley & Sons, Inc., New York, 1965.

D3 Desoer, C. A.: The Bang-Bang Servo Problem Treated by Variational Techniques, *Information and Control*, vol. 2, pp. 333-348, 1959.

D4 Desoer, C. A.: A Generalization of the Popov Criterion, *IEEE Trans. on Automatic Control*, vol. AC-10, no. 2, pp. 182-185, April 1965.

D5 Dewey, A. G., and E. I. Jury: A Note on Aizerman's Conjecture, *IEEE Trans. on Automatic Control*, vol. AC-10, no. 4, pp. 482-483, October 1965.

D6 Dewey, A. G., and E. I. Jury: A Stability Inequality for a Class of Nonlinear Feedback Systems, *IEEE Trans. on Automatic Control*, vol. AC-11, no. 1, pp. 54-62, January 1966.

D7 Doetsch, G.: "Guide to the Applications of Laplace Transforms," D. Van Nostrand Company, Inc., Princeton, N. J., 1961.

D8 Doetsch, G.: "Handbuch der Laplace Transformation," vol. 1, *Birkhäuser Verlag*, Basel, 1950 (In German).

D9 Dorato, P.: On Sensitivity in Optimal Control Systems, *IEEE Trans. on Automatic Control*, vol. AC-8, pp. 256-257, July 1963.

D10 Dreyfus, S. E.: Dynamic Programming and the Calculus of Variations, *J. of Math. Analysis and Applications*, vol. 1, no. 2, pp. 228-239, September 1960.

D11 Dreyfus, S. E.: Dynamic Programming and the Calculus of Variations," Academic Press, Inc., New York, 1965.

D12 Dutilh, J. R.: Théorie des Servo-mecanismes à Relais, *Onde Elect.*, vol. 30, no. 283, pp. 438-445, October 1950.

E1 Elsgolc, L. E.: "Calculus of Variations" (in Russian); English translation, Addison-Wesley Publishing Company, Inc., Reading, Mass., 1962.

F1 Fitts, R. E.: Two Counterexamples to Aizerman's Conjecture, *IEEE Trans. on Automatic Control*, vol. AC-11, no. 3, pp. 553-556, July 1966.

F2 Flügge-Lotz, I., and H. Halkin: Pontryagin's Maximum Principle and Optimal Control, *Tech. Report 130*, Department of Engineering Mechanics, Stanford University, Palo Alto, Calif., September 1961 (AFOSR TN 1489).

F3 Flügge-Lotz, I., and H. A. Titus, Jr.: Optimum and Quasi-Optimum Control of Third- and Fourth-Order Systems, *Proc. of the Second IFAC Congress - Theory*, Basel, Switzerland, pp. 363-370, 1963.

F4 Frame, J. S.: Matrix Functions and Applications, *IEEE Spectrum*, pts. I-V, March-July 1964 (pts. II and III, H. E. Koenig, co-author).

F5 Fukuma, A., and M. Matsubara: Jump Resonance Criteria of Nonlinear Control Systems, *IEEE Trans. on Automatic Control*, vol. AC-11, no. 4, pp. 699-706, October 1966.

G1 Gantmacher, F. R.: "Theory of Matrices," vols. I and II (in Russian); English translation, Chelsea Publishing Company, New York, 1959.

G2 Gelb, A.: The Dynamic Input-Output Analysis of Limit Cycling Control Systems, *Joint Automatic Control Conference*, Paper 9-3, June 1962.

G3 Gibson, J. E.: "Nonlinear Automatic Control," McGraw-Hill Book Company, New York, 1963.

G4 Gille, J.-C., M. J. Pélegrin, and P. Decaulne: "Feedback Control Systems: Analysis, Synthesis, and Design," McGraw-Hill Book Company, New York, 1959.

G5 Gille, J.-C., S. Wergrzyn, and J.-G. Paquet: Oscillations Sous-Harmoniques dans un Asservissement par Plus-ou-Moins in *Automatic and Remote Control - Theory*, vol. 2, pp. 204-209, Butterworths, London, 1964.

G6 Goldfarb, L. C.: On Some Nonlinear Phenomena in Regulatory Systems, *Automatika i Telemekhanika*, Moscow, vol. 8, no. 5, pp. 349-383, September-October 1947 (in Russian); English translation, in R. Oldenburger (ed.), *Frequency Response*, The Macmillan Company New York, pp. 239-257, 1956.

G7 Goldstein, H.: "Classical Mechanics," Addison-Wesley Publishing Company, Inc., Reading, Mass., 1950.

G8 Graham, D., and D. McRuer: "Analysis of Nonlinear Control Systems," John Wiley and Sons, Inc., New York, 1961.

G9 Grayson, L. P.: The Status of Synthesis Using Lyapunov's Method, *Automatica*, vol. 3, no. 2, pp. 91-121, December 1965.

H1 Hadley, G.: "Nonlinear and Dynamic Programming," Addison-Wesley Publishing Company, Inc., Reading, Mass., 1964.

H2 Hahn, W.: "Theory and Application of Liapunov's Direct Method" (in German); English translation, Prentice-Hall, Inc., Englewood Cliffs, N. J., 1963.

H3 Halanay, A.: "Differential Equations: Stability, Oscillations, Time Lags," (in Rumanian); English translation, Academic Press, New York, 1966.

H4 Halkin, H.: A Generalization of LaSalle's "Bang-Bang" Principle, *SIAM Jour. on Control*, Series A, vol. 2, no. 2, pp. 199-202, 1965.

H5 Halkin, H.: "Mathematical Foundations of System Optimization," in G. Leitmann (ed.), *Topics of Optimization*, chap. 6, Academic Press, Inc., New York, 1967.

H6 Hamming, R. W.: "Numerical Methods for Scientists and Engineers," McGraw-Hill Book Company, New York, 1962.

H7 Hatanaka, H.: The Frequency Responses and Jump-Resonance Phenomena of Nonlinear Feedback Control Systems, *J. of Basic Engineering*, vol. 85, no. 2, pp. 236-242, June 1963.

H8 Hayashi, C.: "Nonlinear Oscillations in Physical Systems," McGraw-Hill Book Company, New York, 1964.

H9 Hestenes, M. R.: "Calculus of Variations and Optimal Control Theory," John Wiley & Sons, Inc., New York, 1966.

H10 Hildebrand, F. B.: "Methods of Applied Mathematics," Prentice-Hall, Inc., Englewood Cliffs, N. J., 1952.

H11 Ho, Y. C.: Differential Games (review of book by R. Isaacs), *IEEE Trans. on Automatic Control*, vol. AC-10, no. 4, pp. 501-503, 1965.

H12 Ho, Y. C.: What Constitutes a Controllable System, *IRE Trans. on Automatic Control*, vol. AC-7, no. 3, p. 76, April 1962.

H13 Hobson, E. W.: "The Theory of Functions of a Real Variable and the Theory of Fourier's Series," vol. II, Dover Publications, Inc., New York, 1957.

H14 Hochstadt, H.: "Differential Equations, a Modern Approach," Holt, Rinehart and Winston, New York, 1964.

H15 Holtzman, J. M.: Contraction Maps and Equivalent Linearization, *Bell System Tech. J.*, vol. 46, no. 10, pp. 2405-2435, December, 1967.

H16 Holtzman, J. M., and S. Horing: The Sensitivity of Terminal Conditions of Optimal Control Systems to Parameter Variations, *IEEE Trans. on Automatic Control*, vol. AC–10, pp. 420-426, October 1965.

H17 Hsu, J. C.: Integral Representation of Zero-Memory Nonlinear Functions, *Bell System Tech. J.*, vol. 41, no. 4, pp. 1813-1830, November 1962.

H18 Hsu, J. C., Y. S. Lim, and A. U. Meyer: On Active Attitude Control of Satellites, *IEEE Trans. on MIL Electronics*, vol. MIL-9, no. 2, pp. 107-115, April 1965.

I1 Ince, E. L.: "Ordinary Differential Equations," Dover Publications, Inc., New York, 1956.

I2 Isaacs, R.: "Differential Games; a Mathematical Theory with Applications to Warfare and Pursuit, Control, and Optimization," John Wiley & Sons, Inc., New York, 1965.

J1 Johnson, C. D.: "Singular Solutions in Problems of Optimal Control," in C. T. Leondes (ed.), *Advances in Control Systems: Theory and Applications*, vol. 2, pp. 209-267, Academic Press, Inc., New York, 1965.

J2 Johnson, C. D., and J. E. Gibson: Singular Solutions in Problems of Optimal Control, *IEEE Trans. on Automatic Control*, vol. AC-8, no. 1, pp. 4-15, January 1963.

J3 Johnson, C. D., and W. M. Wonham: On a Problem of Letov in Optimal Control, *Joint Automatic Control Conference*, Preprints of Conference Papers, pp. 317-325, June 1964.

J4 Jones, R. W., and A. U. Meyer: Analysis of Series Generator Series Motor Drive, *Trans. AIEE*, vol. 79, pt. III, pp. 31-39, April 1960.

J5 Jury, E. I.: A Note on the Steady-State Response of a Linear Time-Invariant System to General Periodic Input, *Proc. of the IRE*, vol. 48, no. 5, pp. 942-944, May 1960.

J6 Jury, E. I.: "Theory and Application of the z-Transform Method," John Wiley & Sons, Inc., New York, 1964.

K1 Kahn, D. A.: An Analysis of Relay Servomechanisms, *Trans. AIEE*, vol. 68, pt. II, pp. 1079-1088, 1949.

K2 Kalman, R. E.: Contributions to the Thoery of Optimal Control, *Boletin de la Sociedad Matematica Mexicana*, (2) vol. 5, pp. 102-119, 1960.

K3 Kalman, R. E.: Lyapunov Functions for the Problem of Lur'e in Automatic Control, *National Academy of Sciences, Proceedings*, vol. 49, no. 2, pp. 201-205, February 1963.

K4 Kalman, R. E.: "New Methods and Results in Linear Prediction and Filtering Theory," in J. L. Bogdanoff and F. Kozin (eds.), *Symposium on Engineering Applications of Random*

Function Theory and Probability, John Wiley & Sons, Inc., New York, 1963.

K5 Kalman, R. E.: Physical and Mathematical Mechanisms of Instability in Nonlinear Automatic Control Systems, *Trans. ASME*, vol. 79, no. 3, pp. 553-566, April 1957.

K6 Kalman, R. E.: "The Theory of Optimal Control and the Calculus of Variations" in R. Bellman (ed.), *Mathematical Optimization Techniques*, University of California Press, Berkeley, Calif., 1963.

K7 Kalman, R. E.: When is a Linear Control System Optimal? *J. of Basic Engineering*, vol. 86, no. 1, pp. 51-60, March 1964.

K8 Kalman, R. E., and J. E. Bertram: Control System Analysis and Design via the "Second Method" of Lyapunov, pt. I: Continuous Time Systems, *J. of Basic Engineering*, vol. 82, no. 2, pp. 371-393, June 1960.

K9 Kalman, R. E., Y. C. Ho, and K. S. Narendra: "Controllability of Linear Dynamical Systems" in *Contributions to Differential Equations*, vol. I, no. 2, pp. 189-213, Interscience Publishers, New York, 1963.

K10 Kalman, R. E., and R. W. Koepcke: Optimal Synthesis of Linear Sampling Control Systems Using Generalized Performance Indexes, *Trans. ASME*, vol. 80, no. 8, pp. 1820-1826, November 1958.

K11 Kantorovich, L. V., and G. P. Akilov: "Functional Analysis in Normed Spaces," Oxford, Pergamon Press, London, 1965.

K12 Kaplan, W.: "Operational Methods for Linear Systems," Addison-Wesley Publishing Company, Inc., Reading, Mass., 1962.

K13 Kelley, H. J.: "Method of Gradients," in G. Leitmann (ed.), *Optimization Techniques, with Applications to Aerospace Systems*, pp. 205-254, Academic Press, Inc., New York, 1962.

K14 Kelley, H. J.: A Second Variation Test for Singular Extremals, *AIAA Journal*, vol. 2, no. 8, pp. 1380-1382, August, 1964.

K15 Kenneth, P., and R. McGill: "Two-Point Boundary-Value-Problem Techniques" in C. T. Leondes (ed.), *Advances in Control Systems*, vol. 3, pp. 69-109, Academic Press, Inc., New York, 1966.

K16 Kinariwala, B. K.: Analysis of Time-Varying Networks, *IRE International Convention Record*, vol. 9, pt. 4, pp. 268-276, 1961.

K17 Knopp, K.: "Theory of Functions," pt. I, Dover Publications, Inc., New York, 1945.

K18 Kochenburger, R. J.: A Frequency Response Method for Analyzing Contactor Servomechanisms, *Trans. AIEE*, vol. 69, pt. I, pp. 270-284, 1950.

K19 Kolmogorov, A. N., and S. V. Fomin: "Elements of the Theory of Functions and Functional Analysis," 1954 (in

Russian); English translation, Graylock Press, Rochester, New York, 1957.

K20 Kopp, R. E., R. McGill, H. G. Moyer, and G. Pinkham: "Several Trajectory Optimization Techniques, pt. I - Discussion, pt. II - Application" in A. V. Balakrishnan and L. W. Neustadt (eds.), *Computing Methods in Optimization Problems*, pp. 65-105, Academic Press, Inc., New York, 1964.

K21 Kovatch, G.: A Method for the Computation of Self-Sustained Oscillation in Systems with Piecewise Linear Elements, *IEEE Trans. on Automatic Control*, vol. AC-8, no. 4, pp. 358-365, 1963.

K22 Ku, Y. H.: "Analysis and Control of Nonlinear Systems," The Ronald Press, New York, 1958.

L1 Laning, J. H., Jr., and R. H. Battin: "Random Processes in Automatic Control," McGraw-Hill Book Company, New York, 1956.

L2 Larson, R. E.: Dynamic Programming with Reduced Computational Requirements, *IEEE Trans. on Automatic Control*, vol. AC-10, no. 2, pp. 135-143, April 1965.

L3 Larson, R. E.: A Survey of Dynamic Programming Computational Procedures, *IEEE International Convention Record*, 1967.

L4 LaSalle, J. P.: Complete Stability of a Nonlinear Control System, *Proc. National Academy Science, U.S.A.*, vol. 48, no. 4, pp. 600-603, April 1962.

L5 LaSalle, J. P.: "The Time-Optimal Control Problem," in L. Cesari (ed.), *Contributions to the Theory of Nonlinear Oscillations*, vol. V, Princeton University Press, Princeton, N.J., 1960.

L6 LaSalle, J. P. and S. Lefschetz: "Stability by Liapunov's Direct Method with Applications," Academic Press Inc., New York, 1961

L7 Lee, E. B.: A Sufficient Condition in the Theory of Optimal Control, *SIAM Jour. on Control*, Series A, vol. 1, no. 3, pp. 241-245, 1963.

L8 Lefferts, E. J.: "A Guide of the Application of the Liapunov Direct Method to Flight Control Systems," *NASA-CR-209*, National Aeronautics and Space Administration, Washington, D. C., April 1965.

L9 Lefschetz, S.: "Some Mathematical Considerations on Nonlinear Automatic Controls," in *Contributions to Differential Equations*, vol. I, pp. 1-28, Interscience Publishers, New York, 1963.

L10 Lefschetz, S.: "Stability of Nonlinear Control Systems," Academic Press, Inc., New York, 1965.

L11 Leitmann, G.: "An Introduction to Optimal Control," McGraw-Hill Book Company, New York, 1966.

L12 Leitmann, G. (ed.): "Optimization Techniques with Applications to Aerospace Systems," Academic Press Inc., New York, 1962.

L13 Letov, A. M.: "Stability in Nonlinear Control Systems," 1955 (in Russian); English translation, Princeton University Press, Princeton, New Jersey, 1961.

L14 Lim, Y. S., and L. F. Kazda: A Study of Second Order Nonlinear Systems, *J. of Math. Analysis and Applications*, vol. 8, no. 3, pp. 423-444, June 1964.

L15 Lozier, J. C.: Carrier-Controlled Relay Servos, *Electrical Engineering*, vol. 69, pp. 1052-1056, 1950.

L16 Lozier, J. C.: A Steady State Approach to the Theory of Saturable Servo Systems, *IRE Trans. on Automatic Control*, vol. PGAC-1, pp. 19-39, May 1956.

L17 Lur'e, A. I.: "Some Non-Linear Problems in the Theory of Automatic Control," 1951 (in Russian); English translation, Her Majesty's Stationery Office, London, 1957.

L18 Lyapunov, A. M.: "Stability of Motion" (in Russian); English translation, Academic Press, Inc., New York, 1967.

M1 Magnus, K.: Über den Zusammenhang verschiedener Näherungsverfahren zur Berechnung nichtlinearer Schwingungen, *Z. Angew. Math. Mech.*, vol. 37, nos. 11/12, pp. 471-485, November-December 1957.

M2 Magnus, W., and F. Oberhettinger: "Formulas and Theorems for the Functions of Mathematical Physics," Chelsea Publishing Company, New York, 1954.

M3 Malkin, I. G.: Stability in the Case of Constantly Acting Disturbances, *Prikladnaia Matematika i Mekhanika*, vol. 8, pp. 241-245, 1944 (in Russian with English summary).

M4 Massera, J. L.: Contributions to Stability Theory, *Ann. of Math.* (2) vol. 64, no. 1, pp. 182-206, July 1956.

M5 McColl, L. A.: "Fundamental Theory of Servomechanisms," D. Van Nostrand Company, Inc., Princeton, N. J., 1945.

M6 McGill, R., and P. Kenneth: A Convergence Theorem on the Iterative Solution of Non-Linear Two-Point Boundary-Value Systems, *Proc., XIVth International Astronautical Congress 1963*, vol. 4, Gauthier-Villars, Paris, France, pp. 173-188, 1965.

M7 McLachlan, N. W.: "Theory and Application of Mathieu Functions," Dover Publications, Inc., New York, 1964.

M8 McShane, E. J.: On Multipliers for Lagrange Problems, *American Jour. of Mathematics*, vol. 61, pp. 809-819 (1939).

M9 Merriam, C. W., III: "Optimization Theory and the Design of Feedback Control Systems," McGraw-Hill Book Company, New York, 1964.

M10 Merriam, C. W. III,: A Computational Method for Feedback Control Optimization, *Information and Control*, vol. 8, no. 2, pp. 215-232.

M11 Meyer, A. U.: "Pulse Frequency Modulation and Its Effect in Feedback Systems," Doctoral Thesis, Northwestern University, Evanston, Ill., 1961 (available through University Microfilms, Inc., Ann Arbor, Michigan).

M12 Meyer, A. U., and J. C. Hsu: The Evaluation of Frequency Response Stability Criterion for Nonlinear Systems via Logarithmic Gain-Phase Plots, *Joint Automatic Control Conference*, June, 1968.

M13 Minorsky, N.: "Nonlinear Oscillations," D. Van Nostrand Company, Inc., Princeton, N. J., 1962.

M14 Murphy, G. J.: A Frequency Domain Stability Chart for Nonlinear Feedback Systems, *IEEE Trans. on Automatic Control*, vol. AC-12, no. 6, December 1967.

N1 Naumov, B. N.: An Investigation of Absolute Stability of the Equilibrium State in Nonlinear Automatic Control Systems by Means of Logarithmic Frequency Characteristics, *Automation and Remote Control*, vol. 26, no. 4, pp. 593-601, April 1965.

N2 Naumov, B. N., and Ya. Z. Zsypkin: A Frequency Criterion for Absolute Process Stability in Nonlinear Control Systems, *Automation and Remote Control*, vol. 25, no. 6, pp. 765-778, June 1964.

N3 Nelson, W. L.: On the Use of Optimization Theory for Practical Control System Design, *IEEE Trans. on Automatic Control*. vol. AC-9, no. 4, pp. 469-477, October 1964.

N4 Neuman, C. P.: "Frequency Domain Stability Criteria in Nonlinear Automatic Control," Ph.D. Thesis, Harvard University, Cambridge, Mass., March 1967.

N5 Neustadt, L. W.: The Existence of Optimal Controls in the Absence of Convexity Conditions, *J. of Math. Analysis and Applications*, vol. 7, no. 1, pp. 110-117, August 1963.

N6 Newton, G. C., Jr., L. A. Gould, and J. F. Kaiser: "Analytical Design of Linear Feedback Controls," John Wiley & Sons, Inc., New York, 1957.

O1 Ogata, K.: "State Space Analysis of Control Systems," Prentice-Hall, Inc., Englewood Cliffs, N. J., 1967.

O2 Okamura, K.: Some Mathematical Thoery of the Penalty Method for Solving Optimum Control Problems, *SIAM Jour. on Control*, Series A, vol. 2, no. 3, pp. 317-331, 1964.

O3 Oppelt, W.: Über Ortskurvenverfahren bei Regelvorgangen mit Reibung, *VDI Zeit.*, vol. 90, no. 6, pp. 179-183, June 1948; English translation, Locus Curve Method for Regulators with Friction, *Rep. Nat. Bur. Stand.*, no. 1691.

O4 Ostrowski, A. M.: "Solution of Equations and Systems of Equations," Academic Press, Inc., New York, 1960.

P1 Parks, P. C.: A New Proof of the Routh-Hurwitz Stability Criterion Using the Second Method of Liapunov, *Proc. Cambridge Phil. Soc.*, vol. 58, pt. 4, pp. 694-702, October 1962.

P2 Pars, L. A.: "Introduction to the Calculus of Variations," John Wiley & Sons, Inc., New York, 1962.

P3 Pell, W. H.: Graphical Solution of Single-Degree-of-Freedom Vibration Problem with Arbitrary Damping and Restoring Forces, *J. Appl. Mech.*, vol. 24, no. 2, pp. 311-312, June 1957.

P4 Perron, O.: Die Stabilitätsfrage bei Differentialgleichungen, *Mathematische Zeitschrift*, vol. 32, no. 5, pp. 703-728, December 1930.

P5 Pipes, L. A.: "Matrix Methods for Engineering," Prentice Hall, Inc., Englewood Cliffs, New Jersey, 1963.

P6 Pliss, V. A.: Certain Problems in the Theory of Stability of Motion in the Whole, 1958 (in Russian); English translation, *NASA-TT-F-280*, National Aeronautics and Space Administration, Washington, D. C., August 1965.

P7 Pontryagin, L. S.: "Ordinary Differential Equations," 1960 (in Russian); English translation, Addison-Wesley Publishing Company, Inc., Reading, Mass., 1962.

P8 Pontryagin, L. S., V. G. Boltyanskii, R. V. Gamkrelidze, and E. F. Mishchenko: "Mathematical Theory of Optimal Processes" (in Russian); English translation, Interscience-Wiley, New York, 1962.

P9 Popov, V. M.: "Stability Criteria for Nonlinear Systems of Automatic Control Based on the Use of Laplace Transform" (in Rumanian), *Studii si Cercetari de Energetica*, vol. 9, no. 4, pp. 119-135, 1959.

P10 Porter, W. A.: "Modern Foundations of Systems Engineering," The Macmillan Company, New York, 1966.

P11 Pyati, S.: "A Study of Absolute Stability in Nonlinear Control Systems," Ph.D. Thesis, University of Michigan, 1965.

R1 Reis, G. C.: An Extension of Pell's Method of Phase-Trajectory Construction, *IEEE Trans. on Automatic Control*, vol. AC-9, no. 3, p. 315, July 1964.

R2 Rose, N. J.: Theoretical Aspects of Limit Control, *Report No. 459*, Experimental Towing Tank, Stevens Institute of Technology, Hoboken, N. J., November 1953.

R3 Rosenbrock, H. H.: The Stability of Time-Dependent Control Systems, *J. of Electronics and Control*, vol. 15, no. 1, pp. 73-80, July 1963.

R4 Routh, E. J.: "Dynamics of Rigid Bodies (Advanced Part)," Dover Publications, Inc., New York, 1955.

R5 Roxin, E.: The Existence of Optimal Controls, *Michigan Math. J.*, vol. 9, pp. 109-119, 1962.

R6 Rozonoèr, L. I.: L. S. Pontryagin's Maximum Principle in the Theory of Optimum Systems, *Automation and Remote Control*, vol. 20, 1959. Pt. I, pp. 1288-1302, October 1959; pt. II, pp. 1405-1421, November 1959; pt. III, pp. 1517-1532, December 1959.

R7 Russell, D. L.: Penalty Functions and Bounded Phase Coordinate Control, *SIAM Jour. on Control*, Series A, vol. 2, no. 3, pp. 409-422, 1964.

S1 Sakawa, Y.: Subharmonic Oscillations in Relay-Control Systems, *Automatic and Remote Control*, Butterworths, London, vol. 1, pp. 404-409, 1961.

S2 Sandberg, I. W.: A Frequency-Domain Condition for the Stability of Feedback Systems Containing a Single Time-Varying Nonlinear Element, *Bell System Tech. J.*, vol. 43, no. 4, pt. 2, pp. 1601-1608, July 1964.

S3 Sandberg, I. W.: On the Boundedness of Solutions of Nonlinear Integral Equations, *Bell System Tech. J.*, vol. 44, no. 3, pp. 439-453, March 1965.

S4 Sandberg, I. W.: On the Response of Nonlinear Control Systems to Periodic Input Signals, *Bell System Tech. J.*, vol. 43, no. 43, pp. 911-926, May 1964.

S5 Sandberg, I. W.: Some Results on the Theory of Physical Systems Governed by Nonlinear Functional Equations, *Bell System Tech. J.*, vol. 44, no. 5, pp. 871-898, May-June 1965.

S6 Sandberg, I. W.: Some Stability Results Related to Those of V. M. Popov, *Bell System Tech. J.*, vol. 44, no. 9, pp. 2133-2148, November 1965.

S7 Sansone, G., and R. Conti: "Non-linear Differential Equations," 1956 (in Italian); English translation, with additions, The Macmillan Company, New York, 1964.

S8 Schuck, O. H.: Adaptive Flight Control, *Automatic and Remote Control*, Butterworths, London, vol. 2, pp. 645-652, 1961.

S9 Schultz, D. G.: "The Generation of Liapunov Functions" in C. T. Leondes (ed.), *Advances in Control Systems*, vol. II, pp. 1-64, Academic Press, Inc., New York, 1965.

S10 Schwartz, R. J., and B. Friedland: "Linear Systems," McGraw-Hill Book Company, New York, 1965.

S11 Stiles, J. A.: "Time Optimal Control of a Two Variable System," Ph.D. Thesis, Trinity College, Cambridge University, 1964.

S12 Struble, R. A.: "Nonlinear Differential Equations," McGraw-Hill Book Company, New York, 1962.

S13 Sun, J., and K. Hang: Analysis and Synthesis of Time Optimal Control Systems, *Proc. of the Second IFAC Congress - Theory*, Basel, Switzerland, pp. 347-351, 1963.

T1 Tait, K. S.: "Singular Problems in Optimal Control," Doctoral Thesis, Harvard University, Cambridge, Mass., 1965.

T2 Tchamran, A.: On Bellman's Functional Equation and a Class of Time-Optimal Control Systems, *J. of the Franklin Inst.*, vol. 280, no. 6, pp. 493-505, December 1965.

T3 Timothy, L. K., and B. E. Bona: "An Introduction to State Space Analysis of Systems," McGraw-Hill Book Company, New York, 1967.

T4 Tsien, H. S.: "Engineering Cybernetics," McGraw-Hill Book Company, New York, 1954.

T5 Tsypkin, Ya. S.: "Sampling System Theory and its Application," 1958 (in Russian); English translation, Pergamon Press Ltd., Oxford, vols. 1 and 2, 1964.

T6 Tsypkin, Ya. S.: "Theory of Relay Systems in Automatic Control," Moscow, 1955 (in Russian); German translation, Ja. S. Zypkin, "Theorie der Relaissysteme der automatischen Regelung," Oldenburg, München, 1958.

T7 Tustin, A.: A Method of Analyzing the Effects of Certain Kinds of Nonlinearity in Closed-Cycle Control Systems, *Jour. IEE*, vol. 94, pt. IIA, no. 1, pp. 152-160, 1947.

V1 Valentine, F. A.: "The Problem of Lagrange with Differential Inequalities as Added Side Conditions" in *Contribution to the Calculus of Variations, 1933-1937*, University of Chicago Press, Chicago, Ill., 1937.

V2 Varaiya, P. P., and R. Liu: Bounded-Input Bounded-Output Stability of Nonlinear Time-Varying Differential Systems, *SIAM Jour. on Control*, vol. 4, no. 4, pp. 698-704, 1966.

W1 Wang, P. P.: Comment on "An Extension of Pell's Method of Phase-Trajectory Construction," IEEE Trans. on Automatic Control, vol. AC-12, no. 3, p. 328, June 1967.

W2 West, J. C.: "Analytical Techniques for Non-linear Control Systems," D. Van Nostrand and Company, Inc., Princeton, N. J., 1960.

W3 Whittaker, E. T., and G. N. Watson: "A Course of Modern Analysis," Cambridge University Press, England, 4th ed., 1927.

W4 Wiener, N.: "The Extrapolation, Interpolation and Smoothing of a Stationary Time Series; with Engineering Applications," John Wiley & Sons, Inc., New York, 1949.

W5 Wiener, N.: "The Fourier Integral and Certain of Its Applications," Cambridge University Press, England, 1933 (reprinted by Dover Publications, Inc., New York).

W6 Willems, J. C.: "Perturbation Theory for the Analysis of Instability in Nonlinear Feedback Systems," Paper presented at the 1966 Allerton Conference on Circuit and System Theory.

W7 Wonham, W. M., and C. D. Johnson: Optimal Bang-Bang Control with Quadratic Performance Index, *J. of Basic Engineering*, vol. 86, no. 1, pp. 107-115, March 1964.

Y1 Yakubovich, V. A.: The Conditions for Absolute Stability of a Control System with a Hysteresis-Type Nonlinearity, *Soviet Physics - DOKLADY*, vol. 8, no. 3, pp. 235-237, September 1963.

Y2 Yakubovich, V. A.: The Matrix-Inequality Method in the Theory of the Stability of Nonlinear Control Systems, pt. I: Absolute Stability of Forced Vibrations, *Automation and Remote Control*, vol. 25, no. 7, pp. 905–917, July 1964.

Y3 Yakubovich, V. A.: The Method of Matrix Inequalities in the Stability Theory of Nonlinear Control Systems, pt. II: Absolute Stability in a Class of Nonlinearities with a Condition on the Derivative, *Automation and Remote Control*, vol. 26, no. 4, pp. 577–592, April 1965.

Y4 Yakubovich, V. A.: The Solution of Certain Matrix Inequalities in Automatic Control Theory, *Soviet Mathematics*, American Mathematical Society, vol. 3, no. 2, pp. 620–623, March 1962.

Z1 Zadeh, L. A., and C.A. Desoer: "Linear System Theory; The State-Space Approach," McGraw-Hill Book Company, New York, 1963.

Z2 Zames, G.: On the Input-Output Stability of Time-Varying Nonlinear Feedback Systems, *IEEE Trans. on Automatic Control*. Pt. I: Conditions Derived Using Concepts of Loop Gain, Conicity and Positivity, vol. AC-11, no. 2, pp. 228–239, April 1966; pt. II: Conditions Involving Circles in the Frequency Plane and Sector Nonlinearities, vol. AC-11, no. 3, pp. 465–476, July 1966.

Z3 Zames, G.: On the Input-Output Stability of Nonlinear, Time-Varying Feedback Systems, *National Electronics Conference Proc.*, vol. 20, pp. 725–730, October 1964.

Z4 Zubov, V. I.: The Methods of A. M. Lyapunov and Their Applications, 1957 (in Russian); English translation, *AEC Tr. 4439*, USAEC, Oak Ridge, Tenn., 1961.

Index